Student Solutions Manual

DANIEL S. MILLER Niagara County Community College

Blitzer

PRECALCULUS THIRD EDITION

PEARSON

Prentice Hall

Upper Saddle River, NJ 07458

Acquisitions Editor: Adam Jaworski
Editor-in-Chief: Sally Yagan
Project Manager: Dawn Murrin
Supplements Editor: Christine Whitlock
Executive Managing Editor: Kathleen Schiaparelli
Managing Editor: Nicole M. Jackson
Assistant Managing Editor: Karen Bosch
Production Editor: Traci Douglas
Supplement Cover Manager: Paul Gourhan
Supplement Cover Designer: Christopher Kossa
Manufacturing Buyer: Ilene Kahn
Manufacturing Manager: Alexis Heydt-Long

© 2007 Pearson Education, Inc.
Pearson Prentice Hall
Pearson Education, Inc.
Upper Saddle River, NJ 07458

All rights reserved. No part of this book may be reproduced in any form or by any means, without permission in writing from the publisher.

Pearson Prentice Hall™ is a trademark of Pearson Education, Inc.

The author and publisher of this book have used their best efforts in preparing this book. These efforts include the development, research, and testing of the theories and programs to determine their effectiveness. The author and publisher make no warranty of any kind, expressed or implied, with regard to these programs or the documentation contained in this book. The author and publisher shall not be liable in any event for incidental or consequential damages in connection with, or arising out of, the furnishing, performance, or use of these programs.

This work is protected by United States copyright laws and is provided solely for teaching courses and assessing student learning. Dissemination or sale of any part of this work (including on the World Wide Web) will destroy the integrity of the work and is not permitted. The work and materials from it should never be made available except by instructors using the accompanying text in their classes. All recipients of this work are expected to abide by these restrictions and to honor the intended pedagogical purposes and the needs of other instructors who rely on these materials.

Printed in the United States of America

10 9 8 7 6 5 4 3 2

ISBN   0-13-188039-X

Pearson Education Ltd., *London*
Pearson Education Australia Pty. Ltd., *Sydney*
Pearson Education Singapore, Pte. Ltd.
Pearson Education North Asia Ltd., *Hong Kong*
Pearson Education Canada, Inc., *Toronto*
Pearson Educación de Mexico, S.A. de C.V.
Pearson Education—Japan, *Tokyo*
Pearson Education Malaysia, Pte. Ltd.

Table of Contents

Chapter P

Section P.1

Check Point Exercises

1. $8 + 6(x-3)^2 = 8 + 6(13-3)^2$
    $$= 8 + 6(10)^2$$
    $$= 8 + 6(100)$$
    $$= 8 + 600$$
    $$= 608$$

2. The year 2000 is 40 years after 1960.
    $P = 0.72x^2 + 9.4x + 783$
    $$= 0.72(40)^2 + 9.4(40) + 783$$
    $$= 0.72(1600) + 376 + 783$$
    $$= 1152 + 376 + 783$$
    $$= 2311$$
    The equation's value of 2311 models the data in the bar graph quite well.

3. The elements common to $\{3, 4, 5, 6, 7\}$ and $\{3, 7, 8, 9\}$ are 3 and 7.
    $\{3,4,5,6,7\} \cap \{3,7,8,9\} = \{3,7\}$

4. The union is the set containing all the elements of either set.
    $\{3,4,5,6,7\} \cup \{3,7,8,9\} = \{3,4,5,6,7,8,9\}$

5. $\left\{ -9, \ -1.3, \ 0, \ 0.\overline{3}, \ \dfrac{\pi}{2}, \ \sqrt{9}, \ \sqrt{10} \right\}$

    a. Natural numbers: $\sqrt{9}$ because $\sqrt{9} = 3$

    b. Whole numbers: $0, \ \sqrt{9}$

    c. Integers: $-9, 0, \sqrt{9}$

    d. Rational numbers: $-9, \ -1.3, \ 0, \ 0.\overline{3}, \ \sqrt{9}$

    e. Irrational numbers: $\dfrac{\pi}{2}, \ \sqrt{10}$

    f. Real numbers:
        $\left\{ -9, \ -1.3, \ 0, \ 0.\overline{3}, \ \dfrac{\pi}{2}, \ \sqrt{9}, \ \sqrt{10} \right\}$

6. a. $\left| 1 - \sqrt{2} \right|$

    Because $\sqrt{2} \approx 1.4$, the number inside the absolute value bars is negative. The absolute value of x when $x < 0$ is $-x$. Thus,
    $\left| 1 - \sqrt{2} \right| = -\left(1 - \sqrt{2}\right) = \sqrt{2} - 1$

    b. $\left| \pi - 3 \right|$

    Because $\pi \approx 3.14$, the number inside the absolute value bars is positive. The absolute value of a positive number is the number itself. Thus,
    $\left| \pi - 3 \right| = \pi - 3$.

    c. $\dfrac{|x|}{x}$

    Because $x > 0$, $|x| = x$.

    Thus, $\dfrac{|x|}{x} = \dfrac{x}{x} = 1$

7. $|-4 - (5)| = |-9| = 9$
    The distance between -4 and 5 is 9.

8. $7(4x^2 + 3x) + 2(5x^2 + x)$
    $$= 7(4x^2 + 3x) + 2(5x^2 + x)$$
    $$= 28x^2 + 21x + 10x^2 + 2x$$
    $$= 38x^2 + 23x$$

9. $6 + 4[7 - (x-2)]$
    $$= 6 + 4[7 - x + 2)]$$
    $$= 6 + 4[9 - x]$$
    $$= 6 + 36 - 4x$$
    $$= 42 - 4x$$

Exercise Set P.1

1. $7 + 5(10) = 7 + 50 = 57$

3. $6(3) - 8 = 18 - 8 = 10$

5. $8^2 + 3(8) = 64 + 24 = 88$

7. $7^2 - 6(7) + 3 = 49 - 42 + 3 = 7 + 3 = 10$

9. $4 + 5(9-7)^3 = 4 + 5(2)^3$
$$= 4 + 5(8) = 4 + 40 = 44$$

11. $8^2 - 3(8-2) = 64 - 3(6)$
$$= 64 - 18 = 46$$

13. $\dfrac{5(x+2)}{2x-14} = \dfrac{5(10+2)}{2(10)-14}$
$$= \dfrac{5(12)}{6}$$
$$= 5 \cdot 2$$
$$= 10$$

15. $\dfrac{2x+3y}{x+1}; x = -2, y = 4$
$$= \dfrac{2(-2)+3(4)}{-2+1} = \dfrac{-4+12}{-1} = \dfrac{8}{-1} = -8$$

17. $C = \dfrac{5}{9}(50-32) = \dfrac{5}{9}(18) = 10$
10°C is equivalent to 50°F.

19. $h = 4 + 60t - 16t^2 = 4 + 60(2) - 16(2)^2$
$$= 4 + 120 - 16(4) = 4 + 120 - 64$$
$$= 124 - 64 = 60$$
Two seconds after it is kicked, the ball's height is 60 feet.

21. $\{1,2,3,4\} \cap \{2,4,5\} = \{2,4\}$

23. $\{s,e,t\} \cap \{t,e,s\} = \{s,e,t\}$

25. $\{1,3,5,7\} \cap \{2,4,6,8,10\} = \{\ \}$
The empty set is also denoted by $\varnothing$.

27. $\{a,b,c,d\} \cap \varnothing = \varnothing$

29. $\{1,2,3,4\} \cup \{2,4,5\} = \{1,2,3,4,5\}$

31. $\{1,3,5,7\} \cup \{2,4,6,8,10\}$
$$= \{1,2,3,4,5,6,7,8,10\}$$

33. $\{a,e,i,o,u\} \cup \varnothing = \{a,e,i,o,u\}$

35. a. $\sqrt{100}$

b. $0, \sqrt{100}$

c. $-9, 0, \sqrt{100}$

d. $-9, -\dfrac{4}{5}, 0, 0.25, 9.2, \sqrt{100}$

e. $\sqrt{3}$

f. $-9, -\dfrac{4}{5}, 0, 0.25, \sqrt{3}, 9.2, \sqrt{100}$

37. a. $\sqrt{64}$

b. $0, \sqrt{64}$

c. $-11, 0, \sqrt{64}$

d. $-11, -\dfrac{5}{6}, 0, 0.75, \sqrt{64}$

e. $\sqrt{5}, \pi$

f. $-11, -\dfrac{5}{6}, 0, 0.75, \sqrt{5}, \pi, \sqrt{64}$

39. 0

41. Answers may vary.

43. True; -13 is to the left of -2 on the number line.

45. True; 4 is to the right of -7 on the number line.

47. True; $-\pi = -\pi$

49. True; 0 is to the right of -6 on the number line.

51. $|300| = 300$

53. $|12 - \pi| = 12 - \pi$

55. $\left|\sqrt{2} - 5\right| = 5 - \sqrt{2}$

57. $\dfrac{-3}{|-3|} = \dfrac{-3}{3} = -1$

59. $\left||-3| - |-7|\right| = |3 - 7| = |-4| = 4$

61. $|x + y| = |2 + (-5)| = |-3| = 3$

63. $|x| + |y| = |2| + |-5| = 2 + 5 = 7$

65. $\dfrac{y}{|y|} = \dfrac{-5}{|-5|} = \dfrac{-5}{5} = -1$

67. The distance is $|2-17| = |-15| = 15$.

69. The distance is $|-2-5| = |-7| = 7$.

71. The distance is
$|-19-(-4)| = |-19+4| = |-15| = 15$.

73. The distance is
$|-3.6-(-1.4)| = |-3.6+1.4| = |-2.2| = 2.2$.

75. $6 + (-4) = (-4) + 6$; commutative property of addition

77. $6 + (2 + 7) = (6 + 2) + 7$; associative property of addition

79. $(2 + 3) + (4 + 5) = (4 + 5) + (2 + 3)$; commutative property of addition

81. $2(-8 + 6) = -16 + 12$; distributive property of multiplication over addition

83. $\dfrac{1}{x+3}(x+3) = 1; x \neq -3$, inverse property of multiplication

85. $5(3x + 4) - 4 = 5\cdot 3x + 5\cdot 4 - 4$
$ = 15x + 20 - 4$
$ = 15x + 16$

87. $5(3x - 2) + 12x = 5\cdot 3x - 5\cdot 2 + 12x$
$ = 15x - 10 + 12x$
$ = 27x - 10$

89. $7(3y - 5) + 2(4y + 3)$
$= 7\cdot 3y - 7\cdot 5 + 2\cdot 4y + 2\cdot 3$
$= 21y - 35 + 8y + 6$
$= 29y - 29$

91. $5(3y - 2) - (7y + 2) = 15y - 10 - 7y - 2$
$= 8y - 12$

93. $7 - 4[3 - (4y - 5)] = 7 - 4[3 - 4y + 5]$
$ = 7 - 4[8 - 4y]$
$ = 7 - 32 + 16y$
$ = 16y - 25$

95. $8x^2 + 4 - [6(x^2 - 2) + 5]$
$= 18x^2 + 4 - [6x^2 - 12 + 5]$
$= 18x^2 + 4 - [6x^2 - 7]$
$= 18x^2 + 4 - 6x^2 + 7$
$= 18x^2 - 6x^2 + 4 + 7$
$= (18 - 6)x^2 + 11 = 12x^2 + 11$

97. $-(-14x) = 14x$

99. $-(2x - 3y - 6) = -2x + 3y + 6$

101. $\dfrac{1}{3}(3x) + [(4y) + (-4y)] = x + 0$
$\phantom{\dfrac{1}{3}(3x) + [(4y) + (-4y)]} = x$

103. $|-6| \ \square \ |-3|$
$ 6 \ \square \ 3$
$ 6 > 3$
Since $6 > 3$, $|-6| > |-3|$.

105. $\left|\dfrac{3}{5}\right| \ \square \ |-0.6|$
$ |0.6| \ \square \ |-0.6|$
$ 0.6 \ \square \ 0.6$
$ 0.6 = 0.6$
Since $0.6 = 0.6$, $\left|\dfrac{3}{5}\right| = |-0.6|$.

107. $\dfrac{30}{40} - \dfrac{3}{4} \ \square \ \dfrac{14}{15}\cdot\dfrac{15}{14}$
$\dfrac{30}{40} - \dfrac{30}{40} \ \square \ \dfrac{\cancel{14}}{\cancel{15}}\cdot\dfrac{\cancel{15}}{\cancel{14}}$
$ 0 \ \square \ 1$
$ 0 < 1$
Since $0 < 1$, $\dfrac{30}{40} - \dfrac{3}{4} < \dfrac{14}{15}\cdot\dfrac{15}{14}$.

109. $\dfrac{8}{13} \div \dfrac{8}{13} \ \square \ |-1|$
$ \dfrac{8}{13}\cdot\dfrac{13}{8} \ \square \ 1$
$ 1 \ \square \ 1$
$ 1 = 1$
Since $1 = 1$, $\dfrac{8}{13} \div \dfrac{8}{13} = |-1|$.

111. $x - (x + 4) = x - x - 4 = -4$

113. $6(-5x) = -30x$

115. $5x - 2x = 3x$

117. $8x - (3x + 6) = 8x - 3x - 6 = 5x - 6$

119. $N = 17x^2 - 65.4x + 302.2$
$= 17(4)^2 - 65.4(4) + 302.2$
$= 17(16) - 261.6 + 302.2$
$= 272 - 261.6 + 302.2$
≈ 313
The formula models the graph's data very well.

121. $N = 17x^2 - 65.4x + 302.2$
$= 17(6)^2 - 65.4(6) + 302.2$
$= 17(36) - 392.4 + 302.2$
$= 612 - 392.4 + 302.2$
≈ 522
The formula predicts that there will be 522 U.S. billionaires in 2006.

123. Model 1: $N = -2.04x + 10.24$
$= -2.04(0) + 10.24$
$= 10.24$
Model 2: $N = 0.04x^2 - 3.6x + 11$
$= 0.04(0)^2 - 3.6(0) + 11$
$= 11$
Model 3: $N = 0.76x^3 - 4x^2 + 1.8x + 10.5$
$= 0.76(0)^3 - 4(0)^2 + 1.8(0) + 10.5$
$= 10.5$
Model 3 was the best model for 1999.

125. Model 1: $N = -2.04x + 10.24$
$= -2.04(4) + 10.24$
$= 2.08$
Model 2: $N = 0.04x^2 - 3.6x + 11$
$= 0.04(4)^2 - 3.6(4) + 11$
$= -2.76$

Model 3: $N = 0.76x^3 - 4x^2 + 1.8x + 10.5$
$= 0.76(4)^3 - 4(4)^2 + 1.8(4) + 10.5$
$= 2.34$
Model 3 was the best model for 2003.

127. a. $0.05x + 0.12(10,000 - x)$
$= 0.05x + 1200 - 0.12x$
$= 1200 - 0.07x$

b. $1200 - 0.07x = 1200 - 0.07(6000)$
$= \$780$

141. a. False; x has a coefficient of 1.

b. False; $5 + 3(x - 4) = 5 + 3x - 12 = 3x - 7$

c. False; $-x - x = -2x$.

d. True; $x - 0.02(x + 200)$
$= x - 0.02x - 4$
$= x - 0.02x - 0.02(200)$
$= 0.98x - 4$

(d) is true.

143. $-\pi > -3.5$

145. a. $x = 100$
$\dfrac{0.5x + 5000}{100}$
$= \dfrac{5050}{100}$
$= \$50.50$

$x = 1000$
$\dfrac{0.5(1000) + 5000}{1000}$
$= \dfrac{5500}{1000}$
$= \$5.50$

$x = 10,000$
$\dfrac{0.5(10,000) + 5000}{10,000}$
$= \dfrac{10000}{10000}$
$= \$1$

b. No, they would need make 10,000 clocks for the cost to be \$1 so they can add \$.50.

Section P.2

Check Point Exercises

1. a. $\left(2x^3y^6\right)^4 = (2)^4\left(x^3\right)^4\left(y^6\right)^4 = 16x^{12}y^{24}$

   b. $\left(-6x^2y^5\right)\left(3xy^3\right)$
   $$= (-6)\cdot 3 \cdot x^2 \cdot x \cdot y^5 \cdot y^3$$
   $$= -18x^3y^8$$

   c. $\dfrac{100x^{12}y^2}{20x^{16}y^{-4}} = \left(\dfrac{100}{20}\right)\left(\dfrac{x^{12}}{x^{16}}\right)\left(\dfrac{y^2}{y^{-4}}\right)$
   $$= 5x^{12-16}y^{2-(-4)}$$
   $$= 5x^{-4}y^6$$
   $$= \dfrac{5y^6}{x^4}$$

   d. $\left(\dfrac{5x}{y^4}\right)^{-2} = \dfrac{(5)^{-2}(x)^{-2}}{\left(y^4\right)^{-2}}$
   $$= \dfrac{(5)^{-2}(x)^{-2}}{\left(y^4\right)^{-2}}$$
   $$= \dfrac{5^{-2}x^{-2}}{y^{-8}}$$
   $$= \dfrac{y^8}{5^2x^2}$$
   $$= \dfrac{y^8}{25x^2}$$

2. a. $-2.6\times10^9 = -2,600,000,000$

   b. $3.017\times10^{-6} = 0.000003017$

3. a. $5,210,000,000 = 5.21\times10^9$

   b. $-0.00000006893 = -6.893\times10^{-8}$

4. $410\times10^7 = \left(4.1\times10^2\right)\times10^7$
   $$= 4.1\times\left(10^2\times10^7\right)$$
   $$= 4.1\times10^9$$

5. a. $\left(7.1\times10^5\right)\left(5\times10^{-7}\right)$
   $$= 7.1\cdot5\times10^5\cdot10^{-7}$$
   $$= 35.5\times10^{-2}$$
   $$= \left(3.55\times10^1\right)\times10^{-2}$$
   $$= 3.55\times\left(10^1\times10^{-2}\right)$$
   $$= 3.55\times10^{-1}$$

   b. $\dfrac{1.2\times10^6}{3\times10^{-3}} = \dfrac{1.2}{3}\cdot\dfrac{10^6}{10^{-3}}$
   $$= 0.4\times10^{6-(-3)}$$
   $$= 0.4\times10^9$$
   $$= 4\times10^8$$

6. $\dfrac{2.02\times10^{12}}{2.88\times10^8} = \dfrac{2.02}{2.88}\cdot\dfrac{10^{12}}{10^8}$
   $$\approx 0.7014\times10^4$$
   $$\approx 7014$$
   The per capita tax was \$7014 in 2002.

7. $S = (1.76\times10^5)[(1.44\times10^{-2})-r^2]$
   $$= (1.76\times10^5)[(1.44\times10^{-2})-0^2]$$
   $$= 2534.4$$
   The speed of the blood at the central axis of the artery is 2534.4 centimeters per second.

Exercise Set P.2

1. $5^2\cdot2 = (5\cdot5)\cdot2 = 25\cdot2 = 50$

3. $(-2)^6 = (-2)(-2)(-2)(-2)(-2)(-2) = 64$

5. $-2^6 = -2\cdot2\cdot2\cdot2\cdot2\cdot2 = -64$

7. $(-3)^0 = 1$

9. $-3^0 = -1$

11. $4^{-3} = \dfrac{1}{4^3} = \dfrac{1}{4\cdot4\cdot4} = \dfrac{1}{64}$

13. $2^2\cdot2^3 = 2^{2+3} = 2^5 = 2\cdot2\cdot2\cdot2\cdot2 = 32$

15. $(2^2)^3 = 2^{2\cdot3} = 2^6 = 2\cdot2\cdot2\cdot2\cdot2\cdot2 = 64$

17. $\dfrac{2^8}{2^4} = 2^{8-4} = 2^4 = 2\cdot2\cdot2\cdot2 = 16$

19. $3^{-3} \cdot 3 = 3^{-3+1} = 3^{-2} = \dfrac{1}{3^2} = \dfrac{1}{3 \cdot 3} = \dfrac{1}{9}$

21. $\dfrac{2^3}{2^7} = 2^{3-7} = 2^{-4} = \dfrac{1}{2^4} = \dfrac{1}{2 \cdot 2 \cdot 2 \cdot 2} = \dfrac{1}{16}$

23. $x^{-2}y = \dfrac{\cdot 1}{x^2} \cdot y = \dfrac{y}{x^2}$

25. $x^0 y^5 = 1 \cdot y^5 = y^5$

27. $x^3 \cdot x^7 = x^{3+7} = x^{10}$

29. $x^{-5} \cdot x^{10} = x^{-5+10} = x^5$

31. $(x^3)^7 = x^{3 \cdot 7} = x^{21}$

33. $(x^{-5})^3 = x^{-5 \cdot 3} = x^{-15} = \dfrac{1}{x^{15}}$

35. $\dfrac{x^{14}}{x^7} = x^{14-7} = x^7$

37. $\dfrac{x^{14}}{x^{-7}} = x^{14-(-7)} = x^{14+7} = x^{21}$

39. $(8x^3)^2 = 8^2(x^3)^2 = 8^2 x^{3 \cdot 2} = 64x^6$

41. $\left(-\dfrac{4}{x}\right)^3 = \dfrac{(-4)^3}{x^3} = -\dfrac{64}{x^3}$

43. $(-3x^2 y^5)^2 = (-3)^2 (x^2)^2 \cdot (y^5)^2$
$= 9x^{2 \cdot 2} y^{5 \cdot 2}$
$= 9x^4 y^{10}$

45. $(3x^4)(2x^7) = 3 \cdot 2x^4 \cdot x^7 = 6x^{4+7} = 6x^{11}$

47. $(-9x^3 y)(-2x^6 y^4) = (-9)(-2)x^3 x^6 yy^4$
$= 18x^{3+6} y^{1+4}$
$= 18x^9 y^5$

49. $\dfrac{8x^{20}}{2x^4} = \left(\dfrac{8}{2}\right)\left(\dfrac{x^{20}}{x^4}\right) = 4x^{20-4} = 4x^{16}$

51. $\dfrac{25a^{13} \cdot b^4}{-5a^2 \cdot b^3} = \left(\dfrac{25}{-5}\right)\left(\dfrac{a^{13}}{a^2}\right)\left(\dfrac{b^4}{b^3}\right)$
$= -5a^{13-2} b^{4-3}$
$= -5a^{11} b$

53. $\dfrac{14b^7}{7b^{14}} = \left(\dfrac{14}{7}\right)\left(\dfrac{b^7}{b^{14}}\right) = 2 \cdot b^{7-14} = 2b^{-7} = \dfrac{2}{b^7}$

55. $(4x^3)^{-2} = (4^{-2})(x^3)^{-2}$
$= 4^{-2} x^{-6}$
$= \dfrac{1}{4^2 x^6}$
$= \dfrac{1}{16x^6}$

57. $\dfrac{24x^3 \cdot y^5}{32x^7 y^{-9}} = \dfrac{3}{4} x^{3-7} y^{5-(-9)}$
$= \dfrac{3}{4} x^{-4} y^{14}$
$= \dfrac{3y^{14}}{4x^4}$

59. $\left(\dfrac{5x^3}{y}\right)^{-2} = \dfrac{5^{-2} x^{-6}}{y^{-2}} = \dfrac{y^2}{25x^6}$

61. $\left(\dfrac{-15a^4 b^2}{5a^{10} b^{-3}}\right)^3$
$= \left(\dfrac{-3b^{2-(-3)}}{a^{10-4}}\right)^3$
$= \left(\dfrac{-3b^5}{a^6}\right)^3$
$= \dfrac{-27b^{15}}{a^{18}}$

63. $\left(\dfrac{3a^{-5} b^2}{12a^3 b^{-4}}\right)^0 = 1$

65. $3.8 \times 10^2 = 380$

67. $6 \times 10^{-4} = 0.0006$

69. $-7.16 \times 10^6 = -7,160,000$

71. $7.9 \times 10^{-1} = 0.79$

73. $-4.15 \times 10^{-3} = -0.00415$

75. $-6.00001 \times 10^{10} = -60,000,100,000$

77. $32,000 = 3.2 \times 10^4$

79. $638,000,000,000,000,000$
$= 6.38 \times 10^{17}$

81. $-5716 = -5.716 \times 10^3$

83. $0.0027 = 2.7 \times 10^{-3}$

85. $-0.00000000504 = -5.04 \times 10^{-9}$

87. $\left(3 \times 10^4\right)\left(2.1 \times 10^3\right)$
$= \left(3 \times 2.1\right)\left(10^4 \times 10^3\right)$
$= 6.3 \times 10^{4+3} = 6.3 \times 10^7$

89. $\left(1.6 \times 10^{15}\right)\left(4 \times 10^{-11}\right)$
$= \left(1.6 \times 4\right)\left(10^{15} \times 10^{-11}\right)$
$= 6.4 \times 10^{15+(-11)} = 6.4 \times 10^4$

91. $\left(6.1 \times 10^{-8}\right)\left(2 \times 10^{-4}\right)$
$= \left(6.1 \times 2\right)\left(10^{-8} \times 10^{-4}\right)$
$= 12.2 \times 10^{-8+(-4)}$
$= 12.2 \times 10^{-12} = 1.22 \times 10^{-11}$

93. $\left(4.3 \times 10^8\right)\left(6.2 \times 10^4\right)$
$= \left(4.3 \times 6.2\right)\left(10^8 \times 10^4\right)$
$= 26.66 \times 10^{8+4}$
$= 26.66 \times 10^{12}$
$= 2.666 \times 10^{13} \approx 2.67 \times 10^{13}$

95. $\dfrac{8.4 \times 10^8}{4 \times 10^5} = \dfrac{8.4}{4} \times \dfrac{10^8}{10^5}$
$= 2.1 \times 10^{8-5} = 2.1 \times 10^3$

97. $\dfrac{3.6 \times 10^4}{9 \times 10^{-2}} = \dfrac{3.6}{9} \times \dfrac{10^4}{10^{-2}}$
$= 0.4 \times 10^{4-(-2)}$
$= 0.4 \times 10^6 = 4 \times 10^5$

99. $\dfrac{4.8 \times 10^{-2}}{2.4 \times 10^6} = \dfrac{4.8}{2.4} \times \dfrac{10^{-2}}{10^6}$
$= 2 \times 10^{-2-6} = 2 \times 10^{-8}$

101. $\dfrac{2.4 \times 10^{-2}}{4.8 \times 10^{-6}} = \dfrac{2.4}{4.8} \times \dfrac{10^{-2}}{10^{-6}}$
$= 0.5 \times 10^{-2-(-6)}$
$= 0.5 \times 10^4 = 5 \times 10^3$

103. $\dfrac{480,000,000,000}{0.00012} = \dfrac{4.8 \times 10^{11}}{1.2 \times 10^{-4}}$
$= \dfrac{4.8}{1.2} \times \dfrac{10^{11}}{10^{-4}}$
$= 4 \times 10^{11-(-4)}$
$= 4 \times 10^{15}$

105. $\dfrac{0.00072 \times 0.003}{0.00024}$
$= \dfrac{\left(7.2 \times 10^{-4}\right)\left(3 \times 10^{-3}\right)}{2.4 \times 10^{-4}}$
$= \dfrac{7.2 \times 3}{2.4} \times \dfrac{10^{-4} \cdot 10^{-3}}{10^{-4}} = 9 \times 10^{-3}$

107. $\dfrac{\left(x^{-2}y\right)^{-3}}{\left(x^2 y^{-1}\right)^3} = \dfrac{x^6 y^{-3}}{x^6 y^{-3}}$
$= x^{6-6} y^{-3-(-3)} = x^0 y^0 = 1$

109. $\left(2x^{-3}yz^{-6}\right)\left(2x\right)^{-5} = 2x^{-3}yz^{-6} \cdot 2^{-5} x^{\cdot -5}$
$= 2^{-4} x^{-8} yz^{-6} = \dfrac{y}{2^4 x^8 z^6} = \dfrac{y}{16 x^8 z^6}$

111. $\left(\dfrac{x^3 y^4 z^5}{x^{-3} y^{-4} z^{-5}}\right)^{-2} = \left(x^6 y^8 z^{10}\right)^{-2}$
$= x^{-12} y^{-16} z^{-20} = \dfrac{1}{x^{12} y^{16} z^{20}}$

113. $\dfrac{\left(2^{-1} x^{-2} y^{-1}\right)^{-2}\left(2x^{-4} y^3\right)^{-2}\left(16 x^{-3} y^3\right)^0}{\left(2x^{-3} y^{-5}\right)^2}$
$= \dfrac{\left(2^2 x^2 y^2\right)\left(2^{-2} x^8 y^{-6}\right)(1)}{\left(2^2 x^{-6} y^{-10}\right)}$
$= \dfrac{x^{18} y^6}{4}$

115. $62.6 \text{ million} = 62.6 \times 10^6 = 6.26 \times 10^7$
So, 6.26×10^7 people will be 65 and over in 2025.

117. $131.2 - 34.9 = 96.3$
$96.3 \text{ million} = 96.3 \times 10^6 = 9.63 \times 10^7$ There will be 9.63×10^7 more people 65 and over in the year 2100 than in 2000.

119. 20 billion = 2×10^{10}

$$\frac{2 \times 10^{10}}{2.92 \times 10^{8}} = \frac{2}{2.92} \times \frac{10^{10}}{10^{8}}$$
$$\approx 0.6849 \times 10^{10-8}$$
$$= 0.6849 \times 10^{2}$$
$$= 6.849 \times 10^{1} \approx 68$$

The average American consumes about 68 hotdogs each year.

121. 8 billion = 8×10^{9}

$$\frac{8 \times 10^{9}}{3.2 \times 10^{7}} = \frac{8}{3.2} \times \frac{10^{9}}{10^{7}}$$
$$= 2.5 \times 10^{9-7}$$
$$= 2.5 \times 10^{2} = 250$$

$2.5 \times 10^{2} = 250$ chickens are raised for food each second in the U.S.

123. $\dfrac{6.8 \times 10^{12}}{2.9 \times 10^{8}} = \dfrac{6.8}{2.9} \cdot \dfrac{10^{12}}{10^{8}}$
$$\approx 2.3448 \times 10^{4}$$
$$\approx 23,448$$

If the national debt was divided evenly among every individual in the U.S., each citizen would have to pay \$23,448.

133. a. False, $4^{-2} = \dfrac{1}{16} > 4^{-3} = \dfrac{1}{64}$

b. True, $5^{-2} = \dfrac{1}{25} > 2^{-5} = \dfrac{1}{32}$

c. False, $16 = (-2)^{4} \neq 2^{-4} = \dfrac{1}{16}$

d. False. $5^{2} \cdot 5^{-2} = 5^{2-2} = 5^{0} = 1$
$2^{5} \cdot 2^{-5} = 2^{5-5} = 2^{0} = 1$
1 is not greater than 1

135. $b^{A} = MN, b^{C} = M, b^{D} = N$
$b^{A} = b^{C} b^{D}$
$A = C + D$

Section P.3

Check Point Exercises

1. a. $\sqrt{81} = 9$

b. $-\sqrt{9} = -3$

c. $\sqrt{\dfrac{1}{25}} = \dfrac{1}{5}$

d. $\sqrt{36 + 64} = \sqrt{100} = 10$

e. $\sqrt{36} + \sqrt{64} = 6 + 8 = 14$

2. a. $\sqrt{75} = \sqrt{25 \cdot 3} = \sqrt{25}\sqrt{3} = 5\sqrt{3}$

b. $\sqrt{5x} \cdot \sqrt{10x} = \sqrt{5x \cdot 10x}$
$$= \sqrt{50x^{2}}$$
$$= \sqrt{25 \cdot 2x^{2}}$$
$$= \sqrt{25x^{2}} \cdot \sqrt{2}$$
$$= 5x\sqrt{2}$$

3. a. $\sqrt{\dfrac{25}{16}} = \dfrac{\sqrt{25}}{\sqrt{16}} = \dfrac{5}{4}$

b. $\dfrac{\sqrt{150x^{3}}}{\sqrt{2x}} = \sqrt{\dfrac{150x^{3}}{2x}}$
$$= \sqrt{75x^{2}}$$
$$= \sqrt{25x^{2}} \cdot \sqrt{3}$$
$$= 5x\sqrt{3}$$

4. a. $8\sqrt{13} + 9\sqrt{13} = (8 + 9)\sqrt{3}$
$$= 17\sqrt{13}$$

b. $\sqrt{17x} - 20\sqrt{17x}$
$$= 1\sqrt{17x} - 20\sqrt{17x}$$
$$= (1 - 20)\sqrt{17x}$$
$$= -19\sqrt{17x}$$

5. a. $5\sqrt{27}+\sqrt{12}$
$= 5\sqrt{9\cdot 3}+\sqrt{4\cdot 3}$
$= 5\cdot 3\sqrt{3}+2\sqrt{3}$
$= 15\sqrt{3}+2\sqrt{3}$
$= (15+2)\sqrt{3}$
$= 17\sqrt{3}$

    b. $6\sqrt{18x}-4\sqrt{8x}$
$= 6\sqrt{9\cdot 2x}-4\sqrt{4\cdot 2x}$
$= 6\cdot 3\sqrt{2x}-4\cdot 2\sqrt{2x}$
$= 18\sqrt{2x}-8\sqrt{2x}$
$= (18-8)\sqrt{2x}$
$= 10\sqrt{2x}$

6. a. If we multiply numerator and denominator by $\sqrt{3}$, the denominator becomes $\sqrt{3}\cdot\sqrt{3}=\sqrt{9}=3$. Therefore, multiply by 1, choosing $\dfrac{\sqrt{3}}{\sqrt{3}}$ for 1.

$\dfrac{5}{\sqrt{3}}=\dfrac{5}{\sqrt{3}}\cdot\dfrac{\sqrt{3}}{\sqrt{3}}=\dfrac{5\sqrt{3}}{\sqrt{9}}=\dfrac{5\sqrt{3}}{3}$

    b. The *smallest* number that will produce a perfect square in the denominator of $\dfrac{6}{\sqrt{12}}$ is $\sqrt{3}$ because $\sqrt{12}\cdot\sqrt{3}=\sqrt{36}=6$. So multiply by 1, choosing $\dfrac{\sqrt{3}}{\sqrt{3}}$ for 1.

$\dfrac{6}{\sqrt{12}}=\dfrac{6}{\sqrt{12}}\cdot\dfrac{\sqrt{3}}{\sqrt{3}}=\dfrac{6\sqrt{3}}{\sqrt{36}}=\dfrac{6\sqrt{3}}{6}=\sqrt{3}$

7. Multiply by $\dfrac{4-\sqrt{5}}{4-\sqrt{5}}$.

$\dfrac{8}{4+\sqrt{5}}=\dfrac{8}{4+\sqrt{5}}\cdot\dfrac{4-\sqrt{5}}{4-\sqrt{5}}$

$=\dfrac{8(4-\sqrt{5})}{4^{2}-(\sqrt{5})^{2}}$

$=\dfrac{8(4-\sqrt{5})}{16-5}$

$=\dfrac{8(4-\sqrt{5})}{11}$ or $\dfrac{32-8\sqrt{5}}{11}$

8. a. $\sqrt[3]{40}=\sqrt[3]{8\cdot 5}=\sqrt[3]{8}\cdot\sqrt[3]{5}=2\sqrt[3]{5}$

    b. $\sqrt[5]{8}\cdot\sqrt[5]{8}=\sqrt[5]{64}=\sqrt[5]{32}\cdot\sqrt[5]{2}=2\sqrt[5]{2}$

    c. $\sqrt[3]{\dfrac{125}{27}}=\dfrac{\sqrt[3]{125}}{\sqrt[3]{27}}=\dfrac{5}{3}$

9. $3\sqrt[3]{81}-4\sqrt[3]{3}$
$= 3\sqrt[3]{27\cdot 3}-4\sqrt[3]{3}$
$= 3\cdot 3\sqrt[3]{3}-4\sqrt[3]{3}$
$= 9\sqrt[3]{3}-4\sqrt[3]{3}$
$= (9-4)\sqrt[3]{3}$
$= 5\sqrt[3]{3}$

10. a. $25^{\frac{1}{2}}=\sqrt{25}=5$

    b. $8^{\frac{1}{3}}=\sqrt[3]{8}=2$

    c. $-81^{\frac{1}{4}}=-\sqrt[4]{81}=-3$

    d. $(-8)^{\frac{1}{3}}=\sqrt[3]{-8}=-2$

    e. $27^{-\frac{1}{3}}=\dfrac{1}{27^{\frac{1}{3}}}=\dfrac{1}{\sqrt[3]{27}}=\dfrac{1}{3}$

11. a. $27^{\frac{4}{3}}=\left(\sqrt[3]{27}\right)^{4}=(3)^{4}=81$

    b. $4^{\frac{3}{2}}=\left(\sqrt[2]{4}\right)^{3}=(2)^{3}=8$

    c. $32^{-\frac{2}{5}}=\dfrac{1}{32^{\frac{2}{5}}}=\dfrac{1}{\left(\sqrt[5]{32}\right)^{2}}=\dfrac{1}{2^{2}}=\dfrac{1}{4}$

12. a. $\left(2x^{4/3}\right)\left(5x^{8/3}\right)$
$= 2\cdot 5x^{4/3}\cdot x^{8/3}$
$= 10x^{(4/3)+(8/3)}$
$= 10x^{12/3}$
$= 10x^{4}$

b. $\dfrac{20x^4}{5x^{3/2}} = \left(\dfrac{20}{5}\right)\left(\dfrac{x^4}{x^{3/2}}\right)$

$= 4x^{4-(3/2)}$

$= 4x^{(8/2)-(3/2)}$

$= 4x^{5/2}$

13. $\sqrt[6]{x^3} = x^{3/6} = x^{1/2} = \sqrt{x}$

Exercise Set P.3

1. $\sqrt{36} = \sqrt{6^2} = 6$

3. $-\sqrt{36} = -\sqrt{6^2} = -6$

5. $\sqrt{-36}$, The square root of a negative number is not real.

7. $\sqrt{25-16} = \sqrt{9} = 3$

9. $\sqrt{25} - \sqrt{16} = 5 - 4 = 1$

11. $\sqrt{(-13)^2} = \sqrt{169} = 13$

13. $\sqrt{50} = \sqrt{25 \cdot 2} = \sqrt{25}\sqrt{2} = 5\sqrt{2}$

15. $\sqrt{45x^2} = \sqrt{9x^2 \cdot 5}$

$= \sqrt{9x^2}\sqrt{5}$

$= \sqrt{9}\sqrt{x^2}\sqrt{5}$

$= 3|x|\sqrt{5}$

17. $\sqrt{2x} \cdot \sqrt{6x} = \sqrt{2x \cdot 6x}$

$= \sqrt{12x^2}$

$= \sqrt{4x^2} \cdot \sqrt{3}$

$= 2x\sqrt{3}$

19. $\sqrt{x^3} = \sqrt{x^2} \cdot \sqrt{x} = x\sqrt{x}$

21. $\sqrt{2x^2} \cdot \sqrt{6x} = \sqrt{2x^2 \cdot 6x}$

$= \sqrt{12x^3}$

$= \sqrt{4x^2} \cdot \sqrt{3x}$

$= 2x\sqrt{3x}$

23. $\sqrt{\dfrac{1}{81}} = \dfrac{\sqrt{1}}{\sqrt{81}} = \dfrac{1}{9}$

25. $\sqrt{\dfrac{49}{16}} = \dfrac{\sqrt{49}}{\sqrt{16}} = \dfrac{7}{4}$

27. $\dfrac{\sqrt{48x^3}}{\sqrt{3x}} = \sqrt{\dfrac{48x^3}{3x}} = \sqrt{16x^2} = 4x$

29. $\dfrac{\sqrt{150x^4}}{\sqrt{3x}} = \sqrt{\dfrac{150x^4}{3x}}$

$= \sqrt{50x^3}$

$= \sqrt{25x^2} \cdot \sqrt{2x}$

$= 5x\sqrt{2x}$

31. $\dfrac{\sqrt{200x^3}}{\sqrt{10x^{-1}}}$

$= \sqrt{\dfrac{200x^3}{10x^{-1}}}$

$= \sqrt{20x^{3-(-1)}}$

$= \sqrt{20x^4}$

$= \sqrt{4 \cdot 5x^4}$

$= 2x^2\sqrt{5}$

33. $7\sqrt{3} + 6\sqrt{3} = (7+6)\sqrt{3} = 13\sqrt{3}$

35. $6\sqrt{17x} - 8\sqrt{17x} = (6-8)\sqrt{17x} = -2\sqrt{17x}$

37. $\sqrt{8} + 3\sqrt{2} = \sqrt{4 \cdot 2} + 3\sqrt{2}$

$= 2\sqrt{2} + 3\sqrt{2}$

$= (2+3)\sqrt{2}$

$= 5\sqrt{2}$

39. $\sqrt{50x} - \sqrt{8x} = \sqrt{25 \cdot 2x} - \sqrt{4 \cdot 2x}$

$= 5\sqrt{2x} - 2\sqrt{2x}$

$= (5-2)\sqrt{2x}$

$= 3\sqrt{2x}$

41. $3\sqrt{18} + 5\sqrt{50} = 3\sqrt{9\cdot 2} + 5\sqrt{25\cdot 2}$
$$= 3\cdot 3\sqrt{2} + 5\cdot 5\sqrt{2}$$
$$= 9\sqrt{2} + 25\sqrt{2}$$
$$= (9+25)\sqrt{2}$$
$$= 34\sqrt{2}$$

43. $3\sqrt{8} - \sqrt{32} + 3\sqrt{72} - \sqrt{75}$
$$= 3\sqrt{4\cdot 2} - \sqrt{16\cdot 2} + 3\sqrt{36\cdot 2} - \sqrt{25\cdot 3}$$
$$= 3\cdot 2\sqrt{2} - 4\sqrt{2} + 3\cdot 6\sqrt{2} - 5\sqrt{3}$$
$$= 6\sqrt{2} - 4\sqrt{2} + 18\sqrt{2} - 5\sqrt{3}$$
$$= 20\sqrt{2} - 5\sqrt{3}$$

45. $\dfrac{1}{\sqrt{7}} = \dfrac{1}{\sqrt{7}}\cdot\dfrac{\sqrt{7}}{\sqrt{7}} = \dfrac{\sqrt{7}}{7}$

47. $\dfrac{\sqrt{2}}{\sqrt{5}} = \dfrac{\sqrt{2}}{\sqrt{5}}\cdot\dfrac{\sqrt{5}}{\sqrt{5}} = \dfrac{\sqrt{10}}{5}$

49. $\dfrac{13}{3+\sqrt{11}} = \dfrac{13}{3+\sqrt{11}}\cdot\dfrac{3-\sqrt{11}}{3-\sqrt{11}}$
$$= \dfrac{13(3-\sqrt{11})}{3^2-(\sqrt{11})^2}$$
$$= \dfrac{13(3-\sqrt{11})}{9-11}$$
$$= \dfrac{13(3-\sqrt{11})}{-2}$$

51. $\dfrac{7}{\sqrt{5}-2} = \dfrac{7}{\sqrt{5}-2}\cdot\dfrac{\sqrt{5}+2}{\sqrt{5}+2}$
$$= \dfrac{7(\sqrt{5}+2)}{(\sqrt{5})^2-2^2}$$
$$= \dfrac{7(\sqrt{5}+2)}{5-4}$$
$$= 7(\sqrt{5}+2)$$

53. $\dfrac{6}{\sqrt{5}+\sqrt{3}} = \dfrac{6}{\sqrt{5}+\sqrt{3}}\cdot\dfrac{\sqrt{5}-\sqrt{3}}{\sqrt{5}-\sqrt{3}}$
$$= \dfrac{6(\sqrt{5}-\sqrt{3})}{(\sqrt{5})^2-(\sqrt{3})^2}$$
$$= \dfrac{6(\sqrt{5}-\sqrt{3})}{5-3}$$
$$= \dfrac{6(\sqrt{5}-\sqrt{3})}{2}$$
$$= 3(\sqrt{5}-\sqrt{3})$$

55. $\sqrt[3]{125} = \sqrt[3]{5^3} = 5$

57. $\sqrt[3]{-8} = \sqrt[3]{(-2)^3} = -2$

59. $\sqrt[4]{-16}$ is not a real number.

61. $\sqrt[4]{(-3)^4} = \left|-3\right| = 3$

63. $\sqrt[5]{(-3)^5} = -3$

65. $\sqrt[5]{-\dfrac{1}{32}} = \sqrt[5]{-\dfrac{1}{2^5}} = -\dfrac{1}{2}$

67. $\sqrt[3]{32} = \sqrt[3]{8\cdot 4} = \sqrt[3]{8}\sqrt[3]{4} = 2\cdot\sqrt[3]{4}$

69. $\sqrt[3]{x^4} = \sqrt[3]{x^3\cdot x} = x\cdot\sqrt[3]{x}$

71. $\sqrt[3]{9}\cdot\sqrt[3]{6} = \sqrt[3]{54} = \sqrt[3]{27\cdot 2} = \sqrt[3]{27}\sqrt[3]{2} = 3\sqrt[3]{2}$

73. $\dfrac{\sqrt[5]{64x^6}}{\sqrt[5]{2x}} = \sqrt[5]{\dfrac{64x^6}{2x}} = \sqrt[5]{32x^5} = 2x$

75. $4\sqrt[5]{2} + 3\sqrt[5]{2} = 7\sqrt[5]{2}$

77. $5\sqrt[3]{16} + \sqrt[3]{54} = 5\sqrt[3]{8\cdot 2} + \sqrt[3]{27\cdot 2}$
$$= 5\cdot 2\sqrt[3]{2} + 3\sqrt[3]{2}$$
$$= 10\sqrt[3]{2} + 3\sqrt[3]{2}$$
$$= 13\sqrt[3]{2}$$

79. $\sqrt[3]{54xy^3} - y\sqrt[3]{128x}$
$$= \sqrt[3]{27\cdot 2xy^3} - y\sqrt[3]{64\cdot 2x}$$
$$= 3y\sqrt[3]{2x} - 4y\sqrt[3]{2x}$$
$$= -y\sqrt[3]{2x}$$

81. $\sqrt{2} + \sqrt[3]{8} = \sqrt{2} + 2$

83. $36^{1/2} = \sqrt{36} = 6$

85. $8^{1/3} = \sqrt[3]{8} = 2$

87. $125^{2/3} = \left(\sqrt[3]{125}\right)^2 = 5^2 = 25$

89. $32^{-4/5} = \dfrac{1}{32^{4/5}} = \dfrac{1}{2^4} = \dfrac{1}{16}$

91. $\left(7x^{1/3}\right)\left(2x^{1/4}\right) = 7 \cdot 2x^{1/3} \cdot x^{1/4}$
$\qquad\qquad\qquad = 14 \cdot x^{1/3+1/4}$
$\qquad\qquad\qquad = 14x^{7/12}$

93. $\dfrac{20x^{1/2}}{5x^{1/4}} = \left(\dfrac{20}{5}\right)\left(\dfrac{x^{1/2}}{x^{1/4}}\right)$
$\qquad\quad = 4 \cdot x^{1/2 - 1/4}$
$\qquad\quad = 4x^{1/4}$

95. $\left(x^{2/3}\right)^3 = x^{2/3 \cdot 3} = x^2$

97. $(25x^4 y^6)^{1/2} = 25^{1/2} x^{4 \cdot 1/2} y^{6 \cdot 1/2} = 5x^2 |y|^3$

99. $\dfrac{\left(3y^{\frac{1}{4}}\right)^3}{y^{\frac{1}{12}}} = \dfrac{27y^{\frac{3}{4}}}{y^{\frac{1}{12}}} = 27y^{\frac{3}{4}-\frac{1}{12}}$
$\qquad = 27y^{\frac{8}{12}} = 27y^{\frac{2}{3}}$

101. $\sqrt[4]{5^2} = 5^{2/4} = 5^{1/2} = \sqrt{5}$

103. $\sqrt[3]{x^6} = x^{6/3} = x^2$

105. $\sqrt[6]{x^4} = \sqrt[6/2]{x^{4/2}} = \sqrt[3]{x^2}$

107. $\sqrt[9]{x^6 y^3} = x^{\frac{6}{9}} y^{\frac{3}{9}} = x^{\frac{2}{3}} y^{\frac{1}{3}} = \sqrt[3]{x^2 y}$

109. $\sqrt[3]{\sqrt[4]{16} + \sqrt{625}} = \sqrt[3]{2 + 25} = \sqrt[3]{27} = 3$

111. $\left(49x^{-2} y^4\right)^{-1/2} \left(xy^{1/2}\right)$

$= (49)^{-1/2} \left(x^{-2}\right)^{-1/2} \left(y^4\right)^{-1/2} \left(xy^{1/2}\right)$

$= \dfrac{1}{49^{1/2}} x^{(-2)(-1/2)} y^{(4)(-1/2)} \left(xy^{1/2}\right)$

$= \dfrac{1}{7} x^1 y^{-2} \cdot xy^{1/2} = \dfrac{1}{7} x^{1+1} y^{-2+(1/2)}$

$= \dfrac{1}{7} x^2 y^{-3/2} = \dfrac{x^2}{7y^{3/2}}$

113. $\left(\dfrac{x^{-5/4} y^{1/3}}{x^{-3/4}}\right)^{-6} = \left(x^{(-5/4)-(-3/4)} y^{1/3}\right)^{-6}$

$= \left(x^{-2/4} y^{1/3}\right)^{-6} = x^{(-2/4)(-6)} y^{(1/3)(-6)}$

$= x^3 y^{-2} = \dfrac{x^3}{y^2}$

115. $d(x) = \sqrt{\dfrac{3x}{2}}$

$d(72) = \sqrt{\dfrac{3(72)}{2}}$

$\qquad\quad = \sqrt{3(36)}$

$\qquad\quad = \sqrt{3} \cdot \sqrt{36}$

$\qquad\quad = 6\sqrt{3} \approx 10.4 \text{ miles}$

A passenger on the pool deck can see roughly 10.4 miles.

117. $v = \sqrt{20L}; L = 245$

$\qquad v = \sqrt{20 \cdot 245} = \sqrt{4900} = 70$

The motorist was traveling 70 miles per hour, so he was speeding.

119. $\dfrac{7\sqrt{2 \cdot 2 \cdot 3}}{6} = \dfrac{7 \cdot 2\sqrt{3}}{6} = \dfrac{14\sqrt{3}}{6} = \dfrac{7}{3}\sqrt{3}$

121. a. $C = 35.74 + 0.6215t - 35.74 \sqrt[25]{v^4} + 0.4275t\sqrt[25]{v^4}$

         $C = 35.74 + 0.6215t - 35.74 v^{\frac{4}{25}} + 0.4275tv^{\frac{4}{25}}$

   b. $C = 35.74 + 0.6215(25) - 35.74(30)^{\frac{4}{25}} + 0.4275(25)(30)^{\frac{4}{25}}$

         $\approx 8° \text{ F}$

123. $P = 2l + 2w$

      $= 2\left(2\sqrt{20}\right) + 2\left(\sqrt{125}\right)$

      $= 4\sqrt{20} + 2\sqrt{125}$

      $= 4\sqrt{4 \cdot 5} + 2\sqrt{25 \cdot 5}$

      $= 4 \cdot 2\sqrt{5} + 2 \cdot 5\sqrt{5}$

      $= 8\sqrt{5} + 10\sqrt{5}$

      $= (8 + 10)\sqrt{5} = 18\sqrt{5}$

The perimeter is $18\sqrt{5}$ feet.

$A = lw = 2\sqrt{20} \cdot \sqrt{125}$

      $= 2\sqrt{20 \cdot 125} = 2\sqrt{2500}$

      $= 2 \cdot 50 = 100$

The area is 100 square feet.

133. a.   false; $(-8)^{\frac{1}{3}} = \sqrt[3]{-8} = -2$ is real.

   b.   false; $\sqrt{x^2 + y^2} \neq x + y$

   c.   false; $(8)^{-\frac{1}{3}} = \dfrac{1}{(8)^{\frac{1}{3}}} = \dfrac{1}{\sqrt[3]{8}} = \dfrac{1}{2}$

   d.   true; $2^{\frac{1}{2}} \cdot 2^{\frac{1}{2}} = 2^{\frac{1}{2} + \frac{1}{2}} = 2^1 = 2$

134. $\left(5 + \sqrt{\boxed{3}}\right)\left(5 - \sqrt{\boxed{3}}\right) = 22$

          $25 - \boxed{3} = 22$

            $\boxed{3} = 3$

135. $\sqrt{\boxed{25}x^{\boxed{14}}} = 5x^7$

137. a. $3^{\frac{1}{2}} \boxed{>} 3^{\frac{1}{3}}$

     Calculator Check: $1.7321 > 1.4422$

   b. $\sqrt{7} + \sqrt{18} \boxed{\geq} \sqrt{7 + 18}$

     Calculator Check: $6.8884 > 5$

Section P.4

Check Point Exercises

1.   **a.** $(-17x^3 + 4x^2 - 11x - 5) + (16x^3 - 3x^2 + 3x - 15)$

       $= (-17x^3 + 16x^3) + (4x^2 - 3x^2) + (-11x + 3x) + (-5 - 15)$

       $= -x^3 + x^2 - 8x - 20$

     b. $(13x^2 - 9x^2 - 7x + 1) - (-7x^3 + 2x^2 - 5x + 9)$

       $= (13x^3 - 9x^2 - 7x + 1) + (7x^3 - 2x^2 + 5x - 9)$

       $= (13x^3 + 7x^3) + (-9x^2 - 2x^2) + (-7x + 5x) + (1 - 9)$

       $= 20x^3 - 11x^2 - 2x - 8$

2. $(5x-2)(3x^2-5x+4)$

    $= 5x(3x^2-5x+4)-2(3x^2-5x+4)$

    $= 5x \cdot 3x^2 - 5x \cdot 5x + 5x \cdot 4 - 2 \cdot 3x^2 + 2 \cdot 5x - 2 \cdot 4$

    $= 15x^3 - 25x^2 + 20x - 6x^2 + 10x - 8$

    $= 15x^3 - 31x^2 + 30x - 8$

3. $(7x-5)(4x-3) = 7x \cdot 4x + 7x(-3) + (-5)4x + (-5)(-3)$

    $\qquad\qquad\qquad = 28x^2 - 21x - 20x + 15$

    $\qquad\qquad\qquad = 28x^2 - 41x + 15$

4. a. $(7x-6y)(3x-y) = (7x)(3x) + (7x)(-y) + (-6y)(3x) + (-6y)(-y)$

    $\qquad\qquad\qquad\quad = 21x^2 - 7xy - 18xy + 6y^2$

    $\qquad\qquad\qquad\quad = 21x^2 - 25xy + 6y^2$

    b. $(2x+4y)^2 = (2x)^2 + 2(2x)(4y) + (4y)^2$

    $\qquad\qquad\quad = 4x^2 + 16xy + 16y^2$

5. a. $(3x+2+5y)(3x+2-5y) = (3x+2)^2 - (5y)^2$

    $\qquad\qquad\qquad\qquad\qquad = 9x^2 + 12x + 4 - 25y^2$

    $\qquad\qquad\qquad\qquad\qquad = 9x^2 + 12x - 25y^2 + 4$

    b. $(2x+y+3)^2 = (2x+y)^2 + 2(2x+y)(3) + 3^2$

    $\qquad\qquad\qquad = 4x^2 + 4xy + y^2 + 12x + 6y + 9$

    $\qquad\qquad\qquad = 4x^2 + 4xy + 12x + y^2 + 6y + 9$

Exercise Set P.4

1. Yes; $2x + 3x^2 - 5 = 3x^2 + 2x - 5$

3. No; The form of a polynomial involves addition and subtraction, not division.

5. $3x^2$ has degree 2

    $-5x$ has degree 1

    4 has degree 0

    $3x^2 - 5x + 4$ has degree 2.

7. x^2 has degree 2

    $-4x^3$ has degree 3

    $9x$ has degree 1

    $-12x^4$ has degree 4

    63 has degree 0

    $x^2 - 4x^3 + 9x - 12x^4 + 63$ has degree 4.

9. $(-6x^3 + 5x^2 - 8x + 9) + (17x^3 + 2x^2 - 4x - 13) = (-6x^3 + 17x^3) + (5x^2 + 2x^2) + (-8x - 4x) + (9 - 13)$

    $\qquad\qquad\qquad\qquad\qquad\qquad\qquad\qquad\qquad = 11x^3 + 7x^2 - 12x - 4$

    The degree is 3.

11. $(17x^3 - 5x^2 + 4x - 3) - (5x^3 - 9x^2 - 8x + 11) = (17x^3 - 5x^2 + 4x - 3) + (-5x^3 + 9x^2 + 8x - 11)$
$$= (17x^3 - 5x^3) + (-5x^2 + 9x^2) + (4x + 8x) + (-3 - 11)$$
$$= 12x^3 + 4x^2 + 12x - 14$$

The degree is 3.

13. $(5x^2 - 7x - 8) + (2x^2 - 3x + 7) - (x^2 - 4x - 3) = (5x^2 - 7x - 8) + (2x^2 - 3x + 7) + (-x^2 + 4x + 3)$
$$= (5x^2 + 2x^2 - x^2) + (-7x - 3x + 4x) + (-8 + 7 + 3)$$
$$= 6x^2 - 6x + 2$$

The degree is 2.

15. $(x + 1)(x^2 - x + 1) = x(x^2) - x \cdot x + x \cdot 1 + 1(x^2) - 1 \cdot x + 1 \cdot 1$
$$= x^3 - x^2 + x + x^2 - x + 1$$
$$= x^3 + 1$$

17. $(2x - 3)(x^2 - 3x + 5) = (2x)(x^2) + (2x)(-3x) + (2x)(5) + (-3)(x^2) + (-3)(-3x) + (-3)(5)$
$$= 2x^3 - 6x^2 + 10x - 3x^2 + 9x - 15$$
$$= 2x^3 - 9x^2 + 19x - 15$$

19. $(x + 7)(x + 3) = x^2 + 3x + 7x + 21 = x^2 + 10x + 21$

21. $(x - 5)(x + 3) = x^2 + 3x - 5x - 15 = x^2 - 2x - 15$

23. $(3x + 5)(2x + 1) = (3x)(2x) + 3x(1) + 5(2x) + 5 = 6x^2 + 3x + 10x + 5 = 6x^2 + 13x + 5$

25. $(2x - 3)(5x + 3) = (2x)(5x) + (2x)(3) + (-3)(5x) + (-3)(3) = 10x^2 + 6x - 15x - 9 = 10x^2 - 9x - 9$

27. $(5x^2 - 4)(3x^2 - 7) = (5x^2)(3x^2) + (5x^2)(-7) + (-4)(3x^2) + (-4)(-7) = 15x^4 - 35x^2 - 12x^2 + 28 = 15x^4 - 47x^2 + 28$

29. $(8x^3 + 3)(x^2 - 5) = (8x^3)(x^2) + (8x^3)(-5) + (3)(x^2) + (3)(-5) = 8x^5 - 40x^3 + 3x^2 - 15$

31. $(x + 3)(x - 3) = x^2 - 3^2 = x^2 - 9$

33. $(3x + 2)(3x - 2) = (3x)^2 - 2^2 = 9x^2 - 4$

35. $(5 - 7x)(5 + 7x) = 5^2 - (7x)^2 = 25 - 49x^2$

37. $(4x^2 + 5x)(4x^2 - 5x) = (4x^2)^2 - (5x)^2 = 16x^4 - 25x^2$

39. $(1 - y^5)(1 + y^5) = (1)^2 - (y^5)^2 = 1 - y^{10}$

41. $(x + 2)^2 = x^2 + 2 \cdot x \cdot 2 + 2^2 = x^2 + 4x + 4$

43. $(2x + 3)^2 = (2x)^2 + 2(2x)(3) + 3^2 = 4x^2 + 12x + 9$

45. $(x - 3)^2 = x^2 - 2 \cdot x \cdot 3 + 3^2 = x^2 - 6x + 9$

47. $(4x^2 - 1)^2 = (4x^2)^2 - 2(4x^2)(1) + 1^2 = 16x^4 - 8x^2 + 1$

49. $(7 - 2x)^2 = 7^2 - 2(7)(2x) + (2x)^2 = 49 - 28x + 4x^2 = 4x^2 - 28x + 49$

51. $(x+1)^3 = x^3 + 3 \cdot x^2 \cdot 1 + 3x \cdot 1^2 + 1^3 = x^3 + 3x^2 + 3x + 1$

53. $(2x+3)^3 = (2x)^3 + 3 \cdot (2x)^2 \cdot 3 + 3(2x) \cdot 3^2 + 3^3 = 8x^3 + 36x^2 + 54x + 27$

55. $(x-3)^3 = x^3 - 3 \cdot x^3 \cdot 3 + 3 \cdot x \cdot 3^2 - 3^3 = x^3 - 9x^2 + 27x - 27$

57. $(3x-4)^3 = (3x)^3 - 3(3x)^2 \cdot 4 + 3(3x) \cdot 4^2 - 4^3 = 27x^3 - 108x^2 + 144x - 64$

59. $(x+5y)(7x+3y) = x(7x) + x(3y) + (5y)(7x) + (5y)(3y) = 7x^2 + 3xy + 35xy + 15y^2 = 7x^2 + 38xy + 15y^2$

61. $(x-3y)(2x+7y) = x(2x) + x(7y) + (-3y)(2x) + (-3y)(7y) = 2x^2 + 7xy - 6xy - 21y^2 = 2x^2 + xy - 21y^2$

63. $(3xy-1)(5xy+2) = (3xy)(5xy) + (3xy)(2) + (-1)(5xy) + (-1)(2) = 15x^2y^2 + 6xy - 5xy - 2$
$$= 15x^2y^2 + xy - 2$$

65. $(7x+5y)^2 = (7x)^2 + 2(7x)(5y) + (5y)^2 = 49x^2 + 70xy + 25y^2$

67. $(x^2y^2 - 3)^2 = (x^2y^2)^2 - 2(x^2y^2)(3) + 3^2 = x^4y^4 - 6x^2y^2 + 9$

69. $(x-y)(x^2+xy+y^2) = x(x^2) + x(xy) + x(y^2) + (-y)(x^2) + (-y)(xy) + (-y)(y^2)$
$$= x^3 + x^2y + xy^2 - x^2y - xy^2 - y^3$$
$$= x^3 - y^3$$

71. $(3x+5y)(3x-5y) = (3x)^2 - (5y)^2 = 9x^2 - 25y^2$

73. $(x+y+3)(x+y-3) = (x+y)^2 - 3^2 = x^2 + 2xy + y^2 - 9$

75. $(3x+7-5y)(3x+7+5y) = (3x+7)^2 - (5y)^2 = 9x^2 + 42x + 49 - 25y^2$

77. $[5y-(2x+3)][5y+(2x+3)] = (5y)^2 - (2x+3)^2 = 25y^2 - (4x^2 + 12x + 9) = 25y^2 - 4x^2 - 12x - 9$

79. $(x+y+1)^2 = (x+y)^2 + 2(x+y) + 1 = x^2 + 2xy + y^2 + 2x + 2y + 1$

81. $(2x+y+1)^2 = (2x+y)^2 + 2(2x+y) + 1 = 4x^2 + 4xy + y^2 + 4x + 2y + 1$

83. $(3x+4y)^2 - (3x-4y)^2 = \left[(3x)^2 + 2(3x)(4y) + (4y)^2\right] - \left[(3x)^2 - 2(3x)(4y) + (4y)^2\right]$
$$= \left(9x^2 + 24xy + 16y^2\right) - \left(9x^2 - 24xy + 16y^2\right)$$
$$= 9x^2 + 24xy + 16y^2 - 9x^2 + 24xy - 16y^2$$
$$= 48xy$$

85. $(5x-7)(3x-2) - (4x-5)(6x-1)$
$$= \left[15x^2 - 10x - 21x + 14\right] - \left[24x^2 - 4x - 30x + 5\right]$$
$$= \left(15x^2 - 31x + 14\right) - \left(24x^2 - 34x + 5\right)$$
$$= 15x^2 - 31x + 14 - 24x^2 + 34x - 5$$
$$= -9x^2 + 3x + 9$$

87. $(2x+5)(2x-5)(4x^2+25)$

$= \left[(2x)^2 - 5^2 \right] (4x^2 + 25)$

$= (4x^2 - 25)(4x^2 + 25)$

$= (4x^2)^2 - (25)^2$

$= 16x^4 - 625$

89. $\dfrac{(2x-7)^5}{(2x-7)^3} = (2x-7)^{5-3}$

$= (2x-7)^2$

$= (2x)^2 - 2(2x)(7) + (7)^2$

$= 4x^2 - 28x + 49$

91. Model 4 is not in standard form.
    $N = 0.09x^2 + 0.01x^3 + 1.1x + 5.64$
    Model 4 in standard form:
    $N = 0.01x^3 + 0.09x^2 + 1.1x + 5.64$

93. Model 1:
    $N = 1.8x + 5.1$
    $N = 1.8(2) + 5.1$
    $N = 8.7$
    Model 2:
    $N = 5.6(1.2)^x$
    $N = 5.6(1.2)^2$
    $N = 8.064$
    Model 3:
    $N = 0.17x^2 + 0.95x + 5.68$
    $N = 0.17(2)^2 + 0.95(2) + 5.68$
    $N = 8.26$
    Model 4:
    $N = 0.09x^2 + 0.01x^3 + 1.1x + 5.64$
    $N = 0.09(2)^2 + 0.01(2)^3 + 1.1(2) + 5.64$
    $N = 8.28$
    Model 1 best describes the data in 2000.

95. Model 3 is the model of degree 2.
    $N = 0.17x^2 + 0.95x + 5.68$
    $N = 0.17(5)^2 + 0.95(5) + 5.68$
    $N = 14.68$
    Model 3 best describes the data in 2003 very well.

97. $x(8-2x)(10-2x) = x(80-36x+4x^2)$

$$= 80x - 36x^2 + 4x^3$$

$$= 4x^3 - 36x^2 + 80x$$

99. $(x+9)(x+3)-(x+5)(x+1)$

$= x^2 + 12x + 27 - (x^2 + 6x + 5)$

$= x^2 + 12x + 27 - x^2 - 6x - 5$

$= 6x + 22$

109. $(2x-1)x(x+3) - x(x-2)x$

$= (2x^2 + 5x - 3)(x+2) - x^2(x-2)$

$= 2x^3 + 5x^2 - 3x - x^3 + 2x^2$

$= x^3 + 7x^2 - 3x$

111. $(y^n + 2)(y^n - 2) - (y^n - 3)^2$

$= y^{2n} - 4 - (y^{2n} - 6y^n + 9)$

$= y^{2n} - 4 - y^{2n} + 6y^n - 9$

$= 6y^n - 13$

Section P.5

Check Point Exercises

1. **a.** $10x^3 - 4x^2$

$= 2x^2(5x) - 2x^2(2)$

$= 2x^2(5x-2)$

 b. $2x(x-7) + 3(x-7)$

$= (x-7)(2x+3)$

2. $x^3 + 5x^2 - 2x - 10$

$= (x^3 + 5x^2) - (2x + 10)$

$= x^2(x+5) - 2(x+5)$

$= (x+5)(x^2 - 2)$

3. **a.** Find two numbers whose product is 40 and whose sum is 13. The required integers are 8 and 5. Thus,

$x^2 + 13x + 40 = (x+5)(x+8)$ or $(x+8)(x+5)$

 b. Find two numbers whose product is −14 and whose sum is −5. The required integers are −7 and 2. Thus,

$x^2 - 5x - 14 = (x-7)(x+2)$ or $(x+2)(x-7)$.

4. Find two First terms whose product is $6x^2$.
    $$6x^2 + 19x - 7 = (6x \quad)(x \quad)$$
    $$6x^2 + 19x - 7 = (3x \quad)(2x \quad)$$

    Find two Last terms whose product is -7.
    The possible factors are $1(-7)$ and $-1(7)$.

    Try various combinations of these factors to find the factorization in which the sum of the Outside and Inside products is $19x$.

Possible Factors of $6x^2 + 19x - 7$	Sum of Outside and Inside Products (Should Equal $19x$)
$(6x+1)(x-7)$	$-42x + x = -41x$
$(6x-7)(x+1)$	$6x - 7x = -x$
$(6x-1)(x+7)$	$42x - x = 41x$
$(6x+7)(x-1)$	$-6x + 7x = x$
$(3x+1)(2x-7)$	$-21x + 2x = -19x$
$(3x-7)(2x+1)$	$3x - 14x = -11x$
$(3x-1)(2x+7)$	$21x - 2x = 19x$
$(3x+7)(2x-1)$	$-3x + 14x = 11x$

    Thus, $6x^2 + 19x - 7 = (3x-1)(2x+7)$ or $(2x+7)(3x-1)$.

5. Find two First terms whose product is $3x^2$.
    $$3x^2 - 13xy + 4y^2 = (3x \quad)(x \quad)$$

    Find two Last terms whose product is $4y^2$.
    The possible factors are $(2y)(2y)$, $(-2y)(-2y)$, $(4y)(y)$, and $(-4y)(-y)$.

    Try various combinations of these factors to find the factorization in which the sum of the Outside and Inside products is $-13xy$.

    $$3x^2 - 13xy + y^2 = (3x - y)(x - 4y) \text{ or } (x - 4y)(3x - y).$$

6. Express each term as the square of some monomial. Then use the formula for factoring $A^2 - B^2$.
    a. $x^2 - 81 = x^2 - 9^2 = (x+9)(x-9)$

    b. $36x^2 - 25 = (6x)^2 - 5^2 = (6x+5)(6x-5)$

7. Express $81x^4 - 16$ as the difference of two squares and use the formula for factoring $A^2 - B^2$.
    $$81x^4 - 16 = (9x^2)^2 - 4^2 = (9x^2 + 4)(9x^2 - 4)$$

    The factor $9x^2 - 4$ is the difference of two squares and can be factored. Express $9x^2 - 4$ as the difference of two squares and again use the formula for factoring $A^2 - B^2$.
    $$(9x^2 + 4)(9x^2 - 4) = (9x^2 + 4)\left[(3x)^2 - 2^2\right] = (9x^2 + 4)(3x + 2)(3x - 2)$$

    Thus, factored completely,
    $$81x^4 - 16 = (9x^2 + 4)(3x + 2)(3x - 2).$$

8. a. $x^2 + 14x + 49 = x^2 + 2 \cdot x \cdot 7 + 7^2 = (x+7)^2$

b. Since $16x^2 = (4x)^2$ and $49 = 7^2$, check to see if the middle term can be expressed as twice the product of $4x$ and 7. Since $2 \cdot 4x \cdot 7 = 56x$, $16x^2 - 56x + 49$ is a perfect square trinomial. Thus,

$$16x^2 - 56x + 49 = (4x)^2 - 2 \cdot 4x \cdot 7 + 7^2$$
$$= (4x-7)^2$$

9. a. $= x^3 + 1^3$
$$= (x+1)(x^2 - x \cdot 1 + 1^2)$$
$$= (x+1)(x^2 - x + 1)$$

b. $-8 = (5x)^3 - 2^3$
$$= (5x-2)\left[(5x)^2 + (5x)(2) + 2^2\right]$$
$$= (5x-2)(25x^2 + 10x + 4)$$

10. Factor out the greatest common factor.
$$3x^3 - 30x^2 + 75x = 3x(x^2 - 10x + 25)$$
Factor the perfect square trinomial.
$$3x(x^2 - 10x + 25) = 3x(x-5)^2$$

11. Reorder to write as a difference of squares.
$$x^2 - 36a^2 + 20x + 100$$
$$= x^2 + 20x + 100 - 36a^2$$
$$= (x^2 + 20x + 100) - 36a^2$$
$$= (x+10)^2 - 36a^2$$
$$= (x + 10 + 6a)(x + 10 - 6a)$$

12. $x(x-1)^{-\frac{1}{2}} + (x-1)^{\frac{1}{2}}$
$$= (x-1)^{-\frac{1}{2}}\left[x + (x-1)^{\frac{1}{2}-\left(-\frac{1}{2}\right)}\right]$$
$$= (x-1)^{-\frac{1}{2}}\left[x + (x-1)\right]$$
$$= (x-1)^{-\frac{1}{2}}(2x-1)$$
$$= \frac{(2x-1)}{(x-1)^{\frac{1}{2}}}$$

Exercise Set P.5

1. $18x + 27 = 9 \cdot 2x + 9 \cdot 3 = 9(2x+3)$

3. $3x^2 + 6x = 3x \cdot x + 3x \cdot 2 = 3x(x+2)$

5. $9x^4 - 18x^3 + 27x^2$
$$= 9x^2(x^2) + 9x^2(-2x) + 9x^2(3)$$
$$= 9x^2(x^2 - 2x + 3)$$

7. $x(x+5) + 3(x+5) = (x+5)(x+3)$

9. $x^2(x-3) + 12(x-3) = (x-3)(x^2+12)$

11. $x^3 - 2x^2 + 5x - 10 = x^2(x-2) + 5(x-2)$
$$= (x^2+5)(x-2)$$

13. $x^3 - x^2 + 2x - 2 = x^2(x-1) + 2(x-1)$
$$= (x-1)(x^2+2)$$

15. $3x^3 - 2x^2 - 6x + 4 = x^2(3x-2) - 2(3x-2)$
$$= (3x-2)(x^2-2)$$

17. $x^2 + 5x + 6 = (x+2)(x+3)$

19. $x^2 - 2x - 15 = (x-5)(x+3)$

21. $x^2 - 8x + 15 = (x-5)(x-3)$

23. $3x^2 - x - 2 = (3x+2)(x-1)$

25. $3x^2 - 25x - 28 = (3x-28)(x+1)$

27. $6x^2 - 11x + 4 = (2x-1)(3x-4)$

29. $4x^2 + 16x + 15 = (2x+3)(2x+5)$

31. $9x^2 - 9x + 2 = (3x-1)(3x-2)$

33. $20x^2 + 27x - 8 = (5x+8)(4x-1)$

35. $2x^2 + 3xy + y^2 = (2x+y)(x+y)$

37. $6x^2 - 5xy - 6y^2 = (3x + 2y)(2x - 3y)$

39. $x^2 - 100 = x^2 - 10^2 = (x + 10)(x - 10)$

41. $36x^2 - 49 = (6x)^2 - 7^2 = (6x + 7)(6x - 7)$

43. $9x^2 - 25y^2 = (3x)^2 - (5y)^2$
$$= (3x + 5y)(3x - 5y)$$

45. $x^4 - 16 = (x^2)^2 - 4^2$
$$= (x^2 + 4)(x^2 - 4)$$
$$= (x^2 + 4)(x + 2)(x - 2)$$

47. $16x^4 - 81 = (4x^2)^2 - 9^2$
$$= (4x^2 + 9)(4x^2 - 9)$$
$$= (4x^2 + 9)[(2x)^2 - 3^2]$$
$$= (4x^2 + 9)(2x + 3)(2x - 3)$$

49. $x^2 + 2x + 1 = x^2 + 2 \cdot x \cdot 1 + 1^2 = (x + 1)^2$

51. $x^2 - 14x + 49 = x^2 - 2 \cdot x \cdot 7 + 7^2$
$$= (x - 7)^2$$

53. $4x^2 + 4x + 1 = (2x)^2 + 2 \cdot 2x \cdot 1 + 1^2$
$$= (2x + 1)^2$$

55. $9x^2 - 6x + 1 = (3x)^2 - 2 \cdot 3x \cdot 1 + 1^2$
$$= (3x - 1)^2$$

57. $x^3 + 27 = x^3 + 3^3$
$$= (x + 3)(x^2 - x \cdot 3 + 3^2)$$
$$= (x + 3)(x^2 - 3x + 9)$$

59. $x^3 - 64 = x^3 - 4^3$
$$= (x - 4)(x^2 + x \cdot 4 + 4^2)$$
$$= (x - 4)(x^2 + 4x + 16)$$

61. $8x^3 - 1 = (2x)^3 - 1^3$
$$= (2x - 1)[(2x)^2 + (2x)(1) + 1^2]$$
$$= (2x - 1)(4x^2 + 2x + 1)$$

63. $64x^3 + 27 = (4x)^3 + 3^3$
$$= (4x + 3)[(4x)^2 - (4x)(3) + 3^2]$$
$$= (4x + 3)(16x^2 - 12x + 9)$$

65. $3x^3 - 3x = 3x(x^2 - 1) = 3x(x + 1)(x - 1)$

67. $4x^2 - 4x - 24 = 4(x^2 - x - 6)$
$$= 4(x + 2)(x - 3)$$

69. $2x^4 - 162 = 2(x^4 - 81)$
$$= 2[(x^2)^2 - 9^2]$$
$$= 2(x^2 + 9)(x^2 - 9)$$
$$= 2(x^2 + 9)(x^2 - 3^2)$$
$$= 2(x^2 + 9)(x + 3)(x - 3)$$

71. $x^3 + 2x^2 - 9x - 18 = (x^3 + 2x^2) - (9x + 18)$
$$= x^2(x + 2) - 9(x + 2)$$
$$= (x^2 - 9)(x + 2)$$
$$= (x^2 - 3^2)(x + 2)$$
$$= (x - 3)(x + 3)(x + 2)$$

73. $2x^2 - 2x - 112 = 2(x^2 - x - 56) = 2(x - 8)(x + 7)$

75. $x^3 - 4x = x(x^2 - 4)$
$$= x(x^2 - 2^2)$$
$$= x(x - 2)(x + 2)$$

77. $x^2 + 64$ is prime.

79. $x^3 + 2x^2 - 4x - 8 = (x^3 + 2x^2) + (-4x - 8)$
$$= x^2(x + 2) - 4(x + 2) = (x^2 - 4)(x + 2) = (x^2 - 2^2)(x + 2) = (x - 2)(x + 2)(x + 2) = (x - 2)(x + 2)^2$$

81. $y^5 - 81y$
$$= y(y^4 - 81) = y[(y^2)^2 - 9^2] = y(y^2 + 9)(y^2 - 9) = y(y^2 + 9)(y^2 - 3^2) = y(y^2 + 9)(y + 3)(y - 3)$$

83. $20y^4 - 45y^2 = 5y^2(4y^2 - 9) = 5y^2[(2y)^2 - 3^2] = 5y^2(2y + 3)(2y - 3)$

85. $x^2 - 12x + 36 - 49y^2 = \left(x^2 - 12x + 36\right) - 49y^2 = (x-6)^2 - 49y^2 = (x - 6 + 7y)(x - 6 - 7y)$

87. $9b^2 x - 16y - 16x + 9b^2 y$

$= \left(9b^2 x + 9b^2 y\right) + \left(-16x - 16y\right) = 9b^2\left(x + y\right) - 16\left(x + y\right) = \left(x + y\right)\left(9b^2 - 16\right) = (x + y)(3b + 4)(3b - 4)$

89. $x^2 y - 16y + 32 - 2x^2$

$= \left(x^2 y - 16y\right) + \left(-2x^2 + 32\right) = y\left(x^2 - 16\right) - 2\left(x^2 - 16\right) = \left(x^2 - 16\right)(y - 2) = (x + 4)(x - 4)(y - 2)$

91. $2x^3 - 8a^2 x + 24x^2 + 72x$

$= 2x\left(x^2 - 4a^2 + 12x + 36\right) = 2x\left[\left(x^2 + 12x + 36\right) - 4a^2\right] = 2x\left[(x + 6)^2 - 4a^2\right] = 2x(x + 6 - 2a)(x + 6 + 2a)$

93. $x^{\frac{3}{2}} - x^{\frac{1}{2}} = x^{\frac{1}{2}}\left(x^{\frac{3}{2} - \frac{1}{2}}\right) - 1 = x^{\frac{1}{2}}(x - 1)$

95. $4x^{-\frac{2}{3}} + 8x^{\frac{1}{3}} = 4x^{-\frac{2}{3}}\left(1 + 2x^{\frac{1}{3} - \left(-\frac{2}{3}\right)}\right) = 4x^{-\frac{2}{3}}(1 + 2x) = \dfrac{4(1 + 2x)}{x^{\frac{2}{3}}}$

97. $(x + 3)^{\frac{1}{2}} - (x + 3)^{\frac{3}{2}} = (x + 3)^{\frac{1}{2}}\left[1 - (x + 3)^{\frac{3}{2} - \frac{1}{2}}\right] = (x + 3)^{\frac{1}{2}}\left[1 - (x + 3)\right] = (x + 3)^{\frac{1}{2}}(-x - 2) = -(x + 3)^{\frac{1}{2}}(x + 2)$

99. $(x + 5)^{-\frac{1}{2}} - (x + 5)^{-\frac{3}{2}} = (x + 5)^{-\frac{3}{2}}\left[(x + 5)^{-\frac{1}{2} - \left(-\frac{3}{2}\right)} - 1\right] = (x + 5)^{-\frac{3}{2}}\left[(x + 5) - 1\right] = (x + 5)^{-\frac{3}{2}}(x + 4) = \dfrac{x + 4}{(x + 5)^{\frac{3}{2}}}$

101. $(4x - 1)^{\frac{1}{2}} - \dfrac{1}{3}(4x - 1)^{\frac{3}{2}}$

$= (4x - 1)^{\frac{1}{2}}\left[1 - \dfrac{1}{3}(4x - 1)^{\frac{3}{2} - \frac{1}{2}}\right] = (4x - 1)^{\frac{1}{2}}\left[1 - \dfrac{1}{3}(4x - 1)\right] = (4x - 1)^{\frac{1}{2}}\left[1 - \dfrac{4}{3}x + \dfrac{1}{3}\right]$

$= (4x - 1)^{\frac{1}{2}}\left(\dfrac{4}{3} - \dfrac{4}{3}x\right) = (4x - 1)^{\frac{1}{2}}\dfrac{4}{3}(1 - x) = \dfrac{-4(4x - 1)(x - 1)}{3}$

103. $10x^2(x + 1) - 7x(x + 1) - 6(x + 1) = (x + 1)\left(10x^2 - 7x - 6\right) = (x + 1)(5x - 6)(2x + 1)$

105. $6x^4 + 35x^2 - 6 = \left(x^2 + 6\right)\left(6x^2 - 1\right)$

107. $y^7 + y = y\left(y^6 + 1\right) = y\left[\left(y^2\right)^3 + 1^3\right] = y\left(y^2 + 1\right)\left(y^4 - y^2 + 1\right)$

109. $x^4 - 5x^2 y^2 + 4y^4 = \left(x^2 - 4y^2\right)\left(x^2 - y^2\right) = (x + 2y)(x - 2y)(x + y)(x - y)$

111. $(x - y)^4 - 4(x - y)^2$

$= (x - y)^2\left((x - y)^2 - 4\right) = (x - y)^2\left((x - y) + 2\right)\left((x - y) - 2\right) = (x - y)^2(x - y + 2)(x - y - 2)$

113. $2x^2 - 7xy^2 + 3y^4 = \left(2x - y^2\right)\left(x - 3y^2\right)$

115. a. $(x - 0.4x) - 0.4(x - 0.4x) = (x - 0.4x)(1 - 0.4) = (0.6x)(0.6) = 0.36x$

    b. No, the computer is selling at 36% of its original price.

117. a. $(3x)^2 - 4 \cdot 2^2 = 9x^2 - 16$

    b. $9x^2 - 16 = (3x + 4)(3x - 4)$

119. a. $x(x + y) - y(x + y)$

    b. $x(x + y) - y(x + y) = (x + y)(x - y)$

121. $V_{\text{shaded}} = V_{\text{outside}} - V_{\text{inside}}$
$$= a \cdot a \cdot 4a - b \cdot b \cdot 4a$$
$$= 4a^3 - 4ab^2$$
$$= 4a(a^2 - b^2)$$
$$= 4a(a + b)(a - b)$$

131. $x^{2n} + 6x^n + 8 = (x^n + 4)(x^n + 2)$

133. $x^4 - y^4 - 2x^3y + 2xy^3 = (x^4 - y^4) + (-2x^3y + 2xy^3) = (x^2 - y^2)(x^2 + y^2) - 2xy(x^2 - y^2)$

$$= (x^2 - y^2)(x^2 + y^2 - 2xy) = (x - y)(x + y)(x^2 - 2xy + y^2) = (x - y)(x + y)(x - y)^2 = (x - y)^3(x + y)$$

135. $x^2 + bx + 15$, $b = 16, -16, 8$ or -8

Mid-Chapter P Check Point

1. $(3x + 5)(4x - 7) = (3x)(4x) + (3x)(-7) + (5)(4x) + (5)(-7)$
$$= 12x^2 - 21x + 20x - 35$$
$$= 12x^2 - x - 35$$

2. $(3x + 5) - (4x - 7) = 3x + 5 - 4x + 7$
$$= 3x - 4x + 5 + 7$$
$$= -x + 12$$

3. $\sqrt{6} + 9\sqrt{6} = 10\sqrt{6}$

4. $3\sqrt{12} - \sqrt{27} = 3 \cdot 2\sqrt{3} - 3\sqrt{3} = 6\sqrt{3} - 3\sqrt{3} = 3\sqrt{3}$

5. $7x + 3[9 - (2x - 6)] = 7x + 3[9 - 2x + 6] = 7x + 3[15 - 2x] = 7x + 45 - 6x = x + 45$

6. $(8x - 3)^2 = (8x)^2 - 2(8x)(3) + (3)^2 = 64x^2 - 48x + 9$

7. $\left(x^{\frac{1}{3}}y^{-\frac{1}{2}}\right)^6 = x^{\frac{1}{3}\cdot 6}y^{-\frac{1}{2}\cdot 6} = x^2 y^{-3} = \dfrac{x^2}{y^3}$

8. $\left(\dfrac{2}{7}\right)^0 - 32^{-\frac{2}{5}} = 1 - \dfrac{1}{\left(\sqrt[5]{32}\right)^2} = 1 - \dfrac{1}{(2)^2} = 1 - \dfrac{1}{4} = \dfrac{3}{4}$

9. $(2x-5)-(x^2-3x+1) = 2x-5-x^2+3x-1 = -x^2+5x-6$

10. $(2x-5)(x^2-3x+1) = 2x(x^2-3x+1)-5(x^2-3x+1)$
$\qquad\qquad\qquad\qquad = 2x(x^2-3x+1)-5(x^2-3x+1)$
$\qquad\qquad\qquad\qquad = 2x^3-6x^2+2x-5x^2+15x-5$
$\qquad\qquad\qquad\qquad = 2x^3-6x^2-5x^2+2x+15x-5$
$\qquad\qquad\qquad\qquad = 2x^3-11x^2+17x-5$

11. $x^3+x^3-x^3\cdot x^3 = 2x^3-x^6 = -x^6+2x^3$

12. $(9a-10b)(2a+b) = (9a)(2a)+(9a)(b)+(-10b)(2a)+(-10b)(b)$
$\qquad\qquad\qquad\qquad = (9a)(2a)+(9a)(b)+(-10b)(2a)+(-10b)(b)$
$\qquad\qquad\qquad\qquad = 18a^2+9ab-20ab-10b^2$
$\qquad\qquad\qquad\qquad = 18a^2-11ab-10b^2$

13. $\{a,c,d,e\}\cup\{c,d,f,h\} = \{a,c,d,e,f,h\}$

14. $\{a,c,d,e\}\cap\{c,d,f,h\} = \{c,d\}$

15. $\left(3x^2 y^3 - xy + 4y^2\right) - \left(-2x^2 y^3 - 3xy + 5y^2\right) = 3x^2 y^3 - xy + 4y^2 + 2x^2 y^3 + 3xy - 5y^2$
$\qquad\qquad\qquad\qquad\qquad\qquad = 3x^2 y^3 - xy + 4y^2 + 2x^2 y^3 + 3xy - 5y^2$
$\qquad\qquad\qquad\qquad\qquad\qquad = 3x^2 y^3 + 2x^2 y^3 - xy + 3xy + 4y^2 - 5y^2$
$\qquad\qquad\qquad\qquad\qquad\qquad = 5x^2 y^3 + 2xy - y^2$

16. $\dfrac{24x^2 y^{13}}{-2x^5 y^{-2}} = -12x^{2-5}y^{13-(-2)} = -12x^{-3}y^{15} = -\dfrac{12y^{15}}{x^3}$

17. $\left(\dfrac{1}{3}x^{-5}y^4\right)\left(18x^{-2}y^{-1}\right) = 6x^{-5-2}y^{4-1} = \dfrac{6y^3}{x^7}$

18. $\sqrt[12]{x^4} = x^{\frac{4}{12}} = \left|x^{\frac{1}{3}}\right| = \left|\sqrt[3]{x}\right|$

19. $\left[4y-(3x+2)\right]\left[4y+(3x+2)\right] = (4y)^2-(3x+2)^2 = 16y^2-(9x^2+12x+4) = 16y^2-9x^2-12x-4$

20. $(x-2y-1)^2 = x(x-2y-1)-2y(x-2y-1)-(x-2y-1)$

$$= x^2 - 2xy - x - 2xy + 4y^2 + 2y - x + 2y + 1$$

$$= x^2 - 4xy + 4y^2 - 2x + 4y + 1$$

21. $\dfrac{24 \times 10^3}{2 \times 10^6} = \dfrac{24}{2} \cdot \dfrac{10^3}{10^6} = 12 \times 10^{-3} = \left(1.2 \times 10^1\right) \times 10^{-3} = 1.2 \times \left(10^1 \times 10^{-3}\right) = 1.2 \times 10^{-2}$

22. $\dfrac{\sqrt[3]{32}}{\sqrt[3]{2}} = \sqrt[3]{\dfrac{32}{2}} = \sqrt[3]{16} = \sqrt[3]{2^4} = 2\sqrt[3]{2}$

23. $(x^3+2)(x^3-2) = x^6 - 4$

24. $(x^2+2)^2 = (x^2)^2 + 2(x^2)(2) + (2)^2 = x^4 + 4x^2 + 4$

25. $\sqrt{50} \cdot \sqrt{6} = 5\sqrt{2} \cdot \sqrt{6} = 5\sqrt{2 \cdot 6} = 5\sqrt{12} = 5 \cdot 2\sqrt{3} = 10\sqrt{3}$

26. $\dfrac{11}{7-\sqrt{3}} = \dfrac{11}{7-\sqrt{3}} \cdot \dfrac{7+\sqrt{3}}{7+\sqrt{3}} = \dfrac{77+11\sqrt{3}}{49-3} = \dfrac{77+11\sqrt{3}}{46}$

27. $\dfrac{11}{\sqrt{3}} = \dfrac{11}{\sqrt{3}} \cdot \dfrac{\sqrt{3}}{\sqrt{3}} = \dfrac{11\sqrt{3}}{3}$

28. $7x^2 - 22x + 3 = (7x-1)(x-3)$

29. $x^2 - 2x + 4$ is prime.

30. $7x^2 - 22x + 3 = (7x-1)(x-3)$

31. $3x^2 - 4xy - 7y^2 = (3x-7y)(x+y)$

32. $64y - y^3 = y(64-y^2) = y(8+y)(8-y)$

33. $50x^3 + 20x^2 + 2x = 2x(25x^2+10x+1) = 2x(5x+1)^2$

34. $x^2 - 6x + 9 - 49y^2 = (x-3)^2 - 49y^2 = \left[(x-3)+7y\right]\left[(x-3)-7y\right] = (x-3+7y)(x-3-7y)$

35. $x^{-\frac{3}{2}} - 2x^{-\frac{1}{2}} + x^{\frac{1}{2}} = x^{-\frac{3}{2}}\left(1-2x+x^2\right) = \dfrac{(1-x)^2}{x^{\frac{3}{2}}}$

36. $\left(x^2+1\right)^{\frac{1}{2}} - 10\left(x^2+1\right)^{-\frac{1}{2}} = \left(x^2+1\right)^{-\frac{1}{2}}\left[\left(x^2+1\right)-10\right] = \left(x^2+1\right)^{-\frac{1}{2}}\left(x^2-9\right) = \dfrac{(x+3)(x-3)}{\left(x^2+1\right)^{\frac{1}{2}}}$

37. $\left\{-11, \ -\dfrac{3}{7}, \ 0, \ 0.45, \ \sqrt{25}\right\}$

38. Since $2-\sqrt{13}<0$ then $\left|2-\sqrt{13}\right|=\sqrt{13}-2$

39. Since $x<0$ then $|x|=-x$. Thus $x^2|x|=-x^2x=-x^3$

40. $120\cdot2.9\times10^8=348\times10^8=3.48\times10^2\times10^8=3.48\times10^{10}$
    The total annual spending on ice cream is $\$3.48\times10^{10}$.

41. $\dfrac{3\times10^{10}}{7.5\times10^9}=\dfrac{3}{7.5}\cdot\dfrac{10^{10}}{10^9}=0.4\times10=4$
    A human brain has 4 times as many neurons as a gorilla brain.

42. **a.** Model 1:
    $$D=236(1.5)^x$$
    $$D=236(1.5)^2$$
    $$D=531$$
    Model 2:
    $$D=127x+239$$
    $$D=127(2)+239$$
    $$D=493$$
    Model 3:
    $$D=-54x^2+234x+220$$
    $$D=-54(2)^2+234(2)+220$$
    $$D=472$$

    Model 3 best describes the data in 2004.

    b. Model 2 is the polynomial of degree 1:
    $$D=127x+239$$
    $$D=127(6)+239$$
    $$D=1001$$

    Model 2 predicts Americans will spend 1001 million dollars on online dating in 2008.

Section P.6

Check Point Exercises

1. **a.**   The denominator would equal zero if $x = -5$, so -5 must be excluded from the domain.

    b. $x^2 - 36 = (x + 6)(x - 6)$

    The denominator would equal zero if $x = -6$ or $x = 6$, so -6 and 6 must both be excluded from the domain.

2. **a.** $\dfrac{x^3 + 3x^2}{x + 3} = \dfrac{x^2(x + 3)}{x + 3}$ Because the denominator is $x + 3$, $x \neq -3$

    $\qquad\qquad = \dfrac{x^2(x + 3)}{x + 3}$

    $\qquad\qquad = x^2, \ x \neq -3$

    b. $\dfrac{x^2 - 1}{x^2 + 2x + 1} = \dfrac{(x - 1)(x + 1)}{(x + 1)(x + 1)}$ Because the denominator is

    $\qquad\qquad\qquad = \dfrac{x - 1}{x + 1}, x \neq -1$ $(x + 1)(x + 1), x \neq -1$

3. $\dfrac{x + 3}{x^2 - 4} \cdot \dfrac{x^2 - x - 6}{x^2 + 6x + 9}$

    $= \dfrac{x + 3}{(x + 2)(x - 2)} \cdot \dfrac{(x - 3)(x + 2)}{(x + 3)(x + 3)}$ Because the denominator has factors of

    $= \dfrac{x + 3}{(x + 2)(x - 2)} \cdot \dfrac{(x - 3)(x + 2)}{(x + 3)(x + 3)}$ $x + 2, \ x - 2$, and $x + 3$, $x \neq -2$, $x \neq 2$,

    $= \dfrac{x - 3}{(x - 2)(x + 3)}, \ x \neq -2, \ x \neq 2, \ x \neq -3$ and $x \neq -3$.

4. $\dfrac{x^2 - 2x + 1}{x^3 + x} \div \dfrac{x^2 + x - 2}{3x^2 + 3}$

    $= \dfrac{x^2 - 2x + 1}{x^3 + x} \cdot \dfrac{3x^2 + 3}{x^2 + x - 2}$

    $= \dfrac{(x - 1)(x - 1)}{x(x^2 + 1)} \cdot \dfrac{3(x^2 + 1)}{(x + 2)(x - 1)}$

    $= \dfrac{3(x - 1)}{x(x + 2)}, \ x \neq 0, \ x \neq -2, \ x \neq 1$

5. $\dfrac{x}{x+1} - \dfrac{3x+2}{x+1} = \dfrac{x-3x-2}{x+1}$

$$= \dfrac{-2x-2}{x+1}$$

$$= \dfrac{-2(x+1)}{x+1}$$

$$= -2, x \neq -1$$

6. $\dfrac{3}{x+1} + \dfrac{5}{x-1}$

$$= \dfrac{3x(x-1)+5(x+1)}{(x+1)(x-1)}$$

$$= \dfrac{3x-3+5x+5}{(x+1)(x-1)}$$

$$= \dfrac{8x+2}{(x+1)(x-1)}$$

$$= \dfrac{2(4x+1)}{(x+1)(x-1)}$$

$$= \dfrac{2(4x+1)}{(x+1)(x-1)}, \ x \neq -1 \text{ and } x \neq 1.$$

7. Factor each denominator completely.

$x^2 - 6x + 9 = (x-3)^2$

$x^2 - 9 = (x+3)(x-3)$

List the factors of the first denominator.
$x-3, \ x-3$

Add any unlisted factors from the second denominator.
$x-3, \ x-3, \ x+3$

The least common denominator is the product of all factors in the final list.
$(x-3)(x-3)(x+3)$ or $(x-3)^2(x+3)$ is the least common denominator.

8. Find the least common denominator.

$x^2 - 10x + 25 = (x-5)^2$

$2x - 10 = 2(x-5)$

The least common denominator is $2(x-5)(x-5)$.
Write all rational expressions in terms of the least common denominator.

$$\dfrac{x}{x^2-10x+25} - \dfrac{x-4}{2x-10}$$

$$= \dfrac{x}{(x-5)(x-5)} - \dfrac{x-4}{2(x-5)}$$

$$= \dfrac{2x}{2(x-5)(x-5)} - \dfrac{(x-4)(x-5)}{2(x-5)(x-5)}$$

Add numerators, putting this sum over the least common denominator.

$$= \frac{2x - (x-4)(x-5)}{2(x-5)(x-5)}$$

$$= \frac{2x - (x^2 - 5x - 4x + 20)}{2(x-5)(x-5)}$$

$$= \frac{2x - x^2 + 5x + 4x - 20}{2(x-5)(x-5)}$$

$$= \frac{2x - x^2 + 5x + 4x - 20}{2(x-5)(x-5)}$$

$$= \frac{-x^2 + 11x - 20}{2(x-5)(x-5)}$$

$$= \frac{-x^2 + 11x - 20}{2(x-5)^2}, \ x \neq 5$$

9. $\dfrac{\dfrac{1}{x} - \dfrac{3}{2}}{\dfrac{1}{x} + \dfrac{3}{4}} = \dfrac{\dfrac{2}{2x} - \dfrac{3x}{2x}}{\dfrac{4}{4x} + \dfrac{3x}{4x}}, \ x \neq 0$

$$= \frac{\dfrac{2-3x}{2x}}{\dfrac{4+3x}{4x}}, \ x \neq \frac{-4}{3}$$

$$= \frac{2-3x}{2x} \div \frac{4+3x}{4x}$$

$$= \frac{2-3x}{2x} \cdot \frac{4x}{4+3x}$$

$$= \frac{2-3x}{4+3x} \cdot \frac{4}{2}$$

$$= \frac{2-3x}{4+3x} \cdot \frac{2}{1}$$

$$= \frac{2(2-3x)}{4+3x}, \ x \neq 0 \ and \ x \neq \frac{-4}{3}$$

10. Multiply each of the three terms, $\dfrac{1}{x+7}$, $\dfrac{1}{x}$, and

7 by the least common denominator of $x(x+7)$.

$$\frac{\dfrac{1}{x+7} - \dfrac{1}{x}}{7} = \frac{x(x+7)\left(\dfrac{1}{x+7}\right) - x(x+7)\left(\dfrac{1}{x}\right)}{7x(x+7)}$$

$$= \frac{x - (x+7)}{7x(x+7)}$$

$$= \frac{-7}{7x(x+7)}$$

$$= -\frac{1}{x(x+7)}, \ x \neq 0, \ x \neq -7$$

11. $\dfrac{\sqrt{x} + \dfrac{1}{\sqrt{x}}}{x} = \dfrac{\left(\sqrt{x} + \dfrac{1}{\sqrt{x}}\right)\sqrt{x}}{x\sqrt{x}} = \dfrac{x+1}{x^{3/2}}$

12. $\dfrac{\sqrt{x+3} - \sqrt{x}}{3}$

$$= \frac{\sqrt{x+3} - \sqrt{x}}{3} \cdot \frac{\sqrt{x+3} + \sqrt{x}}{\sqrt{x+3} \cdot \sqrt{x}}$$

$$= \frac{\left(\sqrt{x+3}\right)^2 - \left(\sqrt{x}\right)^2}{3\left(\sqrt{x+3} + \sqrt{x}\right)}$$

$$= \frac{x+3-x}{3\left(\sqrt{x+3} + \sqrt{x}\right)}$$

$$= \frac{1}{\sqrt{x+3} + \sqrt{x}}$$

Exercise Set P.6

1. $\dfrac{7}{x-3}, x \neq 3$

3. $\dfrac{x+5}{x^2-25} = \dfrac{x+5}{(x+5)(x-5)}, x \neq 5, -5$

5. $\dfrac{x-1}{x^2+11x+10} = \dfrac{x-1}{(x+1)(x+10)}, x \neq -1, -10$

7. $\dfrac{3x-9}{x^2-6x+9} = \dfrac{3(x-3)}{(x-3)(x-3)}$

$\qquad = \dfrac{3}{x-3}, x \neq 3$

9. $\dfrac{x^2-12x+36}{4x-24} = \dfrac{(x-6)(x-6)}{4(x-6)} = \dfrac{x-6}{4}.$

$\qquad x \neq 6$

11. $\dfrac{y^2+7y-18}{y^2-3y+2} = \dfrac{(y+9)(y-2)}{(y-2)(y-1)} = \dfrac{y+9}{y-1},$

$\qquad y \neq 1, 2$

13. $\dfrac{x^2+12x+36}{x^2-36} = \dfrac{(x+6)^2}{(x+6)(x-6)} = \dfrac{x+6}{x-6},$

$\qquad x \neq 6, -6$

15. $\dfrac{x-2}{3x+9} \cdot \dfrac{2x+6}{2x-4} = \dfrac{x-2}{3(x+3)} \cdot \dfrac{2(x+3)}{2(x-2)}$

$\qquad = \dfrac{2}{6} = \dfrac{1}{3}, x \neq 2, -3$

17. $\dfrac{x^2-9}{x^2} \cdot \dfrac{x^2-3x}{x^2+x-12}$

$\qquad = \dfrac{(x-3)(x+3)}{x^2} \cdot \dfrac{x(x-3)}{(x+4)(x-3)}$

$\qquad = \dfrac{(x-3)(x+3)}{x(x+4)}, x \neq 0, -4, 3$

19. $\dfrac{x^2-5x+6}{x^2-2x-3} \cdot \dfrac{x^2-1}{x^2-4}$

$\qquad = \dfrac{(x-3)(x-2)}{(x-3)(x+1)} \cdot \dfrac{(x+1)(x-1)}{(x-2)(x+2)}$

$\qquad = \dfrac{x-1}{x+2}, x \neq -2, -1, 2, 3$

21. $\dfrac{x^3-8}{x^2-4} \cdot \dfrac{x+2}{3x} = \dfrac{(x-2)(x^2+2x+4)}{(x-2)(x+2)} \cdot \dfrac{x+2}{3x}$

$\qquad = \dfrac{x^2+2x+4}{3x}, x \neq -2, 0, 2$

23. $\dfrac{x+1}{3} \div \dfrac{3x+3}{7} = \dfrac{x+1}{3} \div \dfrac{3(x+1)}{7}$

$\qquad = \dfrac{x+1}{3} \cdot \dfrac{7}{3(x+1)}$

$\qquad = \dfrac{7}{9}, x \neq -1$

25. $\dfrac{x^2-4}{x} \div \dfrac{x+2}{x-2} = \dfrac{(x-2)(x+2)}{x} \cdot \dfrac{x-2}{x+2}$

$\qquad = \dfrac{(x-2)^2}{x}; x \neq 0, -2, 2$

27. $\dfrac{4x^2+10}{x-3} \div \dfrac{6x^2+15}{x^2-9}$

$\qquad = \dfrac{2(2x^2+5)}{x-3} \div \dfrac{3(2x^2+5)}{(x-3)(x+3)}$

$\qquad = \dfrac{2(2x^2+5)}{x-3} \cdot \dfrac{(x-3)(x+3)}{3(2x^2+5)}$

$\qquad = \dfrac{2(x+3)}{3}, x \neq 3, -3$

29. $\dfrac{x^2-25}{2x-2} \div \dfrac{x^2+10x+25}{x^2+4x-5}$

$\qquad = \dfrac{(x-5)(x+5)}{2(x-1)} \div \dfrac{(x+5)^2}{(x+5)(x-1)}$

$\qquad = \dfrac{(x-5)(x+5)}{2(x-1)} \cdot \dfrac{(x+5)(x-1)}{(x+5)^2}$

$\qquad = \dfrac{x-5}{2}, x \neq 1, -5$

31. $\dfrac{x^2+x-12}{x^2+x-30} \cdot \dfrac{x^2+5x+6}{x^2-2x-3} \div \dfrac{x+3}{x^2+7x+6}$

$\qquad = \dfrac{(x+4)(x-3)}{(x+6)(x-5)} \cdot \dfrac{(x+2)(x+3)}{(x+1)(x-3)} \cdot \dfrac{(x+6)(x+1)}{x+3}$

$\qquad = \dfrac{(x+4)(x+2)}{x-5}$

$\qquad x \neq -6, -3, -1, 3, 5$

33. $\dfrac{4x+1}{6x+5} + \dfrac{8x+9}{6x+5} = \dfrac{4x+1+8x+9}{6x+5}$

$$= \dfrac{12x+10}{6x+5}$$

$$= \dfrac{2(6x+5)}{6x+5} = 2, x \neq -\dfrac{5}{6}$$

35. $\dfrac{x^2-2x}{x^2+3x} + \dfrac{x^2+x}{x^2+3x} = \dfrac{x^2-2x+x^2+x}{x^2+3x}$

$$= \dfrac{2x^2-x}{x^2+3x}$$

$$= \dfrac{x(2x-1)}{x(x+3)}$$

$$= \dfrac{2x-1}{x+3}, x \neq 0, -3$$

37. $\dfrac{4x-10}{x-2} - \dfrac{x-4}{x-2} = \dfrac{4x-10-(x-4)}{x-2}$

$$= \dfrac{4x-10-x+4}{x-2}$$

$$= \dfrac{3x-6}{x-2}$$

$$= \dfrac{3(x-2)}{x-2}$$

$$= 3, x \neq 2$$

39. $\dfrac{x^2+3x}{x^2+x-12} - \dfrac{x^2-12}{x^2+x-12}$

$$= \dfrac{x^2+3x-(x^2-12)}{x^2+x-12}$$

$$= \dfrac{x^2+3x-x^2+12}{x^2+x-12}$$

$$= \dfrac{3x+12}{x^2+x-12}$$

$$= \dfrac{3(x+4)}{(x+4)(x-3)}$$

$$= \dfrac{3}{x-3}, x \neq 3, -4$$

41. $\dfrac{3}{x+4} + \dfrac{6}{x+5} = \dfrac{3(x+5)+6(x+4)}{(x+4)(x+5)}$

$$= \dfrac{3x+15+6x+24}{(x+4)(x+5)}$$

$$= \dfrac{9x+39}{(x+4)(x+5)}, x \neq -4, -5$$

43. $\dfrac{3}{x+1} - \dfrac{3}{x} = \dfrac{3x-3(x+1)}{x(x+1)}$

$$= \dfrac{3x-3x-3}{x(x+1)} = -\dfrac{3}{x(x+1)}, x \neq -1, 0$$

45. $\dfrac{2x}{x+2} + \dfrac{x+2}{x-2} = \dfrac{2x(x-2)+(x+2)(x+2)}{(x+2)(x-2)}$

$$= \dfrac{2x^2-4x+x^2+4x+4}{(x+2)(x-2)}$$

$$= \dfrac{3x^2+4}{(x+2)(x-2)}, x \neq -2, 2$$

47. $\dfrac{x+5}{x-5} + \dfrac{x-5}{x+5}$

$$= \dfrac{(x+5)(x+5)+(x-5)(x-5)}{(x-5)(x+5)}$$

$$= \dfrac{x^2+10x+25+x^2-10x+25}{(x-5)(x+5)}$$

$$= \dfrac{2x^2+50}{(x-5)(x+5)}, x \neq -5, 5$$

49. $\dfrac{4}{x^2+6x+9} + \dfrac{4}{x+3} = \dfrac{4}{(x+3)^2} + \dfrac{4}{x+3}$

$$= \dfrac{4+4(x+3)}{(x+3)^2} = \dfrac{4+4x+12}{(x+3)^2} = \dfrac{4x+16}{(x+3)^2},$$

$$x \neq -3$$

51. $\dfrac{3x}{x^2+3x-10} - \dfrac{2x}{x^2+x-6}$

$$= \dfrac{3x}{(x+5)(x-2)} - \dfrac{2x}{(x+3)(x-2)}$$

$$= \dfrac{3x(x+3)-2x(x+5)}{(x+5)(x-2)(x+3)}$$

$$= \dfrac{3x^2+9x-2x^2-10x}{(x+5)(x-2)(x+3)}$$

$$= \dfrac{x^2-x}{(x+5)(x-2)(x+3)}, x \neq -5, 2, -3$$

53. $\dfrac{4x^2+x-6}{x^2+3x+2}-\dfrac{3x}{x+1}+\dfrac{5}{x+2}$

$=\dfrac{4x^2+x-6}{(x+1)(x+2)}+\dfrac{-3x}{x+1}+\dfrac{5}{x+2}$

$=\dfrac{4x^2+x-5}{(x+1)(x+2)}+\dfrac{-3x(x+2)}{(x+1)(x+2)}+\dfrac{5(x+1)}{(x+1)(x+2)}$

$=\dfrac{4x^2+x-6-3x^2-6x+5x+5}{(x+1)(x+2)}$

$=\dfrac{x^2-1}{(x+1)(x+2)}$

$=\dfrac{(x-1)(x+1)}{(x+1)(x+2)}$

$=\dfrac{x-1}{x+2}; x\neq-2,-1$

55. $\dfrac{\frac{x}{3}-1}{x-3}=\dfrac{3\left[\frac{x}{3}-1\right]}{3[x-3]}=\dfrac{x-3}{3(x-3)}=\dfrac{1}{3},\ x\neq3$

57. $\dfrac{1+\frac{1}{x}}{3-\frac{1}{x}}=\dfrac{x\left[1+\frac{1}{x}\right]}{x\left[3-\frac{1}{x}\right]}=\dfrac{x+1}{3x-1},x\neq0,\frac{1}{3}$

59. $\dfrac{\frac{1}{x}+\frac{1}{y}}{x+y}=\dfrac{xy\left[\frac{1}{x}+\frac{1}{y}\right]}{xy[x+y]}=\dfrac{y+x}{xy(x+y)}=\dfrac{1}{xy},$

$x\neq0,y\neq0,x\neq-y$

61. $\dfrac{x-\frac{x}{x+3}}{x+2}=\dfrac{(x+3)\left[x-\frac{x}{x+3}\right]}{(x+3)(x+2)}=\dfrac{x(x+3)-x}{(x+3)(x+2)}$

$=\dfrac{x^2+3x-x}{(x+3)(x+2)}=\dfrac{x^2+2x}{(x+3)(x+2)}$

$=\dfrac{x(x+2)}{(x+3)(x+2)}=\dfrac{x}{x+3},x\neq-2,-3$

63. $\dfrac{\frac{3}{x-2}-\frac{4}{x+2}}{\frac{7}{x^2-4}}=\dfrac{\frac{3}{x-2}-\frac{4}{x+2}}{\frac{7}{(x-2)(x+2)}}$

$=\dfrac{\left[\frac{3}{x-2}-\frac{4}{x+2}\right](x-2)(x+2)}{\left[\frac{7}{(x-2)(x+2)}\right](x-2)(x+2)}$

$=\dfrac{3(x+2)-4(x-2)}{7}$

$=\dfrac{3x+6-4x+8}{7}=\dfrac{-x+14}{7}$

$=-\dfrac{x-14}{7}\ \ x\neq-2,2$

65. $\dfrac{\frac{1}{x+1}}{\frac{1}{x^2-2x-3}+\frac{1}{x-3}}=\dfrac{\frac{1}{x+1}}{\frac{1}{(x+1)(x-3)}+\frac{1}{x-3}}$

$=\dfrac{\frac{(x+1)(x-3)}{x+1}}{\frac{(x+1)(x-3)}{(x+1)(x-3)}+\frac{(x+1)(x-3)}{x-3}}$

$=\dfrac{x-3}{1+x+1}$

$=\dfrac{x-3}{x+2}\ \ x\neq-2,-1,3$

67. $\dfrac{\frac{1}{(x+h)^2}-\frac{1}{x^2}}{h}=\dfrac{\frac{x^2(x+h)^2}{(x+h)^2}-\frac{x^2(x+h)^2}{x^2}}{hx^2(x+h)^2}$

$=\dfrac{x^2-(x+h)^2}{hx^2(x+h)^2}$

$=\dfrac{x^2-(x^2+2hx+h^2)}{hx^2(x+h)^2}$

$=\dfrac{x^2-x^2-2hx-h^2}{hx^2(x+h)^2}$

$=\dfrac{-2hx-h^2}{hx^2(x+h)^2}$

$=\dfrac{-h(2x+h)}{hx^2(x+h)^2}$

$=-\dfrac{(2x+h)}{x^2(x+h)^2}$

69.
$$\frac{\sqrt{x}-\frac{1}{3\sqrt{x}}}{\sqrt{x}} = \frac{\left(\sqrt{x}-\frac{1}{3\sqrt{x}}\right)(3\sqrt{x})}{\sqrt{x}(3\sqrt{x})}$$
$$= \frac{3x-1}{3x}$$
$$= 1-\frac{1}{3x}, x > 0$$

71.
$$\frac{\frac{x^2}{\sqrt{x^2+2}}-\sqrt{x^2+2}}{x^2}$$
$$= \frac{\left(\frac{x^2}{\sqrt{x^2+2}}-\sqrt{x^2+2}\right)\sqrt{x^2+2}}{x^2\sqrt{x^2+2}}$$
$$= \frac{x^2-(x^2+2)}{x^2\sqrt{x^2+2}}$$
$$= -\frac{2}{x^2\sqrt{x^2+2}}$$

73.
$$\frac{\frac{1}{\sqrt{x+h}}-\frac{1}{\sqrt{x}}}{h} = \frac{\left(\frac{1}{\sqrt{x+h}}-\frac{1}{\sqrt{x}}\right)\sqrt{x+h}\sqrt{x}}{h\sqrt{x+h}\sqrt{x}}$$
$$= \frac{\sqrt{x}-\sqrt{x+h}}{h\sqrt{x(x+h)}}, h \neq 0$$

75.
$$\frac{\sqrt{x+5}-\sqrt{x}}{5} = \frac{\sqrt{x+5}-\sqrt{x}}{5}\cdot\frac{\sqrt{x+5}+\sqrt{x}}{\sqrt{x+5}+\sqrt{x}}$$
$$= \frac{(\sqrt{x+5})^2-(\sqrt{x})^2}{5(\sqrt{x+5}+\sqrt{x})}$$
$$= \frac{x+5-x}{5(\sqrt{x+5}+\sqrt{x})}$$
$$= \frac{1}{\sqrt{x+5}+\sqrt{x}}$$

77.
$$\frac{\sqrt{x}+\sqrt{y}}{x^2-y^2} = \frac{\sqrt{x}+\sqrt{y}}{x^2-y^2}\cdot\frac{\sqrt{x}-\sqrt{y}}{\sqrt{x}-\sqrt{y}}$$
$$= \frac{(\sqrt{x})^2-(\sqrt{y})^2}{(x+y)(x-y)(\sqrt{x}-\sqrt{y})}$$
$$= \frac{x-y}{(x+y)(x-y)(\sqrt{x}-\sqrt{y})}$$
$$= \frac{1}{(x+y)(\sqrt{x}-\sqrt{y})}$$

79.
$$\left(\frac{2x+3}{x+1}\cdot\frac{x^2+4x-5}{2x^2+x-3}\right)-\frac{2}{x+2} = \left(\frac{(2x+3)}{x+1}\cdot\frac{(x+5)(x-1)}{(2x+3)(x-1)}\right)-\frac{2}{x+2} = \frac{x+5}{x+1}-\frac{2}{x+2}$$
$$= \frac{(x+5)(x+2)}{(x+1)(x+2)}-\frac{2(x+1)}{(x+1)(x+2)} = \frac{(x+5)(x+2)-2(x+1)}{(x+1)(x+2)} = \frac{x^2+2x+5x+10-2x-2}{(x+1)(x+2)} = \frac{x^2+5x+8}{(x+1)(x+2)}$$

81.
$$\left(2-\frac{6}{x+1}\right)\left(1+\frac{3}{x-2}\right) = \left(\frac{2(x+1)}{(x+1)}-\frac{6}{(x+1)}\right)\left(\frac{(x-2)}{(x-2)}+\frac{3}{(x-2)}\right)$$
$$= \left(\frac{2x+2-6}{x+1}\right)\left(\frac{x-2+3}{x-2}\right) = \left(\frac{2x-4}{x+1}\right)\left(\frac{x+1}{x-2}\right) = \frac{2(x-2)(x+1)}{(x+1)(x-2)} = 2$$

83. $\dfrac{y^{-1} - (y+5)^{-1}}{5} = \dfrac{\dfrac{1}{y} - \dfrac{1}{y+5}}{5}$

LCD $= y(y+5)$

$\dfrac{\dfrac{1}{y} - \dfrac{1}{y+5}}{5} = \dfrac{y(y+5)\left(\dfrac{1}{y} - \dfrac{1}{y+5}\right)}{y(y+5)(5)} = \dfrac{y+5-y}{5y(y+5)} = \dfrac{5}{5y(y+5)} = \dfrac{1}{y(y+5)}$

85. $\left(\dfrac{1}{a^3 - b^3} \cdot \dfrac{ac + ad - bc - bd}{1}\right) - \dfrac{c-d}{a^2 + ab + b^2} = \left(\dfrac{1}{(a-b)(a^2 + ab + b^2)} \cdot \dfrac{a(c+d) - b(c+d)}{1}\right) - \dfrac{c-d}{a^2 + ab + b^2}$

$= \left(\dfrac{1}{(a-b)(a^2 + ab + b^2)} \cdot \dfrac{(c+d)(a-b)}{1}\right) - \dfrac{c-d}{a^2 + ab + b^2} = \dfrac{c+d}{a^2 + ab + b^2} - \dfrac{c-d}{a^2 + bd + b^2}$

$= \dfrac{c+d-c+d}{a^2 + ab + b^2} = \dfrac{2d}{a^2 + ab + b^2}$

87. **a.** $\dfrac{130x}{100 - x}$ is equal to

1. $\dfrac{130 \cdot 40}{100 - 40} = \dfrac{130 \cdot 40}{60} = 86.67$,

   when $x = 40$

2. $\dfrac{130 \cdot 80}{100 - 80} = \dfrac{130 \cdot 80}{20} = 520$,

   when $x = 80$

3. $\dfrac{130 \cdot 90}{100 - 90} = \dfrac{130 \cdot 90}{10} = 1170$,

   when $x = 90$

   It costs \$86,670,000 to inoculate 40% of the population against this strain of flu, and \$520,000,000 to inoculate 80% of the population, and \$1,170,000,000 to inoculate 90% of the population.

b. For $x = 100$, the function is not defined.

c. As x approaches 100, the value of the function increases rapidly. So it costs an astronomical amount of money to inoculate almost all of the people, and it is impossible to inoculate 100% of the population.

89. **a.** The crime rate is the number of crimes per person. Thus the rational expression is the number of crimes divided by the total population

$\dfrac{-0.3t + 14}{3.6t + 260}$

b. $\dfrac{-0.3t + 14}{3.6t + 260} = \dfrac{-0.3(8) + 14}{3.6(8) + 260} \approx 0.04$

The crime rate in 2002 was 0.04. That is 4000 per 100,000 people.

c. The rational expression models the crime rate in 2002 fairly well.

91. $P = 2L + 2W$

$$= 2\left(\frac{x}{x+3}\right) + 2\left(\frac{x}{x-4}\right)$$

$$= \frac{2x}{x+3} + \frac{2x}{x+4}$$

$$= \frac{2x(x+4)}{(x+3)(x+4)} + \frac{2x(x+}{(x+3)(}$$

$$= \frac{2x^2 + 8x + 2x^2 + 6x}{(x+3)(x+4)}$$

$$= \frac{4x^2 + 14x}{(x+3)(x+4)}$$

93. $R = \dfrac{1}{\dfrac{1}{R_1} + \dfrac{1}{R_2} + \dfrac{1}{R_3}}$

$$= \frac{R_1 R_2 R_3}{\left(\frac{1}{R_1} + \frac{1}{R_2} + \frac{1}{R_3}\right) R_1 R_2 R_3}$$

$$= \frac{R_1 R_2 R_3}{R_2 R_3 + R_1 R_3 + R_1 R_2}$$

$$R(4,\ 8,\ 12) = \frac{4 \cdot 8 \cdot 12}{8 \cdot 12 + 4 \cdot 12 + 4 \cdot 8}$$

$$= \frac{384}{96 + 48 + 32}$$

$$= \frac{384}{176}$$

$$= \frac{24}{11}$$

The parallel resistance is $\dfrac{24}{11}$ ohms.

107. a. false; $\dfrac{a}{b} + \dfrac{a}{c} = \dfrac{ab + ac}{bc}$

b. false; $6 + \dfrac{1}{x} = \dfrac{6x + 1}{x}$

c. false; $\dfrac{1}{x+3} + \dfrac{x+3}{2} = \dfrac{x^2 + 6x + 11}{2(x+3)}$

d. false; $\dfrac{x^2 - 25}{x - 5} = \dfrac{(x+5)(x-5)}{x-5} = x + 5$

e. true

109. $\left(1 - \dfrac{1}{x}\right)\left(1 - \dfrac{1}{x+1}\right)\left(1 - \dfrac{1}{x+2}\right)\left(1 - \dfrac{1}{x+3}\right) = \left(\dfrac{x}{x} - \dfrac{1}{x}\right)\left(\dfrac{x+1}{x+1} - \dfrac{1}{x+1}\right)\left(\dfrac{x+2}{x+2} - \dfrac{1}{x+2}\right)\left(\dfrac{x+3}{x+3} - \dfrac{1}{x+3}\right)$

$$= \left(\frac{x-1}{x}\right)\left(\frac{(x+1)-1}{x+1}\right)\left(\frac{(x+2)-1}{x+2}\right)\left(\frac{(x+3)-1}{x+3}\right)$$

$$= \frac{x-1}{\cancel{x}} \cdot \frac{\cancel{x}}{\cancel{x+1}} \cdot \frac{\cancel{x+1}}{\cancel{x+2}} \cdot \frac{\cancel{x+2}}{x+3} = \frac{x-1}{x+3}$$

111. It cubes x.

$$\frac{\dfrac{1}{x} + \dfrac{1}{x^2} + \dfrac{1}{x^3}}{\dfrac{1}{x^4} + \dfrac{1}{x^5} + \dfrac{1}{x^6}} = \frac{\dfrac{x^6}{x} + \dfrac{x^6}{x^2} + \dfrac{x^6}{x^3}}{\dfrac{x^6}{x^4} + \dfrac{x^6}{x^5} + \dfrac{x^6}{x^6}} = \frac{x^5 + x^4 + x^3}{x^2 + x + 1} = \frac{x^3(x^2 + x + 1)}{x^2 + x + 1} = x^3$$

Section P.7

Check Point Exercises

1. $4(2x+1)-29=3(2x-5)$
    $8x+4-29=6x-15$
    $8x-25=6x-15$
    $8x-25-6x=6x-15-6x$
    $2x-25=-15$
    $2x-25+25=-15+25$
    $2x=10$
    $\dfrac{2x}{2}=\dfrac{10}{2}$
    $x=5$

    Check:
    $4(2x+1)-29=3(2x-5)$
    $4[2(5)+1]-29=3[2(5)-5]$
    $4[10+1]-29=3[10-5]$
    $4[11]-29=3[5]$
    $44-29=15$
    $15=15$ true
    The solution set is $\{5\}$.

2. $\dfrac{x-3}{4}=\dfrac{5}{14}-\dfrac{x+5}{7}$
    $28\cdot\dfrac{x-3}{4}=28\left(\dfrac{5}{14}-\dfrac{x+5}{7}\right)$
    $7(x-3)=2(5)-4(x+5)$
    $7x-21=10-4x-20$
    $7x-21=-4x-10$
    $7x+4x=-10+21$
    $11x=11$
    $\dfrac{11x}{11}=\dfrac{11}{11}$
    $x=1$

    Check:
    $\dfrac{x-3}{4}=\dfrac{5}{14}-\dfrac{x+5}{7}$
    $\dfrac{1-3}{4}=\dfrac{5}{14}-\dfrac{1+5}{7}$
    $\dfrac{-2}{4}=\dfrac{5}{14}-\dfrac{6}{7}$
    $-\dfrac{1}{2}=-\dfrac{1}{2}$
    The solution set is $\{1\}$.

3. $\dfrac{6}{x+3}-\dfrac{5}{x-2}=\dfrac{-20}{x^2+x-6}$
    $\dfrac{6}{x+3}-\dfrac{5}{x-2}=\dfrac{-20}{(x+3)(x-2)}$
    $\dfrac{6(x+3)(x-2)}{x+3}-\dfrac{5(x+3)(x-2)}{x-2}=\dfrac{-20(x+3)(x-2)}{(x+3)(x-2)}$
    $6(x-2)-5(x+3)=-20$
    $6x-12-5x-15=-20$
    $x-27=-20$
    $x=7$

    The solution set is $\{7\}$.

4.

$$\frac{1}{x+2} = \frac{4}{x^2-4} - \frac{1}{x-2}$$

$$\frac{1}{x+2} = \frac{4}{(x+2)(x-2)} - \frac{1}{x-2}$$

$$\frac{1(x+2)(x-2)}{x+2} = \frac{4(x+2)(x-2)}{(x+2)(x-2)} - \frac{1(x+2)(x-2)}{x-2}$$

$$x-2 = 4 - (x+2)$$

$$x-2 = 4 - x - 2$$

$$x-2 = 2 - x$$

$$2x = 4$$

$$x = 2$$

2 must be rejected. The solution set is $\{\ \}$.

5.

$$\frac{1}{p} + \frac{1}{q} = \frac{1}{f}$$

$$\frac{1pqf}{p} + \frac{1pqf}{q} = \frac{1pqf}{f}$$

$$qf + pf = pq$$

$$qf - pq = -pf$$

$$q(f-p) = -pf$$

$$\frac{q(f-p)}{f-p} = \frac{-pf}{f-p}$$

$$q = \frac{pf}{p-f}$$

6. $4|1-2x| - 20 = 0$

$$4|1-2x| = 20$$

$$|1-2x| = 5$$

$$1-2x = 5 \quad \text{or} \quad 1-2x = -5$$

$$-2x = 4 \qquad\qquad -2x = -6$$

$$x = -2 \qquad\qquad x = 3$$

The solution set is $\{-2, 3\}$.

7. a. $3x^2 - 9x = 0$

$$3x(x-3) = 0$$

$$3x = 0 \quad \text{or} \quad x - 3 = 0$$

$$x = 0 \qquad\qquad x = 3$$

The solution set is $\{0, 3\}$.

b. $2x^2 + x = 1$

$$2x^2 + x - 1 = 0$$

$$(2x-1)(x+1) = 0$$

$$2x - 1 = 0 \quad \text{or} \quad x + 1 = 0$$

$$2x = 1 \qquad\qquad x = -1$$

$$x = \frac{1}{2}$$

The solution set is $\left\{\frac{1}{2}, -1\right\}$.

8. a. $3x^2 - 21 = 0$

$$3x^2 = 21$$

$$\frac{3x^2}{3} = \frac{21}{3}$$

$$x^2 = 7$$

$$x = \pm\sqrt{7}$$

The solution set is $\left\{-\sqrt{7}, \sqrt{7}\right\}$.

b. $(x+5)^2 = 11$

$$x + 5 = \pm\sqrt{11}$$

$$x = -5 \pm \sqrt{11}$$

The solution set is $\left\{-5 + \sqrt{11}, -5 - \sqrt{11}\right\}$.

9. $x^2 + 4x - 1 = 0$

$x^2 + 4x = 1$

$x^2 + 4x + 4 = 1 + 4$

$(x+2)^2 = 5$

$x + 2 = \pm\sqrt{5}$

$x = -2 \pm \sqrt{5}$

10. $2x^2 + 2x - 1 = 0$

$a = 2, b = 2, c = -1$

$x = \dfrac{-b \pm \sqrt{b^2 - 4ac}}{2a}$

$= \dfrac{-2 \pm \sqrt{2^2 - 4(2)(-1)}}{2(2)}$

$= \dfrac{-2 \pm \sqrt{4 + 8}}{4}$

$= \dfrac{-2 \pm \sqrt{12}}{4}$

$= \dfrac{-2 \pm 2\sqrt{3}}{4}$

$= \dfrac{2(-1 \pm \sqrt{3})}{4}$

$= \dfrac{-1 \pm \sqrt{3}}{2}$

The solution set is $\left\{ \dfrac{-1+\sqrt{3}}{2}, \dfrac{-1-\sqrt{3}}{2} \right\}$.

11. $3x^2 - 2x + 5 = 0$

$a = 3, \ b = -2, \ c = 5$

$b^2 - 4ac = (-2)^2 - 4 \cdot 3 \cdot 5 = 4 - 60 = -56$

The discriminant is -56. The equation has two complex imaginary solutions.

12. $\sqrt{x+3} + 3 = x$

$\sqrt{x+3} = x - 3$

$\left(\sqrt{x+3}\right)^2 = (x-3)^2$

$x + 3 = x^2 - 6x + 9$

$0 = x^2 - 7x + 6$

$0 = (x-6)(x-1)$

$x - 6 = 0 \quad \text{or} \quad x - 1 = 0$

$x = 6 \qquad\qquad x = 1$

1 does not check and must be rejected.
The solution set is $\{6\}$.

Exercise Set P.7

1. $7x - 5 = 72$

$7x = 77$

$x = 11$

Check:

$7x - 5 = 72$

$7(11) - 5 = 72$

$77 - 5 = 72$

$72 = 72$

The solution set is $\{11\}$.

3. $11x - (6x - 5) = 40$

$11x - 6x + 5 = 40$

$5x + 5 = 40$

$5x = 35$

$x = 7$

The solution set is $\{7\}$.

Check:

$11x - (6x - 5) = 40$

$11(7) - [6(7) - 5] = 40$

$77 - (42 - 5) = 40$

$77 - (37) = 40$

$40 = 40$

5. $2x - 7 = 6 + x$

$x - 7 = 6$

$x = 13$

The solution set is $\{13\}$.

Check:

$2(13) - 7 = 6 + 13$

$26 - 7 = 19$

$19 = 19$

7. $7x + 4 = x + 16$

$6x + 4 = 16$

$6x = 12$

$x = 2$

The solution set is $\{2\}$.

Check:

$7(2) + 4 = 2 + 16$

$14 + 4 = 18$

$18 = 18$

9. $3(x-2) + 7 = 2(x+5)$
$3x - 6 + 7 = 2x + 10$
$3x + 1 = 2x + 10$

$x + 1 = 10$
$x = 9$
The solution set is $\{9\}$.

Check:
$3(9-2) + 7 = 2(9+5)$
$3(7) + 7 = 2(14)$
$21 + 7 = 28$
$28 = 28$

11. $\dfrac{x+3}{6} = \dfrac{3}{8} + \dfrac{x-5}{4}$

$24\left[\dfrac{x+3}{6} = \dfrac{3}{8} + \dfrac{x-5}{4}\right]$

$4x + 12 = 9 + 6x - 30$
$4x - 6x = -21 - 12$
$-2x = -33$
$x = \dfrac{33}{2}$

The solution set is $\left\{\dfrac{33}{2}\right\}$.

13. $\dfrac{x}{4} = 2 + \dfrac{x-3}{3}$

$12\left[\dfrac{x}{4} = 2 + \dfrac{x-3}{3}\right]$

$3x = 24 + 4x - 12$
$3x - 4x = 12$
$-x = 12$
$x = -12$
The solution set is $\{-12\}$.

15. $\dfrac{x+1}{3} = 5 - \dfrac{x+2}{7}$

$21\left[\dfrac{x+1}{3} = 5 - \dfrac{x+2}{7}\right]$

$7x + 7 = 105 - 3x - 6$
$7x + 3x = 99 - 7$
$10x = 92$
$x = \dfrac{92}{10}$
$x = \dfrac{46}{5}$

The solution set is $\left\{\dfrac{46}{5}\right\}$.

17. a. $\dfrac{1}{x-1} + 5 = \dfrac{11}{x-1} \ (x \neq 1)$

b. $\dfrac{1}{x-1} + 5 = \dfrac{11}{x-1}$
$1 + 5(x-1) = 11$
$1 + 5x - 5 = 11$
$5x - 4 = 11$
$5x = 15$
$x = 3$
The solution set is $\{3\}$.

19. a. $\dfrac{8x}{x+1} = 4 - \dfrac{8}{x+1} \ (x \neq -1)$

b. $\dfrac{8x}{x+1} = 4 - \dfrac{8}{x+1}$
$8x = 4(x+1) - 8$
$8x = 4x + 4 - 8$
$4x = -4$
$x = -1 \Rightarrow$ no solution
The solution set is the empty set, $\varnothing$.

21. a. $\dfrac{3}{2x-2} + \dfrac{1}{2} = \dfrac{2}{x-1} \ (x \neq 1)$

b. $\dfrac{3}{2x-2} + \dfrac{1}{2} = \dfrac{2}{x-1}$
$\dfrac{3}{2(x-1)} + \dfrac{1}{2} = \dfrac{2}{x-1}$
$3 + 1(x-1) = 4$
$3 + x - 1 = 4$
$x = 2$
The solution set is $\{2\}$.

23. a. $\dfrac{2}{x+1} - \dfrac{1}{x-1} = \dfrac{2x}{x^2-1} \ (x \neq 1, x \neq -1)$

b. $\dfrac{2}{x+1} - \dfrac{1}{x-1} = \dfrac{2x}{x^2-1}$
$\dfrac{2}{x+1} - \dfrac{1}{x-1} = \dfrac{2x}{(x+1)(x-1)}$
$2(x-1) - 1(x+1) = 2x$
$2x - 2 - x - 1 = 2x$
$-x = 3$
$x = -3$
The solution set is $\{-3\}$.

25. a. $\dfrac{1}{x-4} - \dfrac{5}{x+2} = \dfrac{6}{(x-4)(x+2)}; (x \neq -2, 4)$

b. $\dfrac{1}{x-4} - \dfrac{5}{x+2} = \dfrac{6}{x^2-2x-8}$

$\dfrac{1}{x-4} - \dfrac{5}{x+2} = \dfrac{6}{(x-4)(x+2)}$

$(x \neq 4, x \neq -2)$

$1(x+2) - 5(x-4) = 6$

$x + 2 - 5x + 20 = 6$

$-4x = -16$

$x = 4$

The solution set is the empty set, $\varnothing$.

27. $I = Prt$

$P = \dfrac{I}{rt};$

interest

29. $T = D + pm$

$T - D = pm$

$\dfrac{T-D}{m} = \dfrac{pm}{m}$

$\dfrac{T-D}{m} = p$

total of payment

31. $A = \dfrac{1}{2}h(a+b)$

$2A = h(a+b)$

$\dfrac{2A}{h} = a + b$

$\dfrac{2A}{h} - b = a$

area of trapezoid

33. $S = P + Prt$

$S - P = Prt$

$\dfrac{S-P}{Pt} = r;$

interest

35. $B = \dfrac{F}{S-V}$

$B(S-V) = F$

$S - V = \dfrac{F}{B}$

$S = \dfrac{F}{B} + V$

37. $IR + Ir = E$

$I(R+r) = E$

$I = \dfrac{E}{R+r}$

electric current

39. $\dfrac{1}{p} + \dfrac{1}{q} = \dfrac{1}{f}$

$qf + pf = pq$

$f(q+p) = pq$

$f = \dfrac{pq}{p+q}$

thin lens equation

41. $f = \dfrac{f_1 f_2}{f_1 + f_2}$

$f(f_1 + f_2) = f_1 f_2$

$ff_1 + ff_2 = f_1 f_2$

$ff_1 - f_1 f_2 = -ff_2$

$f_1(f - f_2) = -ff_2$

$\dfrac{f_1(f-f_2)}{f-f_2} = \dfrac{-ff_2}{f-f_2}$

$f_1 = \dfrac{ff_2}{f_2 - f}$

focal length

43. $|x-2| = 7$

$x - 2 = 7 \quad x - 2 = -7$

$x = 9 \qquad x = -5$

The solution set is $\{9, -5\}$.

45. $|2x-1| = 5$

$2x - 1 = 5 \quad 2x - 1 = -5$

$2x = 6 \qquad 2x = -4$

$x = 3 \qquad x = -2$

The solution set is $\{3, -2\}$.

47. $2|3x-2| = 14$

$|3x-2| = 7$

$3x - 2 = 7 \quad 3x - 2 = -7$

$3x = 9 \qquad 3x = -5$

$x = 3 \qquad x = -5/3$

The solution set is $\{3, -5/3\}$

49. $2\left|4-\dfrac{5}{2}x\right|+6=18$

$\qquad 2\left|4-\dfrac{5}{2}x\right|=12$

$\qquad \left|4-\dfrac{5}{2}x\right|=6$

$4-\dfrac{5}{2}x=6 \quad$ or $\quad 4-\dfrac{5}{2}x=-6$

$-\dfrac{5}{2}x=2 \qquad\qquad -\dfrac{5}{2}x=-10$

$x=-\dfrac{4}{5} \qquad\qquad\quad x=4$

The solution set is $\left\{-\dfrac{4}{5},4\right\}$.

51. $|x+1|+5=3$

$\qquad |x+1|=-2$

No solution

The solution set is $\{\ \}$.

53. $|2x-1|+3=3$

$\qquad |2x-1|=0$

$\qquad 2x-1=0$

$\qquad\quad 2x=1$

$\qquad\qquad x=1/2$

The solution set is $\left\{\dfrac{1}{2}\right\}$.

55. $x^2-3x-10=0$

$(x-5)(x+2)=0$

$x-5=0 \quad$ or $\quad x+2=0$

$x=5 \qquad\qquad x=-2$

The solution set is $\{-2,5\}$.

57. $\qquad x^2=8x-15$

$x^2-8x+15=0$

$(x-3)(x-5)=0$

$x-3=0 \quad$ or $\quad x-5=0$

$x=3 \qquad\qquad x=5$

The solution set is $\{3,5\}$.

59. $\qquad 5x^2=20x$

$5x^2-20x=0$

$5x(x-4)=0$

$5x=0 \quad$ or $\quad x-4=0$

$x=0 \qquad\qquad x=4$

The solution set is $\{0,4\}$.

61. $3x^2=27$

$\qquad x^2=9$

$\qquad \sqrt{x^2}=\pm\sqrt{9}$

$\qquad x=\pm3$

The solution set is $\{\pm3\}$.

63. $5x^2+1=51$

$\qquad 5x^2=50$

$\qquad x^2=10$

$\qquad \sqrt{x^2}=\pm\sqrt{10}$

$\qquad x=\pm\sqrt{10}$

The solution set is $\left\{\pm\sqrt{10}\right\}$.

65. $3(x-4)^2=15$

$\qquad (x-4)^2=5$

$\qquad \sqrt{(x-4)^2}=\pm\sqrt{5}$

$\qquad x-4=\pm\sqrt{5}$

$\qquad x=4\pm\sqrt{5}$

The solution set is $\left\{4\pm\sqrt{5}\right\}$.

67. $\qquad x^2+6x=7$

$x^2+6x+9=7+9$

$\qquad (x+3)^2=16$

$\qquad x+3=\pm4$

$\qquad x=-3\pm4$

The solution set is $\{-7,1\}$.

69. $\qquad x^2-2x=2$

$x^2-2x+1=2+1$

$\qquad (x-1)^2=3$

$\qquad x-1=\pm\sqrt{3}$

$\qquad x=1\pm\sqrt{3}$

The solution set is $\left\{1+\sqrt{3},1-\sqrt{3}\right\}$.

71.
$$x^2 - 6x - 11 = 0$$
$$x^2 - 6x = 11$$
$$x^2 - 6x + 9 = 11 + 9$$
$$(x-3)^2 = 20$$
$$x - 3 = \pm\sqrt{20}$$
$$x = 3 \pm 2\sqrt{5}$$
The solution set is $\left\{3 + 2\sqrt{5}, 3 - 2\sqrt{5}\right\}$.

73.
$$x^2 + 4x + 1 = 0$$
$$x^2 + 4x = -1$$
$$x^2 + 4x + 4 = -1 + 4$$
$$(x+2)^2 = 3$$
$$x + 2 = \pm\sqrt{3}$$
$$x = -2 \pm \sqrt{3}$$
The solution set is $\left\{-2 + \sqrt{3}, -2 - \sqrt{3}\right\}$.

75.
$$x^2 + 8x + 15 = 0$$
$$x = \frac{-8 \pm \sqrt{8^2 - 4(1)(15)}}{2(1)}$$
$$x = \frac{-8 \pm \sqrt{64 - 60}}{2}$$
$$x = \frac{-8 \pm \sqrt{4}}{2}$$
$$x = \frac{-8 \pm 2}{2}$$
The solution set is $\{-5, -3\}$.

77.
$$x^2 + 5x + 3 = 0$$
$$x = \frac{-5 \pm \sqrt{5^2 - 4(1)(3)}}{2(1)}$$
$$x = \frac{-5 \pm \sqrt{25 - 12}}{2}$$
$$x = \frac{-5 \pm \sqrt{13}}{2}$$
The solution set is $\left\{\dfrac{-5 + \sqrt{13}}{2}, \dfrac{-5 - \sqrt{13}}{2}\right\}$.

79.
$$3x^2 - 3x - 4 = 0$$
$$x = \frac{3 \pm \sqrt{(-3)^2 - 4(3)(-4)}}{2(3)}$$
$$x = \frac{3 \pm \sqrt{9 + 48}}{6}$$
$$x = \frac{3 \pm \sqrt{57}}{6}$$
The solution set is $\left\{\dfrac{3 + \sqrt{57}}{6}, \dfrac{3 - \sqrt{57}}{6}\right\}$

81.
$$4x^2 = 2x + 7$$
$$4x^2 - 2x - 7 = 0$$
$$x = \frac{2 \pm \sqrt{(-2)^2 - 4(4)(-7)}}{2(4)}$$
$$x = \frac{2 \pm \sqrt{4 + 112}}{8}$$
$$x = \frac{2 \pm \sqrt{116}}{8}$$
$$x = \frac{2 \pm 2\sqrt{29}}{8}$$
$$x = \frac{1 \pm \sqrt{29}}{4}$$
The solution set is $\left\{\dfrac{1 + \sqrt{29}}{4}, \dfrac{1 - \sqrt{29}}{4}\right\}$.

83.
$$x^2 - 4x - 5 = 0$$
$$(-4)^2 - 4(1)(-5)$$
$$= 16 + 20$$
$$= 36; \text{ 2 unequal real solutions}$$

85.
$$2x^2 - 11x + 3 = 0$$
$$(-11)^2 - 4(2)(3)$$
$$= 121 - 24$$
$$= 97; \text{ 2 unequal real solutions}$$

87.
$$x^2 = 2x - 1$$
$$x^2 - 2x + 1 = 0$$
$$(-2)^2 - 4(1)(1)$$
$$= 4 - 4$$
$$= 0; \text{ 1 real solution}$$

89. $x^2 - 3x - 7 = 0$

$(-3)^2 - 4(1)(-7)$

$= 9 + 28$

$= 37$; 2 unequal real solutions

91. $2x^2 - x = 1$

$2x^2 - x - 1 = 0$

$(2x+1)(x-1) = 0$

$2x + 1 = 0$ or $x - 1 = 0$

$2x = -1$

$x = -\dfrac{1}{2}$ or $x = 1$

The solution set is $\left\{ -\dfrac{1}{2}, 1 \right\}$.

93. $5x^2 + 2 = 11x$

$5x^2 - 11x + 2 = 0$

$(5x - 1)(x - 2) = 0$

$5x - 1 = 0$ or $x - 2 = 0$

$5x = 1$

$x = \dfrac{1}{5}$ or $x = 2$

The solution set is $\left\{ \dfrac{1}{5}, 2 \right\}$.

95. $3x^2 = 60$

$x^2 = 20$

$x = \pm\sqrt{20}$

$x = \pm 2\sqrt{5}$

The solution set is $\left\{ -2\sqrt{5}, 2\sqrt{5} \right\}$.

97. $x^2 - 2x = 1$

$x^2 - 2x + 1 = 1 + 1$

$(x-1)^2 = 2$

$x - 1 = \pm\sqrt{2}$

$x = 1 \pm \sqrt{2}$

The solution set is $\left\{ 1+\sqrt{2}, 1-\sqrt{2} \right\}$.

99. $(2x+3)(x+4) = 1$

$2x^2 + 8x + 3x + 12 = 1$

$2x^2 + 11x + 11 = 0$

$x = \dfrac{-11 \pm \sqrt{11^2 - 4(2)(11)}}{2(2)}$

$x = \dfrac{-11 \pm \sqrt{121 - 88}}{4}$

$x = \dfrac{-11 \pm \sqrt{33}}{4}$

The solution set is $\left\{ \dfrac{-11+\sqrt{33}}{4}, \dfrac{-11-\sqrt{33}}{4} \right\}$.

101. $(3x - 4)^2 = 16$

$3x - 4 = \pm\sqrt{16}$

$3x - 4 = \pm 4$

$3x = 4 \pm 4$

$3x = 8$ or $3x = 0$

$x = \dfrac{8}{3}$ or $x = 0$

The solution set is $\left\{ 0, \dfrac{8}{3} \right\}$.

103. $3x^2 - 12x + 12 = 0$

$x^2 - 4x + 4 = 0$

$(x-2)(x-2) = 0$

$x - 2 = 0$

$x = 2$

The solution set is $\{2\}$.

105. $4x^2 - 16 = 0$

$4x^2 = 16$

$x^2 = 4$

$x = \pm 2$

The solution set is $\{-2, 2\}$.

107.
$$x^2 = 4x - 2$$
$$x^2 - 4x + 2 = 0$$
$$x = \frac{-b \pm \sqrt{b^2 - 4ac}}{2a}$$
$$x = \frac{-(-4) \pm \sqrt{(-4)^2 - 4(1)(2)}}{2(1)}$$
$$x = \frac{4 \pm \sqrt{8}}{2}$$
$$x = 2 \pm \sqrt{2}$$
The solution set is $\left\{ 2 \pm \sqrt{2} \right\}$.

109. $2x^2 - 7x = 0$
$$x(2x - 7) = 0$$
$$x = 0 \text{ or } 2x - 7 = 0$$
$$2x = 7$$
$$x = 0 \text{ or } x = \frac{7}{2}$$
The solution set is $\left\{ 0, \frac{7}{2} \right\}$.

111. $\dfrac{1}{x} + \dfrac{1}{x+2} = \dfrac{1}{3}; x \neq 0, -2$
$$3x + 6 + 3x = x^2 + 2x$$
$$0 = x^2 - 4x - 6$$
$$x = \frac{-(-4) \pm \sqrt{(-4)^2 - 4(1)(-6)}}{2(1)}$$
$$x = \frac{4 \pm \sqrt{16 + 24}}{2}$$
$$x = \frac{4 \pm \sqrt{40}}{2}$$
$$x = \frac{4 \pm 2\sqrt{10}}{2}$$
$$x = 2 \pm \sqrt{10}$$
The solution set is $\{2 + \sqrt{10}, \ 2 - \sqrt{10}\}$.

113.
$$\frac{2x}{x-3} + \frac{6}{x+3} = \frac{-28}{x^2 - 9}; x \neq 3, -3$$
$$2x(x+3) + 6(x-3) = -28$$
$$2x^2 + 6x + 6x - 18 = -28$$
$$2x^2 + 12x + 10 = 0$$
$$x^2 + 6x + 5 = 0$$
$$(x+1)(x+5) = 0$$
The solution set is $\{-5, \ -1\}$.

115.
$$\sqrt{3x + 18} = x$$
$$3x + 18 = x^2$$
$$x^2 - 3x - 18 = 0$$
$$(x+3)(x-6) = 0$$
$$x + 3 = 0 \quad x - 6 = 0$$
$$x = -3 \qquad x = 6$$
$$\sqrt{3(-3) + 18} = -3 \quad \sqrt{3(6) + 18} = 6$$
$$\sqrt{-9 + 18} = -3 \qquad \sqrt{18 + 18} = 6$$
$$\sqrt{9} = -3 \text{ False} \quad \sqrt{36} = 6$$
The solution set is $\{6\}$.

117.
$$\sqrt{x + 3} = x - 3$$
$$x + 3 = x^2 - 6x + 9$$
$$x^2 - 7x + 6 = 0$$
$$(x-1)(x-6) = 0$$
$$x - 1 = 0 \quad x - 6 = 0$$
$$x = 1 \qquad x = 6$$
$$\sqrt{1 + 3} = 1 - 3 \qquad \sqrt{6 + 3} = 6 - 3$$
$$\sqrt{4} = -2 \qquad \text{False} \quad \sqrt{9} = 3$$
The solution set is $\{6\}$.

119.
$$\sqrt{2x + 13} = x + 7$$
$$2x + 13 = (x + 7)^2$$
$$2x + 13 = x^2 + 14x + 49$$
$$x^2 + 12x + 36 = 0$$
$$(x + 6)^2 = 0$$
$$x + 6 = 0$$
$$x = -6$$
$$\sqrt{2(-6) + 13} = -6 + 7$$
$$\sqrt{-12 + 13} = 1$$
$$\sqrt{1} = 1$$
The solution set is $\{-6\}$.

121.
$$x - \sqrt{2x+5} = 5$$
$$x - 5 = \sqrt{2x+5}$$
$$(x-5)^2 = 2x+5$$
$$x^2 - 10x + 25 = 2x + 5$$
$$x^2 - 12x + 20 = 0$$
$$(x-2)(x-10) = 0$$
$$x - 2 = 0 \quad x - 10 = 0$$
$$x = 2 \qquad x = 10$$
$$2 - \sqrt{2(2)+5} = 5 \quad 10 - \sqrt{2(10)+5} = 5$$
$$2 - \sqrt{9} = 5 \qquad 10 - \sqrt{25} = 5$$
$$2 - 3 = 5 \quad \text{False} \quad 10 - 5 = 5$$
The solution set is $\{10\}$.

123.
$$\sqrt{2x+19} - 8 = x$$
$$\sqrt{2x+19} = x + 8$$
$$\left(\sqrt{2x+19}\right)^2 = (x+8)^2$$
$$2x + 19 = x^2 + 16x + 64$$
$$0 = x^2 + 14x + 45$$
$$0 = (x+9)(x+5)$$
$$x + 9 = 0 \quad \text{or} \quad x + 5 = 0$$
$$x = -9 \qquad x = -5$$
-9 does not check and must be rejected.
The solution set is $\{-5\}$.

125.
$$25 - [2 + 5y - 3(y+2)] = -3(2y-5) - [5(y-1) - 3y + 3]$$
$$25 - [2 + 5y - 3y - 6] = -6y + 15 - [5y - 5 - 3y + 3]$$
$$25 - [2y - 4] = -6y + 15 - [2y - 2]$$
$$25 - 2y + 4 = -6y + 15 - 2y + 2$$
$$-2y + 29 = -8y + 17$$
$$6y = -12$$
$$y = -2$$
The solution set is $\{-2\}$.

127.
$$7 - 7x = (3x+2)(x-1)$$
$$7 - 7x = 3x^2 - x - 2$$
$$0 = 3x^2 + 6x - 9$$
$$0 = x^2 + 2x - 3$$
$$0 = (x+3)(x-1)$$
$$x + 3 = 0 \quad \text{or} \quad x - 1 = 0$$
$$x = -3 \qquad x = 1$$
The solution set is $\{-3, 1\}$.

129.
$$\left| x^2 + 2x - 36 \right| = 12$$
$$x^2 + 2x - 36 = 12 \qquad x^2 + 2x - 36 = -12$$
$$x^2 + 2x - 48 = 0 \quad \text{or} \quad x^2 + 2x - 24 = 0$$
$$(x+8)(x-6) = 0 \qquad (x+6)(x-4) = 0$$
Setting each of the factors above equal to zero gives $x = -8$, $x = 6$, $x = -6$, and $x = 4$.
The solution set is $\{-8, -6, 4, 6\}$.

131.

$$\frac{1}{x^2 - 3x + 2} = \frac{1}{x+2} + \frac{5}{x^2 - 4}$$

$$\frac{1}{(x-1)(x-2)} = \frac{1}{x+2} + \frac{5}{(x+2)(x-2)}$$

Multiply both sides of the equation by the least common denominator, $(x-1)(x-2)(x+2)$. This results in the following:

$$x + 2 = (x-1)(x-2) + 5(x-1)$$
$$x + 2 = x^2 - 2x - x + 2 + 5x - 5$$
$$x + 2 = x^2 + 2x - 3$$
$$0 = x^2 + x - 5$$

Apply the quadratic formula:
$a = 1 \quad b = 1 \quad c = -5$.

$$x = \frac{-1 \pm \sqrt{1^2 - 4(1)(-5)}}{2(1)} = \frac{-1 \pm \sqrt{1 - (-20)}}{2}$$

$$= \frac{-1 \pm \sqrt{21}}{2}$$

The solutions are $\dfrac{-1 \pm \sqrt{21}}{2}$, and the solution set is

$$\left\{ \frac{-1 \pm \sqrt{21}}{2} \right\}.$$

133. $\sqrt{x+8} - \sqrt{x-4} = 2$

$$\sqrt{x+8} = \sqrt{x-4} + 2$$
$$x + 8 = \left(\sqrt{x-4} + 2\right)^2$$
$$x + 8 = x - 4 + 4\sqrt{x-4} + 4$$
$$x + 8 = x + 4\sqrt{x-4}$$
$$8 = 4\sqrt{x-4}$$
$$2 = \sqrt{x-4}$$
$$4 = x - 4$$
$$x = 8$$

$$\sqrt{8+8} - \sqrt{8-4} = 2$$
$$\sqrt{16} - \sqrt{4} = 2$$
$$4 - 2 = 2$$

The solution set is $\{8\}$.

135. Values that make the denominator zero must be excluded.

$$2x^2 + 4x - 9 = 0$$

$$x = \frac{-b \pm \sqrt{b^2 - 4ac}}{2a}$$

$$x = \frac{-(4) \pm \sqrt{(4)^2 - 4(2)(-9)}}{2(2)}$$

$$x = \frac{-4 \pm \sqrt{88}}{4}$$

$$x = \frac{-4 \pm 2\sqrt{22}}{4}$$

$$x = \frac{-2 \pm \sqrt{22}}{2}$$

137. $D = \dfrac{1}{9}N + \dfrac{26}{9}; \quad D = \dfrac{7}{2}$

$$\frac{7}{2} = \frac{1}{9}N + \frac{26}{9}$$

$$18\left(\frac{7}{2}\right) = 18\left(\frac{1}{9}N + \frac{26}{9}\right)$$

$$63 = 2N + 52$$

$$11 = 2N$$

$$\frac{11}{2} = \frac{2N}{2}$$

$$5.5 = N$$

If the high-humor group averages a level of depression of 3.5 in response to a negative life event, the intensity of that event would be 5.5. The solution is the point along the horizontal axis where the graph for the high-humor group has a value of 3.5 on the vertical axis. This corresponds to the point $(5.5, 3.5)$ on the high-humor graph.

139.

$$C = \frac{x + 0.1(500)}{x + 500}$$

$$0.28 = \frac{x + 0.1(500)}{x + 500}$$

$$0.28(x + 500) = x + 0.1(500)$$

$$0.28x + 140 = x + 50$$

$$-0.72x = -90$$

$$\frac{-0.72x}{-0.72} = \frac{-90}{-0.72}$$

$$x = 125$$

125 liters of pure peroxide must be added.

141. $f(x) = 0.013x^2 - 1.19x + 28.24$

$\qquad 3 = 0.013x^2 - 1.19x + 28.24$

$\qquad 0 = 0.013x^2 - 1.19x + 25.24$

Apply the quadratic formula:

$a = 0.013 \quad b = -1.19 \quad c = 25.24$

$x = \dfrac{-(-1.19) \pm \sqrt{(-1.19)^2 - 4(0.013)(25.24)}}{2(0.013)}$

$= \dfrac{1.19 \pm \sqrt{1.4161 - 1.31248}}{0.026}$

$= \dfrac{1.19 \pm \sqrt{0.10362}}{0.026}$

$\approx \dfrac{1.19 \pm 0.32190}{0.026}$

$\approx 58.15 \text{ or } 33.39$

The solutions are approximately 33.39 and 58.15. Thus, 33 year olds and 58 year olds are expected to be in 3 fatal crashes per 100 million miles driven. The function models the actual data well.

143. For the year 2100, we use $x = 98$.

$H = 0.083(98) + 57.9$

$\quad = 66.034$

$L = 0.36\sqrt{98} + 57.9$

$\quad \approx 61.464$

In the year 2100, the projected high end temperature is about $66°$ and the projected low end temperature is about $61.5°$.

145. Using H:

$0.083x + 57.9 = 57.9 + 1$

$\qquad 0.083x = 1$

$\qquad x = \dfrac{1}{0.083}$

$\qquad x \approx 12$

The projected global temperature will exceed the 2002 average by 1 degree in 2014 (12 years after 2002). Using L:

$0.36\sqrt{x} + 57.9 = 1 + 57.9$

$\qquad 0.36\sqrt{x} = 1$

$\qquad \sqrt{x} = \dfrac{1}{0.36}$

$\qquad \left(\sqrt{x}\right)^2 = \left(\dfrac{1}{0.36}\right)^2$

$\qquad x \approx 8$

The projected global temperature will exceed the 2002 average by 1 degree in 2010 (8 years after 2002).

161. **a.** false; $\quad (2x - 3)^2 = 25$

$\qquad\qquad\qquad \sqrt{(2x-3)^2} = \pm\sqrt{25}$

$\qquad\qquad\qquad\qquad 2x - 3 = \pm 5$

b. false; some quadratics have one number in their solution set.

c. true; some quadratics have one number in their solution set.

d. false; $ax^2 + c = 0$ can be solved using $b = 0$.

(c) is true.

163. $[x - (-3)][x - (5)] = 0$

$\qquad (x + 3)(x - 5) = 0$

$\qquad\quad x^2 - 2x - 15 = 0$

165. $s = -16t^2 + v_0 t$

$\quad 0 = -16t^2 + v_0 t - s$

$\quad a = -16, \ b = v_0, \ c = -s$

$\quad t = \dfrac{-v_0 \pm \sqrt{(v_0)^2 - 4(-16)(-s)}}{2(-16)}$

$\quad t = \dfrac{-v_0 \pm \sqrt{(v_0)^2 - 64s}}{-32}$

$\quad t = \dfrac{v_0 \pm \sqrt{v_0{}^2 - 64s}}{32}$

Section P.8

Check Point Exercises

1. Let x = the number of football injuries
    Let $x + 0.6$ = the number of basketball injuries
    Let $x + 0.3$ = the number of bicycling injuries
    $$x + (x + 0.6) + (x + 0.3) = 3.9$$
    $$x + x + 0.6 + x + 0.3 = 3.9$$
    $$3x + 0.9 = 3.9$$
    $$3x = 3$$
    $$x = 1$$

    $x = 1$
    $x + 0.6 = 1 + 0.6 = 1.6$
    $x + 0.3 = 1 + 0.3 = 1.3$
    In 2004 there were 1 million football injuries, 1.6 million basketball injuries, and 1.3 million bicycling injuries.

2. Let x = the number of years after 2004 that it will take until Americans will purchase 79.9 million gallons of organic milk.
    $$40.7 + 5.6x = 79.9$$
    $$5.6x = 79.9 - 40.7$$
    $$5.6x = 39.2$$
    $$x = \frac{39.2}{5.6}$$
    $$x = 7$$
    Americans will purchase 79.9 million gallons of organic milk 7 years after 2004, or 2011.

3. Let x = the computer's price before the reduction.
    $$x - 0.30x = 840$$
    $$0.70x = 840$$
    $$x = \frac{840}{0.70}$$
    $$x = 1200$$
    Before the reduction the computer's price was $1200.

4. Let x = the width of the court.
    Let $x + 44$ = the length of the court.
    $$2l + 2w = P$$
    $$2(x + 44) + 2x = 288$$
    $$2x + 88 + 2x = 288$$
    $$4x + 88 = 288$$
    $$4x = 200$$
    $$x = \frac{200}{4}$$
    $$x = 50$$
    $$x + 44 = 94$$
    The dimensions of the court are 50 by 94.

5. $$(16 + 2x)(12 + 2x) = 320$$
    $$192 + 56x + 4x^2 = 320$$
    $$4x^2 + 56x - 128 = 0$$
    $$x^2 + 14x - 32 = 0$$
    $$(x + 16)(x - 2) = 0$$
    $$x + 16 = 0 \quad \text{or} \quad x - 2 = 0$$
    $$x = -16 \qquad\qquad x = 2$$
    -16 must be rejected.
    The path must be 2 feet wide.

6. $$a^2 + b^2 = c^2$$
    $$a^2 + (50)^2 = (130)^2$$
    $$a^2 + 2500 = 16,900$$
    $$a^2 = 14,400$$
    $$a = \pm 120$$
    -120 must be rejected.
    The tower is 120 yards tall.

7.

The original amount of money per person.

The new amount of money per person.

reduction per winner

$$\overbrace{\frac{5,000,000}{x}}^{} - \overbrace{375,000}^{} = \overbrace{\frac{5,000,000}{x+3}}^{}$$

$$x(x+3)\left(\frac{5,000,000}{x} - 375,000\right) = x(x+3)\frac{5,000,000}{x+3}$$

$$5,000,000(x+3) - 375,000x(x+3) = 5,000,000x$$

$$5,000,000x + 15,000,000 - 375,000x^2 - 1,125,000x = 5,000,000x$$

$$-375,000x^2 - 1,125,000x + 15,000,000 = 0$$

$$x^2 + 3x - 40 = 0$$

$$(x+8)(x-5) = 0$$

$x + 8 = 0 \quad$ or $\quad x - 5 = 0$

$x = -8 \qquad\quad x = 5$

-8 must be rejected. There were 5 people in the original group.

Exercise Set P.8

1. Let x = the number of births (in thousands)

Let $x - 229$ = the number of deaths (in thousands).

$$x + (x - 229) = 521$$

$$x + x - 229 = 521$$

$$2x - 229 = 521$$

$$2x - 229 + 229 = 521 + 229$$

$$2x = 750$$

$$\frac{2x}{2} = \frac{750}{2}$$

$$x = 375$$

There are 375 thousand births and $375 - 229 = 146$ thousand deaths each day.

3. Let L = the life expectancy of an American man.

y = the number of years after 1900.

$$L = 55 + 0.2y$$

$$85 = 55 + 0.2y$$

$$30 = 0.2y$$

$$150 = y$$

The life expectancy will be 85 years in the year

$1900 + 150 = 2050$.

5. $1.7x + 39.8 = 44.9 + 8.5$

$1.7x + 39.8 = 53.4$

$$1.7x = 13.6$$

$$\frac{1.7x}{1.7} = \frac{13.6}{1.7}$$

$$x = 8$$

The number of Americans without health insurance will exceed 44.9 million by 8.5 million 8 years after 2000, or 2008.

7. Let x = the number of years after 2005
$$13,300 + 1000x = 26,800 - 500x$$
$$1500x = 13,500$$
$$\frac{1500x}{1500} = \frac{13,500}{1500}$$
$$x = 9$$
The two colleges will have the same enrollment about 9 years after 2005, or 2014.
$$13,300 + 1000(9) = 22,300$$
$$\text{and}$$
$$26,800 - 500(9) = 22,300$$
The college's enrollments will be 22,300 at that time.

9. Let x = the cost of the television set.
$$x - 0.20x = 336$$
$$0.80x = 336$$
$$x = 420$$
The television set's price is $420.

11. Let x = the nightly cost
$$x + 0.08x = 162$$
$$1.08x = 162$$
$$x = 150$$
The nightly cost is $150.

13. Let x = the annual salary for men whose highest educational attainment is a high school degree.
$$x + 0.22x = 44,000$$
$$1.22x = 44,000$$
$$x \approx 36,000$$
The annual salary for men whose highest educational attainment is a high school degree is about $36,000.

15. Let c = the dealer's cost
$$584 = c + 0.25c$$
$$584 = 1.25c$$
$$467.20 = c$$
The dealer's cost is $467.20.

17. Let w = the width of the field
Let $2w$ = the length of the field
$$P = 2(\text{length}) + 2(\text{width})$$
$$300 = 2(2w) + 2(w)$$
$$300 = 4w + 2w$$
$$300 = 6w$$
$$50 = w$$
If $w = 50$, then $2w = 100$. Thus, the dimensions are 50 yards by 100 yards.

19. Let w = the width of the field
Let $2w + 6$ = the length of the field
$$228 = 6w + 12$$
$$216 = 6w$$
$$36 = w$$
If $w = 36$, then $2w + 6 = 2(36) + 6 = 78$. Thus, the dimensions are 36 feet by 78 feet.

21. Let x = the width of the frame.
Total length: $16 + 2x$
Total width: $12 + 2x$
$$P = 2(\text{length}) + 2(\text{width})$$
$$72 = 2(16 + 2x) + 2(12 + 2x)$$
$$72 = 32 + 4x + 24 + 4x$$
$$72 = 8x + 56$$
$$16 = 8x$$
$$2 = x$$
The width of the frame is 2 inches.

23. Let w = the width
Let $w + 3$ = the length
$$\text{Area} = lw$$
$$54 = (w + 3)w$$
$$54 = w^2 + 3w$$
$$0 = w^2 + 3w - 54$$
$$0 = (w + 9)(w - 6)$$
$$w + 9 = 0 \qquad w - 6 = 0$$
$$w = -9 \qquad w = 6$$
Disregard -9 because we can't have a negative length measurement. The width is 6 feet and the length is $6 + 3 = 9$ feet.

25. Let x = the length of the side of the original square
Let $x + 3$ = the length of the side of the new, larger square
$$(x + 3)^2 = 64$$
$$x^2 + 6x + 9 = 64$$
$$x^2 + 6x - 55 = 0$$
$$(x + 11)(x - 5) = 0$$
Apply the zero product principle.
$$x + 11 = 0 \qquad x - 5 = 0$$
$$x = -11 \qquad x = 5$$
The solution set is $\{-11, 5\}$. Disregard -11 because we can't have a negative length measurement. This means that x, the length of the side of the original square, is 5 inches.

27. Let x = the width of the path
$$(20+2x)(10+2x) = 600$$
$$200+40x+20x+4x^2 = 600$$
$$200+60x+4x^2 = 600$$
$$4x^2+60x+200 = 600$$
$$4x^2+60x-400 = 0$$
$$4(x^2+15x-100) = 0$$
$$4(x+20)(x-5) = 0$$

Apply the zero product principle.
$$4(x+20) = 0 \qquad x-5 = 0$$
$$x+20 = 0 \qquad x = 5$$
$$x = -20$$

The solution set is $\{-20, 5\}$. Disregard -20 because we can't have a negative width measurement. The width of the path is 5 meters.

29. $(20+2x)(30+2x)-(20)(30) = 336$
$$600+100x+4x^2-600 = 336$$
$$4x^2+100x-336 = 0$$
$$x^2+25x-84 = 0$$
$$(x-3)(x+28) = 0$$
$$x-3 = 0 \quad \text{or} \quad x+28 = 0$$
$$x = 3 \qquad\qquad x = -28$$
-28 must be rejected.
The width of the path is 3 feet

31. $a^2+b^2 = c^2$
$$a^2+15^2 = 20^2$$
$$a^2+225 = 400$$
$$a^2 = 175$$
$$a = \pm\sqrt{175}$$
$$a \approx \pm 13.2$$
-13.2 must be rejected.
The ladder reaches 13.2 feet up the house.

33. $a^2+b^2 = c^2$
$$5^2+x^2 = (x+1)^2$$
$$x^2+25 = x^2+2x+1$$
$$25 = 2x+1$$
$$24 = 2x$$
$$x = 12$$
$$x+1 = 13$$
The wire is 13 feet long.

35. Let x be the width.
$$a^2+b^2 = c^2$$
$$x^2+(2x)^2 = 64^2$$
$$x^2+4x^2 = 4096$$
$$5x^2 = 4096$$
$$x^2 = \frac{4096}{5}$$
$$x = \pm\sqrt{\frac{4096}{5}}$$
$$x \approx 28.62 \text{ feet}$$
$$2x \approx 57.24 \text{ feet}$$
The distance along the length and width is about $28.62 + 57.24$, or about 85.9 feet. A person could save $85.9 - 64$, or about 21.9 feet.

37.

The original amount of money per person

$$\overbrace{\frac{20,000,000}{x}} - \overbrace{500,000}^{\text{reduction per winner}} = \overbrace{\frac{20,000,000}{x+2}}^{\text{The new amount of money per person}}$$

$$x(x+2)\left(\frac{20,000,000}{x} - 500,000\right) = x(x+2)\frac{20,000,000}{x+2}$$

$$20,000,000(x+2) - 500,000x(x+2) = 20,000,000x$$

$$20,000,000x + 40,000,000 - 500,000x^2 - 1,000,000x = 20,000,000x$$

$$40,000,000 - 500,000x^2 - 1,000,000x = 0$$

$$x^2 + 2x - 80 = 0$$

$$(x+10)(x-8) = 0$$

$$x + 10 = 0 \quad \text{or} \quad x - 8 = 0$$
$$x = -10 \qquad\qquad x = 8$$

-10 must be rejected. There were 8 people in the original group.

39. Let x be the car's average velocity.

$$\overbrace{\frac{300}{x}}^{\substack{\text{car's time}\\\text{traveled}}} = \overbrace{\frac{180}{x-20}}^{\substack{\text{bus's time}\\\text{traveled}}}$$

$$300(x-20) = 180x$$
$$300x - 6000 = 180x$$
$$120x = 6000$$
$$x = 50$$
$$x - 20 = 30$$

The average velocity of the car is 50 miles per hour. The average velocity of the bus is 30 miles per hour.

41. Let x be the average velocity on the return trip.

$$\frac{5}{x+9} + \frac{5}{x} = \frac{7}{6}$$

$$6x(x+9)\left(\frac{5}{x+9} + \frac{5}{x}\right) = 6x(x+9)\frac{7}{6}$$

$$30x + 30(x+9) = 7x(x+9)$$

$$30x + 30x + 270 = 7x^2 + 63x$$

$$0 = 7x^2 + 3x - 270$$

$$0 = (x-6)(7x+45)$$

$$x - 6 = 0 \quad \text{or} \quad 7x + 45 = 0$$
$$x = 6 \qquad\qquad x = -\frac{45}{7}$$

$-\dfrac{45}{7}$ must be rejected. The average velocity on the return trip is 6 miles per hour.

43. Let x = number of hours
$$35x = \text{labor cost}$$
$$35x + 63 = 448$$
$$35x = 385$$
$$x = 11$$
It took 11 hours.

45. Let x = inches over 5 feet
$$100 + 5x = 135$$
$$5x = 35$$
$$x = 7$$
A height of 5 feet 7 inches corresponds to 135 pounds.

47. Let x be the number of consecutive hits.
$$\frac{35+x}{140+x} = 0.30$$
$$35 + x = 0.30(140 + x)$$
$$35 + x = 42 + 0.30x$$
$$350 + 10x = 420 + 3x$$
$$7x = 70$$
$$x = 10$$
You must get 10 consecutive hits to increase your batting average to 0.30.

55. Let x be the length of one leg.

$$a^2 + b^2 = c^2$$

$$x^2 + (x+1)^2 = \left[12 - x - (x+1)\right]^2$$

$$x^2 + x^2 + 2x + 1 = \left[12 - x - x - 1\right]^2$$

$$2x^2 + 2x + 1 = (11 - 2x)^2$$

$$2x^2 + 2x + 1 = 121 - 44x + 4x^2$$

$$0 = 2x^2 - 46x + 120$$

$$0 = x^2 - 23x + 60$$

$$0 = (x - 3)(x - 20)$$

$$x - 3 = 0 \quad \text{or} \quad x - 20 = 0$$

$$x = 3 \qquad\qquad x = 20$$

$$x + 1 = 4$$

$$12 - (3 + 4) = 5$$

20 must be rejected, as it is greater than the perimeter.
The lengths of the sides are 3, 4, and 5.

57. Let x = woman's age
$3x$ = Coburn's age

$$3x + 20 = 2(x + 20)$$

$$3x + 20 = 2x + 40$$

$$x + 20 = 40$$

$$x = 20$$

Coburn is 60 years old the woman is 20 years old.

59. Let x = mother's amount
$2x$ = boy's amount

$$\frac{x}{2} = \text{girl's amount}$$

$$x + 2x + \frac{x}{2} = 14,000$$

$$\frac{7}{2}x = 14,000$$

$$x = \$4,000$$

The mother received $4000, the boy received $8000, and the girl received $2000.

Section P.9

Check Point Exercises

1. **a.** $[-2, \ 5) = \left\{x \mid -2 \le x < 5\right\}$

b. $[1, \ 3.5] = \left\{x \mid 1 \le x \le 3.5\right\}$

c. $[-\infty, \ -1) = \left\{x \mid x < -1\right\}$

2. **a.** Graph $[1, 3]$:

Graph $(2, 6)$:

To find the intersection, take the portion of the number line that the two graphs have in common.

Numbers in both $[1, 3]$ and $(2, 6)$:

Thus, $[1, 3] \cap (2, 6) = (2, 3]$.

b. Graph $[1, 3]$:

Graph $(2, 6)$:

To find the union, take the portion of the number line representing the total collection of numbers in the two graphs.

Numbers in either $[1, 3]$ or $(2, 6)$ or both:

Thus, $[1, 3] \cup (2, 6) = [1, 6)$.

3. $2 - 3x \le 5$

$-3x \le 3$

$x \ge -1$

The solution set is $\{x | x \ge -1\}$ or $[-1, \infty)$.

4. $3x + 1 > 7x - 15$

$-4x > -16$

$\dfrac{-4x}{-4} < \dfrac{-16}{-4}$

$x < 4$

The solution set is $\{x | x < 4\}$ or $(-\infty, 4]$.

5. $1 \le 2x + 3 < 11$

$-2 \le 2x < 8$

$-1 \le x < 4$

The solution set is $\{x | -1 \le x < 4\}$ or $[-1, 4)$.

6. $|x - 2| < 5$

$-5 < x - 2 < 5$

$-3 < x < 7$

The solution set is $\{x | -3 < x < 7\}$ or $(-3, 7)$.

7. $-3|5x - 2| + 20 \ge -19$

$-3|5x - 2| \ge -39$

$\dfrac{-3|5x - 2|}{-3} \le \dfrac{-39}{-3}$

$|5x - 2| \le 13$

$-13 \le 5x - 2 \le 13$

$-11 \le 5x \le 15$

$\dfrac{-11}{5} \le \dfrac{5x}{5} \le \dfrac{15}{5}$

$-\dfrac{11}{5} \le x \le 3$

The solution set is

$\left\{ x \middle| -\dfrac{11}{5} \le x \le 3 \right\}$ or $\left[-\dfrac{11}{5}, 3 \right]$.

8. $18 < |6 - 3x|$

$6 - 3x < -18$ or $6 - 3x > 18$

$-3x < -24$ $-3x > 12$

$\dfrac{-3x}{-3} > \dfrac{-24}{-3}$ $\dfrac{-3x}{-3} < \dfrac{12}{-3}$

$x > 8$ $x < -4$

The solution set is $\{x | x < -4 \text{ or } x > 8\}$

or $(-\infty, -4) \cup (8, \infty)$.

9. Let x = the number of miles driven in a week.

$260 < 80 + 0.25x$

$180 < 0.25x$

$720 < x$

Driving more than 720 miles in a week makes Basic the better deal.

Exercise Set P.9

1. $1 < x \le 6$

3. $-5 \le x < 2$

5. $-3 \le x \le 1$

7. $x > 2$

9. $x \ge -3$

11. $x < 3$

13. $x < 5.5$

15.   Graph $(-3, 0)$:

Graph $[-1, 2]$:

To find the intersection, take the portion of the number line that the two graphs have in common.

Numbers in both
$(-3, 0)$ and $[-1, 2]$:

Thus, $(-3, 0) \cap [-1, 2] = [-1, 0)$.

17.   Graph $(-3, 0)$:

Graph $[-1, 2]$:

To find the union, take the portion of the number line representing the total collection of numbers in the two graphs.

Numbers in either $(-3, 0)$
or $[-1, 2]$ or both:

Thus, $(-3, 0) \cup [-1, 2] = (-3, 2]$.

19.   Graph $(-\infty, 5)$:

Graph $[1, 8]$:

To find the intersection, take the portion of the number line that the two graphs have in common.

Numbers in both
$(-\infty, 5)$ and $[1, 8]$:

Thus, $(-\infty, 5) \cap [1, 8] = [1, 5)$.

21.   Graph $(-\infty, 5)$:

Graph $[1, 8]$:

To find the union, take the portion of the number line representing the total collection of numbers in the two graphs.

Numbers in either $(-\infty, 5)$
or $[1, 8]$ or both:

Thus, $(-\infty, 5) \cup [1, 8] = (-\infty, 8]$.

23.   Graph $[3, \infty)$:

Graph $(6, \infty)$:

To find the intersection, take the portion of the number line that the two graphs have in common.

Numbers in both
$[3, \infty)$ and $(6, \infty)$:

Thus, $[3, \infty) \cap (6, \infty) = (6, \infty)$.

25.   Graph $[3, \infty)$:

Graph $(6, \infty)$:

To find the union, take the portion of the number line representing the total collection of numbers in the two graphs.

Numbers in either $[3, \infty)$

or $(6, \infty)$ or both:

Thus, $[3, \infty) \cup (6, \infty) = [3, \infty)$.

27. $5x + 11 < 26$
$5x < 15$
$x < 3$
The solution set is $\{x \mid x < 3\}$, or $(-\infty, 3)$.

29. $3x - 7 \geq 13$
$3x \geq 20$
$x \geq \dfrac{20}{3}$

The solution set is $\left\{x \mid x > \dfrac{20}{3}\right\}$, or $\left[\dfrac{20}{3}, \infty\right)$.

$\dfrac{20}{3}$

31. $-9x \geq 36$
$x \leq -4$
The solution set is $\{x \mid x \leq -4\}$, or $(-\infty, -4]$.

-4

33. $8x - 11 \leq 3x - 13$
$8x - 3x \leq -13 + 11$
$5x \leq -2$

$x \leq -\dfrac{2}{5}$

The solution set is $\left\{x \mid x \leq -\dfrac{2}{5}\right\}$, or $\left(-\infty, -\dfrac{2}{5}\right]$.

$-\dfrac{2}{5}$

35. $4(x + 1) + 2 \geq 3x + 6$
$4x + 4 + 2 \geq 3x + 6$
$4x + 6 \geq 3x + 6$
$4x - 3x \geq 6 - 6$
$x \geq 0$
The solution set is $\{x \mid x > 0\}$, or $[0, \infty)$.

0

37. $2x - 11 < -3(x + 2)$
$2x - 11 < -3x - 6$
$5x < 5$
$x < 1$
The solution set is $\{x \mid x < 1\}$, or $(-\infty, 1)$.

39. $1 - (x + 3) \geq 4 - 2x$
$1 - x - 3 \geq 4 - 2x$
$-x - 2 \geq 4 - 2x$
$x \geq 6$
The solution set is $\{x \mid x \geq 6\}$, or $[6, \infty)$.

6

41. $\dfrac{x}{4} - \dfrac{3}{2} \leq \dfrac{x}{2} + 1$

$\dfrac{4x}{4} - \dfrac{4 \cdot 3}{2} \leq \dfrac{4 \cdot x}{2} + 4 \cdot 1$

$x - 6 \leq 2x + 4$

$-x \leq 10$

$x \geq -10$

The solution set is $\{x \mid x \geq -10\}$, or $[-10, \infty)$.

-10

43. $1 - \dfrac{x}{2} > 4$

$-\dfrac{x}{2} > 3$

$x < -6$

The solution set is $\{x \mid x, -6\}$, or $(-\infty, -6)$.

-6

45. $\dfrac{x-4}{6} \geq \dfrac{x-2}{9} + \dfrac{5}{18}$

$3(x-4) \geq 2(x-2) + 5$

$3x - 12 \geq 2x - 4 + 5$

$x \geq 13$

The solution set is $\{x \mid x \geq 13\}$, or $[13, \infty)$.

47. $3[3(x+5)+8x+7] + 5[3(x-6) - 2(3x-5)] < 2(4x+3)$

$3[3x + 15 + 8x + 7] + 5[3x - 18 - 6x + 10] < 8x + 6$

$3[11x + 22] + 5[-3x - 8] < 8x + 6$

$33x + 66 - 15x - 40 < 8x + 6$

$18x + 26 < 8x + 6$

$10x < -20$

$x < -2$

The solution set is $\{x \mid x < -2\}$ or $[-\infty, -2)$.

49. $6 < x + 3 < 8$

$6 - 3 < x + 3 - 3 < 8 - 3$

$3 < x < 5$

The solution set is $\{x \mid 3 < x < 5\}$, or (3, 5).

51. $-3 \leq x - 2 < 1$

$-1 \leq x < 3$

The solution set is $\{x \mid -1 \leq x < 3\}$, or [-1, 3).

53. $-11 < 2x - 1 \leq -5$

$-10 < 2x \leq -4$

$-5 < x \leq -2$

The solution set is $\{x \mid -5 < x \leq -2\}$, or

$(-5, -2]$.

55. $-3 \leq \dfrac{2}{3}x - 5 < -1$

$2 \leq \dfrac{2}{3}x < 4$

$3 \leq x < 6$

The solution set is $\{x \mid 3 \leq x < 6\}$, or [3, 6).

57. $|x| < 3$

$-3 < x < 3$

The solution set is $\{x \mid -3 < x < 3\}$, or (-3, 3).

59. $|x - 1| \leq 2$

$-2 \leq x - 1 \leq 2$

$-1 \leq x \leq 3$

The solution set is $\{x \mid -1 \leq x \leq 3\}$, or [-1, 3].

61. $|2x - 6| < 8$

$-8 < 2x - 6 < 8$

$-2 < 2x < 14$

$-1 < x < 7$

The solution set is $\{x \mid -1 < x < 7\}$, or (-1, 7).

63. $|2(x - 1) + 4| \leq 8$

$-8 \leq 2(x - 1) + 4 \leq 8$

$-8 \leq 2x - 2 + 4 \leq 8$

$-8 \leq 2x + 2 \leq 8$

$-10 \leq 2x \leq 6$

$-5 \leq x \leq 3$

The solution set is $\{x \mid -5 \leq x \leq 3\}$, or

$[-5, 3]$.

65. $\left| \dfrac{2y+6}{3} \right| < 2$

$-2 < \dfrac{2y+6}{3} < 2$

$-6 < 2y + 6 < 6$

$-12 < 2y < 0$

$-6 < y < 0$

The solution set is $\{x \mid -6 < y < 0\}$, or (-6, 0).

67. $|x| > 3$

$x > 3$ or $x < -3$

The solution set is $\{x \mid x > 3 \text{ or } x < -3\}$, that is,

$(-\infty, -3)$ or $(3, \infty)$.

69. $|x - 1| \geq 2$

$x - 1 \geq 2$ or $x - 1 \leq -2$

$x \geq 3$ $x \leq -1$

The solution set is $\{x \mid x \leq -1 \text{ or } x \geq 3\}$, that is,

$(-\infty, -1]$ or $[3, \infty)$.

71. $|3x - 8| > 7$

$3x - 8 > 7$ or $3x - 8 < -7$

$3x > 15$ $3x < 1$

$x > 5$ $x < \dfrac{1}{3}$

The solution set is $\left\{x \mid x < \dfrac{1}{3} \text{ or } x > 5\right\}$, that is,

$\left(-\infty, \dfrac{1}{3}\right)$ or $(5, \infty)$.

73. $\left|\dfrac{2x + 2}{4}\right| \geq 2$

$\dfrac{2x + 2}{4} \geq 2$ or $\dfrac{2x + 2}{4} \leq -2$

$2x + 2 \geq 8$ $2x + 2 \leq -8$

$2x \geq 6$ $2x \leq -10$

$x \geq 3$ $x \leq -5$

The solution set is $\{x \mid x \leq -5 \text{ or } x \geq 3\}$, that is,

$(-\infty, -5]$ or $[3, \infty)$.

75. $\left|3 - \dfrac{2}{3}x\right| > 5$

$3 - \dfrac{2}{3}x > 5$ or $3 - \dfrac{2}{3}x < -5$

$-\dfrac{2}{3}x > 2$ $-\dfrac{2}{3}x < -8$

$x < -3$ $x > 12$

The solution set is $\{x \mid x < -3 \text{ or } x > 12\}$, that is,

$(-\infty, -3)$ or $(12, \infty)$.

77. $3|x - 1| + 2 \geq 8$

$3|x - 1| \geq 6$

$|x - 1| \geq 2$

$x - 1 \geq 2$ or $x - 1 \leq -2$

$x \geq 3$ $x \leq -1$

The solution set is $\{x \mid x \leq 1 \text{ or } x \geq 3\}$, that is,

$(-\infty, -1]$ or $[3, \infty)$.

79. $-2|x - 4| \geq -4$

$\dfrac{-2|x - 4|}{-2} \leq \dfrac{-4}{-2}$

$|x - 4| \leq 2$

$-2 \leq x - 4 \leq 2$

$2 \leq x \leq 6$

The solution set is $\{x \mid 2 \leq x \leq 6\}$.

81. $-4|1 - x| < -16$

$\dfrac{-4|1 - x|}{-4} > \dfrac{-16}{-4}$

$|1 - x| > 4$

$1 - x > 4$ $1 - x < -4$

$-x > 3$ or $-x < -5$

$x < -3$ $x > 5$

The solution set is $\{x \mid x < -3 \text{ or } x > 5\}$.

83. $3 \leq |2x - 1|$

$2x - 1 \geq 3$ $2x - 1 \leq -3$

$2x \geq 4$ or $2x \leq -2$

$x \geq 2$ $x \leq -1$

The solution set is $\{x \mid x \leq -1 \text{ or } x \geq 2\}$.

85. $5 > |4 - x|$ is equivalent to $|4 - x| < 5$.

$-5 < 4 - x < 5$

$-9 < -x < 1$

$\dfrac{-9}{-1} > \dfrac{-x}{-1} > \dfrac{1}{-1}$

$9 > x > -1$

$-1 < x < 9$

The solution set is $\{x \mid -1 < x < 9\}$.

87. $1 < |2 - 3x|$ is equivalent to $|2 - 3x| > 1$.

$$
\begin{array}{ll}
2 - 3x > 1 & \\
-3x > -1 & \quad 2 - 3x < -1 \\
\dfrac{-3x}{-3} < \dfrac{-1}{-3} \quad \text{or} & \quad -3x < -3 \\
& \quad \dfrac{-3x}{-3} > \dfrac{-3}{-3} \\
x < \dfrac{1}{3} & \quad x > 1
\end{array}
$$

The solution set is $\left\{ x \mid x < \dfrac{1}{3} \text{ or } x > 1 \right\}$.

89. $12 < \left| -2x + \dfrac{6}{7} \right| + \dfrac{3}{7}$

$$
\dfrac{81}{7} < \left| -2x + \dfrac{6}{7} \right|
$$

$$
\begin{array}{ll}
-2x + \dfrac{6}{7} > \dfrac{81}{7} \quad \text{or} & \quad -2x + \dfrac{6}{7} < -\dfrac{81}{7} \\
-2x > \dfrac{75}{7} & \quad -2x < -\dfrac{87}{7} \\
x < -\dfrac{75}{14} & \quad x > \dfrac{87}{14}
\end{array}
$$

The solution set is $\left\{ x \mid x < -\dfrac{75}{14} \text{ or } x > \dfrac{87}{14} \right\}$,

that is, $\left(-\infty, -\dfrac{75}{14} \right)$ or $\left(\dfrac{87}{14}, \infty \right)$.

91. $4 + \left| 3 - \dfrac{x}{3} \right| \ge 9$

$$
\left| 3 - \dfrac{x}{3} \right| \ge 5
$$

$$
\begin{array}{ll}
3 - \dfrac{x}{3} \ge 5 \quad \text{or} & \quad 3 - \dfrac{x}{3} \le -5 \\
-\dfrac{x}{3} \ge 2 & \quad -\dfrac{x}{3} \le -8 \\
x \le -6 & \quad x \ge 24
\end{array}
$$

The solution set is $\{ x \mid x \le -6 \text{ or } x \ge 24 \}$, that is,

$(-\infty, -6]$ or $[24, \infty)$.

93.
$$
\begin{aligned}
y &\ge 4 \\
1 - (x + 3) + 2x &\ge 4 \\
1 - x - 3 + 2x &\ge 4 \\
x - 2 &\ge 4 \\
x &\ge 6
\end{aligned}
$$
The solution set is $[6, \infty)$.

95.
$$
\begin{aligned}
y &\le 4 \\
7 - \left| \dfrac{x}{2} + 2 \right| &\le 4 \\
- \left| \dfrac{x}{2} + 2 \right| &\le -3 \\
\left| \dfrac{x}{2} + 2 \right| &\ge 3
\end{aligned}
$$

$$
\begin{array}{ll}
\dfrac{x}{2} + 2 \ge 3 \quad \text{or} & \quad \dfrac{x}{2} + 2 \le -3 \\
x + 4 \ge 6 & \quad x + 4 \le -6 \\
x \ge 2 & \quad x \le -10
\end{array}
$$

The solution set is $(-\infty, -10] \cup [2, \infty)$.

97. Let x be the number.

$|4 - 3x| \ge 5 \quad$ or $\quad |3x - 4| \ge 5$

$$
\begin{array}{ll}
3x - 4 \ge 5 & \quad 3x - 4 \le -5 \\
3x \ge 9 \quad \text{or} & \quad 3x \le -1 \\
x \ge 3 & \quad x \le -\dfrac{1}{3}
\end{array}
$$

The solution set is $\left\{ x \mid x \le -\dfrac{1}{3} \text{ or } x \ge 3 \right\}$ or

$\left(-\infty, -\dfrac{1}{3} \right] \cup [3, \infty)$.

99. $(0, 4)$

101. passion $\le$ intimacy or intimacy $\ge$ passion

103. passion < commitment or commitment > passion

105. 9, after 3 years

107. $3.1x + 25.8 > 63$

$3.1x > 37.2$

$x > 12$

Since x is the number of years after 1994, we calculate 1994+12=2006. 63% of voters will use electronic systems after 2006.

109.
$$
\begin{aligned}
28 &\le 20 + 0.40(x - 60) \le 40 \\
28 &\le 20 + 0.40x - 24 \le 40 \\
28 &\le 0.40x - 4 \le 40 \\
32 &\le 0.40x \le 44 \\
80 &\le x \le 110
\end{aligned}
$$
Between 80 and 110 ten minutes, inclusive.

111. $\left|\dfrac{h-50}{5}\right| \geq 1.645$

$\dfrac{h-50}{5} \geq 1.645$ or $\dfrac{h-50}{5} \leq -1.645$

$h - 50 \geq 8.225$ $h - 50 \leq -8.225$

$h \geq 58.225$ $h \leq 41.775$

The number of outcomes would be 59 or more, or 41 or less.

113. $15 + 0.08x < 3 + .12x$

$12 < 0.04x$

$300 < x$

Plan A is a better deal when driving more than 300 miles a month.

115. $2 + 0.08x < 8 + 0.05x$

$0.03x < 6$

$x < 200$

The credit union is a better deal when writing less than 200 checks.

117. $3000 + 3x < 5.5x$

$3000 < 2.5x$

$1200 < x$

More then 1200 packets of stationary need to be sold each week to make a profit.

119. $245 + 95x \leq 3000$

$95x \leq 2755$

$x \leq 29$

29 bags or less can be lifted safely.

121. a. $\dfrac{86 + 88 + x}{3} \geq 90$

$\dfrac{174 + x}{3} \geq 90$

$174 + x \geq 270$

$x \geq 96$

You must get at least a 96.

b. $\dfrac{86 + 88 + x}{3} < 80$

$\dfrac{174 + x}{3} < 80$

$174 + x < 240$

$x < 66$

This will happen if you get a grade less than 66.

123. Let x = the number of times the bridge is crossed per three month period
The cost with the 3-month pass is
$C_3 = 7.50 + 0.50x$.

The cost with the 6-month pass is $C_6 = 30$.

Because we need to buy two 3-month passes per 6-month pass, we multiply the cost with the 3-month pass by 2.

$2(7.50 + 0.50x) < 30$

$15 + x < 30$

$x < 15$

We also must consider the cost without purchasing a pass. We need this cost to be less than the cost with a 3-month pass.

$3x > 7.50 + 0.50x$

$2.50x > 7.50$

$x > 3$

The 3-month pass is the best deal when making more than 3 but less than 15 crossings per 3-month period.

133. Because $x > y$, $y - x$ represents a negative number. When both sides are multiplied by $(y - x)$ the inequality must be reversed.

135. Model 1:

$|T - 57| < 7$

$-7 < T - 57 < 7$

$50 < T < 64$

Model 2:

$|T - 50| < 22$

$-22 < T - 50 < 22$

$28 < T < 72$

Model 1 describes a city with monthly temperature averages ranging from 50 degrees to 64 degrees Fahrenheit. Model 2 describes a city with monthly temperature averages ranging from 28 degrees to 72 degrees Fahrenheit.

Model 1 describes San Francisco and model 2 describes Albany.

Chapter P Review Exercises

1. $3+6(x-2)^3 = 3+6(4-2)^3$
$\qquad = 3+6(2)^3$
$\qquad = 3+6(8)$
$\qquad = 3+48$
$\qquad = 51$

2. $x^2-5(x-y) = 6^2-5(6-2)$
$\qquad = 36-5(4)$
$\qquad = 36-20$
$\qquad = 16$

3. $S = 0.015x^2+x+10$
$S = 0.015(60)^2+(60)+10$
$\quad = 0.015(3600)+60+10$
$\quad = 54+60+10$
$\quad = 124$

4. $A=\{a,b,c\} \quad B=\{a,c,d,e\}$
$\{a,b,c\}\cap\{a,c,d,e\}=\{a,c\}$

5. $A=\{a,b,c\} \quad B=\{a,c,d,e\}$
$\{a,b,c\}\cup\{a,c,d,e\}=\{a,b,c,d,e\}$

6. $A=\{a,b,c\} \quad C=\{a,d,f,g\}$
$\{a,b,c\}\cup\{a,d,f,g\}=\{a,b,c,d,f,g\}$

7. $A=\{a,b,c\} \quad C=\{a,d,f,g\}$
$\{a,d,f,g\}\cap\{a,b,c\}=\{a\}$

8. **a.** $\sqrt{81}$

   b. $0,\sqrt{81}$

   c. $-17,0,\sqrt{81}$

   d. $-17,-\dfrac{9}{13},0,0.75,\sqrt{81}$

   e. $\sqrt{2},\pi$

   f. $-17,-\dfrac{9}{13},0,0.75,\sqrt{2},\pi,\sqrt{81}$

9. $|-103|=103$

10. $\left|\sqrt{2}-1\right|=\sqrt{2}-1$

11. $\left|3-\sqrt{17}\right|=\sqrt{17}-3$ since $\sqrt{17}$ is greater than 3.

12. $|4-(-17)|=|4+17|=|21|=21$

13. $3+17=17+3$;
commutative property of addition.

14. $(6\cdot3)\cdot9=6\cdot(3\cdot9)$;
associative property of multiplication.

15. $\sqrt{3}(\sqrt{5}+\sqrt{3})=\sqrt{15}+3$;
distributive property of multiplication over addition.

16. $(6\cdot9)\cdot2=2\cdot(6\cdot9)$;
commutative property of multiplication.

17. $\sqrt{3}(\sqrt{5}+\sqrt{3})=(\sqrt{5}+\sqrt{3})\sqrt{3}$;
commutative property of multiplication.

18. $(3\cdot7)+(4\cdot7)=(4\cdot7)+(3\cdot7)$;
commutative property of addition.

19. $5(2x-3)+7x=10x-15+7x=17x-15$

20. $\dfrac{1}{5}(5x)+[(3y)+(-3y)]-(-x)=x+[0]+x=2x$

21. $3(4y-5)-(7y+2)=12y-15-7y-2=5y-17$

22. $8-2[3-(5x-1)]=8-2[3-5x+1]$
$\qquad =8-2[4-5x]$
$\qquad =8-8+10x$
$\qquad =10x$

23. $E=10x+166$
$E=10(20)+166=366$

$E=0.04x^2+9.2x+169$
$E=0.04(20)^2+9.2(20)+169=369$
The actual number was 368 so the better formula was $E=0.04x^2+9.2x+169$.

24. $(-3)^3(-2)^2=(-27)\cdot(4)=-108$

25. $2^{-4} + 4^{-1} = \dfrac{1}{2^4} + \dfrac{1}{4}$

$= \dfrac{1}{16} + \dfrac{1}{4}$

$= \dfrac{1}{16} + \dfrac{4}{16}$

$= \dfrac{5}{16}$

26. $5^{-3} \cdot 5 = 5^{-3} 5^1 = 5^{-3+1} = 5^{-2} = \dfrac{1}{5^2} = \dfrac{1}{25}$

27. $\dfrac{3^3}{3^6} = 3^{3-6} = 3^{-3} = \dfrac{1}{3^3} = \dfrac{1}{27}$

28. $(-2x^4 y^3)^3 = (-2)^3 (x^4)^3 (y^3)^3$

$= (-2)^3 x^{4 \cdot 3} y^{3 \cdot 3}$

$= -8x^{12} y^9$

29. $(-5x^3 y^2)(-2x^{-11} y^{-2})$

$= (-5)(-2)x^3 x^{-11} y^2 y^{-2}$

$= 10 \cdot x^{3-11} y^{2-2}$

$= 10x^{-8} y^0$

$= \dfrac{10}{x^8}$

30. $(2x^3)^{-4} = (2)^{-4} (x^3)^{-4}$

$= 2^{-4} x^{-12}$

$= \dfrac{1}{2^4 x^{12}}$

$= \dfrac{1}{16x^{12}}$

31. $\dfrac{7x^5 y^6}{28x^{15} y^{-2}} = \left(\dfrac{7}{28}\right)(x^{5-15})(y^{6-(-2)})$

$= \dfrac{1}{4} x^{-10} y^8$

$= \dfrac{y^8}{4x^{10}}$

32. $3.74 \times 10^4 = 37,400$

33. $7.45 \times 10^{-5} = 0.0000745$

34. $3,590,000 = 3.59 \times 10^6$

35. $0.00725 = 7.25 \times 10^{-3}$

36. $(3 \times 10^3)(1.3 \times 10^2) = (3 \times 1.3) \times (10^3 \times 10^2)$

$= 3.9 \times 10^5$

$= 390,000$

37. $\dfrac{6.9 \times 10^3}{3 \times 10^5} = \left(\dfrac{6.9}{3}\right) \times 10^{3-5}$

$= 2.3 \times 10^{-2}$

$= 0.023$

38. $\dfrac{10^9}{10^6} = 10^{9-6} = 10^3$

It would take 10^3 or 1000 years to accumulate $1 billion.

39. $(2.9 \times 10^8) \times 150$

$= (2.9 \times 10^8) \times (1.5 \times 10^2)$

$= (2.9 \times 1.5) \times (10^8 \times 10^2)$

$= 4.35 \times 10^{10}$

The total annual spending on movies is 4.35×10^{10}.

40. $\sqrt{300} = \sqrt{100 \cdot 3} = \sqrt{100} \cdot \sqrt{3} = 10\sqrt{3}$

41. $\sqrt{12x^2} = \sqrt{4x^2 \cdot 3} = \sqrt{4x^2} \cdot \sqrt{3} = 2|x|\sqrt{3}$

42. $\sqrt{10x} \cdot \sqrt{2x} = \sqrt{20x^2}$

$= \sqrt{4x^2} \cdot \sqrt{5}$

$= 2x\sqrt{5}$

43. $\sqrt{r^3} = \sqrt{r^2} \cdot \sqrt{r} = r\sqrt{r}$

44. $\sqrt{\dfrac{121}{4}} = \dfrac{\sqrt{121}}{\sqrt{4}} = \dfrac{11}{2}$

45. $\dfrac{\sqrt{96x^3}}{\sqrt{2x}} = \sqrt{\dfrac{96x^3}{2x}}$

$= \sqrt{48x^2}$

$= \sqrt{16x^2} \cdot \sqrt{3}$

$= 4x\sqrt{3}$

46. $7\sqrt{5} + 13\sqrt{5} = (7 + 13)\sqrt{5} = 20\sqrt{5}$

47. $2\sqrt{50} + 3\sqrt{8} = 2\sqrt{25 \cdot 2} + 3\sqrt{4 \cdot 2}$
$= 2 \cdot 5\sqrt{2} + 3 \cdot 2\sqrt{2}$
$= 10\sqrt{2} + 6\sqrt{2}$
$= 16\sqrt{2}$

48. $4\sqrt{72} - 2\sqrt{48} = 4\sqrt{36 \cdot 2} - 2\sqrt{16 \cdot 3}$
$= 4 \cdot 6\sqrt{2} - 2 \cdot 4\sqrt{3}$
$= 24\sqrt{2} - 8\sqrt{3}$

49. $\dfrac{30}{\sqrt{5}} = \dfrac{30}{\sqrt{5}} \cdot \dfrac{\sqrt{5}}{\sqrt{5}} = \dfrac{30\sqrt{5}}{5} = 6\sqrt{5}$

50. $\dfrac{\sqrt{2}}{\sqrt{3}} = \dfrac{\sqrt{2}}{\sqrt{3}} \cdot \dfrac{\sqrt{3}}{\sqrt{3}} = \dfrac{\sqrt{6}}{3}$

51. $\dfrac{5}{6 + \sqrt{3}} = \dfrac{5}{6 + \sqrt{3}} \cdot \dfrac{6 - \sqrt{3}}{6 - \sqrt{3}}$
$= \dfrac{5(6 - \sqrt{3})}{36 - 3}$
$= \dfrac{5(6 - \sqrt{3})}{33}$

52.
$\dfrac{14}{\sqrt{7} - \sqrt{5}} = \dfrac{14}{\sqrt{7} - \sqrt{5}} \cdot \dfrac{\sqrt{7} + \sqrt{5}}{\sqrt{7} + \sqrt{5}}$
$= \dfrac{14(\sqrt{7} + \sqrt{5})}{7 - 5}$
$= \dfrac{14(\sqrt{7} + \sqrt{5})}{2}$
$= 7(\sqrt{7} + \sqrt{5})$

53. $\sqrt[3]{125} = 5$

54. $\sqrt[5]{-32} = -2$

55. $\sqrt[4]{-125}$ is not a real number.

56. $\sqrt[4]{(-5)^4} = \sqrt[4]{625} = \sqrt[4]{5^4} = 5$

57. $\sqrt[3]{81} = \sqrt[3]{27 \cdot 3} = \sqrt[3]{27} \cdot \sqrt[3]{3} = 3\sqrt[3]{3}$

58. $\sqrt[3]{y^5} = \sqrt[3]{y^3 y^2} = y\sqrt[3]{y^2}$

59. $\sqrt[4]{8} \cdot \sqrt[4]{10} = \sqrt[4]{80} = \sqrt[4]{16 \cdot 5} = \sqrt[4]{16} \cdot \sqrt[4]{5} = 2\sqrt[4]{5}$

60. $4\sqrt[3]{16} + 5\sqrt[3]{2} = 4\sqrt[3]{8 \cdot 2} + 5\sqrt[3]{2}$
$= 4 \cdot 2\sqrt[3]{2} + 5\sqrt[3]{2}$
$= 8\sqrt[3]{2} + 5\sqrt[3]{2}$
$= 13\sqrt[3]{2}$

61. $\dfrac{\sqrt[4]{32x^5}}{\sqrt[4]{16x}} = \sqrt[4]{\dfrac{32x^5}{16x}} = \sqrt[4]{2x^4} = x\sqrt[4]{2}$

62. $16^{1/2} = \sqrt{16} = 4$

63. $25^{-1/2} = \dfrac{1}{25^{1/2}} = \dfrac{1}{\sqrt{25}} = \dfrac{1}{5}$

64. $125^{1/3} = \sqrt[3]{125} = 5$

65. $27^{-1/3} = \dfrac{1}{27^{1/3}} = \dfrac{1}{\sqrt[3]{27}} = \dfrac{1}{3}$

66. $64^{2/3} = (\sqrt[3]{64})^2 = 4^2 = 16$

67. $27^{-4/3} = \dfrac{1}{27^{4/3}} = \dfrac{1}{(\sqrt[3]{27})^4} = \dfrac{1}{3^4} = \dfrac{1}{81}$

68. $(5x^{2/3})(4x^{1/4}) = 5 \cdot 4x^{2/3 + 1/4} = 20x^{11/12}$

69. $\dfrac{15x^{3/4}}{5x^{1/2}} = \left(\dfrac{15}{5}\right)x^{3/4 - 1/2} = 3x^{1/4}$

70. $(125 \cdot x^6)^{2/3} = (\sqrt[3]{125x^6})^2$
$= (5x^2)^2$
$= 25x^4$

71. $\sqrt[6]{y^3} = (y^3)^{1/6} = y^{3 \cdot 1/6} = y^{1/2} = \sqrt{y}$

72. $(-6x^3 + 7x^2 - 9x + 3) + (14x^3 + 3x^2 - 11x - 7) = (-6x^3 + 14x^3) + (7x^2 + 3x^2) + (-9x - 11x) + (3 - 7)$
$$= 8x^3 + 10x^2 - 20x - 4$$

     The degree is 3.

73. $(13x^4 - 8x^3 + 2x^2) - (5x^4 - 3x^3 + 2x^2 - 6) = (13x^4 - 8x^3 + 2x^2) + (-5x^4 + 3x^3 - 2x^2 + 6)$
$$= (13x^4 - 5x^4) + (-8x^3 + 3x^3) + (2x^2 - 2x^2) + 6$$
$$= 8x^4 - 5x^3 + 6$$

     The degree is 4.

74. $(3x - 2)(4x^2 + 3x - 5) = (3x)(4x^2) + (3x)(3x) + (3x)(-5) + (-2)(4x^2) + (-2)(3x) + (-2)(-5)$
$$= 12x^3 + 9x^2 - 15x - 8x^2 - 6x + 10$$
$$= 12x^3 + x^2 - 21x + 10$$

75. $(3x - 5)(2x + 1) = (3x)(2x) + (3x)(1) + (-5)(2x) + (-5)(1)$
$$= 6x^2 + 3x - 10x - 5$$
$$= 6x^2 - 7x - 5$$

76. $(4x + 5)(4x - 5) = (4x^2) - 5^2 = 16x^2 - 25$

77. $(2x + 5)^2 = (2x)^2 + 2(2x) \cdot 5 + 5^2 = 4x^2 + 20x + 25$

78. $(3x - 4)^2 = (3x)^2 - 2(3x) \cdot 4 + (-4)^2 = 9x^2 - 24x + 16$

79. $(2x + 1)^3 = (2x)^3 + 3(2x)^2(1) + 3(2x)(1)^2 + 1^3 = 8x^3 + 12x^2 + 6x + 1$

80. $(5x - 2)^3 = (5x)^3 - 3(5x)^2(2) + 3(5x)(2)^2 - 2^3 = 125x^3 - 150x^2 + 60x - 8$

81. $(x + 7y)(3x - 5y) = x(3x) + (x)(-5y) + (7y)(3x) + (7y)(-5y)$
$$= 3x^2 - 5xy + 21xy - 35y^2$$
$$= 3x^2 + 16xy - 35y^2$$

82. $(3x - 5y)^2 = (3x)^2 - 2(3x)(5y) + (-5y)^2$
$$= 9x^2 - 30xy + 25y^2$$

83. $(3x^2 + 2y)^2 = (3x^2)^2 + 2(3x^2)(2y) + (2y)^2$
$$= 9x^4 + 12x^2y + 4y^2$$

84. $(7x + 4y)(7x - 4y) = (7x)^2 - (4y)^2$
$$= 49x^2 - 16y^2$$

85. $(a - b)(a^2 + ab + b^2)$
$$= a(a^2) + a(ab) + a(b^2) + (-b)(a^2)$$
$$+ (-b)(ab) + (-b)(b^2)$$
$$= a^3 + a^2b + ab^2 - a^2b - ab^2 - b^3$$
$$= a^3 - b^3$$

86. $\left[5y-(2x+1)\right]\left[5y+(2x+1)\right]$

$$= (5y)^2 - (2x+1)^2$$
$$= 25y^2 - (4x^2+4x+1)$$
$$= 25y^2 - 4x^2 - 4x - 1$$

87. $\left(x+2y+4\right)^2$

$$= (x+2y+4)(x+2y+4)$$
$$= x(x+2y+4) + 2y(x+2y+4) + 4(x+2y+4)$$
$$= x^2 + 2xy + 4x + 2xy + 4y^2 + 8y + 4x + 8y + 16$$
$$= x^2 + 4xy + 4y^2 + 8x + 16y + 16$$

88. $15x^3 + 3x^2 = 3x^2 \cdot 5x + 3x^2 \cdot 1$

$$= 3x^2(5x+1)$$

89. $x^2 - 11x + 28 = (x-4)(x-7)$

90. $15x^2 - x - 2 = (3x+1)(5x-2)$

91. $64 - x^2 = 8^2 - x^2 = (8-x)(8+x)$

92. $x^2 + 16$ is prime.

93. $3x^4 - 9x^3 - 30x^2 = 3x^2(x^2 - 3x - 10)$

$$= 3x^2(x-5)(x+2)$$

94. $20x^7 - 36x^3 = 4x^3(5x^4 - 9)$

95. $x^3 - 3x^2 - 9x + 27 = x^2(x-3) - 9(x-3)$

$$= (x^2 - 9)(x-3)$$
$$= (x+3)(x-3)(x-3)$$
$$= (x+3)(x-3)^2$$

96. $16x^2 - 40x + 25 = (4x-5)(4x-5)$

$$= (4x-5)^2$$

97. $x^4 - 16 = (x^2)^2 - 4^2$

$$= (x^2+4)(x^2-4)$$
$$= (x^2+4)(x+2)(x-2)$$

98. $y^3 - 8 = y^3 - 2^3 = (y-2)(y^2 + 2y + 4)$

99. $x^3 + 64 = x^3 + 4^3 = (x+4)(x^2 - 4x + 16)$

100. $3x^4 - 12x^2 = 3x^2(x^2 - 4)$

$$= 3x^2(x-2)(x+2)$$

101. $27x^3 - 125 = (3x)^3 - 5^3$
$$= (3x-5)[(3x)^2 + (3x)(5) + 5^2]$$
$$= (3x-5)(9x^2 + 15x + 25)$$

102. $x^5 - x = x(x^4 - 1)$
$$= x(x^2 - 1)(x^2 + 1)$$
$$= x(x-1)(x+1)(x^2 + 1)$$

103. $x^3 + 5x^2 - 2x - 10 = x^2(x+5) - 2(x+5)$
$$= (x^2 - 2)(x+5)$$

104. $x^2 + 18x + 81 - y^2 = (x^2 + 18x + 81) - y^2$
$$= (x+9)^2 - y^2$$
$$= (x+9-y)(x+9+y)$$

105. $16x^{-\frac{3}{4}} + 32x^{\frac{1}{4}} = 16x^{-\frac{3}{4}}\left(1 + 2x^{\frac{1}{4} - \left(-\frac{3}{4}\right)}\right)$
$$= 16x^{-\frac{3}{4}}(1 + 2x)$$
$$= \frac{16(1+2x)}{x^{\frac{3}{4}}}$$

106. $\left(x^2 - 4\right)\left(x^2 + 3\right)^{\frac{1}{2}} - \left(x^2 - 4\right)^2 \left(x^2 + 3\right)^{\frac{3}{2}}$
$$= \left(x^2 - 4\right)\left(x^2 + 3\right)^{\frac{1}{2}}\left[1 - \left(x^2 - 4\right)\left(x^2 + 3\right)\right]$$
$$= (x-2)(x+2)\left(x^2 + 3\right)^{\frac{1}{2}}\left[1 - (x-2)(x+2)\left(x^2 + 3\right)\right]$$
$$= (x-2)(x+2)(x^2 + 3)^{\frac{1}{2}}(-x^4 + x^2 + 13)$$

107. $12x^{-\frac{1}{2}} + 6x^{-\frac{3}{2}} = 6x^{-\frac{3}{2}}(2x+1) = \frac{6(2x+1)}{x^{\frac{3}{2}}}$

108. $\dfrac{x^3 + 2x^2}{x+2} = \dfrac{x^2(x+2)}{x+2} = x^2, x \neq -2$

109. $\dfrac{x^2 + 3x - 18}{x^2 - 36} = \dfrac{(x+6)(x-3)}{(x+6)(x-6)} = \dfrac{x-3}{x-6}$,
$x \neq -6, 6$

110. $\dfrac{x^2 + 2x}{x^2 + 4x + 4} = \dfrac{x(x+2)}{(x+2)^2} = \dfrac{x}{x+2}$,
$x \neq -2$

111. $\dfrac{x^2+6x+9}{x^2-4} \cdot \dfrac{x+3}{x-2} = \dfrac{(x+3)^2}{(x-2)(x+2)} \cdot \dfrac{x+3}{x-2}$

$\qquad\qquad = \dfrac{(x+3)^3}{(x-2)^2(x+2)}$,

$x \neq 2, -2$

112. $\dfrac{6x+2}{x^2-1} \div \dfrac{3x^2+x}{x-1}$

$= \dfrac{2(3x+1)}{(x-1)(x+1)} \div \dfrac{x(3x+1)}{x-1}$

$= \dfrac{2(3x+1)}{(x-1)(x+1)} \cdot \dfrac{x-1}{x(3x+1)}$

$= \dfrac{2}{x(x+1)}$,

$x \neq 0, 1, -1, -\dfrac{1}{3}$

113. $\dfrac{x^2-5x-24}{x^2-x-12} \div \dfrac{x^2-10x+16}{x^2+x-6}$

$= \dfrac{(x-8)(x+3)}{(x-4)(x+3)} \div \dfrac{(x-2)(x-8)}{(x+3)(x-2)}$

$= \dfrac{x-8}{x-4} \cdot \dfrac{x+3}{x-8}$

$= \dfrac{x+3}{x-4}$,

$x \neq -3, 4, 2, 8$

114. $\dfrac{2x-7}{x^2-9} - \dfrac{x-10}{x^2-9} = \dfrac{2x-7-(x-10)}{x^2-9}$

$\qquad\qquad = \dfrac{x+3}{(x+3)(x-3)}$

$\qquad\qquad = \dfrac{1}{x-3}$,

$x \neq 3, -3$

115. $\dfrac{3x}{x+2} + \dfrac{x}{x-2} = \dfrac{3x}{x+2} \cdot \dfrac{x-2}{x-2} + \dfrac{x}{x-2} \cdot \dfrac{x+2}{x+2}$

$\qquad\qquad = \dfrac{3x^2-6x+x^2+2x}{(x+2)(x-2)}$

$\qquad\qquad = \dfrac{4x^2-4x}{(x+2)(x-2)}$

$\qquad\qquad = \dfrac{4x(x-1)}{(x+2)(x-2)}$,

$x \neq 2, -2$

116. $\dfrac{x}{x^2-9} + \dfrac{x-1}{x^2-5x+6}$

$= \dfrac{x}{(x-3)(x+3)} + \dfrac{x-1}{(x-2)(x-3)}$

$= \dfrac{x}{(x-3)(x+3)} \cdot \dfrac{x-2}{x-2} + \dfrac{x-1}{(x-2)(x-3)} \cdot \dfrac{x+3}{x+3}$

$= \dfrac{x(x-2)+(x-1)(x+3)}{(x-3)(x+3)(x-2)}$

$= \dfrac{x^2-2x+x^2+2x-3}{(x-3)(x+3)(x-2)}$

$= \dfrac{2x^2-3}{(x-3)(x+3)(x-2)}$

$x \neq 3, -3, 2$

117.

$$\frac{4x-1}{2x^2+5x-3} - \frac{x+3}{6x^2+x-2}$$

$$= \frac{4x-1}{(2x-1)(x+3)} - \frac{x+3}{(2x-1)(3x+2)}$$

$$= \frac{4x-1}{(2x-1)(x+3)} \cdot \frac{3x+2}{3x+2}$$

$$- \frac{x+3}{(2x-1)(3x+2)} \cdot \frac{x+3}{x+3}$$

$$= \frac{12x^2+8x-3x-2-x^2-6x-9}{(2x-1)(x+3)(3x+2)}$$

$$= \frac{11x^2-x-11}{(2x-1)(x+3)(3x+2)},$$

$$x \neq \frac{1}{2}, -3, -\frac{2}{3}$$

118.

$$\frac{\dfrac{1}{x}-\dfrac{1}{2}}{\dfrac{1}{3}-\dfrac{x}{6}} = \frac{\dfrac{1}{x}-\dfrac{1}{2}}{\dfrac{1}{3}-\dfrac{x}{6}} \cdot \frac{6x}{6x}$$

$$= \frac{6-3x}{2x-x^2}$$

$$= \frac{-3(x-2)}{-x(x-2)}$$

$$= \frac{3}{x},$$

$$x \neq 0, 2$$

119.

$$\frac{3+\dfrac{12}{x}}{1-\dfrac{16}{x^2}} = \frac{3+\dfrac{12}{x}}{1-\dfrac{16}{x^2}} \cdot \frac{x^2}{x^2}$$

$$= \frac{3x^2+12x}{x^2-16}$$

$$= \frac{3x(x+4)}{(x+4)(x-4)}$$

$$= \frac{3x}{x-4},$$

$$x \neq 0, 4, -4$$

120.

$$\frac{3-\dfrac{1}{x+3}}{3+\dfrac{1}{x+3}} = \frac{3-\dfrac{1}{x+3}}{3+\dfrac{1}{x+3}} \cdot \frac{x+3}{x+3}$$

$$= \frac{3(x+3)-1}{3(x+3)+1}$$

$$= \frac{3x+9-1}{3x+9+1}$$

$$= \frac{3x+8}{3x+10},$$

$$x \neq -3, -\frac{10}{3}$$

121 .

$$\frac{\sqrt{25-x^2}+\dfrac{x^2}{\sqrt{25-x^2}}}{25-x^2}$$

$$= \frac{\left(\sqrt{25-x^2}+\dfrac{x^2}{\sqrt{25-x^2}}\right)\sqrt{25-2x^2}}{(25-x^2)\sqrt{25-x^2}}$$

$$= \frac{25-x^2+x^2}{(25-x^2)\sqrt{25-x^2}}$$

$$= \frac{25}{\sqrt{(25-x^2)^3}}$$

$$= \frac{25}{\sqrt{(25-x^2)^3}} \cdot \frac{\sqrt{25-x^2}}{\sqrt{25-x^2}}$$

$$= \frac{25\sqrt{25-x^2}}{(25-x^2)}$$

$$= \frac{25\sqrt{25-x^2}}{(5-x)^2(5+x)^2}$$

122. $1-2(6-x) = 3x+2$
$1-12+2x = 3x+2$
$-11-x = 2$
$-x = 13$
$x = -13$
The solution set is $\{-13\}$.
This is a conditional equation.

123. $2(x-4)+3(x+5) = 2x-2$
$2x-8+3x+15 = 2x-2$
$5x+7 = 2x-2$
$3x = -9$
$x = -3$
The solution set is $\{-3\}$.
This is a conditional equation.

124. $2x - 4(5x + 1) = 3x + 17$
$2x - 20x - 4 = 3x + 17$
$-18x - 4 = 3x + 17$
$-21x = 21$
$x = -1$
The solution set is $\{-1\}$.
This is a conditional equation.

125. $x \neq 1, x \neq -1$

$$\frac{1}{x-1} - \frac{1}{x+1} = \frac{2}{x^2 - 1}$$

$$\frac{1}{x-1} - \frac{1}{x+1} = \frac{2}{(x+1)(x-1)}$$

$$x + 1 - (x - 1) = 2$$

$$x + 1 - x + 1 = 2$$

$$2 = 2$$

The solution set is all real numbers except 1 and -1.

126. $x \neq -2, x \neq 4$

$$\frac{4}{x+2} + \frac{2}{x-4} = \frac{30}{(x+2)(x-4)}$$

$$4(x - 4) + 2(x + 2) = 30$$

$$4x - 16 + 2x + 4 = 30$$

$$6x - 12 = 30$$

$$6x = 42$$

$$x = 7$$

The solution set is $\{7\}$.

127. $-4|2x+1| + 12 = 0$

$$-4|2x+1| = -12$$

$$|2x+1| = 3$$

$2x + 1 = 3 \quad$ or $\quad 2x + 1 = -3$
$2x = 2 \qquad\qquad 2x = -4$
$x = 1 \qquad\qquad x = -2$

The solution set is $\left\{-2, 1\right\}$.

128. $2x^2 - 11x + 5 = 0$
$(2x - 1)(x - 5) = 0$
$2x - 1 = 0 \quad x - 5 = 0$

$$x = \frac{1}{2} \text{ or } x = 5$$

The solution set is $\left\{\frac{1}{2}, 5\right\}$.

129. $(3x + 5)(x - 3) = 5$
$3x^2 + 5x - 9x - 15 = 5$
$3x^2 - 4x - 20 = 0$

$$x = \frac{4 \pm \sqrt{(-4)^2 - 4(3)(-20)}}{2(3)}$$

$$x = \frac{4 \pm \sqrt{16 + 240}}{6}$$

$$x = \frac{4 \pm \sqrt{256}}{6}$$

$$x = \frac{4 \pm 16}{6}$$

$$x = \frac{20}{6}, \frac{-12}{6}$$

$$x = \frac{10}{3}, -2$$

The solution set is $\left\{-2, \frac{10}{3}\right\}$.

130. $3x^2 - 7x + 1 = 0$

$$x = \frac{7 \pm \sqrt{(-7)^2 - 4(3)(1)}}{2(3)}$$

$$x = \frac{7 \pm \sqrt{49 - 12}}{6}$$

$$x = \frac{7 \pm \sqrt{37}}{6}$$

The solution set is $\left\{\frac{7 + \sqrt{37}}{6}, \frac{7 - \sqrt{37}}{6}\right\}$.

131. $x^2 - 9 = 0$
$x^2 = 9$
$x = \pm 3$
The solution set is $\{-3, 3\}$.

132. $(x - 3)^2 - 24 = 0$

$$(x - 3)^2 = 24$$

$$\sqrt{(x-3)^2} = \pm\sqrt{24}$$

$$x - 3 = \pm 2\sqrt{6}$$

$$x = 3 \pm 2\sqrt{6}$$

133.
$$\frac{2x}{x^2+6x+8} = \frac{x}{x+4} - \frac{2}{x+2}$$

$$\frac{2x}{(x+4)(x+2)} = \frac{x}{x+4} - \frac{2}{x+2}$$

$$\frac{2x(x+4)(x+2)}{(x+4)(x+2)} = (x+4)(x+2)\left(\frac{x}{x+4} - \frac{2}{x+2}\right)$$

$$2x = x(x+2) - 2(x+4)$$

$$2x = x^2 + 2x - 2x - 8$$

$$0 = x^2 - 2x - 8$$

$$0 = (x+2)(x-4)$$

$$x+2 = 0 \quad \text{or} \quad x-4 = 0$$
$$x = -2 \qquad\qquad x = 4$$

−2 must be rejected. The solution set is $\{4\}$.

134. $\sqrt{8-2x} - x = 0$

$$\sqrt{8-2x} = x$$

$$\left(\sqrt{8-2x}\right)^2 = x^2$$

$$8 - 2x = x^2$$

$$0 = x^2 + 2x - 8$$

$$0 = (x+4)(x-2)$$

$$x + 4 = 0 \quad \text{or} \quad x - 2 = 0$$
$$x = -4 \qquad\qquad x = 2$$

−4 must be rejected. The solution set is $\{2\}$.

135. $\sqrt{2x-3} + x = 3$

$$\sqrt{2x-3} = 3 - x$$

$$2x - 3 = 9 - 6x + x^2$$

$$x^2 - 8x + 12 = 0$$

$$x^2 - 8x = -12$$

$$x^2 - 8x + 16 = -12 + 16$$

$$(x-4)^2 = 4$$

$$x - 4 = \pm 2$$

$$x = 4 + 2$$

$$x = 6, 2$$

The solution set is $\{2\}$.

136. $vt + gt^2 = s$

$$gt^2 = s - vt$$

$$\frac{gt^2}{t^2} = \frac{s-vt}{t^2}$$

$$g = \frac{s-vt}{t^2}$$

137.
$$T = \frac{A-P}{\text{Pr}}$$

$$Pr(T) = Pr\frac{A-P}{\text{Pr}}$$

$$PrT = A - P$$

$$PrT + P = A$$

$$P(rT+1) = A$$

$$P = \frac{A}{1+rT}$$

138.
$$x^2 = 2x - 19$$

$$x^2 - 2x + 19 = 0$$

$$b^2 - 4ac = (-2)^2 - 4(1)(19) = -72$$

$-72 < 0$, thus the equation has no real solutions.

139. $9x^2 - 30x + 25 = 0$

$$b^2 - 4ac = (-30)^2 - 4(9)(25) = 0$$

$b^2 - 4ac = 0$, thus the equation has one repeated real solution.

140. Let x = the number of calories in Burger King's Chicken Caesar.
$x + 125$ = the number of calories in Taco Bell's Express Taco Salad.
$x + 95$ = the number of calories in Wendy's Mandarin Chicken Salad.

$$x + (x+125) + (x+95) = 1705$$

$$3x + 220 = 1705$$

$$3x = 1485$$

$$x = 495$$

$$x + 125 = 495 + 125 = 620$$
$$x + 95 = 495 + 95 = 590$$

There are 495 calories in the Chicken Caesar, 620 calories in the Express Taco Salad, and 590 calories in the Mandarin Chicken Salad.

141. Let x = the number of years after 1970.
$$P = -0.5x + 37.4$$

$$18.4 = -0.5x + 37.4$$

$$-19 = -0.5x$$

$$\frac{-19}{-0.5} = \frac{-0.5x}{-0.5}$$

$$38 = x$$

If the trend continues only 18.4% of U.S. adults will smoke cigarettes 38 years after 1970, or 2008.

142. Let x = the original price of the phone
$$48 = x - 0.20x$$
$$48 = 0.80x$$
$$60 = x$$
The original price is $60.

143. Let x = the amount sold to earn $800 in one week
$$800 = 300 + 0.05x$$
$$500 = 0.05x$$
$$10,000 = x$$
Sales must be $10,000 in one week to earn $800.

144. Let w = the width of the playing field,
Let $3w - 6$ = the length of the playing field
$$P = 2(\text{length}) + 2(\text{width})$$
$$340 = 2(3w - 6) + 2w$$
$$340 = 6w - 12 + 2w$$
$$340 = 8w - 12$$
$$352 = 8w$$
$$44 = w$$
The dimensions are 44 yards by 126 yards.

145. b. Check some points to determine that
$y_1 = 14,100 + 1500x$ and
$y_2 = 41,700 - 800x$. Since
$y_1 = y_2 = 32,100$ when $x = 12$, the two colleges will have the same enrollment in the year $2007 + 12 = 2019$. That year the enrollments will be 32,100 students.

146.
$$A = lw$$
$$15 = l(2l - 7)$$
$$15 = 2l^2 - 7l$$
$$0 = 2l^2 - 7l - 15$$
$$0 = (2l + 3)(l - 5)$$
$$l = 5$$
$$2l - 7 = 3$$
The length is 5 yards, the width is 3 yards.

147. Let x = height of building
$2x$ = shadow height
$$x^2 + (2x)^2 = 300^2$$
$$x^2 + 4x^2 = 90,000$$
$$5x^2 = 90,000$$
$$x^2 = 18,000$$
$$x \approx \pm 134.164$$
Discard negative height.

The building is approximately 134 meters high.

148. $(10 + 2x)(16 + 2x) = 280$
$$160 + 52x + 4x^2 = 280$$
$$4x^2 + 52x - 120 = 0$$
$$x^2 + 13x - 30 = 0$$
$$(x + 15)(x - 2) = 0$$
$$x + 15 = 0 \quad \text{or} \quad x - 2 = 0$$
$$x = -15 \qquad \qquad x = 2$$
-15 must be rejected. The width of the frame is 2 inches.

149.
$$\frac{1500}{x} + 100 = \frac{1500}{x - 4}$$
$$x(x - 4)\left(\frac{1500}{x} + 100\right) = x(x - 4)\frac{1500}{x - 4}$$
$$1500(x - 4) + 100x(x - 4) = 1500x$$
$$1500x - 6000 + 100x^2 - 400x = 1500x$$
$$15x - 60 + x^2 - 4x = 15x$$
$$x^2 - 4x - 60 = 0$$
$$(x + 6)(x - 10) = 0$$
$$x + 6 = 0 \quad \text{or} \quad x - 10 = 0$$
$$x = -6 \qquad \qquad x = 10$$
-6 must be rejected. There were originally 10 people.

150. $\{x | -3 \le x < 5\}$

151. $\{x | x > -2\}$

152. $\{x | x \le 0\}$

153. Graph $(-2,1]$:

Graph $[-1,3)$:

To find the intersection, take the portion of the number line that the two graphs have in common.

Numbers in both $(-2,1]$ and $[-1,3)$:

Thus, $(-2,1] \cap [-1,3) = [-1,1]$.

154. Graph $(-2,1]$:

Graph $[-1,3)$:

To find the union, take the portion of the number line representing the total collection of numbers in the two graphs.

Numbers in either $(-2,1]$ or $[-1,3)$ or both:

Thus, $(-2,1] \cup [-1,3) = (-2,3)$.

155. Graph $[1,3)$:

Graph $(0,4)$:

To find the intersection, take the portion of the number line that the two graphs have in common.

Numbers in both $[1,3)$ and $(0,4)$:

Thus, $[1,3) \cap (0,4) = [1,3)$.

156. Graph $[1,3)$:

Graph $(0,4)$:

To find the union, take the portion of the number line representing the total collection of numbers in the two graphs.

Numbers in either $[1,3)$ or $(0,4)$ or both:

Thus, $[1,3) \cup (0,4) = (0,4)$.

157. $-6x + 3 \leq 15$
$-6x \leq 12$
$x \geq 2$

The solution set is $[-2,\infty)$.

158. $6x - 9 \geq -4x - 3$
$10x \geq 6$

$x \geq \dfrac{3}{5}$

The solution set is $\left[\dfrac{3}{5},\infty\right)$.

159. $\dfrac{x}{3} - \dfrac{3}{4} - 1 > \dfrac{x}{2}$

$12\left(\dfrac{x}{3} - \dfrac{3}{4} - 1\right) > 12\left(\dfrac{x}{2}\right)$

$4x - 9 - 12 > 6x$

$-21 > 2x$

$-\dfrac{21}{2} > x$

The solution set is $\left(-\infty, -\dfrac{21}{2}\right)$.

160. $6x + 5 > -2(x - 3) - 25$

$6x + 5 > -2x + 6 - 25$

$8x + 5 > -19$

$8x > -24$

$x > -3$

The solution set is $(-3, \infty)$.

161. $3(2x - 1) - 2(x - 4) \geq 7 + 2(3 + 4x)$

$6x - 3 - 2x + 8 \geq 7 + 6 + 8x$

$4x + 5 \geq 8x + 13$

$-4x \geq 8$

$x \leq -2$

The solution set is $[-\infty, -2)$.

162. $7 < 2x + 3 \leq 9$

$4 < 2x \leq 6$

$2 < x \leq 3$

$(2, 3]$

The solution set is $[2, 3)$.

163. $|2x + 3| \leq 15$

$-15 \leq 2x + 3 \leq 15$

$-18 \leq 2x \leq 12$

$-9 \leq x \leq 6$

The solution set is $[-9, 6]$.

164. $\left|\dfrac{2x + 6}{3}\right| > 2$

$\dfrac{2x + 6}{3} > 2 \qquad \dfrac{2x + 6}{3} < -2$

$2x + 6 > 6 \qquad 2x + 6 < -6$

$2x > 0 \qquad\quad 2x < -12$

$x > 0 \qquad\quad x < -6$

The solution set is $(-\infty, -6)$ or $(0, \infty)$.

165. $|2x + 5| - 7 \geq -6$

$|2x + 5| \geq 1$

$2x + 5 \geq 1$ or $2x + 5 \leq -1$

$2x \geq -4 \qquad\quad 2x \leq -6$

$x \geq -2 \quad$ or $\quad x \leq -3$

The solution set is $(-\infty, -3]$ or $[-2, \infty)$.

166. $-4|x + 2| + 5 \leq -7$

$-4|x + 2| \leq -12$

$|x + 2| \geq 3$

$x + 2 \geq 3 \qquad\quad x + 2 \leq -3$

$\qquad\qquad$ or

$x \geq 1 \qquad\qquad x \leq -5$

The solution set is $(-\infty, -5] \cup [1, \infty)$.

167. $0.20x + 24 \leq 40$

$0.20x \leq 16$

$\dfrac{0.20x}{0.20} \leq \dfrac{16}{0.20}$

$x \leq 80$

A customer can drive no more than 80 miles.

168. $80 \leq \dfrac{95 + 79 + 91 + 86 + x}{5} < 90$

$400 \leq 95 + 79 + 91 + 86 + x < 450$

$400 \leq 351 + x < 450$

$49 \leq x < 99$

A grade of at least 49% but less than 99% will result in a B.

Chapter P Test

1. $5(2x^2 - 6x) - (4x^2 - 3x) = 10x^2 - 30x - 4x^2 + 3x$
$$= 6x^2 - 27x$$

2. $7 + 2[3(x+1) - 2(3x-1)]$
$$= 7 + 2[3x + 3 - 6x + 2]$$
$$= 7 + 2[-3x + 5]$$
$$= 7 - 6x + 10$$
$$= -6x + 17$$

3. $\{1,2,5\} \cap \{5,a\} = \{5\}$

4. $\{1,2,5\} \cup \{5,a\} = \{1,2,5,a\}$

5. $\dfrac{30x^3 y^4}{6x^9 y^{-4}} = 5x^{3-9} y^{4-(-4)} = 5x^{-6} y^8 = \dfrac{5y^8}{x^6}$

6. $\sqrt{6r} \cdot \sqrt{3r} = \sqrt{18r^2} = \sqrt{9r^2} \cdot \sqrt{2} = 3r\sqrt{2}$

7. $4\sqrt{50} - 3\sqrt{18} = 4\sqrt{25 \cdot 2} - 3\sqrt{9 \cdot 2}$
$$= 4 \cdot 5\sqrt{2} - 3 \cdot 3\sqrt{2}$$
$$= 20\sqrt{2} - 9\sqrt{2}$$
$$= 11\sqrt{2}$$

8. $\dfrac{3}{5+\sqrt{2}} = \dfrac{3}{5+\sqrt{2}} \cdot \dfrac{5-\sqrt{2}}{5-\sqrt{2}}$
$$= \dfrac{3(5-\sqrt{2})}{25-2}$$
$$= \dfrac{3(5-\sqrt{2})}{23}$$

9. $\sqrt[3]{16x^4} = \sqrt[3]{8x^3 \cdot 2x}$
$$= \sqrt[3]{8x^3} \cdot \sqrt[3]{2x}$$
$$= 2x\sqrt[3]{2x}$$

10. $\dfrac{x^2 + 2x - 3}{x^2 - 3x + 2} = \dfrac{(x+3)(x-1)}{(x-2)(x-1)} = \dfrac{x+3}{x-2},$
$x \neq 2, 1$

11. $\dfrac{5 \times 10^{-6}}{20 \times 10^{-8}} = \dfrac{5}{20} \cdot \dfrac{10^{-6}}{10^{-8}} = 0.25 \times 10^2 = 2.5 \times 10^1$

12. $(2x-5)(x^2 - 4x + 3)$
$$= 2x^3 - 8x^2 + 6x - 5x^2 + 20x - 15$$
$$= 2x^3 - 13x^2 + 26x - 15$$

13. $(5x+3y)^2 = (5x)^2 + 2(5x)(3y) + (3y)^2$
$$= 25x^2 + 30xy + 9y^2$$

14. $\dfrac{2x+8}{x-3} \div \dfrac{x^2 + 5x + 4}{x^2 - 9}$
$$= \dfrac{2(x+4)}{x-3} \div \dfrac{(x+1)(x+4)}{(x-3)(x+3)}$$
$$= \dfrac{2(x+4)}{x-3} \cdot \dfrac{(x-3)(x+3)}{(x+1)(x+4)}$$
$$= \dfrac{2(x+3)}{x+1},$$
$x \neq 3, -1, -4, -3$

15. $\dfrac{x}{x+3} + \dfrac{5}{x-3}$
$$= \dfrac{x}{x+3} \cdot \dfrac{x-3}{x-3} + \dfrac{5}{x-3} \cdot \dfrac{x+3}{x+3}$$
$$= \dfrac{x(x-3) + 5(x+3)}{(x+3)(x-3)}$$
$$= \dfrac{x^2 - 3x + 5x + 15}{(x+3)(x-3)}$$
$$= \dfrac{x^2 + 2x + 15}{(x+3)(x-3)}, x \neq 3, -3$

16. $\dfrac{2x+3}{x^2 - 7x + 12} - \dfrac{2}{x-3}$
$$= \dfrac{2x+3}{(x-3)(x-4)} - \dfrac{2}{x-3}$$
$$= \dfrac{2x+3}{(x-3)(x-4)} - \dfrac{2}{x-3} \cdot \dfrac{x-4}{x-4}$$
$$= \dfrac{2x+3 - 2(x-4)}{(x-3)(x-4)}$$
$$= \dfrac{2x+3 - 2(x-4)}{(x-3)(x-4)}$$
$$= \dfrac{2x+3 - 2x + 8}{(x-3)(x-4)}$$
$$= \dfrac{11}{(x-3)(x-4)},$$
$x \neq 3, 4$

17. $\dfrac{1-\frac{x}{x+2}}{1+\frac{1}{x}} = \dfrac{\left(1-\frac{x}{x+2}\right)(x+2)x}{\left(1+\frac{1}{x}\right)(x+2)x}$

$= \dfrac{x(x+2)-x^2}{x(x+2)+(x+2)}$

$= \dfrac{x^2+2x-x^2}{(x+1)(x+2)}$

$= \dfrac{2x}{x^2+3x+2}, x \neq 0$

18. $\dfrac{2x\sqrt{x^2+5}-\frac{2x^3}{\sqrt{x^2+5}}}{x^2+5}$

$= \dfrac{\left(2x\sqrt{x^2+5}-\frac{2x^3}{\sqrt{x^2+5}}\right)\sqrt{x^2+5}}{(x^2+5)\sqrt{x^2+5}}$

$= \dfrac{2x(x^2+5)-2x^3}{(x^2+5)\sqrt{x^2+5}}$

$= \dfrac{2x^3+10x-2x^3}{(x^2+5)\sqrt{x^2+5}}$

$= \dfrac{10x}{\sqrt{(x^2+5)^3}}$

19. $x^2-9x+18 = (x-3)(x-6)$

20. $x^3+2x^2+3x+6 = x^2(x+2)+3(x+2)$

$= (x^2+3)(x+2)$

21. $25x^2-9 = (5x)^2-3^2 = (5x-3)(5x+3)$

22. $36x^2-84x+49 = (6x)^2-2(6x)\cdot7+7^2$

$= (6x-7)^2$

23. $y^3-125 = y^3-5^3 = (y-5)(y^2+5y+25)$

24. $(x^2+10x+25)-9y^2$

$= (x+5)^2-9y^2$

$= (x+5-3y)(x+5+3y)$

25. $x(x+3)^{-\frac{3}{5}}+(x+3)^{\frac{2}{5}}$

$= (x+3)^{-\frac{3}{5}}\left[x+(x+3)\right]$

$= (x+3)^{-\frac{3}{5}}(2x+3) = \dfrac{2x+3}{(x+3)^{\frac{3}{5}}}$

26. $-7, -\dfrac{4}{5}, 0, 0.25, \sqrt{4}, \dfrac{22}{7}$ are rational numbers.

27. $3(2+5) = 3(5+2)$;
commutative property of addition

28. $6(7+4) = 6\cdot7+6\cdot4$
distributive property of multiplication over addition

29. $0.00076 = 7.6\times10^{-4}$

30. $27^{-\frac{5}{3}} = \dfrac{1}{27^{\frac{5}{3}}} = \dfrac{1}{\left(\sqrt[3]{27}\right)^5} = \dfrac{1}{(3)^5} = \dfrac{1}{243}$

31. $2\left(6.3\times10^9\right) = 12.6\times10^9 = 1.26\times10^{10}$

32. a. Model 2 describes data for men and Model 1 describes data for women.

b. $E = 0.18t+65$
$E = 0.18(50)+65$
$= 74$
The model predicts that the life expectancy for men in 2000 was 74 years. This fits the data in the graph fairly well.

c. $E = 0.17t+71$
$88 = 0.17t+71$
$17 = 0.17t$
$\dfrac{17}{0.17} = \dfrac{0.17t}{0.17}$
$100 = t$
The life expectancy for women will reach 88 years 100 years after 1950, or 2050.

33. $7(x-2) = 4(x+1)-21$
$7x-14 = 4x+4-21$
$7x-14 = 4x-17$
$3x = -3$
$x = -1$
The solution set is $\{-1\}$.

34. $\dfrac{2x-3}{4} = \dfrac{x-4}{2}-\dfrac{x+1}{4}$
$2x-3 = 2(x-4)-(x+1)$
$2x-3 = 2x-8-x-1$
$2x-3 = x-9$
$x = -6$
The solution set is $\{-6\}$.

35.
$$\frac{2}{x-3} - \frac{4}{x+3} = \frac{8}{(x-3)(x+3)}$$
$$2(x+3) - 4(x-3) = 8$$
$$2x + 6 - 4x + 12 = 8$$
$$-2x + 18 = 8$$
$$-2x = -10$$
$$x = 5$$
The solution set is $\{5\}$.

36. $2x^2 - 3x - 2 = 0$
$(2x+1)(x-2) = 0$
$2x+1 = 0$ or $x - 2 = 0$
$x = -\frac{1}{2}$ or $x = 2$

The solution set is $\left\{-\frac{1}{2}, 2\right\}$.

37. $(3x-1)^2 = 75$
$3x - 1 = \pm\sqrt{75}$
$3x = 1 \pm 5\sqrt{3}$
$x = \frac{1 \pm 5\sqrt{3}}{3}$

The solution set is $\left\{\frac{1-5\sqrt{3}}{3}, \frac{1+5\sqrt{3}}{3}\right\}$.

38. $x(x-2) = 4$
$x^2 - 2x - 4 = 0$
$$x = \frac{-b \pm \sqrt{b^2 - 4ac}}{2a}$$
$$x = \frac{2 \pm \sqrt{(-2)^2 - 4(1)(-4)}}{2}$$
$$x = \frac{2 \pm 2\sqrt{5}}{2}$$
$$x = 1 \pm \sqrt{5}$$
The solution set is $\left\{1 - \sqrt{5}, 1 + \sqrt{5}\right\}$.

39.
$$\sqrt{x-3} + 5 = x$$
$$\sqrt{x-3} = x - 5$$
$$x - 3 = x^2 - 10x + 25$$
$$x^2 - 11x + 28 = 0$$
$$x = \frac{11 \pm \sqrt{11^2 - 4(1)(28)}}{2(1)}$$
$$x = \frac{11 \pm \sqrt{121 - 112}}{2}$$
$$x = \frac{11 \pm \sqrt{9}}{2}$$
$$x = \frac{11 \pm 3}{2}$$
$x = 7$ or $x = 4$
4 does not check and must be rejected.
The solution set is $\{7\}$.

40.
$$\sqrt{8-2x} - x = 0$$
$$\sqrt{8-2x} = x$$
$$\left(\sqrt{8-2x}\right)^2 = (x)^2$$
$$8 - 2x = x^2$$
$$0 = x^2 + 2x - 8$$
$$0 = (x+4)(x-2)$$
$x + 4 = 0$ or $x - 2 = 0$
$x = -4$ $\qquad$ $x = 2$
-4 does not check and must be rejected.
The solution set is $\{2\}$.

41. $\left|\frac{2}{3}x - 6\right| = 2$

$\frac{2}{3}x - 6 = 2 \qquad \frac{2}{3}x - 6 = -2$

$\frac{2}{3}x = 8 \qquad \frac{2}{3}x = 4$

$x = 12 \qquad x = 6$

The solution set is $\{6, 12\}$.

42. $-3|4x-7|+15=0$

$-3|4x-7|=-15$

$|4x-7|=5$

$4x-7=5$ or $4x-7=-5$

$4x=12$ $4x=2$

$x=3$ $x=\dfrac{1}{2}$

The solution set is $\left\{\dfrac{1}{2},3\right\}$

43. $\dfrac{2x}{x^2+6x+8}+\dfrac{2}{x+2}=\dfrac{x}{x+4}$

$\dfrac{2x}{(x+4)(x+2)}+\dfrac{2}{x+2}=\dfrac{x}{x+4}$

$\dfrac{2x(x+4)(x+2)}{(x+4)(x+2)}+\dfrac{2(x+4)(x+2)}{x+2}=\dfrac{x(x+4)(x+2)}{x+4}$

$2x+2(x+4)=x(x+2)$

$2x+2x+8=x^2+2x$

$2x+8=x^2$

$0=x^2-2x-8$

$0=(x-4)(x+2)$

$x-4=0$ or $x+2=0$

$x=4$ $x=-2$ (rejected)

The solution set is $\{4\}$.

44. $3(x+4)\geq 5x-12$

$3x+12\geq 5x-12$

$-2x\geq -24$

$x\leq 12$

The solution set is $(-\infty,12]$.

45. $\dfrac{x}{6}+\dfrac{1}{8}\leq \dfrac{x}{2}-\dfrac{3}{4}$

$4x+3\leq 12x-18$

$-8x\leq -21$

$x\geq \dfrac{21}{8}$

The solution set is $\left[\dfrac{21}{8},\infty\right)$.

46. $-3\leq \dfrac{2x+5}{3}<6$

$-9\leq 2x+5<18$

$-14\leq 2x<13$

$-7\leq x<\dfrac{13}{2}$

The solution set is $\left[-7,\dfrac{13}{2}\right)$.

47. $|3x+2|\geq 3$

$3x+2\geq 3$ or $3x+2\leq -3$

$3x\geq 1$ $3x\leq -5$

$x\geq \dfrac{1}{3}$ $x\leq -\dfrac{5}{3}$

The solution set is $\left(-\infty,-\dfrac{5}{3}\right]\cup\left[\dfrac{1}{3},\infty\right)$.

48. $V=\dfrac{1}{3}lwh$

$3V=lwh$

$\dfrac{3V}{lw}=\dfrac{lwh}{lw}$

$\dfrac{3V}{lw}=h$

$h=\dfrac{3V}{lw}$

49. $y-y_1=m(x-x_1)$

$y-y_1=mx-mx_1$

$-mx=y_1-mx_1-y$

$\dfrac{-mx}{-m}=\dfrac{y_1-mx_1-y}{-m}$

$x=\dfrac{y-y_1}{m}+x_1$

50.
$$R = \frac{as}{a+s}$$
$$R(a+s) = as$$
$$Ra + Rs = as$$
$$Ra - as = -Rs$$
$$a(R-s) = -Rs$$
$$\frac{a(R-s)}{R-s} = \frac{-Rs}{R-s}$$
$$a = \frac{Rs}{s-R}$$

51.
$$43x + 575 = 1177$$
$$43x = 602$$
$$x = 14$$
The system's income will be $1177 billion 14 years after 2004, or 2018.

52.
$$B = 0.07x^2 + 47.4x + 500$$
$$1177 = 0.07x^2 + 47.4x + 500$$
$$0 = 0.07x^2 + 47.4x - 677$$
$$0 = 0.07x^2 + 47.4x - 677$$
$$x = \frac{-b \pm \sqrt{b^2 - 4ac}}{2a}$$
$$x = \frac{-(47.4) \pm \sqrt{(47.4)^2 - 4(0.07)(-677)}}{2(0.07)}$$
$$x \approx 14, \quad x \approx -691 \text{ (rejected)}$$
The system's income will be $1177 billion 14 years after 2004, or 2018.

53. The formulas model the data quite well.

54. Let $x =$ the number of books in 2002.
Let $x + 62 =$ the number of books in 2003.
Let $x + 190 =$ the number of books in 2004.
$$(x) + (x+62) + (x+190) = 2598$$
$$x + x + 62 + x + 190 = 2598$$
$$3x + 252 = 2598$$
$$3x = 2346$$
$$x = 782$$
$$x + 62 = 844$$
$$x + 190 = 972$$
The number of books in 2002, 2003, and 2004 were 782, 844, and 972 respectively.

55.
$$29700 + 150x = 5000 + 1100x$$
$$24700 = 950x$$
$$26 = x$$
In 26 years, the cost will be $33,600.

56.
$$l = 2w + 4$$
$$A = lw$$
$$48 = (2w + 4)w$$
$$48 = 2w^2 + 4w$$
$$0 = 2w^2 + 4w - 48$$
$$0 = w^2 + 2w - 24$$
$$0 = (w+6)(w-4)$$

$$w + 6 = 0 \qquad w - 4 = 0$$
$$w = -6 \qquad w = 4$$
$$2w + 4 = 2(4) + 4 = 12$$
width is 4 feet, length is 12 feet

57.
$$24^2 + x^2 = 26^2$$
$$576 + x^2 = 676$$
$$x^2 = 100$$
$$x = \pm 10$$
The wire should be attached 10 feet up the pole.

58. Let $x =$ the original selling price
$$20 = x - 0.60x$$
$$20 = 0.40x$$
$$50 = x$$
The original price is $50.

59.
$$\frac{600,000}{x} - 6000 = \frac{600,000}{x+5}$$

$$x(x+5)\left(\frac{600,000}{x} - 6000\right) = x(x+5)\frac{600,000}{x+5}$$

$$600,000(x+5) - 6000x(x+5) = 600,000x$$

$$600,000x + 3,000,000 - 6000x^2 - 30,000x = 600,000x$$

$$-6000x^2 - 30,000x + 3,000,000 = 0$$

$$x^2 + 5x - 500 = 0$$

$$(x+25)(x-20) = 0$$

$$x + 25 = 0 \quad \text{or} \quad x - 20 = 0$$

$$x = -25 \qquad x = 20$$

−25 must be rejected. There were originally 20 people.

60. Let x = the number of local calls

The monthly cost using Plan A is $C_A = 25$.

The monthly cost using Plan B is $C_B = 13 + 0.06x$.

For Plan A to be better deal, it must cost less than Plan B.

$$C_A < C_B$$
$$25 < 13 + 0.06x$$
$$12 < 0.06x$$
$$200 < x$$
$$x > 200$$

Plan A is a better deal when more than 200 local calls are made per month.

Chapter 1

Section 1.1

Check Point Exercises

1.

2.

$$y = 4 - x$$

$x = -3, y = 7$

$x = -2, y = 6$

$x = -1, y = 5$

$x = 0, y = 4$

$x = 1, y = 3$

$x = 2, y = 2$

$x = 3, y = 1$

3.

$$y = |x + 1|$$

$x = -4, y = 3$

$x = -3, y = 2$

$x = -2, y = 1$

$x = -1, y = 0$

$x = 0, y = 1$

$x = 1, y = 2$

$x = 2, y = 3$

4. The meaning of a
$[-100, 100, 50]$ by $[-100, 100, 10]$
viewing rectangle is as follows:

$$\underbrace{[-100}_{\substack{\text{minimum} \\ x\text{-value}}}, \underbrace{100}_{\substack{\text{maximum} \\ x\text{-value}}}, \underbrace{50}_{\substack{\text{distance} \\ \text{between} \\ x\text{-axis} \\ \text{tick} \\ \text{marks}}}]$$

by

$$\underbrace{[-100}_{\substack{\text{minimum} \\ y\text{-value}}}, \underbrace{100}_{\substack{\text{maximum} \\ y\text{-value}}}, \underbrace{10}_{\substack{\text{distance} \\ \text{between} \\ y\text{-axis} \\ \text{tick} \\ \text{marks}}}]$$

5. **a.** The graph crosses the x-axis at $(-3, 0)$.
Thus, the x-intercept is -3.
The graph crosses the y-axis at $(0, 5)$.
Thus, the y-intercept is 5.

   b. The graph does not cross the x-axis.
Thus, there is no x-intercept.
The graph crosses the y-axis at $(0, 4)$.
Thus, the y-intercept is 4.

   c. The graph crosses the x- and y-axes at
the origin $(0, 0)$.
Thus, the x-intercept is 0 and the
y-intercept is 0.

6. The number of federal prisoners sentenced for
drug offenses in 2003 is about 57% of 159,275.
This can be estimated by finding 60% of
160,000.

$N \approx 60\%$ of $160,000$

$= 0.60 \times 160,000$

$= 96,000$

Exercise Set 1.1

1.

3.

5.

7.

9.

11.

13.

$$y = x^2 - 2$$

$x = -3, y = 7$

$x = -2, y = 2$

$x = -1, y = -1$

$x = 0, y = -2$

$x = 1, y = -1$

$x = 2, y = 2$

$x = 3, y = 7$

15.

$$y = x - 2$$

$x = -3, y = -5$

$x = -2, y = -4$

$x = -1, y = -3$

$x = 0, y = -2$

$x = 1, y = -1$

$x = 2, y = 0$

$x = 3, y = 1$

17.

$$y = 2x + 1$$

$x = -3, y = -5$
$x = -2, y = -3$
$x = -1, y = -1$
$x = 0, y = 1$
$x = 1, y = 3$
$x = 2, y = 5$
$x = 3, y = 7$

21.

$$y = 2|x|$$

$x = -3, y = 6$
$x = -2, y = 4$
$x = -1, y = 2$
$x = 0, y = 0$
$x = 1, y = 2$
$x = 2, y = 4$
$x = 3, y = 6$

19.

$$y = -\frac{1}{2}x$$

$x = -3, y = \dfrac{3}{2}$

$x = -2, y = 1$

$x = -1, y = \dfrac{1}{2}$

$x = 0, y = 0$

$x = 1, y = -\dfrac{1}{2}$

$x = 2, y = -1$

$x = 3, y = -\dfrac{3}{2}$

23.

$$y = |x| + 1$$

$x = -3, y = 4$
$x = -2, y = 3$
$x = -1, y = 2$
$x = 0, y = 1$
$x = 1, y = 2$
$x = 2, y = 3$
$x = 3, y = 4$

25.

$$y = 9 - x^2$$

$x = -3, y = 0$

$x = -2, y = 5$

$x = -1, y = 8$

$x = 0, y = 9$

$x = 1, y = 8$

$x = 2, y = 5$

$x = 3, y = 0$

27.

$$y = x^3$$

$x = -3, y = -27$

$x = -2, y = -8$

$x = -1, y = 1$

$x = 0, y = 0$

$x = 1, y = 1$

$x = 2, y = 8$

$x = 3, y = 27$

29. (c) x-axis tick marks –5, –4, –3, –2, –1, 0, 1, 2, 3, 4, 5; y-axis tick marks are the same.

31. (b); x-axis tick marks –20, –10, 0, 10, 20, 30, 40, 50, 60, 70, 80; y-axis tick marks –30, –20, –10, 0, 10, 20, 30, 40, 50, 60, 70

33. The equation that corresponds to Y_2 in the table is (c), $y_2 = 2 - x$. We can tell because all of the points $(-3, 5)$, $(-2, 4)$, $(-1, 3)$, $(0, 2)$, $(1, 1)$, $(2, 0)$, and $(3, -1)$ are on the line $y = 2 - x$, but all are not on any of the others.

35. No. It passes through the point $(0, 2)$.

37. $(2, 0)$

39. The graphs of Y_1 and Y_2 intersect at the points $(-2, 4)$ and $(1, 1)$.

41. **a.** 2; The graph intersects the x-axis at $(2, 0)$.

   b. –4; The graph intersects the y-axis at $(0, –4)$.

43. **a.** 1, –2; The graph intersects the x-axis at $(1, 0)$ and $(–2, 0)$.

   b. 2; The graph intersects the y-axis at $(0, 2)$.

45. **a.** –1; The graph intersects the x-axis at $(–1, 0)$.

   b. none; The graph does not intersect the y-axis.

47.

$$y = 2x + 4$$

49.

$$y = 3 - x^2$$

51.

x	(x, y)
-3	$(-3, 5)$
-2	$(-2, 5)$
-1	$(-1, 5)$
0	$(0, 5)$
1	$(1, 5)$
2	$(2, 5)$
3	$(3, 5)$

$$y = 5$$

53.

x	(x, y)
-2	$\left(-2, -\dfrac{1}{2}\right)$
-1	$(-1, -1)$
$-\dfrac{1}{2}$	$\left(-\dfrac{1}{2}, -2\right)$
$-\dfrac{1}{3}$	$\left(-\dfrac{1}{3}, -3\right)$
$\dfrac{1}{3}$	$\left(\dfrac{1}{3}, 3\right)$
$\dfrac{1}{2}$	$\left(\dfrac{1}{2}, 2\right)$
1	$(1, 1)$
2	$\left(2, \dfrac{1}{2}\right)$

55. There were approximately 65 democracies in 1989.

57. The number of democracies increased at the greatest rate between 1989 and 1993.

59. There were 49 democracies in 1977.

61. $R = 165 - 0.75A; \ A = 40$

$R - 165 - 0.75A = 165 - 0.75(40)$

$ = 165 - 30 = 135$

The desirable heart rate during exercise for a 40-year old man is 135 beats per minute. This corresponds to the point (40, 135) on the blue graph.

63. a. At birth we have $x = 0$.

$y = 2.9\sqrt{x} + 36$

$ = 2.9\sqrt{0} + 36$

$ = 2.9(0) + 36$

$ = 36$

According to the model, the head circumference at birth is 36 cm.

b. At 9 months we have $x = 9$.

$y = 2.9\sqrt{x} + 36$

$ = 2.9\sqrt{9} + 36$

$ = 2.9(3) + 36$

$ = 44.7$

According to the model, the head circumference at 9 months is 44.7 cm.

c. At 14 months we have $x = 14$.

$y = 2.9\sqrt{x} + 36$

$ = 2.9\sqrt{14} + 36$

$ \approx 46.9$

According to the model, the head circumference at 14 months is roughly 46.9 cm.

d. The model describes healthy children.

71. $y = 45.48x^2 - 334.35x + 1237.9$

The discharges decreased from 1990 to 1994, but started to increase after 1994. The policy was not a success.

73. (a)

75. (b)

77. (b)

Section 1.2

Check Point Exercises

1.   The domain is the set of all first components: $\{5, 10, 15, 20, 25\}$. The range is the set of all second components: $\{12.8, 16.2, 18.9, 20.7, 21.8\}$.

2.   **a.**   The relation is not a function since the two ordered pairs $(5, 6)$ and $(5, 8)$ have the same first component but different second components.

    b.   The relation is a function since no two ordered pairs have the same first component and different second components.

3.   **a.** $2x + y = 6$
$$y = -2x + 6$$
For each value of x, there is one and only one value for y, so the equation defines y as a function of x.

    b. $x^2 + y^2 = 1$
$$y^2 = 1 - x^2$$
$$y = \pm\sqrt{1 - x^2}$$
Since there are values of x (all values between -1 and 1 exclusive) that give more than one value for y (for example, if $x = 0$, then $y = \pm\sqrt{1 - 0^2} = \pm 1$), the equation does not define y as a function of x.

4.   **a.** $f(-5) = (-5)^2 - 2(-5) + 7$
$$= 25 - (-10) + 7$$
$$= 42$$

    b. $f(x + 4) = (x + 4)^2 - 2(x + 4) + 7$
$$= x^2 + 8x + 16 - 2x - 8 + 7$$
$$= x^2 + 6x + 15$$

    c. $f(-x) = (-x)^2 - 2(-x) + 7$
$$= x^2 - (-2x) + 7$$
$$= x^2 + 2x + 7$$

5.

x	$f(x) = 2x$	(x, y)
-2	–4	$(-2, -4)$
-1	–2	$(-1, -2)$
0	0	$(0, 0)$
1	2	$(1, 2)$
2	4	$(2, 4)$

x	$g(x) = 2x - 3$	(x, y)
-2	$g(-2) = 2(-2) - 3 = -7$	$(-2, -7)$
-1	$g(-1) = 2(-1) - 3 = -5$	$(-1, -5)$
0	$g(0) = 2(0) - 3 = -3$	$(0, -3)$
1	$g(1) = 2(1) - 3 = -1$	$(1, -1)$
2	$g(2) = 2(2) - 3 = 1$	$(2, 1)$

The graph of g is the graph of f shifted down 3 units.

6.   The graph (c) fails the vertical line test and is therefore not a function.
   y is a function of x for the graphs in (a) and (b).

7.   **a.** $f(10) \approx 16$ **b.** $x \approx 8$

8.   **a.**   Domain $= \{x \mid -2 \le x \le 1\}$ or $[-2, 1]$.

   Range $= \{y \mid 0 \le y \le 3\}$ or $[0, 3]$.

   b.   Domain $= \{x \mid -2 < x \le 1\}$ or $(-2, 1]$.

   Range $= \{y \mid -1 \le y < 2\}$ or $[-1, 2)$.

   c.   Domain $= \{x \mid -3 \le x < 0\}$ or $[-3, 0)$.

   Range $= \{y \mid y = -3, -2, -1\}$.

Exercise Set 1.2

1. The relation is a function since no two ordered pairs have the same first component and different second components. The domain is {1, 3, 5} and the range is {2, 4, 5}.

3. The relation is not a function since the two ordered pairs (3, 4) and (3, 5) have the same first component but different second components (the same could be said for the ordered pairs (4, 4) and (4, 5)). The domain is {3, 4} and the range is {4, 5}.

5. The relation is a function because no two ordered pairs have the same first component and different second components The domain is
    {3, 4, 5, 7} and the range is {–2, 1, 9}.

7. The relation is a function since there are no same first components with different second components. The domain is {–3, –2, –1, 0} and the range is {–3, –2, –1, 0}.

9. The relation is not a function since there are ordered pairs with the same first component and different second components. The domain is {1} and the range is {4, 5, 6}.

11. $x + y = 16$
    $$y = 16 - x$$
    Since only one value of y can be obtained for each value of x, y is a function of x.

13. $x^2 + y = 16$
    $$y = 16 - x^2$$
    Since only one value of y can be obtained for each value of x, y is a function of x.

15. $x^2 + y^2 = 16$
    $$y^2 = 16 - x^2$$
    $$y = \pm\sqrt{16 - x^2}$$
    If $x = 0$, $y = \pm 4$.
    Since two values, $y = 4$ and $y = -4$, can be obtained for one value of x, y is not a function of x.

17. $x = y^2$
    $$y = \pm\sqrt{x}$$
    If $x = 1$, $y = \pm 1$.
    Since two values, $y = 1$ and $y = -1$, can be obtained for $x = 1$, y is not a function of x.

19. $y = \sqrt{x + 4}$
    Since only one value of y can be obtained for each value of x, y is a function of x.

21. $x + y^3 = 8$
    $$y^3 = 8 - x$$
    $$y = \sqrt[3]{8 - x}$$
    Since only one value of y can be obtained for each value of x, y is a function of x.

23. $xy + 2y = 1$

$y(x+2) = 1$

$y = \dfrac{1}{x+2}$

Since only one value of y can be obtained for each value of x, y is a function of x.

25. $|x| - y = 2$

$-y = -|x| + 2$

$y = |x| - 2$

Since only one value of y can be obtained for each value of x, y is a function of x.

27. **a.** $f(6) = 4(6) + 5 = 29$

     b. $f(x+1) = 4(x+1) + 5 = 4x + 9$

     c. $f(-x) = 4(-x) + 5 = -4x + 5$

29. **a.** $g(-1) = (-1)^2 + 2(-1) + 3$

                $= 1 - 2 + 3$

                $= 2$

     b. $g(x+5) = (x+5)^2 + 2(x+5) + 3$

                    $= x^2 + 10x + 25 + 2x + 10 + 3$

                    $= x^2 + 12x + 38$

     c. $g(-x) = (-x)^2 + 2(-x) + 3$

                $= x^2 - 2x + 3$

31. **a.** $h(2) = 2^4 - 2^2 + 1$

              $= 16 - 4 + 1$

              $= 13$

     b. $h(-1) = (-1)^4 - (-1)^2 + 1$

               $= 1 - 1 + 1$

               $= 1$

     c. $h(-x) = (-x)^4 - (-x)^2 + 1 = x^4 - x^2 + 1$

     d. $h(3a) = (3a)^4 - (3a)^2 + 1$

               $= 81a^4 - 9a^2 + 1$

33. **a.** $f(-6) = \sqrt{-6+6} + 3 = \sqrt{0} + 3 = 3$

     b. $f(10) = \sqrt{10+6} + 3$

              $= \sqrt{16} + 3$

              $= 4 + 3$

              $= 7$

     c. $f(x-6) = \sqrt{x-6+6} + 3 = \sqrt{x} + 3$

35.   a. $f(2) = \dfrac{4(2)^2 - 1}{2^2} = \dfrac{15}{4}$

     b. $f(-2) = \dfrac{4(-2)^2 - 1}{(-2)^2} = \dfrac{15}{4}$

     c. $f(-x) = \dfrac{4(-x)^2 - 1}{(-x)^2} = \dfrac{4x^2 - 1}{x^2}$

37.   a. $f(6) = \dfrac{6}{|6|} = 1$

     b. $f(-6) = \dfrac{-6}{|-6|} = \dfrac{-6}{6} = -1$

     c. $f(r^2) = \dfrac{r^2}{|r^2|} = \dfrac{r^2}{r^2} = 1$

39.

x	$f(x) = x$	(x, y)
-2	$f(-2) = -2$	$(-2, -2)$
-1	$f(-1) = -1$	$(-1, -1)$
0	$f(0) = 0$	$(0, 0)$
1	$f(1) = 1$	$(1, 1)$
2	$f(2) = 2$	$(2, 2)$

x	$g(x) = x + 3$	(x, y)
-2	$g(-2) = -2 + 3 = 1$	$(-2, 1)$
-1	$g(-1) = -1 + 3 = 2$	$(-1, 2)$
0	$g(0) = 0 + 3 = 3$	$(0, 3)$
1	$g(1) = 1 + 3 = 4$	$(1, 4)$
2	$g(2) = 2 + 3 = 5$	$(2, 5)$

The graph of g is the graph of f shifted up 3 units.

41.

x	$f(x) = -2x$	(x, y)
–2	$f(-2) = -2(-2) = 4$	$(-2, 4)$
–1	$f(-1) = -2(-1) = 2$	$(-1, 2)$
0	$f(0) = -2(0) = 0$	$(0, 0)$
1	$f(1) = -2(1) = -2$	$(1, -2)$
2	$f(2) = -2(2) = -4$	$(2, -4)$

x	$g(x) = -2x - 1$	(x, y)
–2	$g(-2) = -2(-2) - 1 = 3$	$(-2, 3)$
–1	$g(-1) = -2(-1) - 1 = 1$	$(-1, 1)$
0	$g(0) = -2(0) - 1 = -1$	$(0, -1)$
1	$g(1) = -2(1) - 1 = -3$	$(1, -3)$
2	$g(2) = -2(2) - 1 = -5$	$(2, -5)$

$f(x) = -2x$
$g(x) = -2x - 1$

The graph of g is the graph of f shifted down 1 unit.

43.

x	$f(x) = x^2$	(x, y)
–2	$f(-2) = (-2)^2 = 4$	$(-2, 4)$
–1	$f(-1) = (-1)^2 = 1$	$(-1, 1)$
0	$f(0) = (0)^2 = 0$	$(0, 0)$
1	$f(1) = (1)^2 = 1$	$(1, 1)$
2	$f(2) = (2)^2 = 4$	$(2, 4)$

x	$g(x) = x^2 + 1$	(x, y)
–2	$g(-2) = (-2)^2 + 1 = 5$	$(-2, 5)$
–1	$g(-1) = (-1)^2 + 1 = 2$	$(-1, 2)$
0	$g(0) = (0)^2 + 1 = 1$	$(0, 1)$
1	$g(1) = (1)^2 + 1 = 2$	$(1, 2)$
2	$g(2) = (2)^2 + 1 = 5$	$(2, 5)$

$g(x) = x^2 + 1$
$f(x) = x^2$

The graph of g is the graph of f shifted up 1 unit.

45.

x	$f(x) = |x|$	(x, y)
–2	$f(-2) = |-2| = 2$	$(-2, 2)$
–1	$f(-1) = |-1| = 1$	$(-1, 1)$
0	$f(0) = |0| = 0$	$(0, 0)$
1	$f(1) = |1| = 1$	$(1, 1)$
2	$f(2) = |2| = 2$	$(2, 2)$
x	$g(x) = |x| - 2$	(x, y)
–2	$g(-2) = |-2| - 2 = 0$	$(-2, 0)$
–1	$g(-1) = |-1| - 2 = -1$	$(-1, -1)$
0	$g(0) = |0| - 2 = -2$	$(0, -2)$
1	$g(1) = |1| - 2 = -1$	$(1, -1)$
2	$g(2) = |2| - 2 = 0$	$(2, 0)$

$g(x) = |x| - 2$
$f(x) = |x|$

The graph of g is the graph of f shifted down 2 units.

47.

x	$f(x) = x^3$	(x, y)
–2	$f(-2) = (-2)^3 = -8$	$(-2, -8)$
–1	$f(-1) = (-1)^3 = -1$	$(-1, -1)$
0	$f(0) = (0)^3 = 0$	$(0, 0)$
1	$f(1) = (1)^3 = 1$	$(1, 1)$
2	$f(2) = (2)^3 = 8$	$(2, 8)$

x	$g(x) = x^3 + 2$	(x, y)
-2	$g(-2) = (-2)^3 + 2 = -6$	$(-2, -6)$
-1	$g(-1) = (-1)^3 + 2 = 1$	$(-1, 1)$
0	$g(0) = (0)^3 + 2 = 2$	$(0, 2)$
1	$g(1) = (1)^3 + 2 = 3$	$(1, 3)$
2	$g(2) = (2)^3 + 2 = 10$	$(2, 10)$

The graph of g is the graph of f shifted up 2 units.

49.

x	$f(x) = 3$	(x, y)
-2	$f(-2) = 3$	$(-2, 3)$
-1	$f(-1) = 3$	$(-1, 3)$
0	$f(0) = 3$	$(0, 3)$
1	$f(1) = 3$	$(1, 3)$
2	$f(2) = 3$	$(2, 3)$

x	$g(x) = 5$	(x, y)
-2	$g(-2) = 5$	$(-2, 5)$
-1	$g(-1) = 5$	$(-1, 5)$
0	$g(0) = 5$	$(0, 5)$
1	$g(1) = 5$	$(1, 5)$
2	$g(2) = 5$	$(2, 5)$

The graph of g is the graph of f shifted up 2 units.

51.

x	$f(x) = \sqrt{x}$	(x, y)
0	$f(0) = \sqrt{0} = 0$	$(0,0)$
1	$f(1) = \sqrt{1} = 1$	$(1,1)$
4	$f(4) = \sqrt{4} = 2$	$(4,2)$
9	$f(9) = \sqrt{9} = 3$	$(9,3)$

x	$g(x) = \sqrt{x} - 1$	(x, y)
0	$g(0) = \sqrt{0} - 1 = -1$	$(0,-1)$
1	$g(1) = \sqrt{1} - 1 = 0$	$(1,0)$
4	$g(4) = \sqrt{4} - 1 = 1$	$(4,1)$
9	$g(9) = \sqrt{9} - 1 = 2$	$(9,2)$

The graph of g is the graph of f shifted down 1 unit.

53.

x	$f(x) = \sqrt{x}$	(x, y)
0	$f(0) = \sqrt{0} = 0$	$(0,0)$
1	$f(1) = \sqrt{1} = 1$	$(1,1)$
4	$f(4) = \sqrt{4} = 2$	$(4,2)$
9	$f(9) = \sqrt{9} = 3$	$(9,3)$

x	$g(x) = \sqrt{x-1}$	(x, y)
1	$g(1) = \sqrt{1-1} = 0$	$(1,0)$
2	$g(2) = \sqrt{2-1} = 1$	$(2,1)$
5	$g(5) = \sqrt{5-1} = 2$	$(5,2)$
10	$g(10) = \sqrt{10-1} = 3$	$(10,3)$

The graph of g is the graph of f shifted right 1 unit.

55. function

57. function

59. not a function

61. function

63. function

65. $f(-2) = -4$

67. $f(4) = 4$

69. $f(-3) = 0$

71. $g(-4) = 2$

73. $g(-10) = 2$

75. When $x = -2$, $g(x) = 1$.

77. **a.** domain: $(-\infty, \infty)$

   b. range: $[-4, \infty)$

   c. x-intercepts: -3 and 1

   d. y-intercept: -3

   e. $f(-2) = -3$ and $f(2) = 5$

79. **a.** domain: $(-\infty, \infty)$

   b. range: $[1, \infty)$

   c. x-intercept: none

   d. y-intercept: 1

   e. $f(-1) = 2$ and $f(3) = 4$

81. **a.** domain: $[0, 5)$

   b. range: $[-1, 5)$

   c. x-intercept: 2

   d. y-intercept: -1

   e. $f(3) = 1$

83. **a.** domain: $[0, \infty)$

   b. range: $[1, \infty)$

   c. x-intercept: none

   d. y-intercept: 1

   e. $f(4) = 3$

85. **a.** domain: $[-2, 6]$

   b. range: $[-2, 6]$

   c. x-intercept: 4

   d. y-intercept: 4

   e. $f(-1) = 5$

87. **a.** domain: $(-\infty, \infty)$

   b. range: $(-\infty, -2]$

   c. x-intercept: none

   d. y-intercept: -2

   e. $f(-4) = -5$ and $f(4) = -2$

89. **a.** domain: $(-\infty, \infty)$

   b. range: $(0, \infty)$

   c. x-intercept: none

   d. y-intercept: 1.5

   e. $f(4) = 6$

91. a. domain: $\{-5, -2, 0, 1, 3\}$

    b. range: $\{2\}$

    c. x-intercept: none

    d. y-intercept: 2

    e. $f(-5) + f(3) = 2 + 2 = 4$

93. $g(1) = 3(1) - 5 = 3 - 5 = -2$

$$f\big(g(1)\big) = f(-2) = (-2)^2 - (-2) + 4$$
$$= 4 + 2 + 4 = 10$$

95. $\sqrt{3 - (-1)} - (-6)^2 + 6 \div (-6) \cdot 4$

$$= \sqrt{3 + 1} - 36 + 6 \div (-6) \cdot 4$$
$$= \sqrt{4} - 36 + -1 \cdot 4$$
$$= 2 - 36 + -4$$
$$= -34 + -4$$
$$= -38$$

97. $f(-x) - f(x)$

$$= (-x)^3 + (-x) - 5 - (x^3 + x - 5)$$
$$= -x^3 - x - 5 - x^3 - x + 5 = -2x^3 - 2x$$

99. a. $\{(\text{U.S., } 80\%), (\text{Japan, } 64\%),$

        $(\text{France, } 64\%), (\text{Germany, } 61\%),$

        $(\text{England, } 59\%), (\text{China}, 47\%)\}$

    b. Yes, the relation is a function. Each element in the domain corresponds to only one element in the range.

    c. $\{(80\%, \text{U.S.}), (64\%, \text{Japan}),$

        $(64\%, \text{France}), (61\%, \text{Germany}),$

        $(59\%, \text{England}), (47\%, \text{China})\}$

    d. No, the relation is not a function. 64% in the domain corresponds to both Japan and France in the range.

101. $W(16) = 0.07(16) + 4.1$

        $= 1.12 + 4.1 = 5.22$

In 2000 there were 5.22 million women enrolled in U.S. colleges.
$(2000, 5.22)$

103. $W(20) = 0.07(20) + 4.1$

        $= 1.4 + 4.1 = 5.5$

    $M(20) = 0.01(20) + 3.9$

        $= 0.2 + 3.9 = 4.1$

    $W(20) - M(20) = 5.5 - 4.1 = 1.4$

In 2004, there will be 1.4 million more women than men enrolled in U.S. colleges.

105. a. According to the graph, women's earnings were about 73% of men's in 2000.

   b. $P(x) = 0.012x^2 - 0.16x + 60$

        $P(40) = 0.012(40)^2 - 0.16(40) + 60 = 72.8$

        According to the function, women's earnings were about 72.8% of men's in 2000.

   c. $\dfrac{27,355}{37,339} \approx 0.733 = 73.3\%$

        The answers in parts (a) and (b) model the actual data quite well.

107. $C(x) = 100,000 + 100x$

    $C(90) = 100,000 + 100(90) = \$109,000$

    It will cost \$109,000 to produce 90 bicycles.

109.
$$T(x) = \frac{40}{x} + \frac{40}{x+30}$$
$$T(30) = \frac{40}{30} + \frac{40}{30+30}$$
$$= \frac{80}{60} + \frac{40}{60}$$
$$= \frac{120}{60}$$
$$= 2$$

    If you travel 30 mph going and 60 mph returning, your total trip will take 2 hours.

121. a.   false; the domain of f is [–4, 4]

   b.   false; the range of f is [–2, 2)

   c.   true; $f(-1) - f(4) = 1 - (-1) = 2$

   d.   false; $f(0) < 1$ x

   (c) is true.

123. Answers may vary.
    An example is $\{(1,1),(2,1)\}$

Section 1.3

Check Point Exercises

1.   **a.** $f(x) = -2x^2 + x + 5$

$$f(x+h) = -2(x+h)^2 + (x+h) + 5$$
$$= -2(x^2 + 2xh + h^2) + x + h + 5$$
$$= -2x^2 - 4xh - 2h^2 + x + h + 5$$

     b. $\dfrac{f(x+h) - f(x)}{h}$

$$= \frac{-2x^2 - 4xh - 2h^2 + x + h + 5 - \left(-2x^2 + x + 5\right)}{h}$$

$$= \frac{-2x^2 - 4xh - 2h^2 + x + h + 5 + 2x^2 - x - 5}{h}$$

$$= \frac{-4xh - 2h^2 + h}{h}$$

$$= \frac{h\left(-4x - 2h + 1\right)}{h}$$

$$= -4x - 2h + 1$$

2. $C(t) = \begin{cases} 20 & \text{if } 0 \le t \le 60 \\ 20 + 0.40(t - 60) & \text{if } t > 60 \end{cases}$

     a.   Since $0 \le 40 \le 60$, $C(40) = 20$
       With 40 calling minutes, the cost is \$20.
       This is represented by $(40, 20)$.

     b.   Since $80 > 60$, $C(80) = 20 + 0.40(80 - 60) = 28$
       With 80 calling minutes, the cost is \$28.
       This is represented by $(80, 28)$.

3.   The function is increasing on the interval $(-\infty, -1)$, decreasing on the interval $(-1, 1)$, and increasing on the interval $(1, \infty)$.

4.   **a.** $f(-x) = (-x)^2 + 6 = x^2 + 6 = f(x)$
       The function is even.

     b. $g(-x) = 7(-x)^3 - (-x) = -7x^3 + x = -f(x)$
       The function is odd.

     c. $h(-x) = (-x)^5 + 1 = -x^5 + 1$
       The function is neither even nor odd.

Exercise Set 1.3

1. $\dfrac{f(x+h)-f(x)}{h}$

$=\dfrac{4(x+h)-4x}{h}$

$=\dfrac{4x+4h-4x}{h}$

$=\dfrac{4h}{h}$

$=4$

3. $\dfrac{f(x+h)-f(x)}{h}$

$=\dfrac{3(x+h)+7-(3x+7)}{h}$

$=\dfrac{3x+3h+7-3x-7}{h}$

$=\dfrac{3h}{h}$

$=3$

5. $\dfrac{f(x+h)-f(x)}{h}$

$=\dfrac{(x+h)^2-x^2}{h}$

$=\dfrac{x^2+2xh+h^2-x^2}{h}$

$=\dfrac{2xh+h^2}{h}$

$=\dfrac{h(2x+h)}{h}$

$=2x+h$

7. $\dfrac{f(x+h)-f(x)}{h}$

$=\dfrac{(x+h)^2-4(x+h)+3-(x^2-4x+3)}{h}$

$=\dfrac{x^2+2xh+h^2-4x-4h+3-x^2+4x-3}{h}$

$=\dfrac{2xh+h^2-4h}{h}$

$=\dfrac{h(2x+h-4)}{h}$

$=2x+h-4$

9. $\dfrac{f(x+h)-f(x)}{h}$

$=\dfrac{2(x+h)^2+(x+h)-1-(2x^2+x-1)}{h}$

$=\dfrac{2x^2+4xh+2h^2+x+h-1-2x^2-x+1}{h}$

$=\dfrac{4xh+2h^2+h}{h}$

$=\dfrac{h(4x+2h+1)}{h}$

$=4x+2h+1$

11. $\dfrac{f(x+h)-f(x)}{h}$

$=\dfrac{-(x+h)^2+2(x+h)+4-(-x^2+2x+4)}{h}$

$=\dfrac{-x^2-2xh-h^2+2x+2h+4+x^2-2x-4}{h}$

$=\dfrac{-2xh-h^2+2h}{h}$

$=\dfrac{h(-2x-h+2)}{h}$

$=-2x-h+2$

13. $\dfrac{f(x+h)-f(x)}{h}$

$=\dfrac{-2(x+h)^2+5(x+h)+7-(-2x^2+5x+7)}{h}$

$=\dfrac{-2x^2-4xh-2h^2+5x+5h+7+2x^2-5x-7}{h}$

$=\dfrac{-4xh-2h^2+5h}{h}$

$=\dfrac{h(-4x-2h+5)}{h}$

$=-4x-2h+5$

15. $\dfrac{f(x+h)-f(x)}{h}$

$=\dfrac{-2(x+h)^2-(x+h)+3-(-2x^2-x+3)}{h}$

$=\dfrac{-2x^2-4xh-2h^2-x-h+3+2x^2+x-3}{h}$

$=\dfrac{-4xh-2h^2-h}{h}$

$=\dfrac{h(-4x-2h-1)}{h}$

$=-4x-2h-1$

17. $\dfrac{f(x+h)-f(x)}{h}=\dfrac{6-6}{h}=\dfrac{0}{h}=0$

19. $\dfrac{f(x+h)-f(x)}{h}$

$=\dfrac{\dfrac{1}{x+h}-\dfrac{1}{x}}{h}$

$=\dfrac{\dfrac{x}{x(x+h)}+\dfrac{-(x+h)}{x(x+h)}}{h}$

$=\dfrac{\dfrac{x-x-h}{x(x+h)}}{h}$

$=\dfrac{\dfrac{-h}{x(x+h)}}{h}$

$=\dfrac{-h}{x(x+h)}\cdot\dfrac{1}{h}$

$=\dfrac{-1}{x(x+h)}$

21. $\dfrac{f(x+h)-f(x)}{h}$

$=\dfrac{\sqrt{x+h}-\sqrt{x}}{h}$

$=\dfrac{\sqrt{x+h}-\sqrt{x}}{h}\cdot\dfrac{\sqrt{x+h}+\sqrt{x}}{\sqrt{x+h}+\sqrt{x}}$

$=\dfrac{x+h-x}{h\left(\sqrt{x+h}+\sqrt{x}\right)}$

$=\dfrac{h}{h\left(\sqrt{x+h}+\sqrt{x}\right)}$

$=\dfrac{1}{\sqrt{x+h}+\sqrt{x}}$

23. **a.** $f(-2)=3(-2)+5=-1$

 b. $f(0)=4(0)+7=7$

 c. $f(3)=4(3)+7=19$

25. **a.** $g(0)=0+3=3$

 b. $g(-6)=-(-6+3)=-(-3)=3$

 c. $g(-3)=-3+3=0$

27. **a.** $h(5)=\dfrac{5^2-9}{5-3}=\dfrac{25-9}{2}=\dfrac{16}{2}=8$

 b. $h(0)=\dfrac{0^2-9}{0-3}=\dfrac{-9}{-3}=3$

 c. $h(3)=6$

29. **a.** increasing: $(-1,\infty)$

 b. decreasing: $(-\infty,-1)$

 c. constant: none

31. **a.** increasing: $(0,\infty)$

 b. decreasing: none

 c. constant: none

33. **a.** increasing: none

 b. decreasing: $(-2,6)$

 c. constant: none

35. a. increasing: $(-\infty, -1)$

   b. decreasing: none

   c. constant: $(-1, \infty)$

37. a. increasing: $(-\infty, 0)$ or $(1.5, 3)$

   b. decreasing: $(0, 1.5)$ or $(3, \infty)$

   c. constant: none

39. a. increasing: $(-2, 4)$

   b. decreasing: none

   c. constant: $(-\infty, -2)$ or $(4, \infty)$

41. a. $x = 0$, relative maximum $= 4$

   b. $x = -3, 3$, relative minimum $= 0$

43. a. $x = -2$, relative maximum $= 21$

   b. $x = 1$, relative minimum $= -6$

45. $f(x) = x^3 + x$

$f(-x) = (-x)^3 + (-x)$

$f(-x) = -x^3 - x = -(x^3 + x)$

$f(-x) = -f(x)$, odd function

47. $g(x) = x^2 + x$

$g(-x) = (-x)^2 + (-x)$

$g(-x) = x^2 - x$, neither

49. $h(x) = x^2 - x^4$

$h(-x) = (-x)^2 - (-x)^4$

$h(-x) = x^2 - x^4$

$h(-x) = h(x)$, even function

51. $f(x) = x^2 - x^4 + 1$

$f(-x) = (-x)^2 - (-x)^4 + 1$

$f(-x) = x^2 - x^4 + 1$

$f(-x) = f(x)$, even function

53. $f(x) = \dfrac{1}{5}x^6 - 3x^2$

$f(-x) = \dfrac{1}{5}(-x)^6 - 3(-x)^2$

$f(-x) = \dfrac{1}{5}x^6 - 3x^2$

$f(-x) = f(x)$, even function

55. $f(x) = x\sqrt{1 - x^2}$

$f(-x) = -x\sqrt{1 - (-x)^2}$

$f(-x) = -x\sqrt{1 - x^2}$

$ = -\left(x\sqrt{1 - x^2}\right)$

$f(-x) = -f(x)$, odd function

57. The graph is symmetric with respect to the y-axis. The function is even.

59. The graph is symmetric with respect to the origin. The function is odd.

61. a. Domain: $(-\infty, \infty)$

   b. Range: $[-4, \infty)$

   c. x-intercepts: 1, 7

   d. y-intercept: 4

   e. $(4, \infty)$

   f. $(0, 4)$

    g. $(-\infty, 0)$

    h. $x = 4$

    i. $y = -4$

    j. $f(-3) = 4$

    k. $f(2) = -2$ and $f(6) = -2$

    l.   neither ; $f(-x) \neq x$, $f(-x) \neq -x$

63. **a.**   Domain: $(-\infty, 3]$

    b.   Range: $(-\infty, 4]$

    c. x-intercepts: -3, 3

    d. $f(0) = 3$

    e. $(-\infty, 1)$

    f. $(1, 3)$

    g. $(-\infty, -3]$

    h. $f(1) = 4$

    i. $x = 1$

    j.   positive; $f(-1) = +2$

65. $f(1.06) = 1$

67. $f\left(\dfrac{1}{3}\right) = 0$

69. $f(-2.3) = -3$

71. $\sqrt{f(-1.5) + f(-0.9)} - \left[f(\pi)\right]^2 + f(-3) \div f(1) \cdot f(-\pi)$

    $= \sqrt{1 + 0} - \left[-4\right]^2 + 2 \div (-2) \cdot 3$

    $= \sqrt{1} - 16 + (-1) \cdot 3$

    $= 1 - 16 - 3$

    $= -18$

73. $30 + 0.30(t - 120) = 30 + 0.3t - 36 = 0.3t - 6$

75. $C(t) = \begin{cases} 50 & \text{if } 0 \leq t \leq 400 \\ 50 + 0.30(t - 400) & \text{if } t > 400 \end{cases}$

77. $f(60) \approx 3.1$

In 1960, about 3.1% of the population were Jewish-Americans.

79. $x \approx 19$ and $x \approx 64$

In 1919 and 1964, about 3% of the population were Jewish-Americans.

81.   In 1940, the maximum of 3.7% of the population were Jewish-American.

83.   Each year corresponds to only 1 percentage.

85.   Increasing: (45, 74)

Decreasing: (16, 45)

The number of accidents occurring per 50 million miles driven increases with age starting at age 45, while it decreases with age starting at age 16.

87.   Answers may vary. An example is 16 and 74 year olds will have 526.4 accidents per 50 million miles.

89. $f(30) = 61.9(30) + 132 = 1989$ cigarettes per adult

This describes the actual data quite well.

91.   The maximum occurred in 1960. Graph estimates will vary near 4100.

$f(50) = -2.2(50)^2 + 256(50) - 3503 = 3797$ cigarettes per adult

The function does not describe the actual data reasonably well.

93.

107.

Increasing: $(1, \infty)$
Decreasing: $(-\infty, 1)$

103.

The number of doctor visits decreases during childhood and then increases as you get older. The minimum is (20.29, 3.99), which means that the minimum number of doctor visits, about 4, occurs at around age 20.

109.

Increasing: $(-\infty, 0)$
Decreasing: $(0, \infty)$

105.

Increasing: $(-2, 0)$ or $(2, \infty)$
Decreasing: $(-\infty, -2)$ or $(0, 2)$

113. a. h is even if both f and g are even or if both f and g are odd.

f and g are both even:

$$h(-x) = \frac{f(-x)}{g(-x)} = \frac{f(x)}{g(x)} = h(x)$$

f and g are both odd:

$$h(-x) = \frac{f(-x)}{g(-x)} = \frac{-f(x)}{-g(x)} = \frac{f(x)}{g(x)} = h(x)$$

b. h is odd if f is odd and g is even or if f is even and g is odd.

f is odd and g is even:

$$h(-x) = \frac{f(-x)}{g(-x)} = \frac{-f(x)}{g(x)} = -\frac{f(x)}{g(x)} = -h(x)$$

f is even and g is odd:

$$h(-x) = \frac{f(-x)}{g(-x)} = \frac{f(x)}{-g(x)} = -\frac{f(x)}{g(x)} = -h(x)$$

Section 1.4

Check Point Exercises

1. a. $m = \dfrac{-2-4}{-4-(-3)} = \dfrac{-6}{-1} = 6$

    b. $m = \dfrac{5-(-2)}{-1-4} = \dfrac{7}{-5} = -\dfrac{7}{5}$

2. $y - y_1 = m(x - x_1)$

    $y - (-5) = 6(x - 2)$

    $y + 5 = 6x - 12$

    $y = 6x - 17$

3. $m = \dfrac{-6-(-1)}{-1-(-2)} = \dfrac{-5}{1} = -5$,

    so the slope is –5. Using the point (–2, –1), we get the point slope equation:

    $y - y_1 = m(x - x_1)$

    $y - (-1) = -5[x - (-2)]$

    $y + 1 = -5(x + 2)$. Solve the equation for y:

    $y + 1 = -5x - 10$

    $y = -5x - 11$.

4. The slope m is $\frac{3}{5}$ and the y-intercept is 1, so one point on the line is (1, 0). We can find a second point on the line by using the slope $m = \frac{3}{5} = \frac{\text{Rise}}{\text{Run}}$: starting at the point (0, 1), move 3 units up and 5 units to the right, to obtain the point (5, 4).

$f(x) = \dfrac{3}{5}x + 1$

5. All ordered pairs that are solutions of $x = -3$ have a value of x that is always –3. Any value can be used for y.

6. $3x + 6y - 12 = 0$

$$6y = -3x + 12$$

$$y = \frac{-3}{6}x + \frac{12}{6}$$

$$y = -\frac{1}{2}x + 2$$

3x + 6y − 12 = 0

The slope is $-\dfrac{1}{2}$ and the y-intercept is 2.

7.   Find the x-intercept:

$$3x - 2y - 6 = 0$$
$$3x - 2(0) - 6 = 0$$
$$3x - 6 = 0$$
$$3x = 6$$
$$x = 2$$

Find the y-intercept:

$$3x - 2y - 6 = 0$$
$$3(0) - 2y - 6 = 0$$
$$-2y - 6 = 0$$
$$-2y = 6$$
$$y = -3$$

3x − 2y = 6

8. $m = \dfrac{\text{Change in } y}{\text{Change in } x} = \dfrac{32.8 - 30.0}{20 - 10} = \dfrac{2.8}{10} = 0.28$

$$y - y_1 = m(x - x_1)$$

$$y - 30.0 = 0.28(x - 10)$$

$$y - 30.0 = 0.28x - 2.8$$

$$y = 0.28x + 27.2$$

2020 is 50 years after 1970.

$$y = 0.28x + 27.2$$

$$y = 0.28(50) + 27.2$$

$$y = 41.2$$

In 2020 the median age is expected to be 41.2.

Exercise Set 1.4

1. $m = \dfrac{10 - 7}{8 - 4} = \dfrac{3}{4}$; rises

3. $m = \dfrac{2 - 1}{2 - (-2)} = \dfrac{1}{4}$; rises

5. $m = \dfrac{2 - (-2)}{3 - 4} = \dfrac{0}{-1} = 0$; horizontal

7. $m = \dfrac{-1 - 4}{-1 - (-2)} = \dfrac{-5}{1} = -5$; falls

9. $m = \dfrac{-2 - 3}{5 - 5} = \dfrac{-5}{0}$ undefined; vertical

11. $m = 2$, $x_1 = 3$, $y_1 = 5$;
point-slope form: $y - 5 = 2(x - 3)$;
slope-intercept form: $y - 5 = 2x - 6$
$$y = 2x - 1$$

13. $m = 6$, $x_1 = -2$, $y_1 = 5$;
point-slope form: $y - 5 = 6(x + 2)$;
slope-intercept form: $y - 5 = 6x + 12$
$$y = 6x + 17$$

15. $m = -3$, $x_1 = -2$, $y_1 = -3$;
point-slope form: $y + 3 = -3(x + 2)$;
slope-intercept form: $y + 3 = -3x - 6$
$$y = -3x - 9$$

17. $m = -4$, $x_1 = -4$, $y_1 = 0$;
point-slope form: $y - 0 = -4(x + 4)$;
slope-intercept form: $y = -4(x + 4)$
$$y = -4x - 16$$

19. $m = -1$, $x_1 = \dfrac{-1}{2}$, $y_1 = -2$;

point-slope form: $y + 2 = -1\left(x + \dfrac{1}{2}\right)$;

slope-intercept form: $y + 2 = -x - \dfrac{1}{2}$

$$y = -x - \dfrac{5}{2}$$

21. $m = \dfrac{1}{2}$, $x_1 = 0$, $y_1 = 0$;

point-slope form: $y - 0 = \dfrac{1}{2}(x - 0)$;

slope-intercept form: $y = \dfrac{1}{2}x$

23. $m = -\dfrac{2}{3}$, $x_1 = 6$, $y_1 = -2$;

point-slope form: $y + 2 = -\dfrac{2}{3}(x - 6)$;

slope-intercept form: $y + 2 = -\dfrac{2}{3}x + 4$

$$y = -\dfrac{2}{3}x + 2$$

25. $m = \dfrac{10 - 2}{5 - 1} = \dfrac{8}{4} = 2$;

point-slope form: $y - 2 = 2(x - 1)$ using $(x_1, y_1) = (1, 2)$, or $y - 10 = 2(x - 5)$ using $(x_1, y_1) = (5, 10)$;

slope-intercept form: $y - 2 = 2x - 2$ or

$$y - 10 = 2x - 10,$$
$$y = 2x$$

27. $m = \dfrac{3 - 0}{0 - (-3)} = \dfrac{3}{3} = 1$;

point-slope form: $y - 0 = 1(x + 3)$ using $(x_1, y_1) = (-3, 0)$, or $y - 3 = 1(x - 0)$ using $(x_1, y_1) = (0, 3)$; slope-intercept form: $y = x + 3$

29. $m = \dfrac{4 - (-1)}{2 - (-3)} = \dfrac{5}{5} = 1$;

point-slope form: $y + 1 = 1(x + 3)$ using $(x_1, y_1) = (-3, -1)$, or $y - 4 = 1(x - 2)$ using $(x_1, y_1) = (2, 4)$; slope-intercept form: $y + 1 = x + 3$ or

$$y - 4 = x - 2$$
$$y = x + 2$$

31. $m = \dfrac{6 - (-2)}{3 - (-3)} = \dfrac{8}{6} = \dfrac{4}{3}$;

point-slope form: $y + 2 = \dfrac{4}{3}(x + 3)$ using $(x_1, y_1) = (-3, -2)$, or $y - 6 = \dfrac{4}{3}(x - 3)$ using $(x_1, y_1) = (3, 6)$;

slope-intercept form: $y + 2 = \dfrac{4}{3x} + 4$ or

$$y - 6 = \dfrac{4}{3}x - 4,$$
$$y = \dfrac{4}{3}x + 2$$

33. $m = \dfrac{-1 - (-1)}{4 - (-3)} = \dfrac{0}{7} = 0$;

point-slope form: $y + 1 = 0(x + 3)$ using $(x_1, y_1) = (-3, -1)$, or $y + 1 = 0(x - 4)$ using $(x_1, y_1) = (4, -1)$;
slope-intercept form: $y + 1 = 0$, so

$$y = -1$$

35. $m = \dfrac{0-4}{-2-2} = \dfrac{-4}{-4} = 1$;

point-slope form: $y - 4 = 1(x - 2)$ using $(x_1, y_1) = (2, 4)$, or $y - 0 = 1(x + 2)$ using $(x_1, y_1) = (-2, 0)$;

slope-intercept form: $y - 9 = x - 2$, or

$$y = x + 2$$

37. $m = \dfrac{4-0}{0-\left(-\frac{1}{2}\right)} = \dfrac{4}{\frac{1}{2}} = 8$;

point-slope form: $y - 4 = 8(x - 0)$ using $(x_1, y_1) = (0, 4)$, or $y - 0 = 8\left(x + \frac{1}{2}\right)$ using $(x_1, y_1) = \left(-\frac{1}{2}, 0\right)$; or

$y - 0 = 8\left(x + \frac{1}{2}\right)$

slope-intercept form: $y = 8x + 4$

39. $m = 2; b = 1$

$y = 2x + 1$

41. $m = -2; b = 1$

$f(x) = -2x + 1$

43. $m = \dfrac{3}{4}; \ b = -2$

$f(x) = \dfrac{3}{4}x - 2$

45. $m = -\dfrac{3}{5}; \ b = 7$

$y = -\dfrac{3}{5}x + 7$

47. $m = -\dfrac{1}{2}; b = 0$

$g(x) = -\dfrac{1}{2}x$

49. $y = -2$

51. $y = -3$

53. $y = 0$

55. $f(x) = 1$

57. $3x - 18 = 0$
$3x = 18$
$x = 6$

59. **a.** $3x + y - 5 = 0$
$y - 5 = -3x$
$y = -3x + 5$

  b. $m = -3;\ b = 5$

61. **a.** $2x + 3y - 18 = 0$
$2x - 18 = -3y$
$-3y = 2x - 18$
$y = \dfrac{2}{-3}x - \dfrac{18}{-3}$
$y = -\dfrac{2}{3}x + 6$

  b. $m = -\dfrac{2}{3};\ b = 6$

c.

$2x + 3y - 18 = 0$

63. **a.** $8x - 4y - 12 = 0$
$8x - 12 = 4y$
$4y = 8x - 12$
$y = \dfrac{8}{4}x - \dfrac{12}{4}$
$y = 2x - 3$

  b. $m = 2;\ b = -3$

  c.

$8x - 4y - 12 = 0$

65. **a.** $3y - 9 = 0$
$3y = 9$
$y = 3$

  b. $m = 0;\ b = 3$

  c.

$3y - 9 = 0$

67. Find the *x*-intercept:
$$6x - 2y - 12 = 0$$
$$6x - 2(0) - 12 = 0$$
$$6x - 12 = 0$$
$$6x = 12$$
$$x = 2$$
Find the *y*-intercept:
$$6x - 2y - 12 = 0$$
$$6(0) - 2y - 12 = 0$$
$$-2y - 12 = 0$$
$$-2y = 12$$
$$y = -6$$

$$6x - 2y - 12 = 0$$

69. Find the *x*-intercept:
$$2x + 3y + 6 = 0$$
$$2x + 3(0) + 6 = 0$$
$$2x + 6 = 0$$
$$2x = -6$$
$$x = -3$$
Find the *y*-intercept:
$$2x + 3y + 6 = 0$$
$$2(0) + 3y + 6 = 0$$
$$3y + 6 = 0$$
$$3y = -6$$
$$y = -2$$

71. Find the *x*-intercept:
$$8x - 2y + 12 = 0$$
$$8x - 2(0) + 12 = 0$$
$$8x + 12 = 0$$
$$8x = -12$$
$$\frac{8x}{8} = \frac{-12}{8}$$
$$x = \frac{-3}{2}$$
Find the *y*-intercept:
$$8x - 2y + 12 = 0$$
$$8(0) - 2y + 12 = 0$$
$$-2y + 12 = 0$$
$$-2y = -12$$
$$y = -6$$

$$8x - 2y + 12 = 0$$

73.
$$m = \frac{0-a}{b-0} = \frac{-a}{b} = -\frac{a}{b}$$

Since *a* and *b* are both positive, $-\frac{a}{b}$ is negative. Therefore, the line falls.

75.
$$m = \frac{(b+c)-b}{a-a} = \frac{c}{0}$$
The slope is undefined.
The line is vertical.

77.
$$Ax + By = C$$
$$By = -Ax + C$$
$$y = -\frac{A}{B}x + \frac{C}{B}$$

The slope is $-\frac{A}{B}$ and the *y*-intercept is $\frac{C}{B}$.

79.
$$-3 = \frac{4-y}{1-3}$$
$$-3 = \frac{4-y}{-2}$$
$$6 = 4-y$$
$$2 = -y$$
$$-2 = y$$

81. $3x - 4f(x) = 6$
$$-4f(x) = -3x + 6$$
$$f(x) = \frac{3}{4}x - \frac{3}{2}$$

$3x - 4f(x) - 6 = 0$

$\left(0, -\frac{3}{2}\right)$

83. Using the slope-intercept form for the equation of a line:
$$-1 = -2(3) + b$$
$$-1 = -6 + b$$
$$5 = b$$

85. m_1, m_3, m_2, m_4

87. **a.** First we must find the slope using $(10,16)$ and $(16,12.7)$.
$$m = \frac{12.7 - 16}{16 - 10} = -\frac{3.3}{6} = -0.55$$
Then use the slope and one of the points to write the equation in point-slope form.
$$y - y_1 = m(x - x_1)$$
$$y - 16 = -0.55(x - 10)$$
or
$$y - 12.7 = -0.55(x - 16)$$

b. $y - 16 = -0.55(x - 10)$
$$y - 16 = -0.55x + 5.5$$
$$y = -0.55x + 21.5$$
$$f(x) = -0.55x + 21.5$$

c. $f(20) = -0.55(20) + 21.5 = 10.5$
The linear function predicts 10.5% of adult women will be on weight-loss diets in 2007.

89. **a.** points: $(0, 73.7), (5, 74.7), (10, 75.4)$
$(15, 75.8), (19, 76.7), (20, 77.0), (21, 77.2)$

b. $m = \dfrac{\text{Change in } y}{\text{Change in } x} = \dfrac{77.0 - 74.7}{20 - 5} \approx 0.15$
$$y - y_1 = m(x - x_1)$$
$$y - 74.7 = 0.15(x - 5) \quad \text{[point-slope]}$$
$$y - 74.7 = 0.15x - 0.75$$
$$y = 0.15x + 73.95 \quad \text{[slope-intercept]}$$

c. $E(x) = 0.15x + 73.95$
$$E(40) = 0.15(40) + 73.95$$
$$= 79.95$$
In 2020 the life expectancy is expected to be 79.95.

91. $(10, 230)$ $(60, 110)$ Points may vary.
$$m = \frac{110 - 230}{60 - 10} = -\frac{120}{50} = -2.4$$
$$y - 230 = -2.4(x - 10)$$
$$y - 230 = -2.4x + 24$$
$$y = -2.4x + 254$$
Answers may vary for predictions.

101. Two points are $(0, 6)$ and $(10, -24)$.
$$m = \frac{-24 - 6}{10 - 0} = \frac{-30}{10} = -3.$$
Check: $y = mx + b$: $y = -3x + 6$.

103. Two points are $(0, -2)$ and $(10, 5.5)$.

$$m = \frac{5.5 - (-2)}{10 - 0} = \frac{7.5}{10} = 0.75 \text{ or } \frac{3}{4}.$$

Check: $y = mx + b$: $y = \frac{3}{4}x - 2$.

105. Statement **c.** is true.

Statement **a.** is false. One nonnegative slope is 0. A line with slope equal to zero does not rise from left to right.

Statement **b.** is false. Slope-intercept form is $y = mx + b$. Vertical lines have equations of the form $x = a$. Equations of this form have undefined slope and cannot be written in slope-intercept form.

Statement **d.** is false. The graph of $x = 7$ is a vertical line through the point $(7, 0)$.

107.

We are given that the y-intercept is -6 and the slope is $\frac{1}{2}$.

So the equation of the line is $y = \frac{1}{2}x - 6$.

We can put this equation in the form $ax + by = c$ to find the missing coefficients.

$$y = \frac{1}{2}x - 6$$

$$y - \frac{1}{2}x = -6$$

$$2\left(y - \frac{1}{2}x\right) = 2(-6)$$

$$2y - x = -12$$

$$x - 2y = 12$$

Therefore, the coefficient of x is 1 and the coefficient of y is -2.

109. Let $(25, 40)$ and $(125, 280)$ be ordered pairs (M, E) where M is degrees Madonna and E is degrees Elvis. Then

$m = \frac{280 - 40}{125 - 25} = \frac{240}{100} = 2.4$. Using $(x_1, y_1) = (25, 40)$, point-slope form tells us that

$E - 40 = 2.4 \, (M - 25)$ or $E = 2.4 \, M - 20$.

Section 1.5

Check Point Exercises

1. The slope of the line $y = 3x + 1$ is 3.

$$y - y_1 = m(x - x_1)$$
$$y - 5 = 3(x - (-2))$$
$$y - 5 = 3(x + 2) \quad \text{point-slope}$$
$$y - 5 = 3x + 6$$
$$y = 3x + 11 \quad \text{slope-intercept}$$

2. a. Write the equation in slope-intercept form:
   $$x + 3y - 12 = 0$$
   $$3y = -x + 12$$
   $$y = -\frac{1}{3}x + 4$$

   The slope of this line is $-\frac{1}{3}$ thus the slope of any line perpendicular to this line is 3.

   b. Use $m = 3$ and the point $(-2, -6)$ to write the equation.
   $$y - y_1 = m(x - x_1)$$
   $$y - (-6) = 3(x - (-2))$$
   $$y + 6 = 3(x + 2)$$
   $$y + 6 = 3x + 6$$
   $$-3x + y = 0$$
   $$3x - y = 0 \quad \text{general form}$$

3. $m = \dfrac{\text{Change in } y}{\text{Change in } x} = \dfrac{12 - 10}{2010 - 1995} = \dfrac{2}{15} \approx 0.13$

   The slope indicates that the number of U.S. men living alone is projected to increase by 0.13 million each year.

4. a. $\dfrac{f(x_2) - f(x_1)}{x_2 - x_1} = \dfrac{1^3 - 0^3}{1 - 0} = 1$

   b. $\dfrac{f(x_2) - f(x_1)}{x_2 - x_1} = \dfrac{2^3 - 1^3}{2 - 1} = \dfrac{8 - 1}{1} = 7$

   c. $\dfrac{f(x_2) - f(x_1)}{x_2 - x_1} = \dfrac{0^3 - (-2)^3}{0 - (-2)} = \dfrac{8}{2} = 4$

5. $\dfrac{f(x_2) - f(x_1)}{x_2 - x_1} = \dfrac{f(3) - f(1)}{3 - 1} = \dfrac{0.05 - 0.03}{3 - 1} = 0.01$

6.   a. $s(1) = 4(1)^2 = 4$

$s(2) = 4(2)^2 = 16$

$\dfrac{\Delta s}{\Delta t} = \dfrac{16-4}{2-1} = 12$ feet per second

b. $s(1) = 4(1)^2 = 4$

$s(1.5) = 4(1.5)^2 = 9$

$\dfrac{\Delta s}{\Delta t} = \dfrac{9-4}{1.5-1} = 10$ feet per second

c. $s(1) = 4(1)^2 = 4$

$s(1.01) = 4(1.01)^2 = 4.0804$

$\dfrac{\Delta s}{\Delta t} = \dfrac{4.0804-4}{1.01-1} = 8.04$ feet per second

Exercise Set 1.5

1.   Since L is parallel to $y = 2x$, we know it will have slope $m = 2$. We are given that it passes through (4, 2). We use the slope and point to write the equation in point-slope form.

$y - y_1 = m(x - x_1)$

$y - 2 = 2(x - 4)$

Solve for y to obtain slope-intercept form.

$y - 2 = 2(x - 4)$

$y - 2 = 2x - 8$

$y = 2x - 6$

In function notation, the equation of the line is $f(x) = 2x - 6$.

3.   Since L is perpendicular to $y = 2x$, we know it will have slope $m = -\dfrac{1}{2}$. We are given that it passes through (2, 4). We use the slope and point to write the equation in point-slope form.

$y - y_1 = m(x - x_1)$

$y - 4 = -\dfrac{1}{2}(x - 2)$

Solve for y to obtain slope-intercept form.

$y - 4 = -\dfrac{1}{2}(x - 2)$

$y - 4 = -\dfrac{1}{2}x + 1$

$y = -\dfrac{1}{2}x + 5$

In function notation, the equation of the line is $f(x) = -\dfrac{1}{2}x + 5$.

5. $m = -4$ since the line is parallel to $y = -4x + 3$; $x_1 = -8$, $y_1 = -10$;

    point-slope form: $y + 10 = -4(x + 8)$
    slope-intercept form: $y + 10 = -4x - 32$
    $$y = -4x - 42$$

7. $m = -5$ since the line is perpendicular to $y = \frac{1}{5}x + 6$; $x_1 = 2$, $y_1 = -3$;

    point-slope form: $y + 3 = -5(x - 2)$
    slope-intercept form: $y + 3 = -5x + 10$
    $$y = -5x + 7$$

9. $2x - 3y - 7 = 0$
    $$-3y = -2x + 7$$
    $$y = \frac{2}{3}x - \frac{7}{3}$$

    The slope of the given line is $\frac{2}{3}$, so $m = \frac{2}{3}$ since the lines are parallel.

    point-slope form: $y - 2 = \frac{2}{3}(x + 2)$

    general form: $2x - 3y + 10 = 0$

11. $x - 2y - 3 = 0$
    $$-2y = -x + 3$$
    $$y = \frac{1}{2}x - \frac{3}{2}$$

    The slope of the given line is $\frac{1}{2}$, so $m = -2$ since the lines are perpendicular.

    point-slope form: $y + 7 = -2(x - 4)$
    general form: $2x + y - 1 = 0$

13. $\frac{15 - 0}{5 - 0} = \frac{15}{5} = 3$

15. $\frac{5^2 + 2 \cdot 5 - (3^2 + 2 \cdot 3)}{5 - 3}$
    $$= \frac{25 + 10 - (9 + 6)}{2}$$
    $$= \frac{20}{2}$$
    $$= 10$$

17. $\frac{\sqrt{9} - \sqrt{4}}{9 - 4} = \frac{3 - 2}{5} = \frac{1}{5}$

19. a.
$$s(3) = 10(3)^2 = 90$$
$$s(4) = 10(4)^2 = 160$$
$$\frac{\Delta s}{\Delta t} = \frac{160-90}{4-3} = 70 \text{ feet per second}$$

b.
$$s(3) = 10(3)^2 = 90$$
$$s(3.5) = 10(3.5)^2 = 122.5$$
$$\frac{\Delta s}{\Delta t} = \frac{122.5-90}{3.5-3} = 65 \text{ feet per second}$$

c.
$$s(3) = 10(3)^2 = 90$$
$$s(3.01) = 10(3.01)^2 = 90.601$$
$$\frac{\Delta s}{\Delta t} = \frac{90.601-90}{3.01-3} = 60.1 \text{ feet per second}$$

d.
$$s(3) = 10(3)^2 = 90$$
$$s(3.001) = 10(3.001)^2 = 90.06$$
$$\frac{\Delta s}{\Delta t} = \frac{90.06-90}{3.001-3} = 60.01 \text{ feet per second}$$

21. Since the line is perpendicular to $x = 6$ which is a vertical line, we know the graph of f is a horizontal line with 0 slope. The graph of f passes through $(-1,5)$, so the equation of f is $f(x) = 5$.

23. First we need to find the equation of the line with x-intercept of 2 and y-intercept of -4. This line will pass through $(2,0)$ and $(0,-4)$. We use these points to find the slope.

$$m = \frac{-4-0}{0-2} = \frac{-4}{-2} = 2$$

Since the graph of f is perpendicular to this line, it will have slope $m = -\frac{1}{2}$.

Use the point $(-6,4)$ and the slope $-\frac{1}{2}$ to find the equation of the line.

$$y - y_1 = m(x - x_1)$$
$$y - 4 = -\frac{1}{2}(x - (-6))$$
$$y - 4 = -\frac{1}{2}(x + 6)$$
$$y - 4 = -\frac{1}{2}x - 3$$
$$y = -\frac{1}{2}x + 1$$
$$f(x) = -\frac{1}{2}x + 1$$

25. First put the equation $3x - 2y - 4 = 0$ in slope-intercept form.

$$3x - 2y - 4 = 0$$
$$-2y = -3x + 4$$
$$y = \frac{3}{2}x - 2$$

The equation of f will have slope $-\frac{2}{3}$ since it is perpendicular to the line above and the same

$y-$ intercept -2.

So the equation of f is $f(x) = -\frac{2}{3}x - 2$.

27. The slope indicates that the global average temperature is projected to increase by 0.01 degrees Fahrenheit each year.

29. The slope indicates that the percentage of U.S. adults who smoked cigarettes decreased by 0.52% each year.

31. $f(x) = 13x + 222$

33. $f(x) = -2.40x + 52.40$

35. $\dfrac{f(x_2) - f(x_1)}{x_2 - x_1} = \dfrac{f(2003) - f(1997)}{2003 - 1997} = \dfrac{25.2 - 32.5}{2003 - 1997} \approx -1.22$

43.

$$y = \frac{1}{3}x + 1$$
$$y = -3x - 2$$

    a. The lines are perpendicular because their slopes are negative reciprocals of each other. This is verified because product of their slopes is -1.

    b.

The lines do not appear to be perpendicular.

    c.

The lines appear to be perpendicular. The calculator screen is rectangular and does not have the same width and height. This causes the scale of the x–axis to differ from the scale on the y–axis despite using the same scale in the window settings. In part (b), this causes the lines not to appear perpendicular when indeed they are. The zoom square feature compensates for this and in part (c), the lines appear to be perpendicular.

45.

47. The slope of the line containing $(1,-3)$ and $(-2,4)$ has slope

$$m = \frac{4-(-3)}{-2-1} = \frac{4+3}{-3} = \frac{7}{-3} = -\frac{7}{3}.$$

Solve $Ax + y - 2 = 0$ for y to obtain slope-intercept form.

$Ax + y - 2 = 0$

$y = -Ax + 2$

So the slope of this line is $-A$.

This line is perpendicular to the line above so its slope is $\dfrac{3}{7}$. Therefore, $-A = \dfrac{3}{7}$ so $A = -\dfrac{3}{7}$.

Mid-Chapter 1 Check Point

1. The relation is not a function.
The domain is $\{1,2\}$.
The range is $\{-6,4,6\}$.

2. The relation is a function.
The domain is $\{0,2,3\}$.
The range is $\{1,4\}$.

3. The relation is a function.
The domain is $\{x \mid -2 \le x < 2\}$.
The range is $\{y \mid 0 \le y \le 3\}$.

4. The relation is not a function.
The domain is $\{x \mid -3 < x \le 4\}$.
The range is $\{y \mid -1 \le y \le 2\}$.

5. The relation is not a function.
The domain is $\{-2,-1,0,1,2\}$.
The range is $\{-2,-1,1,3\}$.

6. The relation is a function.
The domain is $\{x \mid x \le 1\}$.
The range is $\{y \mid y \ge -1\}$.

7. $x^2 + y = 5$
$$y = -x^2 + 5$$
For each value of x, there is one and only one value for y, so the equation defines y as a function of x.

8. $x + y^2 = 5$
$$y^2 = 5 - x$$
$$y = \pm\sqrt{5-x}$$
Since there are values of x that give more than one value for y (for example, if $x = 4$, then $y = \pm\sqrt{5-4} = \pm 1$), the equation does not define y as a function of x.

9. Each value of x corresponds to exactly one value of y.

10. Domain: $(-\infty, \infty)$

11. Range: $(-\infty, 4]$

12. x-intercepts: -6 and 2

13. y-intercept: 3

14. increasing: $(-\infty, -2)$

15. decreasing: $(-2, \infty)$

16. $x = -2$

17. $f(-2) = 4$

18. $f(-4) = 3$

19. $f(-7) = -2$ and $f(3) = -2$

20. $f(-6) = 0$ and $f(2) = 0$

21. $(-6, 2)$

22. $f(100)$ is negative.

23. neither; $f(-x) \neq x$ and $f(-x) \neq -x$

24. $\dfrac{f(x_2) - f(x_1)}{x_2 - x_1} = \dfrac{f(4) - f(-4)}{4 - (-4)} = \dfrac{-5 - 3}{4 + 4} = -1$

25. $y = -2x$

26. $y = -2$

27. $x + y = -2$

28. $y = \dfrac{1}{3}x - 2$

29. $x = 3.5$

30.

$4x - 2y = 8$

31.

$f(x) = x^2 - 4$

32.

$f(x) = x - 4$

33.

$f(x) = |x| - 4$

34. $5y = -3x$

$$y = -\frac{3}{5}x$$

$5y = -3x$

35. $5y = 20$

$$y = 4$$

$5y = 20$

36.

$$f(x) = \begin{cases} -1 \text{ if } x \le 0 \\ 1 \text{ if } x > 0 \end{cases}$$

37. **a.** $f(-x) = -2(-x)^2 - x - 5 = -2x^2 - x - 5$

neither; $f(-x) \ne x$ and $f(-x) \ne -x$

b. $\dfrac{f(x+h) - f(x)}{h}$

$$= \frac{-2(x+h)^2 + (x+h) - 5 - (-2x^2 + x - 5)}{h}$$

$$= \frac{-2x^2 - 4xh - 2h^2 + x + h - 5 + 2x^2 - x + 5}{h}$$

$$= \frac{-4xh - 2h^2 + h}{h}$$

$$= \frac{h(-4x - 2h + 1)}{h}$$

$$= -4x - 2h + 1$$

38. $C(x) = \begin{cases} 30 & \text{if } 0 \le t \le 200 \\ 30 + 0.40(t - 200) & \text{if } t > 200 \end{cases}$

a. $C(150) = 30$

b. $C(250) = 30 + 0.40(250 - 200) = 50$

39. $y - y_1 = m(x - x_1)$

$y - 3 = -2(x - (-4))$

$y - 3 = -2(x + 4)$

$y - 3 = -2x - 8$

$y = -2x - 5$

$f(x) = -2x - 5$

40. $m = \dfrac{\text{Change in } y}{\text{Change in } x} = \dfrac{1 - (-5)}{2 - (-1)} = \dfrac{6}{3} = 2$

$y - y_1 = m(x - x_1)$

$y - 1 = 2(x - 2)$

$y - 1 = 2x - 4$

$y = 2x - 3$

$f(x) = 2x - 3$

41. $3x - y - 5 = 0$

$-y = -3x + 5$

$y = 3x - 5$

The slope of the given line is 3, and the lines are parallel, so $m = 3$.

$y - y_1 = m(x - x_1)$

$y - (-4) = 3(x - 3)$

$y + 4 = 3x - 9$

$y = 3x - 13$

$f(x) = 3x - 13$

42. $2x - 5y - 10 = 0$

$-5y = -2x + 10$

$\dfrac{-5y}{-5} = \dfrac{-2x}{-5} + \dfrac{10}{-5}$

$y = \dfrac{2}{5}x - 2$

The slope of the given line is $\dfrac{2}{5}$, and the lines are perpendicular, so $m = -\dfrac{5}{2}$.

$$y - y_1 = m(x - x_1)$$

$$y - (-3) = -\frac{5}{2}\big(x - (-4)\big)$$

$$y + 3 = -\frac{5}{2}x - 10$$

$$y = -\frac{5}{2}x - 13$$

$$f(x) = -\frac{5}{2}x - 13$$

43. $m_1 = \dfrac{\text{Change in } y}{\text{Change in } x} = \dfrac{0 - (-4)}{7 - 2} = \dfrac{4}{5}$

$m_2 = \dfrac{\text{Change in } y}{\text{Change in } x} = \dfrac{6 - 2}{1 - (-4)} = \dfrac{4}{5}$

The slope of the lines are equal thus the lines are parallel.

44. The slope indicates that the percentage of U.S. colleges offering distance learning is increasing by 7.8% each year.

45. $\dfrac{f(x_2) - f(x_1)}{x_2 - x_1} = \dfrac{f(2) - f(-1)}{2 - (-1)}$

$$= \dfrac{\big(3(2)^2 - 2\big) - \big(3(-1)^2 - (-1)\big)}{2 + 1}$$

$$= 2$$

Section 1.6

Check Point Exercises

1. Shift up vertically 3 units.

2. Shift to the right 4 units.

3. Shift to the right 1 unit and down 2 units.

4. Reflect about the *x*-axis.

5. Reflect about the *y*-axis.

6. Vertically stretch the graph of $f(x) = |x|$.

7.   **a.**   Horizontally shrink the graph of $y = f(x)$.

$$g(x) = f(2x)$$

     b.   Horizontally stretch the graph of $y = f(x)$.

$$h(x) = f\left(\frac{1}{2}x\right)$$

8.   The graph of $y = f(x)$ is shifted 1 unit left, shrunk by a factor of $\frac{1}{3}$, reflected about the x-axis, then shifted down 2 units.

$$y = -\frac{1}{3}f(x + 1) - 2$$

9.   The graph of $f(x) = x^2$ is shifted 1 unit right, stretched by a factor of 2, then shifted up 3 units.

$$g(x) = 2(x - 1)^2 + 3$$

Exercise Set 1.6

1.

$$g(x) = f(x) + 1$$

3.

$$g(x) = f(x + 1)$$

5.

$$g(x) = f(x - 1) - 2$$

7.

$$g(x) = -f(x)$$

9.

$$g(x) = -f(x) + 3$$

11.

$$g(x) = \frac{1}{2}f(x)$$

13. $g(x) = f\left(\frac{1}{2}x\right)$

15.

$$g(x) = -f\left(\frac{1}{2}x\right) + 1$$

17.

$$g(x) = f(x) - 1$$

19.

$$g(x) = f(x - 1)$$

21.

$$g(x) = f(x - 1) + 2$$

23.

$$g(x) = -f(x)$$

25.

$$g(x) = f(-x) + 1$$

27.

$$g(x) = 2f(x)$$

29.

$$g(x) = f(2x)$$

31.

$$g(x) = 2f(x + 2) + 1$$

33.

$$g(x) = f(x) + 2$$

35.

$$g(x) = f(x + 2)$$

37.

$$g(x) = -f(x + 2)$$

39.

$$g(x) = -\frac{1}{2}f(x + 2)$$

41.

$$g(x) = -\frac{1}{2}f(x + 2) - 2$$

43.

$$g(x) = \frac{1}{2}f(2x)$$

45.

$$g(x) = f(x - 1) - 1$$

47.

$$g(x) = -f(x - 1) + 1$$

49.

$$g(x) = 2f\left(\frac{1}{2}x\right)$$

51.

$$g(x) = \frac{1}{2}f(x + 1)$$

53.

55.

57.

59.

61.

63.

65.

67.

69.

71.

73.

75.

77.

79.

81.

83.

85.

87.

89.

91.

93.

95.

97.

99.

101.

103.

105.

107.

109.

111.

113.

115.

117.

119.

$g(x) = 2 \text{ int } (x + 1)$

121.

$h(x) = \text{int } (-x) + 1$

123. $y = \sqrt{x - 2}$

125. $y = (x + 1)^2 - 4$

127. a.   First, vertically stretch the graph of $f(x) = \sqrt{x}$ by the factor 2.9; then shift the result up 20.1 units.

    b. $f(x) = 2.9\sqrt{x} + 20.1$

          $f(48) = 2.9\sqrt{48} + 20.1 \approx 40.2$

          The model describes the actual data very well.

    c. $\dfrac{f(x_2) - f(x_1)}{x_2 - x_1}$

          $= \dfrac{f(10) - f(0)}{10 - 0}$

          $= \dfrac{\left(2.9\sqrt{10} + 20.1\right) - \left(2.9\sqrt{0} + 20.1\right)}{10 - 0}$

          $= \dfrac{29.27 - 20.1}{10}$

          ≈ 0.9

          0.9 inches per month

    d. $\dfrac{f(x_2) - f(x_1)}{x_2 - x_1}$

          $= \dfrac{f(60) - f(50)}{60 - 50}$

          $= \dfrac{\left(2.9\sqrt{60} + 20.1\right) - \left(2.9\sqrt{50} + 20.1\right)}{60 - 50}$

          $= \dfrac{42.5633 - 40.6061}{10}$

          ≈ 0.2

          This rate of change is lower than the rate of change in part (c). The relative leveling off of the curve shows this difference.

135. a.

    b.

137. a.   False; the graph of g is a translation of three units upward and three units to the left of the graph of f.

    b.   False; the graph of f is a reflection of the graph of $y = \sqrt{x}$ in the x-axis, while the graph of g is a reflection of the graph of $y = \sqrt{x}$ in the y-axis.

c.   False; $g(x) = 5x^2 - 10$, so the graph of g can be obtained by stretching f five units followed by a
      downward shift of ten units.

d.   True

(d) is true.

139. $g(x) = -|x - 5| + 1$ **143.** $(a, 2b)$

145. $(a, b - 3)$

141. $g(x) = -\dfrac{1}{4}\sqrt{16 - x^2} - 1$

Section 1.7

Check Point Exercises

1.   a.   The function $f(x) = x^2 + 3x - 17$ contains neither division nor an even root. The domain of f is the set of
            all real numbers or $(-\infty, \infty)$.

      b.   The denominator equals zero when $x = 7$ or $x = -7$. These values must be excluded from the domain.
            Domain of $g = (-\infty, -7) \cup (-7, 7) \cup (7, \infty)$.

      c.   Since $h(x) = \sqrt{9x - 27}$ contains an even root; the quantity under the radical must be greater than or equal to 0.
            $$9x - 27 \geq 0$$
            $$9x \geq 27$$
            $$x \geq 3$$
            Thus, the domain of h is $\{x \mid x \geq 3\}$, or the interval $[3, \infty)$.

2.   a. $(f + g)(x) = f(x) + g(x)$
            $$= x - 5 + (x^2 - 1)$$
            $$= x - 5 + x^2 - 1$$
            $$= -x^2 + x - 6$$

      b. $(f - g)(x) = f(x) - g(x)$
            $$= x - 5 - (x^2 - 1)$$
            $$= x - 5 - x^2 + 1$$
            $$= -x^2 + x - 4$$

      c. $(fg)(x) = (x - 5)(x^2 - 1)$
            $$= x(x^2 - 1) - 5(x^2 - 1)$$
            $$= x^3 - x - 5x^2 + 5$$
            $$= x^3 - 5x^2 - x + 5$$

      d. $\left(\dfrac{f}{g}\right)(x) = \dfrac{f(x)}{g(x)}$
            $$= \dfrac{x - 5}{x^2 - 1}, \ x \neq \pm 1$$

3. a. $(f+g)(x) = f(x) + g(x)$
        $$= \sqrt{x-3} + \sqrt{x+1}$$

    b. Domain of f: $x - 3 \geq 0$
                                $x \geq 3$
                                $[3, \infty)$
        Domain of g: $x + 1 \geq 0$
                                $x \geq -1$
                                $[-1, \infty)$

        The domain of $f + g$ is the set of all real numbers that are common to the domain of f and the domain of g. Thus, the domain of $f + g$ is $[3, \infty)$.

4. a. $(f \circ g)(x) = f\big(g(x)\big)$
        $$= 5\big(2x^2 - x - 1\big) + 6$$
        $$= 10x^2 - 5x - 5 + 6$$
        $$= 10x^2 - 5x + 1$$

    b. $(g \circ f)(x) = g\big(f(x)\big)$
        $$= 2\big(5x + 6\big)^2 - \big(5x + 6\big) - 1$$
        $$= 2(25x^2 + 60x + 36) - 5x - 6 - 1$$
        $$= 50x^2 + 120x + 72 - 5x - 6 - 1$$
        $$= 50x^2 + 115x + 65$$

5. a. $f \circ g(x) = \dfrac{4}{\dfrac{1}{x} + 2} = \dfrac{4x}{1 + 2x}$

    b. $\left\{ x \middle| x \neq 0, \, x \neq -\dfrac{1}{2} \right\}$

6. $h(x) = f \circ g$ where $f(x) = \sqrt{x}$; $g(x) = x^2 + 5$

Exercise Set 1.7

1. The function contains neither division nor an even root. The domain $= (-\infty, \infty)$

3. The denominator equals zero when $x = 4$. This value must be excluded from the domain.
    Domain: $(-\infty, 4) \cup (4, \infty)$.

5. The function contains neither division nor an even root. The domain $= (-\infty, \infty)$

7. The values that make the denominator equal zero must be excluded from the domain.
    Domain: $(-\infty, -3) \cup (-3, 5) \cup (5, \infty)$

9. The values that make the denominators equal zero must be excluded from the domain.
    Domain: $(-\infty, -7) \cup (-7, 9) \cup (9, \infty)$

11. The first denominator cannot equal zero. The values that make the second denominator equal zero must be excluded from the domain.
Domain: $(-\infty,-1)\cup(-1,1)\cup(1,\infty)$

13. Exclude x for $x = 0$.

Exclude x for $\dfrac{3}{x} - 1 = 0$.

$\dfrac{3}{x} - 1 = 0$

$x\left(\dfrac{3}{x} - 1\right) = x(0)$

$3 - x = 0$

$-x = -3$

$x = 3$

Domain: $(-\infty,0)\cup(0,3)\cup(3,\infty)$

15. Exclude x for $x - 1 = 0$.

$x - 1 = 0$

$x = 1$

Exclude x for $\dfrac{4}{x-1} - 2 = 0$.

$\dfrac{4}{x-1} - 2 = 0$

$(x-1)\left(\dfrac{4}{x-1} - 2\right) = (x-1)(0)$

$4 - 2(x-1) = 0$

$4 - 2x + 2 = 0$

$-2x + 6 = 0$

$-2x = -6$

$x = 3$

Domain: $(-\infty,1)\cup(1,3)\cup(3,\infty)$

17. The expression under the radical must not be negative.

$x - 3 \geq 0$

$x \geq 3$

Domain: $[3,\infty)$

19. The expression under the radical must be positive.

$x - 3 > 0$

$x > 3$

Domain: $(3,\infty)$

21. The expression under the radical must not be negative.

$5x + 35 \geq 0$

$5x \geq -35$

$x \geq -7$

Domain: $[-7,\infty)$

23. The expression under the radical must not be negative.

$24 - 2x \geq 0$

$-2x \geq -24$

$\dfrac{-2x}{-2} \leq \dfrac{-24}{-2}$

$x \leq 12$

Domain: $(-\infty,12]$

25. The expressions under the radicals must not be negative.
$$x - 2 \geq 0 \qquad x + 3 \geq 0$$
$$ \text{and}$$
$$x \geq 2 \qquad\quad x \geq -3$$
To make both inequalities true, $x \geq 2$.
Domain: $[2, \infty)$

27. The expression under the radical must not be negative.
$$x - 2 \geq 0$$
$$x \geq 2$$
The denominator equals zero when $x = 5$.
Domain: $[2, 5) \cup (5, \infty)$.

29. Find the values that make the denominator equal zero and must be excluded from the domain.
$$x^3 - 5x^2 - 4x + 20$$
$$= x^2 (x - 5) - 4(x - 5)$$
$$= (x - 5)(x^2 - 4)$$
$$= (x - 5)(x + 2)(x - 2)$$
-2, 2, and 5 must be excluded.
Domain: $(-\infty, -2) \cup (-2, 2) \cup (2, 5) \cup (5, \infty)$

31. $(f + g)(x) = 3x + 2$
Domain: $(-\infty, \infty)$
$(f - g)(x) = f(x) - g(x)$
$$= (2x + 3) - (x - 1)$$
$$= x + 4$$
Domain: $(-\infty, \infty)$
$(fg)(x) = f(x) \cdot g(x)$
$$= (2x + 3) \cdot (x - 1)$$
$$= 2x^2 + x - 3$$
Domain: $(-\infty, \infty)$
$\left(\dfrac{f}{g}\right)(x) = \dfrac{f(x)}{g(x)} = \dfrac{2x + 3}{x - 1}$
Domain: $(-\infty, 1) \cup (1, \infty)$

33. $(f + g)(x) = 3x^2 + x - 5$
Domain: $(-\infty, \infty)$
$(f - g)(x) = -3x^2 + x - 5$
Domain: $(-\infty, \infty)$
$(fg)(x) = (x - 5)(3x^2) = 3x^3 - 15x^2$
Domain: $(-\infty, \infty)$
$\left(\dfrac{f}{g}\right)(x) = \dfrac{x - 5}{3x^2}$
Domain: $(-\infty, 0) \cup (0, \infty)$

35. $(f + g)(x) = 2x^2 - 2$
Domain: $(-\infty, \infty)$
$(f - g)(x) = 2x^2 - 2x - 4$
Domain: $(-\infty, \infty)$
$(fg)(x) = (2x^2 - x - 3)(x + 1)$
$$= 2x^3 + x^2 - 4x - 3$$
Domain: $(-\infty, \infty)$
$\left(\dfrac{f}{g}\right)(x) = \dfrac{2x^2 - x - 3}{x + 1}$
$$= \dfrac{(2x - 3)(x + 1)}{(x + 1)} = 2x - 3$$
Domain: $(-\infty, -1) \cup (-1, \infty)$

37. $(f + g)(x) = (3 - x^2) + (x^2 + 2x - 15)$
$$= 2x - 12$$
Domain: $(-\infty, \infty)$
$(f - g)(x) = (3 - x^2) - (x^2 + 2x - 15)$
$$= -2x^2 - 2x + 18$$
Domain: $(-\infty, \infty)$
$(fg)(x) = (3 - x^2)(x^2 + 2x - 15)$
$$= -x^4 - 2x^3 + 18x^2 + 6x - 45$$
Domain: $(-\infty, \infty)$
$\left(\dfrac{f}{g}\right)(x) = \dfrac{3 - x^2}{x^2 + 2x - 15}$
Domain: $(-\infty, -5) \cup (-5, 3) \cup (3, \infty)$

39. $(f+g)(x) = \sqrt{x} + x - 4$

Domain: $[0, \infty)$

$(f-g)(x) = \sqrt{x} - x + 4$

Domain: $[0, \infty)$

$(fg)(x) = \sqrt{x}(x-4)$

Domain: $[0, \infty)$

$\left(\dfrac{f}{g}\right)(x) = \dfrac{\sqrt{x}}{x-4}$

Domain: $[0,4) \cup (4,\infty)$

41. $(f+g)(x) = 2 + \dfrac{1}{x} + \dfrac{1}{x} = 2 + \dfrac{2}{x} = \dfrac{2x+2}{x}$

Domain: $(-\infty, 0) \cup (0, \infty)$

$(f-g)(x) = 2 + \dfrac{1}{x} - \dfrac{1}{x} = 2$

Domain: $(-\infty, 0) \cup (0, \infty)$

$(fg)(x) = \left(2 + \dfrac{1}{x}\right) \cdot \dfrac{1}{x} = \dfrac{2}{x} + \dfrac{1}{x^2} = \dfrac{2x+1}{x^2}$

Domain: $(-\infty, 0) \cup (0, \infty)$

$\left(\dfrac{f}{g}\right)(x) = \dfrac{2 + \frac{1}{x}}{\frac{1}{x}} = \left(2 + \dfrac{1}{x}\right) \cdot x = 2x + 1$

Domain: $(-\infty, 0) \cup (0, \infty)$

43. $(f+g)(x) = f(x) + g(x)$

$= \dfrac{5x+1}{x^2-9} + \dfrac{4x-2}{x^2-9}$

$= \dfrac{9x-1}{x^2-9}$

Domain: $(-\infty, -3) \cup (-3, 3) \cup (3, \infty)$

$(f-g)(x) = f(x) - g(x)$

$= \dfrac{5x+1}{x^2-9} - \dfrac{4x-2}{x^2-9}$

$= \dfrac{x+3}{x^2-9}$

$= \dfrac{1}{x-3}$

Domain: $(-\infty, -3) \cup (-3, 3) \cup (3, \infty)$

$(fg)(x) = f(x) \cdot g(x)$

$= \dfrac{5x+1}{x^2-9} \cdot \dfrac{4x-2}{x^2-9}$

$= \dfrac{(5x+1)(4x-2)}{\left(x^2-9\right)^2}$

Domain: $(-\infty, -3) \cup (-3, 3) \cup (3, \infty)$

$\left(\dfrac{f}{g}\right)(x) = \dfrac{\frac{5x+1}{x^2-9}}{\frac{4x-2}{x^2-9}}$

$= \dfrac{5x+1}{x^2-9} \cdot \dfrac{x^2-9}{4x-2}$

$= \dfrac{5x+1}{4x-2}$

The domain must exclude -3, 3, and any values that make $4x - 2 = 0$.

$4x - 2 = 0$

$4x = 2$

$x = \dfrac{1}{2}$

Domain: $(-\infty, -3) \cup \left(-3, \frac{1}{2}\right) \cup \left(\frac{1}{2}, 3\right) \cup (3, \infty)$

45. $(f+g)(x) = \sqrt{x+4} + \sqrt{x-1}$

Domain: $[1, \infty)$

$(f-g)(x) = \sqrt{x+4} - \sqrt{x-1}$

Domain: $[1, \infty)$

$(fg)(x) = \sqrt{x+4} \cdot \sqrt{x-1} = \sqrt{x^2+3x-4}$

Domain: $[1, \infty)$

$\left(\dfrac{f}{g}\right)(x) = \dfrac{\sqrt{x+4}}{\sqrt{x-1}}$

Domain: $(1, \infty)$

47. $(f+g)(x) = \sqrt{x-2} + \sqrt{2-x}$

Domain: $\{2\}$

$(f-g)(x) = \sqrt{x-2} - \sqrt{2-x}$

Domain: $\{2\}$

$(fg)(x) = \sqrt{x-2} \cdot \sqrt{2-x} = \sqrt{-x^2+4x-4}$

Domain: $\{2\}$

$\left(\dfrac{f}{g}\right)(x) = \dfrac{\sqrt{x-2}}{\sqrt{2-x}}$

Domain: $\varnothing$

49. $f(x) = 2x;\ g(x) = x + 7$

a. $(f \circ g)(x) = 2(x+7) = 2x + 14$

b. $(g \circ f)(x) = 2x + 7$

c. $(f \circ g)(2) = 2(2) + 14 = 18$

51. $f(x) = x + 4$; $g(x) = 2x + 1$

    a. $(f \circ g)(x) = (2x + 1) + 4 = 2x + 5$

    b. $(g \circ f)(x) = 2(x + 4) + 1 = 2x + 9$

    c. $(f \circ g)(2) = 2(2) + 5 = 9$

53. $f(x) = 4x - 3$; $g(x) = 5x^2 - 2$

    a. $(f \circ g)(x) = 4(5x^2 - 2) - 3$

                  $= 20x^2 - 11$

    b. $(g \circ f)(x) = 5(4x - 3)^2 - 2$

                  $= 5(16x^2 - 24x + 9) - 2$

                  $= 80x^2 - 120x + 43$

    c. $(f \circ g)(2) = 20(2)^2 - 11 = 69$

55. $f(x) = x^2 + 2$; $g(x) = x^2 - 2$

    a. $(f \circ g)(x) = (x^2 - 2)^2 + 2$

                  $= x^4 - 4x^2 + 4 + 2$

                  $= x^4 - 4x^2 + 6$

    b. $(g \circ f)(x) = (x^2 + 2)^2 - 2$

                  $= x^4 + 4x^2 + 4 - 2$

                  $= x^4 + 4x^2 + 2$

    c. $(f \circ g)(2) = 2^4 - 4(2)^2 + 6 = 6$

57. $f(x) = 4 - x$; $g(x) = 2x^2 + x + 5$

    a. $(f \circ g)(x) = 4 - \left(2x^2 + x + 5\right)$

                  $= 4 - 2x^2 - x - 5$

                  $= -2x^2 - x - 1$

    b. $(g \circ f)(x) = 2(4 - x)^2 + (4 - x) + 5$

                  $= 2(16 - 8x + x^2) + 4 - x + 5$

                  $= 32 - 16x + 2x^2 + 4 - x + 5$

                  $= 2x^2 - 17x + 41$

    c. $(f \circ g)(2) = -2(2)^2 - 2 - 1 = -11$

59. $f(x) = \sqrt{x}$; $g(x) = x - 1$

    a. $(f \circ g)(x) = \sqrt{x - 1}$

    b. $(g \circ f)(x) = \sqrt{x} - 1$

    c. $(f \circ g)(2) = \sqrt{2 - 1} = \sqrt{1} = 1$

61. $f(x) = 2x - 3$; $g(x) = \dfrac{x + 3}{2}$

    a. $(f \circ g)(x) = 2\left(\dfrac{x + 3}{2}\right) - 3$

                  $= x + 3 - 3$

                  $= x$

    b. $(g \circ f)(x) = \dfrac{(2x - 3) + 3}{2} = \dfrac{2x}{2} = x$

    c. $(f \circ g)(2) = 2$

63. $f(x) = \dfrac{1}{x}$; $g(x) = \dfrac{1}{x}$

    a. $(f \circ g)(x) = \dfrac{1}{\frac{1}{x}} = x$

    b. $(g \circ f)(x) = \dfrac{1}{\frac{1}{x}} = x$

    c. $(f \circ g)(2) = 2$

65. a. $(f \circ g)(x) = f\left(\dfrac{1}{x}\right) = \dfrac{2}{\dfrac{1}{x} + 3}, x \neq 0$

$= \dfrac{2(x)}{\left(\dfrac{1}{x} + 3\right)(x)}$

$= \dfrac{2x}{1 + 3x}$

b. We must exclude 0 because it is excluded from g.

We must exclude $-\dfrac{1}{3}$ because it causes the denominator of $f \circ g$ to be 0.

Domain: $\left(-\infty, -\dfrac{1}{3}\right) \cup \left(-\dfrac{1}{3}, 0\right) \cup (0, \infty)$.

67. a. $(f \circ g)(x) = f\left(\dfrac{4}{x}\right) = \dfrac{\dfrac{4}{x}}{\dfrac{4}{x} + 1}$

$= \dfrac{\left(\dfrac{4}{x}\right)(x)}{\left(\dfrac{4}{x} + 1\right)(x)}$

$= \dfrac{4}{4 + x}, x \neq -4$

b. We must exclude 0 because it is excluded from g.
We must exclude -4 because it causes the denominator of $f \circ g$ to be 0.
Domain: $(-\infty, -4) \cup (-4, 0) \cup (0, \infty)$.

69. a. $f \circ g(x) = f(x - 2) = \sqrt{x - 2}$

b. The expression under the radical in $f \circ g$ must not be negative.
$x - 2 \geq 0$
$\quad x \geq 2$
Domain: $[2, \infty)$.

71. a. $(f \circ g)(x) = f(\sqrt{1 - x})$

$= \left(\sqrt{1 - x}\right)^2 + 4$

$= 1 - x + 4$

$= 5 - x$

b. The domain of $f \circ g$ must exclude any values that are excluded from g.
$1 - x \geq 0$
$\quad -x \geq -1$
$\quad\quad x \leq 1$
Domain: $(-\infty, 1]$.

73. $f(x) = x^4$ $g(x) = 3x - 1$

75. $f(x) = \sqrt[3]{x}$ $g(x) = x^2 - 9$

77. $f(x) = |x|$ $g(x) = 2x - 5$

79. $f(x) = \dfrac{1}{x}$ $g(x) = 2x - 3$

81. $(f + g)(-3) = f(-3) + g(-3) = 4 + 1 = 5$

83. $(fg)(2) = f(2)g(2) = (-1)(1) = -1$

85.   The domain of $f + g$ is $[-4, 3]$.

87.   The graph of $f + g$

89. $(f \circ g)(-1) = f(g(-1)) = f(-3) = 1$

91. $(g \circ f)(0) = g(f(0)) = g(2) = -6$

93.
$$(f \circ g)(x) = 7$$
$$2(x^2 - 3x + 8) - 5 = 7$$
$$2x^2 - 6x + 16 - 5 = 7$$
$$2x^2 - 6x + 11 = 7$$
$$2x^2 - 6x + 4 = 0$$
$$x^2 - 3x + 2 = 0$$
$$(x - 1)(x - 2) = 0$$
$$x - 1 = 0 \quad \text{or} \quad x - 2 = 0$$
$$x = 1 \qquad\qquad x = 2$$

95.   Domain: $\{0, 1, 2, 3, 4, 5, 6, 7, 8\}$

97.   **a.** $(B - D)(x) = (26,208x + 3,869,910) - (17,964x + 2,300,198)$
$$= 26,208x + 3,869,910 - 17,964x - 2,300,198$$
$$= 8244x + 1,569,712$$

This function represents the net change in population from births and deaths.

     b. $(B - D)(x) = 8244x + 1,569,712$
$(B - D)(8) = 8244(8) + 1,569,712 = 1,635,664$

The U.S. population increased by 1,635,664 in 2003.

     c. $4,093,000 - 2,423,000 = 1,670,000$

The difference of the functions modeled this value reasonably well.

99. $f + g$ represents the total world population in year x.

101. $(f + g)(2000) \approx 6$ billion people.

103. $(R - C)(20,000)$
$= 65(20,000) - (600,000 + 45(20,000))$
$= -200,000$
The company lost \$200,000 since costs exceeded revenues.
$(R - C)(30,000)$
$= 65(30,000) - (600,000 + 45(30,000))$
$= 0$
The company broke even.

105. a. f gives the price of the computer after a \$400 discount. g gives the price of the computer after a 25% discount.

     b. $(f \circ g)(x) = 0.75x - 400$
This models the price of a computer after first a 25% discount and then a \$400 discount.

c. $(g \circ f)(x) = 0.75(x - 400)$

This models the price of a computer after first a \$400 discount and then a 25% discount.

d.   The function $f \circ g$ models the greater discount, since the 25% discount is taken on the regular price first.

113.

The per capita cost of Medicare is rising.

115.

$(f \circ g)(x) = \sqrt{2 - \sqrt{x}}$

The domain of g is $[0, \infty)$.

The expression under the radical in $f \circ g$ must not be negative.

$2 - \sqrt{x} \geq 0$

$-\sqrt{x} \geq -2$

$\sqrt{x} \leq 2$

$x \leq 4$

Domain: $[0, 4]$

117. $(f \circ g)(x) = (f \circ g)(-x)$

$f(g(x)) = f(g(-x))$ since g is even

$f(g(x)) = f(g(x))$ so $f \circ g$ is even

119.

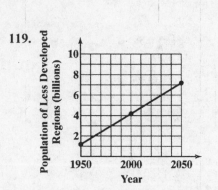

Section 1.8

Check Point Exercises

1. $f\big(g(x)\big) = 4\left(\dfrac{x+7}{4}\right) - 7 = x$

$g\big(f(x)\big) = \dfrac{(4x - 7) + 7}{4} = x$

$f\big(g(x)\big) = g\big(f(x)\big) = x$

2. $f(x) = 2x + 7$

Replace $f(x)$ with y:

$y = 2x + 7$

Interchange x and y:

$x = 2y + 7$

Solve for y:

$x = 2y + 7$

$x - 7 = 2y$

$\dfrac{x - 7}{2} = y$

Replace y with $f^{-1}(x)$:

$f^{-1}(x) = \dfrac{x - 7}{2}$

3. $f(x) = 4x^3 - 1$

Replace $f(x)$ with y:

$y = 4x^3 - 1$

Interchange x and y:

$x = 4y^3 - 1$

Solve for y:

$x = 4y^3 - 1$

$x + 1 = 4y^3$

$\dfrac{x + 1}{4} = y^3$

$\sqrt[3]{\dfrac{x + 1}{4}} = y$

Replace y with $f^{-1}(x)$:

$$f^{-1}(x) = \sqrt[3]{\frac{x+1}{4}}$$

Alternative form for answer:

$$f(x)^{-1} = \sqrt[3]{\frac{x+1}{4}} = \frac{\sqrt[3]{x+1}}{\sqrt[3]{4}}$$

$$= \frac{\sqrt[3]{x+1}}{\sqrt[3]{4}} \cdot \frac{\sqrt[3]{2}}{\sqrt[3]{2}} = \frac{\sqrt[3]{2x+2}}{\sqrt[3]{8}}$$

$$= \frac{\sqrt[3]{2x+2}}{2}$$

4. $f(x) = \dfrac{3}{x} - 1$

Replace $f(x)$ with y:

$$y = \frac{3}{x} - 1$$

Interchange x and y:

$$x = \frac{3}{y} - 1$$

Solve for y:

$$x = \frac{3}{y} - 1$$

$$xy = 3 - y$$

$$xy + y = 3$$

$$y(x+1) = 3$$

$$y = \frac{3}{x+1}$$

Replace y with $f^{-1}(x)$:

$$f^{-1}(x) = \frac{3}{x+1}$$

5. The graphs of (b) and (c) pass the horizontal line test and thus have an inverse.

6. Find points of f^{-1}.

$f(x)$	$f^{-1}(x)$
$(-2,-2)$	$(-2,-2)$
$(-1,0)$	$(0,-1)$
$(1,2)$	$(2,1)$

7. $f(x) = x^2 + 1$

Replace $f(x)$ with y:

$$y = x^2 + 1$$

Interchange x and y:

$$x = y^2 + 1$$

Solve for y:

$$x = y^2 + 1$$

$$x - 1 = y^2$$

$$\sqrt{x-1} = y$$

Replace y with $f^{-1}(x)$:

$$f^{-1}(x) = \sqrt{x-1}$$

Exercise Set 1.8

1. $f(x) = 4x; \, g(x) = \dfrac{x}{4}$

$$f(g(x)) = 4\left(\frac{x}{4}\right) = x$$

$$g(f(x)) = \frac{4x}{4} = x$$

f and g are inverses.

3. $f(x) = 3x + 8; \, g(x) = \dfrac{x-8}{3}$

$$f(g(x)) = 3\left(\frac{x-8}{3}\right) + 8 = x - 8 + 8 = x$$

$$g(f(x)) = \frac{(3x+8)-8}{3} = \frac{3x}{3} = x$$

f and g are inverses.

5. $f(x) = 5x - 9; \ g(x) = \dfrac{x+5}{9}$

$f(g(x)) = 5\left(\dfrac{x+5}{9}\right) - 9$

$\qquad = \dfrac{5x+25}{9} - 9$

$\qquad = \dfrac{5x-56}{9}$

$g(f(x)) = \dfrac{5x-9+5}{9} = \dfrac{5x-4}{9}$

f and *g* are not inverses.

7. $f(x) = \dfrac{3}{x-4}; g(x) = \dfrac{3}{x} + 4$

$f(g(x)) = \dfrac{3}{\frac{3}{x}+4-4} = \dfrac{3}{\frac{3}{x}} = x$

$g(f(x)) = \dfrac{3}{\frac{3}{x-4}} + 4$

$\qquad = 3 \cdot \left(\dfrac{x-4}{3}\right) + 4$

$\qquad = x - 4 + 4$

$\qquad = x$

f and *g* are inverses.

9. $f(x) = -x; g(x) = -x$

$f(g(x)) = -(-x) = x$

$g(f(x)) = -(-x) = x$

f and *g* are inverses.

11. a. $\quad f(x) = x + 3$

$\qquad y = x + 3$

$\qquad x = y + 3$

$\qquad y = x - 3$

$\quad f^{-1}(x) = x - 3$

b. $\quad f(f^{-1}(x)) = x - 3 + 3 = x$

$\qquad f^{-1}(f(x)) = x + 3 - 3 = x$

13. a. $\quad f(x) = 2x$

$\qquad y = 2x$

$\qquad x = 2y$

$\qquad y = \dfrac{x}{2}$

$\quad f^{-1}(x) = \dfrac{x}{2}$

b. $\quad f(f^{-1}(x)) = 2\left(\dfrac{x}{2}\right) = x$

$\qquad f^{-1}(f(x)) = \dfrac{2x}{2} = x$

15. a. $\quad f(x) = 2x + 3$

$\qquad y = 2x + 3$

$\qquad x = 2y + 3$

$\qquad x - 3 = 2y$

$\qquad y = \dfrac{x-3}{2}$

$\quad f^{-1}(x) = \dfrac{x-3}{2}$

b. $\quad f(f^{-1}(x)) = 2\left(\dfrac{x-3}{2}\right) + 3$

$\qquad = x - 3 + 3$

$\qquad = x$

$\quad f^{-1}(f(x)) = \dfrac{2x+3-3}{2} = \dfrac{2x}{2} = x$

17. a.

$\qquad f(x) = x^3 + 2$

$\qquad y = x^3 + 2$

$\qquad x = y^3 + 2$

$\qquad x - 2 = y^3$

$\qquad y = \sqrt[3]{x-2}$

$\quad f^{-1}(x) = \sqrt[3]{x-2}$

b. $\quad f(f^{-1}(x)) = \left(\sqrt[3]{x-2}\right)^3 + 2$

$\qquad = x - 2 + 2$

$\qquad = x$

$\quad f^{-1}(f(x)) = \sqrt[3]{x^3+2-2} = \sqrt[3]{x^3} = x$

19. a.

$$f(x) = (x+2)^3$$
$$y = (x+2)^3$$
$$x = (y+2)^3$$
$$\sqrt[3]{x} = y+2$$
$$y = \sqrt[3]{x} - 2$$
$$f^{-1}(x) = \sqrt[3]{x} - 2$$

b.

$$f(f^{-1}(x)) = \left(\sqrt[3]{x} - 2 + 2\right)^3 = \left(\sqrt[3]{x}\right)^3 = x$$
$$f^{-1}(f(x)) = \sqrt[3]{(x+2)^3} - 2$$
$$= x + 2 - 2$$
$$= x$$

21. a.

$$f(x) = \frac{1}{x}$$
$$y = \frac{1}{x}$$
$$x = \frac{1}{y}$$
$$xy = 1$$
$$y = \frac{1}{x}$$
$$f^{-1}(x) = \frac{1}{x}$$

b.

$$f(f^{-1}(x)) = \frac{1}{\frac{1}{x}} = x$$
$$f^{-1}(f(x)) = \frac{1}{\frac{1}{x}} = x$$

23. a.

$$f(x) = \sqrt{x}$$
$$y = \sqrt{x}$$
$$x = \sqrt{y}$$
$$y = x^2$$
$$f^{-1}(x) = x^2, x \geq 0$$

b.

$$f(f^{-1}(x)) = \sqrt{x^2} = |x| = x \text{ for } x \geq 0.$$
$$f^{-1}(f(x)) = (\sqrt{x})^2 = x$$

25. a.

$$f(x) = \frac{7}{x} - 3$$
$$y = \frac{7}{x} - 3$$
$$x = \frac{7}{y} - 3$$
$$xy = 7 - 3y$$
$$xy + 3y = 7$$
$$y(x+3) = 7$$
$$y = \frac{7}{x+3}$$
$$f^{-1}(x) = \frac{7}{x+3}$$

b.

$$f\left(f^{-1}(x)\right) = \frac{7}{\frac{7}{x+3}} - 3 = x$$
$$f^{-1}\left(f(x)\right) = \frac{7}{\frac{7}{x} - 3 + 3} = x$$

27. a.

$$f\left(x\right) = \frac{2x+1}{x-3}$$
$$y = \frac{2x+1}{x-3}$$
$$x = \frac{2y+1}{y-3}$$
$$x(y-3) = 2y+1$$
$$xy - 3x = 2y+1$$
$$xy - 2y = 3x+1$$
$$y(x-2) = 3x+1$$
$$y = \frac{3x+1}{x-2}$$
$$f^{-1}\left(x\right) = \frac{3x+1}{x-2}$$

b. $f(f^{-1}(x)) = \dfrac{2\left(\dfrac{3x+1}{x-2}\right)+1}{\dfrac{3x+1}{x-2}-3}$

$= \dfrac{2(3x+1)+x-2}{3x+1-3(x-2)} = \dfrac{6x+2+x-2}{3x+1-3x+6}$

$= \dfrac{7x}{7} = x$

$f^{-1}(f(x)) = \dfrac{3\left(\dfrac{2x+1}{x-3}\right)+1}{\dfrac{2x+1}{x-3}-2}$

$= \dfrac{3(2x+1)+x-3}{2x+1-2(x-3)}$

$= \dfrac{6x+3+x-3}{2x+1-2x+6} = \dfrac{7x}{7} = x$

29. The function fails the horizontal line test, so it does not have an inverse function.

31. The function fails the horizontal line test, so it does not have an inverse function.

33. The function passes the horizontal line test, so it does have an inverse function.

35.

37.

39. a. $f(x) = 2x - 1$

$y = 2x - 1$

$x = 2y - 1$

$x + 1 = 2y$

$\dfrac{x+1}{2} = y$

$f^{-1}(x) = \dfrac{x+1}{2}$

b.

c. Domain of f : $(-\infty, \infty)$

Range of f : $(-\infty, \infty)$

Domain of f^{-1} : $(-\infty, \infty)$

Range of f^{-1} : $(-\infty, \infty)$

41. a. $f(x) = x^2 - 4$

$y = x^2 - 4$

$x = y^2 - 4$

$x + 4 = y^2$

$\sqrt{x+4} = y$

$f^{-1}(x) = \sqrt{x+4}$

b.

c. Domain of f : $[0, \infty)$

Range of f : $[-4, \infty)$

Domain of f^{-1} : $[-4, \infty)$

Range of f^{-1} : $[0, \infty)$

43. a. $f(x) = (x-1)^2$

$$y = (x-1)^2$$
$$x = (y-1)^2$$
$$-\sqrt{x} = y-1$$
$$-\sqrt{x}+1 = y$$
$$f^{-1}(x) = 1-\sqrt{x}$$

b.

c. Domain of f: $(-\infty, 1]$
Range of f: $[0, \infty)$
Domain of f^{-1}: $[0, \infty)$
Range of f^{-1}: $(-\infty, 1]$

45. a. $f(x) = x^3 - 1$

$$y = x^3 - 1$$
$$x = y^3 - 1$$
$$x + 1 = y^3$$
$$\sqrt[3]{x+1} = y$$
$$f^{-1}(x) = \sqrt[3]{x+1}$$

b.

c. Domain of f: $(-\infty, \infty)$
Range of f: $(-\infty, \infty)$
Domain of f^{-1}: $(-\infty, \infty)$
Range of f^{-1}: $(-\infty, \infty)$

47. a. $f(x) = (x+2)^3$

$$y = (x+2)^3$$
$$x = (y+2)^3$$
$$\sqrt[3]{x} = y+2$$
$$\sqrt[3]{x} - 2 = y$$
$$f^{-1}(x) = \sqrt[3]{x} - 2$$

b.

c. Domain of f: $(-\infty, \infty)$
Range of f: $(-\infty, \infty)$
Domain of f^{-1}: $(-\infty, \infty)$
Range of f^{-1}: $(-\infty, \infty)$

49. a. $f(x) = \sqrt{x-1}$

$$y = \sqrt{x-1}$$
$$x = \sqrt{y-1}$$
$$x^2 = y-1$$
$$x^2 + 1 = y$$
$$f^{-1}(x) = x^2 + 1$$

b.

c. Domain of f: $[1, \infty)$
Range of f: $[0, \infty)$
Domain of f^{-1}: $[0, \infty)$
Range of f^{-1}: $[1, \infty)$

51. **a.** $f(x) = \sqrt[3]{x} + 1$

$$y = \sqrt[3]{x} + 1$$

$$x = \sqrt[3]{y} + 1$$

$$x - 1 = \sqrt[3]{y}$$

$$(x-1)^3 = y$$

$$f^{-1}(x) = (x-1)^3$$

b.

c.   Domain of f: $(-\infty, \infty)$

Range of f: $(-\infty, \infty)$

Domain of f^{-1}: $(-\infty, \infty)$

Range of f^{-1}: $(-\infty, \infty)$

53. $f(g(1)) = f(1) = 5$

55. $(g \circ f)(-1) = g(f(-1)) = g(1) = 1$

57. $f^{-1}(g(10)) = f^{-1}(-1) = 2$, since $f(2) = -1$.

59. $(f \circ g)(0) = f(g(0))$

$$= f(4 \cdot 0 - 1)$$

$$= f(-1) = 2(-1) - 5 = -7$$

61.   Let $f^{-1}(1) = x$. Then

$$f(x) = 1$$

$$2x - 5 = 1$$

$$2x = 6$$

$$x = 3$$

Thus, $f^{-1}(1) = 3$

63. $g(f[h(1)]) = g(f[1^2 + 1 + 2])$

$$= g(f(4))$$

$$= g(2 \cdot 4 - 5)$$

$$= g(3)$$

$$= 4 \cdot 3 - 1 = 11$$

65. **a.**   {(Zambia, −7.3), (Colombia, −4.5), (Poland, −2.8), (Italy, −2.8), (United States, −1.9)}

b.   {(−7.3, Zambia), (−4.5, Colombia), (−2.8, Poland), (−2.8, Italy), (−1.9, United States)} This relation is not a function because −2.8 corresponds to two elements in the range.

67. **a.**   It passes the horizontal line test and is one-to-one.

b. $f^{-1}(0.25) = 15$ If there are 15 people in the room, the probability that 2 of them have the same birthday is 0.25.
$f^{-1}(0.5) = 21$ If there are 21 people in the room, the probability that 2 of them have the same birthday is 0.5.
$f^{-1}(0.7) = 30$ If there are 30 people in the room, the probability that 2 of them have the same birthday is 0.7.

69.

$$f(g(x)) = \frac{9}{5}\left[\frac{5}{9}(x-32)\right] + 32$$

$$= x - 32 + 32$$

$$= x$$

f and g are inverses.

77.

one-to-one

79.

not one-to-one

81.

not one-to-one

83.

not one-to-one

85.

f and g are inverses

87. a. False. The inverse is $\{(4,1), (7,2)\}$.

   b. False. $f(x) = 5$ is a horizontal line, so it does not pass the horizontal line test.

   c. False. $f^{-1}(x) = \dfrac{x}{3}$.

   d. True. The domain of f is the range of f^{-1} and the range of f is the domain of f^{-1}.

   (d) is true.

89.
$$f(x) = \frac{3x-2}{5x-3}$$
$$y = \frac{3x-2}{5x-3}$$
$$x = \frac{3y-2}{5y-3}$$
$$x(5y-3) = 3y-2$$
$$5xy - 3x = 3y - 2$$
$$5xy - 3y = 3x - 2$$
$$y(5x-3) = 3x - 2$$
$$y = \frac{3x-2}{5x-3}$$
$$f^{-1}(x) = \frac{3x-2}{5x-3}$$

Note: An alternative approach is to show that $(f \circ f)(x) = x$.

91.
$$8 + f^{-1}(x-1) = 10$$
$$f^{-1}(x-1) = 2$$
$$f(2) = x-1$$
$$6 = x - 1$$
$$7 = x$$
$$x = 7$$

Section 1.9

Check Point Exercises

1.
$$d = \sqrt{(x_2 - x_1)^2 + (y_2 - y_1)^2}$$
$$d = \sqrt{(1-(-4))^2 + (-3-9)^2}$$
$$= \sqrt{(5)^2 + (-12)^2}$$
$$= \sqrt{25 + 144}$$
$$= \sqrt{169}$$
$$= 13$$

2. $\left(\dfrac{1+7}{2}, \dfrac{2+(-3)}{2}\right) = \left(\dfrac{8}{2}, \dfrac{-1}{2}\right) = \left(4, -\dfrac{1}{2}\right)$

3. $h = 0,\ k = 0,\ r = 4$;
$$(x-0)^2 + (y-0)^2 = 4^2$$
$$x^2 + y^2 = 16$$

4. $h = 5,\ k = -6,\ r = 10$;
$$(x-5)^2 + [y-(-6)]^2 = 10^2$$
$$(x-5)^2 + (y+6)^2 = 100$$

5. a. $(x+3)^2 + (y-1)^2 = 4$
$$[x-(-3)]^2 + (y-1)^2 = 2^2$$
So in the standard form of the circle's equation $(x-h)^2 + (y-k)^2 = r^2$, we have $h = -3,\ k = 1,\ r = 2$.
center: $(h, k) = (-3, 1)$
radius: $r = 2$

b.

$$(x + 3)^2 + (y - 1)^2 = 4$$

c. Domain: $[-5, -1]$

Range: $[-1, 3]$

6.
$$x^2 + y^2 + 4x - 4y - 1 = 0$$
$$x^2 + y^2 + 4x - 4y - 1 = 0$$
$$\left(x^2 + 4x \quad\right) + \left(y^2 - 4y \quad\right) = 0$$
$$\left(x^2 + 4x + 4\right) + \left(y^2 + 4y + 4\right) = 1 + 4 + 4$$
$$(x + 2)^2 + (y - 2)^2 = 9$$
$$[x - (-x)]^2 + (y - 2)^2 = 3^2$$

So in the standard form of the circle's equation $(x - h)^2 + (y - k)^2 = r^2$, we have $h = -2, k = 2, r = 3$.

$$x^2 + y^2 + 4x - 4y - 1 = 0$$

Exercise Set 1.9

1. $d = \sqrt{(14 - 2)^2 + (8 - 3)^2}$

$= \sqrt{12^2 + 5^2}$

$= \sqrt{144 + 25}$

$= \sqrt{169}$

$= 13$

3. $d = \sqrt{(-6 - 4)^2 + (3 - (-1))^2}$

$= \sqrt{(-10)^2 + (4)^2}$

$= \sqrt{100 + 16}$

$= \sqrt{116}$

$= 2\sqrt{29}$

≈ 10.77

5. $d = \sqrt{(-3 - 0)^2 + (4 - 0)^2}$

$= \sqrt{3^2 + 4^2}$

$= \sqrt{9 + 16}$

$= \sqrt{25}$

$= 5$

7. $d = \sqrt{[3 - (-2)]^2 + [-4 - (-6)]^2}$

$= \sqrt{5^2 + 2^2}$

$= \sqrt{25 + 4}$

$= \sqrt{29}$

≈ 5.39

9. $d = \sqrt{(4 - 0)^2 + [1 - (-3)]^2}$

$= \sqrt{4^2 + 4^2}$

$= \sqrt{16 + 16}$

$= \sqrt{32}$

$= 4\sqrt{2}$

≈ 5.66

11. $d = \sqrt{(-.5 - 3.5)^2 + (6.2 - 8.2)^2}$

$= \sqrt{(-4)^2 + (-2)^2}$

$= \sqrt{16 + 4}$

$= \sqrt{20}$

$= 2\sqrt{5}$

≈ 4.47

13. $d = \sqrt{(\sqrt{5} - 0)^2 + [0 - (-\sqrt{3})]^2}$

$= \sqrt{(\sqrt{5})^2 + (\sqrt{3})^2}$

$= \sqrt{5 + 3}$

$= \sqrt{8}$

$= 2\sqrt{2}$

≈ 2.83

15. $d = \sqrt{(-\sqrt{3} - 3\sqrt{3})^2 + (4\sqrt{5} - \sqrt{5})^2}$

$\quad = \sqrt{(-4\sqrt{3})^2 + (3\sqrt{5})^2}$

$\quad = \sqrt{16(3) + 9(5)}$

$\quad = \sqrt{48 + 45}$

$\quad = \sqrt{93}$

$\quad \approx 9.64$

17. $d = \sqrt{\left(\dfrac{1}{3} - \dfrac{7}{3}\right)^2 + \left(\dfrac{6}{5} - \dfrac{1}{5}\right)^2}$

$\quad = \sqrt{(-2)^2 + 1^2}$

$\quad = \sqrt{4 + 1}$

$\quad = \sqrt{5}$

$\quad \approx 2.24$

19. $\left(\dfrac{6+2}{2}, \dfrac{8+4}{2}\right) = \left(\dfrac{8}{2}, \dfrac{12}{2}\right) = (4, 6)$

21. $\left(\dfrac{-2 + (-6)}{2}, \dfrac{-8 + (-2)}{2}\right)$

$\quad = \left(\dfrac{-8}{2}, \dfrac{-10}{2}\right) = (-4, -5)$

23. $\left(\dfrac{-3+6}{2}, \dfrac{-4 + (-8)}{2}\right)$

$\quad = \left(\dfrac{3}{2}, \dfrac{-12}{2}\right) = \left(\dfrac{3}{2}, -6\right)$

25. $\left(\dfrac{\dfrac{-7}{2} + \left(-\dfrac{5}{2}\right)}{2}, \dfrac{\dfrac{3}{2} + \left(-\dfrac{11}{2}\right)}{2}\right)$

$\quad = \left(\dfrac{\dfrac{-12}{2}}{2}, \dfrac{\dfrac{-8}{2}}{2}\right) = \left(-\dfrac{6}{2}, \dfrac{-4}{2}\right) = (-3, -2)$

27. $\left(\dfrac{8 + (-6)}{2}, \dfrac{3\sqrt{5} + 7\sqrt{5}}{2}\right)$

$\quad = \left(\dfrac{2}{2}, \dfrac{10\sqrt{5}}{2}\right) = \left(1, 5\sqrt{5}\right)$

29. $\left(\dfrac{\sqrt{18} + \sqrt{2}}{2}, \dfrac{-4+4}{2}\right)$

$\quad = \left(\dfrac{3\sqrt{2} + \sqrt{2}}{2}, \dfrac{0}{2}\right) = \left(\dfrac{4\sqrt{2}}{2}, 0\right) = (2\sqrt{2}, 0)$

31. $(x - 0)^2 + (y - 0)^2 = 7^2$

$\qquad\quad x^2 + y^2 = 49$

33. $(x - 3)^2 + (y - 2)^2 = 5^2$

$\quad (x - 3)^2 + (y - 2)^2 = 25$

35. $[x - (-1)]^2 + (y - 4)^2 = 2^2$

$\qquad (x + 1)^2 + (y - 4)^2 = 4$

37. $[x - (-3)]^2 + [y - (-1)]^2 = \left(\sqrt{3}\right)^2$

$\qquad\quad (x + 3)^2 + (y + 1)^2 = 3$

39. $[x - (-4)]^2 + (y - 0)^2 = 10^2$

$\qquad\quad (x + 4)^2 + (y - 0)^2 = 100$

41. $\qquad\quad x^2 + y^2 = 16$

$\quad (x - 0)^2 + (y - 0)^2 = y^2$

$h = 0,\ k = 0,\ r = 4;$

center $= (0, 0);$ radius $= 4$

$x^2 + y^2 = 16$

Domain: $[-4, 4]$

Range: $[-4, 4]$

43. $(x-3)^2 + (y-1)^2 = 36$

$(x-3)^2 + (y-1)^2 = 6^2$

$h = 3,\ k = 1,\ r = 6;$

center $= (3, 1);$ radius $= 6$

$(x - 3)^2 + (y - 1)^2 = 36$

Domain: $[-3, 9]$

Range: $[-5, 7]$

45. $(x+3)^2 + (y-2)^2 = 4$

$[x-(-3)]^2 + (y-2)^2 = 2^2$

$h = -3,\ k = 2,\ r = 2$

center $= (-3, 2);$ radius $= 2$

$(x + 3)^2 + (y - 2)^2 = 4$

Domain: $[-5, -1]$

Range: $[0, 4]$

47. $(x+2)^2 + (y+2)^2 = 4$

$[x-(-2)]^2 + [y-(-2)]^2 = 2^2$

$h = -2,\ k = -2,\ r = 2$

center $= (-2, -2);$ radius $= 2$

$(x + 2)^2 + (y + 2)^2 = 4$

Domain: $[-4, 0]$

Range: $[-4, 0]$

49. $x^2 + y^2 + 6x + 2y + 6 = 0$

$(x^2 + 6x) + (y^2 + 2y) = -6$

$(x^2 + 6x + 9) + (y^2 + 2y + 1) = 9 + 1 - 6$

$(x+3)^2 + (y+1)^2 = 4$

$[x-(-3)]^2 + [9-(-1)]^2 = 2^2$

center $= (-3, -1);$ radius $= 2$

$x^2 + y^2 + 6x + 2y + 6 = 0$

51. $x^2 + y^2 - 10x - 6y - 30 = 0$

$(x^2 - 10x) + (y^2 - 6y) = 30$

$(x^2 - 10x + 25) + (y^2 - 6y + 9) = 25 + 9 + 30$

$(x-5)^2 + (y-3)^2 = 64$

$(x-5)^2 + (y-3)^2 = 8^2$

center $= (5, 3);$ radius $= 8$

$x^2 + y^2 - 10x - 6y - 30 = 0$

53.
$$x^2 + y^2 + 8x - 2y - 8 = 0$$
$$\left(x^2 + 8x\right) + \left(y^2 - 2y\right) = 8$$
$$\left(x^2 + 8x + 16\right) + \left(y^2 - 2y + 1\right) = 16 + 1 + 8$$
$$\left(x + 4\right)^2 + \left(y - 1\right)^2 = 25$$
$$\left[x - (-4)\right]^2 + \left(y - 1\right)^2 = 5^2$$
center = (–4, 1); radius = 5

$$x^2 + y^2 + 8x - 2y - 8 = 0$$

55.
$$x^2 - 2x + y^2 - 15 = 0$$
$$\left(x^2 - 2x\right) + y^2 = 15$$
$$\left(x^2 - 2x + 1\right) + \left(y - 0\right)^2 = 1 + 0 + 15$$
$$\left(x - 1\right)^2 + \left(y - 0\right)^2 = 16$$
$$\left(x - 1\right)^2 + \left(y - 0\right)^2 = 4^2$$
center = (1, 0); radius = 4

$$x^2 - 2x + y^2 - 15 = 0$$

57.
$$x^2 + y^2 - x + 2y + 1 = 0$$
$$x^2 - x \quad + y^2 + 2y \quad = -1$$
$$x^2 - x + \frac{1}{4} + y^2 + 2y + 1 = -1 + \frac{1}{4} + 1$$
$$\left(x - \frac{1}{2}\right)^2 + \left(y + 1\right)^2 = \frac{1}{4}$$
center = $\left(\frac{1}{2}, -1\right)$; radius = $\frac{1}{2}$

$$x^2 + y^2 - x + 2y + 1 = 0$$

59.
$$x^2 + y^2 + 3x - 2y - 1 = 0$$
$$x^2 + 3x \quad + y^2 - 2y \quad = 1$$
$$x^2 + 3x + \frac{9}{4} + y^2 - 2y + 1 = 1 + \frac{9}{4} + 1$$
$$\left(x + \frac{3}{2}\right)^2 + \left(y - 1\right)^2 = \frac{17}{4}$$
center = $\left(-\frac{3}{2}, 1\right)$; radius = $\frac{\sqrt{17}}{2}$

$$x^2 + y^2 + 3x - 2y - 1 = 0$$

61. a. Since the line segment passes through the center, the center is the midpoint of the segment.

$$M = \left(\frac{x_1 + x_2}{2}, \frac{y_1 + y_2}{2}\right)$$

$$= \left(\frac{3+7}{2}, \frac{9+11}{2}\right) = \left(\frac{10}{2}, \frac{20}{2}\right)$$

$$= (5, 10)$$

The center is $(5, 10)$.

b. The radius is the distance from the center to one of the points on the circle. Using the point $(3, 9)$, we get:

$$d = \sqrt{(5-3)^2 + (10-9)^2}$$

$$= \sqrt{2^2 + 1^2} = \sqrt{4+1}$$

$$= \sqrt{5}$$

The radius is $\sqrt{5}$ units.

c.
$$(x-5)^2 + (y-10)^2 = \left(\sqrt{5}\right)^2$$

$$(x-5)^2 + (y-10)^2 = 5$$

63. $x^2 + y^2 = 16$
$x - y = 4$

Intersection points: $(0, -4)$ and $(4, 0)$

Check $(0, -4)$:

$$0^2 + (-4)^2 = 16 \qquad 0 - (-4) = 4$$
$$16 = 16 \text{ true} \qquad\quad 4 = 4 \text{ true}$$

Check $(4, 0)$:

$$4^2 + 0^2 = 16 \qquad 4 - 0 = 4$$
$$16 = 16 \text{ true} \qquad 4 = 4 \text{ true}$$

The solution set is $\{(0, -4), (4, 0)\}$.

65. $(x-2)^2 + (y+3)^2 = 4$
$y = x - 3$

Intersection points: $(0, -3)$ and $(2, -1)$

Check $(0, -3)$:

$$(0-2)^2 + (-3+3)^2 = 9 \qquad -3 = 0 - 3$$
$$(-2)^2 + 0^2 = 4 \qquad\qquad -3 = -3 \text{ true}$$
$$4 = 4$$
$$\text{true}$$

Check $(2, -1)$:

$$(2-2)^2 + (-1+3)^2 = 4 \qquad -1 = 2 - 3$$
$$0^2 + 2^2 = 4 \qquad\qquad\quad -1 = -1 \text{ true}$$
$$4 = 4$$
$$\text{true}$$

The solution set is $\{(0, -3), (2, -1)\}$.

67.
$$d = \sqrt{[65 - (-115)]^2 + (70 - 170)^2}$$

$$d = \sqrt{(65 + 115)^2 + (-100)^2}$$

$$d = \sqrt{180^2 + 10000}$$

$$d = \sqrt{32400 + 10000}$$

$$d = \sqrt{42400}$$

$$d = 205.9 \text{ miles}$$

$$\frac{205.9 \text{ miles}}{400} = 0.5 \text{ hours or } 30 \text{ minutes}$$

69. If we place L.A. at the origin, then we want the equation of a circle with center at $(-2.4, -2.7)$ and radius 30.

$$(x - (-2.4))^2 + (y - (-2.7))^2 = 30^2$$

$$(x + 2.4)^2 + (y + 2.7)^2 = 900$$

77.

79.

81. The distance for A to B:
$$\overline{AB} = \sqrt{(3-1)^2 + [3+d-(1+d)]^2}$$
$$= \sqrt{2^2 + 2^2}$$
$$= \sqrt{4+4}$$
$$= \sqrt{8}$$
$$= 2\sqrt{2}$$

The distance from B to C:
$$\overline{BC} = \sqrt{(6-3)^2 + [3+d-(6+d)]^2}$$
$$= \sqrt{3^2 + (-3)^2}$$
$$= \sqrt{9+9}$$
$$= \sqrt{18}$$
$$= 3\sqrt{2}$$

The distance for A to C:
$$\overline{AC} = \sqrt{(6-1)^2 + [6+d-(1+d)]^2}$$
$$= \sqrt{5^2 + 5^2}$$
$$= \sqrt{25+25}$$
$$= \sqrt{50}$$
$$= 5\sqrt{2}$$
$$\overline{AB} + \overline{BC} = \overline{AC}$$
$$2\sqrt{2} + 3\sqrt{2} = 5\sqrt{2}$$
$$5\sqrt{2} = 5\sqrt{2}$$

83. Both circles have center (2, –3). The smaller circle has radius 5 and the larger circle has radius 6. The smaller circle is inside of the larger circle. The area between them is given by
$$\pi(6)^2 - \pi(5)^2 = 36\pi - 25\pi$$
$$= 11\pi$$
$$\approx 34.56 \text{ square units.}$$

Section 1.10

Check Point Exercises

1. **a.** $f(x) = 15 + 0.08x$

    b. $g(x) = 3 + 0.12x$

    c. $15 + 0.08x = 3 + 0.12x$
    $12 = 0.04x$
    $300 = x$
    The plans cost the same for 300 minutes.

2. **a.** $N(x) = 8000 - 100(x - 100)$
    $= 8000 - 100x + 10000$
    $= 18,000 - 100x$

    b. $R(x) = (18,000 - 100x)x$
    $= -100x^2 + 18,000x$

3. $V(x) = (15 - 2x)(8 - 2x)x$
    $= (120 - 46x + 4x^2)x$
    $= 4x^3 - 46x^2 + 120x$
    Since x represents the inches to be cut off, $x > 0$.
    The smallest side is 8, so must cut less than 4
    off each side. The domain of V is $\{x \mid 0 < x < 4\}$
    or, in interval notation, $(0, 4)$.

4. $2l + 2w = 200$
    $2l = 200 - 2w$
    $l = 100 - w$
    Let x = width, then length = $100 - x$
    $A(x) = x(100 - x)$
    $= 100x - x^2$

5. $V = \pi r^2 h$
    $1000 = \pi r^2 h$
    $\dfrac{1000}{\pi r^2} = h$

    $A = 2\pi r^2 + 2\pi r h$
    $= 2\pi r^2 + 2\pi r \left(\dfrac{1000}{\pi r^2} \right)$
    $= 2\pi r^2 + \dfrac{2000}{r}$

6. $I(x) = 0.07x + 0.09(25,000 - x)$

7. $d = \sqrt{(x - 0)^2 + (y - 0)^2}$
    $= \sqrt{x^2 + y^2}$

    $y = x^3$
    $d = \sqrt{x^2 + \left(x^3 \right)^2}$
    $= \sqrt{x^2 + x^6}$

Exercise Set 1.10

1. **a.** $f(x) = 200 + 0.15x$

    b. $320 = 200 + 0.15x$
    $120 = 01.5x$
    $800 = x$
    800 miles

3. **a.** $M(x) = 239.4 - 0.3x$

    b. $180 = 239.4 - 0.3x$
    $0.3x = 59.4$
    $x = 198$
    198 years after 1954, in 2152,
    someone will run a 3 minute mile.

5. **a.** $f(x) = 1.25x$

    b. $g(x) = 21 + 0.5x$

    c. $1.25x = 21 + 0.5x$
    $0.75x = 21$
    $x = 28$
    $f(28) = 1.25(28) = 35$
    $g(28) = 21 + 0.5(28) = 35$
    If a person crosses the bridge 28 times
    the cost will be $35 for both options

7. **a.** $f(x) = 100 + 0.8x$

    b. $g(x) = 40 + 0.9x$

    c. $100 + 0.8x = 40 + 0.9x$
    $60 = 0.1x$
    $600 = x$
    For $600 worth of merchandise,
    your cost is $580 for both plans

9. **a.** $N(x) = 30,000 - 500(x - 20)$
$$= 30,000 - 500x + 10000$$
$$= 40,000 - 500x$$

   b. $R(x) = (40,000 - 500x)x$
$$= -500x^2 + 40,000$$

11. **a.** $N(x) = 9000 + 50(150 - x)$
$$= 9000 - 50x + 7500$$
$$= 16500 - 50x$$

   b. $R(x) = (16500 - 50x)x$
$$= -50x^2 + 16500x$$

13. **a.** $Y(x) = 320 - 4(x - 50)$
$$= 320 - 4x + 200$$
$$= 520 - 4x$$

   b. $T(x) = (520 - 4x)x$
$$= -4x^2 + 520x$$

15. **a.** $V(x) = (24 - 2x)(24 - 2x)x$
$$= (576 - 96x + 4x^2)x$$
$$= 4x^3 - 96x^2 + 576x$$

   b. $V(2) = 4(2)^3 - 96(2)^2 + 576(2) = 800$ If 2-inch squares are cut off each corner, the volume will be 800 square inches.

$V(3) = 4(3)^3 - 96(3)^2 + 576(3) = 972$ If 3-inch squares are cut off each corner, the volume will be 972 square inches.

$V(4) = 4(4)^3 - 96(4)^2 + 576(4) = 1024$ If 4-inch squares are cut off each corner, the volume will be 1024 square inches.

$V(5) = 4(5)^3 - 96(5)^2 + 576(5) = 980$ If 5-inch squares are cut off each corner, the volume will be 980 square inches.

$V(6) = 4(6)^3 - 96(6)^2 + 576(6) = 864$ If 6-inch squares are cut off each corner, the volume will be 864 square inches.

   c. If x is the inches to be cut off, $x > 0$. Since each side is 24, you must cut less than 12 inches off each end.
$0 < x < 12$

17. $A(x) = x(20 - 2x)$
$$= -2x^2 + 20x$$

19. $P(x) = x(66 - x)$
$$= -x^2 + 66x$$

21. $A(x) = x(400 - x)$
$$= -x^2 + 400x$$

23. $2w + l = 800$
$$l = 800 - 2w$$
Let $x = w$
$$A(x) = x(800 - 2x)$$
$$= -2x^2 + 800x$$

25. $2x + 3y = 1000$
$$3y = 1000 - 2x$$
$$y = \frac{1000 - 2x}{3}$$
$$A(x) = x\left(\frac{1000 - 2x}{3}\right)$$
$$= \frac{x(10000 - 2x)}{3}$$

27. $2x =$ distance around 2 straight sides
  $\pi 2r =$ distance around 2 curved sides

$$2x + 2\pi r = 440$$
$$2x = 440 - 2\pi r$$
$$x = 220 - \pi r$$

$$A(x) = (220 - \pi r)r + \pi r^2$$
$$= 220r - \pi r^2 + \pi r^2$$
$$= 220r$$

29. $xy = 4000$
$$y = \frac{4000}{x}$$

$$C(x) = \left[2x + 2\left(\frac{4000}{x}\right)\right]175 + 125x$$
$$= 350x + \frac{1,400,000}{x} + 125x$$
$$= 4750x + \frac{1,400,000}{x}$$

31.
$$10 = x^2 y$$
$$\frac{10}{x^2} = y$$

$$A(x) = x^2 + 4\left(x \cdot \frac{10}{x^2}\right)$$
$$= x^2 + \frac{40}{x}$$

33.
$$300 = y + 4x$$
$$300 - 4x = y$$

$$A(x) = x^2(300 - 4x)$$
$$= -4x^3 + 300x^2$$

35. a. Let x = amount invested at 15%
$50000 - x$ = amount invested at 7%
$$I(x) = 0.15x + 0.07(50000 - x)$$

   b.
$$6000 = 0.15x + 0.07x(50000 - x)$$
$$6000 = 0.15x + 3500 - 0.07x$$
$$2500 = 0.08x$$
$$31250 = x$$
$$50000 - 31250 = 18750$$
   Invest \$31,250 at 15% and \$18,750 at 7%.

37. Let x = amount invested at 12%
$8000 - x$ = amount invested at 5% loss
$$I(x) = 0.12x - 0.05(8000 - x)$$

39.
$$d = \sqrt{(x-0)^2 + (y-0)^2}$$
$$= \sqrt{x^2 + y^2}$$
$$= \sqrt{x^2 + \left(x^2 - 4\right)^2}$$
$$= \sqrt{x^2 + x^4 - 8x^2 + 16}$$
$$= \sqrt{x^4 - 7x^2 + 16}$$

41.
$$d = \sqrt{(x-1)^2 + y^2}$$
$$= \sqrt{x^2 - 2x + 1 + \left(\sqrt{x}\right)^2}$$
$$= \sqrt{x^2 - 2x + 1 + x}$$
$$= \sqrt{x^2 - x + 1}$$

43. a.
$$A(x) = 2xy$$
$$= 2x\sqrt{4 - x^2}$$

   b.
$$P(x) = 2(2x) + 2y$$
$$= 4x + 2\sqrt{4 - x^2}$$

45. 6-foot pole
$$c^2 = 6^2 + x^2$$
$$x = \sqrt{36 + x^2}$$
8-foot pole
$$c^2 = 8^2 + (10 - x)^2$$
$$c = \sqrt{64 + 100 - 20x + x^2}$$
$$c = \sqrt{x^2 - 20x + 164}$$
total length
$$f(x) = \sqrt{36 + x^2} + \sqrt{x^2 - 20x + 164}$$

47.
$$A(x) = \tfrac{1}{2}x(x-5) + \tfrac{1}{2}x(x+3)$$
$$\qquad\qquad + (x+2)\big[(x-5) + (x+3)\big]$$
$$A(x) = \tfrac{1}{2}x^2 - \tfrac{5}{2}x + \tfrac{1}{2}x^2 + \tfrac{3}{2}x + (x+2)[2x - 2]$$
$$A(x) = x^2 - x + 2x^2 + 2x - 4$$
$$A(x) = 3x^2 + x - 4$$

49.
$$V(x) = (x+5)(2x+1)(x+2) - (x+5)(3)(x)$$
$$V(x) = (x+5)(2x^2 + 5x + 2) - 3x(x+5)$$
$$V(x) = 2x^3 + 15x^2 + 27x + 10 - 3x^2 - 15x$$
$$V(x) = 2x^3 + 12x^2 + 12x + 10$$

63. Distance and time rowed:

$$d^2 = 2^2 + x^2$$
$$d = \sqrt{4 + x^2}$$
$$rt = d$$
$$2t = \sqrt{4 + x^2}$$
$$t = \frac{\sqrt{4 + x^2}}{2}$$

Distance and time walked:
$$d = 6 - x$$
$$rt = d$$
$$5t = 6 - x$$
$$t = \frac{6 - x}{5}$$

Total time:
$$T(x) = \frac{\sqrt{4 + x^2}}{2} + \frac{6 - x}{5}$$

65.
$$P = 2h + 2r + \frac{1}{2}(\pi 2r)$$
$$12 = 2h + 2r + \pi r$$
$$12 - 2r - \pi r = 2h$$
$$\frac{12 - 2r - \pi r}{2} = h$$

$$A = \left(\frac{12 - 2r - \pi r}{2}\right) 2r + \frac{1}{2}\left(\pi r^2\right)$$
$$= 12r - 2r^2 - \pi r^2 + \frac{1}{2}\pi r^2$$
$$= 12r - 2r^2 - \frac{1}{2}\pi r^2$$

Chapter 1 Review Exercises

1.

$$y = 2x - 2$$

$x = -3, y = -8$
$x = -2, y = -6$
$x = -1, y = -4$
$x = 0, y = -2$
$x = 1, y = 0$
$x = 2, y = 2$
$x = 3, y = 4$

2.

$$y = x^2 - 3$$

$x = -3, y = 6$
$x = -2, y = 1$
$x = -1, y = -2$
$x = 0, y = -3$
$x = 1, y = -2$
$x = 2, y = 1$
$x = 3, y = 6$

3.

$$y = x$$

$x = -3, y = -3$
$x = -2, y = -2$
$x = -1, y = -1$
$x = 0, y = 0$
$x = 1, y = 1$
$x = 2, y = 2$
$x = 3, y = 3$

4.

$$y = |x| - 2$$

$x = -3, y = 1$
$x = -2, y = 0$
$x = -1, y = -1$
$x = 0, y = -2$
$x = 1, y = -1$
$x = 2, y = 0$
$x = 3, y = 1$

5. A portion of Cartesian coordinate plane with minimum x-value equal to -20, maximum x-value equal to 40, x-scale equal to 10 and with minimum y-value equal to -5, maximum y-value equal to 5, and y-scale equal to 1.

6. x-intercept: -2; The graph intersects the x-axis at $(-2, 0)$.
y-intercept: 2; The graph intersects the y-axis at $(0, 2)$.

7. x-intercepts: 2, -2; The graph intersects the x-axis at $(-2, 0)$ and $(2, 0)$.
y-intercept: -4; The graph intercepts the y-axis at $(0, -4)$.

8. x-intercept: 5; The graph intersects the x-axis at $(5, 0)$.
y-intercept: None; The graph does not intersect the y-axis.

9. Point A is $(91, 125)$. This means that in 1991, 125,000 acres were used for cultivation

10. Opium cultivation was 150,000 acres in 1997.

11. Opium cultivation was at a minimum in 2001 when approximately 25,000 acres were used.

12. Opium cultivation was at a maximum in 2004 when approximately 300,000 acres were used.

13. Opium cultivation did not change between 1991 and 1992.

14. Opium cultivation increased at the greatest rate between 2001 and 2002. The increase in acres used for opium cultivation in this time period was approximately $180,000 - 25,000 = 155,000$ acres.

15. function
domain: $\{2, 3, 5\}$
range: $\{7\}$

16. function
domain: $\{1, 2, 13\}$
range: $\{10, 500, \pi\}$

17. not a function
domain: $\{12, 14\}$
range: $\{13, 15, 19\}$

18. $2x + y = 8$
$\quad y = -2x + 8$
Since only one value of y can be obtained for each value of x, y is a function of x.

19. $3x^2 + y = 14$
$\quad y = -3x^2 + 14$
Since only one value of y can be obtained for each value of x, y is a function of x.

20. $2x + y^2 = 6$
$\quad y^2 = -2x + 6$
$\quad y = \pm\sqrt{-2x + 6}$
Since more than one value of y can be obtained from some values of x, y is not a function of x.

21. $f(x) = 5 - 7x$

  a. $f(4) = 5 - 7(4) = -23$

  b. $f(x + 3) = 5 - 7(x + 3)$
$\qquad\qquad\quad = 5 - 7x - 21$
$\qquad\qquad\quad = -7x - 16$

  c. $f(-x) = 5 - 7(-x) = 5 + 7x$

22. $g(x) = 3x^2 - 5x + 2$

  a. $g(0) = 3(0)^2 - 5(0) + 2 = 2$

b. $g(-2) = 3(-2)^2 - 5(-2) + 2$
$$= 12 + 10 + 2$$
$$= 24$$

c. $g(x-1) = 3(x-1)^2 - 5(x-1) + 2$
$$= 3(x^2 - 2x + 1) - 5x + 5 + 2$$
$$= 3x^2 - 11x + 10$$

d. $g(-x) = 3(-x)^2 - 5(-x) + 2$
$$= 3x^2 + 5x + 2$$

23. a. $g(13) = \sqrt{13-4} = \sqrt{9} = 3$

b. $g(0) = 4 - 0 = 4$

c. $g(-3) = 4 - (-3) = 7$

24. a. $f(-2) = \dfrac{(-2)^2 - 1}{-2 - 1} = \dfrac{3}{-3} = -1$

b. $f(1) = 12$

c. $f(2) = \dfrac{2^2 - 1}{2 - 1} = \dfrac{3}{1} = 3$

25. The vertical line test shows that this is not the graph of a function.

26. The vertical line test shows that this is the graph of a function.

27. The vertical line test shows that this is the graph of a function.

28. The vertical line test shows that this is not the graph of a function.

29. The vertical line test shows that this is not the graph of a function.

30. The vertical line test shows that this is the graph of a function.

31. $\dfrac{8(x+h) - 11 - (8x - 11)}{h}$
$$= \dfrac{8x + 8h - 11 - 8x + 11}{h}$$
$$= \dfrac{8h}{8}$$
$$= 8$$

32. $\dfrac{-2(x+h)^2 + (x+h) + 10 - \left(-2x^2 + x + 10\right)}{h}$

$$= \dfrac{-2\left(x^2 + 2xh + h^2\right) + x + h + 10 + 2x^2 - x - 10}{h}$$

$$= \dfrac{-2x^2 - 4xh - 2h^2 + x + h + 10 + 2x^2 - x - 10}{h}$$

$$= \dfrac{-4xh - 2h^2 + h}{h}$$

$$= \dfrac{h\left(-4x - 2h + 1\right)}{h}$$

$$-4x - 2h + 1$$

33. a. domain: $[-3, 5)$

b. range: $[-5, 0]$

c. x-intercept: -3

d. y-intercept: -2

e. increasing: $(-2, 0)$ or $(3, 5)$
decreasing: $(-3, -2)$ or $(0, 3)$

f. $f(-2) = -3$ and $f(3) = -5$

34. a. domain: $(-\infty, \infty)$

b. range: $(-\infty, \infty)$

c. x-intercepts: -2 and 3

d. y-intercept: 3

e. increasing: $(-5, 0)$
decreasing: $(-\infty, -5)$ or $(0, \infty)$

f. $f(-2) = 0$ and $f(6) = -3$

35. a. domain: $(-\infty, \infty)$

b. range: $[-2, 2]$

c. x-intercept: 0

d. y-intercept: 0

e. increasing: $(-2, 2)$
constant: $(-\infty, -2)$ or $(2, \infty)$

f. $f(-9) = -2$ and $f(14) = 2$

36. a. 0, relative maximum −2

 b. −2, 3, relative minimum −3, −5

37. a. 0, relative maximum 3

 b. −5, relative minimum −6

38. $f(x) = x^3 - 5x$

$$f(-x) = (-x)^3 - 5(-x)$$
$$= -x^3 + 5x$$
$$= -f(x)$$

The function is odd. The function is symmetric with respect to the origin.

39. $f(x) = x^4 - 2x^2 + 1$

$$f(-x) = (-x)^4 - 2(-x)^2 + 1$$
$$= x^4 - 2x^2 + 1$$
$$= f(x)$$

The function is even. The function is symmetric with respect to the *y*-axis.

40. $f(x) = 2x\sqrt{1 - x^2}$

$$f(-x) = 2(-x)\sqrt{1 - (-x)^2}$$
$$= -2x\sqrt{1 - x^2}$$
$$= -f(x)$$

The function is odd. The function is symmetric with respect to the origin.

41. a. Yes, the eagle's height is a function of time since the graph passes the vertical line test.

 b. Decreasing: (3, 12)
 The eagle descended.

 c. Constant: (0, 3) or (12, 17)
 The eagle's height held steady during the first 3 seconds and the eagle was on the ground for 5 seconds.

 d. Increasing: (17, 30)
 The eagle was ascending.

42.

43. $m = \dfrac{1-2}{5-3} = \dfrac{-1}{2} = -\dfrac{1}{2}$; falls

44. $m = \dfrac{-4-(-2)}{-3-(-1)} = \dfrac{-2}{-2} = 1$; rises

45. $m = \dfrac{\frac{1}{4} - \frac{1}{4}}{6 - (-3)} = \dfrac{0}{9} = 0$; horizontal

46. $m = \dfrac{10-5}{-2-(-2)} = \dfrac{5}{0}$ undefined; vertical

47. point-slope form: $y - 2 = -6(x + 3)$
slope-intercept form: $y = -6x - 16$

48. $m = \dfrac{2-6}{-1-1} = \dfrac{-4}{-2} = 2$
point-slope form: $y - 6 = 2(x - 1)$
or $y - 2 = 2(x + 1)$
slope-intercept form: $y = 2x + 4$

49. $3x + y - 9 = 0$
$y = -3x + 9$
$m = -3$
point-slope form:
$y + 7 = -3(x - 4)$
slope-intercept form:
$y = -3x + 12 - 7$
$y = -3x + 5$

156

50. perpendicular to $y = \dfrac{1}{3}x + 4$

$m = -3$
point-slope form:
$y - 6 = -3(x + 3)$
slope-intercept form:
$y = -3x - 9 + 6$
$y = -3x - 3$

51. Write $6x - y - 4 = 0$ in slope intercept form.

$6x - y - 4 = 0$

$-y = -6x + 4$

$y = 6x - 4$

The slope of the perpendicular line is 6, thus the

slope of the desired line is $m = -\dfrac{1}{6}$.

$$y - y_1 = m(x - x_1)$$
$$y - (-1) = -\tfrac{1}{6}\left(x - (-12)\right)$$
$$y + 1 = -\tfrac{1}{6}(x + 12)$$
$$y + 1 = -\tfrac{1}{6}x - 2$$
$$6y + 6 = -x - 12$$
$$x + 6y + 18 = 0$$

52. slope: $\dfrac{2}{5}$; y-intercept: -1

$$y = \frac{2}{5}x - 1$$

53. slope: -4; y-intercept: 5

$$f(x) = -4x + 5$$

54. $2x + 3y + 6 = 0$

$$3y = -2x - 6$$

$$y = -\frac{2}{3}x - 2$$

slope: $-\dfrac{2}{3}$; y-intercept: -2

$$2x + 3y + 6 = 0$$

55. $2y - 8 = 0$

$$2y = 8$$

$$y = 4$$

slope: 0; y-intercept: 4

$$2y - 8 = 0$$

56. $2x - 5y - 10 = 0$

Find x-intercept:
$2x - 5(0) - 10 = 0$

$$2x - 10 = 0$$

$$2x = 10$$

$$x = 5$$

Find y-intercept:
$2(0) - 5y - 10 = 0$

$$-5y - 10 = 0$$

$$-5y = 10$$

$$y = -2$$

$$2x - 5y - 10 = 0$$

57.
$$2x - 10 = 0$$
$$2x = 10$$
$$x = 5$$

$2x - 10 = 0$

58. a. First, find the slope. $(1, 1.5)$
and $(3, 3.4)$.

$$m = \frac{3.4 - 1.5}{3 - 1} = \frac{1.9}{2} = 0.95$$

Next, use the slope and one of the points to write the point-slope equation of the line.
$$y - 1.5 = 0.95(x - 1) \text{ or } y - 3.4 = 0.95(x - 3)$$

b.
$$y - 1.5 = 0.95(x - 1)$$
$$y - 1.5 = 0.95x - 0.95$$
$$y = 0.95x - 0.55$$

c. Since 2009 is 2009-1999 = 10, let $x = 10$.
$$y = 0.95(10) + 0.55$$
$$= 9.5 + 0.55 = 10.05$$
$10.05 billion in revenue was earned from online gambling in 2009.

59. a. $(1999, 41315)$ and $(2001, 41227)$

$$m = \frac{41227 - 41315}{2001 - 1999} = \frac{-88}{2} = -44$$

The number of new AIDS diagnoses decreased at a rate of 44 each year from 1999 to 2001.

b. $(2001, 41227)$ and $(2003, 43045)$

$$m = \frac{43045 - 41227}{2003 - 2001} = \frac{1818}{2} = 909$$

The number of new AIDS diagnoses increased at a rate of 909 each year from 2001 to 2003.

c. $(1999, 41315)$ and $(2003, 43045)$

$$m = \frac{43045 - 41315}{2003 - 1999} = \frac{1730}{4} = 432.5$$

$$\frac{-44 + 909}{2} = \frac{865}{2} = 432.5$$

Yes, the slope equals the average of the two values.

60.
$$\frac{9^2 - 4(9) - [4^2 - 4 \cdot 5]}{9 - 5} = \frac{40}{4} = 10$$

61. a.
$$S(0) = -16(0)^2 + 64(0) + 80 = 80$$
$$S(2) = -16(2)^2 + 64(2) + 80 = 144$$

$$\frac{144 - 80}{2 - 0} = 32$$

b.
$$S(4) = -16(4)^2 + 64(4) + 80 = 80$$

$$\frac{80 - 144}{4 - 2} = -32$$

c. The ball is traveling up until 2 seconds, then it starts to come down.

62. $y = g(x)$

63. $y = g(x)$

64.

$y = g(x)$

65.

$y = g(x)$

66.

$y = g(x)$

72.

67.

73.

68.

74.

69.

75.

70.

76.

71.

77.

78.

79.

80.

81.

82.

83. domain: $(-\infty, \infty)$

84. The denominator is zero when $x = 7$. The domain is $(-\infty, 7) \cup (7, \infty)$.

85. The expressions under each radical must not be negative.
$$8 - 2x \geq 0$$
$$-2x \geq -8$$
$$x \leq 4$$
Domain: $(-\infty, 4]$.

86. The denominator is zero when $x = -7$ or $x = 3$.
Domain: $(-\infty, -7) \cup (-7, 3) \cup (3, \infty)$

87. The expressions under each radical must not be negative. The denominator is zero when $x = 5$.
$$x - 2 \geq 0$$
$$x \geq 2$$
Domain: $[2, 5) \cup (5, \infty)$

88. The expressions under each radical must not be negative.
$$x - 1 \geq 0 \quad \text{and} \quad x + 5 \geq 0$$
$$x \geq 1 \qquad\qquad x \geq -5$$
Domain: $[1, \infty)$

89. $f(x) = 3x - 1; g(x) = x - 5$
$(f + g)(x) = 4x - 6$
Domain: $(-\infty, \infty)$
$(f - g)(x) = (3x - 1) - (x - 5) = 2x + 4$
Domain: $(-\infty, \infty)$
$(fg)(x) = (3x - 1)(x - 5) = 3x^2 - 16x + 5$
Domain: $(-\infty, \infty)$
$$\left(\frac{f}{g}\right)(x) = \frac{3x - 1}{x - 5}$$
Domain: $(-\infty, 5) \cup (5, \infty)$

90. $f(x) = x^2 + x + 1; g(x) = x^2 - 1$
$(f + g)(x) = 2x^2 + x$
Domain: $(-\infty, \infty)$
$(f - g)(x) = (x^2 + x + 1) - (x^2 - 1) = x + 2$
Domain: $(-\infty, \infty)$
$(fg)(x) = (x^2 + x + 1)(x^2 - 1)$
$$= x^4 + x^3 - x - 1$$
$$\left(\frac{f}{g}\right)(x) = \frac{x^2 + x + 1}{x^2 - 1}$$
Domain: $(-\infty, -1) \cup (-1, 1) \cup (1, \infty)$

91. $f(x) = \sqrt{x+7}; g(x) = \sqrt{x-2}$

$(f+g)(x) = \sqrt{x+7} + \sqrt{x-2}$

Domain: $[2, \infty)$

$(f-g)(x) = \sqrt{x+7} - \sqrt{x-2}$

Domain: $[2, \infty)$

$(fg)(x) = \sqrt{x+7} \cdot \sqrt{x-2}$

$= \sqrt{x^2 + 5x - 14}$

Domain: $[2, \infty)$

$\left(\dfrac{f}{g}\right)(x) = \dfrac{\sqrt{x+7}}{\sqrt{x-2}}$

Domain: $(2, \infty)$

92. $f(x) = x^2 + 3; g(x) = 4x - 1$

a. $(f \circ g)(x) = (4x-1)^2 + 3$

$= 16x^2 - 8x + 4$

b. $(g \circ f)(x) = 4(x^2 + 3) - 1$

$= 4x^2 + 11$

c. $(f \circ g)(3) = 16(3)^2 - 8(3) + 4 = 124$

93. $f(x) = \sqrt{x}; \quad g(x) = x + 1$

a. $(f \circ g)(x) = \sqrt{x+1}$

b. $(g \circ f)(x) = \sqrt{x} + 1$

c. $(f \circ g)(3) = \sqrt{3+1} = \sqrt{4} = 2$

94.   a.

$(f \circ g)(x) = f\left(\dfrac{1}{x}\right)$

$= \dfrac{\dfrac{1}{x}+1}{\dfrac{1}{x}-2} = \dfrac{\left(\dfrac{1}{x}+1\right)x}{\left(\dfrac{1}{x}-2\right)x} = \dfrac{1+x}{1-2x}$

b. $x \neq 0 \qquad 1 - 2x \neq 0$

$x \neq \dfrac{1}{2}$

$(-\infty, 0) \cup \left(0, \dfrac{1}{2}\right) \cup \left(\dfrac{1}{2}, \infty\right)$

95.   a. $(f \circ g)(x) = f(x+3) = \sqrt{x+3-1} = \sqrt{x+2}$

b. $x + 2 \geq 0$

$x \geq -2$ $\qquad [-2, \infty)$

96. $f(x) = x^4 \qquad g(x) = x^2 + 2x - 1$

97. $f(x) = \sqrt[3]{x} \qquad g(x) = 7x + 4$

98. $f(x) = \dfrac{3}{5}x + \dfrac{1}{2}; g(x) = \dfrac{5}{3}x - 2$

$f(g(x)) = \dfrac{3}{5}\left(\dfrac{5}{3}x - 2\right) + \dfrac{1}{2}$

$= x - \dfrac{6}{5} + \dfrac{1}{2}$

$= x - \dfrac{7}{10}$

$g(f(x)) = \dfrac{5}{3}\left(\dfrac{3}{5}x + \dfrac{1}{2}\right) - 2$

$= x + \dfrac{5}{6} - 2$

$= x - \dfrac{7}{6}$

f and *g* are not inverses of each other.

99. $f(x) = 2 - 5x; g(x) = \dfrac{2-x}{5}$

$f(g(x)) = 2 - 5\left(\dfrac{2-x}{5}\right)$

$= 2 - (2-x)$

$= x$

$g(f(x)) = \dfrac{2-(2-5x)}{5} = \dfrac{5x}{5} = x$

f and *g* are inverses of each other.

100. a. $f(x) = 4x - 3$

$y = 4x - 3$

$x = 4y - 3$

$y = \dfrac{x+3}{4}$

$f^{-1}(x) = \dfrac{x+3}{4}$

b. $f(f^{-1}(x)) = 4\left(\dfrac{x+3}{4}\right) - 3$

$\qquad\qquad = x + 3 - 3$

$\qquad\qquad = x$

$f^{-1}(f(x)) = \dfrac{(4x-3)+3}{4} = \dfrac{4x}{4} = x$

101. a. $f(x) = 8x^3 + 1$

$\qquad y = 8x^3 + 1$

$\qquad x = 8y^3 + 1$

$\qquad x - 1 = 8y^3$

$\qquad \dfrac{x-1}{8} = y^3$

$\qquad \sqrt[3]{\dfrac{x-1}{8}} = y$

$\qquad \dfrac{\sqrt[3]{x-1}}{2} = y$

$\qquad f^{-1}(x) = \dfrac{\sqrt[3]{x-1}}{2}$

b. $f\left(f^{-1}(x)\right) = 8\left(\dfrac{\sqrt[3]{x-1}}{2}\right)^3 + 1$

$\qquad\qquad = 8\left(\dfrac{x-1}{8}\right) + 1$

$\qquad\qquad = x - 1 + 1$

$\qquad\qquad = x$

$f^{-1}\left(f(x)\right) = \dfrac{\sqrt[3]{\left(8x^3+1\right)-1}}{2}$

$\qquad\qquad = \dfrac{\sqrt[3]{8x^3}}{2}$

$\qquad\qquad = \dfrac{2x}{2}$

$\qquad\qquad = x$

102. a. $f(x) = \dfrac{2}{x} + 5$

$\qquad y = \dfrac{2}{x} + 5$

$\qquad x = \dfrac{2}{y} + 5$

$\qquad xy = 2 + 5y$

$\qquad xy - 5y = 2$

$\qquad y(x-5) = 2$

$\qquad y = \dfrac{2}{x-5}$

$\qquad f^{-1}(x) = \dfrac{2}{x-5}$

b. $f\left(f^{-1}(x)\right) = \dfrac{2}{\dfrac{2}{x-5}} + 5$

$\qquad\qquad = \dfrac{2(x-5)}{2} + 5$

$\qquad\qquad = x - 5 + 5$

$\qquad\qquad = x$

$f^{-1}\left(f(x)\right) = \dfrac{2}{\dfrac{2}{x} + 5 - 5}$

$\qquad\qquad = \dfrac{2}{\dfrac{2}{x}}$

$\qquad\qquad = \dfrac{2x}{2}$

$\qquad\qquad = x$

103. The inverse function exists.

104. The inverse function does not exist since it does not pass the horizontal line test.

105. The inverse function exists.

106. The inverse function does not exist since it does not pass the horizontal line test.

107.

108. $f(x) = 1 - x^2$

$$y = 1 - x^2$$
$$x = 1 - y^2$$
$$y^2 = 1 - x$$
$$y = \sqrt{1 - x}$$
$$f^{-1}(x) = \sqrt{1 - x}$$

109. $f(x) = \sqrt{x} + 1$

$$y = \sqrt{x} + 1$$
$$x = \sqrt{y} + 1$$
$$x - 1 = \sqrt{y}$$
$$(x-1)^2 = y$$
$$f^{-1}(x) = (x-1)^2, \quad x \ge 1$$

$f(x) = \sqrt{x} + 1$
$g(x) = (x-1)^2, x \ge 1$

110. $d = \sqrt{[3-(-2)]^2 + [9-(-3)]^2}$

$$= \sqrt{5^2 + 12^2}$$
$$= \sqrt{25 + 144}$$
$$= \sqrt{169}$$
$$= 13$$

111. $d = \sqrt{[-2-(-4)]^2 + (5-3)^2}$

$$= \sqrt{2^2 + 2^2}$$
$$= \sqrt{4 + 4}$$
$$= \sqrt{8}$$
$$= 2\sqrt{2}$$
$$\approx 2.83$$

112. $\left(\dfrac{2 + (-12)}{2}, \dfrac{6+4}{2} \right) = \left(\dfrac{-10}{2}, \dfrac{10}{2} \right) = (-5, 5)$

113. $\left(\dfrac{4 + (-15)}{2}, \dfrac{-6+2}{2} \right) = \left(\dfrac{-11}{2}, \dfrac{-4}{2} \right) = \left(\dfrac{-11}{2}, -2 \right)$

114. $x^2 + y^2 = 3^2$

$$x^2 + y^2 = 9$$

115. $(x - (-2))^2 + (y - 4)^2 = 6^2$

$$(x+2)^2 + (y-4)^2 = 36$$

116. center: (0, 0); radius: 1

$x^2 + y^2 = 1$
Domain: $[-1, 1]$
Range: $[-1, 1]$

117. center: (−2, 3); radius: 3

$(x + 2)^2 + (y - 3)^2 = 9$
Domain: $[-5, 1]$
Range: $[0, 6]$

118. $x^2 + y^2 - 4x + 2y - 4 = 0$

$x^2 - 4x \quad + y^2 + 2y \quad = 4$

$x^2 - 4x + 4 + y^2 + 2y + 1 = 4 + 4 + 1$

$(x-2)^2 + (y+1)^2 = 9$

center: $(2, -1)$; radius: 3

$x^2 + y^2 - 4x + 2y - 4 = 0$

Domain: $[-1, 5]$

Range: $[-4, 2]$

119. a. $W(x) = 567 + 15x$

b. $702 = 567 + 15x$

$135 = 15x$

$9 = x$

9 years after 2000, in 2009, the average weekly sales will be \$702.

120. a. $f(x) = 15 + 0.05x$

b. $g(x) = 5 + 0.07x$

c. $15 + 0.05x = 5 + 0.07x$

$10 = 0.02x$

$500 = x$

For 500 minutes, the two plans cost the same.

121. a. $N(x) = 400 - 2(x - 120)$

$= 400 - 2x + 240$

$= 640 - 2x$

b. $R(x) = x(640 - 2x)$

$= -2x^2 + 640x$

122. a. $w = 16 - 2x \quad l = 24 - 2x$

$V(x) = (16 - 2x)(24 - 2x)x$

b. $0 < x < 8$

123. $2l + 3w = 400$

$2l = 400 - 3w$

$l = \dfrac{400 - 3w}{2}$

Let x = width

$A(x) = x \left(\dfrac{400 - 3w}{2} \right)$

$= \dfrac{x(400 - 3w)}{2}$

124. $V = lwh$

$8 = x \cdot x \cdot h$

$\dfrac{8}{x^2} = h$

$A(x) = 2x \cdot x + 4hx$

$= 2x^2 + 4 \left(\dfrac{8}{x^2} \right) x$

$= 2x^2 + \dfrac{32}{x}$

125. $I = 0.08x + 0.12(10,000 - x)$

Chapter 1 Test

1. (b), (c), and (d) are not functions.

2. a. $f(4) - f(-3) = 3 - (-2) = 5$

b. domain: $(-5, 6]$

c. range: $[-4, 5]$

d. increasing: $(-1, 2)$

e. decreasing: $(-5, -1)$ or $(2, 6)$

f. $2, f(2) = 5$

g. $(-1, -4)$

h. x-intercepts: $-4, 1,$ and 5.

i. y-intercept: -3

3.   a.   –2, 2

     b.   –1, 1

     c.   0

     d.   even; $f(-x) = f(x)$

     e.   no; f fails the horizontal line test

     f. $f(0)$ is a relative minimum.

     g.

     h.

     i.

     j. $\dfrac{f(x_2) - f(x_1)}{x_2 - x_1} = \dfrac{-1-0}{1-(-2)} = -\dfrac{1}{3}$

4.

     Domain: $(-\infty, \infty)$

     Range: $(-\infty, \infty)$

5.

     Domain: $[-2, 2]$

     Range: $[-2, 2]$

6.

     Domain: $(-\infty, \infty)$

     Range: $\{4\}$

7.

     $f(x) = -\dfrac{1}{3}x + 2$

     Domain: $(-\infty, \infty)$

     Range: $(-\infty, \infty)$

8.

     $(x + 2)^2 + (y - 1)^2 = 9$

     Domain: $[-5, 1]$

     Range: $[-2, 4]$

9.

$$f(x) = \begin{cases} 2 \text{ if } x \le 0 \\ -1 \text{ if } x > 0 \end{cases}$$

Domain: $(-\infty, \infty)$

Range: $\{-1, 2\}$

10.

$x^2 + y^2 + 4x + 6y - 3 = 0$

Domain: $[-6, 2]$

Range: $[-1, 7]$

11.

Domain of f: $(-\infty, \infty)$

Range of f: $[0, \infty)$

Domain of g: $(-\infty, \infty)$

Range of g: $[-2, \infty)$

12.

Domain of f: $(-\infty, \infty)$

Range of f: $[0, \infty)$

Domain of g: $(-\infty, \infty)$

Range of g: $(-\infty, 4]$

13.

Domain of f: $(-\infty, \infty)$

Range of f: $(-\infty, \infty)$

Domain of f^{-1}: $(-\infty, \infty)$

Range of f^{-1}: $(-\infty, \infty)$

14.

Domain of f: $(-\infty, \infty)$

Range of f: $(-\infty, \infty)$

Domain of f^{-1}: $(-\infty, \infty)$

Range of f^{-1}: $(-\infty, \infty)$

15.

Domain of f: $[0, \infty)$

Range of f: $[-1, \infty)$

Domain of f^{-1}: $[-1, \infty)$

Range of f^{-1}: $[0, \infty)$

16. $f(x) = x^2 - x - 4$

$$\begin{aligned} f(x-1) &= (x-1)^2 - (x-1) - 4 \\ &= x^2 - 2x + 1 - x + 1 - 4 \\ &= x^2 - 3x - 2 \end{aligned}$$

17. $\dfrac{f(x+h)-f(x)}{h}$

$=\dfrac{(x+h)^2-(x+h)-4-\left(x^2-x-4\right)}{h}$

$=\dfrac{x^2+2xh+h^2-x-h-4-x^2+x+4}{h}$

$=\dfrac{2xh+h^2-h}{h}$

$=\dfrac{h(2x+h-1)}{h}$

$=2x+h-1$

18. $(g-f)(x)=2x-6-\left(x^2-x-4\right)$

$\qquad\qquad =2x-6-x^2+x+4$

$\qquad\qquad =-x^2+3x-2$

19. $\left(\dfrac{f}{g}\right)(x)=\dfrac{x^2-x-4}{2x-6}$

Domain: $(-\infty,3)\cup(3,\infty)$

20. $(f\circ g)(x)=f\left(g(x)\right)$

$\qquad\qquad =(2x-6)^2-(2x-6)-4$

$\qquad\qquad =4x^2-24x+36-2x+6-4$

$\qquad\qquad =4x^2-26x+38$

21. $(g\circ f)(x)=g\left(f(x)\right)$

$\qquad\qquad =2\left(x^2-x-4\right)-6$

$\qquad\qquad =2x^2-2x-8-6$

$\qquad\qquad =2x^2-2x-14$

22. $g\left(f(-1)\right)=2\left((-1)^2-(-1)-4\right)-6$

$\qquad\qquad =2\left(1+1-4\right)-6$

$\qquad\qquad =2(-2)-6$

$\qquad\qquad =-4-6$

$\qquad\qquad =-10$

23. $f(x)=x^2-x-4$

$f(-x)=(-x)^2-(-x)-4$

$\qquad\quad =x^2+x-4$

f is neither even nor odd.

24. $m=\dfrac{-8-1}{-1-2}=\dfrac{-9}{-3}=3$

point-slope form: $y-1=3(x-2)$
or $y+8=3(x+1)$
slope-intercept form: $y=3x-5$

25. $y=-\dfrac{1}{4}x+5$ so $m=4$

point-slope form: $y-6=4(x+4)$
slope-intercept form: $y=4x+22$

26. Write $4x+2y-5=0$ in slope intercept form.

$4x+2y-5=0$

$\qquad 2y=-4x+5$

$\qquad y=-2x+\dfrac{5}{2}$

The slope of the parallel line is –2, thus the slope of the desired line is $m=-2$.

$y-y_1=m(x-x_1)$

$y-(-10)=-2\left(x-(-7)\right)$

$y+10=-2(x+7)$

$y+10=-2x-14$

$2x+y+24=0$

27. a. $(2,4.85)$ and $(5,4.49)$

First, find the slope using the points $(2,4.85)$ and $(5,4.49)$

$m=\dfrac{4.49-4.85}{5-2}=\dfrac{-0.36}{3}=-0.12$

Then use the slope and one of the points to write the equation in point-slope form.

$y-y_1=m\left(x-x_1\right)$

$y-4.85=-0.12\left(x-2\right)$

or

$y-4.49=-0.12\left(x-5\right)$

b. Solve for y to obtain slope-intercept form.

$y-4.85=-0.12\left(x-2\right)$

$y-4.85=-0.12x+0.24$

$\qquad y=-0.12x+5.09$

$\quad f(x)=-0.12x+5.09$

c. To predict the minimum hourly inflation-adjusted wages in 2007, let $x=2007-1997=10$.

$f(10)=-0.12\left(10\right)+5.09=3.89$

The linear function predicts the minimum hourly inflation-adjusted wage in 2007 to $3.89.

28.
$$\frac{\left[3(10)^2 - 5\right] - [3(6)^2 - 5]}{10 - 6}$$
$$= \frac{205 - 103}{4}$$
$$= \frac{192}{4}$$
$$= 48$$

29. $g(-1) = 3 - (-1) = 4$
$g(7) = \sqrt{7 - 3} = \sqrt{4} = 2$

30. The denominator is zero when $x = 1$ or $x = -5$.
Domain: $(-\infty, -5) \cup (-5, 1) \cup (1, \infty)$

31. The expressions under each radical must not be negative.
$x + 5 \geq 0$　and　$x - 1 \geq 0$
　$x \geq -5$　　　　　$x \geq 1$
Domain: $[1, \infty)$

32. $(f \circ g)(x) = \dfrac{7}{\dfrac{2}{x} - 4} = \dfrac{7x}{2 - 4x}$

$x \neq 0, \quad 2 - 4x \neq 0$
$\qquad x \neq \dfrac{1}{2}$

Domain: $(-\infty, 0) \cup \left(0, \dfrac{1}{2}\right) \cup \left(\dfrac{1}{2}, \infty\right)$

33. $f(x) = x^7 \qquad g(x) = 2x + 3$

34. $d = \sqrt{(x_2 - x_1)^2 + (y_2 - y_1)^2}$
$d = \sqrt{(x_2 - x_1)^2 + (y_2 - y_1)^2}$
$\quad = \sqrt{(5 - 2)^2 + (2 - (-2))^2}$
$\quad = \sqrt{3^2 + 4^2}$
$\quad = \sqrt{9 + 16}$
$\quad = \sqrt{25}$
$\quad = 5$

$$\left(\frac{x_1 + x_2}{2}, \frac{y_1 + y_2}{2}\right) = \left(\frac{2 + 5}{2}, \frac{-2 + 2}{2}\right)$$
$$= \left(\frac{7}{2}, 0\right)$$

The length is 5 and the midpoint is $\left(\dfrac{7}{2}, 0\right)$.

35.　a.　$T(x) = 41.78 - 0.19x$

b.　$37.22 = 41.78 - 0.19x$
$\quad -4.56 = -0.19x$
$\qquad 24 = x$
24 years after 1908, in 2004, the winning time will be 37.22 seconds.

36.　a.　$Y(x) = 50 - 1.5(x - 30)$
$\qquad\quad = 50 - 1.5x + 45$
$\qquad\quad = 95 - 1.5x$

b.
$T(x) = x(95 - 1.5x)$
$\qquad = -1.5x^2 + 95x$

37.　$2l + 2w = 600$
$\qquad 2l = 600 - 2w$
$\qquad\ l = 300 - w$
Let $x = w$

$A(x) = x(300 - x)$
$\qquad = -x^2 + 300x$

38.　$V = lwh$
$\quad 8000 = x \cdot x \cdot h$
$\quad \dfrac{8000}{x^2} = h$

$A(x) = 2x^2 + 4x\left(\dfrac{8000}{x^2}\right)$
$\qquad = 2x^2 + \dfrac{3200}{x}$

Chapter 2

Check Point Exercises

1. **a.** $(5-2i)+(3+3i)$
   $=5-2i+3+3i$
   $=(5+3)+(-2+3)i$
   $=8+i$

   b. $(2+6i)-(12-i)$
   $=2+6i-12+i$
   $=(2-12)+(6+1)i$
   $=-10+7i$

2. **a.** $7i(2-9i)=7i(2)-7i(9i$
   $=14i-63i^2$
   $=14i-63(-1)$
   $=63+14i$

   b. $(5+4i)(6-7i)=30-35i+24i-28i^2$
   $=30-35i+24i-28(-1)$
   $=30+28-35i+24i$
   $=58-11i$

3. $\dfrac{5+4i}{4-i}=\dfrac{5+4i}{4-i}\cdot\dfrac{4+i}{4+i}$
   $=\dfrac{20+5i+16i+4i^2}{16+4i-4i-i^2}$
   $=\dfrac{20+21i-4}{16+1}$
   $=\dfrac{16+21i}{17}$
   $=\dfrac{16}{17}+\dfrac{21}{17}i$

4. **a.** $\sqrt{-27}+\sqrt{-48}=i\sqrt{27}+i\sqrt{48}$
   $=i\sqrt{9\cdot3}+i\sqrt{16\cdot3}$
   $=3i\sqrt{3}+4i\sqrt{3}$
   $=7i\sqrt{3}$

b. $(-2+\sqrt{-3})^2=(-2+i\sqrt{3})^2$
   $=(-2)^2+2(-2)(i\sqrt{3})+(i\sqrt{3})^2$
   $=4-4i\sqrt{3}+3i^2$
   $=4-4i\sqrt{3}+3(-1)$
   $=1-4i\sqrt{3}$

c. $\dfrac{-14+\sqrt{-12}}{2}=\dfrac{-14+i\sqrt{12}}{2}$
   $=\dfrac{-14+2i\sqrt{3}}{2}$
   $=\dfrac{-14}{2}+\dfrac{2i\sqrt{3}}{2}$
   $=-7+i\sqrt{3}$

5. $x^2-2x+2=0$
   $a=1,b=-2,c=2$
   $x=\dfrac{-b\pm\sqrt{b^2-4ac}}{2a}$
   $x=\dfrac{-(-2)\pm\sqrt{(-2)^2-4(1)(2)}}{2(1)}$
   $x=\dfrac{2\pm\sqrt{4-8}}{2}$
   $x=\dfrac{2\pm\sqrt{-4}}{2}$
   $x=\dfrac{2\pm2i}{2}$
   $x=1\pm i$
   The solution set is $\{1+i,1-i\}$.

Exercise Set 2.1

1. $(7+2i)+(1-4i)=7+2i+1-4i$
   $=7+1+2i-4i$
   $=8-2i$

3. $(3+2i)-(5-7i)=3-5+2i+7i$
   $=3+2i-5+7i$
   $=-2+9i$

5. $6-(-5+4i)-(-13-i)=6+5-4i+13+i$
   $=24-3i$

7. $8i-(14-9i)=8i-14+9i$
   $=-14+8i+9i$
   $=-14+17i$

9. $-3i(7i-5) = -21i^2 + 15i$
$= -21(-1) + 15i$
$= 21 + 15i$

11. $(-5+4i)(3+i) = -15 - 5i + 12i + 4i^2$
$= -15 + 7i - 4$
$= -19 + 7i$

13. $(7-5i)(-2-3i) = -14 - 21i + 10i + 15i^2$
$= -14 - 15 - 11i$
$= -29 - 11i$

15. $(3+5i)(3-5i)$

17. $(-5+i)(-5-i) = 25 + 5i - 5i - i^2$
$= 25 + 1$
$= 26$

19. $(2+3i)^2 = 4 + 12i + 9i^2$
$= 4 + 12i - 9$
$= -5 + 12i$

21. $\dfrac{2}{3-i} = \dfrac{2}{3-i} \cdot \dfrac{3+i}{3+i}$
$= \dfrac{2(3+i)}{9+1}$
$= \dfrac{2(3+i)}{10}$
$= \dfrac{3+i}{5}$
$= \dfrac{3}{5} + \dfrac{1}{5}i$

23. $\dfrac{2i}{1+i} = \dfrac{2i}{1+i} \cdot \dfrac{1-i}{1-i} = \dfrac{2i - 2i^2}{1+1} = \dfrac{2+2i}{2} = 1+i$

25. $\dfrac{8i}{4-3i} = \dfrac{8i}{4-3i} \cdot \dfrac{4+3i}{4+3i}$
$= \dfrac{32i + 24i^2}{16+9}$
$= \dfrac{-24 + 32i}{25}$
$= -\dfrac{24}{25} + \dfrac{32}{25}i$

27. $\dfrac{2+3i}{2+i} = \dfrac{2+3i}{2+i} \cdot \dfrac{2-i}{2-i}$
$= \dfrac{4 + 4i - 3i^2}{4+1}$
$= \dfrac{7+4i}{5}$
$= \dfrac{7}{5} + \dfrac{4}{5}i$

29. $\sqrt{-64} - \sqrt{-25} = i\sqrt{64} - i\sqrt{25}$
$= 8i - 5i = 3i$

31. $5\sqrt{-16} + 3\sqrt{-81} = 5(4i) + 3(9i)$
$= 20i + 27i = 47i$

33. $\left(-2+\sqrt{-4}\right)^2 = \left(-2+2i\right)^2$
$= 4 - 8i + 4i^2$
$= 4 - 8i - 4$
$= -8i$

35. $\left(-3-\sqrt{-7}\right)^2 = \left(-3-i\sqrt{7}\right)^2$
$= 9 + 6i\sqrt{7} + i^2(7)$
$= 9 - 7 + 6i\sqrt{7}$
$= 2 + 6i\sqrt{7}$

37. $\dfrac{-8+\sqrt{-32}}{24} = \dfrac{-8+i\sqrt{32}}{24}$
$= \dfrac{-8+i\sqrt{16\cdot 2}}{24}$
$= \dfrac{-8+4i\sqrt{2}}{24}$
$= -\dfrac{1}{3} + \dfrac{\sqrt{2}}{6}i$

39. $\dfrac{-6-\sqrt{-12}}{48} = \dfrac{-6-i\sqrt{12}}{48}$
$= \dfrac{-6-i\sqrt{4\cdot 3}}{48}$
$= \dfrac{-6-2i\sqrt{3}}{48}$
$= -\dfrac{1}{8} - \dfrac{\sqrt{3}}{24}i$

41. $\sqrt{-8}\left(\sqrt{-3}-\sqrt{5}\right)=i\sqrt{8}(i\sqrt{3}-\sqrt{5})$

$$=2i\sqrt{2}\left(i\sqrt{3}-\sqrt{5}\right)$$

$$=-2\sqrt{6}-2i\sqrt{10}$$

43. $\left(3\sqrt{-5}\right)\left(-4\sqrt{-12}\right)=\left(3i\sqrt{5}\right)\left(-8i\sqrt{3}\right)$

$$=-24i^2\sqrt{15}$$

$$=24\sqrt{15}$$

45. $x^2-6x+10=0$

$$x=\frac{6\pm\sqrt{(-6)^2-4(1)(10)}}{2(1)}$$

$$x=\frac{6\pm\sqrt{36-40}}{2}$$

$$x=\frac{6\pm\sqrt{-4}}{2}$$

$$x=\frac{6\pm2i}{2}$$

$$x=3\pm i$$

The solution set is $\{3+i,3-i\}$.

47. $4x^2+8x+13=0$

$$x=\frac{-8\pm\sqrt{8^2-4(4)(13)}}{2(4)}$$

$$=\frac{-8\pm\sqrt{64-208}}{8}$$

$$=\frac{-8\pm\sqrt{-144}}{8}$$

$$=\frac{-8\pm12i}{8}$$

$$=\frac{4(-2\pm3i)}{8}$$

$$=\frac{-2\pm3i}{2}$$

$$=-1\pm\frac{3}{2}i$$

The solution set is $\left\{-1+\frac{3}{2}i,-1-\frac{3}{2}i\right\}$.

49. $3x^2-8x+7=0$

$$x=\frac{-(-8)\pm\sqrt{(-8)^2-4(3)(7)}}{2(3)}$$

$$=\frac{8\pm\sqrt{64-84}}{6}$$

$$=\frac{8\pm\sqrt{-20}}{6}$$

$$=\frac{8\pm2i\sqrt{5}}{6}$$

$$=\frac{2(4\pm i\sqrt{5})}{6}$$

$$=\frac{4\pm i\sqrt{5}}{3}$$

$$=\frac{4}{3}\pm\frac{\sqrt{5}}{3}i$$

The solution set is $\left\{\frac{4}{3}+\frac{\sqrt{5}}{3}i,\frac{4}{3}-\frac{\sqrt{5}}{3}i\right\}$.

51. $(2-3i)(1-i)-(3-i)(3+i)$

$$=\left(2-2i-3i+3i^2\right)-\left(3^2-i^2\right)$$

$$=2-5i+3i^2-9+i^2$$

$$=-7-5i+4i^2$$

$$=-7-5i+4\left(-1\right)$$

$$=-11-5i$$

53. $(2+i)^2-(3-i)^2$

$$=\left(4+4i+i^2\right)-\left(9-6i+i^2\right)$$

$$=4+4i+i^2-9+6i-i^2$$

$$=-5+10i$$

55. $5\sqrt{-16}+3\sqrt{-81}$

$$=5\sqrt{16}\sqrt{-1}+3\sqrt{81}\sqrt{-1}$$

$$=5\cdot4i+3\cdot9i$$

$$=20i+27i$$

$$=47i \quad \text{or} \quad 0+47i$$

57. $f(x)=x^2-2x+2$

$$f(1+i)=(1+i)^2-2(1+i)+2$$

$$=1+2i+i^2-2-2i+2$$

$$=1+i^2$$

$$=1-1$$

$$=0$$

59. $f(x) = \dfrac{x^2 + 19}{2 - x}$

$f(3i) = \dfrac{(3i)^2 + 19}{2 - 3i}$

$= \dfrac{9i^2 + 19}{2 - 3i}$

$= \dfrac{-9 + 19}{2 - 3i}$

$= \dfrac{10}{2 - 3i}$

$= \dfrac{10}{2 - 3i} \cdot \dfrac{2 + 3i}{2 + 3i}$

$= \dfrac{20 + 30i}{4 - 9i^2}$

$= \dfrac{20 + 30i}{4 + 9}$

$= \dfrac{20 + 30i}{13}$

$= \dfrac{20}{13} + \dfrac{30}{13}i$

61. $E = IR = (4 - 5i)(3 + 7i)$

$= 12 + 28i - 15i - 35i^2$

$= 12 + 13i - 35(-1)$

$= 12 + 35 + 13i = 47 + 13i$

The voltage of the circuit is $(47 + 13i)$ volts.

63. Sum:

$\left(5 + i\sqrt{15}\right) + \left(5 - i\sqrt{15}\right)$

$= 5 + i\sqrt{15} + 5 - i\sqrt{15}$

$= 5 + 5$

$= 10$

Product:

$\left(5 + i\sqrt{15}\right)\left(5 - i\sqrt{15}\right)$

$= 25 - 5i\sqrt{15} + 5i\sqrt{15} - 15i^2$

$= 25 + 15$

$= 40$

73. **a.** False; all irrational numbers are complex numbers.

b. False; $(3 + 7i)(3 - 7i) = 9 + 49 = 58$ is a real number.

c. False; $\dfrac{7 + 3i}{5 + 3i} = \dfrac{7 + 3i}{5 + 3i} \cdot \dfrac{5 - 3i}{5 - 3i}$

$= \dfrac{44 - 6i}{34} = \dfrac{22}{17} - \dfrac{3}{17}i$

d. True;

$(x + yi)(x - yi) = x^2 - (yi)^2 = x^2 + y^2$

(d) is true.

75. $\dfrac{1 + i}{1 + 2i} + \dfrac{1 - i}{1 - 2i}$

$= \dfrac{(1 + i)(1 - 2i)}{(1 + 2i)(1 - 2i)} + \dfrac{(1 - i)(1 + 2i)}{(1 + 2i)(1 - 2i)}$

$= \dfrac{(1 + i)(1 - 2i) + (1 - i)(1 + 2i)}{(1 + 2i)(1 - 2i)}$

$= \dfrac{1 - 2i + i - 2i^2 + 1 + 2i - i - 2i^2}{1 - 4i^2}$

$= \dfrac{1 - 2i + i + 2 + 1 + 2i - i + 2}{1 + 4}$

$= \dfrac{6}{5}$

$= \dfrac{6}{5} + 0i$

Section 2.2

Check Point Exercises

1. $f(x) = -(x-1)^2 + 4$

$$f(x) = \overset{a=-1}{\overset{\frown}{-}}\left(x - \overset{h=1}{\overset{\frown}{1}}\right)^2 + \overset{k=4}{\overset{\frown}{4}}$$

Step 1: The parabola opens down because $a < 0$.
Step 2: find the vertex: (1, 4)
Step 3: find the x-intercepts:

$0 = -(x-1)^2 + 4$

$(x-1)^2 = 4$

$x - 1 = \pm 2$

$x = 1 \pm 2$

$x = 3$ or $x = -1$

Step 4: find the y-intercept:

$f(0) = -(0-1)^2 + 4 = 3$

Step 5: The axis of symmetry is $x = 1$.

$f(x) = -(x-1)^2 + 4$

2. $f(x) = (x-2)^2 + 1$

Step 1: The parabola opens up because $a > 0$.
Step 2: find the vertex: (2, 1)
Step 3: find the x-intercepts:

$0 = (x-2)^2 + 1$

$(x-2)^2 = -1$

$x - 2 = \sqrt{-1}$

$x = 2 \pm i$

The equation has no real roots, thus the parabola has no x-intercepts.
Step 4: find the y-intercept:

$f(0) = (0-2)^2 + 1 = 5$

Step 5: The axis of symmetry is $x = 2$.

$f(x) = (x-2)^2 + 1$

3. $f(x) = -x^2 + 4x + 1$

Step 1: The parabola opens down because $a < 0$.
Step 2: find the vertex:

$x = -\dfrac{b}{2a} = -\dfrac{4}{2(-1)} = 2$

$f(2) = -2^2 + 4(2) + 1 = 5$

The vertex is (2, 5).
Step 3: find the x-intercepts:

$0 = -x^2 + 4x + 1$

$x = \dfrac{-b \pm \sqrt{b^2 - 4ac}}{2a}$

$x = \dfrac{-4 \pm \sqrt{4^2 - 4(-1)(1)}}{2(-1)}$

$x = \dfrac{-4 \pm \sqrt{20}}{-2}$

$x = 2 \pm \sqrt{5}$

The x-intercepts are $x \approx -0.2$ and $x \approx -4.2$.
Step 4: find the y-intercept:

$f(0) = -0^2 + 4(0) + 1 = 1$

Step 5: The axis of symmetry is $x = 2$.

$f(x) = -x^2 + 4x + 1$

4. $f(x) = 4x^2 - 16x + 1000$

a. $a = 4$. The parabola opens upward and has a minimum value.

b. $x = \dfrac{-b}{2a} = \dfrac{16}{8} = 2$

$f(2) = 4(2)^2 - 16(2) + 1000 = 984$

The minimum point is 984 at $x = 2$.

c. Domain: $(-\infty, \infty)$ Range: $[984, \infty)$

5. $f(x) = 0.4x^2 - 36x + 1000$

Because $a > 0$, the function has a minimum value.

$$x = -\frac{b}{2a} = -\frac{-36}{2(0.4)} = 45$$

$$f(45) = 0.4(45)^2 - 36(45) + 1000 = 190$$

The age of a driver having the least number of car accidents is 45. The minimum number of accidents per 50 million miles driven is 190.

6.   Let $x =$ one of the numbers;
$x - 8 =$ the other number.

The product is $f(x) = x(x - 8) = x^2 - 8x$

The x-coordinate of the minimum is

$$x = -\frac{b}{2a} = -\frac{-8}{2(1)} = -\frac{-8}{2} = 4.$$

$$f(4) = (4)^2 - 8(4)$$
$$= 16 - 32 = -16$$

The vertex is $(4, -16)$.

The minimum product is -16. This occurs when the two number are 4 and $4 - 8 = -4$.

7.   Maximize the area of a rectangle constructed with 120 feet of fencing.
Let $x =$ the length of the rectangle. Let $y =$ the width of the rectangle.
Since we need an equation in one variable, use the perimeter to express y in terms of x.
$$2x + 2y = 120$$
$$2y = 120 - 2x$$
$$y = \frac{120 - 2x}{2} = 60 - x$$

We need to maximize $A = xy = x(60 - x)$.
Rewrite A as a function of x.
$$A(x) = x(60 - x) = -x^2 + 60x$$

Since $a = -1$ is negative, we know the function opens downward and has a maximum at

$$x = -\frac{b}{2a} = -\frac{60}{2(-1)} = -\frac{60}{-2} = 30.$$

When the length x is 30, the width y is
$$y = 60 - x = 60 - 30 = 30.$$

The dimensions of the rectangular region with maximum area are 30 feet by 30 feet. This gives an area of $30 \cdot 30 = 900$ square feet.

Exercise Set 2.2

1.   vertex: (1, 1)
$$h(x) = (x - 1)^2 + 1$$

3.   vertex: (1, −1)
$$j(x) = (x - 1)^2 - 1$$

5.   The graph is $f(x) = x^2$ translated down one.
$$h(x) = x^2 - 1$$

7.   The point (1, 0) is on the graph and
$g(1) = 0$. $g(x) = x^2 - 2x + 1$

9. $f(x) = 2(x - 3)^2 + 1$
$h = 3, k = 1$
The vertex is at (3, 1).

11. $f(x) = -2(x + 1)^2 + 5$
$h = -1, k = 5$
The vertex is at (−1, 5).

13. $f(x) = 2x^2 - 8x + 3$
$$x = \frac{-b}{2a} = \frac{8}{4} = 2$$
$$f(2) = 2(2)^2 - 8(2) + 3$$
$$= 8 - 16 + 3 = -5$$
The vertex is at (2, −5).

15. $f(x) = -x^2 - 2x + 8$
$$x = \frac{-b}{2a} = \frac{2}{-2} = -1$$
$$f(-1) = -(-1)^2 - 2(-1) + 8$$
$$= -1 + 2 + 8 = 9$$
The vertex is at (−1, 9).

17. $f(x) = (x - 4)^2 - 1$
vertex: (4, −1)
x-intercepts:
$$0 = (x - 4)^2 - 1$$
$$1 = (x - 4)^2$$
$$\pm 1 = x - 4$$
$$x = 3 \text{ or } x = 5$$
y-intercept:
$$f(0) = (0 - 4)^2 - 1 = 15$$

The axis of symmetry is $x = 4$.

$$f(x) = (x-4)^2 - 1$$

Domain: $(-\infty, \infty)$

Range: $[-1, \infty)$

19. $f(x) = (x-1)^2 + 2$

vertex: $(1, 2)$

x-intercepts:

$0 = (x-1)^2 + 2$

$(x-1)^2 = -2$

$x - 1 = \pm\sqrt{-2}$

$x = 1 \pm i\sqrt{2}$

No x-intercepts.

y-intercept:

$f(0) = (0-1)^2 + 2 = 3$

The axis of symmetry is $x = 1$.

$$f(x) = (x-1)^2 + 2$$

Domain: $(-\infty, \infty)$

Range: $[2, \infty)$

21. $y - 1 = (x-3)^2$

$y = (x-3)^2 + 1$

vertex: $(3, 1)$

x-intercepts:

$0 = (x-3)^2 + 1$

$(x-3)^2 = -1$

$x - 3 = \pm i$

$x = 3 \pm i$

No x-intercepts.

y-intercept: 10

$y = (0-3)^2 + 1 = 10$

The axis of symmetry is $x = 3$.

$$y - 1 = (x-3)^2$$

Domain: $(-\infty, \infty)$

Range: $[1, \infty)$

23. $f(x) = 2(x+2)^2 - 1$

vertex: $(-2, -1)$

x-intercepts:

$0 = 2(x+2)^2 - 1$

$2(x+2)^2 = 1$

$(x+2)^2 = \dfrac{1}{2}$

$x + 2 = \pm\dfrac{1}{\sqrt{2}}$

$x = -2 \pm \dfrac{1}{\sqrt{2}} = -2 \pm \dfrac{\sqrt{2}}{2}$

y-intercept:

$f(0) = 2(0+2)^2 - 1 = 7$

The axis of symmetry is $x = -2$.

$$f(x) = 2(x+2)^2 - 1$$

Domain: $(-\infty, \infty)$

Range: $[-1, \infty)$

25. $f(x) = 4 - (x-1)^2$

$f(x) = -(x-1)^2 + 4$

vertex: (1, 4)

x-intercepts:

$0 = -(x-1)^2 + 4$

$(x-1)^2 = 4$

$x - 1 = \pm 2$

$x = -1 \text{ or } x = 3$

y-intercept:

$f(x) = -(0-1)^2 + 4 = 3$

The axis of symmetry is $x = 1$.

$f(x) = 4 - (x-1)^2$

Domain: $(-\infty, \infty)$

Range: $(-\infty, 4]$

27. $f(x) = x^2 - 2x - 3$

$f(x) = (x^2 - 2x + 1) - 3 - 1$

$f(x) = (x-1)^2 - 4$

vertex: (1, -4)

x-intercepts:

$0 = (x-1)^2 - 4$

$(x-1)^2 = 4$

$x - 1 = \pm 2$

$x = -1 \text{ or } x = 3$

y-intercept: -3

$f(0) = 0^2 - 2(0) - 3 = -3$

The axis of symmetry is $x = 1$.

$f(x) = x^2 + 3x - 10$

Domain: $(-\infty, \infty)$

Range: $[-4, \infty)$

29. $f(x) = x^2 + 3x - 10$

$f(x) = \left(x^2 + 3x + \dfrac{9}{4}\right) - 10 - \dfrac{9}{4}$

$f(x) = \left(x + \dfrac{3}{2}\right)^2 - \dfrac{49}{4}$

vertex: $\left(-\dfrac{3}{2}, -\dfrac{49}{4}\right)$

x-intercepts:

$0 = \left(x + \dfrac{3}{2}\right)^2 - \dfrac{49}{4}$

$\left(x + \dfrac{3}{2}\right)^2 = \dfrac{49}{4}$

$x + \dfrac{3}{2} = \pm \dfrac{7}{2}$

$x = -\dfrac{3}{2} \pm \dfrac{7}{2}$

$x = 2 \text{ or } x = -5$

y-intercept:

$f(x) = 0^2 + 3(0) - 10 = -10$

The axis of symmetry is $x = -\dfrac{3}{2}$.

$f(x) = x^2 + 3x - 10$

Domain: $(-\infty, \infty)$

Range: $\left[-\dfrac{49}{4}, \infty\right)$

31. $f(x) = 2x - x^2 + 3$

$f(x) = -x^2 + 2x + 3$

$f(x) = -(x^2 - 2x + 1) + 3 + 1$

$f(x) = -(x-1)^2 + 4$

vertex: $(1, 4)$

x-intercepts:

$0 = -(x-1)^2 + 4$

$(x-1)^2 = 4$

$x - 1 = \pm 2$

$x = -1$ or $x = 3$

y-intercept:

$f(0) = 2(0) - (0)^2 + 3 = 3$

The axis of symmetry is $x = 1$.

$f(x) = 2x - x^2 + 3$

Domain: $(-\infty, \infty)$

Range: $(-\infty, 4]$

33. $f(x) = x^2 + 6x + 3$

$f(x) = (x^2 + 6x + 9) + 3 - 9$

$f(x) = (x+3)^2 - 6$

vertex: $(-3, -6)$

x-intercepts:

$0 = (x+3)^2 - 6$

$(x+3)^2 = 6$

$x + 3 = \pm\sqrt{6}$

$x = -3 \pm \sqrt{6}$

y-intercept:

$f(0) = (0)^2 + 6(0) + 3$

$f(0) = 3$

The axis of symmetry is $x = -3$.

$f(x) = x^2 + 6x + 3$

Domain: $(-\infty, \infty)$

Range: $[-6, \infty)$

35. $f(x) = 2x^2 + 4x - 3$

$f(x) = 2(x^2 + 2x \quad) - 3$

$f(x) = 2(x^2 + 2x + 1) - 3 - 2$

$f(x) = 2(x+1)^2 - 5$

vertex: $(-1, -5)$

x-intercepts:

$0 = 2(x+1)^2 - 5$

$2(x+1)^2 = 5$

$(x+1)^2 = \dfrac{5}{2}$

$x + 1 = \pm\sqrt{\dfrac{5}{2}}$

$x = -1 \pm \dfrac{\sqrt{10}}{2}$

y-intercept:

$f(0) = 2(0)^2 + 4(0) - 3$

$f(0) = -3$

The axis of symmetry is $x = -1$.

$f(x) = 2x^2 + 4x - 3$

Domain: $(-\infty, \infty)$

Range: $[-5, \infty)$

37. $f(x) = 2x - x^2 - 2$

$f(x) = -x^2 + 2x - 2$

$f(x) = -(x^2 - 2x + 1) - 2 + 1$

$f(x) = -(x - 1)^2 - 1$

vertex: $(1, -1)$

x-intercepts:

$0 = -(x - 1)^2 - 1$

$(x - 1)^2 = -1$

$x - 1 = \pm i$

$x = 1 \pm i$

No x-intercepts.

y-intercept:

$f(0) = 2(0) - (0)^2 - 2 = -2$

The axis of symmetry is $x = 1$.

$f(x) = 2x - x^2 - 2$

Domain: $(-\infty, \infty)$

Range: $(-\infty, -1]$

39. $f(x) = 3x^2 - 12x - 1$

a. $a = 3$. The parabola opens upward and has a minimum value.

b. $x = \dfrac{-b}{2a} = \dfrac{12}{6} = 2$

$f(2) = 3(2)^2 - 12(2) - 1$

$= 12 - 24 - 1 = -13$

The minimum is -13 at $x = 2$.

c. Domain: $(-\infty, \infty)$ Range: $[-13, \infty)$

41. $f(x) = -4x^2 + 8x - 3$

a. $a = -4$. The parabola opens downward and has a maximum value.

b. $x = \dfrac{-b}{2a} = \dfrac{-8}{-8} = 1$

$f(1) = -4(1)^2 + 8(1) - 3$

$= -4 + 8 - 3 = 1$

The maximum is 1 at $x = 1$.

c. Domain: $(-\infty, \infty)$ Range: $(-\infty, 1]$

43. $f(x) = 5x^2 - 5x$

a. $a = 5$. The parabola opens upward and has a minimum value.

b. $x = \dfrac{-b}{2a} = \dfrac{5}{10} = \dfrac{1}{2}$

$f\left(\dfrac{1}{2}\right) = 5\left(\dfrac{1}{2}\right)^2 - 5\left(\dfrac{1}{2}\right)$

$= \dfrac{5}{4} - \dfrac{5}{2} = \dfrac{5}{4} - \dfrac{10}{4} = \dfrac{-5}{4}$

The minimum is $\dfrac{-5}{4}$ at $x = \dfrac{1}{2}$.

c. Domain: $(-\infty, \infty)$ Range: $\left[\dfrac{-5}{4}, \infty\right)$

45. Since the parabola opens up, the vertex $(-1, -2)$ is a minimum point.

Domain: $(-\infty, \infty)$. Range: $[-2, \infty)$

47. Since the parabola has a maximum, it opens down from the vertex $(10, -6)$.

Domain: $(-\infty, \infty)$. Range: $(-\infty, -6]$

49. $(h, k) = (5, 3)$

$f(x) = 2(x - h)^2 + k = 2(x - 5)^2 + 3$

51. $(h, k) = (-10, -5)$

$f(x) = 2(x - h)^2 + k$

$= 2[x - (-10)]^2 + (-5)$

$= 2(x + 10)^2 - 5$

53. Since the vertex is a maximum, the parabola opens down and $a = -3$.

$(h, k) = (-2, 4)$

$f(x) = -3(x - h)^2 + k$

$= -3[x - (-2)]^2 + 4$

$= -3(x + 2)^2 + 4$

55. Since the vertex is a minimum, the parabola opens up and $a = 3$.

$$(h,k) = (11,0)$$

$$
\begin{aligned}
f(x) &= 3(x-h)^2 + k \\
&= 3(x-11)^2 + 0 \\
&= 3(x-11)^2
\end{aligned}
$$

57. $x = -\dfrac{b}{2a} = -\dfrac{-0.104}{2(0.005)} = 10.4$

Wine consumption was at a minimum 10.4 years after 1980, or about 1990.

$$
\begin{aligned}
f(10) &= 0.005(10)^2 - 0.104(10) + 2.626 \\
&= 0.005(100) - 1.04 + 2.626 \\
&= 0.5 - 1.04 + 2.626 \\
&= 2.086 \\
&\approx 2.1
\end{aligned}
$$

In 1990 the function suggests that per capita wine consumption was about 2.1 gallons. This models the graph's data quite well.

59. **a.**

$$t = -\frac{b}{2a} = -\frac{64}{2(-16)} = -\frac{64}{-32} = 2$$

$$
\begin{aligned}
s(2) &= -16(2)^2 + 64(2) + 200 \\
&= -16(4) + 128 + 200 \\
&= -64 + 128 + 200 = 264
\end{aligned}
$$

The ball reaches a maximum height of 264 feet 2 seconds after it is thrown.

b.

$$0 = -16t^2 + 64t + 200$$

$$0 = t^2 - 4t - 12.5$$

$$a = 1 \quad b = -4 \quad c = -12.5$$

$$
\begin{aligned}
t &= \frac{-(-4) \pm \sqrt{(-4)^2 - 4(1)(-12.5)}}{2(1)} \\
&= \frac{4 \pm \sqrt{16 + 50}}{2} = \frac{4 \pm \sqrt{66}}{2} \\
&\approx \frac{4 \pm 8.1}{2}
\end{aligned}
$$

$$
= \frac{4 + 8.1}{2} \quad \text{or} \quad \frac{4 - 8.1}{2}
$$

$$
= \frac{12.1}{2} \qquad\qquad = \frac{-4.1}{2}
$$

$$
\approx 6.1 \qquad\qquad\quad \approx -2.1
$$

We disregard –2.1 because we can't have a negative time measurement. The solution is 6.1 and we conclude that the ball will hit the ground in approximately 6.1 seconds.

c.

$$
\begin{aligned}
s(0) &= -16(0)^2 + 64(0) + 200 \\
&= -16(0) + 0 + 200 = 200
\end{aligned}
$$

At $t = 0$, the ball has not yet been thrown and is at a height of 200 feet. This is the height of the building.

d.

61. Let $x =$ one of the numbers;
$16 - x =$ the other number.

The product is
$$
\begin{aligned}
f(x) &= x(16-x) \\
&= 16x - x^2 = -x^2 + 16x
\end{aligned}
$$

The x-coordinate of the maximum is

$$x = -\frac{b}{2a} = -\frac{16}{2(-1)} = -\frac{16}{-2} = 8.$$

$$f(8) = -8^2 + 16(8) = -64 + 128 = 64$$

The vertex is (8, 64). The maximum product is 64. This occurs when the two number are 8 and $16 - 8 = 8$.

63. Let $x =$ one of the numbers;
$x - 16 =$ the other number.

The product is $f(x) = x(x-16) = x^2 - 16x$

The x-coordinate of the minimum is

$$x = -\frac{b}{2a} = -\frac{-16}{2(1)} = -\frac{-16}{2} = 8.$$

$$
\begin{aligned}
f(8) &= (8)^2 - 16(8) \\
&= 64 - 128 = -64
\end{aligned}
$$

The vertex is $(8, -64)$. The minimum product is -64. This occurs when the two number are 8 and $8 - 16 = -8$.

65. Maximize the area of a rectangle constructed along a river with 600 feet of fencing.

Let x = the width of the rectangle;

$600 - 2x$ = the length of the rectangle

We need to maximize.

$A(x) = x(600 - 2x)$

$\qquad = 600x - 2x^2 = -2x^2 + 600x$

Since $a = -2$ is negative, we know the function opens downward and has a maximum at

$$x = -\frac{b}{2a} = -\frac{600}{2(-2)} = -\frac{600}{-4} = 150.$$

When the width is $x = 150$ feet, the length is $600 - 2(150) = 600 - 300 = 300$ feet.

The dimensions of the rectangular plot with maximum area are 150 feet by 300 feet. This gives an area of $150 \cdot 300 = 45,000$ square feet.

67. Maximize the area of a rectangle constructed with 50 yards of fencing.

Let x = the length of the rectangle. Let y = the width of the rectangle.

Since we need an equation in one variable, use the perimeter to express y in terms of x.

$2x + 2y = 50$

$\qquad 2y = 50 - 2x$

$\qquad y = \frac{50 - 2x}{2} = 25 - x$

We need to maximize $A = xy = x(25 - x)$. Rewrite A as a function of x.

$A(x) = x(25 - x) = -x^2 + 25x$

Since $a = -1$ is negative, we know the function opens downward and has a maximum at

$$x = -\frac{b}{2a} = -\frac{25}{2(-1)} = -\frac{25}{-2} = 12.5.$$

When the length x is 12.5, the width y is
$y = 25 - x = 25 - 12.5 = 12.5$.

The dimensions of the rectangular region with maximum area are 12.5 yards by 12.5 yards. This gives an area of $12.5 \cdot 12.5 = 156.25$ square yards.

69. Maximize the area of the playground with 600 feet of fencing.

Let x = the length of the rectangle. Let y = the width of the rectangle.

Since we need an equation in one variable, use the perimeter to express y in terms of x.

$2x + 3y = 600$

$\qquad 3y = 600 - 2x$

$\qquad y = \frac{600 - 2x}{3}$

$\qquad y = 200 - \frac{2}{3}x$

We need to maximize $A = xy = x\left(200 - \frac{2}{3}x\right)$.

Rewrite A as a function of x.

$A(x) = x\left(200 - \frac{2}{3}x\right) = -\frac{2}{3}x^2 + 200x$

Since $a = -\frac{2}{3}$ is negative, we know the function opens downward and has a maximum at

$$x = -\frac{b}{2a} = -\frac{200}{2\left(-\frac{2}{3}\right)} = -\frac{200}{-\frac{4}{3}} = 150.$$

When the length x is 150, the width y is

$$y = 200 - \frac{2}{3}x = 200 - \frac{2}{3}(150) = 100.$$

The dimensions of the rectangular playground with maximum area are 150 feet by 100 feet. This gives an area of $150 \cdot 100 = 15,000$ square feet.

71. Maximize the cross-sectional area of the gutter:

$A(x) = x(20 - 2x)$

$\qquad = 20x - 2x^2 = -2x^2 + 20x.$

Since $a = -2$ is negative, we know the function opens downward and has a maximum at

$$x = -\frac{b}{2a} = -\frac{20}{2(-2)} = -\frac{20}{-4} = 5.$$

When the height x is 5, the width is
$20 - 2x = 20 - 2(5) = 20 - 10 = 10.$

$A(5) = -2(5)^2 + 20(5)$

$\qquad = -2(25) + 100 = -50 + 100 = 50$

The maximum cross-sectional area is 50 square inches. This occurs when the gutter is 5 inches deep and 10 inches wide.

73. x = increase

$$A = (50 + x)(8000 - 100x)$$
$$= 400,000 + 3000x - 100x^2$$

$$x = \frac{-b}{2a} = \frac{-3000}{2(-100)} = 15$$

The maximum price is 50 + 15 = \$65.
The maximum revenue = 65(800 – 100·15) = \$422,500.

75. x = increase

$$A = (20 + x)(60 - 2x)$$
$$= 1200 + 20x - 2x^2$$

$$x = \frac{-b}{2a} = \frac{-20}{2(-2)} = 5$$

The maximum number of trees is 20 + 5 = 25 trees. The maximum yield is 60 – 2·5=50 pounds per tree, 50 x 25 = 1250 pounds.

85. $y = -0.25x^2 + 40x$

$$x = \frac{-b}{2a} = \frac{-40}{-0.5} = 80$$
$$y = -0.25(80)^2 + 40(80)$$
$$= 1600$$

vertex: (80, 1600)

87. $y = 5x^2 + 40x + 600$

$$x = \frac{-b}{2a} = \frac{-40}{10} = -4$$
$$y = 5(-4)^2 + 40(-4) + 600$$
$$= 80 - 160 + 600 = 520$$

vertex: (–4, 520)

89. a. The values of y increase then decrease.

b. $y = 0.005x^2 - 0.170x + 14.817$

c. $x = \dfrac{-(-0.170)}{2(.005)} = 17; \quad 1940 + 17 = 1957$

$$y = 0.005(17)^2 - 0.170(17) + 14.817$$
$$\approx 13.372$$

The worst gas mileage was 13.372 mpg in 1957.

d.

91. $f(x) = 3(x + 2)^2 - 5; (-1, -2)$
axis: $x = -2$
(–1, –2) is one unit right of (–2, –2). One unit left of (–2, –2) is (–3, –2).
point: (–3, –2)

93. We start with the form $f(x) = a(x - h)^2 + k$.
Since we know the vertex is $(h, k) = (-3, -4)$, we have $f(x) = a(x + 3)^2 - 4$. We also know that the graph passes through the point $(1, 4)$, which allows us to solve for a.

$$4 = a(1 + 3)^2 - 4$$
$$8 = a(4)^2$$
$$8 = 16a$$
$$\frac{1}{2} = a$$

Therefore, the function is

$$f(x) = \frac{1}{2}(x + 3)^2 - 4.$$

95. $2x + y - 2 = 0$

$y = 2 - 2x$

$d = \sqrt{x^2 + (2 - 2x)^2}$

$d = \sqrt{x^2 + 4 - 8x + 4x^2}$

$d = \sqrt{5x^2 - 8x + 4}$

Minimize $5x^2 - 8x + 4$

$x = \dfrac{-(-8)}{2(5)} = \dfrac{4}{5}$

$y = 2 - 2\left(\dfrac{4}{5}\right) = \dfrac{2}{5}$

$\left(\dfrac{4}{5}, \dfrac{2}{5}\right)$

97. $440 = 2x + \pi y$

$440 - 2x = \pi y$

$\dfrac{440 - 2x}{\pi} = y$

Maximize

$A = x\left(\dfrac{440 - 2x}{\pi}\right) = -\dfrac{2}{\pi}x^2 + \dfrac{440}{\pi}x$

$x = \dfrac{-\dfrac{440}{\pi}}{2\left(-\dfrac{2}{\pi}\right)} = \dfrac{\dfrac{-440}{\pi}}{-\dfrac{4}{\pi}} = \dfrac{440}{4} = 110$

$\dfrac{440 - 2(110)}{\pi} = \dfrac{220}{\pi}$

The dimensions are 110 yards by $\dfrac{220}{\pi}$ yards.

Section 2.3

Check Point Exercises

1. Since n is even and $a_n > 0$, the graph rises to the left and to the right.

2. Since n is odd and the leading coefficient is negative, the function falls to the right. Since the ratio cannot be negative, the model won't be appropriate.

3. The graph does not show the function's end behavior. Since $a_n > 0$ and n is odd, the graph should fall to the left.

4. $f(x) = x^3 + 2x^2 - 4x - 8$

$0 = x^2(x + 2) - 4(x + 2)$

$0 = (x + 2)(x^2 - 4)$

$0 = (x + 2)^2(x - 2)$

$x = 2$ or $x = -2$

The zeros are 2 and –2.

5. $f(x) = x^4 - 4x^2$

$x^4 - 4x^2 = 0$

$x^2(x^2 - 4) = 0$

$x^2(x + 2)(x - 2) = 0$

$x = 0$ or $x = -2$ or $x = 2$

The zeros are 0, –2, and 2.

6. $f(x) = -4\left(x + \dfrac{1}{2}\right)^2(x - 5)^3$

$-4\left(x + \dfrac{1}{2}\right)^2(x - 5)^3 = 0$

$x = -\dfrac{1}{2}$ or $x = 5$

The zeros are $-\dfrac{1}{2}$, with multiplicity 2, and 5, with multiplicity 3.

Because the multiplicity of $-\dfrac{1}{2}$ is even, the graph touches the x-axis and turns around at this zero.

Because the multiplicity of 5 is odd, the graph crosses the x-axis at this zero.

7. $f(-3) = 3(-3)^3 - 10(-3) + 9 = -42$

$f(-2) = 3(-2)^3 - 10(-2) + 9 = 5$

The sign change shows there is a zero between –3 and –2.

8. $f(x) = x^3 - 3x^2$

Since $a_n > 0$ and n is odd, the graph falls to the left and rises to the right.

$x^3 - 3x^2 = 0$

$x^2(x - 3) = 0$

$x = 0$ or $x = 3$

The x-intercepts are 0 and 3.

$f(0) = 0^3 - 3(0)^2 = 0$

The y-intercept is 0.

$f(-x) = (-x)^3 - 3(-x)^2 = -x^3 - 3x^2$

No symmetry.

$f(x) = x^3 - 3x^2$

Exercise Set 2.3

1. polynomial function;
   degree: 3

3. polynomial function;
   degree: 5

5. not a polynomial function

7. not a polynomial function

9. not a polynomial function

11. polynomial function

13. Not a polynomial function because graph is not continuous.

15. (b)

17. (a)

19. $f(x) = 5x^3 + 7x^2 - x + 9$

   Since $a_n > 0$ and n is odd, the graph of $f(x)$ falls to the left and rises to the right.

21. $f(x) = 5x^4 + 7x^2 - x + 9$

   Since $a_n > 0$ and n is even, the graph of $f(x)$ rises to the left and to the right.

23. $f(x) = -5x^4 + 7x^2 - x + 9$

   Since $a_n < 0$ and n is even, the graph of $f(x)$ falls to the left and to the right.

25. $f(x) = 2(x - 5)(x + 4)^2$

   x = 5 has multiplicity 1;
   The graph crosses the x-axis.
   x = –4 has multiplicity 2;
   The graph touches the x-axis and turns around.

27. $f(x) = 4(x - 3)(x + 6)^3$

   x = 3 has multiplicity 1;
   The graph crosses the x-axis.
   x = –6 has multiplicity 3;
   The graph crosses the x-axis.

29. $f(x) = x^3 - 2x^2 + x$

   $= x(x^2 - 2x + 1)$

   $= x(x - 1)^2$

   x = 0 has multiplicity 1;
   The graph crosses the x-axis.
   x = 1 has multiplicity 2;
   The graph touches the x-axis and turns around.

31. $f(x) = x^3 + 7x^2 - 4x - 28$

   $= x^2(x + 7) - 4(x + 7)$

   $= (x^2 - 4)(x + 7)$

   $= (x - 2)(x + 2)(x + 7)$

   x = 2, x = –2 and x = –7 have multiplicity 1;
   The graph crosses the x-axis.

33. $f(x) = x^3 - x - 1$

   $f(1) = -1$
   $f(2) = 5$
   The sign change shows there is a zero between the given values.

35. $f(x) = 2x^4 - 4x^2 + 1$

   $f(-1) = -1$
   $f(0) = 1$
   The sign change shows there is a zero between the given values.

37. $f(x) = x^3 + x^2 - 2x + 1$

   $f(-3) = -11$
   $f(-2) = 1$
   The sign change shows there is a zero between the given values.

39. $f(x) = 3x^3 - 10x + 9$

$f(-3) = -42$

$f(-2) = 5$

The sign change shows there is a zero between the given values.

41. $f(x) = x^3 + 2x^2 - x - 2$

a. Since $a_n > 0$ and n is odd, $f(x)$ rises to the right and falls to the left.

b.
$$x^3 + 2x^2 - x - 2 = 0$$
$$x^2(x+2) - (x+2) = 0$$
$$(x+2)(x^2 - 1) = 0$$
$$(x+2)(x-1)(x+1) = 0$$
$$x = -2, x = 1, x = -1$$

The zeros at -2, -1, and 1 have odd multiplicity so $f(x)$ crosses the x-axis at these points.

c.
$$f(0) = (0)^3 + 2(0)^2 - 0 - 2$$
$$= -2$$
The y-intercept is -2.

d.
$$f(-x) = (-x) + 2(-x)^2 - (-x) - 2$$
$$= -x^3 + 2x^2 + x - 2$$
$$-f(x) = -x^3 - 2x^2 + x + 2$$

The graph has neither origin symmetry or y-axis symmetry.

e. The graph has 2 turning points and $2 \le 3 - 1$.

$y = x^3 + 2x^2 - x - 2$

43. $f(x) = x^4 - 9x^2$

a. Since $a_n > 0$ and n is even, $f(x)$ rises to the left and the right.

b.
$$x^4 - 9x^2 = 0$$
$$x^2(x^2 - 9) = 0$$
$$x^2(x-3)(x+3) = 0$$
$$x = 0, x = 3, x = -3$$

The zeros at -3 and 3 have odd multiplicity, so $f(x)$ crosses the x-axis at these points. The root at 0 has even multiplicity, so $f(x)$ touches the x-axis at 0.

c. $f(0) = (0)^4 - 9(0)^2 = 0$
The y-intercept is 0.

d. $f(-x) = x^4 - 9x^2$
$f(-x) = f(x)$
The graph has y-axis symmetry.

e. The graph has 3 turning points and $3 \le 4 - 1$.

$f(x) = x^4 - 9x^2$

45. $f(x) = -x^4 + 16x^2$

a. Since $a_n < 0$ and n is even, $f(x)$ falls to the left and the right.

b.
$$-x^4 + 16x^2 = 0$$
$$x^2(-x^2 + 16) = 0$$
$$x^2(4-x)(4+x) = 0$$
$$x = 0, x = 4, x = -4$$
The zeros at -4 and 4 have odd multiplicity, so $f(x)$ crosses the x-axis at these points. The root at 0 has even multiplicity, so $f(x)$ touches the x-axis at 0.

c. $f(0) = (0)^4 - 9(0)^2 = 0$
The y-intercept is 0.

d. $f(-x) = -x^4 + 16x^2$

$f(-x) = f(x)$

The graph has y-axis symmetry.

e.   The graph has 3 turning points and
$3 \le 4 - 1$.

$f(x) = -x^4 + 16x^2$

47. $f(x) = x^4 - 2x^3 + x^2$

a.   Since $a_n > 0$ and n is even, $f(x)$ rises to the
left and the right.

b. $x^4 - 2x^3 + x^2 = 0$

$x^2(x^2 - 2x + 1) = 0$

$x^2(x-1)(x-1) = 0$

$x = 0, x = 1$

The zeros at 1 and 0 have even
multiplicity, so $f(x)$ touches the x-axis at 0
and 1.

c. $f(0) = (0)^4 - 2(0)^3 + (0)^2 = 0$

The y-intercept is 0.

d. $f(-x) = x^4 + 2x^3 + x^2$

The graph has neither y-axis nor origin
symmetry.

e.   The graph has 3 turning points and
$3 \le 4 - 1$.

$f(x) = x^4 - 2x^3 + x^2$

49. $f(x) = -2x^4 + 4x^3$

a.   Since $a_n < 0$ and n is even, $f(x)$ falls to the
left and the right.

b. $-2x^4 + 4x^3 = 0$

$x^3(-2x + 4) = 0$

$x = 0, x = 2$

The zeros at 0 and 2 have odd multiplicity,
so $f(x)$ crosses the x-axis at these points.

c. $f(0) = -2(0)^4 + 4(0)^3 = 0$

The y-intercept is 0.

d. $f(-x) = -2x^4 - 4x^3$

The graph has neither y-axis nor origin
symmetry.

e.   The graph has 1 turning point and
$1 \le 4 - 1$.

$f(x) = -2x^4 + 4x^3$

51. $f(x) = 6x^3 - 9x - x^5$

a.   Since $a_n < 0$ and n is odd, $f(x)$ rises to the
left and falls to the right.

b. $-x^5 + 6x^3 - 9x = 0$

$-x(x^4 - 6x^2 + 9) = 0$

$-x(x^2 - 3)(x^2 - 3) = 0$

$x = 0, x = \pm\sqrt{3}$

The root at 0 has odd multiplicity so $f(x)$
crosses the x-axis at $(0, 0)$. The zeros at
$-\sqrt{3}$ and $\sqrt{3}$ have even multiplicity so
$f(x)$ touches the x-axis at $\sqrt{3}$ and $-\sqrt{3}$.

c. $f(0) = -(0)^5 + 6(0)^3 - 9(0) = 0$

The y-intercept is 0.

d. $f(-x) = x^5 - 6x^3 + 9x$

$f(-x) = -f(x)$

The graph has origin symmetry.

e.   The graph has 4 turning point and
        $4 \le 5 - 1$.

$$f(x) = 6x^3 - 9x - x^5$$

53. $f(x) = 3x^2 - x^3$

a.   Since $a_n < 0$ and n is odd, $f(x)$ rises to the
        left and falls to the right.

b. $-x^3 + 3x^2 = 0$
        $-x^2(x - 3) = 0$
        $x = 0, x = 3$
        The zero at 3 has odd multiplicity so $f(x)$
        crosses the x-axis at that point. The root at
        0 has even multiplicity so $f(x)$ touches the
        axis at $(0, 0)$.

c. $f(0) = -(0)^3 + 3(0)^2 = 0$
        The y-intercept is 0.

d. $f(-x) = x^3 + 3x^2$
        The graph has neither y-axis nor origin
        symmetry.

e.   The graph has 2 turning point and $2 \le 3 - 1$.

$$f(x) = 3x^2 - x^3$$

55. $f(x) = -3(x-1)^2(x^2 - 4)$

a.   Since $a_n < 0$ and n is even, $f(x)$ falls to the
        left and the right.

b. $-3(x-1)^2(x^2 - 4) = 0$
        $x = 1, x = -2, x = 2$
        The zeros at -2 and 2 have odd
        multiplicity, so $f(x)$ crosses the x-axis at
        these points. The root at 1 has even

multiplicity, so $f(x)$ touches the x-axis at $(1, 0)$.

c. $f(0) = -3(0-1)^2(0^2 - 4)^3$
              $= -3(1)(-4) = 12$
        The y-intercept is 12.

d. $f(-x) = -3(-x-1)^2(x^2 - 4)$
        The graph has neither y-axis nor origin
        symmetry.

e.   The graph has 1 turning point and $1 \le 4 - 1$.

$$f(x) = -3(x - 1)^2(x^2 - 4)$$

57. $f(x) = x^2(x-1)^3(x+2)$

a.   Since $a_n > 0$ and n is even, $f(x)$ rises to the
        left and the right.

b. $x = 0, x = 1, x = -2$
        The zeros at 1 and -2 have odd multiplicity
        so $f(x)$ crosses the x-axis at those points.
        The root at 0 has even multiplicity so $f(x)$
        touches the axis at $(0, 0)$.

c. $f(0) = 0^2(0-1)^3(0+2) = 0$
        The y-intercept is 0.

d. $f(-x) = x^2(-x-1)^3(-x+2)$
        The graph has neither y-axis nor origin
        symmetry.

e.   The graph has 2 turning points and $2 \le 6 - 1$.

$$f(x) = x^2(x - 1)^3(x + 2)$$

59. $f(x) = -x^2(x-1)(x+3)$

    a. Since $a_n < 0$ and n is even, $f(x)$ falls to the left and the right.

    b. $x = 0, x = 1, x = -3$
The zeros at 1 and –3 have odd multiplicity so $f(x)$ crosses the x-axis at those points. The root at 0 has even multiplicity so $f(x)$ touches the axis at (0, 0).

    c. $f(0) = -0^2(0-1)(0+3) = 0$
The y-intercept is 0.

    d. $f(-x) = -x^2(-x-1)(-x+3)$
The graph has neither y-axis nor origin symmetry.

    e. The graph has 3 turning points and $3 \leq 4-1$.

$f(x) = -x^2(x-1)(x+3)$

61. $f(x) = -2x^3(x-1)^2(x+5)$

    a. Since $a_n < 0$ and n is even, $f(x)$ falls to the left and the right.

    b. $x = 0, x = 1, x = -5$
The roots at 0 and –5 have odd multiplicity so $f(x)$ crosses the x-axis at those points. The root at 1 has even multiplicity so $f(x)$ touches the axis at (1, 0).

    c. $f(0) = -2(0)^3(0-1)^2(0+5) = 0$
The y-intercept is 0.

    d. $f(-x) = 2x^3(-x-1)^2(-x+5)$
The graph has neither y-axis nor origin symmetry.

    e. The graph has 2 turning points and $2 \leq 6-1$.

$f(x) = -2x^3(x-1)^2(x+5)$

63. $f(x) = (x-2)^2(x+4)(x-1)$

    a. Since $a_n > 0$ and n is even, $f(x)$ rises to the left and rises the right.

    b. $x = 2, x = -4, x = 1$
The zeros at –4 and 1 have odd multiplicity so $f(x)$ crosses the x-axis at those points. The root at 2 has even multiplicity so $f(x)$ touches the axis at (2, 0).

    c. $f(0) = (0-2)^2(0+4)(0-1) = -16$
The y-intercept is –16.

    d. $f(-x) = (-x-2)^2(-x+4)(-x-1)$
The graph has neither y-axis nor origin symmetry.

    e. The graph has 3 turning points and $3 \leq 4-1$.

$f(x) = (x-2)^2(x+4)(x-1)$

65. **a.** The x-intercepts of the graph are -2, 1, and 4, so they are the zeros. Since the graph actually crosses the x-axis at all three places, all three have odd multiplicity.

    b. Since the graph has two turning points, the function must be at least of degree 3. Since -2, 1, and 4 are the zeros, $x+2$, $x-1$, and $x-4$ are factors of the function. The lowest odd multiplicity is 1. From the end behavior, we can tell that the leading coefficient must be positive. Thus, the function is $f(x) = (x+2)(x-1)(x-4)$.

    c. $f(0) = (0+2)(0-1)(0-4) = 8$

67. a. The x-intercepts of the graph are -1 and 3, so they are the zeros. Since the graph crosses the x-axis at -1, it has odd multiplicity. Since the graph touches the x-axis and turns around at 3, it has even multiplicity.

b. Since the graph has two turning points, the function must be at least of degree 3. Since -1 and 3 are the zeros, $x+1$ and $x-3$ are factors of the function. The lowest odd multiplicity is 1, and the lowest even multiplicity is 2. From the end behavior, we can tell that the leading coefficient must be positive. Thus, the function is $f(x) = (x+1)(x-3)^2$.

c. $f(0) = (0+1)(0-3)^2 = 9$

69. a. The x-intercepts of the graph are -3 and 2, so they are the zeros. Since the graph touches the x-axis and turns around at both -3 and 2, both have even multiplicity.

b. Since the graph has three turning points, the function must be at least of degree 4. Since -3 and 2 are the zeros, $x+3$ and $x-2$ are factors of the function. The lowest even multiplicity is 2. From the end behavior, we can tell that the leading coefficient must be negative. Thus, the function is $f(x) = -(x+3)^2(x-2)^2$.

c. $f(0) = -(0+3)^2(0-2)^2 = -36$

71. a. The x-intercepts of the graph are -2, -1, and 1, so they are the zeros. Since the graph crosses the x-axis at -1 and 1, they both have odd multiplicity. Since the graph touches the x-axis and turns around at -2, it has even multiplicity.

b. Since the graph has five turning points, the function must be at least of degree 6. Since -2, -1, and 1 are the zeros, $x+2$, $x+1$, and $x-1$ are factors of the function. The lowest even multiplicity is 2, and the lowest odd multiplicity is 1. However, to reach degree 6, one of the odd multiplicities must be 3. From the end behavior, we can tell that the leading coefficient must be positive. The function is $f(x) = (x+2)^2(x+1)(x-1)^3$.

c. $f(0) = (0+2)^2(0+1)(0-1)^3 = -4$

73. $f(x) = -2212x^2 + 57,575x + 107,896$

$f(10) = -2212(10)^2 + 57,575(10) + 107,896 = 462,446$

$g(x) = -84x^3 - 702x^2 + 50,609x + 113,435$

$g(10) = -84(10)^3 - 702(10)^2 + 50,609(10) + 113,435 = 465,325$

The graph indicates that f provides a better description because $f(10)$ is closer to the actual amount of $458,551$.

75. The leading coefficient is negative and the degree is even. This means that the graph will fall to the right. This function will not be useful in modeling the number of cumulative AIDS deaths over an extended period of time because the cumulative number of deaths cannot decrease.

77. a. The percentage of white classmates was increasing from 1970 through 1980 and from 1985 through 1990.

b. The percentage of white classmates was decreasing from 1980 through 1985 and from 1990 through 2002.

c. Three turning points are shown in the graph.

d. Since there are three turning points, the degree of the polynomial function of best fit would be 4.

e.   The leading coefficient would be negative because the graph falls to the left and falls to the right.

97.

99.

101.

103. a.   False; $f(x)$ falls to the left and rises to the right.

b.   False

c.   True; There are many 3rd degree polynomials with the same three x-intercepts.

d.   False; a function with origin symmetry either falls to the left and rises to the right, or rises to the left and falls to the right.

(c)   is true.

105. $f(x) = x^3 - 2x^2$

Section 2.4

Check Point Exercises

1.
$$
\begin{array}{r}
x+5 \\
x+9{\overline{\smash{\big)}\,x^2+14x+45}} \\
\underline{x^2+9x} \\
5x+45 \\
\underline{5x+45} \\
0
\end{array}
$$
The answer is $x + 5$.

2.
$$
\begin{array}{r}
2x^2+3x-2 \\
x-3{\overline{\smash{\big)}\,2x^3-3x^2-11x+7}} \\
\underline{2x^3-6x^2} \\
3x^2-11x \\
\underline{3x^2-9x} \\
-2x+7 \\
\underline{-2x+6} \\
1
\end{array}
$$
The answer is $2x^2 + 3x - 2 + \dfrac{1}{x-3}$.

3.
$$
\begin{array}{r}
2x^2+7x+14 \\
x^2-2x{\overline{\smash{\big)}\,2x^4+3x^3+0x^2-7x-10}} \\
\underline{2x^4-4x^3} \\
7x^3+0x^2 \\
\underline{7x^3-14x^2} \\
14x^2-7x \\
\underline{14x^2-28x} \\
21x-10
\end{array}
$$
The answer is $2x^2 + 7x + 14 + \dfrac{21x-10}{x^2-2x}$.

4.
$$
\begin{array}{r|rrrr}
-2 & 1 & 0 & -7 & -6 \\
   &   & -2 & 4 & 6 \\
\hline
   & 1 & -2 & -3 & 0
\end{array}
$$
The answer is $x^2 - 2x - 3$.

5.
$$
\begin{array}{r|rrrr}
-4 & 3 & 4 & -5 & 3 \\
   &   & -12 & 32 & -108 \\
\hline
   & 3 & -8 & 27 & -105
\end{array}
$$
$f(-4) = -105$

6.
$$
\begin{array}{r|rrrr}
-1 & 15 & 14 & -3 & -2 \\
   &   & -15 & 1 & 2 \\
\hline
   & 15 & -1 & -2 & 0
\end{array}
$$
$15x^2 - x - 2 = 0$

$(3x+1)(5x-2) = 0$

$x = -\dfrac{1}{3}$ or $x = \dfrac{2}{5}$

The solution set is $\left\{-1, -\dfrac{1}{3}, \dfrac{2}{5}\right\}$.

Exercise Set 2.4

1.
$$x+5\overline{\smash{\big)}\,x^2+8x+15} \quad \overset{\textstyle x+3}{}$$
$$\underline{x^2+5x}$$
$$3x+15$$
$$\underline{3x+15}$$
$$0$$

The answer is $x+3$.

3.
$$x+2\overline{\smash{\big)}\,x^3+5x^2+7x+2} \quad \overset{\textstyle x^2+3x+1}{}$$
$$\underline{x^3+2x^2}$$
$$3x^2+7x$$
$$\underline{3x^2+6x}$$
$$x+2$$
$$\underline{x+2}$$
$$0$$

The answer is x^2+3x+1.

5.
$$3x-1\overline{\smash{\big)}\,6x^3+7x^2+12x-5} \quad \overset{\textstyle 2x^2+3x+5}{}$$
$$\underline{6x^3-2x^2}$$
$$9x^2+12x$$
$$\underline{9x^2-3x}$$
$$15x-5$$
$$\underline{15x-5}$$
$$0$$

The answer is $2x^2+3x+5$.

7.
$$3x-2\overline{\smash{\big)}\,12x^2+x-4} \quad \overset{\textstyle 4x+3+\frac{2}{3x-2}}{}$$
$$\underline{12x^2-8x}$$
$$9x-4$$
$$\underline{9x-6}$$
$$2$$

The answer is $4x+3+\dfrac{2}{3x-2}$.

9.
$$x+3\overline{\smash{\big)}\,2x^3+7x^2+9x-20} \quad \overset{\textstyle 2x^2+x+6-\frac{38}{x+3}}{}$$
$$\underline{2x^3+6x^2}$$
$$x^2+9x$$
$$\underline{x^2+3x}$$
$$6x-20$$
$$\underline{6x+18}$$
$$-38$$

The answer is $2x^2+x+6-\dfrac{38}{x+3}$.

11.
$$x-4\overline{\smash{\big)}\,4x^4-4x^2+6x} \quad \overset{\textstyle 4x^3+16x^2+60x+246+\frac{984}{x-4}}{}$$
$$\underline{4x^4-16x^3}$$
$$16x^3-4x^2$$
$$\underline{16x^3-64x^2}$$
$$60x^2+6x$$
$$\underline{60x^2-240x}$$
$$246x$$
$$\underline{246x-984}$$
$$984$$

The answer is $4x^3+16x^2+60x+246+\dfrac{984}{x-4}$.

13.
$$3x^2-x-3\overline{\smash{\big)}\,6x^3+13x^2-11x-15} \quad \overset{\textstyle 2x+5}{}$$
$$\underline{6x^3-2x^2-6x}$$
$$15x^2-5x-15$$
$$\underline{15x^2-5x-15}$$
$$0$$

The answer is $2x+5$.

$$6x^2 + 3x - 1$$

15. $3x^2 + 1\overline{)18x^4 + 9x^3 + 3x^2}$

$$\underline{18x^4 + 6x^2}$$
$$9x^3 - 3x^2$$
$$\underline{9x^3 + 3x}$$
$$-3x^2 - 3x$$
$$\underline{-3x^2 - 1}$$
$$-3x + 1$$

The answer is $6x^2 + 3x - 1 - \dfrac{3x-1}{3x^2+1}$.

17. $(2x^2 + x - 10) \div (x - 2)$

$$\begin{array}{r|rrr} 2 & 2 & 1 & -10 \\ & & 4 & 10 \\ \hline & 2 & 5 & 0 \end{array}$$

The answer is $2x + 5$.

19. $(3x^2 + 7x - 20) \div (x + 5)$

$$\begin{array}{r|rrr} -5 & 3 & 7 & -20 \\ & & -15 & 40 \\ \hline & 3 & -8 & 20 \end{array}$$

The answer is $3x - 8 + \dfrac{20}{x+5}$.

21. $(4x^3 - 3x^2 + 3x - 1) \div (x - 1)$

$$\begin{array}{r|rrrr} 1 & 4 & -3 & 3 & -1 \\ & & 4 & 1 & 4 \\ \hline & 4 & 1 & 4 & 3 \end{array}$$

The answer is $4x^2 + x + 4 + \dfrac{3}{x-1}$.

23. $(6x^5 - 2x^3 + 4x^2 - 3x + 1) \div (x - 2)$

$$\begin{array}{r|rrrrrr} 2 & 6 & 0 & -2 & 4 & -3 & 1 \\ & & 12 & 24 & 44 & 96 & 186 \\ \hline & 6 & 12 & 22 & 48 & 93 & 187 \end{array}$$

The answer is

$6x^4 + 12x^3 + 22x^2 + 48x + 93 + \dfrac{187}{x-2}$.

25. $(x^2 - 5x - 5x^3 + x^4) \div (5 + x) \Rightarrow$

$(x^4 - 5x^3 + x^2 - 5x) \div (x + 5)$

$$\begin{array}{r|rrrrr} -5 & 1 & -5 & 1 & -5 & 0 \\ & & -5 & 50 & -255 & 1300 \\ \hline & 1 & -10 & 51 & -260 & 1300 \end{array}$$

The answer is

$x^3 - 10x^2 + 51x - 260 + \dfrac{1300}{x+5}$.

27. $\dfrac{x^5 + x^3 - 2}{x - 1}$

$$\begin{array}{r|rrrrrr} 1 & 1 & 0 & 1 & 0 & 0 & -2 \\ & & 1 & 1 & 2 & 2 & 2 \\ \hline & 1 & 1 & 2 & 2 & 2 & 0 \end{array}$$

The answer is $x^4 + x^3 + 2x^2 + 2x + 2$.

29. $\dfrac{x^4 - 256}{x - 4}$

$$\begin{array}{r|rrrrr} 4 & 1 & 0 & 0 & 0 & -256 \\ & & 4 & 16 & 64 & 256 \\ \hline & 1 & 4 & 16 & 64 & 0 \end{array}$$

The answer is $x^3 + 4x^2 + 16x + 64$.

31. $\dfrac{2x^5 - 3x^4 + x^3 - x^2 + 2x - 1}{x + 2}$

$$\begin{array}{r|rrrrrr} -2 & 2 & -3 & 1 & -1 & 2 & -1 \\ & & -4 & 14 & -30 & 62 & -128 \\ \hline & 2 & -7 & 15 & -31 & 64 & -129 \end{array}$$

The answer is

$2x^4 - 7x^3 + 15x^2 - 31x + 64 - \dfrac{129}{x+2}$.

33. $f(x) = 2x^3 - 11x^2 + 7x - 5$

$$\begin{array}{r|rrrr} 4 & 2 & -11 & 7 & -5 \\ & & 8 & -12 & -20 \\ \hline & 2 & -3 & -5 & -25 \end{array}$$

$f(4) = -25$

35. $f(x) = 3x^3 - 7x^2 - 2x + 5$

$$
\begin{array}{r|rrrr}
-3 & 3 & -7 & -2 & 5 \\
   &   & -9 & 48 & -138 \\
\hline
   & 3 & -16 & 46 & -133
\end{array}
$$

$f(-3) = -133$

37. $f(x) = x^4 + 5x^3 + 5x^2 - 5x - 6$

$$
\begin{array}{r|rrrrr}
3 & 1 & 5 & 5 & -5 & -6 \\
  &   & 3 & 24 & 87 & 246 \\
\hline
  & 1 & 8 & 29 & 82 & 240
\end{array}
$$

$f(3) = 240$

39. $f(x) = 2x^4 - 5x^3 - x^2 + 3x + 2$

$$
\begin{array}{r|rrrrr}
-\frac{1}{2} & 2 & -5 & -1 & 3 & 2 \\
             &   & -1 & 3 & -1 & -1 \\
\hline
             & 2 & -6 & 2 & 2 & 1
\end{array}
$$

$f\left(-\dfrac{1}{2}\right) = 1$

41. Dividend: $x^3 - 4x^2 + x + 6$
Divisor: $x + 1$

$$
\begin{array}{r|rrrr}
-1 & 1 & -4 & 1 & 6 \\
   &   & -1 & 5 & -6 \\
\hline
   & 1 & -5 & 6 & 0
\end{array}
$$

The quotient is $x^2 - 5x + 6$.
$(x+1)(x^2 - 5x + 6) = 0$
$(x + 1)(x - 2)(x - 3) = 0$
$x = -1, x = 2, x = 3$
The solution set is $\{-1, 2, 3\}$.

43. $2x^3 - 5x^2 + x + 2 = 0$

$$
\begin{array}{r|rrrr}
2 & 2 & -5 & 1 & 2 \\
  &   & 4 & -2 & -2 \\
\hline
  & 2 & -1 & -1 & 0
\end{array}
$$

$(x - 2)(2x^2 - x - 1) = 0$
$(x - 2)(2x + 1)(x - 1) = 0$
$x = 2, \ x = -\dfrac{1}{2}, \ x = 1$

The solution set is $\left\{-\dfrac{1}{2}, 1, 2\right\}$.

45. $12x^3 + 16x^2 - 5x - 3 = 0$

$$
\begin{array}{r|rrrr}
-\frac{3}{2} & 12 & 16 & -5 & -3 \\
             &   & -18 & 3 & 3 \\
\hline
             & 12 & -2 & -2 & 0
\end{array}
$$

$\left(x + \dfrac{3}{2}\right)(12x^2 - 2x - 2) = 0$

$\left(x + \dfrac{3}{2}\right)2\left(6x^2 - x - 1\right) = 0$

$\left(x + \dfrac{3}{2}\right)2(3x + 1)(2x - 1) = 0$

$x = -\dfrac{3}{2}, \ x = -\dfrac{1}{3}, \ x = \dfrac{1}{2}$

The solution set is $\left\{-\dfrac{3}{2}, -\dfrac{1}{3}, \dfrac{1}{2}\right\}$.

47. The graph indicates that 2 is a solution to the equation.

$$
\begin{array}{r|rrrr}
2 & 1 & 2 & -5 & -6 \\
  &   & 2 & 8 & 6 \\
\hline
  & 1 & 4 & 3 & 0
\end{array}
$$

The remainder is 0, so 2 is a solution.
$x^3 + 2x^2 - 5x - 6 = 0$
$(x - 2)(x^2 + 4x + 3) = 0$
$(x - 2)(x + 3)(x + 1) = 0$
The solutions are 2, -3, and -1, or $\{-3, -1, 2\}$.

49. The table indicates that 1 is a solution to the equation.

$$\underline{1|}\quad 6 \quad -11 \quad 6 \quad -1$$
$$\phantom{\underline{1|}\quad 6}\quad 6 \quad -5 \quad 1$$
$$\overline{\phantom{\underline{1|}}\quad 6 \quad -5 \quad 1 \quad 0}$$

The remainder is 0, so 1 is a solution.

$$6x^3 - 11x^2 + 6x - 1 = 0$$
$$(x-1)(6x^2 - 5x + 1) = 0$$
$$(x-1)(3x-1)(2x-1) = 0$$

The solutions are 1, $\dfrac{1}{3}$, and $\dfrac{1}{2}$, or $\left\{\dfrac{1}{3}, \dfrac{1}{2}, 1\right\}$.

51. a. $14x^3 - 17x^2 - 16x - 177 = 0$

$$\underline{3|}\quad 14 \quad -17 \quad -16 \quad -177$$
$$\phantom{\underline{3|}\quad 14}\quad 42 \quad 75 \quad 177$$
$$\overline{\phantom{\underline{3|}}\quad 14 \quad 25 \quad 59 \quad 0}$$

The remainder is 0 so 3 is a solution.
$$14x^3 - 17x^2 - 16x - 177$$
$$= (x-3)(14x^2 + 25x + 59)$$

b. $f(x) = 14x^3 - 17x^2 - 16x + 34$

We need to find x when $f(x) = 211$.

$$f(x) = 14x^3 - 17x^2 - 16x + 34$$
$$211 = 14x^3 - 17x^2 - 16x + 34$$
$$0 = 14x^3 - 17x^2 - 16x - 177$$

This is the equation obtained in part **a.** One solution is 3. It can be used to find other solutions (if they exist).

$$14x^3 - 17x^2 - 16x - 177 = 0$$
$$(x-3)(14x^2 + 25x + 59) = 0$$

The polynomial $14x^2 + 25x + 59$ cannot be factored, so the only solution is $x = 3$. The female moth's abdominal width is 3 millimeters.

53. $A = l \cdot w$ so

$$l = \frac{A}{w} = \frac{0.5x^3 - 0.3x^2 + 0.22x + 0.06}{x + 0.2}$$

$$\underline{-0.2|}\quad 0.5 \quad -0.3 \quad 0.22 \quad 0.06$$
$$\phantom{\underline{-0.2|}\quad 0.5}\quad -0.1 \quad 0.08 \quad -0.06$$
$$\overline{\phantom{\underline{-0.2|}}\quad 0.5 \quad -0.4 \quad 0.3 \quad 0}$$

Therefore, the length of the rectangle is $0.5x^2 - 0.4x + 0.3$ units.

55. a.
$$f(30) = \frac{80(30) - 8000}{30 - 110} = 70$$

(30, 70) At a 30% tax rate, the government tax revenue will be \$70 ten billion.

b.
$$\underline{110}\ \Big|\quad 80 \quad -8000$$
$$\phantom{\underline{110}\ \Big|\quad 80}\quad 8800$$
$$\overline{\phantom{\underline{110}\ \Big|}\quad 80 \quad 800}$$

$$f(x) = 80 + \frac{800}{x - 110}$$
$$f(30) = 80 + \frac{800}{80 - 110} = 70$$

(30, 70) same answer as in **a.**

c. $f(x)$ is not a polynomial function. It is a rational function because it is the quotient of two linear polynomials.

65. Exercise 43:

Exercise 44:

Exercise 45

Exercise 46:

67.

$$\begin{array}{r} 5x^2 + 2x - 4 \\ 4x+3\overline{)20x^3 + 23x^2 - 10x + k} \\ \underline{20x^3 + 15x^2} \\ 8x^2 - 10 \\ \underline{8x^2 + 6x} \\ -16x + k \\ \underline{-16x - 12} \end{array}$$

To get a remainder of zero, k must equal -12.
$k = -12$

69.

$$\begin{array}{r} x^{2n} - x^n + 1 \\ x^n+1\overline{)x^{3n} \qquad\qquad +1} \\ \underline{x^{3n} + x^{2n}} \\ -x^{2n} \\ \underline{-x^{2n} - x^n} \\ x^n + 1 \\ \underline{x^n + 1} \\ 0 \end{array}$$

71. $x^4 - 4x^3 - 9x^2 + 16x + 20 = 0$

$$\begin{array}{r|rrrrr} 5 & 1 & -4 & -9 & 16 & 20 \\ & & 5 & 5 & -20 & -20 \\ \hline & 1 & 1 & -4 & -4 & 0 \end{array}$$

The remainder is zero and 5 is a solution to the equation.

$x^4 - 4x^3 - 9x^2 + 16x + 20$

$= (x-5)(x^3 + x^2 - 4x - 4)$

To solve the equation, we set it equal to zero and factor.

$(x-5)(x^3 + x^2 - 4x - 4) = 0$

$(x-5)(x^2(x+1) - 4(x+1)) = 0$

$(x-5)(x+1)(x^2 - 4) = 0$

$(x-5)(x+1)(x+2)(x-2) = 0$

Apply the zero product principle.

$x - 5 = 0 \qquad x + 1 = 0$
$\quad x = 5 \qquad\qquad x = -1$

$x + 2 = 0 \qquad x - 2 = 0$
$\quad x = -2 \qquad\qquad x = 2$

The solutions are -2, -1, 2 and 5 and the solution set is $\{-2, -1, 2, 5\}$.

Section 2.5

Check Point Exercises

1. $p: \pm 1,\ \pm 2,\ \pm 3,\ \pm 6$

$q: \pm 1$

$\dfrac{p}{q}: \pm 1,\ \pm 2,\ \pm 3,\ \pm 6$

are the possible rational zeros.

2. $p: \pm 1,\ \pm 3$

$q: \pm 1,\ \pm 2,\ \pm 4$

$\dfrac{p}{q}: \pm 1,\ \pm 3,\ \pm\dfrac{1}{2},\ \pm\dfrac{1}{4},\ \pm\dfrac{3}{2},\ \pm\dfrac{3}{4}$

are the possible rational zeros.

3. $\pm 1,\ \pm 2,\ \pm 4,\ \pm 5,\ \pm 10,\ \pm 20$ are possible rational zeros

$$\begin{array}{r|rrrr} 1 & 1 & 8 & 11 & -20 \\ & & 1 & 9 & 20 \\ \hline & 1 & 9 & 20 & 0 \end{array}$$

1 is a zero.

$x^2 + 9x + 20 = 0$

$(x+4)(x+5) = 0$

$x = -4 \quad \text{or} \quad x = -5$

The solution set is $\{1, -4, -5\}$.

4. $\pm 1,\ \pm 2$ are possible rational zeros

$$\begin{array}{r|rrrr} 2 & 1 & 1 & -5 & -2 \\ & & 2 & 6 & 2 \\ \hline & 1 & 3 & 1 & 0 \end{array}$$

2 is a zero.

$x^2 + 3x + 1 = 0$

$x = \dfrac{-b \pm \sqrt{b^2 - 4ac}}{2a}$

$x = \dfrac{-3 \pm \sqrt{3^2 - 4(1)(1)}}{2(1)}$

$= \dfrac{-3 \pm \sqrt{5}}{2}$

The solution set is $\left\{ 2, \dfrac{-3+\sqrt{5}}{2}, \dfrac{-3-\sqrt{5}}{2} \right\}$.

5. $\pm 1, \ \pm 13$ are possible rational zeros.

$$
\begin{array}{r|rrrrr}
1 & 1 & -6 & 22 & -30 & 13 \\
  &   & 1 & -5 & 17 & -13 \\
\hline
  & 1 & -5 & 17 & -13 & 0
\end{array}
$$

1 is a zero.

$$
\begin{array}{r|rrrr}
1 & 1 & 5 & 17 & -13 \\
  &   & 1 & -4 & 13 \\
\hline
  & 1 & -4 & 13 & 0
\end{array}
$$

1 is a double root.

$x^2 - 4x + 13 = 0$

$x = \dfrac{4 \pm \sqrt{16-52}}{2} = \dfrac{4 \pm \sqrt{-36}}{2} = 2 + 3i$

The solution set is $\{1, \ 2 + 3i, \ 2 - 3i\}$.

6. $(x+3)(x-i)(x+i) = (x+3)(x^2+1)$

$f(x) = a_n(x+3)(x^2+1)$

$f(1) = a_n(1+3)(1^2+1) = 8a_n = 8$

$a_n = 1$

$f(x) = (x+3)(x^2+1)$ or $x^3 + 3x^2 + x + 3$

7. $f(x) = x^4 - 14x^3 + 71x^2 - 154x + 120$

$f(-x) = x^4 + 14x^3 + 71x^2 + 154x + 120$

Since $f(x)$ has 4 changes of sign, there are 4, 2, or 0 positive real zeros.

Since $f(-x)$ has no changes of sign, there are no negative real zeros.

Exercise Set 2.5

1. $f(x) = x^3 + x^2 - 4x - 4$

$p: \pm 1, \ \pm 2, \ \pm 4$

$q: \pm 1$

$\dfrac{p}{q}: \pm 1, \ \pm 2, \ \pm 4$

3. $f(x) = 3x^4 - 11x^3 - x^2 + 19x + 6$

$p: \pm 1, \pm 2, \pm 3, \pm 6$

$q: \pm 1, \pm 3$

$\dfrac{p}{q}: \pm 1, \pm 2, \pm 3, \pm 6, \pm \dfrac{1}{3}, \pm \dfrac{2}{3}$

5. $f(x) = 4x^4 - x^3 + 5x^2 - 2x - 6$

$p: \pm 1, \pm 2, \pm 3, \pm 6$

$q: \pm 1, \pm 2, \pm 4$

$\dfrac{p}{q}: \pm 1, \pm 2, \pm 3, \pm 6, \pm \dfrac{1}{2}, \pm \dfrac{1}{4}, \pm \dfrac{3}{2}, \pm \dfrac{3}{4}$

7. $f(x) = x^5 - x^4 - 7x^3 + 7x^2 - 12x - 12$

$p: \pm 1, \pm 2, \pm 3 \pm 4 \pm 6 \pm 12$

$q: \pm 1$

$\dfrac{p}{q}: \pm 1, \pm 2, \pm 3 \pm 4 \pm 6 \pm 12$

9. $f(x) = x^3 + x^2 - 4x - 4$

a. $p: \pm 1, \ \pm 2, \ \pm 4$

$q: \pm 1$

$\dfrac{p}{q}: \pm 1, \ \pm 2, \ \pm 4$

b.
$$
\begin{array}{r|rrrr}
2 & 1 & 1 & -4 & -4 \\
  &   & 2 & 6 & 4 \\
\hline
  & 1 & 3 & 2 & 0
\end{array}
$$

2 is a zero.

c. $x^3 + x^2 - 4x - 4 = 0$

$(x-2)(x^2 + 3x + 2) = 0$

$(x-2)(x+2)(x+1) = 0$

$x - 2 = 0 \quad x + 2 = 0 \quad x + 1 = 0$

$x = 2, \ x = -2, \ x = -1$

The solution set is $\{2, -2, -1\}$.

11. $f(x) = 2x^3 - 3x^2 - 11x + 6$

a. $p: \pm 1, \ \pm 2, \ \pm 3, \ \pm 6$

$q: \pm 1, \ \pm 2$

$\dfrac{p}{q}: \pm 1, \pm 2, \pm 3, \pm 6, \pm \dfrac{1}{2}, \pm \dfrac{3}{2}$

b.
$$
\begin{array}{r|rrrr}
3 & 2 & -3 & -11 & 6 \\
  &   & 6 & 9 & -6 \\
\hline
  & 2 & 3 & -2 & 0
\end{array}
$$

3 is a zero.

c. $2x^3 - 3x^2 - 11x + 6 = 0$

$(x-3)(2x^2 + 3x - 2) = 0$

$(x-3)(2x-1)(x+2) = 0$

$x = 3, \; x = \dfrac{1}{2}, \; x = -2$

The solution set is $\left\{ 3, \dfrac{1}{2}, -2 \right\}$.

13. a. $f(x) = x^3 + 4x^2 - 3x - 6$

$p: \pm 1, \pm 2, \pm 3, \pm 6$

$q: \pm 1$

$\dfrac{p}{q}: \pm 1, \pm 2, \pm 3, \pm 6$

b.

-1	1	4	-3	-6
		-1	-3	6
	1	3	-6	0

-1 is a zero.

c. $x^2 + 3x - 6 = 0$

$x = \dfrac{-b \pm \sqrt{b^2 - 4ac}}{2a}$

$x = \dfrac{-3 \pm \sqrt{3^2 - 4(1)(-6)}}{2(1)}$

$= \dfrac{-3 \pm \sqrt{33}}{2}$

The solution set is

$\left\{ -1, \dfrac{-3 + \sqrt{33}}{2}, \dfrac{-3 - \sqrt{33}}{2} \right\}$.

15. a. $f(x) = 2x^3 + 6x^2 + 5x + 2$

$p: \pm 1, \pm 2$

$q: \pm 1, \pm 2$

$\dfrac{p}{q}: \pm 1, \pm 2, \pm \dfrac{1}{2}$

b.

-2	2	6	5	2
		-4	-4	-2
	2	2	1	0

-2 is a zero.

c. $2x^2 + 2x + 1 = 0$

$x = \dfrac{-b \pm \sqrt{b^2 - 4ac}}{2a}$

$x = \dfrac{-2 \pm \sqrt{2^2 - 4(2)(1)}}{2(2)}$

$= \dfrac{-2 \pm \sqrt{-4}}{4}$

$= \dfrac{-2 \pm 2i}{4}$

$= \dfrac{-1 \pm i}{2}$

The solution set is $\left\{ -2, \dfrac{-1+i}{2}, \dfrac{-1-i}{2} \right\}$.

17. $x^3 - 2x^2 - 11x + 12 = 0$

a. $p: \pm 1, \pm 2, \pm 3, \pm 4, \pm 6, \pm 12$

$q: \pm 1$

$\dfrac{p}{q}: \pm 1, \pm 2, \pm 3, \pm 4, \pm 6, \pm 12$

b.

4	1	-2	-11	12
		4	8	-12
	1	2	-3	0

4 is a root.

c. $x^3 - 2x^2 - 11x + 12$

$(x-4)(x^2 + 2x - 3) = 0$

$(x-4)(x+3)(x-1) = 0$

$x - 4 = 0 \quad x + 3 = 0 \quad x - 1 = 0$

$x = 4 \qquad x = -3 \qquad x = 1$

The solution set is $\{-3, 1, 4\}$.

19. $x^3 - 10x - 12 = 0$

    a. $p: \pm 1, \pm 2, \pm 3, \pm 4, \pm 6, \pm 12$

          $q: \pm 1$

          $\dfrac{p}{q}: \pm 1, \pm 2, \pm 3, \pm 4, \pm 6, \pm 12$

    b.

-2	1	0	-10	-12
		-2	4	12
	1	-2	-6	0

        -2 is a root.

    c. $x^3 - 10x - 12 = 0$

          $(x+2)(x^2 - 2x - 6) = 0$

$$x = \frac{2 \pm \sqrt{4+24}}{2} = \frac{2 \pm \sqrt{28}}{2}$$

$$= \frac{2 \pm 2\sqrt{7}}{2} = 1 \pm \sqrt{7}$$

    The solution set is $\left\{ -2, 1+\sqrt{7}, 1-\sqrt{7} \right\}$.

21. $6x^3 + 25x^2 - 24x + 5 = 0$

    a. $p: \pm 1, \pm 5$

          $q: \pm 1, \pm 2, \pm 3, \pm 6$

          $\dfrac{p}{q}: \pm 1, \pm 5, \pm \dfrac{1}{2}, \pm \dfrac{5}{2}, \pm \dfrac{1}{3}, \pm \dfrac{5}{3}, \pm \dfrac{1}{6}, \pm \dfrac{5}{6}$

    b.

-5	6	25	-24	5
		-30	25	-5
	6	-5	1	0

        -5 is a root.

    c. $6x^3 + 25x^2 - 24x + 5 = 0$

          $(x+5)(6x^2 - 5x + 1) = 0$

          $(x+5)(2x-1)(3x-1) = 0$

          $x+5 = 0 \quad 2x-1 = 0 \quad 3x-1 = 0$

          $x = -5, \quad x = \dfrac{1}{2}, \quad x = \dfrac{1}{3}$

    The solution set is $\left\{ -5, \dfrac{1}{2}, \dfrac{1}{3} \right\}$.

23. $x^4 - 2x^3 - 5x^2 + 8x + 4 = 0$

    a. $p: \pm 1, \pm 2, \pm 4$

          $q: \pm 1$

          $\dfrac{p}{q}: \pm 1, \pm 2, \pm 4$

    b.

2	1	-2	-5	8	4
		2	0	-10	-4
	1	0	-5	-2	0

        2 is a root.

    c. $x^4 - 2x^3 - 5x^2 + 8x + 4 = 0$

          $(x-2)(x^3 - 5x - 2) = 0$

-2	1	0	-5	-2
		-2	4	2
	1	-2	-1	0

        -2 is a zero of $x^3 - 5x - 2 = 0$.

$$(x-2)(x+2)\left(x^2 - 2x - 1\right) = 0$$

$$x = \frac{2 \pm \sqrt{4+4}}{2} = \frac{2 \pm \sqrt{8}}{2} = \frac{2 \pm 2\sqrt{2}}{2}$$

$$= 1 \pm \sqrt{2}$$

    The solution set is

    $\left\{ -2, 2, 1+\sqrt{2}, 1-\sqrt{2} \right\}$.

25.

$$(x-1)\,(x+5i)\,(x-5i)$$

$$= (x-1)\left(x^2 + 25\right)$$

$$= x^3 + 25x - x^2 - 25$$

$$= x^3 - x^2 + 25x - 25$$

$$f(x) = a_n \left(x^3 - x^2 + 25x - 25\right)$$

$$f(-1) = a_n(-1 - 1 - 25 - 25)$$

$$-104 = a_n(-52)$$

$$a_n = 2$$

$$f(x) = 2\left(x^3 - x^2 + 25x - 25\right)$$

$$f(x) = 2x^3 - 2x^2 + 50x - 50$$

27. $(x+5)(x-4-3i)(x-4+3i)$

$\quad = (x+5)(x^2 - 4x + 3ix - 4x + 16 - 12i$

$\qquad -3ix + 12i - 9i^2)$

$\quad = (x+5)(x^2 - 8x + 25)$

$\quad = (x^3 - 8x^2 + 25x + 5x^2 - 40x + 125)$

$\quad = x^3 - 3x^2 - 15x + 125$

$\quad f(x) = a_n(x^3 - 3x^2 - 15x + 125)$

$\quad f(2) = a_n\left(2^3 - 3(2)^2 - 15(2) + 125\right)$

$\quad 91 = a_n(91)$

$\quad a_n = 1$

$\quad f(x) = 1(x^3 - 3x^2 - 15x + 125)$

$\quad f(x) = x^3 - 3x^2 - 15x + 125$

29. $(x-i)(x+i)(x-3i)(x+3i)$

$\quad = (x^2 - i^2)(x^2 - 9i^2)$

$\quad = (x^2 + 1)(x^2 + 9)$

$\quad = x^4 + 10x^2 + 9$

$\quad f(x) = a_n(x^4 + 10x^2 + 9)$

$\quad f(-1) = a_n((-1)^4 + 10(-1)^2 + 9)$

$\quad 20 = a_n(20)$

$\quad a_n = 1$

$\quad f(x) = x^4 + 10x^2 + 9$

31. $(x+2)\ (x-5)\ (x-3+2i)\ (x-3-2i)$

$\quad = (x^2 - 3x - 10)(x^2 - 3x - 2ix - 3x + 9 + 6i + 2ix - 6i - 4i)$

$\quad = (x^2 - 3x - 10)\ (x^2 - 6x + 13)$

$\quad = x^4 - 6x + 13x^2 - 3x^3 + 18x^2 - 39x - 10x^2 + 60x - 130$

$\quad = x^4 - 9x^3 + 21x^2 + 21x - 130$

$\quad f(x) = a_n\left(x^4 - 9x^3 + 21x^2 + 21x - 130\right)$

$\quad f(1) = a_n(1 - 9 + 21 + 21 - 130)$

$\quad -96 = a_n(-96)$

$\quad a_n = 1$

$\quad f(x) = x^4 - 9x^3 + 21x^2 + 21x - 130$

33. $f(x) = x^3 + 2x^2 + 5x + 4$

Since $f(x)$ has no sign variations,
no positive real roots exist.

$f(-x) = -x^3 + 2x^2 - 5x + 4$

Since $f(-x)$ has 3 sign variations,
3 or 1 negative real roots exist.

35. $f(x) = 5x^3 - 3x^2 + 3x - 1$

Since $f(x)$ has 3 sign variations, 3 or 1 positive
real roots exist.

$f(-x) = -5x^3 - 3x^2 - 3x - 1$

Since $f(-x)$ has no sign variations, no negative
real roots exist.

37. $f(x) = 2x^4 - 5x^3 - x^2 - 6x + 4$

Since $f(x)$ has 2 sign variations, 2 or 0 positive
real roots exist.

$f(-x) = 2x^4 + 5x^3 - x^2 + 6x + 4$

Since $f(-x)$ has 2 sign variations, 2 or 0 negative
real roots exist.

39. $f(x) = x^3 - 4x^2 - 7x + 10$

$p: \pm 1, \pm 2, \pm 5, \pm 10$

$q: \pm 1$

$\dfrac{p}{q}: \pm 1, \pm 2, \pm 5, \pm 10$

Since $f(x)$ has 2 sign variations, 0 or 2 positive
real zeros exist.

$f(-x) = -x^3 - 4x^2 + 7x + 10$

Since $f(-x)$ has 1 sign variation, exactly one
negative real zeros exists.

$$
\begin{array}{r|rrrr}
-2 & 1 & -4 & -7 & 10 \\
   &   & -2 & 12 & -10 \\
\hline
   & 1 & -6 & 5 & 0
\end{array}
$$

-2 is a zero.

$$f(x) = (x+2)\left(x^2 - 6x + 5\right)$$
$$= (x+2)(x-5)(x-1)$$

$x = -2, x = 5, x = 1$

The solution set is $\{-2, 5, 1\}$.

41. $2x^3 - x^2 - 9x - 4 = 0$

$p: \pm 1, \pm 2, \pm 4$

$q: \pm 1, \pm 2$

$\dfrac{p}{q}: \pm 1, \pm 2, \pm 4 \pm \dfrac{1}{2}$

1 positive real root exists.

$f(-x) = -2x^3 - x^2 + 9x - 4$ 2 or no negative real
roots exist.

$$
\begin{array}{r|rrrr}
-\dfrac{1}{2} & 2 & -1 & -9 & -4 \\
              &   & -1 & 1 & 4 \\
\hline
              & 2 & -2 & -8 & 0
\end{array}
$$

$-\dfrac{1}{2}$ is a root.

$$\left(x + \dfrac{1}{2}\right)\left(2x^2 - 2x - 8\right) = 0$$

$$2\left(x + \dfrac{1}{2}\right)\left(x^2 - x - 4\right) = 0$$

$$x = \dfrac{1 \pm \sqrt{1 + 16}}{2} = \dfrac{1 \pm \sqrt{17}}{2}$$

The solution set is

$$\left\{ -\dfrac{1}{2}, \dfrac{1 + \sqrt{17}}{2}, \dfrac{1 - \sqrt{17}}{2} \right\}.$$

43. $f(x) = x^4 - 2x^3 + x^2 + 12x + 8$

$p: \pm 1, \ \pm 2, \ \pm 4, \ \pm 8$

$q: \pm 1$

$\dfrac{p}{q}: \pm 1, \ \pm 2, \ \pm 4, \ \pm 8$

Since $f(x)$ has 2 sign changes, 0 or 2 positive
roots exist.

$$f(-x) = (-x)^4 - 2(-x)^3 + (-x)^2 - 12x + 8$$
$$= x^4 + 2x^3 + x^2 - 12x + 8$$

Since $f(-x)$ has 2 sign changes, 0 or 2 negative
roots exist.

$$
\begin{array}{r|rrrrr}
-1 & 1 & -2 & 1 & 12 & 8 \\
   &   & -1 & 4 & -4 & -8 \\
\hline
   & 1 & -3 & 4 & 8 & 0
\end{array}
$$

$$
\begin{array}{r|rrrr}
-1 & 1 & -3 & 4 & 8 \\
   &   & -1 & 4 & -8 \\
\hline
   & 1 & -4 & 8 & 0
\end{array}
$$

$0 = x^2 - 4x + 8$

$x = \dfrac{-(-4) \pm \sqrt{(-4)^2 - 4(1)(8)}}{2(1)}$

$x = \dfrac{4 \pm \sqrt{16 - 32}}{2}$

$x = \dfrac{4 \pm \sqrt{-16}}{2}$

$x = \dfrac{4 \pm 4i}{2}$

$x = 2 \pm 2i$

The solution set is $\{-1, -1, 2 + 2i, 2 - 2i\}$.

45. $x^4 - 3x^3 - 20x^2 - 24x - 8 = 0$

$p: \pm 1, \pm 2, \pm 4, \pm 8$

$q: \pm 1$

$\dfrac{p}{q}: \pm 1, \pm 2, \pm 4 \pm 8$

1 positive real root exists.
3 or 1 negative real roots exist.

$$
\begin{array}{r|rrrrr}
-1 & 1 & -3 & -20 & -24 & -8 \\
   &   & -1 & 4   & 16 & 8 \\
\hline
   & 1 & -4 & -16 & -8 & 0
\end{array}
$$

$(x+1)\left(x^3 - 4x^2 - 16x - 8\right) = 0$

$$
\begin{array}{r|rrrr}
-2 & 1 & -4 & -16 & -8 \\
   &   & -2 & 12 & 8 \\
\hline
   & 1 & -6 & -4 & 0
\end{array}
$$

$(x+1)(x+2)\left(x^2 - 6x - 4\right) = 0$

$x = \dfrac{6 \pm \sqrt{36 + 16}}{2} = \dfrac{6 \pm \sqrt{52}}{2}$

$= \dfrac{6 \pm 2\sqrt{13}}{2} = \dfrac{3 \pm \sqrt{13}}{2}$

The solution set is
$\left\{-1, -2, 3 \pm \sqrt{13}, 3 - \sqrt{13}\right\}$.

47. $f(x) = 3x^4 - 11x^3 - x^2 + 19x + 6$

$p: \pm 1, \pm 2, \pm 3, \pm 6$

$q: \pm 1, \pm 3$

$\dfrac{p}{q}: \pm 1, \pm 2, \pm 3, \pm 6, \pm \dfrac{1}{3}, \pm \dfrac{2}{3}$

2 or no positive real zeros exists.

$f(-x) = 3x^4 + 11x^3 - x^2 - 19x + 6$

2 or no negative real zeros exist.

$$
\begin{array}{r|rrrrr}
-1 & 3 & -11 & -1 & 19 & 6 \\
   &   & -3 & 14 & -13 & -6 \\
\hline
   & 3 & -14 & 13 & 6 & 0
\end{array}
$$

$f(x) = (x+1)\left(3x^3 - 14x^2 + 13x + 6\right)$

$$
\begin{array}{r|rrrr}
2 & 3 & -14 & 13 & 6 \\
  &   & 6   & -16 & -6 \\
\hline
  & 3 & -8 & -3 & 0
\end{array}
$$

$f(x) = (x+1)(x-2)\left(3x^2 - 8x - 3\right)$

$ = (x+1)(x-2)(3x+1)(x-3)$

$x = -1, \; x = 2 \; x = -\dfrac{1}{3}, \; x = 3$

The solution set is $\left\{-1, 2, -\dfrac{1}{3}, 3\right\}$.

49. $4x^4 - x^3 + 5x^2 - 2x - 6 = 0$

$p: \pm 1, \pm 2, \pm 3, \pm 6$

$q: \pm 1, \pm 2, \pm 4$

$\dfrac{p}{q}: \pm 1, \pm 2, \pm 3, \pm 6, \pm \dfrac{1}{2}, \pm \dfrac{3}{2}, \pm \dfrac{1}{4}, \pm \dfrac{3}{4}$

3 or 1 positive real roots exists.
1 negative real root exists.

$$
\begin{array}{r|rrrrr}
1 & 4 & -1 & 5 & -2 & -6 \\
  &   & 4 & 3 & 8 & 6 \\
\hline
  & 4 & 3 & 8 & 6 & 0
\end{array}
$$

$(x-1)(4x^3 + 3x^2 + 8x + 6) = 0$

$4x^3 + 3x^2 + 8x + 6 = 0$ has no positive real roots.

$$
\begin{array}{r|rrrr}
-\frac{3}{4} & 4 & 3 & 8 & 6 \\
             &   & -3 & 0 & -6 \\
\hline
             & 4 & 0 & 8 & 0
\end{array}
$$

$(x-1)\left(x + \dfrac{3}{4}\right)\left(4x^2 + 8\right) = 0$

$4(x-1)\left(x + \dfrac{3}{4}\right)\left(x^2 + 2\right) = 0$

$x^2 + 2 = 0$

$x^2 = -2$

$x = \pm i\sqrt{2}$

The solution set is $\left\{1, -\dfrac{3}{4}, i\sqrt{2}, -i\sqrt{2}\right\}$.

51. $2x^5 + 7x^4 - 18x^2 - 8x + 8 = 0$

$p: \pm 1, \pm 2, \pm 4, \pm 8$

$q: \pm 1, \pm 2$

$\dfrac{p}{q}: \pm 1, \pm 2, \pm 4, \pm 8, \pm \dfrac{1}{2}$

2 or no positive real roots exists.
3 or 1 negative real root exist.

$$\begin{array}{r|rrrrrr}
-2 & 2 & 7 & 0 & -18 & -8 & 8 \\
& & -4 & -6 & 12 & 12 & -8 \\
\hline
& 2 & 3 & -6 & -6 & 4 & 0
\end{array}$$

$(x+2)(2x^4 + 3x^3 - 6x^2 - 6x + 4) = 0$

$4x^3 + 3x^2 + 8x + 6 = 0$ has no positive real roots.

$$\begin{array}{r|rrrrr}
-2 & 2 & 3 & -6 & -6 & 4 \\
& & -4 & 2 & 8 & -4 \\
\hline
& 2 & -1 & -4 & 2 & 0
\end{array}$$

$(x+2)^2(2x^3 - x^2 - 4x + 2)$

$$\begin{array}{r|rrrr}
\frac{1}{2} & 2 & -1 & -4 & 2 \\
& & 1 & 0 & 2 \\
\hline
& 2 & 0 & -4 & 0
\end{array}$$

$(x+2)^2\left(x - \dfrac{1}{2}\right)(2x^2 - 4) = 0$

$2(x+2)^2\left(x - \dfrac{1}{2}\right)(x^2 - 2) = 0$

$x^2 - 2 = 0$

$x^2 = 2$

$x = \pm\sqrt{2}$

The solution set is $\left\{-2, \dfrac{1}{2}, \sqrt{2}, -\sqrt{2}\right\}$.

53. $f(x) = -x^3 + x^2 + 16x - 16$

a. From the graph provided, we can see that -4 is an x-intercept and is thus a zero of the function. We verify this below:

$$\begin{array}{r|rrrr}
-4 & -1 & 1 & 16 & -16 \\
& & 4 & -20 & 16 \\
\hline
& -1 & 5 & -4 & 0
\end{array}$$

Thus, $-x^3 + x^2 + 16x - 16 = 0$

$(x+4)(-x^2 + 5x - 4) = 0$

$-(x+4)(x^2 - 5x + 4) = 0$

$-(x+4)(x-1)(x-4) = 0$

$x + 4 = 0$ or $x - 1 = 0$ or $x - 4 = 0$

$x = -4$ $x = 1$ $x = 4$

The zeros are -4, 1, and 4.

b.

$f(x) = -x^3 + x^2 + 16x - 16$

55. $f(x) = 4x^3 - 8x^2 - 3x + 9$

a. From the graph provided, we can see that -1 is an x-intercept and is thus a zero of the function. We verify this below:

$$\begin{array}{r|rrrr}
-1 & 4 & -8 & -3 & 9 \\
& & -4 & 12 & -9 \\
\hline
& 4 & -12 & 9 & 0
\end{array}$$

Thus, $4x^3 - 8x^2 - 3x + 9 = 0$

$(x+1)(4x^2 - 12x + 9) = 0$

$(x+1)(2x-3)^2 = 0$

$x + 1 = 0$ or $(2x-3)^2 = 0$

$x = -1$ $2x - 3 = 0$

                      $2x = 3$

                      $x = \dfrac{3}{2}$

The zeros are -1 and $\dfrac{3}{2}$.

b.

$f(x) = 4x^3 - 8x^2 - 3x + 9$

57. $f(x) = 2x^4 - 3x^3 - 7x^2 - 8x + 6$

  a. From the graph provided, we can see that $\dfrac{1}{2}$ is an x-intercept and is thus a zero of the function. We verify this below:

$$\begin{array}{r|rrrrr} \tfrac{1}{2} & 2 & -3 & -7 & -8 & 6 \\ & & 1 & -1 & -4 & -6 \\ \hline & 2 & -2 & -8 & -12 & 0 \end{array}$$

Thus, $\qquad 2x^4 - 3x^3 - 7x^2 - 8x + 6 = 0$

$$\left(x - \frac{1}{2}\right)\left(2x^3 - 2x^2 - 8x - 12\right) = 0$$

$$2\left(x - \frac{1}{2}\right)\left(x^3 - x^2 - 4x - 6\right) = 0$$

To factor $x^3 - x^2 - 4x - 6$, we use the Rational Zero Theorem to determine possible rational zeros.

Factors of the constant term -6:
$\pm 1, \ \pm 2, \ \pm 3, \ \pm 6$

Factors of the leading coefficient 1: ± 1

The possible rational zeros are:

$$\frac{\text{Factors of} -6}{\text{Factors of } 1} = \frac{\pm 1, \ \pm 2, \ \pm 3, \ \pm 6}{\pm 1}$$
$$= \pm 1, \ \pm 2, \ \pm 3, \ \pm 6$$

We test values from above until we find a zero. One possibility is shown next:

Test 3:

$$\begin{array}{r|rrrr} 3 & 1 & -1 & -4 & -6 \\ & & 3 & 6 & 6 \\ \hline & 1 & 2 & 2 & 0 \end{array}$$

The remainder is 0, so 3 is a zero of f.

$$2x^4 - 3x^3 - 7x^2 - 8x + 6 = 0$$

$$\left(x - \frac{1}{2}\right)\left(2x^3 - 2x^2 - 8x - 12\right) = 0$$

$$2\left(x - \frac{1}{2}\right)\left(x^3 - x^2 - 4x - 6\right) = 0$$

$$2\left(x - \frac{1}{2}\right)(x - 3)\left(x^2 + 2x + 2\right) = 0$$

Note that $x^2 + x + 1$ will not factor, so we use the quadratic formula:
$a = 1 \quad b = 2 \quad c = 2$

$$x = \frac{-2 \pm \sqrt{2^2 - 4(1)(2)}}{2(1)}$$

$$= \frac{-2 \pm \sqrt{-4}}{2} = \frac{-2 \pm 2i}{2} = -1 \pm i$$

The zeros are $\dfrac{1}{2}$, 3, and $-1 \pm i$.

  b.

$$f(x) = 2x^4 - 3x^3 - 7x^2 - 8x + 6$$

59. $f(x) = 3x^5 + 2x^4 - 15x^3 - 10x^2 + 12x + 8$

  a. From the graph provided, we can see that 1 and 2 are x-intercepts and are thus zeros of the function. We verify this below:

$$\begin{array}{r|rrrrrr} 1 & 3 & 2 & -15 & -10 & 12 & 8 \\ & & 3 & 5 & -10 & -20 & -8 \\ \hline & 3 & 5 & -10 & -20 & -8 & 0 \end{array}$$

Thus, $3x^5 + 2x^4 - 15x^3 - 10x^2 + 12x + 8$

$$= (x-1)\left(3x^4 + 5x^3 - 10x^2 - 20x - 8\right)$$

$$\begin{array}{r|rrrrr} 2 & 3 & 5 & -10 & -20 & -8 \\ & & 6 & 22 & 24 & 8 \\ \hline & 3 & 11 & 12 & 4 & 0 \end{array}$$

Thus, $3x^5 + 2x^4 - 15x^3 - 10x^2 + 12x + 8$

$$= (x-1)\left(3x^4 + 5x^3 - 10x^2 - 20x - 8\right)$$

$$= (x-1)(x-2)\left(3x^3 + 11x^2 + 12x + 4\right)$$

To factor $3x^3 + 11x^2 + 12x + 4$, we use the Rational Zero Theorem to determine possible rational zeros.

Factors of the constant term 4:
$\pm 1, \ \pm 2, \ \pm 4$

Factors of the leading coefficient 3: $\pm 1, \ \pm 3$

The possible rational zeros are:

$$\frac{\text{Factors of } 4}{\text{Factors of } 3} = \frac{\pm 1, \ \pm 2, \ \pm 4}{\pm 1, \ \pm 3}$$

$$= \pm 1, \ \pm 2, \ \pm 4, \ \pm \frac{1}{3}, \ \pm \frac{2}{3}, \ \pm \frac{4}{3}$$

We test values from above until we find a zero. One possibility is shown next:

Test -1:

$$
\begin{array}{r|rrrr}
-1 & 3 & 11 & 12 & 4 \\
   &   & -3 & -8 & -4 \\
\hline
   & 3 & 8 & 4 & 0
\end{array}
$$

The remainder is 0, so -1 is a zero of f. We can now finish the factoring:

$$3x^5 + 2x^4 - 15x^3 - 10x^2 + 12x + 8 = 0$$

$$(x-1)(3x^4 + 5x^3 - 10x^2 - 20x - 8) = 0$$

$$(x-1)(x-2)(3x^3 + 11x^2 + 12x + 4) = 0$$

$$(x-1)(x-2)(x+1)(3x^2 + 8x + 4) = 0$$

$$(x-1)(x-2)(x+1)(3x+2)(x+2) = 0$$

$$x = 1, \ x = 2, \ x = -1, \ x = -\frac{2}{3}, \ x = -2$$

The zeros are -2, -1, $-\frac{2}{3}$, 1 and 2.

b.

$$f(x) = 3x^5 + 2x^4 - 15x^3 - 10x^2 + 12x + 8$$

61. a. $f(x) = 27$, $x = 40$ People in the arts complete 27% of their work in their 40's.

b.   The polynomial will have a degree 2 with a negative leading coefficient.

63. If you are 25, the equivalent age for dogs is 3 years.

65. Answers may vary.

67. $x(10 - 2x)(8 - 2x) = 48$

$$x(80 - 36x + 4x^2) = 48$$

$$4x^3 - 36x^2 + 80x - 48 = 0$$

$$x^3 - 9x^2 + 20x - 12 = 0$$

$$
\begin{array}{r|rrrr}
2 & 1 & -9 & 20 & -12 \\
  &   & 2 & -14 & 12 \\
\hline
  & 1 & -7 & 6 & 0
\end{array}
$$

$$(x-2)(x^2 - 7x + 6) = 0$$

$$(x-2)(x-6)(x-1) = 0$$

$$x = 2 \quad x = 6 \quad x = 1$$

If $x = 6$, $10 - 2x < 0$

$x = 1$ in. or $x = 2$ in.

77. $6x^3 - 19x^2 + 16x - 4 = 0$

$p: \pm 1, \pm 2, \pm 4$

$q: \pm 1, \pm 2, \pm 3, \pm 6$

$$\frac{p}{q}: \pm 1, \pm 2, \pm 4, \pm\frac{1}{2}, \pm\frac{1}{3}, \pm\frac{2}{3}, \pm\frac{4}{3}, \pm\frac{1}{6}$$

From the graph, we see that the solutions are $\frac{1}{2}, \frac{2}{3}$ and 2.

79. $4x^4 + 4x^3 + 7x^2 - x - 2 = 0$

$p: \pm 1, \pm 2$

$q: \pm 1, \pm 2, \pm 4$

$$\frac{p}{q}: \pm 1, \pm 2, \pm\frac{1}{2}, \pm\frac{1}{4}$$

From the graph, we see that the solutions are $-\frac{1}{2}$ and $\frac{1}{2}$.

81. $f(x) = x^5 - x^4 + x^3 - x^2 + x - 8$

$f(x)$ has 5 sign variations, so either 5, 3, or 1 positive real roots exist.

$f(-x) = -x^5 - x^4 - x^3 - x^2 - x - 8$

$f(-x)$ has no sign variations, so no negative real roots exist.

83. $f(x) = x^3 - 6x - 9$

1 real zero
2 nonreal complex zeros

85. $f(x) = 3x^4 + 4x^3 - 7x^2 - 2x - 3$

87. a. False; the equation has 0 sign variations, so no positive roots exist.

b. False; Descartes' Rule gives the maximum possible number of real roots.

c. False; every polynomial equation of degree 3 has at least one <u>real</u> root.

d. True

(d) is true.

89. $(2x+1)(x+5)(x+2) - 3x(x+5) = 208$

$(2x^2 + 11x + 5)(x+2) - 3x^2 - 15x = 208$

$2x^3 + 4x^2 + 11x^2 + 22x + 5x$

$+10 - 3x^2 - 15x = 208$

$2x^3 + 15x^2 + 27x - 3x^2 - 15x - 198 = 0$

$2x^3 + 12x^2 + 12x - 198 = 0$

$2(x^3 + 6x^2 + 6x - 99) = 0$

$$
\begin{array}{r|rrrr}
3 & 1 & 6 & 6 & -99 \\
& & 3 & 27 & 99 \\
\hline
& 1 & 9 & 33 & 0
\end{array}
$$

$x^2 + 9x + 33 = 0$

$b^2 - 4ac = -51$

$x = 3$ in.

91. Because the polynomial has two obvious changes of direction; the smallest degree is 3.

93. Because the polynomial has two obvious changes of direction and two roots have multiplicity 2, the smallest degree is 5.

Mid-Chapter 2 Check Point

1. $(6 - 2i) - (7 - i) = 6 - 2i - 7 + i = -1 - i$

2. $3i(2 + i) = 6i + 3i^2 = -3 + 6i$

3. $(1+i)(4-3i) = 4 - 3i + 4i - 3i^2$

$= 4 + i + 3$

$= 7 + i$

4. $\dfrac{1+i}{1-i} = \dfrac{1+i}{1-i} \cdot \dfrac{1+i}{1+i}$

$= \dfrac{1 + i + i + i^2}{1 - i^2}$

$= \dfrac{1 + 2i - 1}{1 + 1}$

$= \dfrac{2i}{2}$

$= i$

5. $\sqrt{-75} - \sqrt{-12} = 5i\sqrt{3} - 2i\sqrt{3} = 3i\sqrt{3}$

6.
$$\left(2-\sqrt{-3}\right)^2 = \left(2-i\sqrt{3}\right)^2$$
$$= 4 - 4i\sqrt{3} + 3i^2$$
$$= 4 - 4i\sqrt{3} - 3$$
$$= 1 - 4i\sqrt{3}$$

7.
$$x(2x-3) = -4$$
$$2x^2 - 3x = -4$$
$$2x^2 - 3x + 4 = 0$$
$$x = \frac{-b \pm \sqrt{b^2 - 4ac}}{2a}$$
$$x = \frac{-(-3) \pm \sqrt{(-3)^2 - 4(2)(4)}}{2(2)}$$
$$x = \frac{3 \pm \sqrt{-23}}{4}$$
$$x = \frac{3}{4} \pm \frac{\sqrt{23}}{4}i$$

8. $f(x) = (x-3)^2 - 4$

The parabola opens up because $a > 0$.

The vertex is $(3, -4)$.

x-intercepts:
$$0 = (x-3)^2 - 4$$
$$(x-3)^2 = 4$$
$$x - 3 = \pm\sqrt{4}$$
$$x = 3 \pm 2$$

The equation has x-intercepts at $x = 1$ and $x = 5$.

y-intercept:
$$f(0) = (0-3)^2 - 4 = 5$$

Domain: $(-\infty, \infty)$ Range: $[-4, \infty)$

$f(x) = (x - 3)^2 - 4$

9. $f(x) = 5 - (x+2)^2$

The parabola opens down because $a < 0$.

The vertex is $(-2, 5)$.

x-intercepts:
$$0 = 5 - (x+2)^2$$
$$(x+2)^2 = 5$$
$$x + 2 = \pm\sqrt{5}$$
$$x = -2 \pm \sqrt{5}$$

y-intercept:
$$f(0) = 5 - (0+2)^2 = 1$$

Domain: $(-\infty, \infty)$ Range: $(-\infty, 5]$

$f(x) = 5 - (x + 2)^2$

10. $f(x) = -x^2 - 4x + 5$

The parabola opens down because $a < 0$.

vertex: $x = -\dfrac{b}{2a} = -\dfrac{-4}{2(-1)} = -2$

$$f(-2) = -(-2)^2 - 4(-2) + 5 = 9$$

The vertex is $(-2, 9)$.

x-intercepts:
$$0 = -x^2 - 4x + 5$$
$$x = \frac{-b \pm \sqrt{b^2 - 4ac}}{2a}$$
$$x = \frac{-(-4) \pm \sqrt{(-4)^2 - 4(-1)(5)}}{2(-1)}$$
$$x = \frac{4 \pm \sqrt{36}}{-2}$$
$$x = -2 \pm 3$$

The x-intercepts are $x = 1$ and $x = -5$.

y-intercept:
$$f(0) = -0^2 - 4(0) + 5 = 5$$

Domain: $(-\infty, \infty)$ Range: $(-\infty, 9]$

$f(x) = -x^2 - 4x + 5$

11. $f(x) = 3x^2 - 6x + 1$

The parabola opens up because $a > 0$.

vertex: $x = -\dfrac{b}{2a} = -\dfrac{-6}{2(3)} = 1$

$f(1) = 3(1)^2 - 6(1) + 1 = -2$

The vertex is $(1, -2)$.

x-intercepts:

$0 = 3x^2 - 6x + 1$

$x = \dfrac{-b \pm \sqrt{b^2 - 4ac}}{2a}$

$x = \dfrac{-(-6) \pm \sqrt{(-6)^2 - 4(3)(1)}}{2(3)}$

$x = \dfrac{6 \pm \sqrt{24}}{6}$

$x = \dfrac{3 \pm \sqrt{6}}{3}$

y-intercept:

$f(0) = 3(0)^2 - 6(0) + 1 = 1$

Domain: $(-\infty, \infty)$ Range: $[-2, \infty)$

$f(x) = 3x^2 - 6x + 1$

12. $f(x) = (x-2)^2 (x+1)^3$

$(x-2)^2 (x+1)^3 = 0$

Apply the zero-product principle:

$(x-2)^2 = 0$ or $(x+1)^3 = 0$

$\quad x - 2 = 0 \qquad\qquad x + 1 = 0$

$\qquad x = 2 \qquad\qquad\quad x = -1$

The zeros are -1 and 2.

The graph of f crosses the x-axis at -1, since the zero has multiplicity 3. The graph touches the x-axis and turns around at 2 since the zero has multiplicity 2.

Since f is an odd-degree polynomial, degree 5, and since the leading coefficient, 1, is positive, the graph falls to the left and rises to the right.

Plot additional points as necessary and construct the graph.

$f(x) = (x - 2)^2 (x + 1)^3$

13. $f(x) = -(x-2)^2 (x+1)^2$

$-(x-2)^2 (x+1)^2 = 0$

Apply the zero-product principle:

$(x-2)^2 = 0$ or $(x+1)^2 = 0$

$\quad x - 2 = 0 \qquad\qquad x + 1 = 0$

$\qquad x = 2 \qquad\qquad\quad x = -1$

The zeros are -1 and 2.

The graph touches the x-axis and turns around both at -1 and 2 since both zeros have multiplicity 2.

Since f is an even-degree polynomial, degree 4, and since the leading coefficient, -1, is negative, the graph falls to the left and falls to the right. Plot additional points as necessary and construct the graph.

$f(x) = -(x - 2)^2 (x + 1)^2$

14. $f(x) = x^3 - x^2 - 4x + 4$

$x^3 - x^2 - 4x + 4 = 0$

$x^2(x-1) - 4(x-1) = 0$

$(x^2 - 4)(x-1) = 0$

$(x+2)(x-2)(x-1) = 0$

Apply the zero-product principle:

$x + 2 = 0$ or $x - 2 = 0$ or $x - 1 = 0$

$\quad x = -2 \qquad\quad x = 2 \qquad\quad x = 1$

The zeros are -2, 1, and 2.

The graph of f crosses the x-axis at all three zeros, -2, 1, and 2, since all have multiplicity 1.

Since f is an odd-degree polynomial, degree 3, and since the leading coefficient, 1, is positive, the graph falls to the left and rises to the right.

Plot additional points as necessary and construct the graph.

$$f(x) = x^3 - x^2 - 4x + 4$$

$$f(x) = -(x+1)^6$$

15. $f(x) = x^4 - 5x^2 + 4$

$$x^4 - 5x^2 + 4 = 0$$

$$\left(x^2 - 4\right)\left(x^2 - 1\right) = 0$$

$$(x+2)(x-2)(x+1)(x-1) = 0$$

Apply the zero-product principle,

$x = -2, \ x = 2, \ x = -1, \ x = 1$

The zeros are $-2, \ -1, \ 1, $ and 2.

The graph crosses the x-axis at all four zeros, $-2, \ -1, \ 1, $ and 2., since all have multiplicity 1.

Since f is an even-degree polynomial, degree 4, and since the leading coefficient, 1, is positive, the graph rises to the left and rises to the right.

Plot additional points as necessary and construct the graph.

$$f(x) = x^4 - 5x^2 + 4$$

16. $f(x) = -(x+1)^6$

$$-(x+1)^6 = 0$$

$$(x+1)^6 = 0$$

$$x + 1 = 0$$

$$x = -1$$

The zero is are -1.

The graph touches the x-axis and turns around at -1 since the zero has multiplicity 6.

Since f is an even-degree polynomial, degree 6, and since the leading coefficient, -1, is negative, the graph falls to the left and falls to the right.

Plot additional points as necessary and construct the graph.

17. $f(x) = -6x^3 + 7x^2 - 1$

To find the zeros, we use the Rational Zero Theorem:

List all factors of the constant term -1: ± 1

List all factors of the leading coefficient -6: $\pm 1, \ \pm 2, \ \pm 3, \ \pm 6$

The possible rational zeros are:

$$\frac{\text{Factors of } -1}{\text{Factors of } -6} = \frac{\pm 1}{\pm 1, \ \pm 2, \ \pm 3, \ \pm 6}$$

$$= \pm 1, \ \pm \frac{1}{2}, \ \pm \frac{1}{3}, \ \pm \frac{1}{6}$$

We test values from the above list until we find a zero. One is shown next:

Test 1:

$$\begin{array}{r|rrrr} \underline{1} & -6 & 7 & 0 & -1 \\ & & -6 & 1 & 1 \\ \hline & -6 & 1 & 1 & 0 \end{array}$$

The remainder is 0, so 1 is a zero. Thus,

$$-6x^3 + 7x^2 - 1 = 0$$

$$(x-1)\left(-6x^2 + x + 1\right) = 0$$

$$-(x-1)\left(6x^2 - x - 1\right) = 0$$

$$-(x-1)(3x+1)(2x-1) = 0$$

Apply the zero-product property:

$$x = 1, \quad x = -\frac{1}{3}, \quad x = \frac{1}{2}$$

The zeros are $-\frac{1}{3}, \frac{1}{2},$ and 1.

The graph of f crosses the x-axis at all three zeros, $-\frac{1}{3}, \frac{1}{2},$ and 1, since all have multiplicity 1.

Since f is an odd-degree polynomial, degree 3, and since the leading coefficient, -6, is negative, the graph rises to the left and falls to the right.

Plot additional points as necessary and construct the graph.

$f(x) = -6x^3 + 7x^2 - 1$

18. $f(x) = 2x^3 - 2x$

$$2x^3 - 2x = 0$$

$$2x(x^2 - 1) = 0$$

$$2x(x+1)(x-1) = 0$$

Apply the zero-product principle:
$$x = 0, \qquad x = -1, \qquad x = 1$$

The zeros are -1, 0, and 1.

The graph of f crosses the x-axis at all three zeros, -1, 0, and 1, since all have multiplicity 1.

Since f is an odd-degree polynomial, degree 3, and since the leading coefficient, 2, is positive, the graph falls to the left and rises to the right.

Plot additional points as necessary and construct the graph.

$f(x) = 2x^3 - 2x$

19. $f(x) = x^3 - 2x^2 + 26x$

$$x^3 - 2x^2 + 26x = 0$$

$$x(x^2 - 2x + 26) = 0$$

Note that $x^2 - 2x + 26$ does not factor, so we use the quadratic formula:
$$x = 0 \quad \text{or} \quad x^2 - 2x + 26 = 0$$
$$a = 1, \ b = -2, \ c = 26$$

$$x = \frac{-(-2) \pm \sqrt{(-2)^2 - 4(1)(26)}}{2(1)}$$

$$= \frac{2 \pm \sqrt{-100}}{2} = \frac{2 \pm 10i}{2} = 1 \pm 5i$$

The zeros are 0 and $1 \pm 5i$.

The graph of f crosses the x-axis at 0 (the only real zero), since it has multiplicity 1.

Since f is an odd-degree polynomial, degree 3, and since the leading coefficient, 1, is positive, the graph falls to the left and rises to the right.

Plot additional points as necessary and construct the graph.

$f(x) = x^3 - 2x^2 + 26x$

20. $f(x) = -x^3 + 5x^2 - 5x - 3$

To find the zeros, we use the Rational Zero Theorem:

List all factors of the constant term -3:
$$\pm 1, \ \pm 3$$

List all factors of the leading coefficient -1:
$$\pm 1$$

The possible rational zeros are:

$$\frac{\text{Factors of } -3}{\text{Factors of } -1} = \frac{\pm 1, \ \pm 3}{\pm 1} = \pm 1, \ \pm 3$$

We test values from the previous list until we find a zero. One is shown next:

Test 3:

$$\underline{3|} \quad \begin{array}{rrrr} -1 & 5 & -5 & -3 \\ & -3 & 6 & 3 \\ \hline -1 & 2 & 1 & 0 \end{array}$$

The remainder is 0, so 3 is a zero. Thus,

$$-x^3 + 5x^2 - 5x - 3 = 0$$

$$(x-3)(-x^2 + 2x + 1) = 0$$

$$-(x-3)(x^2 - 2x - 1) = 0$$

Note that $x^2 - 2x - 1$ does not factor, so we use the quadratic formula:
$$x - 3 = 0 \quad \text{or} \quad x^2 - 2x - 1 = 0$$
$$x = 3 \qquad a = 1, \ b = -2, \ c = -1$$

$$x = \frac{-(-2) \pm \sqrt{(-2)^2 - 4(1)(-1)}}{2(1)}$$

$$= \frac{2 \pm \sqrt{8}}{2} = \frac{2 \pm 2\sqrt{2}}{2} = 1 \pm \sqrt{2}$$

The zeros are 3 and $1 \pm \sqrt{2}$.

The graph of *f* crosses the *x*-axis at all three zeros, 3 and $1 \pm \sqrt{2}$, since all have multiplicity 1.

Since *f* is an odd-degree polynomial, degree 3, and since the leading coefficient, -1, is negative, the graph rises to the left and falls to the right.

Plot additional points as necessary and construct the graph.

$$f(x) = -x^3 + 5x^2 - 5x - 3$$

21. $x^3 - 3x + 2 = 0$

We begin by using the Rational Zero Theorem to determine possible rational roots.

Factors of the constant term 2: $\pm 1, \ \pm 2$

Factors of the leading coefficient 1: ± 1

The possible rational zeros are:

$$\frac{\text{Factors of } 2}{\text{Factors of } 1} = \frac{\pm 1, \ \pm 2}{\pm 1} = \pm 1, \ \pm 2$$

We test values from above until we find a root. One is shown next:

Test 1:

$$\begin{array}{r|rrrr} 1 & 1 & 0 & -3 & 2 \\ & & 1 & 1 & -2 \\ \hline & 1 & 1 & -2 & 0 \end{array}$$

The remainder is 0, so 1 is a root of the equation. Thus,

$$x^3 - 3x + 2 = 0$$
$$(x-1)(x^2 + x - 2) = 0$$
$$(x-1)(x+2)(x-1) = 0$$
$$(x-1)^2 (x+2) = 0$$

Apply the zero-product property:

$(x-1)^2 = 0$ or $x + 2 = 0$

$x - 1 = 0$ $x = -2$

$x = 1$

The solutions are -2 and 1, and the solution set is $\{-2, 1\}$.

22. $6x^3 - 11x^2 + 6x - 1 = 0$

We begin by using the Rational Zero Theorem to determine possible rational roots.

Factors of the constant term -1: ± 1

Factors of the leading coefficient 6: $\pm 1, \ \pm 2, \ \pm 3, \ \pm 6$

The possible rational zeros are:

$$\frac{\text{Factors of } -1}{\text{Factors of } 6} = \frac{\pm 1}{\pm 1, \ \pm 2, \ \pm 3, \ \pm 6}$$

$$= \pm 1, \ \pm \frac{1}{2}, \ \pm \frac{1}{3}, \ \pm \frac{1}{6}$$

We test values from above until we find a root. One is shown next:

Test 1:

$$\begin{array}{r|rrrr} 1 & 6 & -11 & 6 & -1 \\ & & 6 & -5 & 1 \\ \hline & 6 & -5 & 1 & 0 \end{array}$$

The remainder is 0, so 1 is a root of the equation. Thus,

$$6x^3 - 11x^2 + 6x - 1 = 0$$
$$(x-1)(6x^2 - 5x + 1) = 0$$
$$(x-1)(3x-1)(2x-1) = 0$$

Apply the zero-product property:

$x - 1 = 0$ or $3x - 1 = 0$ or $2x - 1 = 0$

$x = 1$ $x = \dfrac{1}{3}$ $x = \dfrac{1}{2}$

The solutions are $\dfrac{1}{3}, \dfrac{1}{2}$ and 1, and the solution

set is $\left\{ \dfrac{1}{3}, \dfrac{1}{2}, 1 \right\}$.

23. $(2x+1)(3x-2)^3 (2x-7) = 0$

Apply the zero-product property:

$2x + 1 = 0$ or $(3x-2)^3 = 0$ or $2x - 7 = 0$

$x = -\dfrac{1}{2}$ $3x - 2 = 0$ $x = \dfrac{7}{2}$

$x = \dfrac{2}{3}$

The solutions are $-\dfrac{1}{2}, \dfrac{2}{3}$ and $\dfrac{7}{2}$, and the

solution set is $\left\{ -\dfrac{1}{2}, \dfrac{2}{3}, \dfrac{7}{2} \right\}$.

24. $2x^3 + 5x^2 - 200x - 500 = 0$

We begin by using the Rational Zero Theorem to determine possible rational roots.

Factors of the constant term -500:
$\pm1, \ \pm2, \ \pm4, \ \pm5, \ \pm10, \ \pm20, \ \pm25,$
$\pm50, \ \pm100, \ \pm125, \ \pm250, \ \pm500$

Factors of the leading coefficient 2: $\pm1, \ \pm2$

The possible rational zeros are:

$\dfrac{\text{Factors of } 500}{\text{Factors of } 2} = \pm1, \ \pm2, \ \pm4, \ \pm5,$

$\pm10, \ \pm20, \ \pm25, \ \pm50, \ \pm100, \ \pm125,$

$\pm250, \ \pm500, \ \pm\dfrac{1}{2}, \ \pm\dfrac{5}{2}, \ \pm\dfrac{25}{2}, \ \pm\dfrac{125}{2}$

We test values from above until we find a root. One is shown next:

Test 10:

$$\begin{array}{r|rrrr}
10 & 2 & 5 & -200 & -500 \\
   &   & 20 & 250 & 500 \\
\hline
   & 2 & 25 & 50 & 0
\end{array}$$

The remainder is 0, so 10 is a root of the equation. Thus,

$2x^3 + 5x^2 - 200x - 500 = 0$

$(x - 10)(2x^2 + 25x + 50) = 0$

$(x - 10)(2x + 5)(x + 10) = 0$

Apply the zero-product property:

$x - 10 = 0 \quad$ or $\quad 2x + 5 = 0 \quad$ or $\quad x + 10 = 0$

$x = 10 \qquad\qquad x = -\dfrac{5}{2} \qquad\qquad x = -10$

The solutions are -10, $-\dfrac{5}{2}$, and 10, and the

solution set is $\left\{-10, \ -\dfrac{5}{2}, \ 10\right\}$.

25. $x^4 - x^3 - 11x^2 = x + 12$

$x^4 - x^3 - 11x^2 - x - 12 = 0$

We begin by using the Rational Zero Theorem to determine possible rational roots.

Factors of the constant term -12:
$\pm1, \ \pm2, \ \pm3, \ \pm4, \ \pm6, \ \pm12$

Factors of the leading coefficient 1: ±1

The possible rational zeros are:

$\dfrac{\text{Factors of } -12}{\text{Factors of } 1}$

$= \dfrac{\pm1, \ \pm2, \ \pm3, \ \pm4, \ \pm6, \ \pm12}{\pm1}$

$= \pm1, \ \pm2, \ \pm3, \ \pm4, \ \pm6, \ \pm12$

We test values from this list we find a root. One possibility is shown next:

Test -3:

$$\begin{array}{r|rrrrr}
-3 & 1 & -1 & -11 & -1 & -12 \\
   &   & -3 & 12 & -3 & 12 \\
\hline
   & 1 & -4 & 1 & -4 & 0
\end{array}$$

The remainder is 0, so -3 is a root of the equation. Using the Factor Theorem, we know that $x - 1$ is a factor. Thus,

$x^4 - x^3 - 11x^2 - x - 12 = 0$

$(x + 3)(x^3 - 4x^2 + x - 4) = 0$

$(x + 3)\left[x^2(x - 4) + 1(x - 4)\right] = 0$

$(x + 3)(x - 4)(x^2 + 1) = 0$

As this point we know that -3 and 4 are roots of the equation. Note that $x^2 + 1$ does not factor, so we use the square-root principle:

$x^2 + 1 = 0$

$x^2 = -1$

$x = \pm\sqrt{-1} = \pm i$

The roots are -3, 4, and $\pm i$, and the solution set is $\{-3, \ 4, \ \pm i\}$.

26. $2x^4 + x^3 - 17x^2 - 4x + 6 = 0$

We begin by using the Rational Zero Theorem to determine possible rational roots.

Factors of the constant term 6:
$\pm1, \ \pm2, \ \pm3, \ \pm6$

Factors of the leading coefficient 4: $\pm1, \ \pm2$

The possible rational roots are:

$\dfrac{\text{Factors of } 6}{\text{Factors of } 2} = \dfrac{\pm1, \ \pm2, \ \pm3, \ \pm6}{\pm1, \ \pm2}$

$= \pm1, \ \pm2, \ \pm3, \ \pm6, \ \pm\dfrac{1}{2}, \ \pm\dfrac{3}{2}$

We test values from above until we find a root. One possibility is shown next:

Test -3:

$$\begin{array}{r|rrrrr} -3 & 2 & 1 & -17 & -4 & 6 \\ & & -6 & 15 & 6 & -6 \\ \hline & 2 & -5 & -2 & 2 & 0 \end{array}$$

The remainder is 0, so -3 is a root. Using the Factor Theorem, we know that $x+3$ is a factor of the polynomial. Thus,

$$2x^4 + x^3 - 17x^2 - 4x + 6 = 0$$
$$(x+3)(2x^3 - 5x^2 - 2x + 2) = 0$$

To solve the equation above, we need to factor $2x^3 - 5x^2 - 2x + 2$. We continue testing potential roots:

Test $\dfrac{1}{2}$:

$$\begin{array}{r|rrrr} \frac{1}{2} & 2 & -5 & -2 & 2 \\ & & 1 & -2 & -2 \\ \hline & 2 & -4 & -4 & 0 \end{array}$$

The remainder is 0, so $\dfrac{1}{2}$ is a zero and $x - \dfrac{1}{2}$ is a factor.

Summarizing our findings so far, we have

$$2x^4 + x^3 - 17x^2 - 4x + 6 = 0$$
$$(x+3)(2x^3 - 5x^2 - 2x + 2) = 0$$
$$(x+3)\left(x - \frac{1}{2}\right)(2x^2 - 4x - 4) = 0$$
$$2(x+3)\left(x - \frac{1}{2}\right)(x^2 - 2x - 2) = 0$$

At this point, we know that -3 and $\dfrac{1}{2}$ are roots of the equation. Note that $x^2 - 2x - 2$ does not factor, so we use the quadratic formula:

$$x^2 - 2x - 2 = 0$$
$$a = 1,\ b = -2,\ c = -2$$

$$x = \frac{-(-2) \pm \sqrt{(-2)^2 - 4(1)(-2)}}{2(1)}$$

$$= \frac{2 \pm \sqrt{4+8}}{2} = \frac{2 \pm \sqrt{12}}{2} = \frac{2 \pm 2\sqrt{3}}{2} = 1 \pm \sqrt{3}$$

The solutions are -3, $\dfrac{1}{2}$, and $1 \pm \sqrt{3}$, and the solution set is $\left\{-3, \dfrac{1}{2}, 1 \pm \sqrt{3}\right\}$.

27. $P(x) = -x^2 + 150x - 4425$

Since $a = -1$ is negative, we know the function opens down and has a maximum at

$$x = -\frac{b}{2a} = -\frac{150}{2(-1)} = -\frac{150}{-2} = 75.$$

$$P(75) = -75^2 + 150(75) - 4425$$
$$= -5625 + 11,250 - 4425 = 1200$$

The company will maximize its profit by manufacturing and selling 75 cabinets per day. The maximum daily profit is $1200.

28. Let $x =$ one of the numbers;
$-18 - x =$ the other number
The product is $f(x) = x(-18 - x) = -x^2 - 18x$
The x-coordinate of the maximum is

$$x = -\frac{b}{2a} = -\frac{-18}{2(-1)} = -\frac{-18}{-2} = -9.$$

$$f(-9) = -9\left[-18 - (-9)\right]$$
$$= -9(-18 + 9) = -9(-9) = 81$$

The vertex is $(-9, 81)$. The maximum product is 81. This occurs when the two number are -9 and $-18 - (-9) = -9$.

29. Let $x =$ height of triangle;
$40 - 2x =$ base of triangle

$$A = \frac{1}{2}bh = \frac{1}{2}x(40 - 2x)$$
$$A(x) = 20x - x^2$$

The height at which the triangle will have maximum area is $x = -\dfrac{b}{2a} = -\dfrac{20}{2(-1)} = 10$.

$$A(10) = 20(10) - (10)^2 = 100$$

The maximum area is 100 squares inches.

30.

$$\begin{array}{r} 2x^2 - x - 3 \\ 3x^2 - 1 \overline{\smash{\big)}\, 6x^4 - 3x^3 - 11x^2 + 2x + 4} \\ \underline{6x^4 - 2x^2 } \\ -3x^3 - 9x^2 + 2x \\ \underline{-3x^3 + x } \\ -9x^2 + x + 4 \\ \underline{-9x^2 + 3} \\ x + 1 \end{array}$$

$$2x^2 - x - 3 + \frac{x+1}{3x^2 - 1}$$

31. $\left(2x^4 - 13x^3 + 17x^2 + 18x - 24\right) \div \left(x - 4\right)$

$$
\begin{array}{r|rrrrr}
4 & 2 & -13 & 17 & 18 & -24 \\
  &   & 8 & -20 & -12 & 24 \\
\hline
  & 2 & -5 & -3 & 6 & 0
\end{array}
$$

The quotient is $2x^3 - 5x^2 - 3x + 6$.

32. $(x-1)(x-i)(x+i) = (x-1)(x^2+1)$

$f(x) = a_n(x-1)(x^2+1)$

$f(-1) = a_n(-1-1)\left((-1)^2+1\right) = -4a_n = 8$

$a_n = -2$

$f(x) = -2(x-1)(x^2+1)$ or $-2x^3 + 2x^2 - 2x + 2$

33. $(x-2)(x-2)(x-3i)(x+3i)$

$= (x-2)(x-2)(x^2+9)$

$f(x) = a_n(x-2)(x-2)(x^2+9)$

$f(0) = a_n(0-2)(0-2)(0^2+9)$

$36 = 36a_n$

$a_n = 1$

$f(x) = 1(x-2)(x-2)(x^2+9)$

$f(x) = x^4 - 4x^3 + 13x^2 - 36x + 36$

34. $f(x) = x^3 - x - 5$

$f(1) = 1^3 - 1 - 5 = -5$

$f(2) = 2^3 - 2 - 5 = 1$

Yes, the function must have a real zero between 1 and 2 because $f(1)$ and $f(2)$ have opposite signs.

Section 2.6

Check Point Exercises

1. **a.** $x - 5 = 0$

$x = 5$

$\{x \mid x \neq 5\}$

b. $x^2 - 25 = 0$

$x^2 = 25$

$x = \pm 5$

$\{x \mid x \neq 5, x \neq -5\}$

c. The denominator cannot equal zero.
All real numbers.

2. **a.** $x^2 - 1 = 0$

$x^2 = 1$

$x = 1, x = -1$

b. $g(x) = \dfrac{x-1}{x^2-1} = \dfrac{x-1}{(x-1)(x+1)} = \dfrac{1}{x+1}$

$x = -1$

c. The denominator cannot equal zero.
No vertical asymptotes.

3. **a.** Since $n = m$, $y = \dfrac{9}{3} = 3$

$y = 3$ is a horizontal asymptote.

b. Since $n < m$, $y = 0$ is a horizontal asymptote.

c. Since $n > m$, there is no horizontal asymptote.

4. Begin with the graph of $f(x) = \dfrac{1}{x}$.

$g(x) = \dfrac{1}{x+2} - 1$

Shift the graph 2 units to the left by subtracting 2 from each x-coordinate. Shift the graph 1 unit down by subtracting 1 from each y-coordinate.

5. $f(x) = \dfrac{3x}{x-2}$

$f(-x) = \dfrac{3(-x)}{-x-2} = \dfrac{3x}{x+2}$

no symmetry

$f(0) = \dfrac{3(0)}{0-2} = 0$

The y-intercept is 0.

$3x = 0$

$x = 0$

The x-intercept is 0.

Vertical asymptote:

$x - 2 = 0$

$x = 2$

Horizontal asymptote:

$y = \dfrac{3}{1} = 3$

$$f(x) = \dfrac{3x}{x-2}$$

6. $f(x) = \dfrac{2x^2}{x^2 - 9}$

$f(-x) = \dfrac{2(-x)^2}{(-x)^2 - 9} = \dfrac{2x^2}{x^2 - 9} = f(x)$

The y-axis symmetry.

$f(0) = \dfrac{2(0)^2}{0^2 - 9} = 0$

The y-intercept is 0.

$2x^2 = 0$

$\quad x = 0$

The x-intercept is 0.

vertical asymptotes:

$x^2 - 9 = 0$

$x = 3, x = -3$

horizontal asymptote:

$y = \dfrac{2}{1} = 2$

$$f(x) = \dfrac{2x^2}{x^2 - 9}$$

7. $f(x) = \dfrac{x^4}{x^2 + 2}$

$f(-x) = \dfrac{(-x)^4}{(-x)^2 + 2} = \dfrac{x^4}{x^2 + 2} = f(x)$

y-axis symmetry

$f(0) = \dfrac{0^4}{0^2 + 2} = 0$

The y-intercept is 0.

$x^4 = 0$

$\quad x = 0$

The x-intercept is 0.

vertical asymptotes:

$x^2 + 2 = 0$

$\quad x^2 = -2$

no vertical asymptotes

horizontal asymptote:

Since $n > m$, there is no horizontal asymptote.

$$f(x) = \dfrac{x^4}{x^2 + 2}$$

8.

$$\begin{array}{r|rrr} 2 & 2 & -5 & 7 \\ & & 4 & -2 \\ \hline & 2 & -1 & 5 \end{array}$$

the equation of the slant asymptote is
$y = 2x - 1$.

9. **a.** $C(x) = 500x + 600,000$

b. $\overline{C}(x) = \dfrac{500x + 600,000}{x}$

c. $\overline{C}(1000) = \dfrac{500(1000) + 600,000}{1000} = 1100$

The cost per computer to replace 1000 computers would be $1100.

$\overline{C}(10000) = \dfrac{500(10000) + 600,000}{10000} = 560$

The cost per computer to replace 10,000 computers would be $560.

$\overline{C}(100,000) = \dfrac{500(100,000) + 600,000}{100,000}$

$\qquad\qquad\quad = 506$

The cost per computer to replace 100,000 computers would be $506.

d. $y = 500$

The more computers the company replaces, the closer the average cost comes to $500.

10. $x - 10 =$ the average velocity on the return trip.
The function that expresses the total time
required to complete the round trip is

$$T(x) = \frac{20}{x} + \frac{20}{x - 10}.$$

Exercise Set 2.6

1. $f(x) = \frac{5x}{x - 4}$

    $\{x \mid x \neq 4\}$

3. $g(x) = \frac{3x^2}{(x - 5)(x + 4)}$

    $\{x \mid x \neq 5, x \neq -4\}$

5. $h(x) = \frac{x + 7}{x^2 - 49}$

    $x^2 - 49 = (x - 7)(x + 7)$

    $\{x \mid x \neq 7, x \neq -7\}$

7. $f(x) = \frac{x + 7}{x^2 + 49}$

    all real numbers

9. $-\infty$

11. $-\infty$

13. 0

15. $+\infty$

17. $-\infty$

19. 1

21. $f(x) = \frac{x}{x + 4}$

    $x + 4 = 0$

    $x = -4$

    vertical asymptote: $x = -4$

23. $g(x) = \frac{x + 3}{x(x + 4)}$

    $x(x + 4) = 0$

    $x = 0, x = -4$

    vertical asymptotes: $x = 0, x = -4$

25. $h(x) = \frac{x}{x(x + 4)} = \frac{1}{x + 4}$

    $x + 4 = 0$

    $x = -4$

    vertical asymptote: $x = -4$

27. $r(x) = \frac{x}{x^2 + 4}$

    $x^2 + 4$ has no real zeros
    There are no vertical asymptotes.

29. $f(x) = \frac{12x}{3x^2 + 1}$

    $n < m$

    horizontal asymptote: $y = 0$

31. $g(x) = \frac{12x^2}{3x^2 + 1}$

    $n = m$,

    horizontal asymptote: $y = \frac{12}{3} = 4$

33. $h(x) = \frac{12x^3}{3x^2 + 1}$

    $n > m$

    no horizontal asymptote

35. $f(x) = \frac{-2x + 1}{3x + 5}$

    $n = m$

    horizontal asymptote: $y = -\frac{2}{3}$

37. $g(x) = \frac{1}{x - 1}$

    Shift the graph of $f(x) = \frac{1}{x}$ 1 unit to the right.

$$g(x) = \frac{1}{x - 1}$$

39. $h(x) = \dfrac{1}{x} + 2$

Shift the graph of $f(x) = \dfrac{1}{x}$ 2 units up.

$h(x) = \dfrac{1}{x} + 2$

41. $g(x) = \dfrac{1}{x+1} - 2$

Shift the graph of $f(x) = \dfrac{1}{x}$ 1 unit left and 2 units down.

$g(x) = \dfrac{1}{x+1} - 2$

43. $g(x) = \dfrac{1}{(x+2)^2}$

Shift the graph of $f(x) = \dfrac{1}{x^2}$ 2 units left.

$g(x) = \dfrac{1}{(x+2)^2}$

45. $h(x) = \dfrac{1}{x^2} - 4$

Shift the graph of $f(x) = \dfrac{1}{x^2}$ 4 units down.

$h(x) = \dfrac{1}{x^2} - 4$

47. $h(x) = \dfrac{1}{(x-3)^2} + 1$

Shift the graph of $f(x) = \dfrac{1}{x^2}$ 3 units right and 1 unit up.

$h(x) = \dfrac{1}{(x-3)^2} + 1$

49. $f(x) = \dfrac{4x}{x-2}$

$f(-x) = \dfrac{4(-x)}{(-x)-2} = \dfrac{4x}{x+2}$

$f(-x) \neq f(x),\, f(-x) \neq -f(x)$

no symmetry

y-intercept: $y = \dfrac{4(0)}{0-2} = 0$

x-intercept: $4x = 0$

$x = 0$

vertical asymptote:

$x - 2 = 0$

$x = 2$

horizontal asymptote:

$n = m$, so $y = \dfrac{4}{1} = 4$

$$f(x) = \dfrac{4x}{x-2}$$

51. $f(x) = \dfrac{2x}{x^2-4}$

$f(-x) = \dfrac{2(-x)}{(-x)^2-4} = -\dfrac{2x}{x^2-4} = -f(x)$

Origin symmetry

y-intercept: $\dfrac{2(0)}{0^2-4} = \dfrac{0}{-4} = 0$

x-intercept:

$2x = 0$

$x = 0$

vertical asymptotes:

$x^2 - 4 = 0$

$x = \pm 2$

horizontal asymptote:

$n < m$ so $y = 0$

$$f(x) = \dfrac{2x}{x^2-4}$$

53. $f(x) = \dfrac{2x^2}{x^2-1}$

$f(-x) = \dfrac{2(-x)^2}{(-x)^2-1} = \dfrac{2x^2}{x^2-1} = f(x)$

y-axis symmetry

y-intercept: $y = \dfrac{2(0)^2}{0^2-1} = \dfrac{0}{1} = 0$

x-intercept:

$2x^2 = 0$

$x = 0$

vertical asymptote:

$x^2 - 1 = 0$

$x^2 = 1$

$x = \pm 1$

horizontal asymptote:

$n = m$, so $y = \dfrac{2}{1} = 2$

$$f(x) = \dfrac{2x^2}{x^2-1}$$

55. $f(x) = \dfrac{-x}{x+1}$

$f(-x) = \dfrac{-(-x)}{(-x)+1} = \dfrac{x}{-x+1}$

$f(-x) \neq f(x), f(-x) \neq -f(x)$

no symmetry

y-intercept: $y = \dfrac{-(0)}{0+1} = \dfrac{0}{1} = 0$

x-intercept:

$-x = 0$

$x = 0$

vertical asymptote:

$x + 1 = 0$

$x = -1$

horizontal asymptote:

$n = m$, so $y = \dfrac{-1}{1} = -1$

$$f(x) = \dfrac{-x}{x+1}$$

57. $f(x) = -\dfrac{1}{x^2 - 4}$

$f(-x) = -\dfrac{1}{(-x)^2 - 4} = -\dfrac{1}{x^2 - 4} = f(x)$

y-axis symmetry

y-intercept: $y = -\dfrac{1}{0^2 - 4} = \dfrac{1}{4}$

x-intercept: $-1 \neq 0$
no x-intercept
vertical asymptotes:

$x^2 - 4 = 0$
$\quad x^2 = 4$
$\quad\quad x = \pm 2$

    horizontal asymptote:
$n < m$ or $y = 0$

$f(x) = -\dfrac{1}{x^2 - 4}$

59. $f(x) = \dfrac{2}{x^2 + x - 2}$

$f(-x) = -\dfrac{2}{(-x)^2 - x - 2} = \dfrac{2}{x^2 - x - 2}$

$f(-x) \neq f(x), f(-x) \neq -f(x)$
no symmetry

y-intercept: $y = \dfrac{2}{0^2 + 0 - 2} = \dfrac{2}{-2} = -1$

x-intercept: none
vertical asymptotes:

$\quad x^2 + x - 2 = 0$
$(x + 2)(x - 1) = 0$
$\quad x = -2, x = 1$

horizontal asymptote:
$n < m$ so $y = 0$

$f(x) = \dfrac{2}{x^2 + x - 2}$

61. $f(x) = \dfrac{2x^2}{x^2 + 4}$

$f(-x) = \dfrac{2(-x)^2}{(-x)^2 + 4} = \dfrac{2x^2}{x^2 + 4} = f(x)$

y axis symmetry

y-intercept: $y = \dfrac{2(0)^2}{0^2 + 4} = 0$

x-intercept: $2x^2 = 0$
$x = 0$
vertical asymptote: none
horizontal asymptote:

$n = m$, so $y = \dfrac{2}{1} = 2$

$f(x) = \dfrac{2x^2}{x^2 + 4}$

63. $f(x) = \dfrac{x + 2}{x^2 + x - 6}$

$f(-x) = \dfrac{-x + 2}{(-x)^2 - (-x) - 6} = \dfrac{-x + 2}{x^2 + x - 6}$

$f(-x) \neq f(x), f(-x) \neq -f(x)$
no symmetry

y-intercept: $y = \dfrac{0 + 2}{0^2 + 0 - 6} = -\dfrac{2}{6} = -\dfrac{1}{3}$

x-intercept:
$x + 2 = 0$
$x = -2$
vertical asymptotes:

$x^2 + x - 6 = 0$
$(x + 3)(x - 2)$
$x = -3, x = 2$

    horizontal asymptote:
$n < m$, so $y = 0$

$f(x) = \dfrac{x + 2}{x^2 + x - 6}$

65. $f(x) = \dfrac{x^4}{x^2 + 2}$

$f(-x) = \dfrac{(-x)^4}{(-x)^2 + 2} = \dfrac{x^4}{x^2 + 2} = f(x)$

y-axis symmetry

y-intercept: $y = \dfrac{0^4}{0^2 + 2} = 0$

x-intercept: $x^4 = 0$
$x = 0$
vertical asymptote: none
horizontal asymptote:
$n > m$, so none

$$f(x) = \dfrac{x^4}{x^2 + 2}$$

67. $f(x) = \dfrac{x^2 + x - 12}{x^2 - 4}$

$f(-x) = \dfrac{(-x)^2 - x - 12}{(-x)^2 - 4} = \dfrac{x^2 - x - 12}{x^2 - 4}$

$f(-x) \neq f(x), f(-x) \neq -f(x)$

no symmetry

y-intercept: $y = \dfrac{0^2 + 0 - 12}{0^2 - 4} = 3$

x-intercept: $x^2 + x - 12 = 0$
$\qquad (x - 3)(x + 4) = 0$
$\qquad\qquad x = 3, x = -4$

vertical asymptotes:
$\qquad x^2 - 4 = 0$
$(x - 2)(x + 2) = 0$
$\qquad\qquad x = 2, x = -2$

horizontal asymptote:
$n = m$, so $y = \dfrac{1}{1} = 1$

$$f(x) = \dfrac{x^2 + x - 12}{x^2 - 4}$$

69. $f(x) = \dfrac{3x^2 + x - 4}{2x^2 - 5x}$

$f(-x) = \dfrac{3(-x)^2 - x - 4}{2(-x)^2 + 5x} = \dfrac{3x^2 - x - 4}{2x^2 + 5x}$

$f(-x) \neq f(x), f(-x) \neq -f(x)$

no symmetry

y-intercept: $y = \dfrac{3(0)^2 + 0 - 4}{2(0)^2 - 5(0)} = \dfrac{-4}{0}$

no y-intercept
x-intercepts:
$\qquad\qquad 3x^2 + x - 4 = 0$
$\qquad\quad (3x + 4)(x - 1) = 0$
$\qquad 3x + 4 = 0 \quad x - 1 = 0$
$\qquad\qquad 3x = -4$
$\qquad\qquad\qquad x = -\dfrac{4}{3}, x = 1$

vertical asymptotes:
$2x^2 - 5x = 0$
$x(2x - 5) = 0$
$x = 0, 2x = 5$
$\qquad x = \dfrac{5}{2}$

horizontal asymptote:
$n = m$, so $y = \dfrac{3}{2}$

$$f(x) = \dfrac{3x^2 + x - 4}{2x^2 - 5x}$$

71. a. Slant asymptote:

$$f(x) = x - \frac{1}{x}$$

$$y = x$$

b. $$f(x) = \frac{x^2 - 1}{x}$$

$$f(-x) = \frac{(-x)^2 - 1}{(-x)} = \frac{x^2 - 1}{-x} = -f(x)$$

Origin symmetry

y-intercept: $$y = \frac{0^2 - 1}{0} = \frac{-1}{0}$$

no y-intercept

x-intercepts: $x^2 - 1 = 0$

$x = \pm 1$

vertical asymptote: $x = 0$

horizontal asymptote:

$n < m$, so none exist.

$$f(x) = \frac{x^2 - 1}{x}$$

73. a. Slant asymptote:

$$f(x) = x + \frac{1}{x}$$

$$y = x$$

b. $$f(x) = \frac{x^2 + 1}{x}$$

$$f(-x) = \frac{(-x)^2 + 1}{-x} = \frac{x^2 + 1}{-x} = -f(x)$$

Origin symmetry

y-intercept: $$y = \frac{0^2 + 1}{0} = \frac{1}{0}$$

no y-intercept

x-intercept:

$x^2 + 1 = 0$

$x^2 = -1$

no x-intercept

vertical asymptote: $x = 0$

horizontal asymptote:

$n > m$, so none exist.

$$f(x) = \frac{x^2 + 1}{x}$$

75. a. Slant asymptote:

$$f(x) = x + 4 + \frac{6}{x - 3}$$

$$y = x + 4$$

b. $$f(x) = \frac{x^2 + x - 6}{x - 3}$$

$$f(-x) = \frac{(-x)^2 + (-x) - 6}{-x - 3} = \frac{x^2 - x - 6}{-x - 3}$$

$f(-x) \neq g(x), g(-x) \neq -g(x)$

No symmetry

y-intercept: $$y = \frac{0^2 + 0 - 6}{0 - 3} = \frac{-6}{-3} = 2$$

x-intercept:

$x^2 + x - 6 = 0$

$(x + 3)(x - 2) = 0$

$x = -3$ and $x = 2$

vertical asymptote:

$x - 3 = 0$

$x = 3$

horizontal asymptote:

$n > m$, so none exist.

$$f(x) = \frac{x^2 + x - 6}{x - 3}$$

77. $f(x) = \dfrac{x^3 + 1}{x^2 + 2x}$

    a.   slant asymptote:

$$
\begin{array}{r}
x - 2 \\
x^2 + 2x \overline{\smash{\big)}\, x^3 \qquad\; + 1} \\
\underline{x^3 + 2x^2 \qquad} \\
-2x^2 \qquad \\
\underline{-2x^2 + 4x} \\
-4x + 1
\end{array}
$$

$$y = x - 2$$

    b.

$$f(-x) = \frac{(-x)^3 + 1}{(-x)^2 + 2(-x)} = \frac{-x^3 + 1}{x^2 - 2x}$$

$$f(-x) \neq f(x),\ f(-x) \neq -f(x)$$

no symmetry

y-intercept: $y = \dfrac{0^3 + 1}{0^2 + 2(0)} = \dfrac{1}{0}$

no y-intercept

x-intercept: $x^3 + 1 = 0$

$x^3 = -1$

$x = -1$

vertical asymptotes:

$x^2 + 2x = 0$

$x(x + 2) = 0$

$x = 0,\ x = -2$

horizontal asymptote:

$n > m$, so none

$$f(x) = \frac{x^3 + 1}{x^2 + 2x}$$

79. $\dfrac{5x^2}{x^2 - 4} \cdot \dfrac{x^2 + 4x + 4}{10x^3}$

$$= \frac{\cancel{5}\, \cancel{x^2}}{(\cancel{x+2})(x-2)} \cdot \frac{(x+2)^{\cancel{2}}}{\underset{2}{\cancel{10}}\, \cancel{x^{3}}^{1}}$$

$$= \frac{x + 2}{2x(x - 2)}$$

So, $f(x) = \dfrac{x + 2}{2x(x - 2)}$

$$f(x) = \frac{x + 2}{2x(x - 2)}$$

81. $\dfrac{\dfrac{x}{2x + 6} - \dfrac{9}{x^2 - 9}}{\dfrac{x}{2x + 6} - \dfrac{9}{x^2 - 9}}$

$$= \frac{x}{2(x + 3)} - \frac{9}{(x + 3)(x - 3)}$$

$$= \frac{x(x - 3) - 9(2)}{2(x + 3)(x - 3)}$$

$$= \frac{x^2 - 3x - 18}{2(x + 3)(x - 3)}$$

$$= \frac{(x - 6)(x + 3)}{2(x + 3)(x - 3)} = \frac{x - 6}{2(x - 3)}$$

So, $f(x) = \dfrac{x - 6}{2(x - 3)}$

$$f(x) = \frac{x - 6}{2(x - 3)}$$

83. $\dfrac{1-\dfrac{3}{x+2}}{1+\dfrac{1}{x-2}} = \dfrac{1-\dfrac{3}{x+2}}{1+\dfrac{1}{x-2}} \cdot \dfrac{(x+2)(x-2)}{(x+2)(x-2)}$

$= \dfrac{(x+2)(x-2)-3(x-2)}{(x+2)(x-2)+(x+2)}$

$= \dfrac{x^2-4-3x+6}{x^2-4+x+2}$

$= \dfrac{x^2-3x+2}{x^2+x-2}$

$= \dfrac{(x-2)\,(x-1)}{(x+2)\,(x-1)} = \dfrac{x-2}{x+2}$

So, $f(x) = \dfrac{x-2}{x+2}$

$f(x) = \dfrac{x-2}{x+2}$

85. $g(x) = \dfrac{2x+7}{x+3} = \dfrac{1}{x+3}+2$

$f(x) = \dfrac{1}{x+3} + 2$

87. $g(x) = \dfrac{3x-7}{x-2} = \dfrac{-1}{x-2}+3$

$f(x) = \dfrac{-1}{x-2} + 3$

89. a. $C(x) = 100x + 100{,}000$

b. $\overline{C}(x) = \dfrac{100x+100{,}000}{x}$

c. $\overline{C}(500) = \dfrac{100(500)+100{,}000}{500} = \$300$

When 500 bicycles are manufactured, it costs \$300 to manufacture each.

$\overline{C}(1000) = \dfrac{100(1000)+100{,}000}{1000} = \$200$

When 1000 bicycles are manufactured, it costs \$200 to manufacture each.

$\overline{C}(2000) = \dfrac{100(2000)+100{,}000}{2000} = \$150$

When 2000 bicycles are manufactured, it costs \$150 to manufacture each.

$\overline{C}(4000) = \dfrac{100(4000)+100{,}000}{4000} = \$125$

When 4000 bicycles are manufactured, it costs \$125 to manufacture each.
The average cost decreases as the number of bicycles manufactured increases.

d. $n = m$, so $y = \dfrac{100}{1} = 100$.

As greater numbers of bicycles are manufactured, the average cost approaches \$100.

91. a. From the graph the pH level of the human mouth 42 minutes after a person eats food containing sugar will be about 6.0.

b. From the graph, the pH level is lowest after about 6 minutes.

$$f(6) = \dfrac{6.5(6)^2 - 20.4(6) + 234}{6^2 + 36}$$

$$= 4.8$$

The pH level after 6 minutes (i.e. the lowest pH level) is 4.8.

c. From the graph, the pH level appears to approach 6.5 as time goes by. Therefore, the normal pH level must be 6.5.

d. $y = 6.5$

Over time, the pH level rises back to the normal level.

e. During the first hour, the pH level drops quickly below normal, and then slowly begins to approach the normal level.

93. $P(10) = \dfrac{100(10-1)}{10} = 90 \quad (10, 90)$

For a disease that smokers are 10 times more likely to contact than non-smokers, 90% of the deaths are smoking related.

95. $y = 100$ As incidence of the diseases increases, the percent of death approaches, but never gets to be, 100%.

97. a. $\dfrac{128.3}{134.5} \approx 0.954$

In 1995, there were 954 males per 1000 females.

b. $\dfrac{141.7}{146.7} \approx 0.966$

In 2002, there were 966 males per 1000 females.

c. $f(x) = \dfrac{1.256x + 74.2}{1.324x + 76.71}$

d. 1995 is 45 years after 1950, so we find

$f(45) = \dfrac{1.256(45) + 74.2}{1.324(45) + 76.71} \approx 0.959$

The model predicts 959 males per 1000 females in 1995. The result from the function modeled the actual number fairly well.

e. 2002 is 52 years after 1950, so we find

$f(52) = \dfrac{1.256(52) + 74.2}{1.324(52) + 76.71} \approx 0.958$

The model predicts 958 males per 1000 females in 2002. The result from the function modeled the actual number fairly well.

f. $y = \dfrac{1.256}{1.324}$ or $y = 0.949$

This means that over time, the number of males per 1000 females will approach 949.

99. $T(x) = \dfrac{90}{9x} + \dfrac{5}{x} = \dfrac{10}{x} + \dfrac{5}{x}$

The function that expresses the total time for driving and hiking is $T(x) = \dfrac{10}{x} + \dfrac{5}{x}$.

101. $A = lw$

$xy = 50$

$l = y + 2 = \dfrac{50}{x} + 2$

$w = x + 1$

$A = \left(\dfrac{50}{x} + 2\right)(x + 1)$

$\quad = 50 + \dfrac{50}{x} + 2x + 2$

$\quad = 2x + \dfrac{50}{x} + 52$

The total area of the page is

$A(x) = 2x + \dfrac{50}{x} + 52.$

113.

The graph approaches the horizontal asymptote faster and the vertical asymptote slower as *n* increases.

115. a. $f(x) = \dfrac{27725(x - 14)}{x^2 + 9} - 5x$

b. The graph increases from late teens until about the age of 25, and then the number of arrests decreases.

c. At age 25 the highest number arrests occurs. There are about 356 arrests for every 100,000 drivers.

117. a. False, $\sqrt{x-3} = (x-3)^{1/2}$ is not a polynomial function.

b. False, $n = m$ so the horizontal asymptote is

$y = \dfrac{4}{1} = 4$

c. False, $n = m$ so the horizontal asymptote is

$y = \dfrac{3000}{1} = 3000$, not 30,000.

d. True

(d) is true.

Section 2.7

Check Point Exercises

1.

$$x^2 - x > 20$$

$$x^2 - x - 20 > 0$$

$$(x + 4)(x - 5) > 0$$

Solve the related quadratic equation.

$$(x + 4)(x - 5) = 0$$

Apply the zero product principle.

$$x + 4 = 0 \quad \text{or} \quad x - 5 = 0$$

$$x = -4 \qquad\qquad x = 5$$

The boundary points are –2 and 4.

Test Interval	Test Number	Test	Conclusion
$(-\infty, -4)$	–5	$(-5)^2 - (-5) > 20$ $30 > 20$, true	$(-\infty, -4)$ belongs to the solution set.
$(-4, 5)$	0	$(0)^2 - (0) > 20$ $0 > 20$, false	$(-4, 5)$ does not belong to the solution set.
$(5, \infty)$	10	$(10)^2 - (10) > 20$ $90 > 20$, true	$(5, \infty)$ belongs to the solution set.

The solution set is $(-\infty, -4) \cup (5, \infty)$ or $\{x \mid x < -4 \text{ or } x > 5\}$.

2.

$$x^3 + 3x^2 \le x + 3$$

$$x^3 + 3x^2 - x - 3 \le 0$$

$$(x + 1)(x - 1)(x + 3) \le 0$$

$$(x + 1)(x - 1)(x + 3) = 0$$

$$x + 1 = 0 \quad \text{or} \quad x - 1 = 0 \quad \text{or} \quad x + 3 = 0$$

$$x = -1 \qquad\qquad x = 1 \qquad\qquad x = -3$$

Test Interval	Test Number	Test	Conclusion
$(-\infty, -3)$	-4	$(-4)^3 + 3(-4)^2 \le (-4) + 3$ $-16 \le -1$ true	$(-\infty, -3)$ belongs to the solution set.
$(-3, -1]$	-2	$(-2)^3 + 3(-2)^2 \le (-2) + 3$ $4 \le 1$ false	$(-3, -1]$ does not belong to the solution set.
$[-1, 1]$	0	$(0)^3 + 3(0)^2 \le (0) + 3$ $0 \le 3$ true	$[-1, 1]$ belongs to the solution set.
$[1, \infty)$	2	$(6 + 3)(6 - 5) > 0$ true	$[1, \infty)$ does not belong to the solution set.

The solution set is $(-\infty, -3] \cup [-1, 1]$ or $\{x \mid x \le -3 \text{ or } -1 \le x \le 1\}$.

3.

$$\frac{2x}{x+1} \geq 1$$

$$\frac{2x}{x+1} - 1 \geq 0$$

$$\frac{x-1}{x+1} \geq 0$$

$$x - 1 = 0 \quad \text{or} \quad x + 1 = 0$$

$$x = 1 \qquad\qquad x = -1$$

Test Interval	Test Number	Test	Conclusion
$(-\infty, -1)$	-2	$\dfrac{2(-2)}{-2+1} \geq 1$ $4 \geq 1, \text{ true}$	$(-\infty, -1)$ belongs to the solution set.
$(-1, 1]$	0	$\dfrac{2(0)}{0+1} \geq 1$ $0 \geq 1, \text{ false}$	$(-1, 1]$ does not belong to the solution set.
$[1, \infty)$	2	$\dfrac{2(2)}{2+1} \geq 1$ $\dfrac{4}{3} \geq 1, \text{ true}$	$[1, \infty)$ belongs to the solution set.

The solution set is $(-\infty, -1) \cup [1, \infty)$ or $\left\{ x \mid x < -1 \text{ or } x \geq 1 \right\}$.

4.

$$-16t^2 + 80t > 64$$

$$-16t^2 + 80t - 64 > 0$$

$$-16(t-1)(t-4) > 0$$

$$t - 1 = 0 \quad \text{or} \quad t - 4 = 0$$

$$t = 1 \qquad\qquad t = 4$$

Test Interval	Test Number	Test	Conclusion
$(-\infty, 1)$	0	$-16(0)^2 + 80(0) > 64$ $0 > 64, \text{ false}$	$(-\infty, 1)$ does not belong to the solution set.
$(1, 4)$	2	$-16(2)^2 + 80(2) > 64$ $96 > 64, \text{ true}$	$(1, 4)$ belongs to the solution set.
$(4, \infty)$	5	$-16(5)^2 + 80(5) > 64$ $0 > 64, \text{ false}$	$(4, \infty)$ does not belong to the solution set.

The object will be more than 64 feet above the ground between 1 and 4 seconds.

Exercise Set 2.7

1. $(x-4)(x+2) > 0$
     $x = 4$ or $x = -2$

T	F	T

       -2 4

     Test -3: $(-3-4)(-3+2) > 0$
                           $7 > 0$ True
     Test 0: $(0-4)(0+2) > 0$
                        $-8 > 0$ False
     Test 5: $(5-4)(5+2) > 0$
                           $7 > 0$ True
     $(-\infty, -2)$ or $(4, \infty)$

3. $(x-7)(x+3) \leq 0$
     $x = 7$ or $x = -3$

F	T	F

       -3 7

     Test -4: $(-4-7)(-4+3) \leq 0$
           $11 \leq 0$ False
     Test 0: $(0-7)(0+3) \leq 0$
           $-21 \leq 0$ True
     Test 8: $(8-7)(8+3) \leq 0$
           $11 \leq 0$ False
     The solution set is $[-3, 7]$.

5. $x^2 - 5x + 4 > 0$
     $(x-4)(x-1) > 0$
     $x = 4$ or $x = 1$

T	F	T

       1 4

     Test 0: $0^2 - 5(0) + 4 > 0$
                    $4 > 0$ True
     Test 2: $2^2 - 5(2) + 4 > 0$
                  $-2 > 0$ False
     Test 5: $5^2 - 5(5) + 4 > 0$
                    $4 > 0$ True
     The solution set is $(-\infty, 1)$ or $(4, \infty)$.

7. $x^2 + 5x + 4 > 0$
     $(x+1)(x+4) > 0$
     $x = -1$ or $x = -4$

T	F	T

       -4 -1

     Test -5: $(-5)^2 + 5(-5) + 4 > 0$
                  $4 > 0$ True
     Test -3: $(-3)^2 + 5(-3) + 4 > 0$
               $-2 > 0$ False
     Test 0: $0^2 + 5(0) + 4 > 0$
                $4 > 0$ True
     The solution set is $(-\infty, -4)$ or $(-1, \infty)$.

9. $x^2 - 6x + 9 < 0$
     $(x-3)(x-3) < 0$
              $x = 3$

F	F

       3

     Test 0: $0^2 - 6(0) + 9 < 0$
                    $9 < 0$ False
     Test 4: $4^2 - 6(4) + 9 < 0$
                    $1 < 0$ False
     The solution set is the empty set, $\varnothing$.

11.
$$3x^2 + 10x - 8 \le 0$$
$$(3x - 2)(x + 4) \le 0$$
$$x = \frac{2}{3} \text{ or } x = -4$$

F	T	F
-4	$\frac{2}{3}$	

Test -5: $3(-5)^2 + 10(-5) - 8 \le 0$
$$17 \le 0 \text{ False}$$
Test 0: $3(0)^2 + 10(0) - 8 \le 0$
$$8 \le 0 \text{ True}$$
Test 1: $3(1)^2 + 10(1) - 8 \le 0$
$$5 \le 0 \text{ False}$$
The solution set is $\left[-4, \frac{2}{3} \right]$.

13.
$$2x^2 + x < 15$$
$$2x^2 + x - 15 < 0$$
$$(2x - 5)(x + 3) < 0$$
$$2x - 5 = 0 \quad \text{or} \quad x + 3 = 0$$
$$2x = 5$$
$$x = \frac{5}{2} \quad \text{or} \quad x = -3$$

F	T	F
-3	$\frac{5}{2}$	

Test -4: $2(-4)^2 + (-4) < 15$
$$28 < 15 \text{ False}$$
Test 0: $2(0)^2 + 0 < 15$
$$0 < 15 \text{ True}$$
Test 3: $2(3)^2 + 3 < 15$
$$21 < 15 \text{ False}$$
The solution set is $\left(-3, \frac{5}{2} \right)$.

15.
$$4x^2 + 7x < -3$$
$$4x^2 + 7x + 3 < 0$$
$$(4x + 3)(x + 1) < 0$$
$$4x + 3 = 0 \quad \text{or} \quad x + 1 = 0$$
$$4x - 3 = 0$$
$$x = -\frac{3}{4} \quad \text{or} \quad x = -1$$

F	T	F
-1	$-\frac{3}{4}$	

Test -2: $4(-2)^2 + 7(-2) < -3$
$$2 < -3 \text{ False}$$
Test $-\frac{7}{8}$: $4\left(-\frac{7}{8} \right)^2 + 7\left(-\frac{7}{8} \right) < -3$
$$\frac{49}{16} - \frac{49}{8} < -3$$
$$-\frac{49}{16} < -3 \text{ True}$$
Test 0: $4(0)^2 + 7(0) < -3$
$$0 < -3 \text{ False}$$
The solution set is $\left(-1, -\frac{3}{4} \right)$.

17.
$$5x \le 2 - 3x^2$$
$$3x^2 + 5x - 2 \le 0$$
$$(3x - 1)(x + 2) \le 0$$
$$3x - 1 = 0 \text{ or } x + 2 = 0$$
$$3x = 1$$
$$3x - 1 = 0 \quad \text{or} \quad x + 2 = 0$$
$$3x = 1$$
$$x = \frac{1}{3} \quad \text{or} \quad x = -2$$

F	T	F
-2	$\frac{1}{3}$	

Test -3: $5(-3) \leq 2 - 3(-3)^2$

$\qquad\qquad -15 \leq -25$ False

Test 0: $5(0) \leq 2 - 3(0)^2$

$\qquad\qquad 0 \leq 2$ True

Test 1: $5(1) \leq 2 - 3(1)^2$

$\qquad\qquad 5 \leq -1$ False

The solution set is $\left[-2, \dfrac{1}{3}\right]$.

19. $x^2 - 4x \geq 0$

$x(x-4) \geq 0$

$x = 0$ or $x - 4 = 0$

$\qquad\qquad x = 4$

T		F		T
	0		4	

Test -1: $(-1)^2 - 4(-1) \geq 0$

$\qquad\qquad\qquad 5 \geq 0$ True

Test 1: $(1)^2 - 4(1) \geq 0$

$\qquad\qquad\qquad -3 \geq 0$ False

$\qquad\qquad 0 \leq 2$ True

Test 5: $5^2 - 4(5) \geq 0$

$\qquad\qquad\qquad 5 \geq 0$ True

The solution set is $(-\infty, 0]$ or $[4, \infty)$.

21. $2x^2 + 3x > 0$

$x(2x + 3) > 0$

$x = 0$ or $x = -\dfrac{3}{2}$

T		F		T
	$-\frac{3}{2}$		0	

Test -2: $2(-2)^2 + 3(-2) > 0$

$\qquad\qquad 2 > 0$ True

Test -1: $2(-1)^2 + 3(-1) > 0$

$\qquad\qquad -1 > 0$ False

Test 1: $2(1)^2 + 3(1) > 0$

$\qquad\qquad 5 > 0$ True

The solution set is $\left(-\infty, -\dfrac{3}{2}\right)$ or $(0, \infty)$.

23. $-x^2 + x \geq 0$

$x^2 - x \leq 0$

$x(x - 1) \leq 0$

$x = 0$ or $x = 1$

F		T		F
	0		1	

Test -1: $-(-1)^2 + (-1) \geq 0$

$\qquad\qquad\qquad -2 \geq 0$ False

Test $\dfrac{1}{2}$: $-\left(\dfrac{1}{2}\right)^2 + \left(\dfrac{1}{2}\right) \geq 0$

$\qquad\qquad\qquad \dfrac{1}{4} \geq 0$ True

Test 2: $-(2)^2 + 2 \geq 0$

$\qquad\qquad\qquad -2 \geq 0$ False

The solution set is $[0, 1]$.

25. $x^2 \leq 4x - 2$

$x^2 - 4x + 2 \leq 0$

Solve $x^2 - 4x + 2 = 0$

$x = \dfrac{-b \pm \sqrt{b^2 - 4ac}}{2a}$

$x = \dfrac{-(-4) \pm \sqrt{(-4)^2 - 4(1)(2)}}{2(1)}$

$\quad = \dfrac{4 \pm \sqrt{8}}{2}$

$\quad = 2 \pm \sqrt{2}$

$x \approx 0.59$ or $x \approx 3.41$

F		T		F
	0.59		3.41	

The solution set is

$\left[2 - \sqrt{2}, 2 + \sqrt{2}\right]$ or $[0.59, 3.41]$.

27. $x^2 - 6x + 9 < 0$

Solve $x^2 - 6x + 9 = 0$

$(x-3)(x-3) = 0$

$(x-3)^2 = 0$

$x = 3$

The solution set is the empty set, $\varnothing$.

29. $(x-1)(x-2)(x-3) \geq 0$

Boundary points: 1, 2, and 3
Test one value in each interval.

The solution set is $[1, 2] \cup [3, \infty)$.

31. $x^3 + 2x^2 - x - 2 \geq 0$

$x^2(x+2) - 1(x+2) \geq 0$

$(x+2)(x^2 - 1) \geq 0$

$(x+2)(x-1)(x+1) \geq 0$

Boundary points: -2, -1, and 2
Test one value in each interval.

The solution set is $[-2, -1] \cup [1, \infty)$.

33. $x^3 + 2x^2 - x - 2 \geq 0$

$x^2(x-3) - 9(x-3) \geq 0$

$(x-3)(x^2 - 9) \geq 0$

$(x-3)(x+3)(x-3) \geq 0$

Boundary points: -3 and 3
Test one value in each interval.

The solution set is $(-\infty, -3]$.

35. $x^3 + x^2 + 4x + 4 > 0$

$x^2(x+1) + 4(x+1) \geq 0$

$(x+1)(x^2 + 4) \geq 0$

Boundary point: -1
Test one value in each interval.

The solution set is $(-1, \infty)$.

37. $x^3 - 9x^2 \geq 0$

$x^2(x-9) \geq 0$

Boundary points: 0 and 9
Test one value in each interval.

The solution set is $[0, 0] \cup [9, \infty)$.

39. $\dfrac{x-4}{x+3} > 0$

$x - 4 = 0 \quad x + 3 = 0$

$x = 4 \quad\quad x = -3$

The solution set is $(-\infty, -3) \cup (4, \infty)$.

41. $\dfrac{x+3}{x+4} < 0$

$x = -3 \quad \text{or} \quad x = -4$

The solution set is $(-4, -3)$.

43. $\dfrac{-x+2}{x-4} \ge 0$

$x = 2$ or $x = 4$

	F		T		F	
		2		4		

The solution set is $[2, 4)$.

45. $\dfrac{4-2x}{3x+4} \le 0$

$x = 2$ or $x = -\dfrac{4}{3}$

	T		F		T	
		$-\frac{4}{3}$		2		

The solution set is $\left(-\infty, \dfrac{-4}{3}\right) \cup [2, \infty)$.

47. $\dfrac{x}{x-3} > 0$

$x = 0$ or $x = 3$

	T		F		T	
		0		3		

The solution set is $(-\infty, 0) \cup (3, \infty)$.

49. $\dfrac{(x+4)(x-1)}{x+2} \le 0$

$x = -4$ or $x = -2$ or $x = 1$.

	T		F		T		F	
		-4		-2		1		

Values of $x = -4$ or $x = 1$ result in $f(x) = 0$
and, therefore must be included in the solution
set.

The solution set is $\left(-\infty, -4\right] \cup \left(-2, 1\right]$.

51. $\dfrac{x+1}{x+3} < 2$

$\dfrac{x+1}{x+3} - 2 < 0$

$\dfrac{x+1-2(x+3)}{x+3} < 0$

$\dfrac{x+1-2x-6}{x+3} < 0$

$\dfrac{-x-5}{x+3} < 0$

$x = $ or $x = -3$

	T		F		T	
		-5		-3		

The solution set is $(-\infty, -5) \cup (-3, \infty)$.

53. $\dfrac{x+4}{2x-1} \le 3$

$\dfrac{x+4}{2x-1} - 3 \le 0$

$\dfrac{x+4-3(2x-1)}{2x-1} \le 0$

$\dfrac{x+4-6x+3}{2x-1} \le 0$

$\dfrac{-5x+7}{2x-1} \le 0$

$x = \dfrac{7}{5}$ or $x = \dfrac{1}{2}$

	T		F		T	
		$\frac{1}{2}$		$\frac{7}{5}$		

55.
$$\frac{x-2}{x+2} \le 2$$
$$\frac{x-2}{x+2} - 2 \le 0$$
$$\frac{x-2-2(x+2)}{x+2} \le 0$$
$$\frac{x-2-2x-4}{x+2} \le 0$$
$$\frac{-x-6}{x+2} \le 0$$
$$x=-6 \quad \text{or} \quad x=-2$$

T	F	T
-6	-2	

The solution set is $(-\infty, -6] \cup (-2, \infty)$.

57. $f(x) = \sqrt{2x^2 - 5x + 2}$

The domain of this function requires that
$2x^2 - 5x + 2 \ge 0$
Solve $2x^2 - 5x + 2 = 0$
$(x-2)(2x-1) = 0$
$x = \frac{1}{2}$ or $x = 2$

T	F	T
$\frac{1}{2}$	2	

The domain is $\left(-\infty, \frac{1}{2}\right] \cup [2, \infty)$.

59. $f(x) = \sqrt{\dfrac{2x}{x+1} - 1}$

The domain of this function requires that
$$\frac{2x}{x+1} - 1 \ge 0 \quad \text{or} \quad \frac{x-1}{x+1} \ge 0$$
$$x=-1 \quad \text{or} \quad x=1$$

T	F	T
-1	1	

The value $x=1$ results in 0 and, thus, it must be included in the domain.
The domain is $(-\infty, -1) \cup [1, \infty)$.

61. $\left| x^2 + 2x - 36 \right| > 12$

Express the inequality without the absolute value symbol:

$x^2 + 2x - 36 < -12$ or $x^2 + 2x - 36 > 12$

$x^2 + 2x - 24 < 0$ $\qquad$ $x^2 + 2x - 48 > 0$

Solve the related quadratic equations.

$\quad x^2 + 2x - 24 = 0$ or $x^2 + 2x - 48 = 0$

$(x + 6)(x - 4) = 0$ $\qquad$ $(x + 8)(x - 6) = 0$

Apply the zero product principle.

$x + 6 = 0$ or $x - 4 = 0$ or $x + 8 = 0$ or $x - 6 = 0$

$\quad x = -6$ $\qquad$ $x = 4$ $\qquad$ $x = -8$ $\qquad$ $x = 6$

The boundary points are -8, -6, 4 and 6.

Test Interval	Test Number	Test	Conclusion
$(-\infty, -8)$	-9	$\left| (-9)^2 + 2(-9) - 36 \right| > 12$ $27 > 12$, True	$(-\infty, -8)$ belongs to the solution set.
$(-8, -6)$	-7	$\left| (-7)^2 + 2(-7) - 36 \right| > 12$ $1 > 12$, False	$(-8, -6)$ does not belong to the solution set.
$(-6, 4)$	0	$\left| 0^2 + 2(0) - 36 \right| > 12$ $36 > 12$, True	$(-6, 4)$ belongs to the solution set.
$(4, 6)$	5	$\left| 5^2 + 2(5) - 36 \right| > 12$ $1 > 12$, False	$(4, 6)$ does not belong to the solution set.
$(6, \infty)$	7	$\left| 7^2 + 2(7) - 36 \right| > 12$ $27 > 12$, True	$(6, \infty)$ belongs to the solution set.

The solution set is $(-\infty, -8) \cup (-6, 4) \cup (6, \infty)$ or $\{ x \mid x < -8 \text{ or } -6 < x < 4 \text{ or } x > 6 \}$.

63. $\dfrac{3}{x+3} > \dfrac{3}{x-2}$

Express the inequality so that one side is zero.

$$\dfrac{3}{x+3} - \dfrac{3}{x-2} > 0$$

$$\dfrac{3(x-2)}{(x+3)(x-2)} - \dfrac{3(x+3)}{(x+3)(x-2)} > 0$$

$$\dfrac{3x-6-3x-9}{(x+3)(x-2)} < 0$$

$$\dfrac{-15}{(x+3)(x-2)} < 0$$

Find the values of x that make the denominator zero.

$x+3=0 \qquad x-2=0$

$\quad x=-3 \qquad\quad x=2$

The boundary points are -3 and 2.

Test Interval	Test Number	Test	Conclusion
$(-\infty,-3)$	-4	$\dfrac{3}{-4+3} > \dfrac{3}{-4-2}$ $-3 > \dfrac{1}{2}$, False	$(-\infty,-3)$ does not belong to the solution set.
$(-3,2)$	0	$\dfrac{3}{0+3} > \dfrac{3}{0-2}$ $1 > -\dfrac{3}{2}$, True	$(-3,2)$ belongs to the solution set.
$(2,\infty)$	3	$\dfrac{3}{3+3} > \dfrac{3}{3-2}$ $\dfrac{1}{2} > 3$, False	$(2,\infty)$ does not belong to the solution set.

The solution set is $(-3,2)$ or $\{x \mid -3 < x < 2\}$.

65. $\dfrac{x^2 - x - 2}{x^2 - 4x + 3} > 0$

Find the values of x that make the numerator and denominator zero.

$x^2 - x - 2 = 0$ $x^2 - 4x + 3 = 0$

$(x - 2)(x + 1) = 0$ $(x - 3)(x - 1) = 0$

Apply the zero product principle.

$x - 2 = 0$ or $x + 1 = 0$ $x - 3 = 0$ or $x - 1 = 0$

$\quad x = 2 \qquad\qquad x = -1 \qquad\qquad x = 3 \qquad\qquad x = 1$

The boundary points are -1, 1, 2 and 3.

Test Interval	Test Number	Test	Conclusion
$(-\infty, -1)$	-2	$\dfrac{(-2)^2 - (-2) - 2}{(-2)^2 - 4(-2) + 3} > 0$ $\dfrac{4}{15} > 0$, True	$(-\infty, -1)$ belongs to the solution set.
$(-1, 1)$	0	$\dfrac{0^2 - 0 - 2}{0^2 - 4(0) + 3} > 0$ $-\dfrac{2}{3} > 0$, False	$(-1, 1)$ does not belong to the solution set.
$(1, 2)$	1.5	$\dfrac{1.5^2 - 1.5 - 2}{1.5^2 - 4(1.5) + 3} > 0$ $\dfrac{5}{3} > 0$, True	$(1, 2)$ belongs to the solution set.
$(2, 3)$	2.5	$\dfrac{2.5^2 - 2.5 - 2}{2.5^2 - 4(2.5) + 3} > 0$ $-\dfrac{7}{3} > 0$, False	$(2, 3)$ does not belong to the solution set.
$(3, \infty)$	4	$\dfrac{4^2 - 4 - 2}{4^2 - 4(4) + 3} > 0$ $\dfrac{10}{3} > 0$, True	$(3, \infty)$ belongs to the solution set.

The solution set is $(-\infty, -1) \cup (1, 2) \cup (3, \infty)$ or $\{x \mid x < -1 \text{ or } 1 < x < 2 \text{ or } x > 3\}$.

67. $\qquad 2x^3 + 11x^2 \geq 7x + 6$

$2x^3 + 11x^2 - 7x - 6 \geq 0$

The graph of $f(x) = 2x^3 + 11x^2 - 7x - 6$ appears to cross the x-axis at -6, $-\dfrac{1}{2}$, and 1. We verify this numerically by substituting these values into the function:

$f(-6) = 2(-6)^3 + 11(-6)^2 - 7(-6) - 6 = 2(-216) + 11(36) - (-42) - 6 = -432 + 396 + 42 - 6 = 0$

$f\left(-\dfrac{1}{2}\right) = 2\left(-\dfrac{1}{2}\right)^3 + 11\left(-\dfrac{1}{2}\right)^2 - 7\left(-\dfrac{1}{2}\right) - 6 = 2\left(-\dfrac{1}{8}\right) + 11\left(\dfrac{1}{4}\right) - \left(-\dfrac{7}{2}\right) - 6 = -\dfrac{1}{4} + \dfrac{11}{4} + \dfrac{7}{2} - 6 = 0$

$f(1) = 2(1)^3 + 11(1)^2 - 7(1) - 6 = 2(1) + 11(1) - 7 - 6 = 2 + 11 - 7 - 6 = 0$

Thus, the boundaries are -6, $-\dfrac{1}{2}$, and 1. We need to find the intervals on which $f(x) \ge 0$. These intervals are indicated on the graph where the curve is above the x-axis. Now, the curve is above the x-axis when $-6 < x < -\dfrac{1}{2}$ and when $x > 1$. Thus, the solution set is $\left\{ x \;\middle|\; -6 \le x \le -\dfrac{1}{2} \ \text{ or } \ x \ge 1 \right\}$ or $\left[-6, -\dfrac{1}{2} \right] \cup \left[1, \infty \right)$.

69.
$$\frac{1}{4(x+2)} \le -\frac{3}{4(x-2)}$$

$$\frac{1}{4(x+2)} + \frac{3}{4(x-2)} \le 0$$

Simplify the left side of the inequality:

$$\frac{x-2}{4(x+2)} + \frac{3(x+2)}{4(x-2)} = \frac{x-2+3x+6}{4(x+2)(x-2)} = \frac{4x+4}{4(x+2)(x-2)} = \frac{4(x+1)}{4(x+2)(x-2)} = \frac{x+1}{x^2-4}.$$

The graph of $f(x) = \dfrac{x+1}{x^2-4}$ crosses the x-axis at -1, and has vertical asymptotes at $x = -2$ and $x = 2$. Thus, the boundaries are -2, -1, and 1. We need to find the intervals on which $f(x) \le 0$. These intervals are indicated on the graph where the curve is below the x-axis. Now, the curve is below the x-axis when $x < -2$ and when $-1 < x < 2$. Thus, the solution set is $\left\{ x \mid x < -2 \ \text{ or } \ -1 \le x < 2 \right\}$ or $(-\infty, -2) \cup [-1, 2)$.

71. $s(t) = -16t^2 + 8t + 87$

The diver's height will exceed that of the cliff when $s(t) > 87$

$$-16t^2 + 8t + 87 > 87$$
$$-16t^2 + 8t > 0$$
$$-8t(2t - 1) > 0$$

The boundaries are 0 and $\dfrac{1}{2}$. Testing each interval shows that the diver will be higher than the cliff for the first half second after beginning the jump. The interval is $\left(0, \dfrac{1}{2} \right)$.

73. $f(8) = 27(8) + 163 = 216 + 163 = 379$

$g(8) = 1.2(8)^2 + 15.2(8) + 181.4 = 1.2(64) + 121.6 + 181.4$
$\qquad = 76.8 + 121.6 + 181.4 = 379.8$

Since the graph indicates that Medicare spending will reach \$379 billion, we conclude that both functions model the data quite well.

75. $g(x) = 1.2x^2 + 15.2x + 181.4$

To find when spending exceeds \$536.6 billion, solve the inequality $1.2x^2 + 15.2x + 181.4 > 536.6$.
Solve the related quadratic equation using the quadratic formula.

$1.2x^2 + 15.2x + 181.4 = 536.6$

$1.2x^2 + 15.2x - 355.2 = 0$

$a = 1.2 \quad b = 15.2 \quad c = -355.2$

$$x = \frac{-15.2 \pm \sqrt{15.2^2 - 4(1.2)(-355.2)}}{2(1.2)} = \frac{-15.2 \pm \sqrt{231.04 + 1704.96}}{2.4}$$

$$= \frac{-15.2 \pm \sqrt{1936}}{2.4} = \frac{-15.2 \pm 44}{2.4}$$

$$= \frac{-15.2 - 44}{2.4} \quad \text{or} \quad \frac{-15.2 + 44}{2.4} = -24\frac{2}{3} \quad \text{or} \quad 12$$

We disregard $-24\frac{2}{3}$ since x represents the number of years after 1995 and cannot be negative. The boundary point is 12.

Test Interval	Test Number	Test	Conclusion
$(0,12)$	1	$1.2(1)^2 + 15.2(1) + 181.4 > 536.6$ $197.8 > 536.6$, false	$(0,12)$ does not belong to the solution set.
$(12,\infty)$	13	$1.2(13)^2 + 15.2(13) + 181.4 > 536.6$ $581.8 > 536.6$, true	$(12,\infty)$ belongs to the solution set.

The solution set is $(12,\infty)$. This means that spending will exceed \$536.6 billion after $1995 + 12 = 2007$.

77. $f(x) = \dfrac{15}{x}$

If the time must be limited to 3 hours, then $\dfrac{15}{x} < 3$.

$$\frac{15}{x} < 3$$

$$\frac{15}{x} - 3 < 0$$

$$\frac{-3(x-5)}{x} < 0$$

The boundaries are 0 and 5. Testing each interval shows that $\dfrac{15}{x} < 3$ on the intervals of $(-\infty, 0)$ and $(5,\infty)$.

However, a rate below 0 does not fit the constraints of this problem. Thus the solution is $(5,\infty)$.

The graph agrees with this solution.
For rates above 5 mph, the height of the graph is always at or below 3 hours.

79.   As $x \to \infty$, the graph approaches 0. This shows that the higher the running rate, the less time it will take to complete the 95 miles.

81. To obtain the function that is displayed on the graph, let x represent the hiking rate and, thus, 9x will represent the driving rate.

$$\overbrace{f(x)}^{\text{total time}} = \frac{\overbrace{\text{driving distance}}^{\text{driving time}}}{\text{driving rate}} + \frac{\overbrace{\text{hiking distance}}^{\text{hiking time}}}{\text{hiking rate}}$$

$$f(x) = \frac{90}{9x} + \frac{5}{x}$$

$$= \frac{10}{x} + \frac{5}{x}$$

$$= \frac{15}{x}$$

83. $2l + 2w = P$

  $2l + 2w = 180$

  $2l = 180 - 2w$

  $l = 90 - w$

We want to restrict the area to 800 square feet. That is,

$$A \le 800$$

$$l \cdot w \le 800$$

$$(90 - w)w \le 800$$

$$90w - w^2 \le 800$$

$$-w^2 + 90w - 800 \le 0$$

$$w^2 - 90w + 800 \ge 0$$

$$w^2 - 90w + 800 = 0$$

$$(w - 80)(w - 10) = 0$$

$$w - 80 = 0 \quad \text{or} \quad w - 10 = 0$$

$$w = 80 \qquad\qquad w = 10$$

Assuming the width is the shorter side, we ignore the larger solution.

Test Interval	Test Number	Test	Conclusion
$(0,10)$	5	$90(5) - (5)^2 \le 800$ true	$(0,10)$ is part of the solution set
$(10,45)$	20	$90(20) - (20)^2 \le 800$ false	$(10,45)$ is not part of the solution set

The solution set is $\{w \mid 0 < w \le 10\}$ or $(0,10]$.

The length of the shorter side cannot exceed 10 feet.

87. Answers will vary.

89.

The solution set is $(-\infty, -5) \cup (2, \infty)$.

91.

The solution set is $(-2, -1)$ or $(2, \infty)$.

93. Graph $y_1 = \dfrac{x+2}{x-3}$ and $y_2 = 2$

y_1 less than or equal to y_2 for $x < 3$ or $x \geq 8$.

The solution set is $(-\infty, 3) \cup [8, \infty)$

95. a. False

$x^2 > 25$

Solution: $(-\infty, -5) \cup (5, \infty)$

b. False

Subtract 2 from both sides and solve.

$\dfrac{x - 2 - 2(x+3)}{x+3} < 0$

Note that when multiplying by $x + 3$, $x + 3$ may be negative.

c. False

The solution set of the first inequality is $(-\infty, -3) \cup (1, \infty)$. The solution set of the second inequality is $(-\infty, -3) \cup (1, \infty)$.

d. True

(d) is true.

97. One possible solution: $\dfrac{x-3}{x+4} \geq 0$

99. Because any number squared other than zero is positive, the solution includes only 2.

101. Because any number squared other than zero is positive, and the reciprocal of zero is undefined, the solution is all real numbers except 2.

103. $\sqrt{27 - 3x^2} \geq 0$

$27 - 3x^2 \geq 0$

$9 - x^2 \geq 0$

$(3 - x)(3 + x) \geq 0$

$3 - x = 0 \qquad 3 + x = 0$

$x = 3$ or $\qquad x = -3$

Test –4: $\sqrt{27 - 3(-4)^2} \geq 0$

$\sqrt{27 - 48} \geq 0$

$\sqrt{-21} \geq 0$

no graph- imaginary

Test 0: $\sqrt{27 - 3(0)^2} \geq 0$

$\sqrt{27} \geq 0$ True

Test 4: $\sqrt{27 - 3(4)^2} \geq 0$

$\sqrt{27 - 48} \geq 0$

$\sqrt{-21} \geq 0$

no graph -imaginary

The solution set is $[-3, 3]$.

Section 2.8

Check Point Exercises

1. y varies directly as x is expressed as $y = kx$.

The volume of water, W, varies directly as the time, t can be expressed as $W = kt$.

Use the given values to find k.

$W = kt$

$30 = k(5)$

$6 = k$

Substitute the value of k into the equation.

$W = kt$

$W = 6t$

Use the equation to find W when $t = 11$.

$W = 6t$

$\quad = 6(11)$

$\quad = 66$

A shower lasting 11 minutes will use 66 gallons of water.

2. y varies directly as the square of x is expressed as $y = kx$.

The distance, s, varies directly as the square of the speed, v can be expressed as $s = kv^2$.

Use the given values to find k.

$s = kv^2$

$200 = k(60)^2$

$0.0556 = k$

Substitute the value of k into the equation.

$s = kv^2$

$s = 0.0556v^2$

Use the equation to find s when $v = 100$.

$s = 0.0556v^2$

$\quad = 0.0556(100)^2$

$\quad = 556$

A car traveling 100 mph will require 556 feet to stop.

3. y varies inversely as x is expressed as $y = \dfrac{k}{x}$.

The length, L, varies inversely as the frequency, f can be expressed as $L = \dfrac{k}{f}$.

Use the given values to find k.

$$L = \frac{k}{f}$$

$$8 = \frac{k}{640}$$

$$5120 = k$$

Substitute the value of k into the equation.

$$L = \frac{k}{f}$$

$$L = \frac{5120}{f}$$

Use the equation to find f when $L = 10$.

$$L = \frac{5120}{f}$$

$$10 = \frac{5120}{f}$$

$$10f = 5120$$

$$f = 512$$

A 10 inch violin string will have a frequency of 512 cycles per second.

4. let M represent the number of minutes
let Q represent the number of problems
let P represent the number of people
M varies directly as Q and inversely as P is expressed as $M = \dfrac{kQ}{P}$.

Use the given values to find k.

$$M = \frac{kQ}{P}$$

$$32 = \frac{k(16)}{4}$$

$$8 = k$$

Substitute the value of k into the equation.

$$M = \frac{kQ}{P}$$

$$M = \frac{8Q}{P}$$

Use the equation to find M when $P = 8$ and $Q = 24$.

$$M = \frac{8Q}{P}$$

$$M = \frac{8(24)}{8}$$

$$M = 24$$

It will take 24 minutes for 8 people to solve 24 problems.

5. V varies jointly with h and r^2 and can be modeled as $V = khr^2$.

Use the given values to find k.

$$V = khr^2$$

$$120\pi = k(10)(6)^2$$

$$\frac{\pi}{3} = k$$

Therefore, the volume equation is $V = \dfrac{1}{3}hr^2$.

$$V = \frac{\pi}{3}(2)(12)^2 = 96\pi \text{ cubic feet}$$

Exercise Set 2.8

1. Use the given values to find k.

$$y = kx$$

$$65 = k \cdot 5$$

$$\frac{65}{5} = \frac{k \cdot 5}{5}$$

$$13 = k$$

The equation becomes $y = 13x$.

When $x = 12$, $y = 13x = 13 \cdot 12 = 156$.

3. Since y varies inversely with x, we have $y = \dfrac{k}{x}$.

Use the given values to find k.

$$y = \frac{k}{x}$$

$$12 = \frac{k}{5}$$

$$5 \cdot 12 = 5 \cdot \frac{k}{5}$$

$$60 = k$$

The equation becomes $y = \dfrac{60}{x}$.

When $x = 2$, $y = \dfrac{60}{2} = 30$.

5. Since y varies inversely as x and inversely as the square of z, we have $y = \dfrac{kx}{z^2}$.

Use the given values to find k.

$$y = \frac{kx}{z^2}$$
$$20 = \frac{k(50)}{5^2}$$
$$20 = \frac{k(50)}{25}$$
$$20 = 2k$$
$$10 = k$$

The equation becomes $y = \dfrac{10x}{z^2}$.

When $x = 3$ and $z = 6$,

$$y = \frac{10x}{z^2} = \frac{10(3)}{6^2} = \frac{10(3)}{36} = \frac{30}{36} = \frac{5}{6}.$$

7. Since y varies jointly as x and z, we have
$y = kxz$.

Use the given values to find k.

$$y = kxz$$
$$25 = k(2)(5)$$
$$25 = k(10)$$
$$\frac{25}{10} = \frac{k(10)}{10}$$
$$\frac{5}{2} = k$$

The equation becomes $y = \dfrac{5}{2}xz$.

When $x = 8$ and $z = 12$, $y = \dfrac{5}{2}(8)(12) = 240$.

9. Since y varies jointly as a and b and inversely as the square root of c, we have $y = \dfrac{kab}{\sqrt{c}}$.

Use the given values to find k.

$$y = \frac{kab}{\sqrt{c}}$$
$$12 = \frac{k(3)(2)}{\sqrt{25}}$$
$$12 = \frac{k(6)}{5}$$
$$12(5) = \frac{k(6)}{5}(5)$$
$$60 = 6k$$
$$\frac{60}{6} = \frac{6k}{6}$$
$$10 = k$$

The equation becomes $y = \dfrac{10ab}{\sqrt{c}}$.

When $a = 5$, $b = 3$, $c = 9$,

$$y = \frac{10ab}{\sqrt{c}} = \frac{10(5)(3)}{\sqrt{9}} = \frac{150}{3} = 50.$$

11. $x = kyz$;

Solving for y:

$$x = kyz$$
$$\frac{x}{kz} = \frac{kyz}{yz}.$$
$$y = \frac{x}{kz}$$

13. $x = \dfrac{kz^3}{y}$;

Solving for y

$$x = \frac{kz^3}{y}$$
$$xy = y \cdot \frac{kz^3}{y}$$
$$xy = kz^3$$
$$\frac{xy}{x} = \frac{kz^3}{x}$$
$$y = \frac{kz^3}{x}$$

15.
$x = \dfrac{kyz}{\sqrt{w}}$;

Solving for y:

$$x = \dfrac{kyz}{\sqrt{w}}$$

$$x\left(\sqrt{w}\right) = \left(\sqrt{w}\right)\dfrac{kyz}{\sqrt{w}}$$

$$x\sqrt{w} = kyz$$

$$\dfrac{x\sqrt{w}}{kz} = \dfrac{kyz}{kz}$$

$$y = \dfrac{x\sqrt{w}}{kz}$$

17. $x = kz(y + w)$;

Solving for y:

$$x = kz(y + w)$$

$$x = kzy + kzw$$

$$x - kzw = kzy$$

$$\dfrac{x - kzw}{kz} = \dfrac{kzy}{kz}$$

$$y = \dfrac{x - kzw}{kz}$$

19. $x = \dfrac{kz}{y - w}$;

Solving for y:

$$x = \dfrac{kz}{y - w}$$

$$(y - w)x = (y - w)\dfrac{kz}{y - w}$$

$$xy - wx = kz$$

$$xy = kz + wx$$

$$\dfrac{xy}{x} = \dfrac{kz + wx}{x}$$

$$y = \dfrac{xw + kz}{x}$$

21. Since T varies directly as B, we have $T = kB$.
Use the given values to find k.

$$T = kB$$

$$3.6 = k(4)$$

$$\dfrac{3.6}{4} = \dfrac{k(4)}{4}$$

$$0.9 = k$$

The equation becomes $T = 0.9B$.
When $B = 6$, $T = 0.9(6) = 5.4$.
The tail length is 5.4 feet.

23. Since B varies directly as D, we have $B = kD$.
Use the given values to find k.

$$B = kD$$

$$8.4 = k(12)$$

$$\dfrac{8.4}{12} = \dfrac{k(12)}{12}$$

$$k = \dfrac{8.4}{12} = 0.7$$

The equation becomes $B = 0.7D$.
When $B = 56$,

$$56 = 0.7D$$

$$\dfrac{56}{0.7} = \dfrac{0.7D}{0.7}$$

$$D = \dfrac{56}{0.7} = 80$$

It was dropped from 80 inches.

25. Since a man's weight varies directly as the cube of his height, we have $w = kh^3$.
Use the given values to find k.

$$w = kh^3$$

$$170 = k(70)^3$$

$$170 = k(343,000)$$

$$\dfrac{170}{343,000} = \dfrac{k(343,000)}{343,000}$$

$$0.000496 = k$$

The equation becomes $w = 0.000496h^3$.
When $h = 107$,

$$w = 0.000496(107)^3$$

$$= 0.000496(1,225,043) \approx 607.$$

Robert Wadlow's weight was approximately 607 pounds.

27. Since the banking angle varies inversely as the turning radius, we have $B = \dfrac{k}{r}$.
Use the given values to find k.

$$B = \dfrac{k}{r}$$

$$28 = \dfrac{k}{4}$$

$$28(4) = 28\left(\dfrac{k}{4}\right)$$

$$112 = k$$

The equation becomes $B = \dfrac{112}{r}$.

When $r = 3.5$, $B = \dfrac{112}{r} = \dfrac{112}{3.5} = 32$.

The banking angle is $32°$ when the turning radius is 3.5 feet.

29. Since intensity varies inversely as the square of the distance, we have pressure, we have

    $I = \dfrac{k}{d}$.

    Use the given values to find k.

    $$I = \dfrac{k}{d^2}.$$

    $$62.5 = \dfrac{k}{3^2}$$

    $$62.5 = \dfrac{k}{9}$$

    $$9(62.5) = 9\left(\dfrac{k}{9}\right)$$

    $$562.5 = k$$

    The equation becomes $I = \dfrac{562.5}{d^2}$.

    When $d = 2.5$, $I = \dfrac{562.5}{2.5^2} = \dfrac{562.5}{6.25} = 90$

    The intensity is 90 milliroentgens per hour.

31. Since index varies directly as weight and inversely as the square of one's height, we have $I = \dfrac{kw}{h^2}$.

    Use the given values to find k.

    $$I = \dfrac{kw}{h^2}$$

    $$35.15 = \dfrac{k(180)}{60^2}$$

    $$35.15 = \dfrac{k(180)}{3600}$$

    $$(3600)35.15 = \dfrac{k(180)}{3600}$$

    $$126540 = k(180)$$

    $$k = \dfrac{126540}{180} = 703$$

    The equation becomes $I = \dfrac{703w}{h^2}$.

    When $w = 170$ and $h = 70$,

    $I = \dfrac{703(170)}{(70)^2} \approx 24.4$.

    This person has a BMI of 24.4 and is not overweight.

33. Since heat loss varies jointly as the area and temperature difference, we have $L = kAD$. Use the given values to find k.

    $$L = kAD$$

    $$1200 = k(3 \cdot 6)(20)$$

    $$1200 = 360k$$

    $$\dfrac{1200}{360} = \dfrac{360k}{360}$$

    $$k = \dfrac{10}{3}$$

    The equation becomes $L = \dfrac{10}{3}AD$

    When $A = 6 \cdot 9 = 54$, $D = 10$,

    $L = \dfrac{10}{3}(9 \cdot 6)(10) = 1800$.

    The heat loss is 1800 Btu.

35. Since intensity varies inversely as the square of the distance from the sound source, we have $I = \dfrac{k}{d^2}$. If you move to a seat twice as far, then $d = 2d$. So we have

    $I = \dfrac{k}{(2d)^2} = \dfrac{k}{4d^2} = \dfrac{1}{4} \cdot \dfrac{k}{d^2}$. The intensity will

    be multiplied by a factor of $\dfrac{1}{4}$. So the sound

    intensity is $\dfrac{1}{4}$ of what it was originally.

37. a. Since the average number of phone calls varies jointly as the product of the populations and inversely as the square of

      the distance, we have $C = \dfrac{kP_1P_2}{d^2}$.

    b. Use the given values to find k.

       $$C = \dfrac{kP_1P_2}{d^2}$$

       $$326,000 = \dfrac{k(777,000)(3,695,000)}{(420)^2}$$

       $$326,000 = \dfrac{k(2.87 \times 10^{12})}{176,400}$$

       $$326,000 = 16269841.27k$$

       $$0.02 \approx k$$

       The equation becomes $C = \dfrac{0.02P_1P_2}{d^2}$.

c.
$$C = \frac{0.02(650,000)(490,000)}{(400)^2}$$

$$\approx 39813$$

The average number of calls is approximately 39,813 daily phone calls.

39. a.

b. Current varies inversely as resistance. Answers will vary.

c. Since the current varies inversely as resistance we have $R = \dfrac{k}{I}$. Using one of the given ordered pairs to find k.

$$12 = \frac{k}{0.5}$$

$$12(0.5) = \frac{k}{0.5}(0.5)$$

$$k = 6$$

The equation becomes $R = \dfrac{6}{I}$.

45. z varies directly as the square root of x and inversely as the square of y.

49. Pressure, P, varies directly as the square of wind velocity, v, can be modeled as $P = kv^2$.

If $v = x$ then $P = k(x)^2 = kx^2$

If $v = 2x$ then $P = k(2x)^2 = 4kx^2$

If the wind speed doubles the pressure is 4 times more destructive.

51. The Heat, H, varies directly as the square of the voltage, v, and inversely as the resistance, r.

$$H = \frac{kv^2}{r}$$

If the voltage remains constant, to triple the heat the resistant must be reduced by a multiple of 3.

Chapter 2 Review Exercises

1. $(8 - 3i) - (17 - 7i) = 8 - 3i - 17 + 7i$
$$= -9 + 4i$$

2. $4i(3i - 2) = (4i)(3i) + (4i)(-2)$
$$= 12i^2 - 8i$$
$$= -12 - 8i$$

3. $(7 - i)(2 + 3i)$
$$= 7 \cdot 2 + 7(3i) + (-i)(2) + (-i)(3i)$$
$$= 14 + 21i - 2i + 3$$
$$= 17 + 19i$$

4. $(3 - 4i)^2 = 3^2 + 2 \cdot 3(-4i) + (-4i)^2$
$$= 9 - 24i - 16$$
$$= -7 - 24i$$

5. $(7 + 8i)(7 - 8i) = 7^2 + 8^2 = 49 + 64 = 113$

6. $\dfrac{6}{5 + i} = \dfrac{6}{5 + i} \cdot \dfrac{5 - i}{5 - i}$

$$= \frac{30 - 6i}{25 + 1}$$

$$= \frac{30 - 6i}{26}$$

$$= \frac{15 - 3i}{13}$$

$$= \frac{15}{13} - \frac{3}{13}i$$

7. $\dfrac{3 + 4i}{4 - 2i} = \dfrac{3 + 4i}{4 - 2i} \cdot \dfrac{4 + 2i}{4 + 2i}$

$$= \frac{12 + 6i + 16i + 8i^2}{16 - 4i^2}$$

$$= \frac{12 + 22i - 8}{16 + 4}$$

$$= \frac{4 + 22i}{20}$$

$$= \frac{1}{5} + \frac{11}{10}i$$

8. $\sqrt{-32} - \sqrt{-18} = i\sqrt{32} - i\sqrt{18}$
$$= i\sqrt{16 \cdot 2} - i\sqrt{9 \cdot 2}$$
$$= 4i\sqrt{2} - 3i\sqrt{2}$$
$$= (4i - 3i)\sqrt{2}$$
$$= i\sqrt{2}$$

9.
$$(-2+\sqrt{-100})^2 = (-2+i\sqrt{100})^2$$
$$= (-2+10i)^2$$
$$= 4-40i+(10i)^2$$
$$= 4-40i-100$$
$$= -96-40i$$

10. $\dfrac{4+\sqrt{-8}}{2} = \dfrac{4+i\sqrt{8}}{2} = \dfrac{4+2i\sqrt{2}}{2} = 2+i\sqrt{2}$

11. $x^2 - 2x + 4 = 0$

$$x = \frac{-(-2)\pm\sqrt{(-2)^2-4(1)(4)}}{2(1)}$$

$$x = \frac{2\pm\sqrt{4-16}}{2}$$

$$x = \frac{2\pm\sqrt{-12}}{2}$$

$$x = \frac{2\pm 2i\sqrt{3}}{2}$$

$$x = 1\pm i\sqrt{3}$$

The solution set is $\left\{1-i\sqrt{3},\ 1+i\sqrt{3}\right\}$

12. $2x^2 - 6x + 5 = 0$

$$x = \frac{-(-6)\pm\sqrt{(-6)^2-4(2)(5)}}{2(2)}$$

$$x = \frac{6\pm\sqrt{36-40}}{4}$$

$$x = \frac{6\pm\sqrt{-4}}{4}$$

$$x = \frac{6\pm 2i}{4}$$

$$x = \frac{6}{4}\pm\frac{2i}{4}$$

$$= \frac{3}{2}\pm\frac{1}{2}i$$

The solution set is $\left\{\dfrac{3}{2}-\dfrac{1}{2}i,\ \dfrac{3}{2}+\dfrac{1}{2}i\right\}$.

13. $f(x) = -(x+1)^2 + 4$
vertex: $(-1, 4)$
x-intercepts:
$$0 = -(x+1)^2 + 4$$
$$(x+1)^2 = 4$$
$$x+1 = \pm 2$$
$$x = -1\pm 2$$

$x = -3$ or $x = 1$
y-intercept:
$$f(0) = -(0+1)^2 + 4 = 3$$
The axis of symmetry is $x = -1$.

$$f(x) = -(x+1)^2 + 4$$

Domain: $(-\infty,\infty)$ Range: $(-\infty, 4]$

14. $f(x) = (x+4)^2 - 2$
vertex: $(-4, -2)$
x-intercepts:
$$0 = (x+4)^2 - 2$$
$$(x+4)^2 = 2$$
$$x+4 = \pm\sqrt{2}$$
$$x = -4\pm\sqrt{2}$$
y-intercept:
$$f(0) = (0+4)^2 - 2 = 14 = -1$$

$$f(x) = (x+4)^2 - 2$$

The axis of symmetry is $x = -4$.
Domain: $(-\infty,\infty)$ Range: $[-2,\infty)$

15. $f(x) = -x^2 + 2x + 3$
$$= -(x^2 - 2x + 1) + 3 + 1$$
$$f(x) = -(x-1)^2 + 4$$

$$f(x) = -x^2 + 2x + 3$$

Domain: $(-\infty,\infty)$ Range: $(-\infty, 4]$

16. $f(x) = 2x^2 - 4x - 6$

$f(x) = 2(x^2 - 2x + 1) - 6 - 2$

$2(x-1)^2 - 8$

$f(x) = 2x^2 - 4x - 6$

axis of symmetry: $x = 1$

Domain: $(-\infty, \infty)$ Range: $[-8, \infty)$

17. $f(x) = -x^2 + 14x - 106$

a. Since $a < 0$ the parabola opens down with the maximum value occurring at

$x = -\dfrac{b}{2a} = -\dfrac{14}{2(-1)} = 7$.

The maximum value is $f(7)$.

$f(7) = -(7)^2 + 14(7) - 106 = -57$

b. Domain: $(-\infty, \infty)$ Range: $(-\infty, -57]$

18. $f(x) = 2x^2 + 12x + 703$

a. Since $a > 0$ the parabola opens up with the minimum value occurring at

$x = -\dfrac{b}{2a} = -\dfrac{12}{2(2)} = -3$.

The minimum value is $f(-3)$.

$f(-3) = 2(-3)^2 + 12(-3) + 703 = 685$

b. Domain: $(-\infty, \infty)$ Range: $[685, \infty)$

19. $f(x) = -0.02x^2 + x + 1$

Since $a = -0.02$ is negative, we know the function opens downward and has a maximum

at $x = -\dfrac{b}{2a} = -\dfrac{1}{2(-0.02)} = -\dfrac{1}{-0.04} = 25$. When

25 inches of rain falls, the maximum growth will occur. The maximum growth is

$f(25) = -0.02(25)^2 + 25 + 1$

$= -0.02(625) + 25 + 1$

$= -12.5 + 25 + 1 = 13.5$.

A maximum yearly growth of 13.5 inches occurs when 25 inches of rain falls per year.

20. According to the graph, the vertex (maximum point) is (25, 5). This means that the maximum divorce rate of 5 divorces per 1000 people occurred in the year $1960 + 25 = 1985$.

21. Maximize the area using $A = lw$.

$A(x) = x(1000 - 2x)$

$A(x) = -2x^2 + 1000x$

Since $a = -2$ is negative, we know the function opens downward and has a maximum at

$x = -\dfrac{b}{2a} = -\dfrac{1000}{2(-2)} = -\dfrac{1000}{-4} = 250$.

The maximum area is achieved when the width is 250 yards. The maximum area is

$A(250) = 250(1000 - 2(250))$

$= 250(1000 - 500)$

$= 250(500) = 125,000$.

The area is maximized at 125,000 square yards when the width is 250 yards and the length is $1000 - 2 \cdot 250 = 500$ yards.

22. Let $x =$ one of the numbers

Let $14 + x =$ the other number

We need to minimize the function

$P(x) = x(14 + x)$

$= 14x + x^2$

$= x^2 + 14x$.

The minimum is at

$x = -\dfrac{b}{2a} = -\dfrac{14}{2(1)} = -\dfrac{14}{2} = -7$.

The other number is $14 + x = 14 + (-7) = 7$.

The numbers which minimize the product are 7 and -7. The minimum product is $-7 \cdot 7 = -49$.

23. $3x + 4y = 1000$

$4y = 1000 - 3x$

$$y = \frac{1000 - 3x}{4}$$

$$A = x\left(\frac{1000 - 3x}{4}\right)$$

$$= -\frac{3}{4}x^2 + 250x$$

$$x = \frac{-b}{2a} = \frac{-250}{2\left(-\dfrac{3}{4}\right)} = 125$$

$$y = \frac{1000 - 3(125)}{4} = 166.7$$

125 feet by 166.7 feet will maximize the area.

24. $y = (35 + x)(150 - 4x)$

$y = 5250 + 10x - 4x^2$

$$x = \frac{-b}{2a} = \frac{-10}{2(-4)} = \frac{5}{4} = 1.25 \text{ or } 1 \text{ tree}$$

The maximum number of trees should be $35 + 1$
     $= 36$ trees.

maximum number of trees should be $35 + 1 = 36$
     trees.

$y = 36(150 - 4x) = 36(150 - 4 \cdot 1) = 5256$

The maximum yield will be 5256 pounds.

25. $f(x) = -x^3 + 12x^2 - x$

The graph rises to the left and falls to the right and goes through the origin, so graph (c) is the best match.

26. $g(x) = x^6 - 6x^4 + 9x^2$

The graph rises to the left and rises to the right, so graph (b) is the best match.

27. $h(x) = x^5 - 5x^3 + 4x$

The graph falls to the left and rises to the right and crosses the *y*-axis at zero, so graph (a) is the best match.

28. $f(x) = -x^4 + 1$

$f(x)$ falls to the left and to the right so graph (d) is the best match.

29. The leading coefficient is –0.87 and the degree is 3. This means that the graph will fall to the right. This function is not useful in modeling the number of thefts over an extended period of time. The model predicts that eventually, the number of thefts would be negative. This is impossible.

30. In the polynomial, $f(x) = -x^4 + 21x^2 + 100$, the leading coefficient is –1 and the degree is 4. Applying the Leading Coefficient Test, we know that even-degree polynomials with negative leading coefficient will fall to the left and to the right. Since the graph falls to the right, we know that the elk population will die out over time.

31. $f(x) = -2(x - 1)(x + 2)^2(x + 5)^3$

$x = 1$, multiplicity 1, the graph crosses the *x*-axis

$x = -2$, multiplicity 2, the graph touches the *x*-axis

$x = -5$, multiplicity 5, the graph crosses the *x*-axis

32. $f(x) = x^3 - 5x^2 - 25x + 125$

$$= x^2(x - 5) - 25(x - 5)$$

$$= (x^2 - 25)(x - 5)$$

$$= (x + 5)(x - 5)^2$$

$x = -5$, multiplicity 1, the graph crosses the *x*-axis

$x = 5$, multiplicity 2, the graph touches the *x*-axis

33. $f(x) = x^3 - 2x - 1$

$f(1) = (1)^3 - 2(1) - 1 = -2$

$f(2) = (2)^3 - 2(2) - 1 = 3$

The sign change shows there is a zero between the given values.

34. $f(x) = x^3 - x^2 - 9x + 9$

a. Since n is odd and $a_n > 0$, the graph falls to the left and rises to the right.

b. $f(-x) = (-x)^3 - (-x)^2 - 9(-x) + 9$

$$= -x^3 - x^2 + 9x + 9$$

$f(-x) \neq f(x), f(-x) \neq -f(x)$

no symmetry

c. $f(x) = (x-3)(x+3)(x-1)$
zeros: 3, −3, 1

$f(x) = x^3 - x^2 - 9x + 9$

35. $f(x) = 4x - x^3$

a.   Since n is odd and $a_n < 0$, the graph rises to the left and falls to the right.

b. $f(-x) = -4x + x^3$
$f(-x) = -f(x)$
origin symmetry

c. $f(x) = x(x^2 - 4) = x(x-2)(x+2)$
zeros: $x = 0, 2, -2$

$f(x) = 4x - x^3$

36. $f(x) = 2x^3 + 3x^2 - 8x - 12$

a.   Since h is odd and $a_n > 0$, the graph falls to the left and rises to the right.

b. $f(-x) = -2x^3 + 3x^2 + 8x - 12$
$f(-x) \neq f(x), \ f(-x) = -f(x)$
no symmetry

c. $f(x) = (x-2)(x+2)(2x+3)$
zeros: $x = 2, -2, -\dfrac{3}{2}$

$f(x) = 2x^3 + 3x^2 - 8x - 12$

37. $g(x) = -x^4 + 25x^2$

a.   The graph falls to the left and to the right.

b. $f(-x) = -(-x)^4 + 25(-x)^2$
$\qquad = -x^4 + 25x^2 = f(x)$
y-axis symmetry

c. $\qquad -x^4 + 25x^2 = 0$
$\qquad -x^2(x^2 - 25) = 0$
$-x^2(x-5)(x+5) = 0$
zeros: $x = -5, 0, 5$

$f(x) = -x^4 + 25x^2$

38. $f(x) = -x^4 + 6x^3 - 9x^2$

a.   The graph falls to the left and to the right.

b. $f(-x) = -(-x)^4 + 6(-x)^3 - 9(-x)$
$\qquad = -x^4 - 6x^3 - 9x^2 \ f(-x) \neq f(x)$
$f(-x) \neq -f(x)$
no symmetry

c. $\qquad = -x^2(x^2 - 6x + 9) = 0$
$\qquad -x^2(x-3)(x-3) = 0$
zeros: $x = 0, 3$

$f(x) = -x^4 + 6x^3 - 9x^2$

39. $f(x) = 3x^4 - 15x^3$

    a.   The graph rises to the left and to the right.

    b. $f(-x) = 3(-x)^4 - 15(-x)^2 = 3x^4 + 15x^3$

           $f(-x) \neq f(x),\ f(-x) \neq -f(x)$

           no symmetry

    c $3x^4 - 15x^3 = 0$

           $3x^3(x - 5) = 0$

           zeros: $x = 0, 5$

         $f(x) = 3x^4 - 15x^3$

40. $f(x) = 2x^2(x-1)^3(x+2)$

     Since $a_n > 0$ and n is even, $f(x)$ rises to the left and the right.

     $x = 0,\ x = 1,\ x = -2$

     The zeros at 1 and −2 have odd multiplicity so $f(x)$ crosses the x-axis at those points. The root at 0 has even multiplicity so $f(x)$ touches the axis at $(0, 0)$

     $f(0) = 2(0)^2(0-1)^3(0+2) = 0$

     The y-intercept is 0.

         $f(x) = 2x^2(x-1)^3(x+2)$

41. $f(x) = -x^3(x+4)^2(x-1)$

     Since $a_n < 0$ and n is even, $f(x)$ falls to the left and the right.

     $x = 0,\ x = -4,\ x = 1$

     The roots at 0 and 1 have odd multiplicity so $f(x)$ crosses the x-axis at those points. The root at −4 has even multiplicity so $f(x)$ touches the axis at $(-4, 0)$

     $f(0) = -(0)^3(0+4)^2(0-1) = 0$

The y-intercept is 0.

$f(x) = -x^3(x+4)^2(x-1)$

42.

$$
\begin{array}{r}
4x^2 - 7x + 5 \\
x+1\overline{\smash{\big)}\,4x^3 - 3x^2 - 2x + 1} \\
\underline{4x^3 + 4x^2} \\
-7x^2 - 2x \\
\underline{-7x^2 - 7x} \\
5x + 1 \\
\underline{5x + 5} \\
-4
\end{array}
$$

Quotient: $4x^2 - 7x + 5 - \dfrac{4}{x+1}$

43.

$$
\begin{array}{r}
2x^2 - 4x + 1 \\
5x-3\overline{\smash{\big)}\,10x^3 - 26x^2 + 17x - 13} \\
\underline{10x^3 + 6x^2} \\
-20x^2 + 17x \\
\underline{-20x^2 + 12x} \\
5x - 13 \\
\underline{5x - 3} \\
-10
\end{array}
$$

Quotient: $2x^2 - 4x + 1 - \dfrac{10}{5x-3}$

44.

$$
\begin{array}{r}
2x^2 + 3x - 1 \\
2x^2+1\overline{\smash{\big)}\,4x^4 + 6x^3 + 3x - 1} \\
\underline{4x^2 + 2x^2} \\
6x^3 - 2x^2 + 3x \\
\underline{6x^2 + 3x} \\
-2x^2 - 1 \\
\underline{-2x^2 - 1} \\
0
\end{array}
$$

45. $(3x^4 + 11x^3 - 20x^3 + 7x + 35) \div (x + 5)$

$$
\begin{array}{r|rrrrr}
-5 & 3 & 11 & -20 & 7 & 35 \\
   &   & -15 & 20 & 0 & -35 \\
\hline
   & 3 & -4 & 0 & 7 & 0
\end{array}
$$

Quotient: $3x^3 - 4x^2 + 7$

46. $(3x^4 - 2x^2 - 10x) \div (x - 2)$

$$
\begin{array}{r|rrrrr}
2 & 3 & 0 & -2 & -10 & 0 \\
  &   & 6 & 12 & 20 & 20 \\
\hline
  & 3 & 6 & 10 & 10 & 20
\end{array}
$$

Quotient: $3x^3 + 6x^2 + 10x + 10 + \dfrac{20}{x - 2}$

47. $f(x) = 2x^3 - 7x^2 + 9x - 3$

$$
\begin{array}{r|rrrr}
-13 & 2 & -7 & 9 & -3 \\
    &   & -26 & 429 & -5694 \\
\hline
    & 2 & -33 & 438 & -5697
\end{array}
$$

Quotient: $f(-13) = -5697$

48. $f(x) = 2x^3 + x^2 - 13x + 6$

$$
\begin{array}{r|rrrr}
2 & 2 & 1 & -13 & 6 \\
  &   & 4 & 10 & -6 \\
\hline
  & 2 & 5 & -3 & 0
\end{array}
$$

$$
\begin{aligned}
f(x) &= (x - 2)(2x^2 + 5x - 3) \\
     &= (x - 2)(2x - 1)(x + 3)
\end{aligned}
$$

Zeros: $x = 2, \dfrac{1}{2}, -3$

49. $x^3 - 17x + 4 = 0$

$$
\begin{array}{r|rrrr}
4 & 1 & 0 & -17 & 4 \\
  &   & 4 & 16 & -4 \\
\hline
  & 1 & 4 & -1 & 0
\end{array}
$$

$(x - 4)(x^2 + 4x - 1) = 0$

$x = \dfrac{-4 \pm \sqrt{16 + 4}}{2} = \dfrac{-4 \pm 2\sqrt{5}}{2} = -2 \pm \sqrt{5}$

The solution set is $\left\{ 4, -2 + \sqrt{5}, -2 - \sqrt{5} \right\}$.

50. $f(x) = x^4 - 6x^3 + 14x^2 - 14x + 5$

$p : \pm 1, \pm 5$

$q : \pm 1$

$\dfrac{p}{q} : \pm 1, \pm 5$

51. $f(x) = 3x^5 - 2x^4 - 15x^3 + 10x^2 + 12x - 8$

$p : \pm 1, \pm 2, \pm 4, \pm 8$

$q : \pm 1, \pm 3$

$\dfrac{p}{q} : \pm 1, \pm 2, \pm 4, \pm 8, \pm \dfrac{8}{3}, \pm \dfrac{4}{3}, \pm \dfrac{2}{3}, \pm \dfrac{1}{3}$

52. $f(x) = 3x^4 - 2x^3 - 8x + 5$

$f(x)$ has 2 sign variations, so $f(x) = 0$ has 2 or 0 positive solutions.

$f(-x) = 3x^4 + 2x^3 + x + 5$

$f(-x)$ has no sign variations, so $f(x) = 0$ has no negative solutions.

53. $f(x) = 2x^5 - 3x^3 - 5x^2 + 3x - 1$

$f(x)$ has 3 sign variations, so $f(x) = 0$ has 3 or 1 positive real roots.

$f(-x) = -2x^5 + 3x^3 - 5x^2 - 3x - 1$

$f(-x)$ has 2 sign variations, so $f(x) = 0$ has 2 or 0 negative solutions.

54. $f(x) = f(-x) = 2x^4 + 6x^2 + 8$

No sign variations exist for either $f(x)$ or $f(-x)$, so no real roots exist.

55. $f(x) = x^3 + 3x^2 - 4$

a. $p : \pm 1, \pm 2, \pm 4$

$q : \pm 1$

$\dfrac{p}{q} : \pm 1, \pm 2, \pm 4$

b. 1 sign variation $\Rightarrow$ 1 positive real zero

$f(-x) = -x^3 + 3x^2 - 4$

2 sign variations $\Rightarrow$ 2 or no negative real zeros

c.
$$
\begin{array}{r|rrrr}
1 & 1 & 3 & 0 & -4 \\
  &   & 1 & 4 & -4 \\
\hline
  & 1 & 4 & 4 & 0
\end{array}
$$

1 is a zero.

d. $(x-1)(x^2 + 4x + 4) = 0$

$(x-1)(x+2)^2 = 0$

$x = 1$ or $x = -2$

The solution set is $\{1, -2\}$.

56. $f(x) = 6x^3 + x^2 - 4x + 1$

a. $p: \pm 1$

$q: \pm 1, \pm 2, \pm 3, \pm 6$

$\dfrac{p}{q}: \pm 1, \pm\dfrac{1}{2}, \pm\dfrac{1}{3}, \pm\dfrac{1}{6}$

b. $f(x) = 6x^3 + x^2 - 4x + 1$

2 sign variations; 2 or 0 positive real zeros.

$f(-x) = -6x^3 + x^2 + 4x + 1$

1 sign variation; 1 negative real zero.

c.

$$\begin{array}{r|rrrr} -1 & 6 & 1 & -4 & 1 \\ & & -6 & 5 & -1 \\ \hline & 6 & -5 & 1 & 0 \end{array}$$

-1 is a zero.

d. $6x^3 + x^2 - 4x + 1 = 0$

$(x+1)(6x^2 - 5x + 1) = 0$

$(x+1)(3x-1)(2x-1) = 0$

$x = -1$ or $x = \dfrac{1}{3}$ or $x = \dfrac{1}{2}$

The solution set is $\left\{-1, \dfrac{1}{3}, \dfrac{1}{2}\right\}$.

57. $f(x) = 8x^3 - 36x^2 + 46x - 15$

a. $p: \pm 1, \pm 3, \pm 5, \pm 15$

$q: \pm 1, \pm 2, \pm 4, \pm 8$

$\dfrac{p}{q}: \pm 1, \pm 3, \pm 5, \pm 15, \pm\dfrac{1}{2}, \pm\dfrac{1}{4}, \pm\dfrac{1}{8},$

$\pm\dfrac{3}{2}, \pm\dfrac{3}{4}, \pm\dfrac{3}{8}, \pm\dfrac{5}{2}, \pm\dfrac{5}{4},$

$\pm\dfrac{5}{8}, \pm\dfrac{15}{2}, \pm\dfrac{15}{4}, \pm\dfrac{15}{8}$

b. $f(x) = 8x^3 - 36x^2 + 46x - 15$

3 sign variations; 3 or 1 positive real solutions.

$f(-x) = -8x^3 - 36x^2 - 46x - 15$

0 sign variations; no negative real solutions.

c.

$$\begin{array}{r|rrrr} \frac{1}{2} & 8 & -36 & 46 & -15 \\ & & 4 & -16 & 15 \\ \hline & 8 & -32 & 30 & 0 \end{array}$$

$\dfrac{1}{2}$ is a zero.

d.

$$8x^3 - 36x^2 + 46x - 15 = 0$$

$$\left(x - \dfrac{1}{2}\right)(8x^2 - 32x + 30) = 0$$

$$2\left(x - \dfrac{1}{2}\right)(4x^2 - 16x + 15) = 0$$

$$2\left(x - \dfrac{1}{2}\right)(2x - 5)(2x - 3) = 0$$

$x = \dfrac{1}{2}$ or $x = \dfrac{5}{2}$ or $x = \dfrac{3}{2}$

The solution set is $\left\{\dfrac{1}{2}, \dfrac{3}{2}, \dfrac{5}{2}\right\}$.

58. $2x^3 + 9x^2 - 7x + 1 = 0$

a. $p: \pm 1$

$q: \pm 1, \pm 2$

$\dfrac{p}{q}: \pm 1, \pm\dfrac{1}{2}$

b. $f(x) = 2x^3 + 9x^2 - 7x + 1$

2 sign variations; 2 or 0 positive real zeros.

$f(-x) = -2x^3 + 9x^2 + 7x + 1$

1 sign variation; 1 negative real zero.

c.

$$\begin{array}{r|rrrr} \frac{1}{2} & 2 & 9 & -7 & 1 \\ & & 1 & 5 & -1 \\ \hline & 2 & 10 & -2 & 0 \end{array}$$

$-\dfrac{1}{2}$ is a zero.

d. $2x^3 + 9x^2 - 7x + 1 = 0$

$\left(x - \dfrac{1}{2}\right)(2x^2 + 10x - 2) = 0$

$2\left(x - \dfrac{1}{2}\right)(x^2 + 5x - 1) = 0$

Solving $x^2 + 5x - 1 = 0$ using the quadratic

formula gives $x = \dfrac{-5 \pm \sqrt{29}}{2}$

The solution set is

$\left\{ \dfrac{1}{2}, \dfrac{-5 + \sqrt{29}}{2}, \dfrac{-5 - \sqrt{29}}{2} \right\}.$

59. $x^4 - x^3 - 7x^2 + x + 6 = 0$

a. $p = \dfrac{p}{q} : \pm 1, \pm 2, \pm 3, \pm 6$

b. $f(x) = x^4 - x^3 - 7x^2 + x + 6$
2 sign variations; 2 or 0 positive real zeros.
$f(-x) = x^4 + x^3 - 7x^2 - x + 6$
2 sign variations; 2 or 0 negative real zeros.

c.

1	1	−1	−7	1	6
		1	0	−7	−6
	1	0	−7	−6	0

−1	1	0	−7	−6
		−1	1	6
	1	−1	−6	0

d. $x^4 - x^3 - 7x^2 + x + 6 = 0$

$(x - 1)(x + 1)(x^2 - x + 6) = 0$

$(x - 1)(x + 1)(x - 3)(x + 2) = 0$

The solution set is $\{-2, -1, 1, 3\}.$

60. $4x^4 + 7x^2 - 2 = 0$

a. $p : \pm 1, \pm 2$
$q : \pm 1, \pm 2, \pm 4$
$\dfrac{p}{q} : \pm 1, \pm 2, \pm \dfrac{1}{2}, \pm \dfrac{1}{4}$

b. $f(x) = 4x^4 + 7x^2 - 2$
1 sign variation; 1 positive real zero.
$f(-x) = 4x^4 + 7x^2 - 2$
1 sign variation; 1 negative real zero.

c.

$\frac{1}{2}$	4	0	7	0	−2
		2	1	4	2
	4	2	8	4	0

$-\frac{1}{2}$	4	2	8	4
		−2	0	−4
	4	0	8	0

d. $4x^4 + 7x^2 - 2 = 0$

$\left(x - \dfrac{1}{2}\right)\left(x + \dfrac{1}{2}\right)(4x^2 + 8) = 0$

$4\left(x - \dfrac{1}{2}\right)\left(x + \dfrac{1}{2}\right)(x^2 + 2) = 0$

Solving $x^2 + 2 = 0$ using the quadratic
formula gives $x = \pm 2i$

The solution set is $\left\{ -\dfrac{1}{2}, \dfrac{1}{2}, 2i, -2i \right\}.$

61. $f(x) = 2x^4 + x^3 - 9x^2 - 4x + 4$

a. $p : \pm 1, \pm 2, \pm 4$
$q : \pm 1, \pm 2$
$\dfrac{p}{q} : \pm 1, \pm 2, \pm 4, \pm \dfrac{1}{2}$

b. $f(x) = 2x^4 + x^3 - 9x^2 - 4x + 4$
2 sign variations; 2 or 0 positive real zeros.
$f(-x) = 2x^4 - x^3 - 9x^2 + 4x + 4$
2 sign variations; 2 or 0 negative real zeros.

c.

2	2	1	−9	−4	4
		4	10	2	−4
	2	5	1	−2	0

−1	2	5	1	−2
		−2	−3	2
	2	3	−2	0

d. $2x^2 + 3x - 2 = 0$

$(2x - 1)(x + 2) = 0$

$x = -2 \quad \text{or} \quad x = \frac{1}{2}$

The solution set is $\left\{ -2, -1, \frac{1}{2}, 2 \right\}$.

62. $f(x) = a_n(x - 2)(x - 2 + 3i)(x - 2 - 3i)$

$f(x) = a_n(x - 2)(x^2 - 4x + 13)$

$f(1) = a_n(1 - 2)\left[1^2 - 4(1) + 13\right]$

$-10 = -10a_n$

$a_n = 1$

$f(x) = 1(x - 2)(x^2 - 4x + 13)$

$f(x) = x^3 - 4x^2 + 13x - 2x^2 + 8x - 26$

$f(x) = x^3 - 6x^2 + 21x - 26$

63. $f(x) = a_n(x - i)(x + i)(x + 3)^2$

$f(x) = a_n(x^2 + 1)(x^2 + 6x + 9)$

$f(-1) = a_n\left[(-1)^2 + 1\right]\left[(-1)^2 + 6(-1) + 9\right]$

$16 = 8a_n$

$a_n = 2$

$f(x) = 2(x^2 + 1)(x^2 + 6x + 9)$

$f(x) = 2(x^4 + 6x^3 + 9x^2 + x^2 + 6x + 9)$

$f(x) = 2x^4 + 12x^3 + 20x^2 + 12x + 18$

64. $f(x) = 2x^4 + 3x^3 + 3x - 2$

$p: \pm 1, \pm 2$

$q: \pm 1, \pm 2$

$\dfrac{p}{q}: \pm 1, \pm 2, \pm \dfrac{1}{2}$

$$
\begin{array}{r|rrrrr}
-2 & 2 & 3 & 0 & 3 & -2 \\
   &   & -4 & 2 & -4 & 2 \\
\hline
   & 2 & -1 & 2 & -1 & 0
\end{array}
$$

$2x^4 + 3x^3 + 3x - 2 = 0$

$(x + 2)(2x^3 - x^2 + 2x - 1) = 0$

$(x + 2)\left[x^2(2x - 1) + (2x - 1)\right] = 0$

$(x + 2)(2x - 1)(x^2 + 1) = 0$

$x = -2, \quad x = \dfrac{1}{2} \quad \text{or} \quad x = \pm i$

The zeros are -2, $\dfrac{1}{2}$, $\pm i$.

$f(x) = (x - i)(x + i)(x + 2)(2x - 1)$

65. $g(x) = x^4 - 6x^3 + x^2 + 24x + 16$

$p: \pm 1, \pm 2, \pm 4, \pm 8, \pm 16$

$q: \pm 1$

$\dfrac{p}{q}: \pm 1, \pm 2, \pm 4, \pm 8, \pm 16$

$$
\begin{array}{r|rrrrr}
-1 & 1 & -6 & 1 & 24 & 16 \\
   &   & -1 & 7 & -8 & -16 \\
\hline
   & 1 & -7 & 8 & 16 & 0
\end{array}
$$

$x^4 - 6x^3 + x^2 + 24x + 16 = 0$

$(x + 1)(x^3 - 7x^2 + 8x + 16) = 0$

$$
\begin{array}{r|rrrr}
-1 & 1 & -7 & 8 & 16 \\
   &   & -1 & 8 & -16 \\
\hline
   & 1 & -8 & 16 & 0
\end{array}
$$

$(x + 1)^2(x^2 - 8x + 16) = 0$

$(x + 1)^2(x - 4)^2 = 0$

$x = -1 \quad \text{or} \quad x = 4$

$g(x) = (x + 1)^2(x - 4)^2$

66. 4 real zeros, one with multiplicity two

67. 3 real zeros; 2 nonreal complex zeros

68. 2 real zeros, one with multiplicity two; 2 nonreal complex zeros

69. 1 real zero; 4 nonreal complex zeros

70. $g(x) = \dfrac{1}{(x+2)^2} - 1$

$$g(x) = \dfrac{1}{(x+2)^2} - 1$$

71. $h(x) = \dfrac{1}{x-1} + 3$

$$h(x) = \dfrac{1}{x-1} + 3$$

72. $f(x) = \dfrac{2x}{x^2 - 9}$

Symmetry: $f(-x) = -\dfrac{2x}{x^2 - 9} = -f(x)$

origin symmetry
x-intercept:

$$0 = \dfrac{2x}{x^2 - 9}$$

$$2x = 0$$

$$x = 0$$

y-intercept: $y = \dfrac{2(0)}{0^2 - 9} = 0$

Vertical asymptote:

$$x^2 - 9 = 0$$

$$(x-3)(x+3) = 0$$

$$x = 3 \text{ and } x = -3$$

Horizontal asymptote:
$n < m$, so $y = 0$

$$f(x) = \dfrac{2x}{x^2 - 9}$$

73. $g(x) = \dfrac{2x - 4}{x + 3}$

Symmetry: $g(-x) = \dfrac{-2x - 4}{x + 3}$

$g(-x) \neq g(x)$, $g(-x) \neq -g(x)$
No symmetry
x-intercept:

$$2x - 4 = 0$$

$$x = 2$$

y-intercept: $y = \dfrac{2(0) - 4}{(0) + 3} = -\dfrac{4}{3}$

Vertical asymptote:

$$x + 3 = 0$$

$$x = -3$$

Horizontal asymptote:

$n = m$, so $y = \dfrac{2}{1} = 2$

$$f(x) = \dfrac{2x - 4}{x + 3}$$

74. $h(x) = \dfrac{x^2 - 3x - 4}{x^2 - x - 6}$

Symmetry: $h(-x) = \dfrac{x^2 + 3x - 4}{x^2 + x - 6}$

$h(-x) \neq h(x)$, $h(-x) \neq -h(x)$
No symmetry
x-intercepts:

$$x^2 - 3x - 4 = 0$$

$$(x - 4)(x + 1)$$

$$x = 4 \quad x = -1$$

y-intercept: $y = \dfrac{0^2 - 3(0) - 4}{0^2 - 0 - 6} = \dfrac{2}{3}$

Vertical asymptotes:
$$x^2 - x - 6 = 0$$
$$(x - 3)(x + 2) = 0$$
$$x = 3, -2$$

Horizontal asymptote:

$n = m$, so $y = \dfrac{1}{1} = 1$

$$h(x) = \dfrac{x^2 - 3x - 4}{x^2 - x - 6}$$

75. $r(x) = \dfrac{x^2 + 4x + 3}{(x + 2)^2}$

Symmetry: $r(-x) = \dfrac{x^2 - 4x + 3}{(-x + 2)^2}$

$r(-x) \ne r(x)$, $r(-x) \ne -r(x)$
No symmetry
x-intercepts:
$$x^2 + 4x + 3 = 0$$
$$(x + 3)(x + 1) = 0$$
$$x = -3, -1$$

y-intercept: $y = \dfrac{0^2 + 4(0) + 3}{(0 + 2)^2} = \dfrac{3}{4}$

Vertical asymptote:
$$x + 2 = 0$$
$$x = -2$$

Horizontal asymptote:

$n = m$, so $y = \dfrac{1}{1} = 1$

$$r(x) = \dfrac{x^2 + 4x + 3}{(x + 4)^2}$$

76. $y = \dfrac{x^2}{x + 1}$

Symmetry: $f(-x) = \dfrac{x^2}{-x + 1}$

$f(-x) \ne f(x)$, $f(-x) \ne -f(x)$
No symmetry
x-intercept:
$$x^2 = 0$$
$$x = 0$$

y-intercept: $y = \dfrac{0^2}{0 + 1} = 0$

Vertical asymptote:
$$x + 1 = 0$$
$$x = -1$$
$n > m$, no horizontal asymptote.
Slant asymptote:

$$y = x - 1 + \dfrac{1}{x + 1}$$

$y = x - 1$

$$y = \dfrac{x^2}{x + 1}$$

77. $y = \dfrac{x^2 + 2x - 3}{x - 3}$

Symmetry: $f(-x) = \dfrac{x^2 - 2x - 3}{-x - 3}$

$f(-x) \ne f(x)$, $f(-x) \ne -f(x)$
No symmetry
x-intercepts:
$$x^2 + 2x - 3 = 0$$
$$(x + 3)(x - 1) = 0$$
$$x = -3, 1$$

y-intercept: $y = \dfrac{0^2 + 2(0) - 3}{0 - 3} = \dfrac{-3}{-3} = 1$

Vertical asymptote:
$$x - 3 = 0$$
$$x = 3$$
Horizontal asymptote:
$n > m$, so no horizontal asymptote.
Slant asymptote:

$$y = x + 5 + \frac{12}{x-3}$$

$$y = x + 5$$

$$f(x) = \frac{x^2 + 2x - 3}{x - 3}$$

78. $f(x) = \frac{-2x^3}{x^2+1}$

Symmetry: $f(-x) = \frac{2}{x^2+1} = -f(x)$

Origin symmetry
x-intercept:
$-2x^3 = 0$
$x = 0$

y-intercept: $y = \frac{-2(0)^3}{0^2+1} = \frac{0}{1} = 0$

Vertical asymptote:
$x^2 + 1 = 0$
$x^2 = -1$
No vertical asymptote.
Horizontal asymptote:
$n > m$, so no horizontal asymptote.

Slant asymptote:

$$f(x) = -2x + \frac{2x}{x^2+1}$$

$$y = -2x$$

$$f(x) = \frac{-2x^3}{x^2+1}$$

79. $g(x) = \frac{4x^2 - 16x + 16}{2x - 3}$

Symmetry: $g(-x) = \frac{4x^2 + 16x + 16}{-2x - 3}$

$g(-x) \neq g(x), g(-x) \neq -g(x)$

No symmetry
x-intercept:
$4x^2 - 16x + 16 = 0$
$4(x-2)^2 = 0$
$x = 2$
y-intercept:

$$y = \frac{4(0)^2 - 16(0) + 16}{2(0) - 3} = -\frac{16}{3}$$

Vertical asymptote:
$2x - 3 = 0$

$$x = \frac{3}{2}$$

Horizontal asymptote:
$n > m$, so no horizontal asymptote.
Slant asymptote:

$$g(x) = 2x - 5 + \frac{1}{2x-3}$$

$$y = 2x - 5$$

$$g(x) = \frac{4x^2 - 16x + 16}{2x - 3}$$

80. a. $C(x) = 50,000 + 25x$

b. $\overline{C}(x) = \frac{25x + 50,000}{x}$

c. $\overline{C}(50) = \frac{25(50) + 50,000}{50} = 1025$

When 50 calculators are manufactured, it costs \$1025 to manufacture each.

$\overline{C}(100) = \frac{25(100) + 50,000}{100} = 525$

When 100 calculators are manufactured, it costs \$525 to manufacture each.

$\overline{C}(1000) = \frac{25(1000) + 50,000}{1000} = 75$

When 1,000 calculators are manufactured, it costs \$75 to manufacture each.

$\overline{C}(100,000) = \frac{25(100,000) + 50,000}{100,000} = 25.5$

When 100,000 calculators are manufactured, it costs \$25.50 to manufacture each.

d. $n = m$, so $y = \dfrac{25}{1} = 25$ is the horizontal asymptote. Minimum costs will approach $25.

81. a. $C(90) - C(50) = \dfrac{200(90)}{100-90} - \dfrac{200(50)}{100-50}$

$C(90) - C(50) = 1800 - 200$
$C(90) - C(50) = 1600$
The difference in cost of removing 90% versus 50% of the contaminants is 16 million dollars.

b. $x = 100$; No amount of money can remove 100% of the contaminants, since $C(x)$ increases without bound as x approaches 100.

82. $f(x) = \dfrac{150x + 120}{0.05x + 1}$

$n = m$, so $y = \dfrac{150}{0.05} = 3000$

The number of fish available in the pond approaches 3000.

83. $P(x) = \dfrac{72{,}900}{100x^2 + 729}$

$n < m$ so $y = 0$

As the number of years of education increases the percentage rate of unemployment approaches zero.

84. a. $f(x) = \dfrac{1.96x + 3.14}{3.04x + 21.79}$

b. $y = \dfrac{1.96}{3.04} = 0.645$

The percentage of inmates that are in for violent crimes will approach 64.5%.

c. Answers may vary.

85. $T(x) = \dfrac{4}{x + 3} + \dfrac{2}{x}$

86. $1000 = lw$

$\dfrac{1000}{w} = l$

$P = 2x + 2\left(\dfrac{1000}{x}\right)$

$P = 2x + \dfrac{2000}{2}$

87. $2x^2 + 5x - 3 < 0$
Solve the related quadratic equation.

$2x^2 + 5x - 3 = 0$
$(2x - 1)(x + 3) = 0$

The boundary points are -3 and $\dfrac{1}{2}$.

Testing each interval gives a solution set of $\left(-3, \dfrac{1}{2}\right)$.

88. $2x^2 + 9x + 4 \geq 0$
Solve the related quadratic equation.

$2x^2 + 9x + 4 = 0$
$(2x + 1)(x + 4) = 0$

The boundary points are -4 and $-\dfrac{1}{2}$.

Testing each interval gives a solution set of $(-\infty, -4] \cup \left[-\dfrac{1}{2}, \infty\right)$.

255

89. $x^3 + 2x^2 > 3x$

Solve the related quadratic equation.

$$x^3 + 2x^2 = 3x$$

$$x^3 + 2x^2 - 3x = 0$$

$$x(x^2 + 2x - 3) = 0$$

$$x(x+3)(x-1) = 0$$

The boundary points are -3, 0, and 1.

Testing each interval gives a solution set of $(-3, 0) \cup (1, \infty)$.

90. $\dfrac{x-6}{x+2} > 0$

Find the values of x that make the numerator and denominator zero.

The boundary points are -2 and 6.

Testing each interval gives a solution set of $(-\infty, -2) \cup (6, \infty)$.

91. $\dfrac{(x+1)(x-2)}{x-1} \geq 0$

Find the values of x that make the numerator and denominator zero.

The boundary points are -1, 1 and 2. We exclude 1 from the solution set, since this would make the denominator zero.

Testing each interval gives a solution set of $[-1, 1) \cup [2, \infty)$.

92. $\dfrac{x+3}{x-4} \leq 5$

Express the inequality so that one side is zero.

$$\frac{x+3}{x-4} - 5 \leq 0$$

$$\frac{x+3}{x-4} - \frac{5(x-4)}{x-4} \leq 0$$

$$\frac{-4x+23}{x-4} \leq 0$$

Find the values of x that make the numerator and denominator zero.

The boundary points are 4 and $\dfrac{23}{4}$. We exclude 4 from the solution set, since this would make the denominator zero.

Testing each interval gives a solution set of $(-\infty, 4) \cup \left[\dfrac{23}{4}, \infty\right)$.

93.
$$s = -16t^2 + v_0 t + s_0$$
$$32 < -16t^2 + 48t + 0$$
$$0 < -16t^2 + 48t - 32$$
$$0 < -16\left(t^2 - 3t + 2\right)$$
$$0 < -16(t-2)(t-1)$$

	F		T		F	
		1		2		

The projectile's height exceeds 32 feet during the time period from 1 to 2 seconds.

94.
$$b = ke$$
$$98 = k \cdot 1400$$
$$k = 0.07$$
$$b = 0.07e$$
$$b = 0.07(2200) = \$154$$

95.
$$d = kt^2$$
$$144 = k(3)^2$$
$$k = 16$$
$$d = 16t^2$$
$$d = 16(10)^2 = 1,600 \text{ ft}$$

96.
$$t = \frac{k}{r}$$
$$4 = \frac{k}{50}$$
$$k = 200$$
$$t = \frac{200}{r}$$
$$t = \frac{200}{40} = 5 \text{ hours}$$

97.
$$l = \frac{k}{d^2}$$
$$28 = \frac{k}{8^2}$$
$$k = 1792$$
$$l = \frac{1792}{d^2}$$
$$l = \frac{1792}{4^2} = 112 \text{ decibels}$$

98.
$$t = \frac{kc}{w}$$
$$10 = \frac{k \cdot 30}{6}$$
$$10 = 5h$$
$$h = 2$$
$$t = \frac{2c}{w}$$
$$t = \frac{2(40)}{5} = 16 \text{ hours}$$

99.
$$V = khB$$
$$175 = k \cdot 15 \cdot 35$$
$$k = \frac{1}{3}$$
$$V = \frac{1}{3}hB$$
$$V = \frac{1}{3} \cdot 20 \cdot 120 = 800 \text{ ft}^3$$

Chapter 2 Test

1.
$$(6-7i)(2+5i) = 12 + 30i - 14i - 35i^2$$
$$= 12 + 16i + 35$$
$$= 47 + 16i$$

2.
$$\frac{5}{2-i} = \frac{5}{2-i} \cdot \frac{2+i}{2+i}$$
$$= \frac{5(2+i)}{4+1}$$
$$= \frac{5(2+i)}{5}$$
$$= 2+i$$

3.
$$2\sqrt{-49} + 3\sqrt{-64} = 2(7i) + 3(8i)$$
$$= 14i + 24i$$
$$= 38i$$

4.
$$x^2 = 4x - 8$$
$$x^2 - 4x + 8 = 0$$
$$x = \frac{-b \pm \sqrt{b^2 - 4ac}}{2a}$$
$$x = \frac{-(-4) \pm \sqrt{(-4)^2 - 4(1)(8)}}{2(1)}$$
$$x = \frac{4 \pm \sqrt{-16}}{2}$$
$$x = \frac{4 \pm 4i}{2}$$
$$x = 2 \pm 2i$$

5. $f(x) = (x+1)^2 + 4$
vertex: $(-1, 4)$
axis of symmetry: $x = -1$
x-intercepts:
$$(x+1)^2 + 4 = 0$$
$$x^2 + 2x + 5 = 0$$
$$x = \frac{-2 \pm \sqrt{4 - 20}}{2} = -1 \pm 2i$$
no x-intercepts
y-intercept:
$$f(0) = (0+1)^2 + 4 = 5$$

$f(x) = (x + 1)^2 + 4$
Domain: $(-\infty, \infty)$; Range: $[4, \infty)$

6. $f(x) = x^2 - 2x - 3$
$$x = \frac{-b}{2a} = \frac{2}{2} = 1$$
$$f(1) = 1^2 - 2(1) - 3 = -4$$
vertex: $(1, -4)$
axis of symmetry $x = 1$
x-intercepts:
$$x^2 - 2x - 3 = 0$$
$$(x - 3)(x + 1) = 0$$
$$x = 3 \text{ or } x = -1$$

y-intercept:
$$f(0) = 0^2 - 2(0) - 3 = -3$$

$f(x) = x^2 - 2x - 3$
Domain: $(-\infty, \infty)$; Range: $[-4, \infty)$

7. $f(x) = -2x^2 + 12x - 16$
Since the coefficient of x^2 is negative, the graph of $f(x)$ opens down and $f(x)$ has a maximum point.
$$x = \frac{-12}{2(-2)} = 3$$

$$f(3) = -2(3)^2 + 12(3) - 16$$
$$= -18 + 36 - 16$$
$$= 2$$
Maximum point: $(3, 2)$
Domain: $(-\infty, \infty)$; Range: $(-\infty, 2]$

8. $f(x) = -x^2 + 46x - 360$
$$x = -\frac{b}{2a} = \frac{-46}{-2} = 23$$
23 computers will maximize profit.
$$f(23) = -(23)^2 + 46(23) - 360 = 169$$
Maximum daily profit = \$16,900.

9.   Let $x =$ one of the numbers;
$14 - x =$ the other number.
The product is $f(x) = x(14 - x)$
$$f(x) = x(14 - x) = -x^2 + 14x$$
The x-coordinate of the maximum is
$$x = -\frac{b}{2a} = -\frac{14}{2(-1)} = -\frac{14}{-2} = 7.$$
$$f(7) = -7^2 + 14(7) = 49$$
The vertex is $(7, 49)$. The maximum product is 49. This occurs when the two number are 7 and $14 - 7 = 7$.

10.   **a.** $f(x) = x^3 - 5x^2 - 4x + 20$
$$x^3 - 5x^2 - 4x + 20 = 0$$
$$x^2(x - 5) - 4(x - 5) = 0$$
$$(x - 5)(x - 2)(x + 2) = 0$$
$$x = 5, 2, -2$$
The solution set is $\{5, 2, -2\}$.

b. The degree of the polynomial is odd and the leading coefficient is positive. Thus the graph falls to the left and rises to the right.

11. $f(x) = x^5 - x$

Since the degree of the polynomial is odd and the leading coefficient is positive, the graph of f should fall to the left and rise to the right. The x-intercepts should be -1 and 1.

12. a. The integral root is 2.

b.

$$\begin{array}{r|rrrr} 2 & 6 & -19 & 16 & -4 \\ & & 12 & -14 & 4 \\ \hline & 6 & -7 & 2 & 0 \end{array}$$

$$6x^2 - 7x + 2 = 0$$
$$(3x - 2)(2x - 1) = 0$$
$$x = \frac{2}{3} \text{ or } x = \frac{1}{2}$$

The other two roots are $\frac{1}{2}$ and $\frac{2}{3}$.

13. $2x^3 + 11x^2 - 7x - 6 = 0$

$p: \pm 1, \pm 2, \pm 3, \pm 6$

$q: \pm 1, \pm 2$

$\frac{p}{q}: \pm 1, \pm 2, \pm 3, \pm 6, \pm \frac{1}{2}, \pm \frac{3}{2}$

14. $f(x) = 3x^5 - 2x^4 - 2x^2 + x - 1$

$f(x)$ has 3 sign variations.

$f(-x) = -3x^5 - 2x^4 - 2x^2 - x - 1$

$f(-x)$ has no sign variations.

There are 3 or 1 positive real solutions and no negative real solutions.

15. $x^3 + 9x^2 + 16x - 6 = 0$

Since the leading coefficient is 1, the possible rational zeros are the factors of 6

$$p = \frac{p}{q} : \pm 1, \pm 2, \pm 3, \pm 6$$

$$\begin{array}{r|rrrr} -3 & 1 & 9 & 16 & -6 \\ & & -3 & -18 & 6 \\ \hline & 1 & 6 & -2 & 0 \end{array}$$

Thus $x = 3$ is a root.

Solve the quotient $x^2 + 6x - 2 = 0$ using the quadratic formula to find the remaining roots.

$$x = \frac{-b \pm \sqrt{b^2 - 4ac}}{2a}$$

$$x = \frac{-(6) \pm \sqrt{(6)^2 - 4(1)(-2)}}{2(1)}$$

$$= \frac{-6 \pm \sqrt{44}}{2}$$

$$= -3 \pm \sqrt{11}$$

The zeros are -3, $-3 + \sqrt{11}$, and $-3 - \sqrt{11}$.

16. $f(x) = 2x^4 - x^3 - 13x^2 + 5x + 15$

a. Possible rational zeros are:

$p: \pm 1, \pm 3, \pm 5, \pm 15$

$q: \pm 1, \pm 2$

$\frac{p}{q} : \pm 1, \pm 3, \pm 5, \pm 15, \pm \frac{1}{2}, \pm \frac{3}{2}, \pm \frac{5}{2}, \pm \frac{15}{2}$

b. Verify that -1 and $\frac{3}{2}$ are zeros as it appears in the graph:

$$\begin{array}{r|rrrrr} -1 & 2 & -1 & -13 & 5 & 15 \\ & & -2 & 3 & 10 & -15 \\ \hline & 2 & -3 & -10 & 15 & 0 \end{array}$$

$$\begin{array}{r|rrrr} \frac{3}{2} & 2 & -3 & -10 & 15 \\ & & 3 & 0 & -15 \\ \hline & 2 & 0 & -10 & 0 \end{array}$$

Thus, -1 and $\frac{3}{2}$ are zeros, and the polynomial factors as follows:

$$2x^4 - x^3 - 13x^2 + 5x + 15 = 0$$

$$(x + 1)(2x^3 - 3x^2 - 10x + 15) = 0$$

$$(x + 1)\left(x - \frac{3}{2}\right)(2x^2 - 10) = 0$$

Find the remaining zeros by solving:

$$2x^2 - 10 = 0$$
$$2x^2 = 10$$
$$x^2 = 5$$
$$x = \pm\sqrt{5}$$

The zeros are -1, $\dfrac{3}{2}$, and $\pm\sqrt{5}$.

17. $f(x)$ has zeros at -2 and 1. The zero at -2 has multiplicity of 2.

$$x^3 + 3x^2 - 4 = (x-1)(x+2)^2$$

18. $f(x) = a_0(x+1)(x-1)(x+i)(x-i)$

$\quad = a_0(x^2 - 1)(x^2 + 1)$

$\quad = a_0(x^4 - 1)$

Since $f(3) = 160$, then

$$a_0(3^4 - 1) = 160$$
$$a_0(80) = 160$$
$$a_0 = \frac{160}{80}$$
$$a_0 = 2$$
$$f(x) = 2(x^4 - 1) = 2x^4 - 2$$

19. $f(x) = -3x^3 - 4x^2 + x + 2$

The graph shows a root at $x = -1$.
Use synthetic division to verify this root.

-1	-3	-4	1	2
		3	1	4
	-3	-1	2	0

Factor the quotient to find the remaining zeros.

$$-3x^2 - x + 2 = 0$$
$$-(3x - 2)(x + 1) = 0$$

The zeros (x-intercepts) are -1 and $\dfrac{2}{3}$.

The y-intercept is $f(0) = 2$.

$f(x) = -3x^3 - 4x^2 + x + 2$

20. $f(x) = \dfrac{1}{(x+3)^2}$

Domain: $\{x \mid x \neq -3\}$ or $(-\infty, -3) \cup (-3, \infty)$

$f(x) = \dfrac{1}{(x+3)^2}$

21. $f(x) = \dfrac{1}{x-1} + 2$

Domain: $\{x \mid x \neq 1\}$ or $(-\infty, 1) \cup (1, \infty)$

$f(x) = \dfrac{1}{x-1} + 2$

22. $f(x) = \dfrac{x}{x^2 - 16}$

Domain: $\{x \mid x \neq 4, x \neq -4\}$

Symmetry: $f(-x) = \dfrac{-x}{x^2 - 16} = -f(x)$

y-axis symmetry
x-intercept: $x = 0$

y-intercept: $y = \dfrac{0}{0^2 - 16} = 0$

Vertical asymptotes:
$$x^2 - 16 = 0$$
$$(x - 4)(x + 4) = 0$$
$$x = 4, -4$$

Horizontal asymptote:
$n < m$, so $y = 0$ is the horizontal asymptote.

$f(x) = \dfrac{x}{x^2 - 16}$

23. $f(x) = \dfrac{x^2 - 9}{x - 2}$

Domain: $\{x \mid x \neq 2\}$

Symmetry: $f(-x) = \dfrac{x^2 - 9}{-x - 2}$

$f(-x) \neq f(x), f(-x) \neq -f(x)$
No symmetry

x-intercepts:
$x^2 - 9 = 0$
$(x - 3)(x + 3) = 0$
$x = 3, -3$

y-intercept: $y = \dfrac{0^2 - 9}{0 - 2} = \dfrac{9}{2}$

Vertical asymptote:
$x - 2 = 0$
$x = 2$

Horizontal asymptote:
$n > m$, so no horizontal asymptote exists.

Slant asymptote: $f(x) = x + 2 - \dfrac{5}{x - 2}$

$y = x + 2$

$$f(x) = \dfrac{x^2 - 9}{x - 2}$$

24. $f(x) = \dfrac{x + 1}{x^2 + 2x - 3}$

$x^2 + 2x - 3 = (x + 3)(x - 1)$

Domain: $\{x \mid x \neq -3, x \neq 1\}$

Symmetry: $f(-x) = \dfrac{-x + 1}{x^2 - 2x - 3}$

$f(-x) \neq f(x), f(-x) \neq -f(x)$
No symmetry
x-intercept:
$x + 1 = 0$
$x = -1$

y-intercept: $y = \dfrac{0 + 1}{0^2 + 2(0) - 3} = -\dfrac{1}{3}$

Vertical asymptotes:
$x^2 + 2x - 3 = 0$
$(x + 3)(x - 1) = 0$
$x = -3, 1$

Horizontal asymptote:
$n < m$, so $y = 0$ is the horizontal asymptote.

$$f(x) = \dfrac{x + 1}{x^2 + 2x - 3}$$

25. $f(x) = \dfrac{4x^2}{x^2 + 3}$

Domain: all real numbers

Symmetry: $f(-x) = \dfrac{4x^2}{x^2 + 3} = f(x)$

y-axis symmetry
x-intercept:
$4x^2 = 0$
$x = 0$

y-intercept: $y = \dfrac{4(0)^2}{0^2 + 3} = 0$

Vertical asymptote:
$x^2 + 3 = 0$
$x^2 = -3$
No vertical asymptote.
Horizontal asymptote:
$n = m$, so $y = \dfrac{4}{1} = 4$ is the horizontal asymptote.

$$f(x) = \dfrac{4x^2}{x^2 + 3}$$

26. **a.** $\overline{C}(x) = \dfrac{300,000 + 10x}{x}$

b. Since the degree of the numerator equals the degree of the denominator, the

horizontal asymptote is $x = \dfrac{10}{1} = 10$.

This represents the fact that as the number of televisions produced increases, the average approaches $10 per unit.

27. a. When $x = 5$, $y = 0.89$
After 5 learning tries, 89% of the responses were correct.

b. When $x = 11$, $y = 0.95$
After 11 learning tries, 95% of the responses were correct.

c. $y = .9/.9 = 1$
As the number of learning tries increases, the correct responses approaches 100%.

28. $\qquad x^2 < x + 12$

$x^2 - x - 12 < 0$

$(x + 3)(x - 4) < 0$

Boundary values: -3 and 4

Solution set: $(-3, 4)$

29. $\dfrac{2x+1}{x-3} \le 3$

$\dfrac{2x+1}{x-3} - 3 \le 0$

$\dfrac{10-x}{x-3} \le 0$

Boundary values: 3 and 10

Solution set: $(-\infty, 3) \cup [10, \infty)$

30. $i = \dfrac{k}{d^2}$

$20 = \dfrac{k}{15^2}$

$4500 = k$

$i = \dfrac{4500}{d^2} = \dfrac{4500}{10^2} = 45$ foot-candles

Cumulative Review Exercises (Chapters P–2)

1. Domain: $(-2, 2)$ Range: $[0, \infty)$

2. The zero at -1 touches the x-axis at turns around so it must have a minimum multiplicity of 2. The zero at 1 touches the x-axis at turns around so it must have a minimum multiplicity of 2.

3. There is a relative maximum at the point $(0, 3)$.

4. $(f \circ f)(-1) = f\big(f(-1)\big) = f(0) = 3$

5. $f(x) \to \infty$ as $\underline{x \to -2^+}$ or as $\underline{x \to 2^-}$

6.

7. $|2x - 1| = 3$

$2x - 1 = 3$

$\qquad 2x = 4$

$\qquad x = 2$

$2x - 1 = -3$

$\qquad 2x = -2$

$\qquad x = -1$

The solution set is $\{2, -1\}$.

8. $3x^2 - 5x + 1 = 0$

$x = \dfrac{5 \pm \sqrt{25 - 12}}{6} = \dfrac{5 \pm \sqrt{13}}{6}$

The solution set is $\left\{ \dfrac{5 + \sqrt{13}}{6}, \dfrac{5 - \sqrt{13}}{6} \right\}$.

9. $9 + \dfrac{3}{x} = \dfrac{2}{x^2}$

$9x^2 + 3x = 2$

$9x^2 + 3x - 2 = 0$

$(3x - 1)(3x + 2) = 0$

$3x - 1 = 0 \qquad 3x + 2 = 0$

$x = \dfrac{1}{3} \quad$ or $\quad x = -\dfrac{2}{3}$

The solution set is $\left\{ \dfrac{1}{3}, -\dfrac{2}{3} \right\}$.

10. $x^3 + 2x^2 - 5x - 6 = 0$

$p: \pm 1, \pm 2, \pm 3, \pm 6$

$q: \pm 1$

$\dfrac{p}{q}: \pm 1, \pm 2, \pm 3, \pm 6$

$$\begin{array}{r|rrrr} -3 & 1 & 2 & -5 & -6 \\ & & -3 & 3 & 6 \\ \hline & 1 & -1 & -2 & 0 \end{array}$$

$x^3 + 2x^2 - 5x - 6 = 0$

$(x+3)(x^2 - x - 2) = 0$

$(x+3)(x+1)(x-2) = 0$

$x = -3$ or $x = -1$ or $x = 2$

The solution set is $\{-3, -1, 2\}$.

11. $|2x - 5| > 3$

$2x - 5 > 3$

$2x > 8$

$x > 4$

$2x - 5 < -3$

$2x < 2$

$x < 1$

$(-\infty, 1)$ or $(4, \infty)$

12. $3x^2 > 2x + 5$

$3x^2 - 2x - 5 > 0$

$3x^2 - 2x - 5 = 0$

$(3x - 5)(x + 1) = 0$

$x = \dfrac{5}{3}$ or $x = -1$

Test intervals are $(-\infty, -1)$, $\left(-1, \dfrac{5}{3}\right)$, $\left(\dfrac{5}{3}, \infty\right)$.

Testing points, the solution is

$(-\infty, -1)$ or $\left(\dfrac{5}{3}, \infty\right)$.

13. $f(x) = x^3 - 4x^2 - x + 4$

x-intercepts:

$x^3 - 4x^2 - x + 4 = 0$

$x^2(x - 4) - 1(x - 4) = 0$

$(x - 4)(x^2 - 1) = 0$

$(x - 4)(x + 1)(x - 1) = 0$

$x = -1, 1, 4$

x-intercepts:

$f(0) = 0^3 - 4(0)^2 - 0 + 4 = 4$

The degree of the polynomial is odd and the leading coefficient is positive. Thus the graph falls to the left and rises to the right.

$f(x) = x^3 - 4x^2 - x + 4$

14. $f(x) = x^2 + 2x - 8$

$x = \dfrac{-b}{2a} = \dfrac{-2}{2} = -1$

$f(-1) = (-1)^2 + 2(-1) - 8$

$= 1 - 2 - 8 = -9$

vertex: $(-1, -9)$

x-intercepts:

$x^2 + 2x - 8 = 0$

$(x + 4)(x - 2) = 0$

$x = -4$ or $x = 2$

y-intercept: $f(0) = -8$

$f(x) = x^2 + 2x - 8$

15. $f(x) = x^2(x - 3)$

zeros: $x = 0$ (multiplicity 2) and $x = 3$

y-intercept: $y = 0$

$f(x) = x^3 - 3x^2$

$n = 3, a_n = 0$ so the graph falls to the left and rises to the right.

$f(x) = x^2(x - 3)$

16. $f(x) = \dfrac{x-1}{x-2}$

vertical asymptote: $x = 2$
horizontal asymptote: $y = 1$
x-intercept: $x = 1$

y-intercept: $y = \dfrac{1}{2}$

17.

18.

$x^2 + y^2 - 2x + 4y - 4 = 0$

19. $(f \circ g)(x) = f\big(g(x)\big)$

$$= 2(4x-1)^2 - (4x-1) - 1$$
$$= 32x^2 - 20x + 2$$

20. $\dfrac{f(x+h) - f(x)}{h} = \dfrac{\left[2(x+h)^2 - (x+h) - 1\right] - \left[2x^2 - x - 1\right]}{h}$

$$= \dfrac{2x^2 + 4hx - x + 2h^2 - h - 1 - 2x^2 + x + 1}{h}$$

$$= \dfrac{4hx + 2h^2 - h}{h}$$

$$= 4x + 2h - 1$$

Chapter 3

Section 3.1

Check Point Exercises

1. Substitute 60 for x and evaluate the function at 60. $f(60) = 13.49(0.967)^{-60} - 1 \approx 1$
   Thus, one O-ring is expected to fail at a temperature of 60°F.

2. Begin by setting up a table of coordinates.

x	$f(x) = 3^x$
-3	$f(-3) = 3^{-3} = \frac{1}{27}$
-2	$f(-2) = 3^{-2} = \frac{1}{9}$
-1	$f(-1) = 3^{-1} = \frac{1}{3}$
0	$f(0) = 3^0 = 1$
1	$f(1) = 3^1 = 3$
2	$f(2) = 3^2 = 9$
3	$f(3) = 3^3 = 27$

   Plot these points, connecting them with a continuous curve.

   $$f(x) = 3^x$$

3. Begin by setting up a table of coordinates.

x	$f(x) = \left(\frac{1}{3}\right)^x$
-2	$\left(\frac{1}{3}\right)^{-2} = 9$
-1	$\left(\frac{1}{3}\right)^{-1} = 3$
0	$\left(\frac{1}{3}\right)^{0} = 1$
1	$\left(\frac{1}{3}\right)^{1} = \frac{1}{3}$
2	$\left(\frac{1}{3}\right)^{2} = \frac{1}{9}$

   Plot these points, connecting them with a continuous curve.

$$f(x) = \left(\frac{1}{3}\right)^x$$

4. Note that the function $g(x) = 3^{x-1}$ has the general form $g(x) = b^{x+c}$ where $c = -1$. Because $c < 0$, we graph $g(x) = 3^{x-1}$ by shifting the graph of $f(x) = 3^x$ one unit to the right. Construct a table showing some of the coordinates for f and g.

x	$f(x) = 3^x$	$g(x) = 3^{x-1}$
-2	$3^{-2} = \frac{1}{9}$	$3^{-2-1} = 3^{-3} = \frac{1}{27}$
-1	$3^{-1} = \frac{1}{3}$	$3^{-1-1} = 3^{-2} = \frac{1}{9}$
0	$3^{0} = 1$	$3^{0-1} = 3^{-1} = \frac{1}{3}$
1	$3^{1} = 3$	$3^{1-1} = 3^{0} = 1$
2	$3^{2} = 9$	$3^{2-1} = 3^{1} = 3$

   $$f(x) = 3^x$$
   $$g(x) = 3^{x} - 1$$

5. Note that the function $g(x) = 2^x + 1$ has the general form $g(x) = b^x + c$ where $c = 1$. Because $c > 0$, we graph $g(x) = 2^x + 1$ by shifting the graph of $f(x) = 2^x$ up one unit. Construct a table showing some of the coordinates for f and g.

x	$f(x) - 2^x$	$g(x) = 2^x + 1$
-2	$2^{-2} = \frac{1}{4}$	$2^{-2} + 1 = \frac{1}{4} + 1 = \frac{5}{4}$
-1	$2^{-1} = \frac{1}{2}$	$2^{-1} + 1 = \frac{1}{2} + 1 = \frac{3}{2}$
0	$2^0 = 1$	$2^0 + 1 = 1 + 1 = 2$
1	$2^1 = 2$	$2^1 + 1 = 2 + 1 = 3$
2	$2^2 = 4$	$2^2 + 1 = 4 + 1 = 5$

$$f(x) = 2^x$$
$$g(x) = 2^x + 1$$

6. $f(x) = 6.4e^{0.0123x}$

The year 2050 is 46 years after 2004. Find $f(46)$.

$$f(x) = 6.4e^{0.0123x}$$
$$f(46) = 6.4e^{0.0123(46)}$$
$$\approx 11.27$$

The world population is predicted to be 11.27 billion in 2050.

7. a. $A = P\left(1 + \frac{r}{n}\right)^{nt}$

$$A = 10,000\left(1 + \frac{0.08}{4}\right)^{4(5)}$$
$$= \$14,859.47$$

b. $A = Pe^{rt}$
$$A = 10,000e^{0.08(5)}$$
$$= \$14,918.25$$

Exercise Set 3.1

1. $2^{3.4} \approx 10.556$

3. $3^{\sqrt{5}} \approx 11.665$

5. $4^{-1.5} = 0.125$

7. $e^{2.3} \approx 9.974$

9. $e^{-0.95} \approx 0.387$

11.

x	$f(x) = 4^x$
-2	$4^{-2} = \frac{1}{16}$
-1	$4^{-1} = \frac{1}{4}$
0	$4^0 = 1$
1	$4^1 = 4$
2	$4^2 = 16$

$$f(x) = 4^x$$

13.

x	$g(x) = \left(\frac{3}{2}\right)^x$
-2	$\left(\frac{3}{2}\right)^{-2} = \frac{4}{9}$
-1	$\left(\frac{3}{2}\right)^{-1} = \frac{2}{3}$
0	$\left(\frac{3}{2}\right)^0 = 1$
1	$\left(\frac{3}{2}\right)^1 = \frac{3}{2}$
2	$\left(\frac{3}{2}\right)^2 = \frac{9}{4}$

$$g(x) = \left(\frac{3}{2}\right)^x$$

15.

x	$h(x) = \left(\frac{1}{2}\right)^x$
-2	$\left(\frac{1}{2}\right)^{-2} = 4$
-1	$\left(\frac{1}{2}\right)^{-1} = 2$
0	$\left(\frac{1}{2}\right)^{0} = 1$
1	$\left(\frac{1}{2}\right)^{1} = \frac{1}{2}$
2	$\left(\frac{1}{2}\right)^{2} = \frac{1}{4}$

$$h(x) = \left(\frac{1}{2}\right)^x$$

17.

x	$f(x) = (0.6)^x$
-2	$(0.6)^{-2} = 2.\overline{7}$
-1	$(0.6)^{-1} = 1.\overline{6}$
0	$(0.6)^{0} = 1$
1	$(0.6)^{1} = 0.6$
2	$(0.6)^{2} = 0.36$

$$f(x) = (0.6)^x$$

19. This is the graph of $f(x) = 3^x$ reflected about the x-axis and about the y-axis, so the function is $H(x) = -3^{-x}$.

21. This is the graph of $f(x) = 3^x$ reflected about the x-axis, so the function is $F(x) = -3^x$.

23. This is the graph of $f(x) = 3^x$ shifted one unit downward, so the function is $h(x) = 3^x - 1$.

25. The graph of $g(x) = 2^{x+1}$ can be obtained by shifting the graph of $f(x) = 2^x$ one unit to the left.

$$f(x) = 2^x$$
$$g(x) = 2^x + 1$$

Asymptote: $y = 0$

Domain: $(-\infty, \infty)$; Range: $(0, \infty)$

27. The graph of $g(x) = 2^x - 1$ can be obtained by shifting the graph of $f(x) = 2^x$ downward one unit.

$$f(x) = 2^x$$
$$g(x) = 2^x - 1$$

Asymptote: $y = -1$

Domain: $(-\infty, \infty)$; Range: $(-1, \infty)$

29. The graph of $h(x) = 2^{x+1} - 1$ can be obtained by shifting the graph of $f(x) = 2^x$ one unit to the left and one unit downward.

$$f(x) = 2^x$$
$$h(x) = 2^x + 1 - 1$$

Asymptote: $y = -1$

Domain: $(-\infty, \infty)$; Range: $(-1, \infty)$

31. The graph of $g(x) = -2^x$ can be obtained by reflecting the graph of $f(x) = 2^x$ about the x-axis.

$f(x) = 2^x$
$g(x) = -2^x$

Asymptote: $y = 0$

Domain: $(-\infty, \infty)$; Range: $(-\infty, 0)$

33. The graph of $g(x) = 2 \cdot 2^x$ can be obtained by vertically stretching the graph of $f(x) = 2^x$ by a factor of two.

$f(x) = 2^x$
$g(x) = 2 \cdot 2^x$

Asymptote: $y = 0$

Domain: $(-\infty, \infty)$; Range: $(0, \infty)$

35. The graph of $g(x) = e^{x-1}$ can be obtained by moving $f(x) = e^x$ 1 unit right.

$g(x) = e^x - 1$

Asymptote: $y = 0$

Domain: $(-\infty, \infty)$; Range: $(0, \infty)$

37. The graph of $g(x) = e^x + 2$ can be obtained by moving $f(x) = e^x$ 2 units up.

$g(x) = e^x + 2$

Asymptote: $y = 2$

Domain: $(-\infty, \infty)$; Range: $(2, \infty)$

39. The graph of $h(x) = e^{x-1} + 2$ can be obtained by moving $f(x) = e^x$ 1 unit right and 2 units up.

$h(x) = e^{x-1} + 2$

Asymptote: $y = 2$

Domain: $(-\infty, \infty)$; Range: $(2, \infty)$

41. The graph of $h(x) = e^{-x}$ can be obtained by reflecting $f(x) = e^x$ about the y-axis.

$h(x) = e^{-x}$

Asymptote: $y = 0$

Domain: $(-\infty, \infty)$; Range: $(0, \infty)$

43. The graph of $g(x) = 2e^x$ can be obtained by stretching $f(x) = e^x$ vertically by a factor of 2.

$$g(x) = 2e^x$$

Asymptote: $y = 0$

Domain: $(-\infty, \infty)$; Range: $(0, \infty)$

45. The graph of $h(x) = e^{2x} + 1$ can be obtained by stretching $f(x) = e^x$ horizontally by a factor of 2 and then moving the graph up 1 unit.

$$h(x) = e^{2x} + 1$$

Asymptote: $y = 1$

Domain: $(-\infty, \infty)$; Range: $(1, \infty)$

47. The graph of $g(x)$ can be obtained by reflecting $f(x)$ about the y-axis.

$$f(x) = 3^x$$
$$g(x) = 3^{-x}$$

Asymptote of $f(x)$: $y = 0$

Asymptote of $g(x)$: $y = 0$

49. The graph of $g(x)$ can be obtained by vertically shrinking $f(x)$ by a factor of $\frac{1}{3}$.

$$f(x) = 3^x$$
$$g(x) = \frac{1}{3} \cdot 3^x$$

Asymptote of $f(x)$: $y = 0$

Asymptote of $g(x)$: $y = 0$

51. The graph of $g(x)$ can be obtained by moving the graph of $f(x)$ one space to the right and one space up.

$$f(x) = \left(\frac{1}{2}\right)^x$$

$$g(x) = \left(\frac{1}{2}\right)^{x-1} + 1$$

Asymptote of $f(x)$: $y = 0$

Asymptote of $g(x)$: $y = 1$

53. **a.** $A = 10,000\left(1 + \dfrac{0.055}{2}\right)^{2(5)}$

   $\approx \$13,116.51$

b. $A = 10,000\left(1 + \dfrac{0.055}{4}\right)^{4(5)}$

   $\approx \$13,140.67$

c. $A = 10,000\left(1 + \dfrac{0.055}{12}\right)^{12(5)}$

   $\approx \$13,157.04$

d. $A = 10,000e^{0.055(5)}$

   $\approx \$13,165.31$

55. $A = 12,000\left(1 + \dfrac{0.07}{12}\right)^{12(3)}$

$\approx 14,795.11$ (7% yield)

$A = 12,000e^{0.0685(3)}$

$\approx 14,737.67$ (6.85% yield)

Investing \$12,000 for 3 years at 7% compounded monthly yields the greater return.

57.

x	$f(x) = 2^x$	$g(x) = 2^{-x}$
-2	$\dfrac{1}{4}$	4
-1	$\dfrac{1}{2}$	2
0	1	1
1	2	$\dfrac{1}{2}$
2	4	$\dfrac{1}{4}$

The point of intersection is $(0,1)$.

59

x	$y = 2^x$
-2	$\dfrac{1}{4}$
-1	$\dfrac{1}{2}$
0	1
1	2
2	4

y	$x = 2^y$
-2	$\dfrac{1}{4}$
-1	$\dfrac{1}{2}$
0	1
1	2
2	4

61. The graph is of the form $y = b^x$.

Substitute values from the point $(1, 4)$ to find b.

$y = b^x$

$4 = b^1$

$4 = b$

The equation of the graph is $y = 4^x$

63. The graph is of the form $y = -b^x$.

Substitute values from the point $(1, -e)$ to find b.

$y = -b^x$

$-e = -b^1$

$e = b$

The equation of the graph is $y = -e^x$

65.   **a.** $f(0) = 574(1.026)^0$

$= 574(1) = 574$

India's population in 1974 was 574 million.

b. $f(27) = 574(1.026)^{27} \approx 1148$

India's population in 2001 will be 1148 million.

c.   Since $2028 - 1974 = 54$, find

$f(54) = 574(1.026)^{54} \approx 2295$.

India's population in 2028 will be 2295 million.

d. $2055 - 1974 = 81$, find

$f(54) = 574(1.026)^{81} \approx 4590$.

India's population in 2055 will be 4590 million.

e.   India's population appears to be doubling every 27 years.

67. $S = 465,000(1 + 0.06)^{10}$

$= 465,000(1.06)^{10} \approx \$832,744$

69. $2^{1.7} \approx 3.249009585$

$2^{1.73} \approx 3.317278183$

$2^{1.732} \approx 3.321880096$

$2^{1.73205} \approx 3.321995226$

$2^{1.7320508} \approx 3.321997068$

$2^{\sqrt{3}} \approx 3.321997085$

The closer the exponent is to $\sqrt{3}$, the closer the value is to $2^{\sqrt{3}}$.

71. $f(45) = 0.16(45) + 1.43 = 8.63$

$g(45) = 1.8e^{0.04(45)} \approx 10.9$

The linear function is a better model for the graph's value of 8.9.

73. a. $f(0) = 80e^{-0.5(0)} + 20$

$= 80e^0 + 20$

$= 80(1) + 20$

$= 100$

100% of the material is remembered at the moment it is first learned.

b. $f(1) = 80e^{-0.5(1)} + 20 \approx 68.5$

68.5% of the material is remembered 1 week after it is first learned.

c. $f(4) = 80e^{-0.5(4)} + 20 \approx 30.8$

30.8% of the material is remembered 4 week after it is first learned.

d. $f(52) = 80e^{-0.5(52)} + 20 \approx 20$

20% of the material is remembered 1 year after it is first learned.

75. $f(4) = \dfrac{258,051}{1 + 6.78e^{-1.21(4)}} \approx 244,921$

$g(4) = 55,979.5(4) + 36,217.8 \approx 260,136$

$f(x)$ is a better model for the graph's value of 246,570.

83.

When $x = 31$, $y \approx 3.77$. NASA would not have launched the *Challenger*, since nearly 4 O-rings are expected to fail.

85. a.

b.

c.

d. Answers may vary.

87. $y = 3^x$ is (d). y increases as x increases, but not as quickly as $y = 5^x$. $y = 5^x$ is (c). $y = \left(\dfrac{1}{3}\right)^x$ is (a).

$y = \left(\dfrac{1}{3}\right)^x$ is the same as $y = 3^{-x}$, so it is (d) reflected about the y-axis. $y = \left(\dfrac{1}{5}\right)^x$ is (b).

$y = \left(\dfrac{1}{5}\right)^x$ is the same as $y = 5^{-x}$, so it is (c) reflected about the y-axis.

89. a.

$\cosh(-x) = \dfrac{e^{-x} + e^{-(-x)}}{2}$

$= \dfrac{e^{-x} + e^x}{2}$

$= \dfrac{e^x + e^{-x}}{2}$

$= \cosh x$

b.

$\sinh(-x) = \dfrac{e^{-x} - e^{-(-x)}}{2}$

$= \dfrac{e^{-x} - e^x}{2}$

$= \dfrac{-\left(-e^{-x} + e^x\right)}{2}$

$= -\dfrac{e^x - e^{-x}}{2}$

$= -\sinh x$

c.

$$(\cosh x)^2 - (\sinh x)^2 \overset{?}{=} 1$$

$$\left(\frac{e^x + e^{-x}}{2}\right)^2 - \left(\frac{e^x - e^{-x}}{2}\right)^2 \overset{?}{=} 1$$

$$\frac{e^{2x} + 2 + e^{-2x}}{4} - \frac{e^{2x} - 2 + e^{-2x}}{4} \overset{?}{=} 1$$

$$\frac{e^{2x} + 2 + e^{-2x} - e^{2x} + 2 - e^{-2x}}{4} \overset{?}{=} 1$$

$$\frac{4}{4} \overset{?}{=} 1$$

$$1 = 1$$

Section 3.2

Check Point Exercises

1. **a.** $3 = \log_7 x$ means $7^3 = x$.

   b. $2 = \log_b 25$ means $b^2 = 25$.

   c. $\log_4 26 = y$ means $4^y = 26$.

2. **a.** $2^5 = x$ means $5 = \log_2 x$.

   b. $b^3 = 27$ means $3 = \log_b 27$.

   c. $e^y = 33$ means $y = \log_e 33$.

3. **a.** Question: 10 to what power gives 100?
   $\log_{10} 100 = 2$ because $10^2 = 100$.

   b. Question: 3 to what power gives 3?
   $\log_3 3 = 1$ because $3^1 = 3$.

   c. Question: 36 to what power gives 6?
   $\log_{36} 6 = \frac{1}{2}$ because $36^{\frac{1}{2}} = \sqrt{36} = 6$

4. **a.** Because $\log_b b = 1$, we conclude
   $\log_9 9 = 1$.

   b. Because $\log_b 1 = 0$, we conclude
   $\log_8 1 = 0$.

5. **a.** Because $\log_b b^x = x$, we conclude
   $\log_7 7^8 = 8$.

   b. Because $b^{\log_b x} = x$, we conclude
   $3^{\log_3 17} = 17$.

6. First, set up a table of coordinates for $f(x) = 3^x$.

x	-2	-1	0	1	2	3
$f(x) = 3^x$	$\frac{1}{9}$	$\frac{1}{3}$	1	3	9	27

Reversing these coordinates gives the coordinates for the inverse function
$g(x) = \log_3 x$.

x	$\frac{1}{9}$	$\frac{1}{3}$	1	3	9	27
$g(x) = \log_3 x$	-2	-1	0	1	2	3

The graph of the inverse can also be drawn by reflecting the graph of $f(x) = 3^x$ about the line $y = x$.

$f(x) = 3^x$

$g(x) = \log_3 x$

7. The domain of h consists of all x for which $x - 5 > 0$. Solving this inequality for x, we obtain $x > 5$. Thus, the domain of h is $(5, \infty)$.

8. Substitute the boy's age, 10, for x and evaluate the function at 10.
   $$f(10) = 29 + 48.8 \log(10 + 1)$$
   $$= 29 + 48.8 \log(11)$$
   $$\approx 80$$
   Thus, a 10-year-old boy is approximately 80% of his adult height.

9. Because $I = 10,000\, I_0$,
   $$R = \log \frac{10,000 I_0}{I_0}$$
   $$= \log 10,000$$
   $$= 4$$
   The earthquake registered 4.0 on the Richter scale.

10. **a.** The domain of f consists of all x for which $4 - x > 0$. Solving this inequality for x, we obtain $x < 4$. Thus, the domain of f is $(-\infty, 4)$

b. The domain of g consists of all x for which $x^2 > 0$. Solving this inequality for x, we obtain $x < 0$ or $x > 0$. Thus the domain of g is $(-\infty, 0) \cup (0, \infty)$.

11. Find the temperature increase after 30 minutes by substituting 30 for x and evaluating the function at 30.

$$f(x) = 13.4 \ln x - 11.6$$
$$f(30) = 13.4 \ln 30 - 11.6$$
$$\approx 34$$

The function models the actual increase shown in the graph quite well.

Exercise Set 3.2

1. $2^4 = 16$

3. $3^2 = x$

5. $b^5 = 32$

7. $6^y = 216$

9. $\log_2 8 = 3$

11. $\log_2 \dfrac{1}{16} = -4$

13. $\log_8 2 = \dfrac{1}{3}$

15. $\log_{13} x = 2$

17. $\log_b 1000 = 3$

19. $\log_7 200 = y$

21. $\log_4 16 = 2$ because $4^2 = 16$.

23. $\log_2 64 = 6$ because $2^6 = 64$.

25. $\log_5 \dfrac{1}{5} = -1$ because $5^{-1} = \dfrac{1}{5}$.

27. $\log_2 \dfrac{1}{8} = -3$ because $2^{-3} = \dfrac{1}{8}$.

29. $\log_7 \sqrt{7} = \dfrac{1}{2}$ because $7^{\frac{1}{2}} = \sqrt{7}$.

31. $\log_2 \dfrac{1}{\sqrt{2}} = -\dfrac{1}{2}$ because $2^{-\frac{1}{2}} = \dfrac{1}{\sqrt{2}}$.

33. $\log_{64} 8 = \dfrac{1}{2}$ because $64^{\frac{1}{2}} = \sqrt{64} = 8$.

35. Because $\log_b b = 1$, we conclude $\log_5 5 = 1$.

37. Because $\log_b 1 = 0$, we conclude $\log_4 1 = 0$.

39. Because $\log_b b^x = x$, we conclude $\log_5 5^7 = 7$.

41. Because $b^{\log_b x} = x$, we conclude $8^{\log_8 19} = 19$.

43. First, set up a table of coordinates for $f(x) = 4^x$.

x	-2	-1	0	1	2	3
$f(x) = 4x$	$\frac{1}{16}$	$\frac{1}{4}$	1	4	16	64

Reversing these coordinates gives the coordinates for the inverse function $g(x) = \log_4 x$.

x	$\frac{1}{16}$	$\frac{1}{4}$	1	4	16	64
$g(x) = \log_{4x}$	-2	-1	0	1	2	3

$$f(x) = 4^x$$
$$g(x) = \log_4 x$$

45. First, set up a table of coordinates for

$$f(x) = \left(\frac{1}{2}\right)^x.$$

x	-2	-1	0	1	2	3
$f(x) = \left(\frac{1}{2}\right)^x$	4	2	1	$\frac{1}{2}$	$\frac{1}{4}$	$\frac{1}{8}$

Reversing these coordinates gives the coordinates for the inverse function $g(x) = \log_{1/2} x$.

x	4	2	1	$\frac{1}{2}$	$\frac{1}{4}$	$\frac{1}{8}$
$g(x) = \log_{1/2} x$	-2	-1	0	1	2	3

$$f(x) = \left(\frac{1}{2}\right)^x$$

$$g(x) = \log_{1/2}x$$

47. This is the graph of $f(x) = \log_3 x$ reflected about the x-axis and shifted up one unit, so the function is $H(x) = 1 - \log_3 x$.

49. This is the graph of $f(x) = \log_3 x$ shifted down one unit, so the function is $h(x) = \log_3 x - 1$.

51. This is the graph of $f(x) = \log_3 x$ shifted right one unit, so the function is $g(x) = \log_3(x-1)$.

53.

$$f(x) = \log_2 x$$

$$g(x) = \log_2(x+1)$$

vertical asymptote: $x = -1$
Domain: $(-1, \infty)$; Range: $(-\infty, \infty)$

55.

$$f(x) = \log_2 x$$

$$g(x) = 1 + \log_2 x$$

vertical asymptote: $x = 0$
Domain: $(0, \infty)$; Range: $(-\infty, \infty)$

57.

$$f(x) = \log_2 x$$

$$g(x) = \frac{1}{2}\log_2 x$$

vertical asymptote: $x = 0$
Domain: $(0, \infty)$; Range: $(-\infty, \infty)$

59.

$$g(x) = \log(x-1)$$

vertical asymptote: $x = 1$
Domain: $(1, \infty)$; Range: $(-\infty, \infty)$

61.

$$h(x) = \log x - 1$$

vertical asymptote: $x = 0$
Domain: $(0, \infty)$; Range: $(-\infty, \infty)$

63.

$$g(x) = 1 - \log x$$

vertical asymptote: $x = 0$
Domain: $(0, \infty)$; Range: $(-\infty, \infty)$

65.

$$g(x) = \ln(x + 2)$$

vertical asymptote: $x = -2$
Domain: $(-2, \infty)$; Range: $(-\infty, \infty)$

67.

$$h(x) = \ln(2x)$$

vertical asymptote: $x = 0$
Domain: $(0, \infty)$; Range: $(-\infty, \infty)$

69.

$$g(x) = 2 \ln x$$

vertical asymptote: $x = 0$
Domain: $(0, \infty)$; Range: $(-\infty, \infty)$

71.

$$h(x) = -\ln x$$

vertical asymptote: $x = 0$
Domain: $(0, \infty)$; Range: $(-\infty, \infty)$

73.

$$g(x) = 2 - \ln x$$

vertical asymptote: $x = 0$
Domain: $(0, \infty)$; Range: $(-\infty, \infty)$

75. The domain of f consists of all x for which $x + 4 > 0$. Solving this inequality for x, we obtain $x > -4$. Thus, the domain of f is $(-4, \infty)$.

77. The domain of f consists of all x for which $2 - x > 0$. Solving this inequality for x, we obtain $x < 2$. Thus, the domain of f is $(-\infty, 2)$.

79. The domain of f consists of all x for which $(x - 2)^2 > 0$. Solving this inequality for x, we obtain $x < 2$ or $x > 2$. Thus, the domain of f is $(-\infty, 2)$ or $(2, \infty)$.

81. $\log 100 = \log_{10} 100 = 2$
because $10^2 = 100$.

83. Because $\log 10^x = x$, we
conclude $\log 10^7 = 7$.

85. Because $10^{\log x} = x$, we
conclude $10^{\log 33} = 33$.

87. $\ln 1 = 0$ because $e^0 = 1$.

89. Because $\ln e^x = x$, we
conclude $\ln e^6 = 6$.

91. $\ln\dfrac{1}{e^6} = \ln e^{-6}$

Because $\ln e^x = x$ we conclude

$\ln e^{-6} = -6$, so $\ln\dfrac{1}{e^6} = -6$.

93. Because $e^{\ln x} = x$, we conclude $e^{\ln 125} = 125$.

95. Because $\ln e^x = x$, we conclude $\ln e^{9x} = 9x$.

97. Because $e^{\ln x} = x$, we conclude $e^{\ln 5x^2} = 5x^2$.

99. Because $10^{\log x} = x$, we conclude $10^{\log\sqrt{x}} = \sqrt{x}$.

101. $\log_3(x-1) = 2$

$$3^2 = x - 1$$
$$9 = x - 1$$
$$10 = x$$

The solution is 10, and the solution set is $\{10\}$.

103. $\log_4 x = -3$

$$4^{-3} = x$$
$$x = \dfrac{1}{4^3} = \dfrac{1}{64}$$

The solution is $\dfrac{1}{64}$, and the solution set is $\left\{\dfrac{1}{64}\right\}$.

105. $\log_3\left(\log_7 7\right) = \log_3 1 = 0$

107. $\log_2\left(\log_3 81\right) = \log_2\left(\log_3 3^4\right)$

$$= \log_2 4 = \log_2 2^2 = 2$$

109. For $f(x) = \ln(x^2 - x - 2)$ to be real,

$x^2 - x - 2 > 0$.

Solve the related equation to find the boundary points:

$$x^2 - x - 2 = 0$$
$$(x+1)(x-2) = 0$$

The boundary points are -1 and 2. Testing each interval gives a domain of $(-\infty, -1) \cup (2, \infty)$.

111. For $f(x) = \ln\left(\dfrac{x+1}{x-5}\right)$ to be real, $\dfrac{x+1}{x-5} > 0$.

The boundary points are -1 and 5. Testing each interval gives a domain of $(-\infty, -1) \cup (5, \infty)$.

113. $f(13) = 62 + 35\log(13-4) \approx 95.4$

She is approximately 95.4% of her adult height.

115. Since $2003 - 1997 = 6$, we find $f(6)$:

$$f(6) = -4.9\ln 6 + 73.8 \approx 65$$

In 2003, approximately 65% of U.S. companies performed drug tests. The function modeled the actual number very well. It gives the actual percent.

117. $D = 10\log\left[10^{12}(6.3 \times 10^6)\right] \approx 188$

Yes, the sound can rupture the human eardrum.

119. a. $f(0) = 88 - 15\ln(0+1) = 88$

The average score on the original exam was 88.

b. $f(2) = 88 - 15\ln(2+1) = 71.5$
$f(4) = 88 - 15\ln(4+1) = 63.9$
$f(6) = 88 - 15\ln(6+1) = 58.8$
$f(8) = 88 - 15\ln(8+1) = 55$
$f(10) = 88 - 15\ln(10+1) = 52$
$f(12) = 88 - 15\ln(12+1) = 49.5$

The average score after 2 months was about 71.5, after 4 months was about 63.9, after 6 months was about 58.8, after 8 months was about 55, after 10 months was about 52, and after one year was about 49.5.

c.

Material retention decreases as time passes.

129.

$g(x)$ is $f(x)$ shifted 3 units upward.

131.

g(x) is f(x) shifted right 2 units and upward 1 unit.

133. a.

b.

c.

d They are the same.
$$\log_b MN = \log_b M + \log_b N$$

e. The sum of the logarithms of its factors.

135. a. False; $\dfrac{\log_2 8}{\log_2 4} = \dfrac{3}{2}$

b. False; $\log x$ is not defined for $x < 0$.

c. False; the domain is $(0, \infty)$.

d. True

(d) is true.

137. $\log_4 \left[\log_3 \left(\log_2 8 \right) \right]$
$$= \log_4 \left[\log_3 \left(\log_2 2^3 \right) \right]$$
$$= \log_4 \left[\log_3 3 \right] = \log_4 1 = 0$$

Section 3.3

Check Point Exercises

1. a. $\log_6 (7 \cdot 11) = \log_6 7 + \log_6 11$

b. $\log(100x) = \log 100 + \log x$
$$= 2 + \log x$$

2. a. $\log_8 \left(\dfrac{23}{x} \right) = \log_8 23 - \log_8 x$

b. $\ln \left(\dfrac{e^5}{11} \right) = \ln e^5 - \ln 11$
$$= 5 - \ln 11$$

3. a. $\log_6 3^9 = 9 \log_6 3$

b. $\ln \sqrt[3]{x} = \ln x^{1/3} = \dfrac{1}{3} \ln x$

c. $\log(x+4)^2 = 2 \log(x+4)$

4. a. $\log_b x^4 \sqrt[3]{y}$
$$= \log_b x^4 y^{1/3}$$
$$= \log_b x^4 + \log_b y^{1/3}$$
$$= 4 \log_b x + \dfrac{1}{3} \log_b y$$

b. $\log_5 \dfrac{\sqrt{x}}{25y^3}$
$$= \log_5 \dfrac{x^{1/2}}{25y^3}$$
$$= \log_5 x^{1/2} - \log_5 25y^3$$
$$= \log_5 x^{1/2} - \left(\log_5 5^2 + \log_5 y^3 \right)$$
$$= \tfrac{1}{2} \log_5 x - \log_5 5^2 - \log_5 y^3$$
$$= \tfrac{1}{2} \log_5 x - 2 \log_5 5 - 3 \log_5 y$$
$$= \tfrac{1}{2} \log_5 x - 2 - 3 \log_5 y$$

5. a. $\log 25 + \log 4 = \log(25 \cdot 4) = \log 100 = 2$

b. $\log(7x+6) - \log x = \log \dfrac{7x+6}{x}$

6.   **a.** $\ln x^2 + \dfrac{1}{3}\ln(x+5)$

            $= \ln x^2 + \ln(x+5)^{1/3}$

            $= \ln x^2 (x+5)^{1/3}$

            $= \ln x^2 \sqrt[3]{x+5}$

   b. $2\log(x-3) - \log x$

            $= \log(x-3)^2 - \log x$

            $= \log\dfrac{(x-3)^2}{x}$

   c. $\dfrac{1}{4}\log_b x - 2\log_b 5 - 10\log_b y$

            $= \log_b x^{1/4} - \log_b 5^2 - \log_b y^{10}$

            $= \log_b x^{1/4} - \left(\log_b 25 - \log_b y^{10}\right)$

            $= \log_b x^{1/4} - \log_b 25 y^{10}$

            $= \log_b \dfrac{x^{1/4}}{25 y^{10}}$ or $\log_b \dfrac{\sqrt[4]{x}}{25 y^{10}}$

7. $\log_7 2506 = \dfrac{\log 2506}{\log 7} \approx 4.02$

8. $\log_7 2506 = \dfrac{\ln 2506}{\ln 7} \approx 4.02$

Exercise Set 3.3

1. $\log_5(7 \cdot 3) = \log_5 7 + \log_5 3$

3. $\log_7(7x) = \log_7 7 + \log_7 x = 1 + \log_7 x$

5. $\log(1000x) = \log 1000 + \log x = 3 + \log x$

7. $\log_7\left(\dfrac{7}{x}\right) = \log_7 7 - \log_7 x = 1 - \log_7 x$

9. $\log\left(\dfrac{x}{100}\right) = \log x - \log 100 = \log_x - 2$

11. $\log_4\left(\dfrac{64}{y}\right) = \log_4 64 - \log_4 y$

               $= 3 - \log_4 y$

13. $\ln\left(\dfrac{e^2}{5}\right) = \ln e^2 - \ln 5 = 2\ln e - \ln 5 = 2 - \ln 5$

15. $\log_b x^3 = 3\log_b x$

17. $\log N^{-6} = -6\log N$

19. $\ln \sqrt[5]{x} = \ln x^{(1/5)} = \dfrac{1}{5}\ln x$

21. $\log_b x^2 y = \log_b x^2 + \log_b y = 2\log_b x + \log_b y$

23. $\log_4\left(\dfrac{\sqrt{x}}{64}\right) = \log_4 x^{1/2} - \log_4 64 = \dfrac{1}{2}\log_4 x - 3$

25. $\log_6\left(\dfrac{36}{\sqrt{x+1}}\right) = \log_6 36 - \log_6 (x+1)^{1/2}$

                     $= 2 - \dfrac{1}{2}\log_6 (x+1)$

27. $\log_b\left(\dfrac{x^2 y}{z^2}\right) = \log_b\left(x^2 y\right) - \log_b z^2$

               $= \log_b x^2 + \log_b y - \log_b z^2$

               $= 2\log_b x + \log_b y - 2\log_b z$

29. $\log\sqrt{100x} = \log(100x)^{1/2}$

           $= \dfrac{1}{2}\log(100x)$

           $= \dfrac{1}{2}(\log 100 + \log x)$

           $= \dfrac{1}{2}(2 + \log x)$

           $= 1 + \dfrac{1}{2}\log x$

31. $\log \sqrt[3]{\dfrac{x}{y}} = \log\left(\dfrac{x}{y}\right)^{1/3}$

         $= \dfrac{1}{3}\left[\log\left(\dfrac{x}{y}\right)\right]$

         $= \dfrac{1}{3}(\log x - \log y)$

         $= \dfrac{1}{3}\log x - \dfrac{1}{3}\log y$

33. $\log_b \dfrac{\sqrt{x}y^3}{z^3}$

        $= \log_b x^{1/2} + \log_b y^3 - \log_b z^3$

        $= \dfrac{1}{2}\log_b x + 3\log_b y - 3\log_b z$

35.
$$\log_5 \sqrt[3]{\frac{x^2 y}{25}}$$
$$= \log_5 x^{2/3} + \log_5 y^{1/3} - \log_5 25^{1/3}$$
$$= \frac{2}{3}\log_5 x + \frac{1}{3}\log_5 y - \log_5 5^{2/3}$$
$$= \frac{2}{3}\log_5 x + \frac{1}{3}\log_5 y - \frac{2}{3}$$

37.
$$\ln\left[\frac{x^3 \sqrt{x^2+1}}{(x+1)^4}\right]$$
$$= \ln x^3 + \ln\sqrt{x^2+1} - \ln(x+1)^4$$
$$= 3\ln x + \frac{1}{2}\ln(x^2+1) - 4\ln(x+1)$$

39.
$$\log\left[\frac{10x^2 \sqrt[3]{1-x}}{7(x+1)^2}\right]$$
$$= \log 10 + \log x^2 + \log\sqrt[3]{1-x} - \log 7 - \log(x+1)^2$$
$$= 1 + 2\log x + \frac{1}{3}\log(1-x) - \log 7 - 2\log(x+1)$$

41. $\log 5 + \log 2 = \log(5\cdot 2) = \log 10 = 1$

43. $\ln x + \ln 7 = \ln(7x)$

45. $\log_2 96 - \log_2 3 = \log_2\left(\frac{96}{3}\right) = \log_2 32 = 5$

47. $\log(2x+5) - \log x = \log\left(\frac{2x+5}{x}\right)$

49. $\log x + 3\log y = \log x + \log y^3 = \log(xy^3)$

51. $\frac{1}{2}\ln x + \ln y = \ln x^{1/2} + \ln y$
$$= \ln\left(x^{\frac{1}{2}}y\right) \text{ or } \ln\left(y\sqrt{x}\right)$$

53. $2\log_b x + 3\log_b y = \log_b x^2 + \log_b y^3$
$$= \log_b(x^2 y^3)$$

55. $5\ln x - 2\ln y = \ln x^5 - \ln y^2 = \ln\left(\frac{x^5}{y^2}\right)$

57. $3\ln x - \frac{1}{3}\ln y = \ln x^3 - \ln y^{1/3}$
$$= \ln\left(\frac{x^3}{y^{1/3}}\right) \text{ or } \ln\left(\frac{x^3}{\sqrt[3]{y}}\right)$$

59. $4\ln(x+6) - 3\ln x = \ln(x+6)^4 - \ln x^3$
$$= \ln\frac{(x+6)^4}{x^3}$$

61. $3\ln x + 5\ln y - 6\ln z$
$$= \ln x^3 + \ln y^5 - \ln z^6$$
$$= \ln\frac{x^3 y^5}{z^6}$$

63. $\frac{1}{2}\left(\log x + \log y\right)$
$$= \frac{1}{2}(\log xy)$$
$$= \log(xy)^{1/2}$$
$$= \log\sqrt{xy}$$

65. $\frac{1}{2}(\log_5 x + \log_5 y) - 2\log_5(x+1)$
$$= \frac{1}{2}\log_5 xy - \log_5(x+1)^2$$
$$= \log_5(xy)^{1/2} - \log_5(x+1)^2$$
$$= \log_5 \frac{(xy)^{1/2}}{(x+1)^2}$$
$$= \log_5 \frac{\sqrt{xy}}{(x+1)^2}$$

67. $\frac{1}{3}[2\ln(x+5) - \ln x - \ln(x^2-4)]$
$$= \frac{1}{3}[\ln(x+5)^2 - \ln x - \ln(x^2-4)]$$
$$= \frac{1}{3}\left[\ln\frac{(x+5)^2}{x(x^2-4)}\right]$$
$$= \ln\left[\frac{(x+5)^2}{x(x^2-4)}\right]^{1/3}$$
$$= \ln\sqrt[3]{\frac{(x+5)^2}{x(x^2-4)}}$$

69. $\log x + \log\left(x^2 - 1\right) - \log 7 - \log(x+1)$

$= \log x + \log\left(x^2 - 1\right) - \left(\log 7 + \log(x+1)\right)$

$= \log\left(x\left(x^2 - 1\right)\right) - \log\left(7(x+1)\right)$

$= \log\dfrac{x\left(x^2 - 1\right)}{7(x+1)}$

$= \log\dfrac{x(x+1)(x-1)}{7(x+1)}$

$= \log\dfrac{x(x-1)}{7}$

71. $\log_5 13 = \dfrac{\log 13}{\log 5} \approx 1.5937$

73. $\log_{14} 87.5 = \dfrac{\ln 87.5}{\ln 14} \approx 1.6944$

75. $\log_{0.1} 17 = \dfrac{\log 17}{\log 0.1} \approx -1.2304$

77. $\log_\pi 63 = \dfrac{\ln 63}{\ln \pi} \approx 3.6193$

79.

$y = \log_3 x = \dfrac{\log x}{\log 3}$

81.

$y = \log_2(x+2) = \dfrac{\log(x+2)}{\log 2}$

83.

$\log_b \dfrac{3}{2} = \log_b 3 - \log_b 2 = C - A$

85. $\log_b 8 = \log_b 2^3 = 3\log_b 2 = 3A$

87.

$\log_b \sqrt{\dfrac{2}{27}} = \log_b \left(\dfrac{2}{27}\right)^{\frac{1}{2}}$

$= \dfrac{1}{2}\log_b\left(\dfrac{2}{3^3}\right)$

$= \dfrac{1}{2}\left(\log_b 2 - \log_b 3^3\right)$

$= \dfrac{1}{2}\left(\log_b 2 - 3\log_b 3\right)$

$= \dfrac{1}{2}\log_b 2 - \dfrac{3}{2}\log_b 3$

$= \dfrac{1}{2}A - \dfrac{3}{2}C$

89. false; $\ln e = 1$

91. false; $\log_4\left(2x\right)^3 = 3\log_4\left(2x\right)$

93. true; $x\log 10^x = x \cdot x = x^2$

95. true; $\ln(5x) + \ln 1 = \ln 5x + 0 = \ln 5x$

97. false; $\log(x+3) - \log(2x) = \log\dfrac{x+3}{2x}$

99. true; quotient rule

101. true; $\log_3 7 = \dfrac{\log 7}{\log 3} = \dfrac{1}{\frac{\log 3}{\log 7}} = \dfrac{1}{\log_7 3}$

103. a. $D = 10\log\left(\dfrac{I}{I_0}\right)$

b. $D_1 = 10\log\left(\dfrac{100I}{I_0}\right)$

$= 10\log\left(100I - I_0\right)$

$= 10\log 100 + 10\log I - 10\log I_0$

$= 10(2) + 10\log I - 10\log I_0$

$= 20 + 10\log\left(\dfrac{I}{I_0}\right)$

This is 20 more than the loudness level of the softer sound. This means that the 100 times louder sound will be 20 decibels louder.

113. a. $y = \log_3 x = \dfrac{\ln x}{\ln 3}$

b.

To obtain the graph of $y = 2 + \log_3 x$, shift the graph of $y = \log_3 x$ two units upward. To obtain the graph of $y = \log_3(x + 2)$, shift the graph of $y = \log_3 x$ two units left. To obtain the graph of $y = -\log_3 x$, reflect the graph of $y = \log_3 x$ about the x-axis.

115. $\log_3 x = \dfrac{\log x}{\log 3}$;

$\log_{25} x = \dfrac{\log x}{\log 25}$;

$\log_{100} x = \dfrac{\log x}{\log 100}$

a.   top graph: $y = \log_{100} x$
bottom graph: $y = \log_3 x$

b.   top graph: $y = \log_3 x$
bottom graph: $y = \log_{100} x$

c.   Comparing graphs of $\log_b x$ for $b > 1$, the graph of the equation with the largest b will be on the top in the interval $(0, 1)$ and on the bottom in the interval $(1, \infty)$.

121. a.   False;

$\log_7 49 - \log_7 7 = \log_7 \dfrac{49}{7} = \log_7 7 = 1$

$\dfrac{\log_7 49}{\log_7 7} = \dfrac{2}{1} = 2$

b.   False;

$3 \log_b x + 3 \log_b y = \log_b (xy)^3$
$\neq \log_b \left(x^3 + y^3 \right)$

c.   False;

$\log_b (xy)^5 = 5 \log_b (xy)$
$= 5(\log_b x + \log_b y)$
$\neq (\log_b x + \log_b y)^5$

d.   True;

$\ln \sqrt{2} = \ln 2^{1/2}$
$= \dfrac{1}{2} \ln 2 = \dfrac{\ln 2}{2}$

(d) is true.

123. $\log_7 9 = \dfrac{\log 9}{\log 7} = \dfrac{\log 3^2}{\log 7} = \dfrac{2 \log 3}{\log 7}$

$= \dfrac{2A}{B}$

125. $\dfrac{\log_b (x + h) - \log_b x}{h}$

$= \dfrac{\log_b \dfrac{x + h}{x}}{h}$

$= \dfrac{\log_b \left(1 + \dfrac{h}{x} \right)}{h}$

$= \dfrac{1}{h} \log_b \left(1 + \dfrac{h}{x} \right)$

$= \log_b \left(1 + \dfrac{x}{h} \right)^{1/h}$

Mid-Chapter 3 Check Point

1.

$$f(x) = 2^x$$
$$g(x) = 2^x - 3$$

Asymptote of f: $y = 0$
Asymptote of g: $y = -3$
Domain of f = Domain of g = $(-\infty, \infty)$
Range of f = $(0, \infty)$
Range of g = $(-3, \infty)$

2.

$$f(x) = \left(\frac{1}{2}\right)^x$$

$$g(x) = \left(\frac{1}{2}\right)^{x-1}$$

Asymptote of f: $y = 0$
Asymptote of g: $y = 0$
Domain of f = Domain of g = $(-\infty, \infty)$
Range of f = Range of g = $(0, \infty)$

3.

$$f(x) = e^x$$
$$g(x) = \ln x$$

Asymptote of f: $y = 0$
Asymptote of g: $x = 0$
Domain of f = Range of g = $(-\infty, \infty)$
Range of f = Domain of g = $(0, \infty)$

4.

$$f(x) = \log_2 x$$
$$g(x) = \log_2 (x - 1) + 1$$

Asymptote of f: $x = 0$
Asymptote of g: $x = 1$
Domain of f = $(0, \infty)$
Domain of g = $(1, \infty)$
Range of f = Range of g = $(-\infty, \infty)$

5.

$$f(x) = \log_{1/2} x$$
$$g(x) = -2 \log_{1/2} x$$

Asymptote of f: $x = 0$
Asymptote of g: $x = 0$
Domain of f = Domain of g = $(0, \infty)$
Range of f = Range of g = $(-\infty, \infty)$

6. $f(x) = \log_3 (x + 6)$
The argument of the logarithm must be positive:
$x + 6 > 0$
$\quad x > -6$
Domain: $\{x \mid x > -6\}$ or $(-6, \infty)$.

7. $f(x) = \log_3 x + 6$
The argument of the logarithm must be positive:
$x > 0$
Domain: $\{x \mid x > 0\}$ or $(0, \infty)$.

8. $\log_3 (x + 6)^2$
The argument of the logarithm must be positive.
Now $(x + 6)^2$ is always positive, except when
$x = -6$
Domain: $\{x \mid x \neq 0\}$ or $(-\infty, -6) \cup (-6, \infty)$.

9. $f(x) = 3^{x+6}$

Domain: $\{x \mid x \text{ is a real number}\}$ or $(-\infty, \infty)$.

10. $\log_2 8 + \log_5 25 = \log_2 2^3 + \log_5 5^2$

$\qquad\qquad\qquad\qquad = 3 + 2 = 5$

11. $\log_3 \dfrac{1}{9} = \log_3 \dfrac{1}{3^2} = \log_3 3^{-2} = -2$

12.   Let $\log_{100} 10 = y$

$\qquad\qquad 100^y = 10$

$\qquad\qquad \left(10^2\right)^y = 10^1$

$\qquad\qquad 10^{2y} = 10^1$

$\qquad\qquad 2y = 1$

$\qquad\qquad y = \dfrac{1}{2}$

13. $\log \sqrt[3]{10} = \log 10^{\frac{1}{3}} = \dfrac{1}{3}$

14. $\log_2 \left(\log_3 81\right) = \log_2 \left(\log_3 3^4\right)$

$\qquad\qquad\qquad\qquad = \log_2 4 = \log_2 2^2 = 2$

15. $\log_3 \left(\log_2 \dfrac{1}{8}\right) = \log_3 \left(\log_2 \dfrac{1}{2^3}\right)$

$\qquad\qquad\qquad\qquad = \log_3 \left(\log_2 2^{-3}\right)$

$\qquad\qquad\qquad\qquad = \log_3 (-3)$

$\qquad\qquad\qquad\qquad = \text{not possible}$

This expression is impossible to evaluate.

16. $6^{\log_6 5} = 5$

17. $\ln e^{\sqrt{7}} = \sqrt{7}$

18. $10^{\log 13} = 13$

19. $\log_{100} 0.1 = y$

$\qquad\qquad 100^y = 0.1$

$\qquad\qquad \left(10^2\right)^y = \dfrac{1}{10}$

$\qquad\qquad 10^{2y} = 10^{-1}$

$\qquad\qquad 2y = -1$

$\qquad\qquad y = -\dfrac{1}{2}$

20. $\log_\pi \pi^{\sqrt{\pi}} = \sqrt{\pi}$

21. $\log \left(\dfrac{\sqrt{xy}}{1000}\right) = \log\left(\sqrt{xy}\right) - \log 1000$

$\qquad\qquad\qquad\qquad = \log (xy)^{\frac{1}{2}} - \log 10^3$

$\qquad\qquad\qquad\qquad = \dfrac{1}{2} \log(xy) - 3$

$\qquad\qquad\qquad\qquad = \dfrac{1}{2}\left(\log x + \log y\right) - 3$

$\qquad\qquad\qquad\qquad = \dfrac{1}{2} \log x + \dfrac{1}{2} \log y - 3$

22. $\ln \left(e^{19} x^{20}\right) = \ln e^{19} + \ln x^{20}$

$\qquad\qquad\qquad\qquad = 19 + 20 \ln x$

23. $8 \log_7 x - \dfrac{1}{3} \log_7 y = \log_7 x^8 - \log_7 y^{\frac{1}{3}}$

$\qquad\qquad\qquad\qquad = \log_7 \left(\dfrac{x^8}{y^{\frac{1}{3}}}\right)$

$\qquad\qquad\qquad\qquad = \log_7 \left(\dfrac{x^8}{\sqrt[3]{y}}\right)$

24. $7 \log_5 x + 2 \log_5 x = \log_5 x^7 + \log_5 x^2$

$\qquad\qquad\qquad\qquad = \log_5 \left(x^7 \cdot x^2\right)$

$\qquad\qquad\qquad\qquad = \log_5 x^9$

25. $\dfrac{1}{2} \ln x - 3 \ln y - \ln(z-2)$

$\qquad = \ln x^{\frac{1}{2}} - \ln y^3 - \ln(z-2)$

$\qquad = \ln \sqrt{x} - \left[\ln y^3 + \ln(z-2)\right]$

$\qquad = \ln \sqrt{x} - \ln\left[y^3 (z-2)\right]$

$\qquad = \ln \left[\dfrac{\sqrt{x}}{y^3 (z-2)}\right]$

26.   Continuously: $A = 8000 e^{0.08(3)}$

$\qquad\qquad\qquad\qquad \approx 10{,}170$

Monthly: $A = 8000 \left(1 + \dfrac{0.08}{12}\right)^{12 \cdot 3}$

$\qquad\qquad\qquad \approx 10{,}162$

$10{,}170 - 10{,}162 = 8$

Interest returned will be \$8 more if compounded continuously.

Section 3.4

Check Point Exercises

1.   **a.** $5^{3x-6} = 125$

$$5^{3x-6} = 5^3$$
$$3x - 6 = 3$$
$$3x = 9$$
$$x = 3$$

    b. $8^{x+2} = 4^{x-3}$

$$\left(2^3\right)^{x+2} = \left(2^2\right)^{x-3}$$
$$2^{3x+6} = 2^{2x-6}$$
$$3x + 6 = 2x - 6$$
$$x = -12$$

2. $5^x = 134$

$$\ln 5^x = \ln 134$$
$$x \ln 5 = \ln 134$$
$$x = \frac{\ln 134}{\ln 5} \approx 3.04$$

The solution set is $\left\{ \dfrac{\ln 134}{\ln 5} \right\}$, approximately 3.04.

3. $7e^{2x} = 63$

$$e^{2x} = 9$$
$$\ln e^{2x} = \ln 9$$
$$2x = \ln 9$$
$$x = \frac{\ln 9}{2} \approx 1.10$$

The solution set is $\left\{ \dfrac{\ln 9}{2} \right\}$, approximately 1.10.

4. $3^{2x-1} = 7^{x+1}$

$$\ln 3^{2x-1} = \ln 7^{x+1}$$
$$(2x - 1)\ln 3 = (x + 1)\ln 7$$
$$2x \ln 3 - \ln 3 = x \ln 7 + \ln 7$$
$$2x \ln 3 - x \ln 7 = \ln 3 + \ln 7$$
$$x(2 \ln 3 - \ln 7) = \ln 3 + \ln 7$$
$$x = \frac{\ln 3 + \ln 7}{2 \ln 3 - \ln 7}$$
$$x \approx 12.11$$

5. $e^{2x} - 8e^x + 7 = 0$

$$\left(e^x - 7\right)\left(e^x - 1\right) = 0$$

$$e^x - 7 = 0 \quad \text{or} \quad e^x - 1 = 0$$
$$e^x = 7 \qquad\qquad e^x = 1$$
$$\ln e^x = \ln 7 \qquad \ln e^x = \ln 1$$
$$x = \ln 7 \qquad\qquad x = 0$$

The solution set is $\{0, \ln 7\}$. The solutions are 0 and (approximately) 1.95.

6.   **a.** $\log_2(x - 4) = 3$

$$2^3 = x - 4$$
$$8 = x - 4$$
$$12 = x$$

Check:
$$\log_2(x - 4) = 3$$
$$\log_2(12 - 4) = 3$$
$$\log_2 8 = 3$$
$$3 = 3$$

The solution set is $\{12\}$.

    b. $4 \ln 3x = 8$

$$\ln 3x = 2$$
$$e^{\ln 3x} = e^2$$
$$3x = e^2$$
$$x = \frac{e^2}{3} \approx 2.46$$

Check
$$4 \ln 3x = 8$$
$$4 \ln 3\left(\frac{e^2}{3}\right) = 8$$
$$4 \ln e^2 = 8$$
$$4(2) = 8$$
$$8 = 8$$

The solution set is $\left\{ \dfrac{e^2}{3} \right\}$, approximately 2.46.

7.

$$\log x + \log(x-3) = 1$$
$$\log x(x-3) = 1$$
$$10^1 = x(x-3)$$
$$10 = x^2 - 3x$$
$$0 = x^2 - 3x - 10$$
$$0 = (x-5)(x+2)$$
$$x - 5 = 0 \quad \text{or} \quad x + 2 = 0$$
$$x = 5 \quad \text{or} \quad x = -2$$

Check
Checking 5:
$$\log 5 + \log(5-3) = 1$$
$$\log 5 + \log 2 = 1$$
$$\log(5 \cdot 2) = 1$$
$$\log 10 = 1$$
$$1 = 1$$

Checking -2:
$$\log x + \log(x-3) = 1$$
$$\log(-2) + \log(-2-3) \ 0 \ 1$$

Negative numbers do not have logarithms so -2 does not check.
The solution set is $\{5\}$.

8.

$$\ln(x-3) = \ln(7x-23) - \ln(x+1)$$
$$\ln(x-3) = \ln\frac{7x-23}{x+1}$$
$$x - 3 = \frac{7x-23}{x+1}$$
$$(x-3)(x+1) = 7x - 23$$
$$x^2 - 2x - 3 = 7x - 23$$
$$x^2 - 9x + 20 = 0$$
$$(x-4)(x-5) = 0$$
$$x = 4 \quad \text{or} \quad x = 5$$

Both values produce true statements.
The solution set is $\{4, 5\}$

9. For a risk of 7%, let $R = 7$ in
$$R = 6e^{12.77x}$$
$$6e^{12.77x} = 7$$
$$e^{12.77x} = \frac{7}{6}$$
$$\ln e^{12.77x} = \ln\left(\frac{7}{6}\right)$$
$$12.77x = \ln\left(\frac{7}{6}\right)$$
$$x = \frac{\ln\left(\frac{7}{6}\right)}{12.77} \approx 0.01$$

For a blood alcohol concentration of 0.01, the risk of a car accident is 7%.

10.
$$A = P\left(1 + \frac{r}{n}\right)^{nt}$$
$$3600 = 1000\left(1 + \frac{0.08}{4}\right)^{4t}$$
$$1000\left(1 - \frac{0.08}{4}\right)^{4t} = 3600$$
$$1000(1+0.02)^{4t} = 3600$$
$$1000(1.02)^{4t} = 3600$$
$$(1.02)^{4t} = \ln 3.6$$
$$4t \ln(1.02) = \ln 3.6$$
$$t = \frac{\ln 3.6}{4 \ln 1.02}$$
$$\approx 16.2$$

After approximately 16.2 years, the $1000 will grow to an accumulated value of $3600.

11. $f(x) = 34.1 \ln x + 117.7$

Solve equation when $f(x) = 210$.
$$34.1 \ln x + 117.7 = 210$$
$$34.1 \ln x = 92.3$$
$$\ln x = \frac{92.3}{34.1}$$
$$\log_e x = \frac{92.3}{34.1}$$
$$e^{\frac{92.3}{34.1}} = x$$
$$15 \approx x$$

Approximately 15 years after 1999, in the year 2014, there will be 210 million Internet users in the United States.

Exercise Set 3.4

1. $2^x = 64$

$2^x = 2^6$

$x = 6$

The solution is 6, and the solution set is $\{6\}$.

3. $5^x = 125$

$5^x = 5^3$

$x = 3$

The solution is 3, and the solution set is $\{3\}$.

5. $2^{2x-1} = 32$

$2^{2x-1} = 2^5$

$2x - 1 = 5$

$2x = 6$

$x = 3$

The solution is 3, and the solution set is $\{3\}$.

7. $4^{2x-1} = 64$

$4^{2x-1} = 4^3$

$2x - 1 = 3$

$2x = 4$

$x = 2$

The solution is 2, and the solution set is $\{2\}$.

9. $32^x = 8$

$\left(2^5\right)^x = 2^3$

$2^{5x} = 2^3$

$5x = 3$

$x = \dfrac{3}{5}$

The solution is $\dfrac{3}{5}$, and the solution set is $\left\{\dfrac{3}{5}\right\}$.

11. $9^x = 27$

$\left(3^2\right)^x = 3^3$

$3^{2x} = 3^3$

$2x = 3$

$x = \dfrac{3}{2}$

The solution is $\dfrac{3}{2}$, and the solution set is $\left\{\dfrac{3}{2}\right\}$.

13. $3^{1-x} = \dfrac{1}{27}$

$3^{1-x} = \dfrac{1}{3^3}$

$3^{1-x} = 3^{-3}$

$1 - x = -3$

$-x = -4$

$x = 4$

The solution set is $\{4\}$.

15. $6^{\frac{x-3}{4}} = \sqrt{6}$

$6^{\frac{x-3}{4}} = 6^{\frac{1}{2}}$

$\dfrac{x-3}{4} = \dfrac{1}{2}$

$2(x-3) = 4(1)$

$2x - 6 = 4$

$2x = 10$

$x = 5$

The solution is 5, and the solution set is $\{5\}$.

17. $4^x = \dfrac{1}{\sqrt{2}}$

$\left(2^2\right)^x = \dfrac{1}{2^{\frac{1}{2}}}$

$2^{2x} = 2^{-\frac{1}{2}}$

$2x = -\dfrac{1}{2}$

$x = \dfrac{1}{2}\left(-\dfrac{1}{2}\right) = -\dfrac{1}{4}$

The solution is $-\dfrac{1}{4}$, and the solution set is $\left\{-\dfrac{1}{4}\right\}$.

19. $8^{x+3} = 16^{x-1}$

$\left(2^3\right)^{x+3} = \left(2^4\right)^{x-1}$

$2^{3x+9} = 2^{4x-4}$

$3x + 9 = 4x - 4$

$13 = x$

The solution set is $\{13\}$.

21. $e^{x+1} = \dfrac{1}{e}$

$e^{x+1} = e^{-1}$

$x + 1 = -1$

$x = -2$

The solution set is $\{-2\}$.

23.
$$10^x = 3.91$$
$$\ln 10^x = \ln 3.91$$
$$x \ln 10 = \ln 3.91$$
$$x = \frac{\ln 3.91}{\ln 10} \approx 0.59$$

25.
$$e^x = 5.7$$
$$\ln e^x = 5.7$$
$$x = \ln 5.7 \approx 1.74$$

27.
$$5^x = 17$$
$$\ln 5^x = \ln 17$$
$$x \ln 5 = \ln 17$$
$$x = \frac{\ln 17}{\ln 5} \approx 1.76$$

29.
$$5e^x = 23$$
$$e^x = \frac{23}{5}$$
$$\ln e^x = \ln \frac{23}{5}$$
$$x = \ln \frac{23}{5} \approx 1.53$$

31.
$$3e^{5x} = 1977$$
$$e^{5x} = 659$$
$$\ln e^{5x} = \ln 659$$
$$x = \frac{\ln 659}{5} \approx 1.30$$

33.
$$e^{1-5x} = 793$$
$$\ln e^{1-5x} = \ln 793$$
$$(1-5x)(\ln e) = \ln 793$$
$$1 - 5x = \ln 793$$
$$5x = 1 - \ln 793$$
$$x = \frac{1 - \ln 793}{5} \approx -1.14$$

35.
$$e^{5x-3} - 2 = 10,476$$
$$e^{5x-3} = 10,478$$
$$\ln e^{5x-3} = \ln 10,478$$
$$(5x-3)\ln e = \ln 10,478$$
$$5x - 3 = \ln 10,478$$
$$5x = \ln 10,478 + 3$$
$$x = \frac{\ln 10,478 + 3}{5} \approx 2.45$$

37.
$$7^{x+2} = 410$$
$$\ln 7^{x+2} = \ln 410$$
$$(x+2)\ln 7 = \ln 410$$
$$x + 2 = \frac{\ln 410}{\ln 7}$$
$$x = \frac{\ln 410}{\ln 7} - 2 \approx 1.09$$

39.
$$7^{0.3x} = 813$$
$$\ln 7^{0.3x} = \ln 813$$
$$0.3x \ln 7 = \ln 813$$
$$x = \frac{\ln 813}{0.3 \ln 7} \approx 11.48$$

41.
$$5^{2x+3} = 3^{x-1}$$
$$\ln 5^{2x+3} = \ln 3^{x-1}$$
$$(2x+3)\ln 5 = (x-1)\ln 3$$
$$2x \ln 5 + 3 \ln 5 = x \ln 3 - \ln 3$$
$$3 \ln 5 + \ln 3 = x \ln 3 - 2x \ln 5$$
$$3 \ln 5 + \ln 3 = x(\ln 3 - 2 \ln 5)$$
$$\frac{3 \ln 5 + \ln 3}{\ln 3 - 2 \ln 5} = x$$
$$-2.80 \approx x$$

43.
$$e^{2x} - 3e^x + 2 = 0$$
$$\left(e^x - 2\right)\left(e^x - 1\right) = 0$$
$$e^x - 2 = 0 \quad \text{or} \quad e^x - 1 = 0$$
$$e^x = 2 \qquad\qquad e^x = 1$$
$$\ln e^x = \ln 2 \qquad \ln e^x = \ln 1$$
$$x = \ln 2 \qquad\qquad x = 0$$
The solution set is {0, ln 2). The solutions are 0 and (approximately) 0.69.

45.
$$e^{4x} + 5e^{2x} - 24 = 0$$
$$\left(e^{2x} + 8\right)\left(e^{2x} - 3\right) = 0$$
$$e^{2x} + 8 = 0 \qquad\qquad \text{or} \quad e^{2x} - 3 = 0$$
$$e^{2x} = -8 \qquad\qquad e^{2x} = 3$$
$$\ln e^{2x} = \ln(-8) \qquad \ln e^{2x} = \ln 3$$
$$2x = \ln(-8) \qquad\quad 2x = \ln 3$$
$$\ln(-8) \text{ does not exist} \qquad x = \frac{\ln 3}{2}$$
$$x = \frac{\ln 3}{2} \approx 0.55$$

47.
$$3^{2x} + 3^x - 2 = 0$$
$$(3^x + 2)(3^x - 1) = 0$$

$3^x + 2 = 0$	$3^x - 1 = 0$
$3^x = -2$	$3^x = 1$
$\log 3^x = \log(-2)$	$\log 3^x = \log 1$
can't do	$x \log 3 = 0$

$$x = \frac{0}{\log 3}$$
$$x = 0$$

The solution set is $\{0\}$.

49.
$$\log_3 x = 4$$
$$3^4 = x$$
$$81 = x$$

51.
$$\ln x = 2$$
$$e^2 = x$$
$$7.39 \approx x$$

53.
$$\log_4(x + 5) = 3$$
$$4^3 = x + 5$$
$$59 = x$$

55.
$$\log_3(x - 4) = -3$$
$$3^{-3} = x - 4$$
$$\frac{1}{27} = x - 4$$
$$4\frac{1}{27} = x$$
$$4.04 \approx x$$

57.
$$\log_4(3x + 2) = 3$$
$$4^3 = 3x + 2$$
$$64 = 3x + 2$$
$$62 = 3x$$
$$\frac{62}{3} = x$$
$$20.67 \approx x$$

59.
$$5 \ln 2x = 20$$
$$\ln 2x = 4$$
$$e^{\ln 2x} = e^4$$
$$2x = e^4$$
$$x = \frac{e^4}{2} \approx 27.30$$

61.
$$6 + 2 \ln x = 5$$
$$2 \ln x = -1$$
$$\ln x = -\frac{1}{2}$$
$$e^{\ln x} = e^{-1/2}$$
$$x = e^{-1/2} \approx 0.61$$

63.
$$\ln \sqrt{x + 3} = 1$$
$$e^{\ln \sqrt{x+3}} = e^1$$
$$\sqrt{x + 3} = e$$
$$x + 3 = e^2$$
$$x = e^2 - 3 \approx 4.39$$

65.
$$\log_5 x + \log_5(4x - 1) = 1$$
$$\log_5(4x^2 - x) = 1$$
$$4x^2 - x = 5$$
$$4x^2 - x - 5 = 0$$
$$(4x - 5)(x + 1) = 0$$
$$x = \frac{5}{4} \text{ or } x = -1$$

$x = -1$ does not check because $\log_5(-1)$ does not exist.

The solution set is $\left\{\dfrac{5}{4}\right\}$.

67.
$$\log_3(x - 5) + \log_3(x + 3) = 2$$
$$\log_3\left[(x - 5)(x + 3)\right] = 2$$
$$(x - 5)(x + 3) = 3^2$$
$$x^2 - 2x - 15 = 9$$
$$x^2 - 2x - 24 = 0$$
$$(x - 6)(x + 4) = 0$$
$$x = 6 \text{ or } x = -4$$

$x = -4$ does not check because $\log_3(-4 - 5)$ does not exist. The solution set is $\{6\}$.

69. $\log_2 (x+2) - \log_2 (x-5) = 3$

$$\log_2 \left(\frac{x+2}{x-5}\right) = 3$$

$$\frac{x+2}{x-5} = 2^3$$

$$\frac{x+2}{x-5} = 8$$

$$x+2 = 8(x-5)$$

$$x+2 = 8x - 40$$

$$7x = 42$$

$$x = 6$$

71. $2\log_3 (x+4) = \log_3 9 + 2$

$$2\log_3 (x+4) = 2 + 2$$

$$2\log_3 (x+4) = 4$$

$$\log_3 (x+4) = 2$$

$$3^2 = x+4$$

$$9 = x+4$$

$$5 = x$$

73. $\log_2 (x-6) + \log_2 (x-4) - \log_2 x = 2$

$$\log_2 \frac{(x-6)(x-4)}{x} = 2$$

$$\frac{(x-6)(x-4)}{x} = 2^2$$

$$x^2 - 10x + 24 = 4x$$

$$x^2 - 14x + 24 = 0$$

$$(x-12)(x-2) = 0$$

$$x - 12 = 0 \qquad x - 2 = 0$$

$$x = 12 \qquad x = 2$$

The solution set is {12} since $\log_2 (2-6) = \log_2 (-4)$ is not possible.

75. $\log(x+4) = \log x + \log 4$

$$\log(x+4) = \log 4x$$

$$x + 4 = 4x$$

$$4 = 3x$$

$$x = \frac{4}{3}$$

This value is rejected. The solution set is $\left\{\frac{4}{3}\right\}$.

77. $\log(3x-3) = \log(x+1) + \log 4$

$$\log(3x-3) = \log(4x+4)$$

$$3x - 3 = 4x + 4$$

$$-7 = x$$

This value is rejected. The solution set is $\{\ \}$.

79. $2\log x = \log 25$

$$\log x^2 = \log 25$$

$$x^2 = 25$$

$$x = \pm 5$$

-5 is rejected. The solution set is {5}.

81. $\log(x+4) - \log 2 = \log(5x+1)$

$$\log \frac{x+4}{2} = \log(5x+1)$$

$$\frac{x+4}{2} = 5x + 1$$

$$x + 4 = 10x + 2$$

$$-9x = -2$$

$$x = \frac{2}{9}$$

$$x \approx 0.22$$

83. $2\log x - \log 7 = \log 112$

$$\log x^2 - \log 7 = \log 112$$

$$\log \frac{x^2}{7} = \log 112$$

$$\frac{x^2}{7} = 112$$

$$x^2 = 784$$

$$x = \pm 28$$

-28 is rejected. The solution set is {28}.

85. $\log x + \log(x+3) = \log 10$

$$\log(x^2 + 3x) = \log 10$$

$$x^2 + 3x = 10$$

$$x^2 + 3x - 10 = 0$$

$$(x+5)(x-2) = 0$$

$$x = -5 \ \text{ or } \ x = 2$$

-5 is rejected. The solution set is {2}.

87. $\ln(x-4)+\ln(x+1)=\ln(x-8)$

$\ln(x^2-3x-4)=\ln(x-8)$

$x^2-3x-4=x-8$

$x^2-4x+4=0$

$(x-2)(x-2)=0$

$x=2$

2 is rejected. The solution set is $\{\ \}$.

89. $\ln(x-2)-\ln(x+3)=\ln(x-1)-\ln(x+7)$

$\ln\dfrac{x-2}{x+3}=\ln\dfrac{x-1}{x+7}$

$\dfrac{x-2}{x+3}=\dfrac{x-1}{x+7}$

$(x-2)(x+7)=(x+3)(x-1)$

$x^2+5x-14=x^2+2x-3$

$3x=11$

$x=\dfrac{11}{3}$

$x\approx 3.67$

91. $5^{2x}\cdot 5^{4x}=125$

$5^{2x+4x}=5^3$

$5^{6x}=5^3$

$6x=3$

$x=\dfrac{1}{2}$

93. $2|\ln x|-6=0$

$2|\ln x|=6$

$|\ln x|=3$

$\ln x=3$ or $\ln x=-3$

$x=e^3$ $x=e^{-3}$

$x\approx 20.09$ $x\approx 0.05$

95. $3^{x^2}=45$

$\ln 3^{x^2}=\ln 45$

$x^2\ln 3=\ln 45$

$x^2=\dfrac{\ln 45}{\ln 3}$

$x=\pm\sqrt{\dfrac{\ln 45}{\ln 3}}\approx \pm 1.86$

97. $\ln(2x+1)+\ln(x-3)-2\ln x=0$

$\ln(2x+1)+\ln(x-3)-\ln x^2=0$

$\ln\dfrac{(2x+1)(x-3)}{x^2}=0$

$\dfrac{(2x+1)(x-3)}{x^2}=e^0$

$\dfrac{2x^2-5x-3}{x^2}=1$

$2x^2-5x-3=x^2$

$x^2-5x-3=0$

$x=\dfrac{-b\pm\sqrt{b^2-4ac}}{2a}$

$x=\dfrac{-(-5)\pm\sqrt{(-5)^2-4(1)(-3)}}{2(1)}$

$x=\dfrac{5\pm\sqrt{37}}{2}$

$x=\dfrac{5+\sqrt{37}}{2}\approx 5.54$

$x=\dfrac{5-\sqrt{37}}{2}\approx -0.54$ (rejected)

The solution set is $\left\{\dfrac{5+\sqrt{37}}{2}\right\}$.

99. $5^{x^2-12}=25^{2x}$

$5^{x^2-12}=\left(5^2\right)^{2x}$

$5^{x^2-12}=5^{4x}$

$x^2-12=4x$

$x^2-4x-12=0$

$(x-6)(x+2)=0$

Apply the zero product property:

$x-6=0$ or $x+2=0$

$x=6$ $x=-2$

The solutions are -2 and 6, and the solution set is $\{-2,\ 6\}$.

101. $25 = 6e^{12.77x}$

$\dfrac{25}{6} = e^{12.77x}$

$\ln\dfrac{25}{6} = \ln e^{12.77x}$

$\ln\dfrac{25}{6} = 12.77x$

$\dfrac{\ln\dfrac{25}{6}}{12.77} = x$

$0.112 \approx x$

A blood alcohol level of about 0.11 corresponds to a 25% risk of a car accident.

103. a. $A = 18.9e^{0.005(0)}$

$A = 18.9$ million

b. $19.6 = 18.9e^{0.0055t}$

$\dfrac{19.6}{18.9} = e^{0.0055t}$

$\ln\dfrac{19.6}{18.9} = \ln e^{0.0055t}$

$\ln\dfrac{19.6}{18.9} = 0.0055t$

$\dfrac{\ln\dfrac{19.6}{18.9}}{0.0055} = t$

$6.6 \approx t$

In 2007 the population of New York will reach 19.6 million.

105. $20,000 = 12,500\left(1 + \dfrac{0.0575}{4}\right)^{4t}$

$12,500(1.014375)^{4t} = 20,000$

$(1.014375)^{4t} = 1.6$

$\ln(1.014375)^{4t} = \ln 1.6$

$4t\ln(1.014375) = \ln 1.6$

$t = \dfrac{\ln 1.6}{4\ln 1.014375} \approx 8.2$

8.2 years

107. $1400 = 1000\left(1 + \dfrac{r}{360}\right)^{360\cdot 2}$

$\left(1 + \dfrac{r}{360}\right)^{720} = 1.4$

$\ln\left(1 + \dfrac{r}{360}\right)^{720} = \ln 1.4$

$720\ln\left(1 + \dfrac{r}{360}\right) = \ln 1.4$

$\ln\left(1 + \dfrac{r}{360}\right) = \dfrac{\ln 1.4}{720}$

$e^{\ln(1 + r/360)} = e^{(\ln 1.4)/720}$

$1 + \dfrac{r}{360} = e^{(\ln 1.4)/720} - 1$

$r = 360(e^{(\ln 1.4)/720}) - 1$

≈ 0.168

16.8%

109. accumulated amount = 2(8000) = 16,000

$16,000 = 8000e^{0.08t}$

$e^{0.08t} = 2$

$\ln e^{0.08t} = \ln 2$

$0.08t = \ln 2$

$t = \dfrac{\ln 2}{0.08}$

$t \approx 8.7$

The amount would double in 8.7 years.

111. accumulated amount = 3(2350) = 7050

$7050 = 2350e^{r \cdot 7}$

$e^{7r} = 3$

$\ln e^{7r} = \ln 3$

$7r = \ln 3$

$r = \dfrac{\ln 3}{7} \approx 0.157$

15.7%

113. a. $f(x) = 13.4 + 46.3 \ln x$

$f(3) = 13.4 + 46.3 \ln 3 \approx 64.3$

The function result of 64.3% models the actual value of 63% very well.

b. $f(x) = 13.4 + 46.3 \ln x$

$96 = 13.4 + 46.3 \ln x$

$82.6 = 46.3 \ln x$

$\dfrac{82.6}{46.3} = \ln x$

$x = e^{\frac{82.6}{46.3}}$

$x \approx 6$

The function predicts that 96% of email will be spam 6 years after 2000, or 2006.

115. $30 \log_2 x = 45$

$\log_2 x = 1.5$

$x = 2^{1.5} \approx 2.8$

Only half the students recall the important features of the lecture after 2.8 days. (2.8, 50)

117. $2.4 = -\log x$

$\log x = -2.4$

$x = 10^{-2.4} \approx 0.004$

The hydrogen ion concentration was $10^{-2.4}$, approximately 0.004 moles per liter.

123.

The intersection point is (2, 8).
Verify: $x = 2$

$2^{x+1} = 8$

$2^{2+1} = 2$

$2^3 = 8$

$8 = 8$

The solution set is {2}.

125.

The intersection point is (4, 2).
Verify: $x = 4$

$\log_3(4 \cdot 4 - 7) = 2$

$\log_3 9 = 2$

$2 = 2$

The solution set is {4}.

127.

The intersection point is (2, 1).
Verify: $x = 2$

$\log(2 + 3) + \log 2 = 1$

$\log 5 + \log 2 = 1$

$\log(5 \cdot 2) = 1$

$\log 10 = 1$

$1 = 1$

The solution set is {2}.

129.

There are 2 points of intersection, approximately
$(-1.391606, 0.21678798)$ and
$(1.6855579, 6.3711158)$.
Verify $x \approx -1.391606$

$3^x = 2x + 3$

$3^{-1.391606} \approx 2(-1.391606) + 3$

$0.2167879803 \approx 0.216788$

Verify $x \approx 1.6855579$

$3^x = 2x + 3$

$3^{1.6855579} \approx 2(1.6855579) + 3$

$6.37111582 \approx 6.371158$

The solution set is $\{-1.391606, 1.6855579\}$.

131.

As the distance from the eye increases, barometric air pressure increases, leveling off at about 30 inches of mercury.

133.

When $P = 70$, $t \approx 7.9$, so it will take about 7.9 minutes.
Verify:
$$70 = 45e^{-0.092(7.9)}$$

$$70 \approx 70.10076749$$
The runner's pulse will be 70 beats per minute after about 7.9 minutes.

135. a. False; $\log(x+3) = 2$ means $x+3 = 10^2$

  b. False; $\log(7x+3) - \log(2x+5) = 4$ means
  $\log \dfrac{7x+3}{2x+5} = 4$ which means $\dfrac{7x+3}{2x+5} = 10^4$

  c. True; $x = \dfrac{1}{k} \ln y$
  $kx = \ln y$
  $e^{kx} = e^{\ln y}$
  $e^{kx} = y$

  d. False; The equation $x^{10} = 5.71$ has no variable in an exponent so is not an exponential equation.

  (c) is true

137.
$$(\ln x)^2 = \ln x^2$$
$$(\ln x)^2 = 2 \ln x$$
$$(\ln x)^2 - 2 \ln x = 0$$
$$\ln x (\ln x - 2) = 0$$
$$\ln x = 2 \qquad \ln x = 0$$
$$e^{\ln x} = e^2 \quad \text{or} \qquad x = 1$$
$$x = e^2$$
The solution set is $\left\{ 1, e^2 \right\}$.

Check with graphing utility:

There are two points of intersection: (1, 0) and approximately (7.3890561, 4). Since $e^2 \approx 7.3890566099$, the graph verifies $x = 1$ and $x = e^2$, so the solution set is $\{1, e^2\}$ as determined algebraically.

139. $\ln(\ln x) = 0$
$e^{\ln(\ln x)} = e^0$
$\ln x = 1$
$e^{\ln x} = e^1$
$x = e$
The solution set is $\{e\}$.

The graph of $\ln(\ln(x))$ crosses the graph $y = 0$ at approximately 2.718.

Section 3.5

Check Point Exercises

1. **a.** Use the exponential growth model
$A = A_0 e^{kt}$ with 1990 corresponding to $t = 0$
when the population was 643 million:
$A = 643 e^{kt}$
Substitute $t = 2000 - 1990 = 10$ when the
population was 813 million, so $A = 813$, to
find k.

$$813 = 643 e^{k10}$$

$$\frac{813}{643} = e^{k10}$$

$$\ln \frac{813}{643} = \ln e^{k10}$$

$$\ln \frac{813}{643} = 10k$$

$$\frac{\ln \frac{813}{643}}{10} = k$$

$$0.023 \approx k$$

So the exponential growth function is
$A = 643 e^{0.023t}$

b. Substitute 2000 for A in the model from
part (a) and solve for t.

$$2000 = 643 e^{0.023t}$$

$$\frac{2000}{643} = e^{0.023t}$$

$$\ln \frac{2000}{643} = \ln e^{0.023t}$$

$$\ln \frac{2000}{643} = 0.023t$$

$$\frac{\ln \frac{2000}{643}}{0.023} = t$$

$$49 \approx t$$

The population will reach 2000 million, or
two billion, about 49 years after 1990, in
2039.

2. **a.** In the exponential decay model $A = A_0 e^{kt}$,
substitute $\frac{A_0}{2}$ for A since the amount present
after 28 years is half the original amount.

$$\frac{A_0}{2} = A_0 e^{k \cdot 28}$$

$$e^{28k} = \frac{1}{2}$$

$$\ln e^{28k} = \ln \frac{1}{2}$$

$$28k = \ln \frac{1}{2}$$

$$k = \frac{\ln^{1/2}}{28} \approx -0.0248$$

So the exponential decay model is
$A = A_0 e^{-0.0248t}$

b. Substitute 60 for A_0 and 10 for A in the
model from part (a) and solve for t.

$$10 = 60 e^{-0.0248t}$$

$$e^{-0.0248t} = \frac{1}{6}$$

$$\ln e^{-0.0248t} = \ln \frac{1}{6}$$

$$-0.0248t = \ln \frac{1}{6}$$

$$t = \frac{\ln \frac{1}{6}}{-0.0248} \approx 72$$

The strontium-90 will decay to a level of
10 grams about 72 years after the accident.

3. **a.** The time prior to learning trials
corresponds to $t = 0$.

$$f(0) = \frac{0.8}{1 + e^{-0.2(0)}} = 0.4$$

The proportion of correct responses prior
to learning trials was 0.4.

b. Substitute 10 for t in the model:

$$f(10) = \frac{0.8}{1 + e^{-0.2(10)}} \approx 0.7$$

The proportion of correct responses after
10 learning trials was 0.7.

c. In the logistic growth model,

$f(t) = \frac{c}{1 + ae^{-bt}}$, the constant c represents

the limiting size that $f(t)$ can attain. The
limiting size of the proportion of correct
responses as continued learning trials take
place is 0.8.

4. a.

$$T = C + (T_o - C)e^{kt}$$
$$80 = 30 + (100 - 30)e^{k5}$$
$$80 = 30 + 70e^{5k}$$
$$50 = 70e^{5k}$$
$$\frac{5}{7} = e^{5k}$$
$$\ln\frac{5}{7} = \ln e^{5k}$$
$$\ln\frac{5}{7} = 5k$$
$$\frac{\ln\frac{5}{7}}{5} = k$$
$$-0.0673 \approx k$$
$$T = 30 + 70e^{-0.0673t}$$

b. $T = 30 + 70e^{-0.0673(20)} \approx 48°$
After 20 minutes, the temperature will be 48°.

c.
$$35 = 30 + 70e^{-0.0673t}$$
$$5 = 70e^{-0.0673t}$$
$$\frac{1}{14} = e^{-0.0673t}$$
$$\ln\frac{1}{14} = \ln e^{-0.0673t}$$
$$\ln\frac{1}{14} = -0.0673t$$
$$\frac{\ln\frac{1}{14}}{-0.0673} = t$$
$$39 \approx t$$
The temperature will reach 35° after 39 min.

5. Scatter plot:

Because the data in the scatter plot increase rapidly at first and then begin to level off, the shape suggests that a logarithmic function is a good choice for modeling the data.

6. Scatter plot:

Because the data in the scatter plot appear to increase more and more rapidly, the shape suggests that an exponential function is a good choice for modeling the data.

7. $y = ab^x$ is equivalent to $y = ae^{(\ln b)x}$.
For $y = 4(7.8)^x$, $a = 4$, $b = 7.8$.
Thus, $y = 4(7.8)^x$ is equivalent to $y = 4e^{(\ln 7.8)x}$ in terms of a natural logarithm. Rounded to three decimal places, the model is approximately equivalent to $y = 4e^{2.054x}$.

Exercise Set 3.5

1. Since 2003 is 0 years after 2003, find A when $t = 0$:
$$A = 127.2e^{0.001t}$$
$$A = 127.2e^{0.001(0)}$$
$$A = 127.2e^0$$
$$A = 127.2(1)$$
$$A = 127.2$$
In 2003, the population was 127.2 million.

3. Iraq has the greatest growth rate at 2.8% per year.

5. Substitute $A = 1238$ into the model for India and solve for t:

$$1238 = 1049.7e^{0.015t}$$

$$\frac{1238}{1049.7} = e^{0.015t}$$

$$\ln\frac{1238}{1049.7} = \ln e^{0.015t}$$

$$\ln\frac{1238}{1049.7} = 0.015t$$

$$t = \frac{\ln\dfrac{1238}{1049.7}}{0.015} \approx 11$$

Now, $2003 + 11 = 2014$. The population of India will be 1238 million in approximately the year 2014.

7. **a.** $A_0 = 6.04$. Since 2050 is 50 years after 2000, when $t = 50$, $A = 10$.

$$A = A_0e^{kt}$$

$$10 = 6.04e^{k(50)}$$

$$\frac{10}{6.04} = e^{50k}$$

$$\ln\left(\frac{10}{6.04}\right) = \ln e^{50k}$$

$$\ln\left(\frac{10}{6.04}\right) = 50k$$

$$k = \frac{\ln\left(\dfrac{10}{6.04}\right)}{50} \approx 0.01$$

Thus, the growth function is $A = 6.04e^{0.01t}$.

b.
$$9 = 6.04e^{0.01t}$$

$$\frac{9}{6.04} = e^{0.01t}$$

$$\ln\left(\frac{9}{6.04}\right) = \ln e^{0.01t}$$

$$\ln\left(\frac{9}{6.04}\right) = 0.01t$$

$$t = \frac{\ln\left(\dfrac{9}{6.04}\right)}{0.01} \approx 40$$

Now, $2000 + 40 = 2040$, so the population will be 9 million is approximately the year 2040.

9.
$$A = 16e^{-0.000121t}$$

$$A = 16e^{-0.000121(5715)}$$

$$A = 16e^{-0.691515}$$

$$A \approx 8.01$$

Approximately 8 grams of carbon-14 will be present in 5715 years.

11. After 10 seconds, there will be $16 \cdot \frac{1}{2} = 8$ grams present. After 20 seconds, there will be $8 \cdot \frac{1}{2} = 4$ grams present. After 30 seconds, there will be $4 \cdot \frac{1}{2} = 2$ grams present. After 40 seconds, there will be $2 \cdot \frac{1}{2} = 1$ grams present. After 50 seconds, there will be $1 \cdot \frac{1}{2} = \frac{1}{2}$ gram present.

13.
$$A = A_0e^{-0.000121t}$$

$$15 = 100e^{-0.000121t}$$

$$\frac{15}{100} = e^{-0.000121t}$$

$$\ln 0.15 = \ln e^{-0.000121t}$$

$$\ln 0.15 = -0.000121t$$

$$t = \frac{\ln 0.15}{-0.000121} \approx 15{,}679$$

The paintings are approximately 15,679 years old.

15. **a.**
$$\frac{1}{2} = 1e^{k1.31}$$

$$\ln\frac{1}{2} = \ln e^{1.31k}$$

$$\ln\frac{1}{2} = 1.31k$$

$$k = \frac{\ln\dfrac{1}{2}}{1.31} \approx -0.52912$$

The exponential model is given by $A = A_0e^{-0.52912t}$.

b.
$$A = A_0 e^{-0.52912t}$$
$$0.945 A_0 = A_0 e^{-0.52912t}$$
$$0.945 = e^{-0.52912t}$$
$$\ln 0.945 = \ln e^{-0.52912t}$$
$$\ln 0.945 = -0.52912t$$
$$t = \frac{\ln 0.945}{-0.52912} \approx 0.1069$$

The age of the dinosaur ones is approximately 0.1069 billion or 106,900,000 years old.

17.
$$2A_0 = A_0 e^{kt}$$
$$2 = e^{kt}$$
$$\ln 2 = \ln e^{kt}$$
$$\ln 2 = kt$$
$$t = \frac{\ln 2}{k}$$

The population will double in $t = \dfrac{\ln 2}{k}$ years.

19. $A = e^{0.007t}$

a. $k = 0.007$, so New Zealand's growth rate is 0.7%.

b.
$$t = \frac{\ln 2}{k}$$
$$t = \frac{\ln 2}{0.007} \approx 99$$

New Zealand's population will double in approximately 99 years.

21. a. When the epidemic began, $t = 0$.
$$f(0) = \frac{100,000}{1 + 5000e^0} \approx 20$$
Twenty people became ill when the epidemic began.

b. $f(4) = \dfrac{100,000}{1 + 5,000e^{-4}} \approx 1080$

About 1080 people were ill at the end of the fourth week.

c. In the logistic growth model,
$$f(t) = \frac{c}{1 + ae^{-bt}},$$
the constant c represents the limiting size that $f(t)$ can attain. The limiting size of the population that becomes ill is 100,000 people.

23.
$$f(x) = \frac{12.85}{1 + 4.21e^{-0.026(x)}}$$
$$f(54) = \frac{12.85}{1 + 4.21e^{-0.026(54)}} \approx 6.3$$
The function models the data very well.

25.
$$f(x) = \frac{12.85}{1 + 4.21e^{-0.026(x)}}$$
$$8 = \frac{12.85}{1 + 4.21e^{-0.026(x)}}$$
$$8\left(1 + 4.21e^{-0.026(x)}\right) = 12.85$$
$$8 + 33.68e^{-0.026(x)} = 12.85$$
$$33.68e^{-0.026(x)} = 4.85$$
$$e^{-0.026(x)} = \frac{4.85}{33.68}$$
$$\ln e^{-0.026(x)} = \ln \frac{4.85}{33.68}$$
$$-0.026x = \ln \frac{4.85}{33.68}$$
$$x = \frac{\ln \frac{4.85}{33.68}}{-0.026}$$
$$x \approx 75$$

The world population will reach 8 billion 75 years after 1949, or 2024.

27. $P(20) = \dfrac{90}{1 + 271e^{-0.122(20)}} \approx 3.7$

The probability that a 20-year-old has some coronary heart disease is about 3.7%.

29.
$$0.5 = \frac{0.9}{1 + 271e^{-0.122t}}$$
$$0.5\left(1 + 271e^{-0.122t}\right) = 0.9$$
$$1 + 271e^{-0.122t} = 1.8$$
$$271e^{-0.122t} = 0.8$$
$$e^{-0.122t} = \frac{0.8}{271}$$
$$\ln e^{-0.122t} = \ln \frac{0.8}{271}$$
$$-0.122t = \ln \frac{0.8}{271}$$
$$t = \frac{\ln \frac{0.8}{271}}{-0.122} \approx 48$$

The probability of some coronary heart disease is 0.5 at about age 48.

31. a.
$$55 = 45 + (70 - 45)e^{k10}$$
$$10 = 25e^{10k}$$
$$\frac{2}{5} = e^{10k}$$
$$\ln\frac{2}{5} = \ln e^{10k}$$
$$\ln\frac{2}{5} = 10k$$
$$\frac{\ln\frac{2}{5}}{10} = k$$
$$-0.0916 \approx k$$
$$T = 45 + 25e^{-0.0916t}$$

b. $T = 45 + 25e^{-0.0916(15)} \approx 51°$

After 15 minutes, the temperature will be 51°.

c.
$$50 = 45 + 25e^{-0.0916t}$$
$$5 = 25e^{-0.0916t}$$
$$\frac{1}{5} = e^{-0.0916t}$$
$$\ln\frac{1}{5} = \ln e^{-0.0916t}$$
$$\ln\frac{1}{5} = -0.0916t$$
$$\frac{\ln\frac{1}{5}}{-0.0916} = t$$
$$18 \approx t$$

The temperature will reach 50° after 18 min.

33.
$$T = C + (T_o - C)e^{kt}$$
$$38 = 75 + (28 - 75)e^{k10}$$
$$-37 = -47e^{10k}$$
$$\frac{-37}{-47} = e^{10k}$$
$$\ln\frac{37}{47} = \ln e^{10k}$$
$$\ln\frac{37}{47} = 10k$$
$$\frac{\ln\frac{37}{47}}{10} = k$$
$$-0.0239 \approx k$$
$$T = 75 - 47e^{-0.0239t}$$

$$50 = 75 - 47e^{-0.0239t}$$
$$-25 = -47e^{-0.0239t}$$
$$\frac{-25}{-47} = e^{-0.0239t}$$
$$\ln\frac{25}{47} = \ln e^{-0.0239t}$$
$$\ln\frac{25}{47} = -0.0239t$$
$$\frac{\ln\frac{17}{47}}{-0.0239} = t$$
$$26 = t$$

The temperature will reach 50° after 26 min.

35. a.

b. An exponential function appears to be the best choice for modeling the data.

37. a.

b. A linear function appear to be the best choice for modeling the data.

39. a.

b. An exponential function appears to be the best choice for modeling the data.

41. $y = 100(4.6)^x$ is equivalent to

$y = 100e^{(\ln 4.6)x}$;

Using $\ln 4.6 \approx 1.526$,

$y = 100e^{1.526x}$.

43. $y = 2.5(0.7)^x$ is equivalent to

$y = 2.5e^{(\ln 0.7)x}$;

Using $\ln 0.7 \approx -0.357$,

$y = 2.5e^{-0.357x}$.

For Exercises 55. – 57, enter the data in L1 and L2:

55.

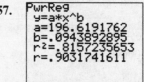

The logarithmic model is

$y = 194.328 + 22.758 \ln x$. Since $r = 0.881$ is

fairly close to 1, the model fits the data okay, but not great.

57.

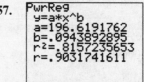

The power regression model is

$y = 196.619x^{0.094}$. Since $r = 0.903$, the model

fits the data fairly well.

59.

The probability of coronary heart disease starts increasing at a more rapid rate at about age 20. At about age 60, the rate of increase starts to slow down.

63.

$$827 = 70 + (85.6 - 70)e^{k30}$$

$$12.7 = 15.6e^{30k}$$

$$\frac{12.7}{15.6} = e^{30k}$$

$$\ln\frac{12.7}{15.6} = \ln e^{30k}$$

$$\ln\frac{12.7}{15.6} = 30k$$

$$\frac{\ln\dfrac{12.7}{15.6}}{30} = k$$

$$-0.0069 \approx k$$

$$85.6 = 70 + (98.6 - 70)e^{-0.0069t}$$

$$15.6 = 28.6e^{-0.0069t}$$

$$\frac{15.6}{28.6} = e^{-0.0069t}$$

$$\ln\frac{15.6}{28.6} = \ln e^{-0.0069t}$$

$$\ln\frac{15.6}{28.6} = -0.0069$$

$$\frac{\ln\dfrac{15.6}{28.6}}{-0.0069} = t$$

$$88 \approx t$$

The death occurred at 88 minutes before 9:30, or 8:22 am.

Chapter 3 Review Exercises

1. This is the graph of $f(x) = 4^x$ reflected about the y-axis, so the function is $g(x) = 4^{-x}$.

2. This is the graph of $f(x) = 4^x$ reflected about the x-axis and about the y-axis, so the function is $h(x) = -4^{-x}$.

3. This is the graph of $f(x) = 4^x$ reflected about the x-axis and about the y-axis then shifted upward 3 units, so the function is $r(x) = -4^{-x} + 3$.

4. This is the graph of $f(x) = 4^x$.

5. The graph of $g(x)$ shifts the graph of $f(x)$ one unit to the right.

$$f(x) = 2^x$$
$$g(x) = 2^{x-1}$$

Asymptote of f: $y = 0$

Asymptote of g: $y = 0$

Domain of f = Domain of g = $(-\infty, \infty)$

Range of f = Range of g = $(0, \infty)$

6. The graph of $g(x)$ shifts the graph of $f(x)$ one unit down.

$$f(x) = 3^x$$
$$g(x) = 3^x - 1$$

Asymptote of f: $y = 0$

Asymptote of g: $y = -1$

Domain of f = Domain of g = $(-\infty, \infty)$

Range of f = $(0, \infty)$

Range of g = $(-1, \infty)$

7. The graph of $g(x)$ reflects the graph of $f(x)$ about the y – axis.

$$f(x) = 3^x$$
$$g(x) = -3^x$$

Asymptote of f: $y = 0$

Asymptote of g: $y = 0$

Domain of f = Domain of g = $(-\infty, \infty)$

Range of f = $(0, \infty)$

Range of g = $(-\infty, 0)$

8. The graph of $g(x)$ reflects the graph of $f(x)$ about the x – axis.

    $$f(x) = \left(\frac{1}{2}\right)^x$$

    $$g(x) = \left(\frac{1}{2}\right)^{-x}$$

    Asymptote of f: $y = 0$

    Asymptote of g: $y = 0$

    Domain of $f =$ Domain of $g = (-\infty, \infty)$

    Range of $f =$ Range of $g = (0, \infty)$

9. The graph of $g(x)$ vertically stretches the graph of $f(x)$ by a factor of 2.

    $$f(x) = e^x$$
    $$g(x) = 2e^{x/2}$$

    Asymptote of f: $y = 0$

    Asymptote of g: $y = 0$

    Domain of $f =$ Domain of $g = (-\infty, \infty)$

    Range of $f =$ Range of $g = (0, \infty)$

10. 5.5% compounded semiannually:

    $$A = 5000\left(1 + \frac{0.055}{2}\right)^{2 \cdot 5} \approx 6558.26$$

    5.25% compounded monthly:

    $$A = 5000\left(1 + \frac{0.0525}{12}\right)^{12 \cdot 5} \approx 6497.16$$

    5.5% compounded semiannually yields the greater return.

11. 7% compounded monthly:

    $$A = 14,000\left(1 + \frac{0.07}{12}\right)^{12 \cdot 10} \approx 28,135.26$$

    6.85% compounded continuously:

    $$A = 14,000e^{0.0685(10)} \approx 27,772.81$$

    7% compounded monthly yields the greater return.

12. a. When first taken out of the microwave, the temperature of the coffee was 200°.

    b. After 20 minutes, the temperature of the coffee was about 120°.

    $$T = 70 + 130e^{-0.04855(20)} \approx 119.23$$

    Using a calculator, the temperature is about 119°.

    c. The coffee will cool to about 70°; The temperature of the room is 70°.

13. $49^{1/2} = 7$

14. $4^3 = x$

15. $3^y = 81$

16. $\log_6 216 = 3$

17. $\log_b 625 = 4$

18. $\log_{13} 874 = y$

19. $\log_4 64 = 3$ because $4^3 = 64$.

20. $\log_5 \dfrac{1}{25} = -2$ because $5^{-2} = \dfrac{1}{25}$.

21. $\log_3(-9)$ cannot be evaluated since $\log_b x$ is defined only for $x > 0$.

22. $\log_{16} 4 = \dfrac{1}{2}$ because $16^{1/2} = \sqrt{16} = 4$.

23. Because $\log_b b = 1$, we conclude $\log_{17} 17 = 1$.

24. Because $\log_b b^x = x$, we conclude $\log_3 3^8 = 8$.

25. Because $\ln e^x = x$, we conclude $\ln e^5 = 5$.

26. $\log_3 \dfrac{1}{\sqrt{3}} = \log_3 \dfrac{1}{3^{\frac{1}{2}}} = \log_3 3^{-\frac{1}{2}} = -\dfrac{1}{2}$

27. $\ln \dfrac{1}{e^2} = \ln e^{-2} = -2$

28. $\log \dfrac{1}{1000} = \log \dfrac{1}{10^3} = \log 10^{-3} = -3$

29. Because $\log_b = 1$,
we conclude $\log_8 8 = 1$.
So, $\log_3 (\log_8 8) = \log_3 1$.
Because $\log_b 1 = 0$
we conclude $\log_3 1 = 0$.
Therefore, $\log_3 (\log_8 8) = 0$.

30.

$f(x) = 2^x$
$g(x) = \log_2 x$

31.

$f(x) = \left(\dfrac{1}{3}\right)^x$

$g(x) = \log_{1/3} x$

32. This is the graph of $f(x) = \log x$ reflected about the y-axis, so the function is
$g(x) = \log(-x)$.

33. This is the graph of $f(x) = \log x$ shifted left 2 units, reflected about the y-axis, then shifted upward one unit, so the function is $r(x) = 1 + \log(2 - x)$.

34. This is the graph of $f(x) = \log x$ shifted left 2 units then reflected about the y-axis, so the function is $h(x) = \log(2 - x)$.

35. This is the graph of $f(x) = \log x$.

36.

$f(x) = \log_2 x$
$g(x) = \log_2(x - 2)$

x-intercept: $(3, 0)$
vertical asymptote: $x = 2$
Domain: $(2, \infty)$
Range: $(-\infty, \infty)$

37.

$f(x) = \log_2 x$
$h(x) = -1 + \log_2 x$

x-intercept: $(2, 0)$
vertical asymptote: $x = 0$
Domain: $(0, \infty)$
Range: $(-\infty, \infty)$

38.

$f(x) = \log_2 x$
$r(x) = \log_2(-x)$

x-intercept: $(-1, 0)$
vertical asymptote: $x = 0$
Domain: $(-\infty, 0)$
Range: $(-\infty, \infty)$

39. $x = -3$

$f(x) = \log x$

$g(x) = -\log (x + 3)$

Asymptote of f: $\quad x = 0$

Asymptote of g: $\quad x = -3$

Domain of $f = (0, \infty)$

Domain of $g = (-3, \infty)$

Range of f = Range of $g = (-\infty, \infty)$

40.

$f(x) = \ln x$

$g(x) = -\ln (2x)$

Asymptote of f: $\quad x = 0$

Asymptote of g: $\quad x = 0$

Domain of f = Domain of $g = (0, \infty)$

Range of f = Range of $g = (-\infty, \infty)$

41. The domain of f consists of all x for which $x + 5 > 0$.

Solving this inequality for x, we obtain $x > -5$.

Thus the domain of f is $(-5, \infty)$

42. The domain of f consists of all x for which $3 - x > 0$.

Solving this inequality for x, we obtain $x < 3$.

Thus, the domain of f is $(-\infty, 3)$.

43. The domain of f consists of all x for which $(x-1)^2 > 0$.

Solving this inequality for x, we obtain $x < 1$ or $x > 1$. Thus, the domain of f is $(-\infty, 1) \cup (1, \infty)$.

44. Because $\ln e^x = x$, we conclude $\ln e^{6x} = 6x$.

45. Because $e^{\ln x} = x$, we conclude $e^{\ln \sqrt{x}} = \sqrt{x}$.

46. Because $10^{\log x} = x$, we conclude $10^{\log 4x^2} = 4x^2$.

47. $R = \log \dfrac{1000 I_0}{I_0} = \log 1000 = 3$

The Richter scale magnitude is 3.0.

48. a. $f(0) = 76 - 18 \log(0+1) = 76$

When first given, the average score was 76.

b. $f(2) = 76 - 18 \log(2+1) \approx 67$

$f(4) = 76 - 18 \log(4+1) \approx 63$

$f(6) = 76 - 18 \log(6+1) \approx 61$

$f(8) = 76 - 18 \log(8+1) \approx 59$

$f(12) = 76 - 18 \log(12+1) \approx 56$

After 2, 4, 6, 8, and 12 months, the average scores are about 67, 63, 61, 59, and 56, respectively.

c.

Time (months)

Retention decreases as time passes.

49. $t = \dfrac{1}{0.06} \ln \left(\dfrac{12}{12-5} \right) \approx 8.98$

It will take about 9 weeks.

50. $\log_6 \left(36 x^3 \right)$

$= \log_6 36 + \log_6 x^3$

$= \log_6 36 + 3 \log_6 x$

$= 2 + 3 \log_6 x$

51. $\log_4 \dfrac{\sqrt{x}}{64} = \log_4 x^{1/2} - \log_4 64$

$= \dfrac{1}{2} \log_4 x - 3$

52. $\log_2 \dfrac{xy^2}{64} = \log_2 xy^2 - \log_2 64$

$$= \log_2 x + \log_2 y^2 - \log_2 64$$

$$= \log_2 x + 2\log_2 y - 6$$

53. $\ln \sqrt[3]{\dfrac{x}{e}}$

$$= \ln\left(\dfrac{x}{e}\right)^{1/3}$$

$$= \dfrac{1}{3}\left[\ln x - \ln e\right]$$

$$= \dfrac{1}{3}\ln x - \dfrac{1}{3}\ln e$$

$$= \dfrac{1}{3}\ln x - \dfrac{1}{3}$$

54. $\log_b 7 + \log_b 3$

$$= \log_b(7 \cdot 3)$$

$$= \log_b 21$$

55. $\log 3 - 3\log x$

$$= \log 3 - \log x^3$$

$$= \log \dfrac{3}{x^3}$$

56. $3\ln x + 4\ln y$

$$= \ln x^3 + \ln y^4$$

$$= \ln\left(x^3 y^4\right)$$

57. $\dfrac{1}{2}\ln x - \ln y$

$$= \ln x^{1/2} - \ln y$$

$$= \ln \dfrac{\sqrt{x}}{y}$$

58. $\log_6 72{,}348 = \dfrac{\log 72{,}348}{\log 6} \approx 6.2448$

59. $\log_4 0.863 = \dfrac{\ln 0.863}{\ln 4} \approx -0.1063$

60. true; $(\ln x)(\ln 1) = (\ln x)(0) = 0$

61. false; $\log(x+9) - \log(x+1) = \log \dfrac{(x+9)}{(x+1)}$

62. false; $\log_2 x^4 = 4\log_2 x$

63. true; $\ln e^x = x\ln e$

64. $2^{4x-2} = 64$

$$2^{4x-2} = 2^6$$

$$4x - 2 = 6$$

$$4x = 8$$

$$x = 2$$

65. $125^x = 25$

$$\left(5^3\right)^x = 5^2$$

$$5^{3x} = 5^2$$

$$3x = 2$$

$$x = \dfrac{2}{3}$$

66. $9^{x+2} = 27^{-x}$

$$\left(3^2\right)^{x+2} = \left(3^3\right)^{-x}$$

$$3^{2x+4} = 3^{-3x}$$

$$2x + 4 = -3x$$

$$5x = -4$$

$$x = -\dfrac{4}{5}$$

67. $8^x = 12{,}143$

$$\ln 8^x = \ln 12{,}143$$

$$x\ln 8 = \ln 12{,}143$$

$$x = \dfrac{\ln 12{,}143}{\ln 8} \approx 4.52$$

68. $9e^{5x} = 1269$

$$e^{5x} = 141$$

$$\ln e^{5x} = \ln 141$$

$$5x = \ln 141$$

$$x = \dfrac{\ln 141}{5} \approx 0.99$$

69. $e^{12-5x} - 7 = 123$

$$e^{12-5x} = 130$$

$$\ln e^{12-5x} = \ln 130$$

$$12 - 5x = \ln 130$$

$$5x = 12 - \ln 130$$

$$x = \dfrac{12 - \ln 130}{5} \approx 1.43$$

70.
$$5^{4x+2} = 37,500$$
$$\ln 5^{4x+2} = \ln 37,500$$
$$(4x+2)\ln 5 = \ln 37,500$$
$$4x\ln 5 + 2\ln 5 = \ln 37,500$$
$$4x\ln 5 = \ln 37,500 - 2\ln 5$$
$$x = \frac{\ln 37,500 - 2\ln 5}{4\ln 5} \approx 1.14$$

71.
$$3^{x+4} = 7^{2x-1}$$
$$\ln 3^{x+4} = \ln 7^{2x-1}$$
$$(x+4)\ln 3 = (2x-1)\ln 7$$
$$x\ln 3 + 4\ln 3 = 2x\ln 7 - \ln 7$$
$$x\ln 3 - 2x\ln 7 = -4\ln 3 - \ln 7$$
$$x(\ln 3 - 2\ln 7) = -4\ln 3 - \ln 7$$
$$x = \frac{-4\ln 3 - \ln 7}{\ln 3 - 2\ln 7}$$
$$x = \frac{4\ln 3 + \ln 7}{2\ln 7 - \ln 3}$$
$$x \approx 2.27$$

72.
$$e^{2x} - e^x - 6 = 0$$
$$(e^x - 3)(e^x + 2) = 0$$
$$e^x - 3 = 0 \quad \text{or} \quad e^x + 2 = 0$$
$$e^x = 3 \qquad\qquad e^x = -2$$
$$\ln e^x = \ln 3 \quad \ln e^x = \ln(-2)$$
$$x = \ln 3 \qquad\qquad x = \ln(-2)$$
$$x = \ln 3 \approx 1.099 \quad \ln(-2) \text{ does not exist.}$$

The solution set is $\{\ln 3\}$,
approximately 1.10.

73. $\log_4 (3x-5) = 3$
$$3x - 5 = 4^3$$
$$3x - 5 = 64$$
$$3x = 69$$
$$x = 23$$
The solutions set is $\{23\}$.

74.
$$3 + 4\ln(2x) = 15$$
$$4\ln(2x) = 12$$
$$\ln(2x) = 3$$
$$2x = e^3$$
$$x = \frac{e^3}{2}$$
$$x \approx 10.04$$

The solutions set is $\left\{\dfrac{e^3}{2}\right\}$.

75. $\log_2 (x+3) + \log_2 (x-3) = 4$
$$\log_2 (x+3)(x-3) = 4$$
$$\log_2 (x^2 - 9) = 4$$
$$x^2 - 9 = 2^4$$
$$x^2 - 9 = 16$$
$$x^2 = 25$$
$$x = \pm 5$$
$x = -5$ does not check because $\log_2(-5+3)$
does not exist.
The solution set is $\{5\}$.

76. $\log_3 (x-1) - \log_3 (x+2) = 2$
$$\log_3 \frac{x-1}{x+2} = 2$$
$$\frac{x-1}{x-2} = 3^2$$
$$\frac{x-1}{x+2} = 9$$
$$x - 1 = 9(x+2)$$
$$x - 1 = 9x + 18$$
$$8x = -19$$
$$x = -\frac{19}{8}$$
$x = -\dfrac{19}{8}$ does not check because

$\log_3\left(-\dfrac{19}{8} - 1\right)$ does not exist.

The solution set is $\varnothing$.

77. $\ln(x+4) - \ln(x+1) = \ln x$

$$\ln\frac{x+4}{x+1} = \ln x$$

$$\frac{x+4}{x+1} = x$$

$$x(x+1) = x+4$$

$$x^2 + x = x + 4$$

$$x^2 = 4$$

$$x = \pm 2$$

$x = -2$ does not check and must be rejected. The solution set is $\{2\}$.

78. $\log_4(2x+1) = \log_4(x-3) + \log_4(x+5)$

$$\log_4(2x+1) = \log_4(x-3) + \log_4(x+5)$$

$$\log_4(2x+1) = \log_4(x^2 + 2x - 15)$$

$$2x+1 = x^2 + 2x - 15$$

$$16 = x^2$$

$$x^2 = 16$$

$$x = \pm 4$$

$x = -4$ does not check and must be rejected. The solution set is $\{4\}$.

79. $P(x) = 14.7 e^{-0.21x}$

$$4.6 = 14.7 e^{-0.21x}$$

$$\frac{4.6}{14.7} = e^{-0.21x}$$

$$\ln\frac{4.6}{14.7} = \ln e^{-0.21x}$$

$$\ln\frac{4.6}{14.7} = -0.21x$$

$$t = \frac{\ln\dfrac{4.6}{14.7}}{-0.21} \approx 5.5$$

The peak of Mt. Everest is about 5.5 miles above sea level.

80. $f(t) = 364(1.005)^t$

$$560 = 364(1.005)^t$$

$$\frac{560}{364} = (1.005)^t$$

$$\ln\frac{560}{364} = \ln(1.005)^t$$

$$\ln\frac{560}{364} = t\ln 1.005$$

$$t = \frac{\ln\dfrac{560}{364}}{\ln 1.005} \approx 86.4$$

The carbon dioxide concentration will be double the pre-industrial level approximately 86 years after the year 2000 in the year 2086.

81. $W(x) = 0.37\ln x + 0.05$

$$3.38 = 0.37\ln x + 0.05$$

$$3.33 = 0.37\ln x$$

$$\frac{3.33}{0.37} = \ln x$$

$$9 = \ln x$$

$$e^9 = e^{\ln x}$$

$$x = e^9 \approx 8103$$

The population of New York City is approximately 8103 thousand, or 8,103,000.

82. $20,000 = 12,500\left(1 + \dfrac{0.065}{4}\right)^{4t}$

$$12,500(1.01625)^{4t} = 20,000$$

$$(1.01625)^{4t} = 1.6$$

$$\ln(1.01625)^{4t} = \ln 1.6$$

$$4t\ln 1.01625 = \ln 1.6$$

$$t = \frac{\ln 1.6}{4\ln 1.01625} \approx 7.3$$

It will take about 7.3 years.

83. $3 \cdot 50,000 = 50,000 e^{0.075t}$

$$50,000 e^{0.075t} = 150,000$$

$$e^{0.075} = 3$$

$$\ln e^{0.075t} = \ln 3$$

$$0.075t = \ln 3$$

$$t = \frac{\ln 3}{0.075} \approx 14.6$$

It will take about 14.6 years.

84. When an investment value triples, $A = 3P$.

$$3P = Pe^{5r}$$

$$e^{5r} = 3$$

$$\ln e^{5r} = \ln 3$$

$$5r = \ln 3$$

$$r = \frac{\ln 3}{5} \approx 0.2197$$

The interest rate would need to be about 22%

85. a.

$$35.3 = 22.4e^{k10}$$

$$\frac{35.3}{22.4} = e^{10k}$$

$$\ln \frac{35.3}{22.4} = \ln e^{10k}$$

$$\ln \frac{35.3}{22.4} = 10k$$

$$\frac{\ln \frac{35.3}{22.4}}{10} = k$$

$$0.045 \approx k$$

$$A = 22.4e^{0.045t}$$

b. $A = 22.4e^{0.045(20)} \approx 55.1$

In 2010, the population will be about 55.1 million.

c.

$$60 = 22.4e^{0.045t}$$

$$\frac{60}{22.4} = e^{0.045t}$$

$$\ln \frac{60}{22.4} = \ln e^{0.045t}$$

$$\ln \frac{60}{22.4} = 0.045t$$

$$\frac{\ln \frac{60}{22.4}}{0.045} = t$$

$$22 \approx t$$

The population will reach 60 million about 22 years after 1990, in 2012.

86. Use the half-life of 140 days to find k.

$$A = A_0 e^{kt}$$

$$\tfrac{1}{2} = e^{k \cdot 140}$$

$$\tfrac{1}{2} = e^{140k}$$

$$\ln \tfrac{1}{2} = \ln e^{140k}$$

$$\ln \tfrac{1}{2} = 140k$$

$$\frac{\ln \tfrac{1}{2}}{140} = k$$

$$k \approx -0.004951$$

Use $A = A_0 e^{kt}$ to find t.

$$A = A_0 e^{-0.004951t}$$

$$0.2 = e^{-0.004951t}$$

$$\ln 0.2 = \ln e^{-0.004951t}$$

$$\ln 0.2 = -0.004951t$$

$$t = \frac{\ln 0.2}{-0.004951}$$

$$t \approx 325$$

It will take about 325 days for the substance to decay to 20% of its original amount.

87. a. $f(0) = \dfrac{500,000}{1 + 2499e^{-0.92(0)}} = 200$

200 people became ill when the epidemic began.

b. $f(6) = \dfrac{500,000}{1 + 2499e^{-0.92(6)}} = 45,411$

45,410 were ill after 6 weeks.

c. 500,000 people

88. a.

$$T = C + (T_o - C)e^{kt}$$

$$150 = 65 + (185 - 65)e^{k2}$$

$$90 = 120e^{2k}$$

$$\frac{90}{120} = e^{2k}$$

$$\ln \frac{3}{4} = \ln e^{2k}$$

$$\ln \frac{3}{4} = 2k$$

$$\frac{\ln \frac{3}{4}}{2} = k$$

$$-0.1438 \approx k$$

$$T = 65 + 120e^{-0.1438t}$$

b. $105 = 65 + 120e^{-0.1438t}$

$40 = 120e^{-0.1438t}$

$\dfrac{1}{3} = e^{-0.1438t}$

$\ln\dfrac{1}{3} = \ln e^{-0.1438t}$

$\ln\dfrac{1}{3} = -0.1438t$

$\dfrac{\ln\dfrac{1}{3}}{-0.1438} = t$

$7.6 \approx t$

The temperature will reach $105°$ after 8 min.

89. a.

b.   An exponential or linear function appears to be the best choice for modeling the data.

90. a.

b.   An exponential function appears to be the best choice for modeling the data.

91. $y = 73(2.6)^x$

$y = 73e^{(\ln 2.6)x}$

$y = 73e^{0.956x}$

92. $y = 6.5(0.43)^x$

$y = 6.5e^{(\ln 0.43)x}$

$y = 6.5e^{-0.844x}$

Chapter 3 Test

1.

$f(x) = 2^x$
$g(x) = 2^x + 1$

2.

$x = 1$

$f(x) = \log_2 x$
$g(x) = \log_2(x - 1)$

3. $5^3 = 125$

4. $\log_{36} 6 = \dfrac{1}{2}$

5.   The domain of f consists of all x for which $3 - x > 0$. Solving this inequality for x, we obtain $x < 3$.
Thus, the domain of f is $(-\infty, 3)$.

6. $\log_4\left(64x^5\right) = \log_4 64 + \log_4 x^5$

$= 3 + 5\log_4 x$

7. $\log_3 \dfrac{\sqrt[3]{x}}{81} = \log_3 x^{\frac{1}{3}} - \log_3 81$

$= \dfrac{1}{3}\log_3 x - 4$

8. $6\log x + 2\log y = \log x^6 + \log y^2$

$= \log\left(x^6 y^2\right)$

9. $\ln 7 - 3\ln x = \ln 7 - \ln x^3$

$= \ln\dfrac{7}{x^3}$

10. $\log_{15} 71 = \dfrac{\log 71}{\log 15} \approx 1.5741$

11. $3^{x-2} = 9^{x+4}$

$3^{x-2} = \left(3^2\right)^{x+4}$

$3^{x-2} = 3^{2x+8}$

$x - 2 = 2x + 8$

$-x = 10$

$x = -10$

12. $5^x = 1.4$

$\ln 5^x = \ln 1.4$

$x \ln 5 = \ln 1.4$

$x = \dfrac{\ln 1.4}{\ln 5} \approx 0.2091$

13. $400e^{0.005x} = 1600$

$e^{0.005x} = 4$

$\ln e^{0.005x} = \ln 4$

$0.005x = \ln 4$

$x = \dfrac{\ln 4}{0.005} \approx 277.2589$

14. $e^{2x} - 6e^x + 5 = 0$

$\left(e^x - 5\right)\left(e^x - 1\right) = 0$

$e^x - 5 = 0$ or $e^x - 1 = 0$

$e^x = 5$ $e^x = 1$

$\ln e^x = \ln 5$ $\ln e^x = \ln 1$

$x = \ln 5$ $x = \ln 1$

$x \approx 1.6094$ $x = 0$

The solution set is $\{0, \ln 5\}$; $\ln \approx 1.6094$.

15. $\log_6 (4x - 1) = 3$

$4x - 1 = 6^3$

$4x - 1 = 216$

$4x = 217$

$x = \dfrac{217}{4} = 54.25$

16. $2 \ln 3x = 8$

$\ln 3x = 4$

$3x = e^4$

$x = \dfrac{e^4}{3} \approx 18.1994$

17. $\log x + \log (x + 15) = 2$

$\log\left(x^2 + 15x\right) = 2$

$x^2 + 15x = 10^2$

$x^2 + 15x - 100 = 0$

$(x + 20)(x - 5) = 0$

$x + 20 = 0$ or $x - 5 = 0$

$x = -20$ $x = 5$

$x = -20$ does not check because $\log(-20)$ does not exist.

The solution set is $\{5\}$.

18. $\ln (x - 4) - \ln (x + 1) = \ln 6$

$\ln \dfrac{x - 4}{x + 1} = \ln 6$

$\dfrac{x - 4}{x + 1} = 6$

$6(x + 1) = x - 4$

$6x + 6 = x - 4$

$5x = -10$

$x = -2$

$x = -2$ does not check and must be rejected.

The solution set is $\{\ \}$.

19. $D = 10 \log \dfrac{10^{12} I_0}{I_0}$

$= 10 \log 10^{12}$

$= 10 \cdot 12$

$= 120$

The loudness of the sound is 120 decibels.

20. Since $\ln e^x = x$, $\ln e^{5x} = 5x$.

21. $\log_b b = 1$ because $b^1 = b$.

22. $\log_6 1 = 0$ because $6^0 = 1$.

23. 6.5% compounded semiannually:

$A = 3{,}000\left(1 + \dfrac{0.065}{2}\right)^{2(10)} \approx \$5{,}687.51$

6% compounded continuously:

$A = 3{,}000 e^{0.06(10)} \approx \$5{,}466.36$

6.5% compounded semiannually yields about \$221 more than 6% compounded continuously.

24.

$$8000 = 4000\left(1 + \frac{0.05}{4}\right)^{4t}$$

$$\frac{8000}{4000} = (1 + 0.0125)^{4t}$$

$$2 = (1.0125)^{4t}$$

$$\ln 2 = \ln(1.0125)^{4t}$$

$$\ln 2 = 4t \ln(1.0125)$$

$$\frac{\ln 2}{4 \ln(1.0125)} = \frac{4t \ln(1.0125)}{4 \ln(1.0125)}$$

$$t = \frac{\ln 2}{4 \ln(1.0125)} \approx 13.9$$

It will take approximately 13.9 years for the money to grow to $8000.

25.

$$2 = 1e^{r10}$$

$$2 = e^{10r}$$

$$\ln 2 = \ln e^{10r}$$

$$\ln 2 = 10r$$

$$r = \frac{\ln 2}{10} \approx 0.069$$

The money will double in 10 years with an interest rate of approximately 6.9%.

26. a.

$$P(0) = 82.3e^{-0.002(0)}$$

$$= 82.3e^0 = 82.3(1) = 82.3$$

In 2003, the population of Germany was 82.3 million.

b. The population of Germany is decreasing. We can tell the model has a negative, $k = -0.002$.

c.

$$81.5 = 82.3e^{-0.002t}$$

$$\frac{81.5}{82.3} = e^{-0.002t}$$

$$\ln \frac{81.5}{82.3} = \ln e^{-0.002t}$$

$$\ln \frac{81.5}{82.3} = -0.002t$$

$$t = \frac{\ln \frac{81.5}{82.3}}{-0.002} \approx 5$$

The population of Germany will be 81.5 million approximately 5 years after 2003 in the year 2008.

27. In 1990, $t = 0$ and $A_0 = 509$
In 2000, $t = 2000 - 1990 = 10$ and $A = 729$.

$$729 = 509e^{k10}$$

$$\frac{729}{509} = e^{10k}$$

$$\ln \frac{729}{509} = \ln e^{10k}$$

$$\ln \frac{729}{509} = 10k$$

$$\frac{\ln \frac{729}{509}}{10} = k$$

$$0.036 \approx k$$

The exponential growth function is $A = 509e^{0.036t}$.

28. When the amount remaining is 5%, $A = 0.05A_0$.

$$0.05A_0 = A_0e^{-0.000121t}$$

$$e^{-0.000121t} = 0.05$$

$$\ln e^{-0.000121t} = \ln 0.05$$

$$-0.000121t = \ln 0.05$$

$$t = \frac{\ln 0.05}{-0.000121} \approx 24,758$$

The man died about 24,758 years ago.

29. a.

$$f(0) = \frac{140}{1 + 9e^{-0.165(0)}} = 14$$

Fourteen elk were initially introduced to the habitat.

b.

$$f(10) = \frac{140}{1 + 9e^{-0.165(10)}} \approx 51$$

After 10 years, about 51 elk are expected.

c. In the logistic growth model,

$$f(t) = \frac{c}{1 + ae^{-bt}},$$

the constant c represents the limiting size that $f(t)$ can attain. The limiting size of the elk population is 140 elk.

30. Plot the ordered pairs.

The values appear to belong to a linear function.

31. Plot the ordered pairs.

The values appear to belong to a logarithmic function.

32. Plot the ordered pairs.

The values appear to belong to an exponential function.

33. Plot the ordered pairs.

The values appear to belong to a quadratic function.

34.
$$y = 96(0.38)^x$$
$$y = 96e^{(\ln 0.38)x}$$
$$y = 96e^{-0.968x}$$

Cumulative Review Exercises (Chapters P–3)

1. $|3x - 4| = 2$

$3x - 4 = 2$ or $3x - 4 = -2$
$3x = 6$ $3x = 2$
$x = 2$ $x = \dfrac{2}{3}$

The solution set is $\left\{\dfrac{2}{3}, 2\right\}$.

2. $x^2 + 2x + 5 = 0$

$$x = \frac{-b \pm \sqrt{b^2 - 4ac}}{2a}$$

$$x = \frac{-(2) \pm \sqrt{(2)^2 - 4(1)(5)}}{2(1)}$$

$$x = \frac{-2 \pm \sqrt{-16}}{2}$$

$$x = \frac{-2 \pm 4i}{2}$$

$$x = -1 \pm 2i$$

3. $x^4 + x^3 - 3x^2 - x + 2 = 0$
$p: \pm 1, \pm 2$
$q: \pm 1$

$\dfrac{p}{q}: \pm 1, \pm 2$

-2	1	1	-3	-1	2
		-2	2	2	-2
	1	-1	-1	1	0

$(x + 2)(x^3 - x^2 - x + 1) = 0$
$(x + 2)[x^2(x - 1) - (x - 1)] = 0$
$(x + 2)(x^2 - 1)(x - 1) = 0$
$(x + 2)(x + 1)(x - 1)(x - 1) = 0$
$(x + 2)(x + 1)(x - 1)^2 = 0$

$x + 2 = 0$ or $x + 1 = 0$ or $x - 1 = 0$
$x = -2$ $x = -1$ $x = 1$

The solution set is $\{-2, -1, 1\}$.

4.
$$e^{5x} - 32 = 96$$
$$e^{5x} = 128$$
$$\ln e^{5x} = \ln 128$$
$$5x = \ln 128$$
$$x = \frac{\ln 128}{5} \approx 0.9704$$

The solution set is $\left\{\dfrac{\ln 128}{5}\right\}$, approximately 0.9704.

5.

$$\log_2(x+5)+\log_2(x-1)=4$$
$$\log_2[(x+5)(x-1)]=4$$
$$(x+5)(x-1)=2^4$$
$$x^2+4x-5=16$$
$$x^2+4x-21=0$$
$$(x+7)(x-3)=0$$

$$x+7=0 \quad \text{or} \quad x-3=0$$
$$x=-7 \qquad\qquad x=3$$

$x=-7$ does not check because $\log_2(-7+5)$ does not exist.
The solution set is $\{3\}$.

6.

$$\ln(x+4)+\ln(x+1)=2\ln(x+3)$$
$$\ln((x+4)(x+1))=\ln(x+3)^2$$
$$(x+4)(x+1)=(x+3)^2$$
$$x^2+5x+4=x^2+6x+9$$
$$5x+4=6x+9$$
$$-x=5$$
$$x=-5$$

$x=-5$ does not check and must be rejected.
The solution set is $\{\ \}$.

7.

$$14-5x\geq-6$$
$$-5x\geq-20$$
$$x\leq4$$

The solution set is $(-\infty,4]$.

8.

$$|2x-4|\leq2$$
$$2x-4\leq2 \text{ and } 2x-4\geq-2$$
$$2x\leq6 \qquad\quad 2x\geq2$$
$$x\leq3 \qquad \text{and} \quad x\geq1$$

The solution set is $[1,3]$.

9. Circle with center: $(3,-2)$ and radius of 2

$$(x-3)^2+(y+2)^2=4$$

10. Parabola with vertex: $(2,-1)$

$$f(x)=(x-2)^2-1$$

11. *x*-intercepts:

$$x^2-1=0$$
$$x^2=1$$
$$x=\pm1$$

The *x*-intercepts are $(1,0)$ and $(-1,0)$.
vertical asymptotes:

$$x^2-4=0$$
$$x^2=4$$
$$x=\pm2$$

The vertical asymptotes are $x=2$ and $x=-2$.
Horizontal asymptote: $y\ 5\ 1$

$$f(x)=\frac{x^2-1}{x^2-4}$$

12. *x*-intercepts:

$$x-2=0 \quad \text{or} \quad x+1=0$$
$$x=2 \qquad \text{or} \quad x=-1$$

The *x*-intercepts are $(2,0)$ and $(-1,0)$.

$$f(x)=(x-2)^2(x+1)$$

13.

$$f(x) = 2x - 4$$

$$f^{-1}(x) = \frac{x+4}{2}$$

14.

$$x = 2$$

$$f(x) = \ln x$$

$$g(x) = \ln(x-2) + 1$$

15. $m = \dfrac{3-(-3)}{1-3} = \dfrac{6}{-2} = -3$

Using (1, 3) point-slope form:

$$y - 3 = -3(x-1)$$

slope-intercept form:

$$y - 3 = -3(x-1)$$

$$y - 3 = -3x + 3$$

$$y = -3x + 6$$

16. $(f \circ g)(x) = f(x+2)$

$$= (x+2)^2$$

$$= x^2 + 4x + 4$$

$$(g \circ f)(x) = g(x^2)$$

$$= x^2 + 2$$

17. y varies inversely as the square of x is expressed

as $y = \dfrac{k}{x^2}$.

The hours, H, vary inversely as the square of the number of cups of coffee, C can be

expressed as $H = \dfrac{k}{C^2}$.

Use the given values to find k.

$$H = \frac{k}{C^2}$$

$$8 = \frac{k}{2^2}$$

$$32 = k$$

Substitute the value of k into the equation.

$$H = \frac{k}{C^2}$$

$$H = \frac{32}{C^2}$$

Use the equation to find H when $C = 4$.

$$H = \frac{32}{C^2}$$

$$H = \frac{32}{4^2}$$

$$H = 2$$

If 4 cups of coffee are consumed you should expect to sleep 2 hours.

18. $s(t) = -16t^2 + 64t + 5$

The ball reaches its maximum height at

$$t = \frac{-b}{2a} = \frac{-(64)}{2(-16)} = 2 \text{ seconds.}$$

The maximum height is $s(2)$.

$$s(2) = -16(2)^2 + 64(2) + 5 = 69 \text{ feet.}$$

19. $s(t) = -16t^2 + 64t + 5$

Let $s(t) = 0$:

$$0 = -16t^2 + 64t + 5$$

Use the quadratic formula to solve.

$$t = \frac{-b \pm \sqrt{b^2 - 4ac}}{2a}$$

$$t = \frac{-(64) \pm \sqrt{(64)^2 - 4(-16)(5)}}{2(-16)}$$

$$t \approx 4.1, \quad t \approx -0.1$$

The negative value is rejected.
The ball hits the ground after about 4.1 seconds.

20. $40x + 10(1.5x) = 660$

$$40x + 15x = 660$$

$$55x = 660$$

$$x = 12$$

Your normal hourly salary is $12 per hour.

Chapter 4

Check Point Exercises

1. The radian measure of a central angle is the length of the intercepted arc, s, divided by the circle's radius, r. The length of the intercepted arc is 42 feet: $s = 42$ feet. The circle's radius is 12 feet: $r = 12$ feet. Now use the formula for radian measure to find the radian measure of θ.

    $$\theta = \frac{s}{r} = \frac{42 \text{ feet}}{12 \text{ feet}} = 3.5$$

    Thus, the radian measure of θ is 3.5

2. a. $60° = 60° \cdot \frac{\pi \text{ radians}}{180°} = \frac{60\pi}{180}$ radians

    $= \frac{\pi}{3}$ radians

    b. $270° = 270° \cdot \frac{\pi \text{ radians}}{180°} = \frac{270\pi}{180}$ radians

    $= \frac{3\pi}{2}$ radians

    c. $-300° = -300° \cdot \frac{\pi \text{ radians}}{180°} = \frac{-300\pi}{180}$ radians

    $= -\frac{5\pi}{3}$ radians

3. a. $\frac{\pi}{4}$ radians $= \frac{\pi \text{ radians}}{4} \cdot \frac{180°}{\pi \text{ radians}}$

    $= \frac{180°}{4} = 45°$

    b. $-\frac{4\pi}{3}$ radians $= -\frac{4\pi \text{ radians}}{3} \cdot \frac{180°}{\pi}$

    $= -\frac{4 \cdot 180°}{3} = -240°$

    c. 6 radians $= 6$ radians $\cdot \frac{180°}{\pi \text{ radians}}$

    $= \frac{6 \cdot 180°}{\pi} \approx 343.8°$

4. a.

    b.

    c.

    d.

5. a. For a 400° angle, subtract 360° to find a positive coterminal angle.
        $400° - 360° = 40°$

    b. For a –135° angle, add 360° to find a positive coterminal angle.
        $-135° + 360° = 225°$

6. a. $\frac{13\pi}{5} - 2\pi = \frac{13\pi}{5} - \frac{10\pi}{5} = \frac{3\pi}{5}$

    b. $-\frac{\pi}{15} + 2\pi = -\frac{\pi}{15} + \frac{30\pi}{15} = \frac{29\pi}{15}$

7. a. $855° - 360° \cdot 2 = 855° - 720° = 135°$

    b. $\frac{17\pi}{3} - 2\pi \cdot 2 = \frac{17\pi}{3} - 4\pi$

    $= \frac{17\pi}{3} - \frac{12\pi}{3} = \frac{5\pi}{3}$

c. $-\dfrac{25\pi}{6} + 2\pi \cdot 3 = -\dfrac{25\pi}{6} + 6\pi$

       $= -\dfrac{25\pi}{6} + \dfrac{36\pi}{6} = \dfrac{11\pi}{6}$

8. The formula $s = r\theta$ can only be used when θ is expressed in radians. Thus, we begin by converting 45° to radians. Multiply by $\dfrac{\pi \text{ radians}}{180°}$.

$45° = 45° \cdot \dfrac{\pi \text{ radians}}{180°} = \dfrac{45}{180}\pi \text{ radians}$

      $= \dfrac{\pi}{4} \text{ radians}$

Now we can use the formula $s = r\theta$ to find the length of the arc. The circle's radius is 6 inches : $r = 6$ inches. The measure of the central angle in radians is $\dfrac{\pi}{4}$: $\theta = \dfrac{\pi}{4}$. The length of the arc intercepted by this central angle is

$s = r\theta = (6 \text{ inches})\left(\dfrac{\pi}{4}\right) = \dfrac{6\pi}{4} \text{ inches} \approx 4.71 \text{ inches.}$

9. We are given ω, the angular speed.
$\omega = 45$ revolutions per minute
We use the formula $v = r\omega$ to find v, the linear speed. Before applying the formula, we must express ω in radians per minute.

$\omega = \dfrac{45 \text{ revolutions}}{1 \text{ minute}} \cdot \dfrac{2\pi \text{ radians}}{1 \text{ revolution}}$

    $= \dfrac{90\pi \text{ radians}}{1 \text{ minute}}$

The angular speed of the propeller is 90π radians per minute. The linear speed is

$v = r\omega = 1.5 \text{ inches} \cdot \dfrac{90\pi}{1 \text{ minute}} = \dfrac{135\pi \text{ inches}}{\text{minute}}$

The linear speed is 135π inches per minute, which is approximately 424 inches per minute.

Exercise Set 4.1

1. obtuse

3. acute

5. straight

7. $\theta = \dfrac{s}{r} = \dfrac{40 \text{ inches}}{10 \text{ inches}} = 4 \text{ radians}$

9. $\theta = \dfrac{s}{r} = \dfrac{8 \text{ yards}}{6 \text{ yards}} = \dfrac{4}{3} \text{ radians}$

11. $\theta = \dfrac{s}{r} = \dfrac{400 \text{ centimeters}}{100 \text{ centimeters}} = 4 \text{ radians}$

13. $45° = 45° \cdot \dfrac{\pi \text{ radians}}{180°}$

      $= \dfrac{45\pi}{180} \text{ radians}$

      $= \dfrac{\pi}{4} \text{ radians}$

15. $135° = 135° \cdot \dfrac{\pi \text{ radians}}{180°}$

      $= \dfrac{135\pi}{180} \text{ radians}$

      $= \dfrac{3\pi}{4} \text{ radians}$

17. $300° = 300° \cdot \dfrac{\pi \text{ radians}}{180°}$

      $= \dfrac{300\pi}{180} \text{ radians}$

      $= \dfrac{5\pi}{3} \text{ radians}$

19. $-225° = -225° \cdot \dfrac{\pi \text{ radians}}{180°}$

      $= -\dfrac{225\pi}{180} \text{ radians}$

      $= -\dfrac{5\pi}{4} \text{ radians}$

21. $\dfrac{\pi}{2} \text{ radians} = \dfrac{\pi \text{ radians}}{2} \cdot \dfrac{180°}{\pi \text{ radians}}$

      $= \dfrac{180°}{2}$

      $= 90°$

23. $\dfrac{2\pi}{3} \text{ radians} = \dfrac{2\pi \text{ radians}}{3} \cdot \dfrac{180°}{\pi \text{ radians}}$

      $= \dfrac{2 \cdot 180°}{3}$

      $= 120°$

25. $\dfrac{7\pi}{6}$ radians $= \dfrac{7\pi \text{ radians}}{6} \cdot \dfrac{180^{\text{O}}}{\pi \text{ radians}}$

$\qquad\qquad = \dfrac{7 \cdot 180^{\text{O}}}{6}$

$\qquad\qquad = 210^{\text{O}}$

27. -3π radians $= -3\pi$ radians $\cdot \dfrac{180^{\text{O}}}{\pi \text{ radians}}$

$\qquad\qquad = -3 \cdot 180^{\text{O}}$

$\qquad\qquad = -540^{\text{O}}$

29. $18° = 18° \cdot \dfrac{\pi \text{ radians}}{180°}$

$\qquad = \dfrac{18\pi}{180}$ radians

$\qquad \approx 0.31$ radians

31. $-40° = -40° \cdot \dfrac{\pi \text{ radians}}{180°}$

$\qquad = -\dfrac{40\pi}{180}$ radians

$\qquad \approx -0.70$ radians

33. $200° = 200° \cdot \dfrac{\pi \text{ radians}}{180°}$

$\qquad = \dfrac{200\pi}{180}$ radians

$\qquad \approx 3.49$ radians

35. 2 radians $= 2$ radians $\cdot \dfrac{180^{\text{O}}}{\pi \text{ radians}}$

$\qquad\qquad = \dfrac{2 \cdot 180^{\text{O}}}{\pi}$

$\qquad\qquad \approx 114.59^{\text{O}}$

37. $\dfrac{\pi}{13}$ radians $= \dfrac{\pi \text{ radians}}{13} \cdot \dfrac{180^{\text{O}}}{\pi \text{ radians}}$

$\qquad\qquad = \dfrac{180^{\text{O}}}{13}$

$\qquad\qquad \approx 13.85^{\text{O}}$

39. -4.8 radians $= -4.8$ radians $\cdot \dfrac{180^{\text{O}}}{\pi \text{ radians}}$

$\qquad\qquad = \dfrac{-4.8 \cdot 180^{\text{O}}}{\pi}$

$\qquad\qquad \approx -275.02^{\text{O}}$

41.

43.

45.

47.

49.

51.

53.

55.

57. $395° - 360° = 35°$

59. $-150° + 360° = 210°$

61. $-765° + 360° \cdot 3 = -765° + 1080° = 315°$

63. $\dfrac{19\pi}{6} - 2\pi = \dfrac{19\pi}{6} - \dfrac{12\pi}{6} = \dfrac{7\pi}{6}$

65. $\dfrac{23\pi}{5} - 2\pi \cdot 2 = \dfrac{23\pi}{5} - 4\pi = \dfrac{23\pi}{5} - \dfrac{20\pi}{5} = \dfrac{3\pi}{5}$

67. $-\dfrac{\pi}{50} + 2\pi = -\dfrac{\pi}{50} + \dfrac{100\pi}{50} = \dfrac{99\pi}{50}$

69. $-\dfrac{31\pi}{7} + 2\pi \cdot 3 = -\dfrac{31\pi}{7} + 6\pi$

$= -\dfrac{31\pi}{7} + \dfrac{42\pi}{7} = \dfrac{11\pi}{7}$

71. $r = 12$ inches, $\theta = 45°$

Begin by converting $45°$ to radians, in order to use the formula $s = r\theta$.

$45° = 45° \cdot \dfrac{\pi \text{ radians}}{180°} = \dfrac{\pi}{4}$ radians

Now use the formula $s = r\theta$.

$s = r\theta = 12 \cdot \dfrac{\pi}{4} = 3\pi$ inches ≈ 9.42 inches

73. $r = 8$ feet, $\theta = 225°$

Begin by converting $225°$ to radians, in order to use the formula $s = r\theta$.

$225° = 225° \cdot \dfrac{\pi \text{ radians}}{180°} = \dfrac{5\pi}{4}$ radians

Now use the formula $s = r\theta$.

$s = r\theta = 8 \cdot \dfrac{5\pi}{4} = 10\pi$ feet ≈ 31.42 feet

75. 6 revolutions per second

$= \dfrac{6 \text{ revolutions}}{1 \text{ second}} \cdot \dfrac{2\pi \text{ radians}}{1 \text{ revolutions}} = \dfrac{12\pi \text{ radians}}{1 \text{ seconds}}$

$= 12\pi$ radians per second

77. $-\dfrac{4\pi}{3}$ and $\dfrac{2\pi}{3}$

79. $-\dfrac{3\pi}{4}$ and $\dfrac{5\pi}{4}$

81. $-\dfrac{\pi}{2}$ and $\dfrac{3\pi}{2}$

83. $\dfrac{55}{60} \cdot 2\pi = \dfrac{11\pi}{6}$

85. 3 minutes and 40 seconds equals 220 seconds.

$\dfrac{220}{60} \cdot 2\pi = \dfrac{22\pi}{3}$

87. First, convert to degrees.

$\dfrac{1}{6}$ revolution $= \dfrac{1}{6}$ revolution $\cdot \dfrac{360°}{1 \text{ revolution}}$

$= \dfrac{1}{6} \cdot 360° = 60°$

Now, convert $60°$ to radians.

$60° = 60° \cdot \dfrac{\pi \text{ radians}}{180°} = \dfrac{60\pi}{180}$ radians

$= \dfrac{\pi}{3}$ radians

Therefore, $\dfrac{1}{6}$ revolution is equivalent to $60°$ or $\dfrac{\pi}{3}$ radians.

89. The distance that the tip of the minute hand moves is given by its arc length, s. Since $s = r\theta$, we begin by finding r and θ. We are given that $r = 8$ inches. The minute hand moves from 12 to 2 o'clock, or $\dfrac{1}{6}$ of a complete revolution. The formula $s = r\theta$ can only be used when θ is expressed in radians. We must convert $\dfrac{1}{6}$ revolution to radians.

$\dfrac{1}{6}$ revolution $= \dfrac{1}{6}$ revolution $\cdot \dfrac{2\pi \text{ radians}}{1 \text{ revolution}}$

$= \dfrac{\pi}{3}$ radians

The distance the tip of the minute hand moves is

$s = r\theta = (8 \text{ inches})\left(\dfrac{\pi}{3}\right) = \dfrac{8\pi}{3}$ inches

≈ 8.38 inches.

91. The length of each arc is given by $s = r\theta$. We are given that $r = 24$ inches and $\theta = 90°$. The formula $s = r\theta$ can only be used when θ is expressed in radians.

$$90° = 90° \cdot \frac{\pi \text{ radians}}{180°} = \frac{90\pi}{180} \text{ radians}$$

$$= \frac{\pi}{2} \text{ radians}$$

The length of each arc is

$$s = r\theta = (24 \text{ inches})\left(\frac{\pi}{2}\right) = 12\pi \text{ inches}$$

$$\approx 37.70 \text{ inches.}$$

93. Recall that $\theta = \frac{s}{r}$. We are given that $s = 8000$ miles and $r = 4000$ miles.

$$\theta = \frac{s}{r} = \frac{8000 \text{ miles}}{4000 \text{ miles}} = 2 \text{ radians}$$

Now, convert 2 radians to degrees.

$$2 \text{ radians} = 2 \text{ radians} \cdot \frac{180°}{\pi \text{ radians}} \approx 114.59°$$

95. Recall that $s = r\theta$. We are given that $r = 4000$ miles and $\theta = 30°$. The formula $s = r\theta$ can only be used when θ is expressed in radians.

$$30° = 30° \cdot \frac{\pi \text{ radians}}{180°} = \frac{30\pi}{180} \text{ radians}$$

$$= \frac{\pi}{6} \text{ radians}$$

$$s = r\theta = (4000 \text{ miles})\left(\frac{\pi}{6}\right) \approx 2094 \text{ miles}$$

To the nearest mile, the distance from A to B is 2094 miles.

97. Linear speed is given by $v = r\omega$. We are given that $\omega = \frac{\pi}{12}$ radians per hour and $r = 4000$ miles. Therefore,

$$v = r\omega = (4000 \text{ miles})\left(\frac{\pi}{12}\right)$$

$$= \frac{4000\pi}{12} \text{ miles per hour}$$

$$\approx 1047 \text{ miles per hour}$$

The linear speed is about 1047 miles per hour.

99. Linear speed is given by $v = r\omega$. We are given that $r = 12$ feet and the wheel rotates at 20 revolutions per minute.
20 revolutions per minute

$$= 20 \text{ revolutions per minute} \cdot \frac{2\pi \text{ radians}}{1 \text{ revolution}}$$

$$= 40\pi \text{ radians per minute}$$

$$v = r\omega = (12 \text{ feet})(40\pi)$$

$$\approx 1508 \text{ feet per minute}$$

The linear speed of the wheel is about 1508 feet per minute.

113.

30.25°

115.

30° 25'12"

117. A right angle measures 90° and

$$90° = \frac{\pi}{2} \text{ radians} \approx 1.57 \text{ radians.}$$

If $\theta = \frac{3}{2}$ radians $= 1.5$ radians, θ is smaller than a right angle.

119. $s = r\theta$

Begin by changing $\theta = 26°$ to radians.

$$26° = 26° \cdot \frac{\pi}{180°} = \frac{13\pi}{90} \text{ radians}$$

$$s = 4000 \cdot \frac{13\pi}{90}$$

$$\approx 1815 \text{ miles}$$

To the nearest mile, Miami, Florida is 1815 miles north of the equator.

Section 4.2

Check Point Exercises

1.　$P\left(\dfrac{\sqrt{3}}{2}, \dfrac{1}{2}\right)$

$\sin t = y = \dfrac{1}{2}$

$\cos t = x = \dfrac{\sqrt{3}}{2}$

$\tan t = \dfrac{y}{x} = \dfrac{\frac{1}{2}}{\frac{\sqrt{3}}{2}} = \dfrac{\sqrt{3}}{3}$

$\csc t = \dfrac{1}{y} = 2$

$\sec t = \dfrac{1}{x} = \dfrac{2\sqrt{3}}{3}$

$\cot t = \dfrac{x}{y} = \sqrt{3}$

2.　The point P on the unit circle that corresponds to $t = \pi$ has coordinates $(-1, 0)$. Use $x = -1$ and $y = 0$ to find the values of the trigonometric functions.

$\sin \pi = y = 0$

$\cos \pi = x = -1$

$\tan \pi = \dfrac{y}{x} = \dfrac{0}{-1} = 0$

$\sec \pi = \dfrac{1}{x} = \dfrac{1}{-1} = -1$

$\cot \pi = \dfrac{x}{y} = \dfrac{-1}{0} = $ undefined

$\csc \pi = \dfrac{1}{y} = \dfrac{1}{0} = $ undefined

3.　$t = \dfrac{\pi}{4},\ P\left(\dfrac{1}{\sqrt{2}}, \dfrac{1}{\sqrt{2}}\right)$

$\csc \dfrac{\pi}{4} = \dfrac{1}{y} = \sqrt{2}$

$\sec \dfrac{\pi}{4} = \dfrac{1}{x} = \sqrt{2}$

$\cot \dfrac{\pi}{4} = \dfrac{x}{y} = \dfrac{\frac{1}{y}}{\frac{1}{\sqrt{2}}} = 1$

4.　a.　$\sec\left(-\dfrac{\pi}{4}\right) = \sec\left(\dfrac{\pi}{4}\right) = \sqrt{2}$

b.　$\sin\left(-\dfrac{\pi}{4}\right) = -\sin\left(\dfrac{\pi}{4}\right) = -\dfrac{\sqrt{2}}{2}$

5.　$\tan \theta = \dfrac{\sin \theta}{\cos \theta} = \dfrac{\frac{2}{3}}{\frac{\sqrt{5}}{3}}$

$= \dfrac{2}{3} \cdot \dfrac{3}{\sqrt{5}} = \dfrac{2}{\sqrt{5}}$

$= \dfrac{2}{\sqrt{5}} \cdot \dfrac{\sqrt{5}}{\sqrt{5}} = \dfrac{2\sqrt{5}}{5}$

$\csc \theta = \dfrac{1}{\sin \theta} = \dfrac{1}{\frac{2}{3}} = \dfrac{3}{2}$

$\sec \theta = \dfrac{1}{\cos \theta} = \dfrac{1}{\frac{\sqrt{5}}{3}} = \dfrac{3}{\sqrt{5}}$

$= \dfrac{3}{\sqrt{5}} \cdot \dfrac{\sqrt{5}}{\sqrt{5}} = \dfrac{3\sqrt{5}}{5}$

$\cot \theta = \dfrac{1}{\tan \theta} = \dfrac{1}{\frac{2}{\sqrt{5}}} = \dfrac{\sqrt{5}}{2}$

6.　$\sin t = \dfrac{1}{2},\ 0 \le t < \dfrac{\pi}{2}$

$\sin^2 t + \cos^2 t = 1$

$\left(\dfrac{1}{2}\right)^2 + \cos^2 t = 1$

$\cos^2 t = 1 - \dfrac{1}{4}$

$\cos t = \sqrt{\dfrac{3}{4}} = \dfrac{\sqrt{3}}{2}$

Because $0 \le t < \dfrac{\pi}{2}$, $\cos t$ is positive.

7.　a.　$\cot \dfrac{5\pi}{4} = \cot\left(\dfrac{\pi}{4} + \pi\right) = \cot \dfrac{\pi}{4} = 1$

b.　$\cos\left(-\dfrac{9\pi}{4}\right) = \cos\left(-\dfrac{9\pi}{4} + 4\pi\right)$

$= \cos \dfrac{7\pi}{4}$

$= \dfrac{\sqrt{2}}{2}$

8. a. $\sin\dfrac{\pi}{4} \approx 0.7071$

b. $\csc 1.5 \approx 1.0025$

Exercise Set 4.2

1. The point P on the unit circle has coordinates $\left(-\dfrac{15}{17}, \dfrac{8}{17}\right)$. Use $x=-\dfrac{15}{17}$ and $y=\dfrac{8}{17}$ to find the values of the trigonometric functions.

$\sin t = y = \dfrac{8}{17}$

$\cos t = x = -\dfrac{15}{17}$

$\tan t = \dfrac{y}{x} = \dfrac{\frac{8}{17}}{-\frac{15}{17}} = -\dfrac{8}{15}$

$\csc t = \dfrac{1}{y} = \dfrac{17}{8}$

$\sec t = \dfrac{1}{x} = -\dfrac{17}{15}$

$\cot t = \dfrac{x}{y} = -\dfrac{15}{8}$

3. The point P on the unit circle that corresponds to $t=-\dfrac{\pi}{4}$ has coordinates $\left(\dfrac{\sqrt{2}}{2}, -\dfrac{\sqrt{2}}{2}\right)$. Use $x=\dfrac{\sqrt{2}}{2}$ and $y=-\dfrac{\sqrt{2}}{2}$ to find the values of the trigonometric functions.

$\sin t = y = -\dfrac{\sqrt{2}}{2}$

$\cos t = x = \dfrac{\sqrt{2}}{2}$

$\tan t = \dfrac{y}{x} = \dfrac{-\frac{\sqrt{2}}{2}}{\frac{\sqrt{2}}{2}} = -1$

$\csc t = \dfrac{1}{y} = -\sqrt{2}$

$\sec t = \dfrac{1}{x} = \sqrt{2}$

$\cot t = \dfrac{x}{y} = -1$

5. $\sin\dfrac{\pi}{6} = \dfrac{1}{2}$

7. $\cos\dfrac{5\pi}{6} = -\dfrac{\sqrt{3}}{2}$

9. $\tan\pi = \dfrac{0}{-1} = 0$

11. $\csc\dfrac{7\pi}{6} = \dfrac{1}{-\frac{1}{2}} = -2$

13. $\sec\dfrac{11\pi}{6} = \dfrac{1}{\frac{\sqrt{3}}{2}} = \dfrac{2\sqrt{3}}{3}$

15. $\sin\dfrac{3\pi}{2} = -1$

17. $\sec\dfrac{3\pi}{2} = $ undefined

19. a. $\cos\dfrac{\pi}{6} = \dfrac{\sqrt{3}}{2}$

b. $\cos\left(-\dfrac{\pi}{6}\right) = \cos\dfrac{\pi}{6} = \dfrac{\sqrt{3}}{2}$

21. a. $\sin\dfrac{5\pi}{6} = \dfrac{1}{2}$

b. $\sin\left(-\dfrac{5\pi}{6}\right) = -\sin\dfrac{5\pi}{6} = -\dfrac{1}{2}$

23. a. $\tan\dfrac{5\pi}{3} = \dfrac{-\frac{\sqrt{3}}{2}}{\frac{1}{2}} = -\sqrt{3}$

b. $\tan\left(-\dfrac{5\pi}{3}\right) = -\tan\dfrac{5\pi}{3} = \sqrt{3}$

25. $\sin t = \dfrac{8}{17}, \cos t = \dfrac{15}{17}$

$\tan t = \dfrac{\frac{8}{17}}{\frac{15}{17}} = \dfrac{8}{15}$

$\csc t = \dfrac{17}{8}$

$\sec t = \dfrac{17}{15}$

$\cot t = \dfrac{15}{8}$

27. $\sin t = \dfrac{1}{3}, \cos t = \dfrac{2\sqrt{2}}{3}$

$\tan t = \dfrac{\frac{1}{3}}{\frac{2\sqrt{2}}{3}} = \dfrac{\sqrt{2}}{4}$

$\csc t = 3$

$\sec t = \dfrac{3\sqrt{2}}{4}$

$\cot t = 2\sqrt{2}$

29. $\sin t = \dfrac{6}{7}, 0 \le t < \dfrac{\pi}{2}$

$\sin^2 t + \cos^2 t = 1$

$\left(\dfrac{6}{7}\right)^2 + \cos^2 t = 1$

$\cos^2 t = 1 - \dfrac{36}{49}$

$\cos t = \sqrt{\dfrac{13}{49}} = \dfrac{\sqrt{13}}{7}$

Because $0 \le t < \dfrac{\pi}{2}$, $\cos t$ is positive.

31. $\sin t = \dfrac{\sqrt{39}}{8}, 0 \le t < \dfrac{\pi}{2}$

$\sin^2 t + \cos^2 t = 1$

$\left(\dfrac{\sqrt{39}}{8}\right)^2 + \cos^2 t = 1$

$\cos^2 t = 1 - \dfrac{39}{64}$

$\cos t = \sqrt{\dfrac{25}{64}} = \dfrac{5}{8}$

Because $0 \le t < \dfrac{\pi}{2}$, $\cos t$ is positive.

33. $\sin 1.7 \csc 1.7 = \sin 1.7 \left(\dfrac{1}{\sin 1.7}\right) = 1$

35. $\sin^2 \dfrac{\pi}{6} + \cos^2 \dfrac{\pi}{2} = 1$ by the Pythagorean identity.

37. $\sec^2 \dfrac{\pi}{3} - \tan^2 \dfrac{\pi}{3} = 1$ because $1 + \tan^2 t = \sec^2 t$.

39. $\cos \dfrac{9\pi}{4} = \cos\left(\dfrac{\pi}{4} + 2\pi\right) = \cos \dfrac{\pi}{4} = \dfrac{\sqrt{2}}{2}$

41. $\sin\left(-\dfrac{9\pi}{4}\right) = \sin\left(-\dfrac{9\pi}{4} + 4\pi\right) = \sin \dfrac{7\pi}{4} = -\dfrac{\sqrt{2}}{2}$

43. $\tan \dfrac{5\pi}{4} = \tan\left(\dfrac{\pi}{4} + \pi\right) = \tan \dfrac{\pi}{4} = 1$

45. $\cot\left(-\dfrac{5\pi}{4}\right) = \cot\left(\dfrac{3\pi}{4} - 2\pi\right) = \cot \dfrac{3\pi}{4} = -1$

47. $-\tan\left(\dfrac{\pi}{4} + 15\pi\right) = -\tan \dfrac{\pi}{4} = -1$

49. $\sin\left(-\dfrac{\pi}{4} - 1000\pi\right) = \sin\left(-\dfrac{\pi}{4} + 2\pi\right)$

$= \sin \dfrac{7\pi}{4}$

$= -\dfrac{\sqrt{2}}{2}$

51. $\cos\left(-\dfrac{\pi}{4} - 1000\pi\right) = \cos\left(-\dfrac{\pi}{4} + 2\pi\right)$

$= \cos \dfrac{7\pi}{4}$

$= \dfrac{\sqrt{2}}{2}$

53. a. $\sin \dfrac{3\pi}{4} = \dfrac{\sqrt{2}}{2}$

b. $\sin \dfrac{11\pi}{4} = \sin\left(\dfrac{3\pi}{4} + 2\pi\right) = \sin \dfrac{3\pi}{4} = \dfrac{\sqrt{2}}{2}$

55. a. $\cos \dfrac{\pi}{2} = 0$

b. $\cos \dfrac{9\pi}{2} = \cos\left(\dfrac{\pi}{2} + 4\pi\right)$

$= \cos\left[\dfrac{\pi}{2} + 2(2\pi)\right]$

$= \cos \dfrac{\pi}{2}$

$= 0$

57. a. $\tan \pi = \dfrac{0}{-1} = 0$

b. $\tan 17\pi = \tan(\pi + 16\pi)$
$= \tan[\pi + 8(2\pi)]$
$= \tan \pi$
$= 0$

59. a. $\sin \dfrac{7\pi}{4} = -\dfrac{\sqrt{2}}{2}$

b. $\sin \dfrac{47\pi}{4} = \sin\left(\dfrac{7\pi}{4} + 10\pi\right)$
$= \sin\left[\dfrac{7\pi}{4} + 5(2\pi)\right]$
$= \sin \dfrac{7\pi}{4}$
$= -\dfrac{\sqrt{2}}{2}$

61. $\sin 0.8 \approx 0.7174$

63. $\tan 3.4 \approx 0.2643$

65. $\csc 1 \approx 1.1884$

67. $\cos \dfrac{\pi}{10} \approx 0.9511$

69. $\cot \dfrac{\pi}{12} \approx 3.7321$

71. $\sin(-t) - \sin t = -\sin t - \sin t = -2\sin t = -2a$

73. $4\cos(-t) - \cos t = 4\cos t - \cos t = 3\cos t = 3b$

75. $\sin(t + 2\pi) - \cos(t + 4\pi) + \tan(t + \pi)$
$= \sin(t) - \cos(t) + \tan(t)$
$= a - b + c$

77. $\sin(-t - 2\pi) - \cos(-t - 4\pi) - \tan(-t - \pi)$
$= -\sin(t + 2\pi) - \cos(t + 4\pi) + \tan(t + \pi)$
$= -\sin(t) - \cos(t) + \tan(t)$
$= -a - b + c$

79. $\cos t + \cos(t + 1000\pi) - \tan t - \tan(t + 999\pi)$
$\qquad\qquad - \sin t + 4\sin(t - 1000\pi)$
$= \cos t + \cos t - \tan t - \tan t - \sin t + 4\sin t$
$= 2\cos t - 2\tan t + 3\sin t$
$= 3a + 2b - 2c$

81. a. $H = 12 + 8.3\sin\left[\dfrac{2\pi}{365}(80 - 80)\right]$
$= 12 + 8.3\sin 0 = 12 + 8.3(0)$
$= 12$
There are 12 hours of daylight in Fairbanks on March 21.

b. $H = 12 + 8.3\sin\left[\dfrac{2\pi}{365}(172 - 80)\right]$
$\approx 12 + 8.3\sin 1.5837$
≈ 20.3
There are about 20.3 hours of daylight in Fairbanks on June 21.

c. $H = 12 + 8.3\sin\left[\dfrac{2\pi}{365}(355 - 80)\right]$
$\approx 12 + 8.3\sin 4.7339$
≈ 3.7
There are about 3.7 hours of daylight in Fairbanks on December 21.

83. a. For $t = 7$,
$E = \sin \dfrac{\pi}{14} \cdot 7 = \sin \dfrac{\pi}{2} = 1$

For $t = 14$,
$E = \sin \dfrac{\pi}{14} \cdot 14 = \sin \pi = 0$

For $t = 21$,
$E = \sin \dfrac{\pi}{14} \cdot 21 = \sin \dfrac{3\pi}{2} = -1$

For $t = 28$,
$E = \sin \dfrac{\pi}{14} \cdot 28 = \sin 2\pi = \sin 0 = 0$

For $t = 35$,
$E = \sin \dfrac{\pi}{14} \cdot 35 = \sin \dfrac{5\pi}{2} = \sin \dfrac{\pi}{2} = 1$
Observations may vary.

b. Because $E(35) = E(7) = 1$, the period is $35 - 7 = 28$ or 28 days.

97. t is in the third quadrant therefore $\sin t < 0$, $\tan t > 0$, and $\cot t > 0$.
Thus, only choice (c) is true.

99. $f(x) = \sin x$ and $f(a) = \dfrac{1}{4}$

$f(a) + 2f(-a) = f(a) - 2f(a)$

$\qquad = \dfrac{1}{4} - 2\left(\dfrac{1}{4}\right)$

$\qquad = -\dfrac{1}{4}$

$f(-a) = -f(a)$ because $\sin(-x) = -\sin x$.
Sine is an odd function.

Section 4.3

Checkpoint Exercises

1. Use the Pythagorean Theorem, $c^2 = a^2 + b^2$, to find c.

$a = 3, b = 4$

$c^2 = a^2 + b^2 = 3^2 + 4^2 = 9 + 16 = 25$

$c = \sqrt{25} = 5$

Referring to these lengths as opposite, adjacent, and hypotenuse, we have

$\sin\theta = \dfrac{\text{opposite}}{\text{hypotenuse}} = \dfrac{3}{5}$

$\cos\theta = \dfrac{\text{adjacent}}{\text{hypotenuse}} = \dfrac{4}{5}$

$\tan\theta = \dfrac{\text{opposite}}{\text{adjacent}} = \dfrac{3}{4}$

$\csc\theta = \dfrac{\text{hypotenuse}}{\text{opposite}} = \dfrac{5}{3}$

$\sec\theta = \dfrac{\text{hypotenuse}}{\text{adjacent}} = \dfrac{5}{4}$

$\cot\theta = \dfrac{\text{adjacent}}{\text{opposite}} = \dfrac{4}{3}$

2. Use the Pythagorean Theorem, $c^2 = a^2 + b^2$, to find b.

$a^2 + b^2 = c^2$

$1^2 + b^2 = 5^2$

$1 + b^2 = 25$

$b^2 = 24$

$b = \sqrt{24} = 2\sqrt{6}$

Note that side a is opposite θ and side b is adjacent to θ.

$\sin\theta = \dfrac{\text{opposite}}{\text{hypotenuse}} = \dfrac{1}{5}$

$\cos\theta = \dfrac{\text{adjacent}}{\text{hypotenuse}} = \dfrac{2\sqrt{6}}{5}$

$\tan\theta = \dfrac{\text{opposite}}{\text{adjacent}} = \dfrac{1}{2\sqrt{6}} = \dfrac{\sqrt{6}}{12}$

$\csc\theta = \dfrac{\text{hypotenuse}}{\text{opposite}} = \dfrac{5}{1} = 5$

$\sec\theta = \dfrac{\text{hypotenuse}}{\text{adjacent}} = \dfrac{5}{2\sqrt{6}} = \dfrac{5\sqrt{6}}{12}$

$\cot\theta = \dfrac{\text{adjacent}}{\text{opposite}} = \dfrac{2\sqrt{6}}{1} = 2\sqrt{6}$

3. Apply the definitions of these three trigonometric functions.

$\csc 45° = \dfrac{\text{length of hypotenuse}}{\text{length of side opposite } 45°}$

$\qquad = \dfrac{\sqrt{2}}{1} = \sqrt{2}$

$\sec 45° = \dfrac{\text{length of hypotenuse}}{\text{length of side adjacent to } 45°}$

$\qquad = \dfrac{\sqrt{2}}{1} = \sqrt{2}$

$\cot 45° = \dfrac{\text{length of side adjacent to } 45°}{\text{length of side opposite } 45°}$

$\qquad = \dfrac{1}{1} = 1$

4.

$\tan 60° = \dfrac{\text{length of side opposite } 60°}{\text{length of side adjacent to } 60°}$

$\qquad = \dfrac{\sqrt{3}}{1} = \sqrt{3}$

$\tan 30° = \dfrac{\text{length of side opposite } 30°}{\text{length of side adjacent to } 30°}$

$\qquad = \dfrac{1}{\sqrt{3}} = \dfrac{1}{\sqrt{3}} \cdot \dfrac{\sqrt{3}}{3} = \dfrac{\sqrt{3}}{3}$

5.   **a.** $\sin 46^{\circ} = \cos(90^{\circ} - 46^{\circ}) = \cos 44^{\circ}$

      b. $\cot \dfrac{\pi}{12} = \tan\left(\dfrac{\pi}{2} - \dfrac{\pi}{12}\right)$

$$= \tan\left(\dfrac{6\pi}{12} - \dfrac{\pi}{12}\right)$$

$$= \tan \dfrac{5\pi}{12}$$

6.   Because we have a known angle, an unknown opposite side, and a known adjacent side, we select the tangent function.

$$\tan 24^{0} = \dfrac{a}{750}$$

$$a = 750 \tan 24^{0}$$

$$a \approx 750(0.4452) \approx 334$$

The distance across the lake is approximately 334 yards.

7. $\tan \theta = \dfrac{\text{side opposite}}{\text{side adjacent}} = \dfrac{14}{10}$

Use a calculator in degree mode to find θ.

Many Scientific Calculators	Many Graphing Calculators
TAN⁻¹ (14 ÷ 10) ENTER	TAN (14 ÷ 10) ENTER

The display should show approximately 54. Thus, the angle of elevation of the sun is approximately 54°.

Exercise Set 4.3

1. $c^2 = 9^2 + 12^2 = 225$

$c = \sqrt{225} = 15$

$\sin \theta = \dfrac{\text{opposite}}{\text{hypotenuse}} = \dfrac{9}{15} = \dfrac{3}{5}$

$\cos \theta = \dfrac{\text{adjacent}}{\text{hypotenuse}} = \dfrac{12}{15} = \dfrac{4}{5}$

$\tan \theta = \dfrac{\text{opposite}}{\text{adjacent}} = \dfrac{9}{12} = \dfrac{3}{4}$

$\csc \theta = \dfrac{\text{hypotenuse}}{\text{opposite}} = \dfrac{15}{9} = \dfrac{5}{3}$

$\sec \theta = \dfrac{\text{hypotenuse}}{\text{adjacent}} = \dfrac{15}{12} = \dfrac{5}{4}$

$\cot \theta = \dfrac{\text{adjacent}}{\text{opposite}} = \dfrac{12}{9} = \dfrac{4}{3}$

3. $a^2 + 21^2 = 29^2$

$a^2 = 841 - 441 = 400$

$a = \sqrt{400} = 20$

$\sin \theta = \dfrac{\text{opposite}}{\text{hypotenuse}} = \dfrac{20}{29}$

$\cos \theta = \dfrac{\text{adjacent}}{\text{hypotenuse}} = \dfrac{21}{29}$

$\tan \theta = \dfrac{\text{opposite}}{\text{adjacent}} = \dfrac{20}{21}$

$\csc \theta = \dfrac{\text{hypotenuse}}{\text{opposite}} = \dfrac{29}{20}$

$\sec \theta = \dfrac{\text{hypotenuse}}{\text{adjacent}} = \dfrac{29}{21}$

$\cot \theta = \dfrac{\text{adjacent}}{\text{opposite}} = \dfrac{21}{20}$

5. $10^2 + b^2 = 26^2$

$$b^2 = 676 - 100 = 576$$

$$b = \sqrt{576} = 24$$

$$\sin\theta = \frac{\text{opposite}}{\text{hypotenuse}} = \frac{10}{26} = \frac{5}{13}$$

$$\cos\theta = \frac{\text{adjacent}}{\text{hypotenuse}} = \frac{24}{26} = \frac{12}{13}$$

$$\tan\theta = \frac{\text{opposite}}{\text{adjacent}} = \frac{10}{24} = \frac{5}{12}$$

$$\csc\theta = \frac{\text{hypotenuse}}{\text{opposite}} = \frac{26}{10} = \frac{13}{5}$$

$$\sec\theta = \frac{\text{hypotenuse}}{\text{adjacent}} = \frac{26}{24} = \frac{13}{12}$$

$$\cot\theta = \frac{\text{adjacent}}{\text{opposite}} = \frac{24}{10} = \frac{12}{5}$$

7. $21^2 + b^2 = 35^2$

$$b^2 = 1225 - 441 = 784$$

$$b = \sqrt{784} = 28$$

$$\sin\theta = \frac{\text{opposite}}{\text{hypotenuse}} = \frac{28}{35} = \frac{4}{5}$$

$$\cos\theta = \frac{\text{adjacent}}{\text{hypotenuse}} = \frac{21}{35} = \frac{3}{5}$$

$$\tan\theta = \frac{\text{opposite}}{\text{adjacent}} = \frac{28}{21} = \frac{4}{3}$$

$$\csc\theta = \frac{\text{hypotenuse}}{\text{opposite}} = \frac{35}{28} = \frac{5}{4}$$

$$\sec\theta = \frac{\text{hypotenuse}}{\text{adjacent}} = \frac{35}{21} = \frac{5}{3}$$

$$\cot\theta = \frac{\text{adjacent}}{\text{opposite}} = \frac{21}{28} = \frac{3}{4}$$

9. $\cos 30° = \dfrac{\text{length of side adjacent to } 30°}{\text{length of hypotenuse}}$

$$= \frac{\sqrt{3}}{2}$$

11. $\sec 45° = \dfrac{\text{length of hypotenuse}}{\text{length of side adjacent to } 45°}$

$$= \frac{\sqrt{2}}{1} = \sqrt{2}$$

13. $\tan\dfrac{\pi}{3} = \tan 60°$

$$= \frac{\text{length of side opposite } 60°}{\text{length of side adjacent to } 60°}$$

$$= \frac{\sqrt{3}}{1} = \sqrt{3}$$

15. $\sin\dfrac{\pi}{4} - \cos\dfrac{\pi}{4} = \sin 45° - \cos 45°$

$$= \frac{1}{\sqrt{2}} - \frac{1}{\sqrt{2}} = 0$$

17. $\sin\dfrac{\pi}{3}\cos\dfrac{\pi}{4} - \tan\dfrac{\pi}{4} = \left(\dfrac{\sqrt{3}}{2}\right)\left(\dfrac{\sqrt{2}}{2}\right) - 1$

$$= \frac{\sqrt{6}}{4} - 1$$

$$= \frac{\sqrt{6} - 4}{4}$$

19. $2\tan\dfrac{\pi}{3} + \cos\dfrac{\pi}{4}\tan\dfrac{\pi}{6} = 2\left(\sqrt{3}\right) + \left(\dfrac{\sqrt{2}}{2}\right)\left(\dfrac{\sqrt{3}}{3}\right)$

$$= 2\sqrt{3} + \frac{\sqrt{6}}{6}$$

$$= \frac{12\sqrt{3} + \sqrt{6}}{6}$$

21. $\sin 7° = \cos(90° - 7°) = \cos 83°$

23. $\csc 25° = \sec(90° - 25°) = \sec 65°$

25. $\tan\dfrac{\pi}{9} = \cot\left(\dfrac{\pi}{2} - \dfrac{\pi}{9}\right)$

$$= \cot\left(\frac{9\pi}{18} - \frac{2\pi}{18}\right)$$

$$= \cot\frac{7\pi}{18}$$

27. $\cos\dfrac{2\pi}{5} = \sin\left(\dfrac{\pi}{2} - \dfrac{2\pi}{5}\right)$

$$= \sin\left(\frac{5\pi}{10} - \frac{4\pi}{10}\right)$$

$$= \sin\frac{\pi}{10}$$

29. $\tan 37° = \dfrac{a}{250}$

$a = 250 \tan 37°$

$a \approx 250(0.7536) \approx 188$ cm

31. $\cos 34° = \dfrac{b}{220}$

$b = 220 \cos 34°$

$b \approx 220(0.8290) \approx 182$ in.

33. $\sin 23° = \dfrac{16}{c}$

$c = \dfrac{16}{\sin 23°} \approx \dfrac{16}{0.3907} \approx 41$ m

35.

Scientific Calculator	Graphing Calculator	Display (rounded to the nearest degree)
.2974 $\boxed{\text{SIN}^{-1}}$	$\boxed{\text{SIN}^{-1}}$ .2974 $\boxed{\text{ENTER}}$	17

If $\sin \theta = 0.2974$, then $\theta \approx 17°$.

37.

Scientific Calculator	Graphing Calculator	Display (rounded to the nearest degree)
4.6252 $\boxed{\text{TAN}^{-1}}$	$\boxed{\text{TAN}^{-1}}$ 4.6252 $\boxed{\text{ENTER}}$	78

If $\tan \theta = 4.6252$, then $\theta \approx 78°$.

39.

Scientific Calculator	Graphing Calculator	Display (rounded to three places)
.4112 $\boxed{\text{COS}^{-1}}$	$\boxed{\text{COS}^{-1}}$ .4112 $\boxed{\text{ENTER}}$	1.147

If $\cos \theta = 0.4112$, then $\theta \approx 1.147$ radians.

41.

Scientific Calculator	Graphing Calculator	Display (rounded to three places)
.4169 $\boxed{\text{TAN}^{-1}}$	$\boxed{\text{TAN}^{-1}}$ .4169 $\boxed{\text{ENTER}}$	.395

If $\tan \theta = 0.4169$, then $\theta \approx 0.395$ radians.

43. $\dfrac{\tan \dfrac{\pi}{3}}{2} - \dfrac{1}{\sec \dfrac{\pi}{6}} = \dfrac{\sqrt{3}}{2} - \dfrac{1}{\dfrac{1}{\cos \frac{\pi}{6}}}$

$= \dfrac{\sqrt{3}}{2} - \dfrac{1}{\dfrac{1}{\frac{\sqrt{3}}{2}}}$

$= \dfrac{\sqrt{3}}{2} - \dfrac{\sqrt{3}}{2}$

$= 0$

45. $1 + \sin^2 40° + \sin^2 50°$

$= 1 + \sin^2(90° - 50°) + \sin^2 50°$

$= 1 + \cos^2 50° + \sin^2 50°$

$= 1 + 1$

$= 2$

47. $\csc 37° \sec 53° - \tan 53° \cot 37°$

$= \sec 53° \sec 53° - \tan 53° \tan 53°$

$= \sec^2 53° - \tan^2 53°$

$= 1$

49. $f(\theta) = 2\cos \theta - \cos 2\theta$

$f\left(\dfrac{\pi}{6}\right) = 2\cos \dfrac{\pi}{6} - \cos\left(2 \cdot \dfrac{\pi}{6}\right)$

$= 2\left(\dfrac{\sqrt{3}}{2}\right) - \cos\left(\dfrac{\pi}{3}\right)$

$= \dfrac{2\sqrt{3}}{2} - \dfrac{1}{2}$

$= \dfrac{2\sqrt{3} - 1}{2}$

51. $\tan\left(\dfrac{\pi}{2}-\theta\right)=\cot\theta=\dfrac{1}{4}$

53. $\tan 40° = \dfrac{a}{630}$

$a = 630\tan 40°$

$a \approx 630(0.8391) \approx 529$

The distance across the lake is approximately
529 yards.

55. $\tan\theta = \dfrac{125}{172}$

Use a calculator in degree mode to find θ.

Many Scientific Calculators	Many Graphing Calculators
125 ÷ 172 = TAN⁻¹	TAN⁻¹ (125 ÷ 172) ENTER

The display should show approximately 36. Thus, the angle of elevation of the sun is approximately 36°.

57. $\sin 10° = \dfrac{500}{c}$

$c = \dfrac{500}{\sin 10°} \approx \dfrac{500}{0.1736} \approx 2880$

The plane has flown approximately 2880 feet.

59. $\cos\theta = \dfrac{60}{75}$

Use a calculator in degree mode to find θ.

Many Scientific Calculators	Many Graphing Calculators
60 ÷ 75 = COS⁻¹	COS⁻¹ (60 ÷ 75) ENTER

The display should show approximately 37. Thus, the angle between the wire and the pole is approximately 37°.

69.

θ	0.4	0.3	0.2	0.1	0.01	0.001	0.0001	0.00001
$\cos\theta$	0.92106	0.95534	0.98007	0.99500	0.99995	0.9999995	0.999999995	1
$\dfrac{\cos\theta-1}{\theta}$	−0.19735	−0.148878	−0.099667	−0.04996	−0.005	−0.0005	−0.00005	0

$\dfrac{\cos\theta-1}{\theta}$ approaches 0 as θ approaches 0.

71. In a right triangle, the hypotenuse is greater than either other side. Therefore both
$\dfrac{\text{opposite}}{\text{hypotenuse}}$ and $\dfrac{\text{adjacent}}{\text{hypotenuse}}$ must be less than 1 for an acute angle in a right triangle.

73. **a.** Let a = distance of the ship from the lighthouse.

$$\tan 35° = \frac{250}{a}$$

$$a = \frac{250}{\tan 35°} \approx \frac{250}{0.7002} \approx 357$$

The ship is approximately 357 feet from the lighthouse.

b. Let b = the plane's height above the lighthouse.

$$\tan 22° = \frac{b}{357}$$

$$b = 357 \tan 22° \approx 357(0.4040) \approx 144$$

$$144 + 250 = 394$$

The plane is approximately 394 feet above the water.

Section 4.4

Checkpoint Exercises

1. $r = \sqrt{x^2 + y^2}$

$r = \sqrt{1^2 + (-3)^2} = \sqrt{1+9} = \sqrt{10}$

Now that we know x, y, and r, we can find the six trigonometric functions of θ.

$\sin \theta = \frac{y}{r} = \frac{-3}{\sqrt{10}} = -\frac{3\sqrt{10}}{10}$

$\cos \theta = \frac{x}{r} = \frac{1}{\sqrt{10}} = \frac{\sqrt{10}}{10}$

$\tan \theta = \frac{y}{x} = \frac{-3}{1} = -3$

$\csc \theta = \frac{r}{y} = \frac{\sqrt{10}}{-3} = -\frac{\sqrt{10}}{3}$

$\sec \theta = \frac{r}{x} = \frac{\sqrt{10}}{1} = \sqrt{10}$

$\cot \theta = \frac{x}{y} = \frac{1}{-3} = -\frac{1}{3}$

2. **a.** $\theta = 0° = 0$ radians
The terminal side of the angle is on the positive x-axis. Select the point
$P = (1,0)$: $x = 1, y = 0, r = 1$
Apply the definitions of the cosine and cosecant functions.

$\cos 0° = \cos 0 = \frac{x}{r} = \frac{1}{1} = 1$

$\csc 0° = \csc 0 = \frac{r}{y} = \frac{1}{0}$, undefined

b. $\theta = 90° = \frac{\pi}{2}$ radians
The terminal side of the angle is on the positive y-axis. Select the point
$P = (0,1)$: $x = 0, y = 1, r = 1$
Apply the definitions of the cosine and cosecant functions.

$\cos 90° = \cos \frac{\pi}{2} = \frac{x}{r} = \frac{0}{1} = 0$

$\csc 90° = \csc \frac{\pi}{2} = \frac{r}{y} = \frac{1}{1} = 1$

c. $\theta = 180° = \pi$ radians
The terminal side of the angle is on the negative x-axis. Select the point
$P = (-1,0)$: $x = -1, y = 0, r = 1$
Apply the definitions of the cosine and cosecant functions.

$\cos 180° = \cos \pi = \frac{x}{r} = \frac{-1}{1} = -1$

$\csc 180° = \csc \pi = \frac{r}{y} = \frac{1}{0}$, undefined

d. $\theta = 270° = \frac{3\pi}{2}$ radians
The terminal side of the angle is on the negative y-axis. Select the point
$P = (0,-1)$: $x = 0, y = -1, r = 1$
Apply the definitions of the cosine and cosecant functions.

$\cos 270° = \cos \frac{3\pi}{2} = \frac{x}{r} = \frac{0}{1} = 0$

$\csc 270° = \csc \frac{3\pi}{2} = \frac{r}{y} = \frac{1}{-1} = -1$

3. Because $\sin\theta < 0$, θ cannot lie in quadrant I; all the functions are positive in quadrant I. Furthermore, θ cannot lie in quadrant II; $\sin\theta$ is positive in quadrant II. Thus, with $\sin\theta < 0$, θ lies in quadrant III or quadrant IV. We are also given that $\cos\theta < 0$. Because quadrant III is the only quadrant in which cosine is negative and the sine is negative, we conclude that θ lies in quadrant III.

4. Because the tangent is negative and the cosine is negative, θ lies in quadrant II. In quadrant II, x is negative and y is positive. Thus,

   $$\tan\theta = -\frac{1}{3} = \frac{y}{x} = \frac{1}{-3}$$

   $x = -3$, $y = 1$

   Furthermore,

   $$r = \sqrt{x^2 + y^2} = \sqrt{(-3)^2 + 1^2} = \sqrt{9+1} = \sqrt{10}$$

   Now that we know x, y, and r, we can find $\sin\theta$ and $\sec\theta$.

   $$\sin\theta = \frac{y}{r} = \frac{1}{\sqrt{10}} = \frac{1}{\sqrt{10}} \cdot \frac{\sqrt{10}}{\sqrt{10}} = \frac{\sqrt{10}}{10}$$

   $$\sec\theta = \frac{r}{x} = \frac{\sqrt{10}}{-3} = -\frac{\sqrt{10}}{3}$$

5. **a.** Because $210°$ lies between $180°$ and $270°$, it is in quadrant III. The reference angle is $\theta' = 210° - 180° = 30°$.

   b. Because $\frac{7\pi}{4}$ lies between $\frac{3\pi}{2} = \frac{6\pi}{4}$ and $2\pi = \frac{8\pi}{4}$, it is in quadrant IV. The reference angle is

   $$\theta' = 2\pi - \frac{7\pi}{4} = \frac{8\pi}{4} - \frac{7\pi}{4} = \frac{\pi}{4}.$$

   c. Because $-240°$ lies between $-180°$ and $-270°$, it is in quadrant II. The reference angle is $\theta = 240 - 180 = 60°$.

   d. Because 3.6 lies between $\pi \approx 3.14$ and $\frac{3\pi}{2} \approx 4.71$, it is in quadrant III. The reference angle is $\theta' = 3.6 - \pi \approx 0.46$.

6. **a.** $665° - 360° = 305°$
   This angle is in quadrant IV, thus the reference angle is $\theta' = 360° - 305° = 55°$.

   b. $\frac{15\pi}{4} - 2\pi = \frac{15\pi}{4} - \frac{8\pi}{4} = \frac{7\pi}{4}$
   This angle is in quadrant IV, thus the reference angle is

   $$\theta' = 2\pi - \frac{7\pi}{4} = \frac{8\pi}{4} - \frac{7\pi}{4} = \frac{\pi}{4}.$$

   c. $-\frac{11\pi}{3} + 2\cdot 2\pi = -\frac{11\pi}{3} + \frac{12\pi}{3} = \frac{\pi}{3}$
   This angle is in quadrant I, thus the reference angle is $\theta' = \frac{\pi}{3}$.

7. **a.** $300°$ lies in quadrant IV. The reference angle is $\theta' = 360° - 300° = 60°$.

   $$\sin 60° = \frac{\sqrt{3}}{2}$$

   Because the sine is negative in quadrant IV, $\sin 300° = -\sin 60° = -\frac{\sqrt{3}}{2}$.

   b. $\frac{5\pi}{4}$ lies in quadrant III. The reference angle is $\theta' = \frac{5\pi}{4} - \pi = \frac{5\pi}{4} - \frac{4\pi}{4} = \frac{\pi}{4}$.

   $$\tan\frac{\pi}{4} = 1$$

   Because the tangent is positive in quadrant III, $\tan\frac{5\pi}{4} = +\tan\frac{\pi}{4} = 1$.

   c. $-\frac{\pi}{6}$ lies in quadrant IV. The reference angle is $\theta' = \frac{\pi}{6}$.

   $$\sec\frac{\pi}{6} = \frac{2\sqrt{3}}{3}$$

   Because the secant is positive in quadrant IV, $\sec\left(-\frac{\pi}{6}\right) = +\sec\frac{\pi}{6} = \frac{2\sqrt{3}}{3}$.

8.   **a.** $\dfrac{17\pi}{6} - 2\pi = \dfrac{17\pi}{6} - \dfrac{12\pi}{6} = \dfrac{5\pi}{6}$ lies in

quadrant II. The reference angle is

$\theta' = \pi - \dfrac{5\pi}{6} = \dfrac{\pi}{6}$.

The function value for the reference angle

is $\cos\dfrac{\pi}{6} = \dfrac{\sqrt{3}}{2}$.

Because the cosine is negative in quadrant

II, $\cos\dfrac{17\pi}{6} = \cos\dfrac{5\pi}{6} = -\cos\dfrac{\pi}{6} = -\dfrac{\sqrt{3}}{2}$.

  b. $\dfrac{-22\pi}{3} + 8\pi = \dfrac{-22\pi}{3} + \dfrac{24\pi}{3} = \dfrac{2\pi}{3}$ lies in

quadrant II. The reference angle is

$\theta' = \pi - \dfrac{2\pi}{3} = \dfrac{\pi}{3}$.

The function value for the reference angle

is $\sin\dfrac{\pi}{3} = \dfrac{\sqrt{3}}{2}$.

Because the sine is positive in quadrant II,

$\sin\dfrac{-22\pi}{3} = \sin\dfrac{2\pi}{3} = \sin\dfrac{\pi}{3} = \dfrac{\sqrt{3}}{2}$.

Exercise Set 4.4

1.   We need values for x, y, and r. Because
$P = (-4, 3)$ is a point on the terminal side of
θ, $x = -4$ and $y = 3$. Furthermore,

$r = \sqrt{x^2 + y^2} = \sqrt{(-4)^2 + 3^2} = \sqrt{16 + 9} = \sqrt{25} = 5$

Now that we know x, y, and r, we can find the
six trigonometric functions of θ.

$\sin\theta = \dfrac{y}{r} = \dfrac{3}{5}$

$\cos\theta = \dfrac{x}{r} = \dfrac{-4}{5} = -\dfrac{4}{5}$

$\tan\theta = \dfrac{y}{x} = \dfrac{3}{-4} = -\dfrac{3}{4}$

$\csc\theta = \dfrac{r}{y} = \dfrac{5}{3}$

$\sec\theta = \dfrac{r}{x} = \dfrac{5}{-4} = -\dfrac{5}{4}$

$\cot\theta = \dfrac{x}{y} = \dfrac{-4}{3} = -\dfrac{4}{3}$

3.   We need values for x, y, and r. Because
$P = (2, 3)$ is a point on the terminal side of
θ, $x = 2$ and $y = 3$. Furthermore,

$r = \sqrt{x^2 + y^2} = \sqrt{2^2 + 3^2} = \sqrt{4 + 9} = \sqrt{13}$

Now that we know x, y, and r, we can find the
six trigonometric functions of θ.

$\sin\theta = \dfrac{y}{r} = \dfrac{3}{\sqrt{13}} = \dfrac{3}{\sqrt{13}} \cdot \dfrac{\sqrt{13}}{\sqrt{13}} = \dfrac{3\sqrt{13}}{13}$

$\cos\theta = \dfrac{x}{r} = \dfrac{2}{\sqrt{13}} = \dfrac{2}{\sqrt{13}} \cdot \dfrac{\sqrt{13}}{\sqrt{13}} = \dfrac{2\sqrt{13}}{13}$

$\tan\theta = \dfrac{y}{x} = \dfrac{3}{2}$

$\csc\theta = \dfrac{r}{y} = \dfrac{\sqrt{13}}{3}$

$\sec\theta = \dfrac{r}{x} = \dfrac{\sqrt{13}}{2}$

$\cot\theta = \dfrac{x}{y} = \dfrac{2}{3}$

5.   We need values for x, y, and r. Because
$P = (3, -3)$ is a point on the terminal side of
θ, $x = 3$ and $y = -3$. Furthermore,

$r = \sqrt{x^2 + y^2} = \sqrt{3^2 + (-3)^2} = \sqrt{9 + 9}$

$= \sqrt{18} = 3\sqrt{2}$

Now that we know x, y, and r, we can find the
six trigonometric functions of θ.

$\sin\theta = \dfrac{y}{r} = \dfrac{-3}{3\sqrt{2}} = \dfrac{-1}{\sqrt{2}} \cdot \dfrac{\sqrt{2}}{\sqrt{2}} = -\dfrac{\sqrt{2}}{2}$

$\cos\theta = \dfrac{x}{r} = \dfrac{3}{3\sqrt{2}} = \dfrac{1}{\sqrt{2}} \cdot \dfrac{\sqrt{2}}{\sqrt{2}} = \dfrac{\sqrt{2}}{2}$

$\tan\theta = \dfrac{y}{x} = \dfrac{-3}{3} = -1$

$\csc\theta = \dfrac{r}{y} = \dfrac{3\sqrt{2}}{-3} = -\sqrt{2}$

$\sec\theta = \dfrac{r}{x} = \dfrac{3\sqrt{2}}{3} = \sqrt{2}$

$\cot\theta = \dfrac{x}{y} = \dfrac{3}{-3} = -1$

7.　We need values for x, y, and r. Because $P = (-2, -5)$ is a point on the terminal side of θ, $x = -2$ and $y = -5$. Furthermore,

$$r = \sqrt{x^2 + y^2} = \sqrt{(-2)^2 + (-5)^2} = \sqrt{4 + 25} = \sqrt{29}$$

Now that we know x, y, and r, we can find the six trigonometric functions of θ.

$$\sin\theta = \frac{y}{r} = \frac{-5}{\sqrt{29}} = \frac{-5}{\sqrt{29}} \cdot \frac{\sqrt{29}}{\sqrt{29}} = -\frac{5\sqrt{29}}{29}$$

$$\cos\theta = \frac{x}{r} = \frac{-2}{\sqrt{29}} = \frac{-2}{\sqrt{29}} \cdot \frac{\sqrt{29}}{\sqrt{29}} = -\frac{2\sqrt{29}}{29}$$

$$\tan\theta = \frac{y}{x} = \frac{-5}{-2} = \frac{5}{2}$$

$$\csc\theta = \frac{r}{y} = \frac{\sqrt{29}}{-5} = -\frac{\sqrt{29}}{5}$$

$$\sec\theta = \frac{r}{x} = \frac{\sqrt{29}}{-2} = -\frac{\sqrt{29}}{2}$$

$$\cot\theta = \frac{x}{y} = \frac{-2}{-5} = \frac{2}{5}$$

9.　$\theta = \pi$ radians

The terminal side of the angle is on the negative x-axis. Select the point $P = (-1, 0)$:
$x = -1$, $y = 0$, $r = 1$ Apply the definition of the cosine function.

$$\cos\pi = \frac{x}{r} = \frac{-1}{1} = -1$$

11.　$\theta = \pi$ radians

The terminal side of the angle is on the negative x-axis. Select the point $P = (-1, 0)$:
$x = -1$, $y = 0$, $r = 1$ Apply the definition of the secant function.

$$\sec\pi = \frac{r}{x} = \frac{1}{-1} = -1$$

13.　$\theta = \frac{3\pi}{2}$ radians

The terminal side of the angle is on the negative y-axis. Select the point $P = (0, -1)$:
$x = 0$, $y = -1$, $r = 1$ Apply the definition of the tangent function.

$$\tan\frac{3\pi}{2} = \frac{y}{x} = \frac{-1}{0}, \text{ undefined}$$

15.　$\theta = \frac{\pi}{2}$ radians

The terminal side of the angle is on the positive y-axis. Select the point $P = (0, 1)$:
$x = 0$, $y = 1$, $r = 1$ Apply the definition of the cotangent function.

$$\cot\frac{\pi}{2} = \frac{x}{y} = \frac{0}{1} = 0$$

17.　Because $\sin\theta > 0$, θ cannot lie in quadrant III or quadrant IV; the sine function is negative in those quadrants. Thus, with $\sin\theta > 0$, θ lies in quadrant I or quadrant II. We are also given that $\cos\theta > 0$. Because quadrant I is the only quadrant in which the cosine is positive and sine is positive, we conclude that θ lies in quadrant I.

19.　Because $\sin\theta < 0$, θ cannot lie in quadrant I or quadrant II; the sine function is positive in those two quadrants. Thus, with $\sin\theta < 0$, θ lies in quadrant III or quadrant IV. We are also given that $\cos\theta < 0$. Because quadrant III is the only quadrant in which the cosine is positive and the sine is negative, we conclude that θ lies in quadrant III.

21.　Because $\tan\theta < 0$, θ cannot lie in quadrant I or quadrant III; the tangent function is positive in those quadrants. Thus, with $\tan\theta < 0$, θ lies in quadrant II or quadrant IV. We are also given that $\cos\theta < 0$. Because quadrant II is the only quadrant in which the cosine is negative and the tangent is negative, we conclude that θ lies in quadrant II.

23. In quadrant III x is negative and y is negative.

Thus, $\cos\theta = -\dfrac{3}{5} = \dfrac{x}{r} = \dfrac{-3}{5}$, $x = -3$, $r = 5$.

Furthermore,

$r^2 = x^2 + y^2$

$5^2 = (-3)^2 + y^2$

$y^2 = 25 - 9 = 16$

$y = -\sqrt{16} = -4$

Now that we know x, y, and r, we can find the remaining trigonometric functions of θ.

$\sin\theta = \dfrac{y}{r} = \dfrac{-4}{5} = -\dfrac{4}{5}$

$\tan\theta = \dfrac{y}{x} = \dfrac{-4}{-3} = \dfrac{4}{3}$

$\csc\theta = \dfrac{r}{y} = \dfrac{5}{-4} = -\dfrac{5}{4}$

$\sec\theta = \dfrac{r}{x} = \dfrac{5}{-3} = -\dfrac{5}{3}$

$\cot\theta = \dfrac{x}{y} = \dfrac{-3}{-4} = \dfrac{3}{4}$

25. In quadrant II x is negative and y is positive.

Thus, $\sin\theta = \dfrac{5}{13} = \dfrac{y}{r}$, $y = 5$, $r = 13$.

Furthermore,

$x^2 + y^2 = r^2$

$x^2 + 5^2 = 13^2$

$x^2 = 169 - 25 = 144$

$x = -\sqrt{144} = -12$

Now that we know x, y, and r, we can find the remaining trigonometric functions of θ.

$\cos\theta = \dfrac{x}{r} = \dfrac{-12}{13} = -\dfrac{12}{13}$

$\tan\theta = \dfrac{y}{x} = \dfrac{5}{-12} = -\dfrac{5}{12}$

$\csc\theta = \dfrac{r}{y} = \dfrac{13}{5}$

$\sec\theta = \dfrac{r}{x} = \dfrac{13}{-12} = -\dfrac{13}{12}$

$\cot\theta = \dfrac{x}{y} = \dfrac{-12}{5} = -\dfrac{12}{5}$

27. Because $270° < \theta < 360°$, θ is in quadrant IV. In quadrant IV x is positive and y is negative.

Thus, $\cos\theta = \dfrac{8}{17} = \dfrac{x}{r}$, $x = 8$,

$r = 17$. Furthermore

$x^2 + y^2 = r^2$

$8^2 + y^2 = 17^2$

$y^2 = 289 - 64 = 225$

$y = -\sqrt{225} = -15$

Now that we know x, y, and r, we can find the remaining trigonometric functions of θ.

$\sin\theta = \dfrac{y}{r} = \dfrac{-15}{17} = -\dfrac{15}{17}$

$\tan\theta = \dfrac{y}{x} = \dfrac{-15}{8} = -\dfrac{15}{8}$

$\csc\theta = \dfrac{r}{y} = \dfrac{17}{-15} = -\dfrac{17}{15}$

$\sec\theta = \dfrac{r}{x} = \dfrac{17}{8}$

$\cot\theta = \dfrac{x}{y} = \dfrac{8}{-15} = -\dfrac{8}{15}$

29. Because the tangent is negative and the sine is positive, θ lies in quadrant II. In quadrant II, x is negative and y is positive. Thus,

$\tan\theta = -\dfrac{2}{3} = \dfrac{y}{x} = \dfrac{2}{-3}$, $x = -3$, $y = 2$.

Furthermore,

$r = \sqrt{x^2 + y^2} = \sqrt{(-3)^2 + 2^2} = \sqrt{9 + 4} = \sqrt{13}$

Now that we know x, y, and r, we can find the remaining trigonometric functions of θ.

$\sin\theta = \dfrac{y}{r} = \dfrac{2}{\sqrt{13}} = \dfrac{2}{\sqrt{13}} \cdot \dfrac{\sqrt{13}}{\sqrt{13}} = \dfrac{2\sqrt{13}}{13}$

$\cos\theta = \dfrac{x}{r} = \dfrac{-3}{\sqrt{13}} = \dfrac{-3}{\sqrt{13}} \cdot \dfrac{\sqrt{13}}{\sqrt{13}} = -\dfrac{3\sqrt{13}}{13}$

$\csc\theta = \dfrac{r}{y} = \dfrac{\sqrt{13}}{2}$

$\sec\theta = \dfrac{r}{x} = \dfrac{\sqrt{13}}{-3} = -\dfrac{\sqrt{13}}{3}$

$\cot\theta = \dfrac{x}{y} = \dfrac{-3}{2} = -\dfrac{3}{2}$

31. Because the tangent is positive and the cosine is negative, θ lies in quadrant III. In quadrant III, x is negative and y is negative. Thus,

$$\tan\theta = \frac{4}{3} = \frac{y}{x} = \frac{-4}{-3}, \ x = -3, y = -4.$$

Furthermore,

$$r = \sqrt{x^2 + y^2} = \sqrt{(-3)^2 + (-4)^2} = \sqrt{9 + 16}$$
$$= \sqrt{25} = 5$$

Now that we know x, y, and r, we can find the remaining trigonometric functions of θ.

$$\sin\theta = \frac{y}{r} = \frac{-4}{5} = -\frac{4}{5}$$

$$\cos\theta = \frac{x}{r} = \frac{-3}{5} = -\frac{3}{5}$$

$$\csc\theta = \frac{r}{y} = \frac{5}{-4} = -\frac{5}{4}$$

$$\sec\theta = \frac{r}{x} = \frac{5}{-3} = -\frac{5}{3}$$

$$\cot\theta = \frac{x}{y} = \frac{-3}{-4} = \frac{3}{4}$$

33. Because the secant is negative and the tangent is positive, θ lies in quadrant III. In quadrant III, x is negative and y is negative. Thus,

$$\sec\theta = -3 = \frac{r}{x} = \frac{3}{-1}, \ x = -1, r = 3.$$

Furthermore,

$$x^2 + y^2 = r^2$$
$$(-1)^2 + y^2 = 3^2$$
$$y^2 = 9 - 1 = 8$$
$$y = -\sqrt{8} = -2\sqrt{2}$$

Now that we know x, y, and r, we can find the remaining trigonometric functions of θ.

$$\sin\theta = \frac{y}{r} = \frac{-2\sqrt{2}}{3} = -\frac{2\sqrt{2}}{3}$$

$$\cos\theta = \frac{x}{r} = \frac{-1}{3} = -\frac{1}{3}$$

$$\tan\theta = \frac{y}{x} = \frac{-2\sqrt{2}}{-1} = 2\sqrt{2}$$

$$\csc\theta = \frac{r}{y} = \frac{3}{-2\sqrt{2}} = \frac{3}{-2\sqrt{2}} \cdot \frac{\sqrt{2}}{\sqrt{2}} = -\frac{3\sqrt{2}}{4}$$

$$\cot\theta = \frac{x}{y} = \frac{-1}{-2\sqrt{2}} = \frac{1}{2\sqrt{2}} \cdot \frac{\sqrt{2}}{\sqrt{2}} = \frac{\sqrt{2}}{4}$$

35. Because $160°$ lies between $90°$ and $180°$, it is in quadrant II. The reference angle is $\theta' = 180° - 160° = 20°$.

37. Because $205°$ lies between $180°$ and $270°$, it is in quadrant III. The reference angle is $\theta' = 205° - 180° = 25°$.

39. Because $355°$ lies between $270°$ and $360°$, it is in quadrant IV. The reference angle is $\theta' = 360° - 355° = 5°$.

41. Because $\frac{7\pi}{4}$ lies between $\frac{3\pi}{2} = \frac{6\pi}{4}$ and $2\pi = \frac{8\pi}{4}$, it is in quadrant IV. The reference angle is $\theta' = 2\pi - \frac{7\pi}{4} = \frac{8\pi}{4} - \frac{7\pi}{4} = \frac{\pi}{4}$.

43. Because $\frac{5\pi}{6}$ lies between $\frac{\pi}{2} = \frac{3\pi}{6}$ and $\pi = \frac{6\pi}{6}$, it is in quadrant II. The reference angle is $\theta' = \pi - \frac{5\pi}{6} = \frac{6\pi}{6} - \frac{5\pi}{6} = \frac{\pi}{6}$.

45. $-150° + 360° = 210°$

Because the angle is in quadrant III, the reference angle is $\theta' = 210° - 180° = 30°$.

47. $-335° + 360° = 25°$

Because the angle is in quadrant I, the reference angle is $\theta' = 25°$.

49. Because 4.7 lies between $\pi \approx 3.14$ and $\frac{3\pi}{2} \approx 4.71$, it is in quadrant III. The reference angle is $\theta' = 4.7 - \pi \approx 1.56$.

51. $565° - 360° = 205°$

Because the angle is in quadrant III, the reference angle is $\theta' = 205° - 180° = 25°$.

53. $\frac{17\pi}{6} - 2\pi = \frac{17\pi}{6} - \frac{12\pi}{6} = \frac{5\pi}{6}$

Because the angle is in quadrant II, the reference angle is $\theta' = \pi - \frac{5\pi}{6} = \frac{\pi}{6}$.

55. $\dfrac{23\pi}{4} - 4\pi = \dfrac{23\pi}{4} - \dfrac{16\pi}{4} = \dfrac{7\pi}{4}$

Because the angle is in quadrant IV, the

reference angle is $\theta' = 2\pi - \dfrac{7\pi}{4} = \dfrac{\pi}{4}$.

57. $-\dfrac{11\pi}{4} + 4\pi = -\dfrac{11\pi}{4} + \dfrac{16\pi}{4} = \dfrac{5\pi}{4}$

Because the angle is in quadrant III, the

reference angle is $\theta' = \dfrac{5\pi}{4} - \pi = \dfrac{\pi}{4}$.

59. $-\dfrac{25\pi}{6} + 6\pi = -\dfrac{25\pi}{6} + \dfrac{36\pi}{6} = \dfrac{11\pi}{6}$

Because the angle is in quadrant IV, the

reference angle is $\theta' = 2\pi - \dfrac{11\pi}{6} = \dfrac{\pi}{6}$.

61. $225°$ lies in quadrant III. The reference angle is
$\theta' = 225° - 180° = 45°$.

$\cos 45° = \dfrac{\sqrt{2}}{2}$

Because the cosine is negative in quadrant III,

$\cos 225° = -\cos 45° = -\dfrac{\sqrt{2}}{2}$.

63. $210°$ lies in quadrant III. The reference angle is
$\theta' = 210° - 180° = 30°$.

$\tan 30° = \dfrac{\sqrt{3}}{3}$

Because the tangent is positive in quadrant III,

$\tan 210° = \tan 30° = \dfrac{\sqrt{3}}{3}$.

65. $420°$ lies in quadrant I. The reference angle is
$\theta' = 420° - 360° = 60°$.

$\tan 60° = \sqrt{3}$
Because the tangent is positive in quadrant I,
$\tan 420° = \tan 60° = \sqrt{3}$.

67. $\dfrac{2\pi}{3}$ lies in quadrant II. The reference angle is

$\theta' = \pi - \dfrac{2\pi}{3} = \dfrac{3\pi}{3} - \dfrac{2\pi}{3} = \dfrac{\pi}{3}$.

$\sin \dfrac{\pi}{3} = \dfrac{\sqrt{3}}{2}$

Because the sine is positive in quadrant II,

$\sin \dfrac{2\pi}{3} = \sin \dfrac{\pi}{3} = \dfrac{\sqrt{3}}{2}$.

69. $\dfrac{7\pi}{6}$ lies in quadrant III. The reference angle is

$\theta' = \dfrac{7\pi}{6} - \pi = \dfrac{7\pi}{6} - \dfrac{6\pi}{6} = \dfrac{\pi}{6}$.

$\csc \dfrac{\pi}{6} = 2$

Because the cosecant is negative in quadrant III,

$\csc \dfrac{7\pi}{6} = -\csc \dfrac{\pi}{6} = -2$.

71. $\dfrac{9\pi}{4}$ lies in quadrant I. The reference angle is

$\theta' = \dfrac{9\pi}{4} - 2\pi = \dfrac{9\pi}{4} - \dfrac{8\pi}{4} = \dfrac{\pi}{4}$.

$\tan \dfrac{\pi}{4} = 1$

Because the tangent is positive in quadrant I,

$\tan \dfrac{9\pi}{4} = \tan \dfrac{\pi}{4} = 1$

73. $-240°$ lies in quadrant II. The reference angle is
$\theta' = 240° - 180° = 60°$.

$\sin 60° = \dfrac{\sqrt{3}}{2}$

Because the sine is positive in quadrant II,

$\sin(-240°) = \sin 60° = \dfrac{\sqrt{3}}{2}$.

75. $-\dfrac{\pi}{4}$ lies in quadrant IV. The reference angle is

$\theta' = \dfrac{\pi}{4}$.

$\tan \dfrac{\pi}{4} = 1$

Because the tangent is negative in quadrant IV,

$\tan\left(-\dfrac{\pi}{4}\right) = -\tan \dfrac{\pi}{4} = -1$.

77. $\sec 495° = \sec 135° = -\sqrt{2}$

79. $\cot \dfrac{19\pi}{6} = \cot \dfrac{7\pi}{6} = \sqrt{3}$

81. $\cos \dfrac{23\pi}{4} = \cos \dfrac{7\pi}{4} = \dfrac{\sqrt{2}}{2}$

83. $\tan\left(-\dfrac{17\pi}{6}\right) = \tan \dfrac{7\pi}{6} = \dfrac{\sqrt{3}}{3}$

85. $\sin\left(-\dfrac{17\pi}{3}\right) = \sin\dfrac{\pi}{3} = \dfrac{\sqrt{3}}{2}$

87. $\sin\dfrac{\pi}{3}\cos\pi - \cos\dfrac{\pi}{3}\sin\dfrac{3\pi}{2}$

$= \left(\dfrac{\sqrt{3}}{2}\right)(-1) - \left(\dfrac{1}{2}\right)(-1)$

$= -\dfrac{\sqrt{3}}{2} + \dfrac{1}{2}$

$= \dfrac{1-\sqrt{3}}{2}$

89. $\sin\dfrac{11\pi}{4}\cos\dfrac{5\pi}{6} + \cos\dfrac{11\pi}{4}\sin\dfrac{5\pi}{6}$

$= \left(\dfrac{\sqrt{2}}{2}\right)\left(-\dfrac{\sqrt{3}}{2}\right) + \left(-\dfrac{\sqrt{2}}{2}\right)\left(\dfrac{1}{2}\right)$

$= -\dfrac{\sqrt{6}}{4} - \dfrac{\sqrt{2}}{4}$

$= -\dfrac{\sqrt{6}+\sqrt{2}}{4}$

91. $\sin\dfrac{3\pi}{2}\tan\left(-\dfrac{15\pi}{4}\right) - \cos\left(-\dfrac{5\pi}{3}\right)$

$= (-1)(1) - \left(\dfrac{1}{2}\right)$

$= -1 - \dfrac{1}{2}$

$= -\dfrac{2}{2} - \dfrac{1}{2}$

$= -\dfrac{3}{2}$

93. $f\left(\dfrac{4\pi}{3} + \dfrac{\pi}{6}\right) + f\left(\dfrac{4\pi}{3}\right) + f\left(\dfrac{\pi}{6}\right)$

$= \sin\left(\dfrac{4\pi}{3} + \dfrac{\pi}{6}\right) + \sin\dfrac{4\pi}{3} + \sin\dfrac{\pi}{6}$

$= \sin\dfrac{3\pi}{2} + \sin\dfrac{4\pi}{3} + \sin\dfrac{\pi}{6}$

$= (-1) + \left(-\dfrac{\sqrt{3}}{2}\right) + \left(\dfrac{1}{2}\right)$

$= -\dfrac{\sqrt{3}+1}{2}$

95. $(h \circ g)\left(\dfrac{17\pi}{3}\right) = h\left(g\left(\dfrac{17\pi}{3}\right)\right)$

$= 2\left(\cos\left(\dfrac{17\pi}{3}\right)\right)$

$= 2\left(\dfrac{1}{2}\right)$

$= 1$

97. The average rate of change is the slope of the line through the points $\left(x_1, f(x_1)\right)$ and $\left(x_2, f(x_2)\right)$

$m = \dfrac{f(x_2) - f(x_1)}{x_2 - x_1}$

$= \dfrac{\sin\left(\dfrac{3\pi}{2}\right) - \sin\left(\dfrac{5\pi}{4}\right)}{\dfrac{3\pi}{2} - \dfrac{5\pi}{4}}$

$= \dfrac{-1 - \left(-\dfrac{\sqrt{2}}{2}\right)}{\dfrac{\pi}{4}}$

$= \dfrac{-1 + \dfrac{\sqrt{2}}{2}}{\dfrac{\pi}{4}}$

$= \dfrac{4\left(-1 + \dfrac{\sqrt{2}}{2}\right)}{4\left(\dfrac{\pi}{4}\right)}$

$= \dfrac{2\sqrt{2} - 4}{\pi}$

99. $\sin \theta = \dfrac{\sqrt{2}}{2}$ when the reference angle is $\dfrac{\pi}{4}$ and

θ is in quadrants I or II.

$\underline{\text{QI}}$	$\underline{\text{QII}}$
$\theta = \dfrac{\pi}{4}$	$\theta = \pi - \dfrac{\pi}{4}$
	$= \dfrac{3\pi}{4}$

$\theta = \dfrac{\pi}{4}, \dfrac{3\pi}{4}$

101. $\sin \theta = -\dfrac{\sqrt{2}}{2}$ when the reference angle is $\dfrac{\pi}{4}$

and θ is in quadrants III or IV.

$\underline{\text{QIII}}$	$\underline{\text{QIV}}$
$\theta = \pi + \dfrac{\pi}{4}$	$\theta = 2\pi - \dfrac{\pi}{4}$
$= \dfrac{5\pi}{4}$	$= \dfrac{7\pi}{4}$

$\theta = \dfrac{5\pi}{4}, \dfrac{7\pi}{4}$

103. $\tan \theta = -\sqrt{3}$ when the reference angle is $\dfrac{\pi}{3}$ and

θ is in quadrants II or IV.

$\underline{\text{QII}}$	$\underline{\text{QIV}}$
$\theta = \pi - \dfrac{\pi}{3}$	$\theta = 2\pi - \dfrac{\pi}{3}$
$= \dfrac{2\pi}{3}$	$= \dfrac{5\pi}{3}$

$\theta = \dfrac{2\pi}{3}, \dfrac{5\pi}{3}$

Mid-Chapter 4 Check Point

1. $10° = 10° \cdot \dfrac{\pi \text{ radians}}{180°} = \dfrac{10\pi}{180}$ radians

$= \dfrac{\pi}{18}$ radians

2. $-105° = -105° \cdot \dfrac{\pi \text{ radians}}{180°} = -\dfrac{105\pi}{180}$ radians

$= -\dfrac{7\pi}{12}$ radians

3. $\dfrac{5\pi}{12}$ radians $= \dfrac{5\pi \text{ radians}}{12} \cdot \dfrac{180°}{\pi \text{ radians}} = 75°$

4. $-\dfrac{13\pi}{20}$ radians $= -\dfrac{13\pi \text{ radians}}{20} \cdot \dfrac{180°}{\pi \text{ radians}}$

$= -117°$

5. **a.** $\dfrac{11\pi}{3} - 2\pi = \dfrac{11\pi}{3} - \dfrac{6\pi}{3} = \dfrac{5\pi}{3}$

b.

c. Since $\dfrac{5\pi}{3}$ is in quadrant IV, the reference

angle is $2\pi - \dfrac{5\pi}{3} = \dfrac{6\pi}{3} - \dfrac{5\pi}{3} = \dfrac{\pi}{3}$

6. **a.** $-\dfrac{19\pi}{4} + 6\pi = -\dfrac{19\pi}{4} + \dfrac{24\pi}{4} = \dfrac{5\pi}{4}$

b.

c. Since $\dfrac{5\pi}{4}$ is in quadrant III, the reference

angle is $\dfrac{5\pi}{4} - \pi = \dfrac{5\pi}{4} - \dfrac{4\pi}{4} = \dfrac{\pi}{4}$

7. **a.** $510° - 360° = 150°$

b.

c. Since $150°$ is in quadrant II, the reference

angle is $180° - 150° = 30°$

8. $r = \sqrt{x^2 + y^2}$

$$r = \sqrt{\left(-\frac{3}{5}\right)^2 + \left(-\frac{4}{5}\right)^2} = \sqrt{\frac{9}{25} + \frac{16}{25}} = \sqrt{\frac{25}{25}} = 1$$

Now that we know x, y, and r, we can find the six trigonometric functions of θ.

$$\sin\theta = \frac{y}{r} = \frac{-\frac{4}{5}}{1} = -\frac{4}{5}$$

$$\cos\theta = \frac{x}{r} = \frac{-\frac{3}{5}}{1} = -\frac{3}{5}$$

$$\tan\theta = \frac{y}{x} = \frac{-\frac{4}{5}}{-\frac{3}{5}} = \frac{4}{3}$$

$$\csc\theta = \frac{r}{y} = \frac{1}{-\frac{4}{5}} = -\frac{5}{4}$$

$$\sec\theta = \frac{r}{x} = \frac{1}{-\frac{3}{5}} = -\frac{5}{3}$$

$$\cot\theta = \frac{x}{y} = \frac{-\frac{3}{5}}{-\frac{4}{5}} = \frac{3}{4}$$

9.   Use the Pythagorean theorem to find b.

$$a^2 + b^2 = c^2$$
$$5^2 + b^2 = 6^2$$
$$25 + b^2 = 36$$
$$b^2 = 11$$
$$b = \sqrt{11}$$

$$\sin\theta = \frac{\text{opposite}}{\text{hypotenuse}} = \frac{5}{6}$$

$$\cos\theta = \frac{\text{adjacent}}{\text{hypotenuse}} = \frac{\sqrt{11}}{6}$$

$$\tan\theta = \frac{\text{opposite}}{\text{adjacent}} = \frac{5\sqrt{11}}{11}$$

$$\csc\theta = \frac{\text{hypotenuse}}{\text{opposite}} = \frac{6}{5}$$

$$\sec\theta = \frac{\text{hypotenuse}}{\text{adjacent}} = \frac{6}{\sqrt{11}} = \frac{6\sqrt{11}}{11}$$

$$\cot\theta = \frac{\text{adjacent}}{\text{opposite}} = \frac{\sqrt{11}}{5}$$

10. $r = \sqrt{x^2 + y^2}$

$$r = \sqrt{3^2 + (-2)^2} = \sqrt{9+4} = \sqrt{13}$$

Now that we know x, y, and r, we can find the six trigonometric functions of θ.

$$\sin\theta = \frac{y}{r} = \frac{-2}{\sqrt{13}} = -\frac{2\sqrt{13}}{13}$$

$$\cos\theta = \frac{x}{r} = \frac{3}{\sqrt{13}} = \frac{3\sqrt{13}}{13}$$

$$\tan\theta = \frac{y}{x} = \frac{-2}{3} = -\frac{2}{3}$$

$$\csc\theta = \frac{r}{y} = \frac{\sqrt{13}}{-2} = -\frac{\sqrt{13}}{2}$$

$$\sec\theta = \frac{r}{x} = \frac{\sqrt{13}}{3}$$

$$\cot\theta = \frac{x}{y} = \frac{3}{-2} = -\frac{3}{2}$$

11.   Because the tangent is negative and the cosine is negative, θ is in quadrant II. In quadrant II, x is negative and y is positive. Thus,

$$\tan\theta = -\frac{3}{4} = \frac{x}{y}, \quad x = -4,\ y = 3.$$ Furthermore,

$$r^2 = x^2 + y^2$$
$$r^2 = (-3)^2 + 4^2$$
$$r^2 = 9 + 16 = 25$$
$$r = 5$$

Now that we know x, y, and r, we can find the remaining trigonometric functions of θ.

$$\sin\theta = \frac{y}{r} = \frac{3}{5}$$

$$\cos\theta = \frac{x}{r} = \frac{-4}{5} = -\frac{4}{5}$$

$$\csc\theta = \frac{r}{y} = \frac{5}{3}$$

$$\sec\theta = \frac{r}{x} = \frac{5}{-3} = -\frac{5}{4}$$

$$\cot\theta = \frac{x}{y} = \frac{-3}{4} = -\frac{4}{3}$$

12. Since $\cos\theta = \dfrac{3}{7} = \dfrac{x}{r}$, $x = 3$, $r = 7$. Furthermore,

$$x^2 + y^2 = r^2$$
$$3^2 + y^2 = 7^2$$
$$9 + y^2 = 49$$
$$y^2 = 40$$
$$y = \pm\sqrt{40} = \pm 2\sqrt{10}$$

Because the cosine is positive and the sine is negative, θ is in quadrant IV. In quadrant IV, x is positive and y is negative.

Therefore $y = -2\sqrt{10}$

Use x, y, and r to find the remaining trigonometric functions of θ.

$$\sin\theta = \frac{y}{r} = \frac{-2\sqrt{10}}{7} = -\frac{2\sqrt{10}}{7}$$

$$\tan\theta = \frac{y}{x} = \frac{-2\sqrt{10}}{3} = -\frac{2\sqrt{10}}{3}$$

$$\csc\theta = \frac{r}{y} = \frac{7}{-2\sqrt{10}} = -\frac{7\sqrt{10}}{20}$$

$$\sec\theta = \frac{r}{x} = \frac{7}{3}$$

$$\cot\theta = \frac{x}{y} = \frac{3}{-2\sqrt{10}} = -\frac{3\sqrt{10}}{20}$$

13. $\tan\theta = \dfrac{\text{side opposite } \theta}{\text{side adjacent } \theta}$

$$\tan 41° = \frac{a}{60}$$
$$a = 60\tan 41°$$
$$a \approx 52 \text{ cm}$$

14. $\cos\theta = \dfrac{\text{side adjacent } \theta}{\text{hypotenuse}}$

$$\cos 72° = \frac{250}{c}$$
$$c = \frac{250}{\cos 72°}$$
$$c \approx 809 \text{ m}$$

15. Since $\cos\theta = \dfrac{1}{6} = \dfrac{x}{r}$, $x = 1$, $r = 6$. Furthermore,

$$x^2 + y^2 = r^2$$
$$1^2 + y^2 = 6^2$$
$$1 + y^2 = 36$$
$$y^2 = 35$$
$$y = \pm\sqrt{35}$$

Since θ is acute, $y = +\sqrt{35} = \sqrt{35}$

$$\cot\left(\frac{\pi}{2} - \theta\right) = \tan\theta = \frac{y}{x} = \frac{\sqrt{35}}{1} = \sqrt{35}$$

16. $\tan 30° = \dfrac{\sqrt{3}}{3}$

17. $\cot 120° = \dfrac{1}{\tan 120°} = \dfrac{1}{-\tan 60°} = \dfrac{1}{-\sqrt{3}} = -\dfrac{\sqrt{3}}{3}$

18. $\cos 240° = -\cos 60° = -\dfrac{1}{2}$

19. $\sec\dfrac{11\pi}{6} = \dfrac{1}{\cos\dfrac{11\pi}{6}} = \dfrac{1}{\cos\dfrac{\pi}{6}} = \dfrac{1}{\dfrac{\sqrt{3}}{2}} = \dfrac{2}{\sqrt{3}} = \dfrac{2\sqrt{3}}{3}$

20. $\sin^2\dfrac{\pi}{7} + \cos^2\dfrac{\pi}{7} = 1$

21. $\sin\left(-\dfrac{2\pi}{3}\right) = \sin\left(-\dfrac{2\pi}{3} + 2\pi\right)$

$$= \sin\frac{4\pi}{3} = -\sin\frac{\pi}{3}$$
$$= -\frac{\sqrt{3}}{2}$$

22. $\csc\left(\dfrac{22\pi}{3}\right) = \csc\left(\dfrac{22\pi}{3} - 6\pi\right) = \csc\dfrac{4\pi}{3}$

$$= \frac{1}{\sin\dfrac{4\pi}{3}} = \frac{1}{-\sin\dfrac{\pi}{3}} = \frac{1}{-\dfrac{\sqrt{3}}{2}}$$

$$= -\frac{2}{\sqrt{3}} = -\frac{2\sqrt{3}}{3}$$

23. $\cos 495° = \cos(495° - 360°) = \cos 135°$

$$= -\cos 45° = -\frac{\sqrt{2}}{2}$$

24. $\tan\left(-\dfrac{17\pi}{6}\right) = \tan\left(-\dfrac{17\pi}{6} + 4\pi\right) = \tan\dfrac{7\pi}{6}$

$\qquad\qquad = \tan\dfrac{\pi}{6} = \dfrac{\sqrt{3}}{3}$

25. $\sin^2\dfrac{\pi}{2} - \cos\pi = (1)^2 - (-1) = 1 + 1 = 2$

26. $\cos\left(\dfrac{5\pi}{6} + 2\pi n\right) + \tan\left(\dfrac{5\pi}{6} + n\pi\right)$

$\qquad = \cos\dfrac{5\pi}{6} + \tan\dfrac{5\pi}{6} = -\cos\dfrac{\pi}{6} - \tan\dfrac{\pi}{6}$

$\qquad = -\dfrac{\sqrt{3}}{2} - \dfrac{\sqrt{3}}{3} = -\dfrac{3\sqrt{3}}{6} - \dfrac{2\sqrt{3}}{6}$

$\qquad = -\dfrac{5\sqrt{3}}{6}$

27. Begin by converting from degrees to radians.

$36° = 36° \cdot \dfrac{\pi \text{ radians}}{180°} = \dfrac{\pi}{5} \text{ radians}$

$s = r\theta = 40 \cdot \dfrac{\pi}{5} = 8\pi \approx 25.13 \text{ cm}$

28. Linear speed is given by $v = r\omega$. It is given that $r = 10$ feet and the merry-go-round rotates at 8 revolutions per minute. Convert 8 revolutions per minute to radians per minute.
8 revolutions per minute

$= 8 \text{ revolutions per minute} \cdot \dfrac{2\pi \text{ radians}}{1 \text{ revolution}}$

$= 16\pi \text{ radians per minute}$

$v = r\omega = (10)(16\pi) = 160\pi \approx 502.7 \text{ feet per minute}$

The linear speed of the horse is about 502.7 feet per minute.

29. $\sin\theta = \dfrac{\text{side opposite }\theta}{\text{hypotenuse}}$

$\sin 6° = \dfrac{h}{5280}$

$\qquad h = 5280\sin 6°$

$\qquad h \approx 551.9 \text{ feet}$

30. $\tan\theta = \dfrac{\text{side opposite }\theta}{\text{side adjacent }\theta}$

$\tan\theta = \dfrac{50}{60}$

$\qquad \theta = \tan^{-1}\left(\dfrac{50}{60}\right)$

$\qquad \theta \approx 40°$

Section 4.5

Checkpoint Exercises

1. The equation $y = 3\sin x$ is of the form $y = A\sin x$ with $A = 3$. Thus, the amplitude is $|A| = |3| = 3$ The period for both $y = 3\sin x$ and $y = \sin x$ is 2π. We find the three x-intercepts, the maximum point, and the minimum point on the interval $[0, 2\pi]$ by dividing the period, 2π, by 4, $\dfrac{\text{period}}{4} = \dfrac{2\pi}{4} = \dfrac{\pi}{2}$, then by adding quarter-periods to generate x-values for each of the key points. The five x-values are

$x = 0$

$x = 0 + \dfrac{\pi}{2} = \dfrac{\pi}{2}$

$x = \dfrac{\pi}{2} + \dfrac{\pi}{2} = \pi$

$x = \pi + \dfrac{\pi}{2} = \dfrac{3\pi}{2}$

$x = \dfrac{3\pi}{2} + \dfrac{\pi}{2} = 2\pi$

Evaluate the function at each value of x.

x	$y = 3\sin x$	coordinates
0	$y = 3\sin 0 = 3\cdot 0 = 0$	$(0, 0)$
$\dfrac{\pi}{2}$	$y = 3\sin\dfrac{\pi}{2} = 3\cdot 1 = 3$	$\left(\dfrac{\pi}{2}, 3\right)$
π	$y = 3\sin x = 3\cdot 0 = 0$	$(\pi, 0)$
$\dfrac{3\pi}{2}$	$y = 3\sin\dfrac{3\pi}{2}$ $= 3(-1) = -3$	$\left(\dfrac{3\pi}{2}, -3\right)$
2π	$y = 3\sin 2\pi = 3\cdot 0 = 0$	$(2\pi, 0)$

Connect the five points with a smooth curve and graph one complete cycle of the given function with the graph of $y = \sin x$.

2. The equation $y = -\dfrac{1}{2}\sin x$ is of the form

$y = A\sin x$ with $A = -\dfrac{1}{2}$. Thus, the amplitude is

$|A| = \left|-\dfrac{1}{2}\right| = \dfrac{1}{2}$. The period for both

$y = -\dfrac{1}{2}\sin x$ and $y = \sin x$ is 2π.

Find the x–values for the five key points by dividing the period, 2π, by 4,

$\dfrac{\text{period}}{4} = \dfrac{2\pi}{4} = \dfrac{\pi}{2}$, then by adding quarter-

periods. The five x-values are
$x = 0$

$x = 0 + \dfrac{\pi}{2} = \dfrac{\pi}{2}$

$x = \dfrac{\pi}{2} + \dfrac{\pi}{2} = \pi$

$x = \pi + \dfrac{\pi}{2} = \dfrac{3\pi}{2}$

$x = \dfrac{3\pi}{2} + \dfrac{\pi}{2} = 2\pi$

Evaluate the function at each value of x.

x	$y = -\dfrac{1}{2}\sin x$	coordinates
0	$y = -\dfrac{1}{2}\sin 0$ $= -\dfrac{1}{2}\cdot 0 = 0$	$(0, 0)$
$\dfrac{\pi}{2}$	$y = -\dfrac{1}{2}\sin\dfrac{\pi}{2}$ $= -\dfrac{1}{2}\cdot 1 = -\dfrac{1}{2}$	$\left(\dfrac{\pi}{2}, -\dfrac{1}{2}\right)$
π	$y = -\dfrac{1}{2}\sin \pi$ $= -\dfrac{1}{2}\cdot 0 = 0$	$(\pi, 0)$
$\dfrac{3\pi}{2}$	$y = -\dfrac{1}{2}\sin\dfrac{3\pi}{2}$ $= -\dfrac{1}{2}(-1) = \dfrac{1}{2}$	$\left(\dfrac{3\pi}{2}, \dfrac{1}{2}\right)$
2π	$y = -\dfrac{1}{2}\sin 2\pi$ $= -\dfrac{1}{2}\cdot 0 = 0$	$(2\pi, 0)$

Connect the five key points with a smooth curve and graph one complete cycle of the given function with the graph of $y = \sin x$. Extend the pattern of each graph to the left and right as desired.

3. The equation $y = 2\sin\dfrac{1}{2}x$ is of the form

$y = A\sin Bx$ with $A = 2$ and $B = \dfrac{1}{2}$.
The amplitude is $|A| = |2| = 2$.

The period is $\dfrac{2\pi}{B} = \dfrac{2\pi}{\frac{1}{2}} = 4\pi$.

Find the x–values for the five key points by dividing the period, 4π, by 4,

$\dfrac{\text{period}}{4} = \dfrac{4\pi}{4} = \pi$, then by adding quarter-

periods.
The five x-values are
$x = 0$

$x = 0 + \pi = \pi$

$x = \pi + \pi = 2\pi$

$x = 2\pi + \pi = 3\pi$

$x = 3\pi + \pi = 4\pi$

Evaluate the function at each value of x.

x	$y = 2\sin\dfrac{1}{2}x$	coordinates
0	$y = 2\sin\left(\dfrac{1}{2}\cdot 0\right)$ $= 2\sin 0$ $= 2\cdot 0 = 0$	$(0, 0)$
π	$y = 2\sin\left(\dfrac{1}{2}\cdot \pi\right)$ $= 2\sin\dfrac{\pi}{2} = 2\cdot 1 = 2$	$(\pi, 2)$
2π	$y = 2\sin\left(\dfrac{1}{2}\cdot 2\pi\right)$ $= 2\sin \pi = 2\cdot 0 = 0$	$(2\pi, 0)$

3π	$y = 2\sin\left(\frac{1}{2}\cdot 3\pi\right)$ $= 2\sin\frac{3\pi}{2}$ $= 2\cdot(-1) = -2$	$(3\pi, -2)$
4π	$y = 2\sin\left(\frac{1}{2}\cdot 4\pi\right)$ $= 2\sin 2\pi = 2\cdot 0 = 0$	$(4\pi, 0)$

Connect the five key points with a smooth curve and graph one complete cycle of the given function. Extend the pattern of the graph another full period to the right.

$$y = 2\sin\frac{1}{2}x$$

4. The equation $y = 3\sin\left(2x - \frac{\pi}{3}\right)$ is of the form

   $y = A\sin(Bx - C)$ with $A = 3$, $B = 2$, and $C = \frac{\pi}{3}$.

   The amplitude is $|A| = |3| = 3$.

   The period is $\frac{2\pi}{B} = \frac{2\pi}{2} = \pi$.

   The phase shift is $\frac{C}{B} = \frac{\frac{\pi}{3}}{2} = \frac{\pi}{3}\cdot\frac{1}{2} = \frac{\pi}{6}$.

   Find the x-values for the five key points by

   dividing the period, π, by 4, $\frac{\text{period}}{4} = \frac{\pi}{4}$, then

   by adding quarter-periods to the value of x

   where the cycle begins, $x = \frac{\pi}{6}$.

   The five x-values are

$x = \frac{\pi}{6}$

$x = \frac{\pi}{6} + \frac{\pi}{4} = \frac{2\pi}{12} + \frac{3\pi}{12} = \frac{5\pi}{12}$

$x = \frac{5\pi}{12} + \frac{\pi}{4} = \frac{5\pi}{12} + \frac{3\pi}{12} = \frac{8\pi}{12} = \frac{2\pi}{3}$

$x = \frac{2\pi}{3} + \frac{\pi}{4} = \frac{8\pi}{12} + \frac{3\pi}{12} = \frac{11\pi}{12}$

$x = \frac{11\pi}{12} + \frac{\pi}{4} = \frac{11\pi}{12} + \frac{3\pi}{12} = \frac{14\pi}{12} = \frac{7\pi}{6}$

Evaluate the function at each value of x.

x	$y = 3\sin\left(2x - \frac{\pi}{3}\right)$	coordinates
$\frac{\pi}{6}$	$y = 3\sin\left(2\cdot\frac{\pi}{6} - \frac{\pi}{3}\right)$ $= 3\sin 0 = 3\cdot 0 = 0$	$\left(\frac{\pi}{6}, 0\right)$
$\frac{5\pi}{12}$	$y = 3\sin\left(2\cdot\frac{5\pi}{12} - \frac{\pi}{3}\right)$ $= 3\sin\frac{3\pi}{6} = 3\sin\frac{\pi}{2}$ $= 3\cdot 1 = 3$	$\left(\frac{5\pi}{12}, 3\right)$
$\frac{2\pi}{3}$	$y = 3\sin\left(2\cdot\frac{2\pi}{3} - \frac{\pi}{3}\right)$ $= 3\sin\frac{3\pi}{3} = 3\sin\pi$ $= 3\cdot 0 = 0$	$\left(\frac{2\pi}{3}, 0\right)$
$\frac{11\pi}{12}$	$y = 3\sin\left(2\cdot\frac{11\pi}{12} - \frac{\pi}{3}\right)$ $= 3\sin\frac{9\pi}{6} = 3\sin\frac{3\pi}{2}$ $= 3(-1) = -3$	$\left(\frac{11\pi}{12}, -3\right)$
$\frac{7\pi}{6}$	$y = 3\sin\left(2\cdot\frac{7\pi}{6} - \frac{\pi}{3}\right)$ $= 3\sin\frac{6\pi}{3} = 3\sin 2\pi$ $= 3\cdot 0 = 0$	$\left(\frac{7\pi}{6}, 0\right)$

Connect the five key points with a smooth curve and graph one complete cycle of the given graph.

$$y = 3\sin\left(2x - \frac{\pi}{3}\right)$$

5. The equation $y = -4\cos\pi x$ is of the form
    $y = A\cos Bx$ with $A = -4$, and $B = \pi$.
    Thus, the amplitude is $|A| = |-4| = 4$.

    The period is $\frac{2\pi}{B} = \frac{2\pi}{\pi} = 2$.

    Find the x-values for the five key points by

    dividing the period, 2, by 4, $\frac{\text{period}}{4} = \frac{2}{4} = \frac{1}{2}$,

    then by adding quarter periods to the value of x
    where the cycle begins. The five x-values are
    $x = 0$

    $x = 0 + \frac{1}{2} = \frac{1}{2}$

    $x = \frac{1}{2} + \frac{1}{2} = 1$

    $x = 1 + \frac{1}{2} = \frac{3}{2}$

    $x = \frac{3}{2} + \frac{1}{2} = 2$

    Evaluate the function at each value of x.

x	$y = -4\cos\pi x$	coordinates
0	$y = -4\cos(\pi \cdot 0)$ $= -4\cos 0 = -4$	$(0, -4)$
$\frac{1}{2}$	$y = -4\cos\left(\pi \cdot \frac{1}{2}\right)$ $= -4\cos\frac{\pi}{2} = 0$	$\left(\frac{1}{2}, 0\right)$
1	$y = -4\cos(\pi \cdot 1)$ $= -4\cos\pi = 4$	$(1, 4)$
$\frac{3}{2}$	$y = -4\cos\left(\pi \cdot \frac{3}{2}\right)$ $= -4\cos\frac{3\pi}{2} = 0$	$\left(\frac{3}{2}, 0\right)$
2	$y = -4\cos(\pi \cdot 2)$ $= -4\cos 2\pi = -4$	$(2, -4)$

Connect the five key points with a smooth curve
and graph one complete cycle of the given
function. Extend the pattern of the graph another
full period to the left.

$$y = -4\cos\pi x$$

6. $y = \frac{3}{2}\cos(2x + \pi) = \frac{3}{2}\cos(2x - (-\pi))$

    The equation is of the form $y = A\cos(Bx - C)$

    with $A = \frac{3}{2}$, $B = 2$, and $C = -\pi$.

    Thus, the amplitude is $|A| = \left|\frac{3}{2}\right| = \frac{3}{2}$.

    The period is $\frac{2\pi}{B} = \frac{2\pi}{2} = \pi$.

    The phase shift is $\frac{C}{B} = \frac{-\pi}{2} = -\frac{\pi}{2}$.

    Find the x-values for the five key points by

    dividing the period, π, by 4, $\frac{\text{period}}{4} = \frac{\pi}{4}$, then

    by adding quarter-periods to the value of x

    where the cycle begins, $x = -\frac{\pi}{2}$.

    The five x-values are

    $x = -\frac{\pi}{2}$

    $x = -\frac{\pi}{2} + \frac{\pi}{4} = -\frac{\pi}{4}$

    $x = -\frac{\pi}{4} + \frac{\pi}{4} = 0$

    $x = 0 + \frac{\pi}{4} = \frac{\pi}{4}$

    $x = \frac{\pi}{4} + \frac{\pi}{4} = \frac{\pi}{2}$

    Evaluate the function at each value of x.

x	$y = \frac{3}{2}\cos(2x + \pi)$	coordinates
$-\frac{\pi}{2}$	$y = \frac{3}{2}\cos(-\pi + \pi)$ $= \frac{3}{2} \cdot 1 = \frac{3}{2}$	$\left(-\frac{\pi}{2}, \frac{3}{2}\right)$

$-\dfrac{\pi}{4}$	$y = \dfrac{3}{2}\cos\left(-\dfrac{\pi}{2}+\pi\right)$ $= \dfrac{3}{2}\cdot 0 = 0$	$\left(-\dfrac{\pi}{4},\,0\right)$
0	$y = \dfrac{3}{2}\cos(0+\pi)$ $= \dfrac{3}{2}\cdot -1 = -\dfrac{3}{2}$	$\left(0,\,-\dfrac{3}{2}\right)$
$\dfrac{\pi}{4}$	$y = \dfrac{3}{2}\cos\left(\dfrac{\pi}{2}+\pi\right)$ $= \dfrac{3}{2}\cdot 0 = 0$	$\left(\dfrac{\pi}{4},\,0\right)$
$\dfrac{\pi}{2}$	$y = \dfrac{3}{2}\cos(\pi+\pi)$ $= \dfrac{3}{2}\cdot 1 = \dfrac{3}{2}$	$\left(\dfrac{\pi}{2},\,\dfrac{3}{2}\right)$

Connect the five key points with a smooth curve and graph one complete cycle of the given graph.

$$y = \frac{3}{2}\cos(2x + \pi)$$

7. The graph of $y = 2\cos x + 1$ is the graph of $y = 2\cos x$ shifted one unit upwards. The period for both functions is 2π. The quarter-period is $\dfrac{2\pi}{4}$ or $\dfrac{\pi}{2}$. The cycle begins at $x = 0$. Add quarter-periods to generate x-values for the key points.

$x = 0$

$x = 0 + \dfrac{\pi}{2} = \dfrac{\pi}{2}$

$x = \dfrac{\pi}{2} + \dfrac{\pi}{2} = \pi$

$x = \pi + \dfrac{\pi}{2} = \dfrac{3\pi}{2}$

$x = \dfrac{3\pi}{2} + \dfrac{\pi}{2} = 2\pi$

Evaluate the function at each value of x.

x	$y = 2\cos x + 1$	coordinates
0	$y = 2\cos 0 + 1$ $= 2\cdot 1 + 1 = 3$	$(0,\,3)$
$\dfrac{\pi}{2}$	$y = 2\cos\dfrac{\pi}{2} + 1$ $= 2\cdot 0 + 1 = 1$	$\left(\dfrac{\pi}{2},\,1\right)$
π	$y = 2\cos\pi + 1$ $= 2\cdot(-1)+1 = -1$	$(\pi,\,-1)$
$\dfrac{3\pi}{2}$	$y = 2\cos\dfrac{3\pi}{2} + 1$ $= 2\cdot 0 + 1 = 1$	$\left(\dfrac{3\pi}{2},\,1\right)$
2π	$y = 2\cos 2\pi + 1$ $= 2\cdot 1 + 1 = 3$	$(2\pi,\,3)$

By connecting the points with a smooth curve, we obtain one period of the graph.

$$y = 2\cos x + 1$$

8. A, the amplitude, is the maximum value of y. The graph shows that this maximum value is 4,

Thus, $A = 4$. The period is $\dfrac{\pi}{2}$, and period

$= \dfrac{2\pi}{B}$.

Thus, $\dfrac{\pi}{2} = \dfrac{2\pi}{B}$

$\pi B = 4\pi$

$B = 4$

Substitute these values into $y = A\sin Bx$.
The graph is modeled by $y = 4\sin 4x$.

9. Because the hours of daylight ranges from a minimum of 10 hours to a maximum of 14 hours, the curve oscillates about the middle value, 12 hours. Thus, $D = 12$. The maximum number of hours is 2 hours above 12 hours. Thus, $A = 2$. The graph shows that one complete cycle occurs in 12–0, or 12 months. The period is 12. Thus,

$$12 = \frac{2\pi}{B}$$

$$12B = 2\pi$$

$$B = \frac{2\pi}{12} = \frac{\pi}{6}$$

The graph shows that the starting point of the cycle is shifted from 0 to 3. The phase shift, $\frac{C}{B}$, is 3.

$$3 = \frac{C}{B}$$

$$3 = \frac{C}{\frac{\pi}{6}}$$

$$\frac{\pi}{2} = C$$

Substitute these values into $y = A\sin(Bx - C) + D$. The number of hours of daylight is modeled by $y = 2\sin\left(\frac{\pi}{6}x - \frac{\pi}{2}\right) + 12$.

Exercise Set 4.5

1. The equation $y = 4\sin x$ is of the form $y = A\sin x$ with $A = 4$. Thus, the amplitude is $|A| = |4| = 4$. The period is 2π. The quarter-period is $\frac{2\pi}{4}$ or $\frac{\pi}{2}$. The cycle begins at $x = 0$. Add quarter-periods to generate x-values for the key points.

    $x = 0$

    $x = 0 + \frac{\pi}{2} = \frac{\pi}{2}$

    $x = \frac{\pi}{2} + \frac{\pi}{2} = \pi$

    $x = \pi + \frac{\pi}{2} = \frac{3\pi}{2}$

    $x = \frac{3\pi}{2} + \frac{\pi}{2} = 2\pi$

    Evaluate the function at each value of x.

x	$y = 4\sin x$	coordinates
0	$y = 4\sin 0 = 4 \cdot 0 = 0$	$(0, 0)$
$\frac{\pi}{2}$	$y = 4\sin\frac{\pi}{2} = 4 \cdot 1 = 4$	$\left(\frac{\pi}{2}, 4\right)$
π	$y = 4\sin\pi = 4 \cdot 0 = 0$	$(\pi, 0)$
$\frac{3\pi}{2}$	$y = 4\sin\frac{3\pi}{2}$ $= 4(-1) = -4$	$\left(\frac{3\pi}{2}, -4\right)$
2π	$y = 4\sin 2\pi = 4 \cdot 0 = 0$	$(2\pi, 0)$

Connect the five key points with a smooth curve and graph one complete cycle of the given function with the graph of $y = \sin x$.

3. The equation $y = \frac{1}{3}\sin x$ is of the form

$y = A\sin x$ with $A = \frac{1}{3}$. Thus, the amplitude is

$|A| = \left|\frac{1}{3}\right| = \frac{1}{3}$. The period is 2π. The quarter-

period is $\frac{2\pi}{4}$ or $\frac{\pi}{2}$. The cycle begins at $x = 0$.

Add quarter-periods to generate x-values for the key points.

$x = 0$

$x = 0 + \frac{\pi}{2} = \frac{\pi}{2}$

$x = \frac{\pi}{2} + \frac{\pi}{2} = \pi$

$x = \pi + \frac{\pi}{2} = \frac{3\pi}{2}$

$x = \frac{3\pi}{2} + \frac{\pi}{2} = 2\pi$

Evaluate the function at each value of x.

x	$y = \frac{1}{3}\sin x$	coordinates
0	$y = \frac{1}{3}\sin 0 = \frac{1}{3}\cdot 0 = 0$	$(0, 0)$
$\frac{\pi}{2}$	$y = \frac{1}{3}\sin\frac{\pi}{2} = \frac{1}{3}\cdot 1 = \frac{1}{3}$	$\left(\frac{\pi}{2}, \frac{1}{3}\right)$
π	$y = \frac{1}{3}\sin\pi = \frac{1}{3}\cdot 0 = 0$	$(\pi, 0)$
$\frac{3\pi}{2}$	$y = \frac{1}{3}\sin\frac{3\pi}{2}$ $= \frac{1}{3}(-1) = -\frac{1}{3}$	$\left(\frac{3\pi}{2}, -\frac{1}{3}\right)$
2π	$y = \frac{1}{3}\sin 2\pi = \frac{1}{3}\cdot 0 = 0$	$(2\pi, 0)$

Connect the five key points with a smooth curve and graph one complete cycle of the given function with the graph of $y = \sin x$.

5. The equation $y = -3\sin x$ is of the form
$y = A\sin x$ with $A = -3$. Thus, the amplitude is
$|A| = |-3| = 3$. The period is 2π. The quarter-
period is $\frac{2\pi}{4}$ or $\frac{\pi}{2}$. The cycle begins at $x = 0$.
Add quarter-periods to generate x-values for the key points.

$x = 0$

$x = 0 + \frac{\pi}{2} = \frac{\pi}{2}$

$x = \frac{\pi}{2} + \frac{\pi}{2} = \pi$

$x = \pi + \frac{\pi}{2} = \frac{3\pi}{2}$

$x = \frac{3\pi}{2} + \frac{\pi}{2} = 2\pi$

Evaluate the function at each value of x.

x	$y = -3\sin x$	coordinates
0	$y = -3\sin x$ $= -3\cdot 0 = 0$	$(0, 0)$
$\frac{\pi}{2}$	$y = -3\sin\frac{\pi}{2}$ $= -3\cdot 1 = -3$	$\left(\frac{\pi}{2}, -3\right)$
π	$y = -3\sin\pi$ $= -3\cdot 0 = 0$	$(\pi, 0)$
$\frac{3\pi}{2}$	$y = -3\sin\frac{3\pi}{2}$ $= -3(-1) = 3$	$\left(\frac{3\pi}{2}, 3\right)$
2π	$y = -3\sin 2\pi$ $= -3\cdot 0 = 0$	$(2\pi, 0)$

Connect the five key points with a smooth curve and graph one complete cycle of the given function with the graph of $y = \sin x$.

7. The equation $y = \sin 2x$ is of the form
$y = A \sin Bx$ with $A = 1$ and $B = 2$. The
amplitude is $|A| = |1| = 1$. The period is
$\frac{2\pi}{B} = \frac{2\pi}{2} = \pi$. The quarter-period is $\frac{\pi}{4}$. The
cycle begins at $x = 0$. Add quarter-periods to
generate x-values for the key points.
$x = 0$

$x = 0 + \frac{\pi}{4}$

$x = \frac{\pi}{4} + \frac{\pi}{4} = \frac{\pi}{2}$

$x = \frac{\pi}{2} + \frac{\pi}{4} = \frac{3\pi}{4}$

$x = \frac{3\pi}{4} + \frac{\pi}{4} = \pi$

Evaluate the function at each value of x.

x	$y = \sin 2x$	coordinates
0	$y = \sin 2 \cdot 0 = \sin 0 = 0$	$(0, 0)$
$\frac{\pi}{4}$	$y = \sin\left(2 \cdot \frac{\pi}{4}\right)$ $= \sin\frac{\pi}{2} = 1$	$\left(\frac{\pi}{4}, 1\right)$
$\frac{\pi}{2}$	$y = \sin\left(2 \cdot \frac{\pi}{2}\right)$ $= \sin \pi = 0$	$\left(\frac{\pi}{2}, 0\right)$
$\frac{3\pi}{4}$	$y = \sin\left(2 \cdot \frac{3\pi}{4}\right)$ $= \sin\frac{3\pi}{2} = -1$	$\left(\frac{3\pi}{4}, -1\right)$
π	$y = \sin(2 \cdot \pi)$ $= \sin 2\pi = 0$	$(\pi, 0)$

Connect the five key points with a smooth curve
and graph one complete cycle of the given
function.

$y = \sin 2x$

9. The equation $y = 3\sin\frac{1}{2}x$ is of the form

$y = A \sin Bx$ with $A = 3$ and $B = \frac{1}{2}$. The

amplitude is $|A| = |3| = 3$. The period is
$\frac{2\pi}{B} = \frac{2\pi}{\frac{1}{2}} = 2\pi \cdot 2 = 4\pi$. The quarter-period is

$\frac{4\pi}{4} = \pi$. The cycle begins at $x = 0$. Add quarter-

periods to generate x-values for the key points.
$x = 0$

$x = 0 + \pi = \pi$

$x = \pi + \pi = 2\pi$

$x = 2\pi + \pi = 3\pi$

$x = 3\pi + \pi = 4\pi$

Evaluate the function at each value of x.

x	$y = 3\sin\frac{1}{2}x$	coordinates
0	$y = 3\sin\left(\frac{1}{2} \cdot 0\right)$ $= 3\sin 0 = 3 \cdot 0 = 0$	$(0, 0)$
π	$y = 3\sin\left(\frac{1}{2} \cdot \pi\right)$ $= 3\sin\frac{\pi}{2} = 3 \cdot 1 = 3$	$(\pi, 3)$
2π	$y = 3\sin\left(\frac{1}{2} \cdot 2\pi\right)$ $= 3\sin \pi = 3 \cdot 0 = 0$	$(2\pi, 0)$
3π	$y = 3\sin\left(\frac{1}{2} \cdot 3\pi\right)$ $= 3\sin\frac{3\pi}{2}$ $= 3(-1) = -3$	$(3\pi, -3)$
4π	$y = 3\sin\left(\frac{1}{2} \cdot 4\pi\right)$ $= 3\sin 2\pi = 3 \cdot 0 = 0$	$(4\pi, 0)$

Connect the five points with a smooth curve and graph one complete cycle of the given function.

$$y = 3\sin\frac{1}{2}x$$

Connect the five points with a smooth curve and graph one complete cycle of the given function.

$$y = 4\sin\pi x$$

11. The equation $y = 4\sin\pi x$ is of the form $y = A\sin Bx$ with $A = 4$ and $B = \pi$. The amplitude is $|A| = |4| = 4$. The period is $\dfrac{2\pi}{B} = \dfrac{2\pi}{\pi} = 2$. The quarter-period is $\dfrac{2}{4} = \dfrac{1}{2}$. The cycle begins at $x = 0$. Add quarter-periods to generate x-values for the key points.

$x = 0$

$x = 0 + \dfrac{1}{2} = \dfrac{1}{2}$

$x = \dfrac{1}{2} + \dfrac{1}{2} = 1$

$x = 1 + \dfrac{1}{2} = \dfrac{3}{2}$

$x = \dfrac{3}{2} + \dfrac{1}{2} = 2$

Evaluate the function at each value of x.

x	$y = 4\sin\pi x$	coordinates
0	$y = 4\sin(\pi \cdot 0)$ $= 4\sin 0 = 4 \cdot 0 = 0$	$(0, 0)$
$\dfrac{1}{2}$	$y = 4\sin\left(\pi \cdot \dfrac{1}{2}\right)$ $= 4\sin\dfrac{\pi}{2} = 4(1) = 4$	$\left(\dfrac{1}{2}, 4\right)$
1	$y = 4\sin(\pi \cdot 1)$ $= 4\sin\pi = 4 \cdot 0 = 0$	$(1, 0)$
$\dfrac{3}{2}$	$y = 4\sin\left(\pi \cdot \dfrac{3}{2}\right)$ $= 4\sin\dfrac{3\pi}{2}$ $= 4(-1) = -4$	$\left(\dfrac{3}{2}, -4\right)$
2	$y = 4\sin(\pi \cdot 2)$ $= 4\sin 2\pi = 4 \cdot 0 = 0$	$(2, 0)$

13. The equation $y = -3\sin 2\pi x$ is of the form $y = A\sin Bx$ with $A = -3$ and $B = 2\pi$. The amplitude is $|A| = |-3| = 3$. The period is $\dfrac{2\pi}{B} = \dfrac{2\pi}{2\pi} = 1$. The quarter-period is $\dfrac{1}{4}$. The cycle begins at $x = 0$. Add quarter-periods to generate x-values for the key points.

$x = 0$

$x = 0 + \dfrac{1}{4} = \dfrac{1}{4}$

$x = \dfrac{1}{4} + \dfrac{1}{4} = \dfrac{1}{2}$

$x = \dfrac{1}{2} + \dfrac{1}{4} = \dfrac{3}{4}$

$x = \dfrac{3}{4} + \dfrac{1}{4} = 1$

Evaluate the function at each value of x.

x	$y = -3\sin 2\pi x$	coordinates
0	$y = -3\sin(2\pi \cdot 0)$ $= -3\sin 0$ $= -3 \cdot 0 = 0$	$(0, 0)$
$\dfrac{1}{4}$	$y = -3\sin\left(2\pi \cdot \dfrac{1}{4}\right)$ $= -3\sin\dfrac{\pi}{2}$ $= -3 \cdot 1 = -3$	$\left(\dfrac{1}{4}, -3\right)$
$\dfrac{1}{2}$	$y = -3\sin\left(2\pi \cdot \dfrac{1}{2}\right)$ $= -3\sin\pi$ $= -3 \cdot 0 = 0$	$\left(\dfrac{1}{2}, 0\right)$

$\dfrac{3}{4}$	$y = -3\sin\left(2\pi \cdot \dfrac{3}{4}\right)$ $= -3\sin\dfrac{3\pi}{2}$ $= -3(-1) = 3$	$\left(\dfrac{3}{4},\,3\right)$
1	$y = -3\sin(2\pi \cdot 1)$ $= -3\sin 2\pi$ $= -3 \cdot 0 = 0$	$(1,\,0)$

Connect the five points with a smooth curve and graph one complete cycle of the given function.

$y = -3\sin 2\pi x$

15. The equation $y = -\sin\dfrac{2}{3}x$ is of the form

$y = A\sin Bx$ with $A = -1$ and $B = \dfrac{2}{3}$. The amplitude is $|A| = |-1| = 1$. The period is $\dfrac{2\pi}{B} = \dfrac{2\pi}{\frac{2}{3}} = 2\pi \cdot \dfrac{3}{2} = 3\pi$. The quarter-period is $\dfrac{3\pi}{4}$. The cycle begins at $x = 0$. Add quarter-periods to generate x-values for the key points.

$x = 0$

$x = 0 + \dfrac{3\pi}{4} = \dfrac{3\pi}{4}$

$x = \dfrac{3\pi}{4} + \dfrac{3\pi}{4} = \dfrac{3\pi}{2}$

$x = \dfrac{3\pi}{2} + \dfrac{3\pi}{4} = \dfrac{9\pi}{4}$

$x = \dfrac{9\pi}{4} + \dfrac{3\pi}{4} = 3\pi$

Evaluate the function at each value of x.

x	$y = -\sin\dfrac{2}{3}x$	coordinates
0	$y = -\sin\left(\dfrac{2}{3} \cdot 0\right)$ $= -\sin 0 = 0$	$(0,\,0)$
$\dfrac{3\pi}{4}$	$y = -\sin\left(\dfrac{2}{3} \cdot \dfrac{3\pi}{4}\right)$ $= -\sin\dfrac{\pi}{2} = -1$	$\left(\dfrac{3\pi}{4},\,-1\right)$
$\dfrac{3\pi}{2}$	$y = -\sin\left(\dfrac{2}{3} \cdot \dfrac{3\pi}{2}\right)$ $= -\sin\pi = 0$	$\left(\dfrac{3\pi}{2},\,0\right)$
$\dfrac{9\pi}{4}$	$y = -\sin\left(\dfrac{2}{3} \cdot \dfrac{9\pi}{4}\right)$ $= -\sin\dfrac{3\pi}{2}$ $= -(-1) = 1$	$\left(\dfrac{9\pi}{4},\,1\right)$
3π	$y = -\sin\left(\dfrac{2}{3} \cdot 3\pi\right)$ $= -\sin 2\pi = 0$	$(3\pi,\,0)$

Connect the five points with a smooth curve and graph one complete cycle of the given function.

$y = -\sin\dfrac{2}{3}x$

17. The equation $y = \sin(x - \pi)$ is of the form $y = A\sin(Bx - C)$ with $A = 1$, $B = 1$, and $C = \pi$. The amplitude is $|A| = |1| = 1$. The period is $\frac{2\pi}{B} = \frac{2\pi}{1} = 2\pi$. The phase shift is $\frac{C}{B} = \frac{\pi}{1} = \pi$.

The quarter-period is $\frac{2\pi}{4} = \frac{\pi}{2}$. The cycle begins at $x = \pi$. Add quarter-periods to generate x-values for the key points.

$$x = \pi$$
$$x = \pi + \frac{\pi}{2} = \frac{3\pi}{2}$$
$$x = \frac{3\pi}{2} + \frac{\pi}{2} = 2\pi$$
$$x = 2\pi + \frac{\pi}{2} = \frac{5\pi}{2}$$
$$x = \frac{5\pi}{2} + \frac{\pi}{2} = 3\pi$$

Evaluate the function at each value of x.

x	$y = \sin(x - \pi)$	coordinates
π	$y = \sin(\pi - \pi)$ $= \sin 0 = 0$	$(\pi, 0)$
$\frac{3\pi}{2}$	$y = \sin\left(\frac{3\pi}{2} - \pi\right)$ $= \sin\frac{\pi}{2} = 1$	$\left(\frac{3\pi}{2}, 1\right)$
2π	$y = \sin(2\pi - \pi)$ $= \sin \pi = 0$	$(2\pi, 0)$
$\frac{5\pi}{2}$	$y = \sin\left(\frac{5\pi}{2} - \pi\right)$ $= \sin\frac{3\pi}{2} = -1$	$\left(\frac{5\pi}{2}, -1\right)$
3π	$y = \sin(3\pi - \pi)$ $= \sin 2\pi = 0$	$(3\pi, 0)$

Connect the five points with a smooth curve and graph one complete cycle of the given function.

$y = \sin(x - \pi)$

19. The equation $y = \sin(2x - \pi)$ is of the form $y = A\sin(Bx - C)$ with $A = 1$, $B = 2$, and $C = \pi$. The amplitude is $|A| = |1| = 1$. The period is $\frac{2\pi}{B} = \frac{2\pi}{2} = \pi$. The phase shift is $\frac{C}{B} = \frac{\pi}{2}$. The quarter-period is $\frac{\pi}{4}$. The cycle begins at $x = \frac{\pi}{2}$. Add quarter-periods to generate x-values for the key points.

$$x = \frac{\pi}{2}$$
$$x = \frac{\pi}{2} + \frac{\pi}{4} = \frac{3\pi}{4}$$
$$x = \frac{3\pi}{4} + \frac{\pi}{4} = \pi$$
$$x = \pi + \frac{\pi}{4} = \frac{5\pi}{4}$$
$$x = \frac{5\pi}{4} + \frac{\pi}{4} = \frac{3\pi}{2}$$

Evaluate the function at each value of x.

x	$y = \sin(2x - \pi)$	coordinates
$\frac{\pi}{2}$	$y = \sin\left(2 \cdot \frac{\pi}{2} - \pi\right)$ $= \sin(\pi - \pi)$ $= \sin 0 = 0$	$\left(\frac{\pi}{2}, 0\right)$
$\frac{3\pi}{4}$	$y = \sin\left(2 \cdot \frac{3\pi}{4} - \pi\right)$ $= \sin\left(\frac{3\pi}{2} - \pi\right)$ $= \sin\frac{\pi}{2} = 1$	$\left(\frac{3\pi}{4}, 1\right)$
π	$y = \sin(2 \cdot \pi - \pi)$ $= \sin(2\pi - \pi)$ $= \sin \pi = 0$	$(\pi, 0)$
$\frac{5\pi}{4}$	$y = \sin\left(2 \cdot \frac{5\pi}{4} - \pi\right)$ $= \sin\left(\frac{5\pi}{2} - \pi\right)$ $= \sin\frac{3\pi}{2} = -1$	$\left(\frac{5\pi}{4}, -1\right)$
$\frac{3\pi}{2}$	$y = \sin\left(2 \cdot \frac{3\pi}{2} - \pi\right)$ $= \sin(3\pi - \pi)$ $= \sin 2\pi = 0$	$\left(\frac{3\pi}{2}, 0\right)$

Connect the five points with a smooth curve and graph one complete cycle of the given function.

$y = \sin(2x - \pi)$

21. The equation $y = 3\sin(2x - \pi)$ is of the form $y = A\sin(Bx - C)$ with $A = 3$, $B = 2$, and $C = \pi$. The amplitude is $|A| = |3| = 3$. The period is $\dfrac{2\pi}{B} = \dfrac{2\pi}{2} = \pi$. The phase shift is $\dfrac{C}{B} = \dfrac{\pi}{2}$. The quarter-period is $\dfrac{\pi}{4}$. The cycle begins at $x = \dfrac{\pi}{2}$. Add quarter-periods to generate x-values for the key points.

$$x = \frac{\pi}{2}$$

$$x = \frac{\pi}{2} + \frac{\pi}{4} = \frac{3\pi}{4}$$

$$x = \frac{3\pi}{4} + \frac{\pi}{4} = \pi$$

$$x = \pi + \frac{\pi}{4} = \frac{5\pi}{4}$$

$$x = \frac{5\pi}{4} + \frac{\pi}{4} = \frac{3\pi}{2}$$

Evaluate the function at each value of x.

x	$y = 3\sin(2x - \pi)$	coordinates
$\dfrac{\pi}{2}$	$y = 3\sin\left(2 \cdot \dfrac{\pi}{2} - \pi\right)$ $= 3\sin(\pi - \pi)$ $= 3\sin 0 = 3 \cdot 0 = 0$	$\left(\dfrac{\pi}{2}, 0\right)$
$\dfrac{3\pi}{4}$	$y = 3\sin\left(2 \cdot \dfrac{3\pi}{4} - \pi\right)$ $= 3\sin\left(\dfrac{3\pi}{2} - \pi\right)$ $= 3\sin\dfrac{\pi}{2} = 3 \cdot 1 = 3$	$\left(\dfrac{3\pi}{4}, 3\right)$
π	$y = 3\sin(2 \cdot \pi - \pi)$ $= 3\sin(2\pi - \pi)$ $= 3\sin \pi = 3 \cdot 0 = 0$	$(\pi, 0)$

| $\dfrac{5\pi}{4}$ | $y = 3\sin\left(2 \cdot \dfrac{5\pi}{4} - \pi\right)$ $= 3\sin\left(\dfrac{5\pi}{2} - \pi\right)$ $= 3\sin\dfrac{3\pi}{2}$ $= 3(-1) = -3$ | $\left(\dfrac{5\pi}{4}, -3\right)$ |
| $\dfrac{3\pi}{2}$ | $y = 3\sin\left(2 \cdot \dfrac{3\pi}{2} - \pi\right)$ $= 3\sin(3\pi - \pi)$ $= 3\sin 2\pi = 3 \cdot 0 = 0$ | $\left(\dfrac{3\pi}{2}, 0\right)$ |

Connect the five points with a smooth curve and graph one complete cycle of the given function.

$y = 3 \sin (2x - \pi)$

23. $y = \dfrac{1}{2}\sin\left(x + \dfrac{\pi}{2}\right) = \dfrac{1}{2}\sin\left(x - \left(-\dfrac{\pi}{2}\right)\right)$

The equation $y = \dfrac{1}{2}\sin\left(x - \left(-\dfrac{\pi}{2}\right)\right)$ is of the form $y = A\sin(Bx - C)$ with $A = \dfrac{1}{2}$, $B = 1$, and $C = -\dfrac{\pi}{2}$. The amplitude is $|A| = \left|\dfrac{1}{2}\right| = \dfrac{1}{2}$. The period is $\dfrac{2\pi}{B} = \dfrac{2\pi}{1} = 2\pi$. The phase shift is $\dfrac{C}{B} = \dfrac{-\frac{\pi}{2}}{1} = -\dfrac{\pi}{2}$. The quarter-period is $\dfrac{2\pi}{4} = \dfrac{\pi}{2}$. The cycle begins at $x = -\dfrac{\pi}{2}$. Add quarter-periods to generate x-values for the key points.

$$x = -\frac{\pi}{2}$$

$$x = -\frac{\pi}{2} + \frac{\pi}{2} = 0$$

$$x = 0 + \frac{\pi}{2} = \frac{\pi}{2}$$

$$x = \frac{\pi}{2} + \frac{\pi}{2} = \pi$$

$$x = \pi + \frac{\pi}{2} = \frac{3\pi}{2}$$

Evaluate the function at each value of x.

x	$y = \frac{1}{2}\sin\left(x + \frac{\pi}{2}\right)$	coordinates
$-\frac{\pi}{2}$	$y = \frac{1}{2}\sin\left(-\frac{\pi}{2} + \frac{\pi}{2}\right)$ $= \frac{1}{2}\sin 0 = \frac{1}{2}\cdot 0 = 0$	$\left(-\frac{\pi}{2}, 0\right)$
0	$y = \frac{1}{2}\sin\left(0 + \frac{\pi}{2}\right)$ $= \frac{1}{2}\sin\frac{\pi}{2} = \frac{1}{2}\cdot 1 = \frac{1}{2}$	$\left(0, \frac{1}{2}\right)$
$\frac{\pi}{2}$	$y = \frac{1}{2}\sin\left(\frac{\pi}{2} + \frac{\pi}{2}\right)$ $= \frac{1}{2}\sin \pi = \frac{1}{2}\cdot 0 = 0$	$\left(\frac{\pi}{2}, 0\right)$
π	$y = \frac{1}{2}\sin\left(\pi + \frac{\pi}{2}\right)$ $= \frac{1}{2}\sin\frac{3\pi}{2}$ $= \frac{1}{2}\cdot(-1) = -\frac{1}{2}$	$\left(\pi, -\frac{1}{2}\right)$
$\frac{3\pi}{2}$	$y = \frac{1}{2}\sin\left(\frac{3\pi}{2} + \frac{\pi}{2}\right)$ $= \frac{1}{2}\sin 2\pi$ $= \frac{1}{2}\cdot 0 = 0$	$\left(\frac{3\pi}{2}, 0\right)$

Connect the five points with a smooth curve and graph one complete cycle of the given function.

$$y = \frac{1}{2}\sin\left(x + \frac{\pi}{2}\right)$$

25. $y = -2\sin\left(2x + \frac{\pi}{2}\right) = -2\sin\left(2x - \left(-\frac{\pi}{2}\right)\right)$

The equation $y = -2\sin\left(2x - \left(-\frac{\pi}{2}\right)\right)$ is of the

form $y = A\sin(Bx - C)$ with $A = -2$,

$B = 2$, and $C = -\frac{\pi}{2}$. The amplitude is

$|A| = |-2| = 2$. The period is $\frac{2\pi}{B} = \frac{2\pi}{2} = \pi$.

The phase shift is $\frac{C}{B} = \frac{-\frac{\pi}{2}}{2} = -\frac{\pi}{2}\cdot\frac{1}{2} = -\frac{\pi}{4}$. The

quarter-period is $\frac{\pi}{4}$. The cycle begins at

$x = -\frac{\pi}{4}$. Add quarter-periods to generate x-

values for the key points.

$$x = -\frac{\pi}{4}$$

$$x = -\frac{\pi}{4} + \frac{\pi}{4} = 0$$

$$x = 0 + \frac{\pi}{4} = \frac{\pi}{4}$$

$$x = \frac{\pi}{4} + \frac{\pi}{4} = \frac{\pi}{2}$$

$$x = \frac{\pi}{2} + \frac{\pi}{4} = \frac{3\pi}{4}$$

Evaluate the function at each value of x.

x	$y = -2\sin\left(2x + \dfrac{\pi}{2}\right)$	coordinates
$-\dfrac{\pi}{4}$	$y = -2\sin\left(2\cdot\left(-\dfrac{\pi}{4}\right) + \dfrac{\pi}{2}\right)$ $= -2\sin\left(-\dfrac{\pi}{2} + \dfrac{\pi}{2}\right)$ $= -2\sin 0 = -2\cdot 0 = 0$	$\left(-\dfrac{\pi}{4}, 0\right)$
0	$y = -2\sin\left(2\cdot 0 + \dfrac{\pi}{2}\right)$ $= -2\sin\left(0 + \dfrac{\pi}{2}\right)$ $= -2\sin\dfrac{\pi}{2}$ $= -2\cdot 1 = -2$	$(0, -2)$
$\dfrac{\pi}{4}$	$y = -2\sin\left(2\cdot\dfrac{\pi}{4} + \dfrac{\pi}{2}\right)$ $= -2\sin\left(\dfrac{\pi}{2} + \dfrac{\pi}{2}\right)$ $= -2\sin\pi$ $= -2\cdot 0 = 0$	$\left(\dfrac{\pi}{4}, 0\right)$
$\dfrac{\pi}{2}$	$y = -2\sin\left(2\cdot\dfrac{\pi}{2} + \dfrac{\pi}{2}\right)$ $= -2\sin\left(\pi + \dfrac{\pi}{2}\right)$ $= -2\sin\dfrac{3\pi}{2}$ $= -2(-1) = 2$	$\left(\dfrac{\pi}{2}, 2\right)$
$\dfrac{3\pi}{4}$	$y = -2\sin\left(2\cdot\dfrac{3\pi}{4} + \dfrac{\pi}{2}\right)$ $= -2\sin\left(\dfrac{3\pi}{2} + \dfrac{\pi}{2}\right)$ $= -2\sin 2\pi$ $= -2\cdot 0 = 0$	$\left(\dfrac{3\pi}{4}, 0\right)$

Connect the five points with a smooth curve and graph one complete cycle of the given function.

$$y = -2\sin\left(2x + \dfrac{\pi}{2}\right)$$

27. $y = 3\sin(\pi x + 2)$

The equation $y = 3\sin(\pi x - (-2))$ is of the form $y = A\sin(Bx - C)$ with $A = 3$, $B = \pi$, and $C = -2$. The amplitude is $|A| = |3| = 3$. The period is $\dfrac{2\pi}{B} = \dfrac{2\pi}{\pi} = 2$. The phase shift is $\dfrac{C}{B} = \dfrac{-2}{\pi} = -\dfrac{2}{\pi}$. The quarter-period is $\dfrac{2}{4} = \dfrac{1}{2}$.

The cycle begins at $x = -\dfrac{2}{\pi}$. Add quarter-periods to generate x-values for the key points.

$x = -\dfrac{2}{\pi}$

$x = -\dfrac{2}{\pi} + \dfrac{1}{2} = \dfrac{\pi - 4}{2\pi}$

$x = \dfrac{\pi - 4}{2\pi} + \dfrac{1}{2} = \dfrac{\pi - 2}{\pi}$

$x = \dfrac{\pi - 2}{\pi} + \dfrac{1}{2} = \dfrac{3\pi - 4}{2\pi}$

$x = \dfrac{3\pi - 4}{2\pi} + \dfrac{1}{2} = \dfrac{2\pi - 2}{\pi}$

Evaluate the function at each value of x.

x	$y = 3\sin(\pi x + 2)$	coordinates
$-\dfrac{2}{\pi}$	$y = 3\sin\left(\pi\left(-\dfrac{2}{\pi}\right) + 2\right)$ $= 3\sin(-2 + 2)$ $= 3\sin 0 = 3\cdot 0 = 0$	$\left(-\dfrac{2}{\pi}, 0\right)$
$\dfrac{\pi - 4}{2\pi}$	$y = 3\sin\left(\pi\left(\dfrac{\pi - 4}{2\pi}\right) + 2\right)$ $= 3\sin\left(\dfrac{\pi - 4}{2} + 2\right)$ $= 3\sin\left(\dfrac{\pi}{2} - 2 + 2\right)$ $= 3\sin\dfrac{\pi}{2}$ $= 3\cdot 1 = 3$	$\left(\dfrac{\pi - 4}{2\pi}, 3\right)$

$\dfrac{\pi-2}{\pi}$	$y = 3\sin\left(\pi\left(\dfrac{\pi-2}{\pi}\right)+2\right)$ $= 3\sin(\pi-2+2)$ $= 3\sin\pi = 3\cdot 0 = 0$	$\left(\dfrac{\pi-2}{\pi},\ 0\right)$
$\dfrac{3\pi-4}{2\pi}$	$y = 3\sin\left(\pi\left(\dfrac{3\pi-4}{2\pi}\right)+2\right)$ $= 3\sin\left(\dfrac{3\pi-4}{2}+2\right)$ $= 3\sin\left(\dfrac{3\pi}{2}-2+2\right)$ $= 3\sin\dfrac{3\pi}{2}$ $= 3(-1) = -3$	$\left(\dfrac{5\pi}{4},\ -3\right)$
$\dfrac{2\pi-2}{\pi}$	$y = 3\sin\left(\pi\left(\dfrac{2\pi-2}{\pi}\right)+2\right)$ $= 3\sin(2\pi-2+2)$ $= 3\sin 2\pi = 3\cdot 0 = 0$	$\left(\dfrac{2\pi-2}{\pi},\ 0\right)$

Connect the five points with a smooth curve and graph one complete cycle of the given function.

$y = 3\sin(\pi x + 2)$

29. $y = -2\sin(2\pi x + 4\pi) = -2\sin(2\pi x - (-4\pi))$
The equation $y = -2\sin(2\pi x - (-4\pi))$ is of the form $y = A\sin(Bx - C)$ with $A = -2$, $B = 2\pi$, and $C = -4\pi$. The amplitude is

$|A| = |-2| = 2$. The period is $\dfrac{2\pi}{B} = \dfrac{2\pi}{2\pi} = 1$.

The phase shift is $\dfrac{C}{B} = \dfrac{-4\pi}{2\pi} = -2$. The quarter-

period is $\dfrac{1}{4}$. The cycle begins at $x = -2$. Add

quarter-periods to generate x-values for the key points.

$x = -2$

$x = -2 + \dfrac{1}{4} = -\dfrac{7}{4}$

$x = -\dfrac{7}{4} + \dfrac{1}{4} = -\dfrac{3}{2}$

$x = -\dfrac{3}{2} + \dfrac{1}{4} = -\dfrac{5}{4}$

$x = -\dfrac{5}{4} + \dfrac{1}{4} = -1$

Evaluate the function at each value of x.

x	$y = -2\sin(2\pi x + 4\pi)$	coordinates
-2	$y = -2\sin(2\pi(-2) + 4\pi)$ $= -2\sin(-4\pi + 4\pi)$ $= -2\sin 0$ $= -2\cdot 0 = 0$	$(-2, 0)$
$-\dfrac{7}{4}$	$y = -2\sin\left(2\pi\left(-\dfrac{7}{4}\right) + 4\pi\right)$ $= -2\sin\left(-\dfrac{7\pi}{2} + 4\pi\right)$ $= -2\sin\dfrac{\pi}{2} = -2\cdot 1 = -2$	$\left(-\dfrac{7}{4}, -2\right)$
$-\dfrac{3}{2}$	$y = -2\sin\left(2\pi\left(-\dfrac{3}{2}\right) + 4\pi\right)$ $= -2\sin(-3\pi + 4\pi)$ $= -2\sin\pi = -2\cdot 0 = 0$	$\left(-\dfrac{3}{2}, 0\right)$
$-\dfrac{5}{4}$	$y = -2\sin\left(2\pi\left(-\dfrac{5}{4}\right) + 4\pi\right)$ $= -2\sin\left(-\dfrac{5\pi}{2} + 4\pi\right)$ $= -2\sin\dfrac{3\pi}{2}$ $= -2(-1) = 2$	$\left(-\dfrac{5}{4}, 2\right)$
-1	$y = -2\sin(2\pi(-1) + 4\pi)$ $= -2\sin(-2\pi + 4\pi)$ $= -2\sin 2\pi$ $= -2\cdot 0 = 0$	$(-1, 0)$

Connect the five points with a smooth curve and graph one complete cycle of the given function.

$y = -2 \sin (2\pi x + 4\pi)$

31. The equation $y = 2 \cos x$ is of the form $y = A \cos x$ with $A = 2$. Thus, the amplitude is $|A| = |2| = 2$. The period is 2π. The quarter-period is $\frac{2\pi}{4}$ or $\frac{\pi}{2}$. The cycle begins at $x = 0$. Add quarter-periods to generate x-values for the key points.

$x = 0$

$x = 0 + \frac{\pi}{2} = \frac{\pi}{2}$

$x = \frac{\pi}{2} + \frac{\pi}{2} = \pi$

$x = \pi + \frac{\pi}{2} = \frac{3\pi}{2}$

$x = \frac{3\pi}{2} + \frac{\pi}{2} = 2\pi$

Evaluate the function at each value of x.

x	$y = 2 \cos x$	coordinates
0	$y = 2 \cos 0$ $= 2 \cdot 1 = 2$	$(0, 2)$
$\frac{\pi}{2}$	$y = 2 \cos \frac{\pi}{2}$ $= 2 \cdot 0 = 0$	$\left(\frac{\pi}{2}, 0\right)$
π	$y = 2 \cos \pi$ $= 2 \cdot (-1) = -2$	$(\pi, -2)$
$\frac{3\pi}{2}$	$y = 2 \cos \frac{3\pi}{2}$ $= 2 \cdot 0 = 0$	$\left(\frac{3\pi}{2}, 0\right)$
2π	$y = 2 \cos 2\pi$ $= 2 \cdot 1 = 2$	$(2\pi, 2)$

Connect the five points with a smooth curve and graph one complete cycle of the given function with the graph of $y = 2 \cos x$.

33. The equation $y = -2 \cos x$ is of the form $y = A \cos x$ with $A = -2$. Thus, the amplitude is $|A| = |-2| = 2$. The period is 2π. The quarter-period is $\frac{2\pi}{4}$ or $\frac{\pi}{2}$. The cycle begins at $x = 0$. Add quarter-periods to generate x-values for the key points.

$x = 0$

$x = 0 + \frac{\pi}{2} = \frac{\pi}{2}$

$x = \frac{\pi}{2} + \frac{\pi}{2} = \pi$

$x = \pi + \frac{\pi}{2} = \frac{3\pi}{2}$

$x = \frac{3\pi}{2} + \frac{\pi}{2} = 2\pi$

Evaluate the function at each value of x.

x	$y = -2 \cos x$	coordinates
0	$y = -2 \cos 0$ $= -2 \cdot 1 = -2$	$(0, -2)$
$\frac{\pi}{2}$	$y = -2 \cos \frac{\pi}{2}$ $= -2 \cdot 0 = 0$	$\left(\frac{\pi}{2}, 0\right)$
π	$y = -2 \cos \pi$ $= -2 \cdot (-1) = 2$	$(\pi, 2)$
$\frac{3\pi}{2}$	$y = -2 \cos \frac{3\pi}{2}$ $= -2 \cdot 0 = 0$	$\left(\frac{3\pi}{2}, 0\right)$
2π	$y = -2 \cos 2\pi$ $= -2 \cdot 1 = -2$	$(2\pi, -2)$

Connect the five points with a smooth curve and graph one complete cycle of the given function with the graph of $y = \cos x$.

35. The equation $y = \cos 2x$ is of the form $y = A\cos Bx$ with $A = 1$ and $B = 2$. Thus, the amplitude is $|A| = |1| = 1$. The period is $\frac{2\pi}{B} = \frac{2\pi}{2} = \pi$. The quarter-period is $\frac{\pi}{4}$. The cycle begins at $x = 0$. Add quarter-periods to generate x-values for the key points.
$x = 0$

$x = 0 + \frac{\pi}{4} = \frac{\pi}{4}$

$x = \frac{\pi}{4} + \frac{\pi}{4} = \frac{\pi}{2}$

$x = \frac{\pi}{2} + \frac{\pi}{4} = \frac{3\pi}{4}$

$x = \frac{3\pi}{4} + \frac{\pi}{4} = \pi$

Evaluate the function at each value of x.

x	$y = \cos 2x$	coordinates
0	$y = \cos(2 \cdot 0)$ $= \cos 0 = 1$	$(0, 1)$
$\frac{\pi}{4}$	$y = \cos\left(2 \cdot \frac{\pi}{4}\right)$ $= \cos\frac{\pi}{2} = 0$	$\left(\frac{\pi}{4}, 0\right)$
$\frac{\pi}{2}$	$y = \cos\left(2 \cdot \frac{\pi}{2}\right)$ $= \cos\pi = -1$	$\left(\frac{\pi}{2}, -1\right)$
$\frac{3\pi}{4}$	$y = \cos\left(2 \cdot \frac{3\pi}{4}\right)$ $= \cos\frac{3\pi}{2} = 0$	$\left(\frac{3\pi}{4}, 0\right)$
π	$y = \cos(2 \cdot \pi)$ $= \cos 2\pi = 1$	$(\pi, 1)$

Connect the five points with a smooth curve and graph one complete cycle of the given function.

$y = \cos 2x$

37. The equation $y = 4\cos 2\pi x$ is of the form $y = A\cos Bx$ with $A = 4$ and $B = 2\pi$. Thus, the amplitude is $|A| = |4| = 4$. The period is $\frac{2\pi}{B} = \frac{2\pi}{2\pi} = 1$. The quarter-period is $\frac{1}{4}$. The cycle begins at $x = 0$. Add quarter-periods to generate x-values for the key points.
$x = 0$

$x = 0 + \frac{1}{4} = \frac{1}{4}$

$x = \frac{1}{4} + \frac{1}{4} = \frac{1}{2}$

$x = \frac{1}{2} + \frac{1}{4} = \frac{3}{4}$

$x = \frac{3}{4} + \frac{1}{4} = 1$

Evaluate the function at each value of x.

x	$y = 4\cos 2\pi x$	coordinates
0	$y = 4\cos(2\pi \cdot 0)$ $= 4\cos 0$ $= 4 \cdot 1 = 4$	$(0, 4)$
$\frac{1}{4}$	$y = 4\cos\left(2\pi \cdot \frac{1}{4}\right)$ $= 4\cos\frac{\pi}{2}$ $= 4 \cdot 0 = 0$	$\left(\frac{1}{4}, 0\right)$
$\frac{1}{2}$	$y = 4\cos\left(2\pi \cdot \frac{1}{2}\right)$ $= 4\cos\pi$ $= 4 \cdot (-1) = -4$	$\left(\frac{1}{2}, -4\right)$
$\frac{3}{4}$	$y = 4\cos\left(2\pi \cdot \frac{3}{4}\right)$ $= 4\cos\frac{3\pi}{2}$ $= 4 \cdot 0 = 0$	$\left(\frac{3}{4}, 0\right)$

1	$y = 4\cos(2\pi \cdot 1)$ $= 4\cos 2\pi$ $= 4 \cdot 1 = 4$	(1, 4)

Connect the five points with a smooth curve and graph one complete cycle of the given function.

y = 4 cos 2πx

39. The equation $y = -4\cos\frac{1}{2}x$ is of the form

$y = A\cos Bx$ with $A = -4$ and $B = \frac{1}{2}$. Thus, the

amplitude is $|A| = |-4| = 4$. The period is

$\frac{2\pi}{B} = \frac{2\pi}{\frac{1}{2}} = 2\pi \cdot 2 = 4\pi$. The quarter-period is

$\frac{4\pi}{4} = \pi$. The cycle begins at $x = 0$. Add

quarter-periods to generate x-values for the key points.
$x = 0$

$x = 0 + \pi = \pi$

$x = \pi + \pi = 2\pi$

$x = 2\pi + \pi = 3\pi$

$x = 3\pi + \pi = 4\pi$

Evaluate the function at each value of x.

x	$y = -4\cos\frac{1}{2}x$	coordinates
0	$y = -4\cos\left(\frac{1}{2}\cdot 0\right)$ $= -4\cos 0$ $= -4 \cdot 1 = -4$	(0, –4)
π	$y = -4\cos\left(\frac{1}{2}\cdot \pi\right)$ $= -4\cos\frac{\pi}{2}$ $= -4 \cdot 0 = 0$	(π, 0)

2π	$y = -4\cos\left(\frac{1}{2}\cdot 2\pi\right)$ $= -4\cos \pi$ $= -4 \cdot (-1) = 4$	(2π, 4)
3π	$y = -4\cos\left(\frac{1}{2}\cdot 3\pi\right)$ $= -4\cos\frac{3\pi}{2}$ $= -4 \cdot 0 = 0$	(3π, 0)
4π	$y = -4\cos\left(\frac{1}{2}\cdot 4\pi\right)$ $= -4\cos 2\pi$ $= -4 \cdot 1 = -4$	(4π, – 4)

Connect the five points with a smooth curve and graph one complete cycle of the given function.

$y = -4 \cos \frac{1}{2}\, x$

41. The equation $y = -\frac{1}{2}\cos\frac{\pi}{3}x$ is of the form

$y = A\cos Bx$ with $A = -\frac{1}{2}$ and $B = \frac{\pi}{3}$. Thus,

the amplitude is $|A| = \left|-\frac{1}{2}\right| = \frac{1}{2}$. The period is

$\frac{2\pi}{B} = \frac{2\pi}{\frac{\pi}{3}} = 2\pi \cdot \frac{3}{\pi} = 6$. The quarter-period is

$\frac{6}{4} = \frac{3}{2}$. The cycle begins at $x = 0$. Add quarter-

periods to generate x-values for the key points.
$x = 0$

$x = 0 + \frac{3}{2} = \frac{3}{2}$

$x = \frac{3}{2} + \frac{3}{2} = 3$

$x = 3 + \frac{3}{2} = \frac{9}{2}$

$x = \frac{9}{2} + \frac{3}{2} = 6$

Evaluate the function at each value of x.

x	$y = -\dfrac{1}{2}\cos\dfrac{\pi}{3}x$	coordinates
0	$y = -\dfrac{1}{2}\cos\left(\dfrac{\pi}{3}\cdot 0\right)$ $= -\dfrac{1}{2}\cos 0$ $= -\dfrac{1}{2}\cdot 1 = -\dfrac{1}{2}$	$\left(0, -\dfrac{1}{2}\right)$
$\dfrac{3}{2}$	$y = -\dfrac{1}{2}\cos\left(\dfrac{\pi}{3}\cdot\dfrac{3}{2}\right)$ $= -\dfrac{1}{2}\cos\dfrac{\pi}{2}$ $= -\dfrac{1}{2}\cdot 0 = 0$	$\left(\dfrac{3}{2}, 0\right)$
3	$y = -\dfrac{1}{2}\cos\left(\dfrac{\pi}{3}\cdot 3\right)$ $= -\dfrac{1}{2}\cos\pi$ $= -\dfrac{1}{2}\cdot(-1) = \dfrac{1}{2}$	$\left(3, \dfrac{1}{2}\right)$
$\dfrac{9}{2}$	$y = -\dfrac{1}{2}\cos\left(\dfrac{\pi}{3}\cdot\dfrac{9}{2}\right)$ $= -\dfrac{1}{2}\cos\dfrac{3\pi}{2}$ $= -\dfrac{1}{2}\cdot 0 = 0$	$\left(\dfrac{9}{2}, 0\right)$
6	$y = -\dfrac{1}{2}\cos\left(\dfrac{\pi}{3}\cdot 6\right)$ $= -\dfrac{1}{2}\cos 2\pi$ $= -\dfrac{1}{2}\cdot 1 = -\dfrac{1}{2}$	$\left(6, -\dfrac{1}{2}\right)$

Connect the five points with a smooth curve and graph one complete cycle of the given function.

$$y = -\frac{1}{2}\cos\frac{\pi}{3}x$$

43. The equation $y = \cos\left(x - \dfrac{\pi}{2}\right)$ is of the form $y = A\cos(Bx - C)$ with $A = 1$, and $B = 1$, and $C = \dfrac{\pi}{2}$. Thus, the amplitude is $|A| = |1| = 1$.

The period is $\dfrac{2\pi}{B} = \dfrac{2\pi}{1} = 2\pi$. The phase shift is $\dfrac{C}{B} = \dfrac{\frac{\pi}{2}}{1} = \dfrac{\pi}{2}$. The quarter-period is $\dfrac{2\pi}{4} = \dfrac{\pi}{2}$.

The cycle begins at $x = \dfrac{\pi}{2}$. Add quarter-periods to generate x-values for the key points.

$x = \dfrac{\pi}{2}$

$x = \dfrac{\pi}{2} + \dfrac{\pi}{2} = \pi$

$x = \pi + \dfrac{\pi}{2} = \dfrac{3\pi}{2}$

$x = \dfrac{3\pi}{2} + \dfrac{\pi}{2} = 2\pi$

$x = 2\pi + \dfrac{\pi}{2} = \dfrac{5\pi}{2}$

Evaluate the function at each value of x.

x	coordinates
$\dfrac{\pi}{2}$	$\left(\dfrac{\pi}{2}, 1\right)$
π	$(\pi, 0)$
$\dfrac{3\pi}{2}$	$\left(\dfrac{3\pi}{2}, -1\right)$
2π	$(2\pi, 0)$
$\dfrac{5\pi}{2}$	$\left(\dfrac{5\pi}{2}, 1\right)$

Connect the five points with a smooth curve and graph one complete cycle of the given function

$$y = \cos\left(x - \frac{\pi}{2}\right)$$

45. The equation $y = 3\cos(2x - \pi)$ is of the form $y = A\cos(Bx - C)$ with $A = 3$, and $B = 2$, and $C = \pi$. Thus, the amplitude is $|A| = |3| = 3$. The period is $\frac{2\pi}{B} = \frac{2\pi}{2} = \pi$. The phase shift is $\frac{C}{B} = \frac{\pi}{2}$. The quarter-period is $\frac{\pi}{4}$. The cycle begins at $x = \frac{\pi}{2}$. Add quarter-periods to generate x-values for the key points.

$x = \frac{\pi}{2}$

$x = \frac{\pi}{2} + \frac{\pi}{4} = \frac{3\pi}{4}$

$x = \frac{3\pi}{4} + \frac{\pi}{4} = \pi$

$x = \pi + \frac{\pi}{4} = \frac{5\pi}{4}$

$x = \frac{5\pi}{4} + \frac{\pi}{4} = \frac{3\pi}{2}$

Evaluate the function at each value of x.

x	coordinates
$\frac{\pi}{2}$	$\left(\frac{\pi}{2}, 3\right)$
$\frac{3\pi}{4}$	$\left(\frac{3\pi}{4}, 0\right)$
π	$(\pi, -3)$
$\frac{5\pi}{4}$	$\left(\frac{5\pi}{4}, 0\right)$
$\frac{3\pi}{2}$	$\left(\frac{3\pi}{2}, 3\right)$

Connect the five points with a smooth curve and graph one complete cycle of the given function

$y = 3\cos(2x - \pi)$

47. $y = \frac{1}{2}\cos\left(3x + \frac{\pi}{2}\right) = \frac{1}{2}\cos\left(3x - \left(-\frac{\pi}{2}\right)\right)$

The equation $y = \frac{1}{2}\cos\left(3x - \left(-\frac{\pi}{2}\right)\right)$ is of the form $y = A\cos(Bx - C)$ with $A = \frac{1}{2}$, and $B = 3$, and $C = -\frac{\pi}{2}$. Thus, the amplitude is $|A| = \left|\frac{1}{2}\right| = \frac{1}{2}$. The period is $\frac{2\pi}{B} = \frac{2\pi}{3}$. The phase shift is $\frac{C}{B} = \frac{-\frac{\pi}{2}}{3} = -\frac{\pi}{2} \cdot \frac{1}{3} = -\frac{\pi}{6}$. The quarter-period is $\frac{\frac{2\pi}{3}}{4} = \frac{2\pi}{3} \cdot \frac{1}{4} = \frac{\pi}{6}$. The cycle begins at $x = -\frac{\pi}{6}$. Add quarter-periods to generate x-values for the key points.

$x = -\frac{\pi}{6}$

$x = -\frac{\pi}{6} + \frac{\pi}{6} = 0$

$x = 0 + \frac{\pi}{6} = \frac{\pi}{6}$

$x = \frac{\pi}{6} + \frac{\pi}{6} = \frac{\pi}{3}$

$x = \frac{\pi}{3} + \frac{\pi}{6} = \frac{\pi}{2}$

Evaluate the function at each value of x.

x	coordinates
$-\frac{\pi}{6}$	$\left(-\frac{\pi}{6}, \frac{1}{2}\right)$
0	$(0, 0)$
$\frac{\pi}{6}$	$\left(\frac{\pi}{6}, -\frac{1}{2}\right)$
$\frac{\pi}{3}$	$\left(\frac{\pi}{3}, 0\right)$
$\frac{\pi}{2}$	$\left(\frac{\pi}{2}, \frac{1}{2}\right)$

Connect the five points with a smooth curve and graph one complete cycle of the given function

$$y = \frac{1}{2}\cos\left(3x + \frac{\pi}{2}\right)$$

49. The equation $y = -3\cos\left(2x - \frac{\pi}{2}\right)$ is of the form

$y = A\cos(Bx - C)$ with $A = -3$, and

$B = 2$, and $C = \frac{\pi}{2}$. Thus, the amplitude is

$|A| = |-3| = 3$. The period is $\frac{2\pi}{B} = \frac{2\pi}{2} = \pi$.

The phase shift is $\frac{C}{B} = \frac{\frac{\pi}{2}}{2} = \frac{\pi}{2} \cdot \frac{1}{2} = \frac{\pi}{4}$. The

quarter-period is $\frac{\pi}{4}$. The cycle begins at $x = \frac{\pi}{4}$.

Add quarter-periods to generate x-values for the key points.

$$x = \frac{\pi}{4}$$

$$x = \frac{\pi}{4} + \frac{\pi}{4} = \frac{\pi}{2}$$

$$x = \frac{\pi}{2} + \frac{\pi}{4} = \frac{3\pi}{4}$$

$$x = \frac{3\pi}{4} + \frac{\pi}{4} = \pi$$

$$x = \pi + \frac{\pi}{4} = \frac{5\pi}{4}$$

Evaluate the function at each value of x.

x	coordinates
$\frac{\pi}{4}$	$\left(\frac{\pi}{4}, -3\right)$
$\frac{\pi}{2}$	$\left(\frac{\pi}{2}, 0\right)$
$\frac{3\pi}{4}$	$\left(\frac{3\pi}{4}, 3\right)$
π	$(\pi, 0)$
$\frac{5\pi}{4}$	$\left(\frac{5\pi}{4}, -3\right)$

Connect the five points with a smooth curve and graph one complete cycle of the given function

$$y = -3\cos\left(2x - \frac{\pi}{2}\right)$$

51. $y = 2\cos(2\pi x + 8\pi) = 2\cos(2\pi x - (-8\pi))$

The equation $y = 2\cos(2\pi x - (-8\pi))$ is of the

form $y = A\cos(Bx - C)$ with $A = 2$, $B = 2\pi$, and

$C = -8\pi$. Thus, the amplitude is $|A| = |2| = 2$.

The period is $\frac{2\pi}{B} = \frac{2\pi}{2\pi} = 1$. The phase shift is

$\frac{C}{B} = \frac{-8\pi}{2\pi} = -4$. The quarter-period is $\frac{1}{4}$. The

cycle begins at $x = -4$. Add quarter-periods to generate x-values for the key points.

$x = -4$

$$x = -4 + \frac{1}{4} = -\frac{15}{4}$$

$$x = -\frac{15}{4} + \frac{1}{4} = -\frac{7}{2}$$

$$x = -\frac{7}{2} + \frac{1}{4} = -\frac{13}{4}$$

$$x = -\frac{13}{4} + \frac{1}{4} = -3$$

Evaluate the function at each value of x.

x	coordinates
-4	$(-4, 2)$
$-\dfrac{15}{4}$	$\left(-\dfrac{15}{4}, 0\right)$
$-\dfrac{7}{2}$	$\left(-\dfrac{7}{2}, -2\right)$
$-\dfrac{13}{4}$	$\left(-\dfrac{13}{4}, 0\right)$
-3	$(-3, 2)$

Connect the five points with a smooth curve and graph one complete cycle of the given function

$y = 2 \cos (2\pi x + 8\pi)$

53. The graph of $y = \sin x + 2$ is the graph of $y = \sin x$ shifted up 2 units upward. The period for both functions is 2π. The quarter-period is $\dfrac{2\pi}{4}$ or $\dfrac{\pi}{2}$. The cycle begins at $x = 0$. Add quarter-periods to generate x-values for the key points.

$x = 0$

$x = 0 + \dfrac{\pi}{2} = \dfrac{\pi}{2}$

$x = \dfrac{\pi}{2} + \dfrac{\pi}{2} = \pi$

$x = \pi + \dfrac{\pi}{2} = \dfrac{3\pi}{2}$

$x = \dfrac{3\pi}{2} + \dfrac{\pi}{2} = 2\pi$

Evaluate the function at each value of x.

x	$y = \sin x + 2$	coordinates
0	$y = \sin 0 + 2$ $= 0 + 2 = 2$	$(0, 2)$
$\dfrac{\pi}{2}$	$y = \sin \dfrac{\pi}{2} + 2$ $= 1 + 2 = 3$	$\left(\dfrac{\pi}{2}, 3\right)$
π	$y = \sin \pi + 2$ $= 0 + 2 = 2$	$(\pi, 2)$

$\dfrac{3\pi}{2}$	$y = \sin \dfrac{3\pi}{2} + 2$ $= -1 + 2 = 1$	$\left(\dfrac{3\pi}{2}, 1\right)$
2π	$y = \sin 2\pi + 2$ $= 0 + 2 = 2$	$(2\pi, 2)$

By connecting the points with a smooth curve we obtain one period of the graph.

$y = \sin x + 2$

55. The graph of $y = \cos x - 3$ is the graph of $y = \cos x$ shifted 3 units downward. The period for both functions is 2π. The quarter-period is $\dfrac{2\pi}{4}$ or $\dfrac{\pi}{2}$. The cycle begins at $x = 0$. Add quarter-periods to generate x-values for the key points.

$x = 0$

$x = 0 + \dfrac{\pi}{2} = \dfrac{\pi}{2}$

$x = \dfrac{\pi}{2} + \dfrac{\pi}{2} = \pi$

$x = \pi + \dfrac{\pi}{2} = \dfrac{3\pi}{2}$

$x = \dfrac{3\pi}{2} + \dfrac{\pi}{2} = 2\pi$

Evaluate the function at each value of x.

x	$y = \cos x - 3$	coordinates
0	$y = \cos 0 - 3$ $= 1 - 3 = -2$	$(0, -2)$
$\dfrac{\pi}{2}$	$y = \cos \dfrac{\pi}{2} - 3$ $= 0 - 3 = -3$	$\left(\dfrac{\pi}{2}, -3\right)$
π	$y = \cos \pi - 3$ $= -1 - 3 = -4$	$(\pi, -4)$
$\dfrac{3\pi}{2}$	$y = \cos \dfrac{3\pi}{2} - 3$ $= 0 - 3 = -3$	$\left(\dfrac{3\pi}{2}, -3\right)$
2π	$y = \cos 2\pi - 3$ $= 1 - 3 = -2$	

By connecting the points with a smooth curve we obtain one period of the graph.

$$y = \cos x - 3$$

57. The graph of $y = 2\sin\frac{1}{2}x + 1$ is the graph of $y = 2\sin\frac{1}{2}x$ shifted one unit upward. The amplitude for both functions is $|\,2\,| = 2$. The period for both functions is $\frac{2\pi}{\frac{1}{2}} = 2\pi \cdot 2 = 4\pi$.

The quarter-period is $\frac{4\pi}{4} = \pi$. The cycle begins at $x = 0$. Add quarter-periods to generate x-values for the key points.
$x = 0$
$x = 0 + \pi = \pi$
$x = \pi + \pi = 2\pi$
$x = 2\pi + \pi = 3\pi$
$x = 3\pi + \pi = 4\pi$
Evaluate the function at each value of x.

x	$y = 2\sin\frac{1}{2}x + 1$	coordinates
0	$y = 2\sin\left(\frac{1}{2}\cdot 0\right) + 1$ $= 2\sin 0 + 1$ $= 2 \cdot 0 + 1 = 0 + 1 = 1$	$(0, 1)$
π	$y = 2\sin\left(\frac{1}{2}\cdot \pi\right) + 1$ $= 2\sin\frac{\pi}{2} + 1$ $= 2 \cdot 1 + 1 = 2 + 1 = 3$	$(\pi, 3)$
2π	$y = 2\sin\left(\frac{1}{2}\cdot 2\pi\right) + 1$ $= 2\sin \pi + 1$ $= 2 \cdot 0 + 1 = 0 + 1 = 1$	$(2\pi, 1)$

3π	$y = 2\sin\left(\frac{1}{2}\cdot 3\pi\right) + 1$ $= 2\sin\frac{3\pi}{2} + 1$ $= 2 \cdot (-1) + 1$ $= -2 + 1 = -1$	$(3\pi, -1)$
4π	$y = 2\sin\left(\frac{1}{2}\cdot 4\pi\right) + 1$ $= 2\sin 2\pi + 1$ $= 2 \cdot 0 + 1 = 0 + 1 = 1$	$(4\pi, 1)$

By connecting the points with a smooth curve we obtain one period of the graph.

$$y = 2\sin\frac{1}{2}x + 1$$

59. The graph of $y = -3\cos 2\pi x + 2$ is the graph of $y = -3\cos 2\pi x$ shifted 2 units upward. The amplitude for both functions is $|\,-3\,| = 3$. The period for both functions is $\frac{2\pi}{2\pi} = 1$. The quarter-period is $\frac{1}{4}$. The cycle begins at $x = 0$. Add quarter-periods to generate x-values for the key points.
$x = 0$
$x = 0 + \frac{1}{4} = \frac{1}{4}$
$x = \frac{1}{4} + \frac{1}{4} = \frac{1}{2}$
$x = \frac{1}{2} + \frac{1}{4} = \frac{3}{4}$
$x = \frac{3}{4} + \frac{1}{4} = 1$

Evaluate the function at each value of *x*.

x	$y = -3\cos 2\pi x + 2$	coordinates
0	$y = -3\cos(2\pi \cdot 0) + 2$ $\quad = -3\cos 0 + 2$ $\quad = -3 \cdot 1 + 2$ $\quad = -3 + 2 = -1$	$(0, -1)$
$\dfrac{1}{4}$	$y = -3\cos\left(2\pi \cdot \dfrac{1}{4}\right) + 2$ $\quad = -3\cos\dfrac{\pi}{2} + 2$ $\quad = -3 \cdot 0 + 2$ $\quad = 0 + 2 = 2$	$\left(\dfrac{1}{4}, 2\right)$
$\dfrac{1}{2}$	$y = -3\cos\left(2\pi \cdot \dfrac{1}{2}\right) + 2$ $\quad = -3\cos\pi + 2$ $\quad = -3 \cdot (-1) + 2$ $\quad = 3 + 2 = 5$	$\left(\dfrac{1}{2}, 5\right)$
$\dfrac{3}{4}$	$y = -3\cos\left(2\pi \cdot \dfrac{3}{4}\right) + 2$ $\quad = -3\cos\dfrac{3\pi}{2} + 2$ $\quad = -3 \cdot 0 + 2$ $\quad = 0 + 2 = 2$	$\left(\dfrac{3}{4}, 2\right)$
1	$y = -3\cos(2\pi \cdot 1) + 2$ $\quad = -3\cos 2\pi + 2$ $\quad = -3 \cdot 1 + 2$ $\quad = -3 + 2 = -1$	$(1, -1)$

By connecting the points with a smooth curve we obtain one period of the graph.

$y = -3\cos 2\pi x + 2$

61. Using $y = A\cos Bx$ the amplitude is 3 and $A = 3$, The period is 4π and thus

$$B = \frac{2\pi}{\text{period}} = \frac{2\pi}{4\pi} = \frac{1}{2}$$

$$y = A\cos Bx$$

$$y = 3\cos\frac{1}{2}x$$

63. Using $y = A\sin Bx$ the amplitude is 2 and $A = -2$, The period is π and thus

$$B = \frac{2\pi}{\text{period}} = \frac{2\pi}{\pi} = 2$$

$$y = A\sin Bx$$

$$y = -2\sin 2x$$

65. Using $y = A\sin Bx$ the amplitude is 2 and $A = 2$, The period is 4 and thus

$$B = \frac{2\pi}{\text{period}} = \frac{2\pi}{4} = \frac{\pi}{2}$$

$$y = A\sin Bx$$

$$y = 2\sin\left(\frac{\pi}{2}x\right)$$

67.

$$y = \left|2\cos\frac{x}{2}\right|$$

69.

$$y = -\left|3\sin \pi x\right|$$

71.

73.

75. The period of the physical cycle is 33 days.

77. The period of the intellectual cycle is 23 days.

79. In the month of March, March 21 would be the best day to meet an on-line friend for the first time, because the emotional cycle is at a maximum.

81. Answers may vary.

83. The information gives the five key point of the graph.
(0, 14) corresponds to June,
(3, 12) corresponds to September,
(6, 10) corresponds to December,
(9, 12) corresponds to March,
(12, 14) corresponds to June
By connecting the five key points with a smooth curve we graph the information from June of one year to June of the following year.

85. The function $y = 3\sin\frac{2\pi}{365}(x-79)+12$ is of the

form $y = A\sin B\left(x-\frac{C}{B}\right)+D$ with

$A = 3$ and $B = \frac{2\pi}{365}$.

a. The amplitude is $|A| = |3| = 3$.

b. The period is $\frac{2\pi}{B} = \frac{2\pi}{\frac{2\pi}{365}} = 2\pi \cdot \frac{365}{2\pi} = 365$.

c. The longest day of the year will have the most hours of daylight. This occurs when the sine function equals 1.

$$y = 3\sin\frac{2\pi}{365}(x-79)+12$$

$$y = 3(1)+12$$

$$y = 15$$

There will be 15 hours of daylight.

d. The shortest day of the year will have the least hours of daylight. This occurs when the sine function equals −1.

$$y = 3\sin\frac{2\pi}{365}(x-79)+12$$

$$y = 3(-1)+12$$

$$y = 9$$

There will be 9 hours of daylight.

e. The amplitude is 3. The period is 365. The

phase shift is $\frac{C}{B} = 79$. The quarter-period

is $\frac{365}{4} = 91.25$. The cycle begins at $x =$

79. Add quarter-periods to find the x-values of the key points.

$x = 79$

$x = 79 + 91.25 = 170.25$

$x = 170.25 + 91.25 = 261.5$

$x = 261.5 + 91.25 = 352.75$

$x = 352.75 + 91.25 = 444$

Because we are graphing for $0 \le x \le 365$, we will evaluate the function for the first four x-values along with $x = 0$ and $x = 365$. Using a calculator we have the following points.

(0, 9.07) (79, 12) (170.25, 15)
(261.5, 12) (352.75, 9) (365, 9.07)

By connecting the points with a smooth curve we obtain one period of the graph, starting on January 1.

363

87. Because the depth of the water ranges from a minimum of 6 feet to a maximum of 12 feet, the curve oscillates about the middle value, 9 feet. Thus, $D = 9$. The maximum depth of the water is 3 feet above 9 feet. Thus, $A = 3$. The graph shows that one complete cycle occurs in 12-0, or 12 hours. The period is 12. Thus,

$$12 = \frac{2\pi}{B}$$

$$12B = 2\pi$$

$$B = \frac{2\pi}{12} = \frac{\pi}{6}$$

Substitute these values into $y = A\cos Bx + D$. The depth of the water is modeled by

$$y = 3\cos\frac{\pi x}{6} + 9.$$

101. The function $y = 3\sin(2x + \pi) = 3\sin(2x - (-\pi))$ is of the form $y = A\sin(Bx - C)$ with $A = 3$, $B = 2$, and $C = -\pi$. The amplitude is $|A| = |3| = 3$. The period is $\frac{2\pi}{B} = \frac{2\pi}{2} = \pi$.

The cycle begins at $x = \frac{C}{B} = \frac{-\pi}{2} = -\frac{\pi}{2}$. We choose $-\frac{\pi}{2} \le x \le \frac{3\pi}{2}$, and $-4 \le y \le 4$ for our graph.

103. The function

$$y = 0.2\sin\left(\frac{\pi}{10}x + \pi\right) = 0.2\sin\left(\frac{\pi}{10}x - (-\pi)\right) \text{ is}$$

of the form $y = A\sin(Bx - C)$ with

$A = 0.2$, $B = \frac{\pi}{10}$, and $C = -\pi$. The amplitude is $|A| = |0.2| = 0.2$. The period is

$\frac{2\pi}{B} = \frac{2\pi}{\frac{\pi}{10}} = 2\pi \cdot \frac{10}{\pi} = 20$. The cycle begins at

$x = \frac{C}{B} = \frac{-\pi}{\frac{\pi}{10}} = -\pi \cdot \frac{10}{\pi} = -10$. We choose

$-10 \le x \le 30$, and $-1 \le y \le 1$ for our graph.

105.

The graphs appear to be the same from

$-\frac{\pi}{2}$ to $\frac{\pi}{2}$.

107.

The graph is similar to $y = \sin x$, except the amplitude is greater and the curve is less smooth.

109. a.

  b. $y = 22.61\sin(0.50x - 2.04) + 57.17$

111. a. Since $A = 3$ and $D = -2$, the maximum will occur at $3 - 2 = 1$ and the minimum will occur at $-3 - 2 = -5$. Thus the range is $[-5, 1]$

Viewing rectangle: $\left[-\frac{\pi}{6}, \frac{23\pi}{6}, \frac{\pi}{6}\right]$ by

$[-5, 1, 1]$

b. Since $A = 1$ and $D = -2$, the maximum will occur at $1 - 2 = -1$ and the minimum will occur at $-1 - 2 = -3$. Thus the range is $[-3, -1]$

Viewing rectangle: $\left[-\dfrac{\pi}{6}, \dfrac{7\pi}{6}, \dfrac{\pi}{6} \right]$ by

$[-3, -1, 1]$

113. $y = \sin^2 x = \dfrac{1}{2} - \dfrac{1}{2}\cos 2x$

$y = \sin^2 x$

or $y = \dfrac{1}{2} - \dfrac{1}{2}\cos 2x$

Section 4.6

Check Point Exercises

1. Solve the equations
$$2x = -\dfrac{\pi}{2} \quad \text{and} \quad 2x = \dfrac{\pi}{2}$$
$$x = -\dfrac{\pi}{4} \qquad x = \dfrac{\pi}{4}$$

Thus, two consecutive asymptotes occur at $x = -\dfrac{\pi}{4}$ and $x = \dfrac{\pi}{4}$. Midway between these asymptotes is $x = 0$. An x-intercept is 0 and the graph passes through $(0, 0)$. Because the coefficient of the tangent is 3, the points on the graph midway between an x-intercept and the asymptotes have y-coordinates of -3 and 3. Use the two asymptotes, the x-intercept, and the points midway between to graph one period of $y = 3\tan 2x$ from $-\dfrac{\pi}{4}$ to $\dfrac{\pi}{4}$. In order to graph for $-\dfrac{\pi}{4} < x < \dfrac{3\pi}{4}$, Continue the pattern and extend the graph

another full period to the right.

$y = 3 \tan 2x$

2. Solve the equations
$$x - \dfrac{\pi}{2} = -\dfrac{\pi}{2} \quad \text{and} \quad x - \dfrac{\pi}{2} = \dfrac{\pi}{2}$$
$$x = \dfrac{\pi}{2} - \dfrac{\pi}{2} \qquad\quad x = \dfrac{\pi}{2} + \dfrac{\pi}{2}$$
$$x = 0 \qquad\qquad\quad x = \pi$$

Thus, two consecutive asymptotes occur at $x = 0$ and $x = \pi$.

x-intercept $= \dfrac{0 + \pi}{2} = \dfrac{\pi}{2}$

An x-intercept is $\dfrac{\pi}{2}$ and the graph passes

through $\left(\dfrac{\pi}{2}, 0 \right)$. Because the coefficient of the tangent is 1, the points on the graph midway between an x-intercept and the asymptotes have y-coordinates of -1 and 1. Use the two consecutive asymptotes, $x = 0$ and $x = \pi$, to graph one full period of

$y = \tan\left(x - \dfrac{\pi}{2} \right)$ from 0 to π. Continue the

pattern and extend the graph another full period to the right.

$y = \tan\left(x - \dfrac{\pi}{2} \right)$

3. Solve the equations
$$\dfrac{\pi}{2}x = 0 \quad \text{and} \quad \dfrac{\pi}{2}x = \pi$$
$$x = 0 \qquad\qquad x = \dfrac{\pi}{\frac{\pi}{2}}$$
$$x = 2$$

Two consecutive asymptotes occur at $x = 0$ and $x = 2$. Midway between $x = 0$ and $x = 2$ is $x = 1$.

An *x*-intercept is 1 and the graph passes through (1, 0). Because the coefficient of the cotangent is $\frac{1}{2}$, the points on the graph midway between an *x*-intercept and the asymptotes have *y*-coordinates of $-\frac{1}{2}$ and $\frac{1}{2}$. Use the two consecutive asymptotes, $x = 0$ and $x = 2$, to graph one full period of $y = \frac{1}{2}\cot\frac{\pi}{2}x$. The curve is repeated along the *x*-axis one full period as shown.

$$y = \frac{1}{2}\cot\frac{\pi}{2}x$$

4. The *x*-intercepts of $y = \sin\left(x + \frac{\pi}{4}\right)$ correspond to vertical asymptotes of $y = \csc\left(x + \frac{\pi}{4}\right)$.

$$y = \csc\left(x + \frac{\pi}{4}\right)$$

5. Graph the reciprocal cosine function, $y = 2\cos 2x$. The equation is of the form $y = A\cos Bx$ with $A = 2$ and $B = 2$.

amplitude: $|A| = |2| = 2$

period: $\frac{2\pi}{B} = \frac{2\pi}{2} = \pi$

Use quarter-periods, $\frac{\pi}{4}$, to find *x*-values for the five key points. Starting with $x = 0$, the *x*-values are $0, \frac{\pi}{4}, \frac{\pi}{2}, \frac{3\pi}{4}$, and π. Evaluating the function at each value of *x*, the key points are

$(0, 2), \left(\frac{\pi}{4}, 0\right), \left(\frac{\pi}{2}, -2\right), \left(\frac{3\pi}{4}, 0\right), (\pi, 2)$. In

order to graph for $-\frac{3\pi}{4} \le x \le \frac{3\pi}{4}$, Use the first

four points and extend the graph $-\frac{3\pi}{4}$ units to the left. Use the graph to obtain the graph of the reciprocal function. Draw vertical asymptotes through the *x*-intercepts, and use them as guides to graph $y = 2\sec 2x$.

$$y = 2\sec 2x$$

Exercise Set 4.6

1. The graph has an asymptote at $x = -\frac{\pi}{2}$.

The phase shift, $\frac{C}{B}$, from $\frac{\pi}{2}$ to $-\frac{\pi}{2}$ is $-\pi$

units. Thus, $\frac{C}{B} = \frac{C}{1} = -\pi$
$$C = -\pi$$
The function with $C = -\pi$ is $y = \tan(x + \pi)$.

3. The graph has an asymptote at $x = \pi$.

$$\pi = \frac{\pi}{2} + C$$

$$C = \frac{\pi}{2}$$

The function is $y = -\tan\left(x - \frac{\pi}{2}\right)$.

5. Solve the equations

$$\frac{x}{4} = -\frac{\pi}{2} \qquad \text{and} \qquad \frac{x}{4} = \frac{\pi}{2}$$

$$x = \left(-\frac{\pi}{2}\right)4 \qquad x = \left(\frac{\pi}{2}\right)4$$

$$x = -2\pi \qquad x = 2\pi$$

Thus, two consecutive asymptotes occur at $x = -2\pi$ and $x = 2\pi$.

$$x\text{-intercept} = \frac{-2\pi + 2\pi}{2} = \frac{0}{2} = 0$$

An x-intercept is 0 and the graph passes through $(0, 0)$. Because the coefficient of the tangent is 3, the points on the graph midway between an x-intercept and the asymptotes have y-coordinates of -3 and 3. Use the two consecutive asymptotes, $x = -2\pi$ and $x = 2\pi$, to graph one full period of $y = 3\tan\frac{x}{4}$ from -2π to 2π.

Continue the pattern and extend the graph another full period to the right.

$y = 3\tan\dfrac{x}{4}$

7. Solve the equations $2x = -\dfrac{\pi}{2}$ and $2x = \dfrac{\pi}{2}$

$$x = \frac{-\frac{\pi}{2}}{2} \qquad x = \frac{\frac{\pi}{2}}{2}$$

$$x = -\frac{\pi}{4} \qquad x = \frac{\pi}{4}$$

Thus, two consecutive asymptotes occur at $x = -\dfrac{\pi}{4}$ and $x = \dfrac{\pi}{4}$.

$$x\text{-intercept} = \frac{-\frac{\pi}{4} + \frac{\pi}{4}}{2} = \frac{0}{2} = 0$$

An x-intercept is 0 and the graph passes through

$(0, 0)$. Because the coefficient of the tangent is $\dfrac{1}{2}$, the points on the graph midway between an x-intercept and the asymptotes have y-coordinates of $-\dfrac{1}{2}$ and $\dfrac{1}{2}$. Use the two consecutive asymptotes, $x = -\dfrac{\pi}{4}$ and $x = \dfrac{\pi}{4}$, to graph one full period of $y = \dfrac{1}{2}\tan 2x$ from $-\dfrac{\pi}{4}$ to $\dfrac{\pi}{4}$. Continue the pattern and extend the graph another full period to the right.

$y = \dfrac{1}{2}\tan 2x$

9. Solve the equations

$$\frac{1}{2}x = -\frac{\pi}{2} \qquad \text{and} \qquad \frac{1}{2}x = \frac{\pi}{2}$$

$$x = \left(-\frac{\pi}{2}\right)2 \qquad x = \left(\frac{\pi}{2}\right)2$$

$$x = -\pi \qquad x = \pi$$

Thus, two consecutive asymptotes occur at $x = -\pi$ and $x = \pi$.

$$x\text{-intercept} = \frac{-\pi + \pi}{2} = \frac{0}{2} = 0$$

An x-intercept is 0 and the graph passes through $(0, 0)$. Because the coefficient of the tangent is -2, the points on the graph midway between an x-intercept and the asymptotes have y-coordinates of 2 and -2. Use the two consecutive asymptotes, $x = -\pi$ and $x = \pi$, to graph one full period of $y = -2\tan\dfrac{1}{2}x$ from $-\pi$ to π.

Continue the pattern and extend the graph another full period to the right.

$y = -2\tan\dfrac{1}{2}x$

11. Solve the equations

$$x - \pi = -\frac{\pi}{2} \quad \text{and} \quad x - \pi = \frac{\pi}{2}$$

$$x = -\frac{\pi}{2} + \pi \qquad x = \frac{\pi}{2} + \pi$$

$$x = \frac{\pi}{2} \qquad\qquad x = \frac{3\pi}{2}$$

Thus, two consecutive asymptotes occur at

$$x = \frac{\pi}{2} \text{ and } x = \frac{3\pi}{2}.$$

$$x\text{-intercept} = \frac{\frac{\pi}{2} + \frac{3\pi}{2}}{2} = \frac{\frac{4\pi}{2}}{2} = \frac{4\pi}{4} = \pi$$

An x-intercept is π and the graph passes through $(\pi, 0)$. Because the coefficient of the tangent is 1, the points on the graph midway between an x-intercept and the asymptotes have y-coordinates of -1 and 1. Use the two consecutive asymptotes, $x = \frac{\pi}{2}$ and $x = \frac{3\pi}{2}$, to graph one full period of $y = \tan(x - \pi)$ from $\frac{\pi}{2}$ to $\frac{3\pi}{2}$. Continue the pattern and extend the graph another full period to the right.

$$y = \tan (x - \pi)$$

13. There is no phase shift. Thus,

$$\frac{C}{B} = \frac{C}{1} = 0$$

$$C = 0$$

Because the points on the graph midway between an x-intercept and the asymptotes have y-coordinates of -1 and 1, $A = -1$. The function with $C = 0$ and $A = -1$ is $y = -\cot x$.

15. The graph has an asymptote at $-\frac{\pi}{2}$. The phase shift, $\frac{C}{B}$, from 0 to $-\frac{\pi}{2}$ is $-\frac{\pi}{2}$ units. Thus,

$$\frac{C}{B} = \frac{C}{1} = -\frac{\pi}{2}$$

$$C = -\frac{\pi}{2}$$

The function with $C = -\frac{\pi}{2}$ is $y = \cot\left(x + \frac{\pi}{2}\right)$.

17. Solve the equations $x = 0$ and $x = \pi$. Two consecutive asymptotes occur at $x = 0$ and $x = \pi$.

$$x\text{-intercept} = \frac{0 + \pi}{2} = \frac{\pi}{2}$$

An x-intercept is $\frac{\pi}{2}$ and the graph passes through $\left(\frac{\pi}{2}, 0\right)$. Because the coefficient of the cotangent is 2, the points on the graph midway between an x-intercept and the asymptotes have y-coordinates of 2 and -2. Use the two consecutive asymptotes, $x = 0$ and $x = \pi$, to graph one full period of $y = 2\cot x$. The curve is repeated along the x-axis one full period as shown.

$$y = 2\cot x$$

19. Solve the equations

$$2x = 0 \quad \text{and} \quad 2x = \pi$$

$$x = 0 \qquad\qquad x = \frac{\pi}{2}$$

Two consecutive asymptotes occur at $x = 0$ and $x = \frac{\pi}{2}$.

$$x\text{-intercept} = \frac{0 + \frac{\pi}{2}}{2} = \frac{\frac{\pi}{2}}{2} = \frac{\pi}{4}$$

An x-intercept is $\frac{\pi}{4}$ and the graph passes through $\left(\frac{\pi}{4}, 0\right)$. Because the coefficient of the cotangent is $\frac{1}{2}$, the points on the graph midway between an x-intercept and the asymptotes have y-coordinates of $\frac{1}{2}$ and $-\frac{1}{2}$. Use the two consecutive asymptotes, $x = 0$ and $x = \frac{\pi}{2}$, to graph one full period of $y = \frac{1}{2}\cot 2x$. The curve is repeated along the x-axis one full period as shown.

$$y = \frac{1}{2}\cot 2x$$

21. Solve the equations

$$\frac{\pi}{2}x = 0 \quad \text{and} \quad \frac{\pi}{2}x = \pi$$

$$x = 0 \qquad\qquad x = \frac{\pi}{\frac{\pi}{2}}$$

$$\qquad\qquad\qquad x = 2$$

Two consecutive asymptotes occur at $x = 0$ and $x = 2$.

x-intercept $= \frac{0+2}{2} = \frac{2}{2} = 1$

An x-intercept is 1 and the graph passes through (1, 0). Because the coefficient of the cotangent is -3, the points on the graph midway between an x-intercept and the asymptotes have y-coordinates of -3 and 3. Use the two consecutive asymptotes, $x = 0$ and $x = 2$, to graph one full period of

$y = -3\cot\frac{\pi}{2}x$. The curve is repeated along the x-axis one full period as shown.

$$y = -3\cot\frac{\pi}{2}x$$

23. Solve the equations

$$x + \frac{\pi}{2} = 0 \quad \text{and} \quad x + \frac{\pi}{2} = \pi$$

$$x = 0 - \frac{\pi}{2} \qquad\qquad x = \pi - \frac{\pi}{2}$$

$$x = -\frac{\pi}{2} \qquad\qquad x = \frac{\pi}{2}$$

Two consecutive asymptotes occur at $x = -\frac{\pi}{2}$ and $x = \frac{\pi}{2}$.

x-intercept $= \frac{-\frac{\pi}{2} + \frac{\pi}{2}}{2} = \frac{0}{2} = 0$

An x-intercept is 0 and the graph passes through (0, 0). Because the coefficient of the cotangent is 3, the points on the graph midway between an x-intercept and the asymptotes have y-coordinates of 3 and -3. Use the two consecutive asymptotes, $x = -\frac{\pi}{2}$ and $x = \frac{\pi}{2}$, to graph one full period of $y = 3\cot\left(x + \frac{\pi}{2}\right)$. The curve is repeated along the x-axis one full period as shown.

$$y = 3\cot\left(x + \frac{\pi}{2}\right)$$

25. The x-intercepts of $y = -\frac{1}{2}\sin\frac{x}{2}$ corresponds to vertical asymptotes of $y = -\frac{1}{2}\csc\frac{x}{2}$. Draw the vertical asymptotes, and use them as a guide to sketch the graph of $y = -\frac{1}{2}\csc\frac{x}{2}$.

$$y = -\frac{1}{2}\csc\frac{x}{2}$$

27. The x-intercepts of $y = \frac{1}{2}\cos 2\pi x$ corresponds to vertical asymptotes of $y = \frac{1}{2}\sec 2\pi x$. Draw the vertical asymptotes, and use them as a guide to sketch the graph of $y = \frac{1}{2}\sec 2\pi x$.

$y = \frac{1}{2}\sec 2\pi x$

29. Graph the reciprocal sine function, $y = 3\sin x$. The equation is of the form $y = A\sin Bx$ with $A = 3$ and $B = 1$.
amplitude: $|A| = |3| = 3$
period: $\frac{2\pi}{B} = \frac{2\pi}{1} = 2\pi$

Use quarter-periods, $\frac{\pi}{2}$, to find x-values for the five key points. Starting with $x = 0$, the x-values are 0, $\frac{\pi}{2}$, π, $\frac{3\pi}{2}$, and 2π. Evaluating the function at each value of x, the key points are $(0, 0)$, $\left(\frac{\pi}{2}, 3\right)$, $(\pi, 0)$, $\left(\frac{3\pi}{2}, -3\right)$, and $(2\pi, 0)$. Use these key points to graph $y = 3\sin x$ from 0 to 2π. Extend the graph one cycle to the right.
Use the graph to obtain the graph of the reciprocal function. Draw vertical asymptotes through the x-intercepts, and use them as guides to graph $y = 3\csc x$.

$y = 3\csc x$

31. Graph the reciprocal sine function, $y = \frac{1}{2}\sin\frac{x}{2}$. The equation is of the form $y = A\sin Bx$ with $A = \frac{1}{2}$ and $B = \frac{1}{2}$.
amplitude: $|A| = \left|\frac{1}{2}\right| = \frac{1}{2}$
period: $\frac{2\pi}{B} = \frac{2\pi}{\frac{1}{2}} = 2\pi \cdot 2 = 4\pi$

Use quarter-periods, π, to find x-values for the five key points. Starting with $x = 0$, the x-values are 0, π, 2π, 3π, and 4π. Evaluating the function at each value of x, the key points are $(0, 0)$, $\left(\pi, \frac{1}{2}\right)$, $(2\pi, 0)$, $\left(3\pi, -\frac{1}{2}\right)$, and $(4\pi, 0)$.

Use these key points to graph $y = \frac{1}{2}\sin\frac{x}{2}$ from 0 to 4π. Extend the graph one cycle to the right. Use the graph to obtain the graph of the reciprocal function. Draw vertical asymptotes through the x-intercepts, and use them as guides to graph $y = \frac{1}{2}\csc\frac{x}{2}$.

$y = \frac{1}{2}\csc\frac{x}{2}$

33. Graph the reciprocal cosine function, $y = 2\cos x$. The equation is of the form $y = A\cos Bx$ with $A = 2$ and $B = 1$.
amplitude: $|A| = |2| = 2$
period: $\frac{2\pi}{B} = \frac{2\pi}{1} = 2\pi$

Use quarter-periods, $\frac{\pi}{2}$, to find x-values for the five key points. Starting with $x = 0$, the x-values are 0, $\frac{\pi}{2}$, π, $\frac{3\pi}{2}$, 2π. Evaluating the function at each value of x, the key points are $(0, 2)$, $\left(\frac{\pi}{2}, 0\right)$, $(\pi, -2)$, $\left(\frac{3\pi}{2}, 0\right)$, and $(2\pi, 2)$. Use these key points to graph $y = 2\cos x$ from 0 to 2π. Extend the graph one cycle to the right. Use the graph to obtain the graph of the reciprocal function. Draw vertical asymptotes through the *x*-intercepts, and use them as guides to graph $y = 2\sec x$.

$y = 2\sec x$

35. Graph the reciprocal cosine function, $y = \cos\dfrac{x}{3}$.

The equation is of the form $y = A\cos Bx$ with $A = 1$ and $B = \dfrac{1}{3}$.

amplitude: $|A| = |1| = 1$

period: $\dfrac{2\pi}{B} = \dfrac{2\pi}{\frac{1}{3}} = 2\pi \cdot 3 = 6\pi$

Use quarter-periods, $\dfrac{6\pi}{4} = \dfrac{3\pi}{2}$, to find *x*-values for the five key points. Starting with $x = 0$, the *x*-values are 0, $\dfrac{3\pi}{2}$, 3π, $\dfrac{9\pi}{2}$, and 6π. Evaluating the function at each value of *x*, the key points are $(0, 1)$, $\left(\dfrac{3\pi}{2}, 0\right)$, $(3\pi, -1)$,

$\left(\dfrac{9\pi}{2}, 0\right)$, and $(6\pi, 1)$. Use these key points to graph $y = \cos\dfrac{x}{3}$ from 0 to 6π. Extend the graph one cycle to the right. Use the graph to obtain the graph of the reciprocal function. Draw vertical asymptotes through the *x*-intercepts, and use them as guides to graph $y = \sec\dfrac{x}{3}$.

$y = \sec\dfrac{x}{3}$

37. Graph the reciprocal sine function, $y = -2\sin \pi x$. The equation is of the form $y = A\sin Bx$ with $A = -2$ and $B = \pi$.

amplitude: $|A| = |-2| = 2$

period: $\dfrac{2\pi}{B} = \dfrac{2\pi}{\pi} = 2$

Use quarter-periods, $\dfrac{2}{4} = \dfrac{1}{2}$, to find *x*-values for the five key points. Starting with $x = 0$, the *x*-values are 0, $\dfrac{1}{2}$, 1, $\dfrac{3}{2}$, and 2. Evaluating the function at each value of *x*, the key points are $(0, 0)$, $\left(\dfrac{1}{2}, -2\right)$, $(1, 0)$,

$\left(\dfrac{3}{2}, 2\right)$, and $(2, 0)$. Use these key points to graph $y = -2\sin \pi x$ from 0 to 2. Extend the graph one cycle to the right. Use the graph to obtain the graph of the reciprocal function. Draw vertical asymptotes through the *x*-intercepts, and use them as guides to graph $y = -2\csc \pi x$.

$y = -2\csc \pi x$

39. Graph the reciprocal cosine function, $y = -\dfrac{1}{2}\cos \pi x$. The equation is of the form $y = A\cos Bx$ with $A = -\dfrac{1}{2}$ and $B = \pi$.

amplitude: $|A| = \left|-\dfrac{1}{2}\right| = \dfrac{1}{2}$

period: $\dfrac{2\pi}{B} = \dfrac{2\pi}{\pi} = 2$

Use quarter-periods, $\dfrac{2}{4} = \dfrac{1}{2}$, to find *x*-values for the five key points. Starting with $x = 0$, the *x*-values are 0, $\dfrac{1}{2}$, 1, $\dfrac{3}{2}$, and 2. Evaluating the function at each value of *x*, the key points are $\left(0, -\dfrac{1}{2}\right)$, $\left(\dfrac{1}{2}, 0\right)$, $\left(1, \dfrac{1}{2}\right)$, $\left(\dfrac{3}{2}, 0\right)$, $\left(2, -\dfrac{1}{2}\right)$.

Use these key points to graph $y = -\dfrac{1}{2}\cos \pi x$

from 0 to 2. Extend the graph one cycle to the right. Use the graph to obtain the graph of the reciprocal function. Draw vertical asymptotes through the

x-intercepts, and use them as guides to graph

$y = -\dfrac{1}{2}\sec \pi x$.

$y = -\dfrac{1}{2}\sec \pi x$

41. Graph the reciprocal sine function,
$y = \sin(x - \pi)$. The equation is of the form
$y = A\sin(Bx - C)$ with $A = 1$, and $B = 1$, and
$C = \pi$.

amplitude: $|A| = |1| = 1$

period: $\dfrac{2\pi}{B} = \dfrac{2\pi}{1} = 2\pi$

phase shift: $\dfrac{C}{B} = \dfrac{\pi}{1} = \pi$

Use quarter-periods, $\dfrac{2\pi}{4} = \dfrac{\pi}{2}$, to find

x-values for the five key points. Starting with

$x = \pi$, the x-values are $\pi, \dfrac{3\pi}{2}, 2\pi,$

$\dfrac{5\pi}{2}$, and 3π . Evaluating the function at each

value of x, the key points are $(\pi, 0)$,

$\left(\dfrac{3\pi}{2}, 1\right)$, $(2\pi, 0)$, $\left(\dfrac{5\pi}{2}, -1\right)$, $(3\pi, 0)$. Use

these key points to graph $y = \sin(x - \pi)$ from π
to 3π . Extend the graph one cycle to the right.
Use the graph to obtain the graph of the
reciprocal function. Draw vertical asymptotes
through the x-intercepts, and use them as guides

to graph $y = \csc(x - \pi)$.

$y = \csc (x - \pi)$

43. Graph the reciprocal cosine function,
$y = 2\cos(x + \pi)$. The equation is of the form
$y = A\cos(Bx + C)$ with $A = 2$, $B = 1$, and
$C = -\pi$.

amplitude: $|A| = |2| = 2$

period: $\dfrac{2\pi}{B} = \dfrac{2\pi}{1} = 2\pi$

phase shift: $\dfrac{C}{B} = \dfrac{-\pi}{1} = -\pi$

Use quarter-periods, $\dfrac{2\pi}{4} = \dfrac{\pi}{2}$, to find

x-values for the five key points. Starting with

$x = -\pi$, the x-values are $-\pi, -\dfrac{\pi}{2},$

$0, \dfrac{\pi}{2}$, and π . Evaluating the function at each

value of x, the key points are $(-\pi, 2)$,

$\left(-\dfrac{\pi}{2}, 0\right)$, $(0, -2)$, $\left(\dfrac{\pi}{2}, 0\right)$, and $(\pi, 2)$. Use

these key points to graph $y = 2\cos(x + \pi)$ from
$-\pi$ to π . Extend the graph one cycle to the
right. Use the graph to obtain the graph of the
reciprocal function. Draw vertical asymptotes
through the x-intercepts, and use them as guides
to graph $y = 2\sec(x + \pi)$.

$y = 2 \sec (x + \pi)$

45.

$$y = 2\tan\left(x - \frac{\pi}{6}\right) + 1$$

47.

$$y = \sec\left(2x + \frac{\pi}{2}\right) - 1$$

49.

51.

53. $y = (f \circ h)(x) = f(h(x)) = 2\sec\left(2x - \frac{\pi}{2}\right)$

55. Use a graphing utility with $y_1 = \tan x$ and $y_2 = -1$. For the window use $\text{Xmin} = -2\pi$, $\text{Xmax} = 2\pi$, $\text{Ymin} = -2$, and $\text{Ymax} = 2$.

$$x = -\frac{5\pi}{4}, \ -\frac{\pi}{4}, \ \frac{3\pi}{4}, \ \frac{7\pi}{4}$$

$$x \approx -3.93, \ -0.79, \ 2.36, \ 5.50$$

57. Use a graphing utility with $y_1 = 1/\sin x$ and $y_2 = 1$. For the window use $\text{Xmin} = -2\pi$, $\text{Xmax} = 2\pi$, $\text{Ymin} = -2$, and $\text{Ymax} = 2$.

$$x = -\frac{3\pi}{2}, \ \frac{\pi}{2}$$

$$x \approx -4.71, \ 1.57$$

59. $d = 12\tan 2\pi t$

a. Solve the equations

$$2\pi t = -\frac{\pi}{2} \quad \text{and} \quad 2\pi t = \frac{\pi}{2}$$

$$t = \frac{-\frac{\pi}{2}}{2\pi} \qquad\qquad t = \frac{\frac{\pi}{2}}{2\pi}$$

$$t = -\frac{1}{4} \qquad\qquad t = \frac{1}{4}$$

Thus, two consecutive asymptotes occur at

$$x = -\frac{1}{4} \quad \text{and} \quad x = \frac{1}{4}.$$

$$x\text{-intercept} = \frac{-\frac{1}{4} + \frac{1}{4}}{2} = \frac{0}{2} = 0$$

An x-intercept is 0 and the graph passes through (0, 0). Because the coefficient of the tangent is 12, the points on the graph midway between an x-intercept and the asymptotes have y-coordinates of -12 and 12. Use the two consecutive asymptotes,

$$x = -\frac{1}{4} \quad \text{and} \quad x = \frac{1}{4}, \text{ to graph one full}$$

period of $d = 12\tan 2\pi t$. To graph on [0, 2], continue the pattern and extend the graph to 2. (Do not use the left hand side of the first period of the graph on [0, 2].)

$$d = 12\tan 2\pi t$$

b. The function is undefined for $t = 0.25$, 0.75, 1.25, and 1.75.
The beam is shining parallel to the wall at these times.

61. Use the function that relates the acute angle with the hypotenuse and the adjacent leg, the secant function.

$$\sec x = \frac{d}{10}$$

$$d = 10\sec x$$

Graph the reciprocal cosine function, $y = 10\cos x$. The equation is of the form $y = A\cos Bx$ with $A = 10$ and $B = 1$.

amplitude: $|A| = |10| = 10$

period: $\frac{2\pi}{B} = \frac{2\pi}{1} = 2\pi$

For $-\frac{\pi}{2} < x < \frac{\pi}{2}$, use the x-values $-\frac{\pi}{2}$, 0, and

$\frac{\pi}{2}$ to find the key points $\left(-\frac{\pi}{2}, 0\right)$,

$(0, 10)$, and $\left(\frac{\pi}{2}, 0\right)$. Connect these points with

a smooth curve, then draw vertical asymptotes through the x-intercepts, and use them as guides to graph $d = 10\sec x$ on $\left[-\frac{\pi}{2}, \frac{\pi}{2}\right]$.

Number of Years

63.

Seconds after dive

77. period: $\frac{\pi}{B} = \frac{\pi}{\frac{1}{4}} = \pi \cdot 4 = 4\pi$

Graph $y = \tan\frac{x}{4}$ for $0 \le x \le 8\pi$.

79. period: $\frac{\pi}{B} = \frac{\pi}{2}$

Graph $y = \cot 2x$ for $0 \le x \le \pi$.

81. period: $\frac{\pi}{B} = \frac{\pi}{\pi} = 1$

Graph $y = \frac{1}{2}\tan \pi x$ for $0 \le x \le 2$.

83. period: $\frac{2\pi}{B} = \frac{2\pi}{\frac{1}{2}} = 2\pi \cdot 2 = 4\pi$

Graph the functions for $0 \le x \le 8\pi$.

85. period: $\frac{2\pi}{B} = \frac{2\pi}{2} = \pi$

phase shift: $\frac{C}{B} = \frac{\frac{\pi}{6}}{2} = \frac{\pi}{12}$

Thus, we include $\frac{\pi}{12} \le x \le \frac{25\pi}{12}$ in our graph,

and graph for $0 \le x \le \frac{5\pi}{2}$.

87.

The graph shows that carbon dioxide concentration rises and falls each year, but over all the concentration increased from 1990 to 2005.

89. The graph has the shape of a cotangent function with consecutive asymptotes at

$x = 0$ and $x = \dfrac{2\pi}{3}$. The period is $\dfrac{2\pi}{3} - 0 = \dfrac{2\pi}{3}$.

Thus,

$$\frac{\pi}{B} = \frac{2\pi}{3}$$
$$2\pi B = 3\pi$$
$$B = \frac{3\pi}{2\pi} = \frac{3}{2}$$

The points on the graph midway between an x-intercept and the asymptotes have y-coordinates of 1 and -1. Thus, $A = 1$. There is no phase shift. Thus, $C = 0$. An equation for this graph is

$$y = \cot \frac{3}{2} x.$$

91. The range shows that $A = 2$.

Since the period is 3π, the coefficient of x is given by B where $\dfrac{2\pi}{B} = 3\pi$

$$\frac{2\pi}{B} = 3\pi$$
$$3B\pi = 2\pi$$
$$B = \frac{2}{3}$$

Thus, $y = 2\csc \dfrac{2x}{3}$

93. a. Since $A=1$, the range is $(-\infty, -1] \cup [1, \infty)$

Viewing rectangle: $\left[-\dfrac{\pi}{6}, \pi, \dfrac{7\pi}{6} \right]$ by

$[-3, 3, 1]$

b. Since $A=3$, the range is $(-\infty, -3] \cup [3, \infty)$

Viewing rectangle: $\left[-\dfrac{1}{2}, \dfrac{7}{2}, 1 \right]$ by

$[-6, 6, 1]$

Section 4.7

Check Point Exercises

1. Let $\theta = \sin^{-1} \dfrac{\sqrt{3}}{2}$, then $\sin\theta = \dfrac{\sqrt{3}}{2}$.

The only angle in the interval $\left[-\dfrac{\pi}{2}, \dfrac{\pi}{2} \right]$ that

satisfies $\sin\theta = \dfrac{\sqrt{3}}{2}$ is $\dfrac{\pi}{3}$. Thus, $\theta = \dfrac{\pi}{3}$, or

$$\sin^{-1} \frac{\sqrt{3}}{2} = \frac{\pi}{3}.$$

2. Let $\theta = \sin^{-1}\left(-\dfrac{\sqrt{2}}{2} \right)$, then $\sin\theta = -\dfrac{\sqrt{2}}{2}$.

The only angle in the interval $\left[-\dfrac{\pi}{2}, \dfrac{\pi}{2} \right]$ that

satisfies $\cos\theta = -\dfrac{\sqrt{2}}{2}$ is $-\dfrac{\pi}{4}$. Thus $\theta = -\dfrac{\pi}{4}$,

or $\sin^{-1}\left(-\dfrac{\sqrt{2}}{2} \right) = -\dfrac{\pi}{4}$.

3. Let $\theta = \cos^{-1}\left(-\dfrac{1}{2} \right)$, then $\cos\theta = -\dfrac{1}{2}$. The only

angle in the interval $[0, \pi]$ that satisfies

$\cos\theta = -\dfrac{1}{2}$ is $\dfrac{2\pi}{3}$. Thus, $\theta = \dfrac{2\pi}{3}$, or

$$\cos^{-1}\left(-\frac{1}{2} \right) = \frac{2\pi}{3}.$$

4. Let $\theta = \tan^{-1}(-1)$, then $\tan\theta = -1$. The only

angle in the interval $\left(-\dfrac{\pi}{2}, \dfrac{\pi}{2} \right)$ that satisfies

$\tan\theta = -1$ is $-\dfrac{\pi}{4}$. Thus $\theta = -\dfrac{\pi}{4}$ or

$$\tan^{-1}\theta = -\frac{\pi}{4}.$$

5.

Scientific Calculator Solution			
Function	**Mode**	**Keystrokes**	**Display** (rounded to four places)
a. $\cos^{-1}\left(\dfrac{1}{3}\right)$	Radian	1 ÷ 3 = COS⁻¹	1.2310
b. $\tan^{-1}(-35.85)$	Radian	35.85 +/− TAN⁻¹	−1.5429

Graphing Calculator Solution			
Function	**Mode**	**Keystrokes**	**Display** (rounded to four places)
a. $\cos^{-1}\left(\dfrac{1}{3}\right)$	Radian	COS⁻¹ (1 ÷ 3) ENTER	1.2310
b. $\tan^{-1}(-35.85)$	Radian	TAN⁻¹ − 35.85 ENTER	−1.5429

6. a. $\cos\left(\cos^{-1} 0.7\right)$

$x = 0.7$, x is in $[-1,1]$ so $\cos(\cos^{-1} 0.7) = 0.7$

b. $\sin^{-1}(\sin \pi)$

$x = \pi$, x is not in $\left[-\dfrac{\pi}{2}, \dfrac{\pi}{2}\right]$. x is in the domain of $\sin x$, so $\sin^{-1}(\sin \pi) = \sin^{-1}(0) = 0$

c. $\cos\left(\cos^{-1} \pi\right)$

$x = \pi$, x is not in $[-1,1]$ so $\cos\left(\cos^{-1} \pi\right)$ is not defined.

7. Let $\theta = \tan^{-1}\left(\dfrac{3}{4}\right)$, then $\tan\theta = \dfrac{3}{4}$. Because $\tan\theta$ is positive, θ is in the first quadrant.

Use the Pythagorean Theorem to find r.

$r^2 = 3^2 + 4^2 = 9 + 16 = 25$

$r = \sqrt{25} = 5$

Use the right triangle to find the exact value.

$\sin\left(\tan^{-1}\dfrac{3}{4}\right) = \sin\theta = \dfrac{\text{side opposite } \theta}{\text{hypotenuse}} = \dfrac{3}{5}$

8. Let $\theta = \sin^{-1}\left(-\dfrac{1}{2}\right)$, then $\sin\theta = -\dfrac{1}{2}$. Because $\sin\theta$ is negative, θ is in quadrant IV.

Use the Pythagorean Theorem to find x.

$x^2 + (-1)^2 = 2^2$

$\quad x^2 + 1 = 4$

$\quad\quad x^2 = 3$

$\quad\quad\ x = \sqrt{3}$

Use values for x and r to find the exact value.

$$\cos\left[\sin^{-1}\left(-\dfrac{1}{2}\right)\right] = \cos\theta = \dfrac{x}{r} = \dfrac{\sqrt{3}}{2}$$

9. Let $\theta = \tan^{-1}x$, then $\tan\theta = x = \dfrac{x}{1}$.

Use the Pythagorean Theorem to find the third side, a.

$a^2 = x^2 + 1^2$

$a = \sqrt{x^2 + 1}$

Use the right triangle to write the algebraic expression.

$$\sec\left(\tan^{-1}x\right) = \sec\theta = \dfrac{\sqrt{x^2+1}}{1} = \sqrt{x^2+1}$$

Exercise Set 4.7

1. Let $\theta = \sin^{-1}\dfrac{1}{2}$, then $\sin\theta = \dfrac{1}{2}$. The only angle in the interval $\left[-\dfrac{\pi}{2}, \dfrac{\pi}{2}\right]$ that satisfies $\sin\theta = \dfrac{1}{2}$ is $\dfrac{\pi}{6}$. Thus,

$\theta = \dfrac{\pi}{6}$, or $\sin^{-1}\dfrac{1}{2} = \dfrac{\pi}{6}$.

3. Let $\theta = \sin^{-1}\dfrac{\sqrt{2}}{2}$, then $\sin\theta = \dfrac{\sqrt{2}}{2}$. The only angle in the interval $\left[-\dfrac{\pi}{2}, \dfrac{\pi}{2}\right]$ that satisfies $\sin\theta = \dfrac{\sqrt{2}}{2}$ is $\dfrac{\pi}{4}$.

Thus $\theta = \dfrac{\pi}{4}$, or $\sin^{-1}\dfrac{\sqrt{2}}{2} = \dfrac{\pi}{4}$.

5. Let $\theta = \sin^{-1}\left(-\dfrac{1}{2}\right)$, then $\sin\theta = -\dfrac{1}{2}$. The only angle in the interval $\left[-\dfrac{\pi}{2}, \dfrac{\pi}{2}\right]$ that satisfies $\sin\theta = -\dfrac{1}{2}$ is

    $-\dfrac{\pi}{6}$. Thus $\theta = -\dfrac{\pi}{6}$, or $\sin^{-1}\left(-\dfrac{1}{2}\right) = -\dfrac{\pi}{6}$.

7. Let $\theta = \cos^{-1}\dfrac{\sqrt{3}}{2}$, then $\cos\theta = \dfrac{\sqrt{3}}{2}$. The only angle in the interval $[0, \pi]$ that satisfies $\cos\theta = \dfrac{\sqrt{3}}{2}$ is $\dfrac{\pi}{6}$. Thus

    $\theta = \dfrac{\pi}{6}$, or $\cos^{-1}\dfrac{\sqrt{3}}{2} = \dfrac{\pi}{6}$.

9. Let $\theta = \cos^{-1}\left(-\dfrac{\sqrt{2}}{2}\right)$, then $\cos\theta = -\dfrac{\sqrt{2}}{2}$. The only angle in the interval $[0, \pi]$ that satisfies $\cos\theta = -\dfrac{\sqrt{2}}{2}$ is

    $\dfrac{3\pi}{4}$. Thus $\theta = \dfrac{3\pi}{4}$, or $\cos^{-1}\left(-\dfrac{\sqrt{2}}{2}\right) = \dfrac{3\pi}{4}$.

11. Let $\theta = \cos^{-1}0$, then $\cos\theta = 0$. The only angle in the interval $[0, \pi]$ that satisfies $\cos\theta = 0$ is $\dfrac{\pi}{2}$.

    Thus $\theta = \dfrac{\pi}{2}$, or $\cos^{-1}0 = \dfrac{\pi}{2}$.

13. Let $\theta = \tan^{-1}\dfrac{\sqrt{3}}{3}$, then $\tan\theta = \dfrac{\sqrt{3}}{3}$. The only angle in the interval $\left(-\dfrac{\pi}{2}, \dfrac{\pi}{2}\right)$ that satisfies $\tan\theta = \dfrac{\sqrt{3}}{3}$ is $\dfrac{\pi}{6}$.

    Thus $\theta = \dfrac{\pi}{6}$, or $\tan^{-1}\dfrac{\sqrt{3}}{3} = \dfrac{\pi}{6}$.

15. Let $\theta = \tan^{-1}0$, then $\tan\theta = 0$. The only angle in the interval $\left(-\dfrac{\pi}{2}, \dfrac{\pi}{2}\right)$ that satisfies $\tan\theta = 0$ is 0. Thus

    $\theta = 0$, or $\tan^{-1}0 = 0$.

17. Let $\theta = \tan^{-1}\left(-\sqrt{3}\right)$, then $\tan\theta = -\sqrt{3}$. The only angle in the interval $\left(-\dfrac{\pi}{2}, \dfrac{\pi}{2}\right)$ that satisfies $\tan\theta = -\sqrt{3}$ is

    $-\dfrac{\pi}{3}$. Thus $\theta = -\dfrac{\pi}{3}$, or $\tan^{-1}\left(-\sqrt{3}\right) = -\dfrac{\pi}{3}$.

19.

Scientific Calculator Solution			
Function	**Mode**	**Keystrokes**	**Display** (rounded to two places)
$\sin^{-1}0.3$	Radian	0.3 $\boxed{\text{SIN}^{-1}}$	0.30

Graphing Calculator Solution			
Function	**Mode**	**Keystrokes**	**Display** (rounded to two places)
$\sin^{-1}0.3$	Radian	$\boxed{\text{SIN}^{-1}}$ 0.3 $\boxed{\text{ENTER}}$	0.30

21.

Scientific Calculator Solution			
Function	**Mode**	**Keystrokes**	**Display** (rounded to two places)
$\sin^{-1}(-0.32)$	Radian	0.32 $\boxed{+/-}$ $\boxed{\text{SIN}^{-1}}$	−0.33

Graphing Calculator Solution			
Function	**Mode**	**Keystrokes**	**Display** (rounded to two places)
$\sin^{-1}(-0.32)$	Radian	$\boxed{\text{SIN}^{-1}}$ $\boxed{-}$ 0.32 $\boxed{\text{ENTER}}$	−0.33

23.

Scientific Calculator Solution			
Function	**Mode**	**Keystrokes**	**Display** (rounded to two places)
$\cos^{-1}\left(\dfrac{3}{8}\right)$	Radian	3 $\boxed{\div}$ 8 $\boxed{=}$ $\boxed{\text{COS}^{-1}}$	1.19

Graphing Calculator Solution			
Function	**Mode**	**Keystrokes**	**Display** (rounded to two places)
$\cos^{-1}\left(\dfrac{3}{8}\right)$	Radian	$\boxed{\text{COS}^{-1}}$ $\boxed{(}$ 3 $\boxed{\div}$ 8 $\boxed{)}$ $\boxed{\text{ENTER}}$	1.19

25.

Scientific Calculator Solution			
Function	**Mode**	**Keystrokes**	**Display** (rounded to two places)
$\cos^{-1}\dfrac{\sqrt{5}}{7}$	Radian	5 $\boxed{\sqrt{\ }}$ $\boxed{\div}$ 7 $\boxed{=}$ $\boxed{\text{COS}^{-1}}$	1.25

Graphing Calculator Solution			
Function	**Mode**	**Keystrokes**	**Display** (rounded to two places)
$\cos^{-1}\dfrac{\sqrt{5}}{7}$	Radian	$\boxed{\text{COS}^{-1}}$ $\boxed{(}$ $\boxed{\sqrt{\ }}$ 5 $\boxed{\div}$ 7 $\boxed{)}$ $\boxed{\text{ENTER}}$	1.25

27.

Scientific Calculator Solution			
Function	**Mode**	**Keystrokes**	**Display** (rounded to two places)
$\tan^{-1}(-20)$	Radian	20 $\boxed{+/-}$ $\boxed{\text{TAN}^{-1}}$	−1.52

Graphing Calculator Solution			
Function	**Mode**	**Keystrokes**	**Display** (rounded to two places)
$\tan^{-1}(-20)$	Radian	$\boxed{\text{TAN}^{-1}}$ $\boxed{-}$ 20 $\boxed{\text{ENTER}}$	−1.52

29.

Scientific Calculator Solution			
Function	Mode	Keystrokes	Display (rounded to two places)
$\tan^{-1}\left(-\sqrt{473}\right)$	Radian	473 $\boxed{\sqrt{}}$ $\boxed{+/-}$ $\boxed{\text{TAN}^{-1}}$	-1.52

Graphing Calculator Solution			
Function	Mode	Keystrokes	Display (rounded to two places)
$\tan^{-1}\left(-\sqrt{473}\right)$	Radian	$\boxed{\text{TAN}^{-1}}$ $\boxed{(}$ $\boxed{-}$ $\boxed{\sqrt{}}$ 473 $\boxed{)}$ $\boxed{\text{ENTER}}$	-1.52

31. $\sin\left(\sin^{-1} 0.9\right)$

$x = 0.9$, x is in $[-1, 1]$, so $\sin(\sin^{-1} 0.9) = 0.9$

33. $\sin^{-1}\left(\sin\dfrac{\pi}{3}\right)$

$x = \dfrac{\pi}{3}$, x is in $\left[-\dfrac{\pi}{2}, \dfrac{\pi}{2}\right]$, so $\sin^{-1}\left(\sin\dfrac{\pi}{3}\right) = \dfrac{\pi}{3}$

35. $\sin^{-1}\left(\sin\dfrac{5\pi}{6}\right)$

$x = \dfrac{5\pi}{6}$, x is not in $\left[-\dfrac{\pi}{2}, \dfrac{\pi}{2}\right]$, x is in the domain of $\sin x$, so

$\sin^{-1}\left(\sin\dfrac{5\pi}{6}\right) = \sin^{-1}\left(\dfrac{1}{2}\right) = \dfrac{\pi}{6}$

37. $\tan\left(\tan^{-1} 125\right)$

$x = 125$, x is a real number, so

$\tan\left(\tan^{-1} 125\right) = 125$

39. $\tan^{-1}\left[\tan\left(-\dfrac{\pi}{6}\right)\right]$

$x = -\dfrac{\pi}{6}$, x is in $\left(-\dfrac{\pi}{2}, \dfrac{\pi}{2}\right)$, so

$\tan^{-1}\left[\tan\left(-\dfrac{\pi}{6}\right)\right] = -\dfrac{\pi}{6}$

41. $\tan^{-1}\left(\tan\dfrac{2\pi}{3}\right)$

$x = \dfrac{2\pi}{3}$, x is not in $\left(-\dfrac{\pi}{2}, \dfrac{\pi}{2}\right)$, x is in the domain of $\tan x$, so

$\tan^{-1}\left(\tan\dfrac{2\pi}{3}\right) = \tan^{-1}\left(-\sqrt{3}\right) = -\dfrac{\pi}{3}$

43. $\sin^{-1}(\sin\pi)$

$x = \pi$, x is not in $\left[-\dfrac{\pi}{2}, \dfrac{\pi}{2}\right]$, x is in the domain of $\sin x$, so

$\sin^{-1}(\sin\pi) = \sin^{-1} 0 = 0$

45. $\sin\left(\sin^{-1}\pi\right)$

$x = \pi$, x is not in $[-1, 1]$, so $\sin\left(\sin^{-1}\pi\right)$ is not defined.

47. Let $\theta = \sin^{-1}\dfrac{4}{5}$, then $\sin\theta = \dfrac{4}{5}$. Because $\sin\theta$ is positive, θ is in the first quadrant.

$x^2 + y^2 = r^2$

$x^2 + 4^2 = 5^2$

$x^2 = 25 - 16 = 9$

$x = 3$

$\cos\left(\sin^{-1}\dfrac{4}{5}\right) = \cos\theta = \dfrac{x}{r} = \dfrac{3}{5}$

49. Let $\theta = \cos^{-1}\dfrac{5}{13}$, then $\cos\theta = \dfrac{5}{13}$. Because $\cos\theta$ is positive, θ is in the first quadrant.

$$x^2 + y^2 = r^2$$
$$5^2 + y^2 = 13^2$$
$$y^2 = 169 - 25$$
$$y^2 = 144$$
$$y = 12$$
$$\tan\left(\cos^{-1}\frac{5}{13}\right) = \tan\theta = \frac{y}{x} = \frac{12}{5}$$

51. Let $\theta = \sin^{-1}\left(-\dfrac{3}{5}\right)$, then $\sin\theta = -\dfrac{3}{5}$. Because $\sin\theta$ is negative, θ is in quadrant IV.

$$x^2 + y^2 = r^2$$
$$x^2 + (-3)^2 = 5^2$$
$$x^2 = 16$$
$$x = 4$$
$$\tan\left[\sin^{-1}\left(-\frac{3}{5}\right)\right] = \tan\theta = \frac{y}{x} = -\frac{3}{4}$$

53. Let, $\theta = \cos^{-1}\dfrac{\sqrt{2}}{2}$, then $\cos\theta = \dfrac{\sqrt{2}}{2}$. Because $\cos\theta$ is positive, θ is in the first quadrant.

$$x^2 + y^2 = r^2$$
$$\left(\sqrt{2}\right)^2 + y^2 = 2^2$$
$$y^2 = 2$$
$$y = \sqrt{2}$$
$$\sin\left(\cos^{-1}\frac{\sqrt{2}}{2}\right) = \sin\theta = \frac{y}{r} = \frac{\sqrt{2}}{2}$$

55. Let $\theta = \sin^{-1}\left(-\dfrac{1}{4}\right)$, then $\sin\theta = -\dfrac{1}{4}$. Because $\sin\theta$ is negative, θ is in quadrant IV.

$$x^2 + y^2 = r^2$$
$$x^2 + (-1)^2 = 4^2$$
$$x^2 = 15$$
$$x = \sqrt{15}$$
$$\sec\left[\sin^{-1}\left(-\frac{1}{4}\right)\right] = \sec\theta = \frac{r}{x} = \frac{4}{\sqrt{15}} = \frac{4\sqrt{15}}{15}$$

57. Let $\theta = \cos^{-1}\left(-\dfrac{1}{3}\right)$, then $\cos\theta = -\dfrac{1}{3}$. Because $\cos\theta$ is negative, θ is in quadrant II.

$$x^2 + y^2 = r^2$$
$$(-1)^2 + y^2 = 3^2$$
$$y^2 = 8$$
$$y = \sqrt{8}$$
$$y = 2\sqrt{2}$$

Use the right triangle to find the exact value.

$$\tan\left[\cos^{-1}\left(-\frac{1}{3}\right)\right] = \tan\theta = \frac{y}{x} = \frac{2\sqrt{2}}{-1} = -2\sqrt{2}$$

59. Let $\theta = \cos^{-1}\left(-\dfrac{\sqrt{3}}{2}\right)$, then $\cos\theta = -\dfrac{\sqrt{3}}{2}$.

Because $\cos\theta$ is negative, θ is in quadrant II.

$$x^2 + y^2 = r^2$$

$$\left(-\sqrt{3}\right)^2 + y^2 = 2^2$$

$$y^2 = 1$$

$$y = 1$$

$$\csc\left[\cos^{-1}\left(-\dfrac{\sqrt{3}}{2}\right)\right] = \csc\theta = \dfrac{r}{y} = \dfrac{2}{1} = 2$$

61. Let $\theta = \tan^{-1}\left(-\dfrac{2}{3}\right)$, then $\tan\theta = -\dfrac{2}{3}$.

Because $\tan\theta$ is negative, θ is in quadrant IV.

$$r^2 = x^2 + y^2$$

$$r^2 = 3^2 + \left(-2\right)^2$$

$$r^2 = 9 + 4$$

$$r^2 = 13$$

$$r = \sqrt{13}$$

$$\cos\left[\tan^{-1}\left(-\dfrac{2}{3}\right)\right] = \cos\theta = \dfrac{x}{r} = \dfrac{3}{\sqrt{13}} = \dfrac{3\sqrt{13}}{13}$$

63. Let $\theta = \cos^{-1}x$, then $\cos\theta = x = \dfrac{x}{1}$.

Use the Pythagorean Theorem to find the third side, b.

$$x^2 + b^2 = 1^2$$

$$b^2 = 1 - x^2$$

$$b = \sqrt{1 - x^2}$$

Use the right triangle to write the algebraic expression.

$$\tan\left(\cos^{-1}x\right) = \tan\theta = \dfrac{\sqrt{1 - x^2}}{x}$$

65. Let $\theta = \sin^{-1}2x$, then $\sin\theta = 2x$

$$y = 2x, r = 1$$

Use the Pythagorean Theorem to find x.

$$x^2 + (2x)^2 = 1^2$$

$$x^2 = 1 - 4x^2$$

$$x = \sqrt{1 - 4x^2}$$

$$\cos(\sin^{-1}2x) = \sqrt{1 - 4x^2}$$

67. Let $\theta = \sin^{-1}\dfrac{1}{x}$, then $\sin\theta = \dfrac{1}{x}$.

Use the Pythagorean Theorem to find the third side, a.

$$a^2 + 1^2 = x^2$$

$$a^2 = x^2 - 1$$

$$a = \sqrt{x^2 - 1}$$

Use the right triangle to write the algebraic expression.

$$\cos\left(\sin^{-1}\dfrac{1}{x}\right) = \cos\theta = \dfrac{\sqrt{x^2 - 1}}{x}$$

69. $\cot\left(\tan^{-1}\dfrac{x}{\sqrt{3}}\right) = \dfrac{\sqrt{3}}{x}$

71. Let $\theta = \sin^{-1} \dfrac{x}{\sqrt{x^2+4}}$, then $\sin\theta = \dfrac{x}{\sqrt{x^2+4}}$.

Use the Pythagorean Theorem to find the third side, a.

$$a^2 + x^2 = \left(\sqrt{x^2+4}\right)^2$$

$$a^2 = x^2 + 4 - x^2 = 4$$

$$a = 2$$

Use the right triangle to write the algebraic expression.

$$\sec\left(\sin^{-1}\dfrac{x}{\sqrt{x^2+4}}\right) = \sec\theta = \dfrac{\sqrt{x^2+4}}{2}$$

73. a. $y = \sec x$ is the reciprocal of $y = \cos x$. The x-values for the key points in the interval $[0, \pi]$ are $0, \dfrac{\pi}{4}, \dfrac{\pi}{2}, \dfrac{3\pi}{4}$, and π.

The key points are $(0, 1)$, $\left(\dfrac{\pi}{4}, \dfrac{\sqrt{2}}{2}\right)$,

$\left(\dfrac{\pi}{2}, 0\right)$, $\left(\dfrac{3\pi}{4}, -\dfrac{\sqrt{2}}{2}\right)$, and $(\pi, -1)$,

Draw a vertical asymptote at $x = \dfrac{\pi}{2}$. Now draw our graph from $(0, 1)$ through

$\left(\dfrac{\pi}{4}, \sqrt{2}\right)$ to ∞ on the left side of the asymptote. From $-\infty$ on the right side of the asymptote through $\left(\dfrac{3\pi}{4}, -\sqrt{2}\right)$ to

$(\pi, -1)$.

$$y = \sec x$$

b.   With this restricted domain, no horizontal line intersects the graph of $y = \sec x$ more

than once, so the function is one-to-one and has an inverse function.

c.   Reflecting the graph of the restricted secant function about the line $y = x$, we get the graph of $y = \sec^{-1} x$.

$$y = \sec x$$
$$y = \sec^{-1} x$$

75.

$$f(x) = \sin^{-1} x + \dfrac{\pi}{2}$$

Domain: $[-1, 1]$;
Range: $[0, \pi]$

77.

$$g(x) = \cos^{-1}(x + 1)$$

Domain: $[-2, 0]$;
Range: $[0, \pi]$

79.

$$f(x) = -2\tan^{-1} x$$

Domain: $(-\infty, \infty)$;
Range: $(-\pi, \pi)$

81.

$$f(x) = \sin^{-1}(x-2) - \frac{\pi}{2}$$

Domain: $(1, 3]$;
Range: $[-\pi, 0]$

83.

$$g(x) = \cos^{-1}\frac{\pi}{2}$$

Domain: $[-2, 2]$;
Range: $[0, \pi]$

85. The inner function, $\sin^{-1} x$, accepts values on the interval $[-1,1]$. Since the inner and outer functions are inverses of each other, the domain and range are as follows.
Domain: $[-1,1]$; Range: $[-1,1]$

87. The inner function, $\cos x$, accepts values on the interval $(-\infty,\infty)$. The outer function returns values on the interval $[0,\pi]$
Domain: $(-\infty,\infty)$; Range: $[0,\pi]$

89. The inner function, $\cos x$, accepts values on the interval $(-\infty,\infty)$. The outer function returns values on the interval $\left[-\dfrac{\pi}{2},\dfrac{\pi}{2}\right]$
Domain: $(-\infty,\infty)$; Range: $\left[-\dfrac{\pi}{2},\dfrac{\pi}{2}\right]$

91. The functions $\sin^{-1} x$ and $\cos^{-1} x$ accept values on the interval $[-1,1]$. The sum of these values is always $\dfrac{\pi}{2}$.
Domain: $[-1,1]$
Range: $\left\{\dfrac{\pi}{2}\right\}$

93. $\theta = \tan^{-1}\dfrac{33}{x} - \tan^{-1}\dfrac{8}{x}$

x	θ
5	$\tan^{-1}\dfrac{33}{5} - \tan^{-1}\dfrac{8}{5} \approx 0.408$ radians
10	$\tan^{-1}\dfrac{33}{10} - \tan^{-1}\dfrac{8}{10} \approx 0.602$ radians
15	$\tan^{-1}\dfrac{33}{15} - \tan^{-1}\dfrac{8}{15} \approx 0.654$ radians
20	$\tan^{-1}\dfrac{33}{20} - \tan^{-1}\dfrac{8}{20} \approx 0.645$ radians
25	$\tan^{-1}\dfrac{33}{25} - \tan^{-1}\dfrac{8}{25} \approx 0.613$ radians

95. $\theta = 2\tan^{-1}\dfrac{21.634}{28} \approx 1.3157$ radians;
$1.3157\left(\dfrac{180}{\pi}\right) \approx 75.4°$

97. $\tan^{-1} b - \tan^{-1} a = \tan^{-1} 2 - \tan^{-1} 0$
≈ 1.1071 square units

111. The domain of $y = \cos^{-1} x$ is the interval $[-1, 1]$, and the range is the interval $[0, \pi]$. Because the second equation is the first equation with 1 subtracted from the variable, we will move our x max to π, and graph in a $\left[-\dfrac{\pi}{2}, \pi, \dfrac{\pi}{4}\right]$ by $[0, 4, 1]$ viewing rectangle.

The graph of the second equation is the graph of the first equation shifted right 1 unit.

113. The domain of $y = \sin^{-1} x$ is the interval

$[-1, 1]$, and the range is $\left[-\dfrac{\pi}{2}, \dfrac{\pi}{2}\right]$. Because the

second equation is the first equation plus 1, and
with 2 added to the variable, we will move our y
max to 3, and move our x min to $-\pi$, and graph

in a $\left[-\pi, \dfrac{\pi}{2}, \dfrac{\pi}{2}\right]$ by

$[-2, 3, 1]$ viewing rectangle.

The graph of the second equation is the
graph of the first equation shifted left
2 units and up 1 unit.

115.

It seems $\sin^{-1} x + \cos^{-1} x = \dfrac{\pi}{2}$ for $-1 \le x \le 1$.

117. $2\sin^{-1} x = \dfrac{\pi}{4}$

$\sin^{-1} x = \dfrac{\pi}{8}$

$x = \sin\dfrac{\pi}{8}$

119. Let α equal the acute angle in the smaller right
triangle.

$\tan \alpha = \dfrac{8}{x}$

so $\tan^{-1}\dfrac{8}{x} = \alpha$

$\tan(\alpha + \theta) = \dfrac{33}{x}$

so $\tan^{-1}\dfrac{33}{x} = \alpha + \theta$

$\theta = \alpha + \theta - \alpha = \tan^{-1}\dfrac{33}{x} - \tan^{-1}\dfrac{8}{x}$

Section 4.8

Check Point Exercises

1. We begin by finding the measure of angle B.
Because $C = 90°$ and the sum of a triangle's
angles is $180°$, we see that $A + B = 90°$. Thus, $B
= 90° - A = 90° - 62.7° = 27.3°$.
Now we find b. Because we have a known
angle, a known opposite side, and an unknown
adjacent side, use the tangent function.

$\tan 62.7° = \dfrac{8.4}{b}$

$b = \dfrac{8.4}{\tan 62.7°} \approx 4.34$

Finally, we need to find c. Because we have a
known angle, a known opposite side and an
unknown hypotenuse, use the sine function.

$\sin 62.7° = \dfrac{8.4}{c}$

$c = \dfrac{8.4}{\sin 62.7} \approx 9.45$

In summary, $B = 27.3°$, $b \approx 4.34$, and
$c \approx 9.45$.

2. Using a right triangle, we have a known angle,
an unknown opposite side, a, and a known
adjacent side. Therefore, use the tangent
function.

$\tan 85.4° = \dfrac{a}{80}$

$a = 80\tan 85.4° \approx 994$

The Eiffel tower is approximately 994 feet high.

3. Using a right triangle, we have an unknown
angle, A, a known opposite side, and a known
hypotenuse. Therefore, use the sine function.

$\sin A = \dfrac{6.7}{13.8}$

$A = \sin^{-1}\dfrac{6.7}{13.8} \approx 29.0°$

The wire makes an angle of approximately $29.0°$
with the ground.

4. Using two right triangles, a smaller right triangle
corresponding to the smaller angle of elevation
drawn inside a larger right triangle
corresponding to the larger angle of elevation,
we have a known angle, an unknown opposite
side, a in the smaller triangle, b in the larger
triangle, and a known adjacent side in each
triangle. Therefore, use the tangent function.

$$\tan 32° = \frac{a}{800}$$

$$a = 800\tan 32° \approx 499.9$$

$$\tan 35° = \frac{b}{800}$$

$$b = 800\tan 35° \approx 560.2$$

The height of the sculpture of Lincoln's face is 560.2 – 499.9, or approximately 60.3 feet.

5. **a.** We need the acute angle between ray OD and the north-south line through O. The measurement of this angle is given to be 25°. The angle is measured from the south side of the north-south line and lies east of the north-south line. Thus, the bearing from O to D is S 25°E.

   b. We need the acute angle between ray OC and the north-south line through O. This angle measures $90° − 75° = 15°$. This angle is measured from the south side of the north-south line and lies west of the north-south line. Thus the bearing from O to C is S 15° W.

6. **a.** Your distance from the entrance to the trail system is represented by the hypotenuse, c, of a right triangle. Because we know the length of the two sides of the right triangle, we find c using the Pythagorean Theorem. We have

$$c^2 = a^2 + b^2 = (2.3)^2 + (3.5)^2 = 17.54$$

$$c = \sqrt{17.54} \approx 4.2$$

You are approximately 4.2 miles from the entrance to the trail system.

   b. To find your bearing from the entrance to the trail system, consider a north-south line passing through the entrance. The acute angle from this line to the ray on which you lie is $31° + \theta$. Because we are measuring the angle from the south side of the line and you are west of the entrance, your bearing from the entrance is S $(31° + \theta)$ W. To find θ, Use a right triangle and the tangent function.

$$\tan\theta = \frac{3.5}{2.3}$$

$$\theta = \tan^{-1}\frac{3.5}{2.3} \approx 56.7°$$

Thus, $31° + \theta = 31° + 56.7° = 87.7°$. Your bearing from the entrance to the trail system is S 87.7° W.

7. When the object is released $(t = 0)$, the ball's distance, d, from its rest position is 6 inches down. Because it is down, d is negative: when $t = 0$, $d = -6$. Notice the greatest distance from rest position occurs at $t = 0$. Thus, we will use the equation with the cosine function, $y = a\cos\omega t$, to model the ball's motion. Recall that $|a|$ is the maximum distance. Because the ball's initial position is down, $a = -6$. The value of ω can be found using the formula for the period.

$$\text{period} = \frac{2\pi}{\omega} = 4$$

$$2\pi = 4\omega$$

$$\omega = \frac{2\pi}{4} = \frac{\pi}{2}$$

Substitute these values into $d = a\cos wt$. The equation for the ball's simple harmonic motion is $d = -6\cos\frac{\pi}{2}t$.

8. We begin by identifying values for a and ω.

$d = 12\cos\frac{\pi}{4}t$, $a = 12$ and $\omega = \frac{\pi}{4}$.

   a. The maximum displacement from the rest position is the amplitude. Because $a = 12$, the maximum displacement is 12 centimeters.

   b. The frequency, f, is

$$f = \frac{\omega}{2\pi} = \frac{\frac{\pi}{4}}{2\pi} = \frac{\pi}{4}\cdot\frac{1}{2\pi} = \frac{1}{8}$$

The frequency is $\frac{1}{8}$ cycle per second.

   c. The time required for one cycle is the period.

$$\text{period} = \frac{2\pi}{\omega} = \frac{2\pi}{\frac{\pi}{4}} = 2\pi\cdot\frac{4}{\pi} = 8$$

The time required for one cycle is 8 seconds.

Exercise Set 4.8

1. Find the measure of angle B. Because
$C = 90°$, $A + B = 90°$. Thus,
$B = 90° - A = 90° - 23.5° = 66.5°$.
Because we have a known angle, a known
adjacent side, and an unknown opposite side,
use the tangent function.

$$\tan 23.5° = \frac{a}{10}$$

$$a = 10 \tan 23.5° \approx 4.35$$

Because we have a known angle, a known
adjacent side, and an unknown hypotenuse, use
the cosine function.

$$\cos 23.5° = \frac{10}{c}$$

$$c = \frac{10}{\cos 23.5°} \approx 10.90$$

In summary, $B = 66.5°$, $a \approx 4.35$, and
$c \approx 10.90$.

3. Find the measure of angle B. Because
$C = 90°$, $A + B = 90°$.
Thus, $B = 90° - A = 90° - 52.6° = 37.4°$.
Because we have a known angle, a known
hypotenuse, and an unknown opposite side, use
the sine function.

$$\sin 52.6 = \frac{a}{54}$$

$$a = 54 \sin 52.6° \approx 42.90$$

Because we have a known angle, a known
hypotenuse, and an unknown adjacent side, use
the cosine function.

$$\cos 52.6° = \frac{b}{54}$$

$$b = 54 \cos 52.6° \approx 32.80$$

In summary, $B = 37.4°$, $a \approx 42.90$, and $b \approx 32.80$.

5. Find the measure of angle A. Because
$C = 90°$, $A + B = 90°$.
Thus, $A = 90° - B = 90° - 16.8° = 73.2°$.
Because we have a known angle, a known
opposite side and an unknown adjacent side, use
the tangent function.

$$\tan 16.8° = \frac{30.5}{a}$$

$$a = \frac{30.5}{\tan 16.8°} \approx 101.02$$

Because we have a known angle, a known
opposite side, and an unknown hypotenuse, use
the sine function.

$$\sin 16.8° = \frac{30.5}{c}$$

$$c = \frac{30.5}{\sin 16.8°} \approx 105.52$$

In summary, $A = 73.2°$, $a \approx 101.02$, and
$c \approx 105.52$.

7. Find the measure of angle A. Because we have a
known hypotenuse, a known opposite side, and
an unknown angle, use the sine function.

$$\sin A = \frac{30.4}{50.2}$$

$$A = \sin^{-1}\left(\frac{30.4}{50.2}\right) \approx 37.3°$$

Find the measure of angle B. Because
$C = 90°$, $A + B = 90°$. Thus,

$$B = 90° - A \approx 90° - 37.3° = 52.7°.$$

Because we have a known hypotenuse, a known
opposite side, and an unknown adjacent side,
use the Pythagorean Theorem.

$$a^2 + b^2 = c^2$$

$$(30.4)^2 + b^2 = (50.2)^2$$

$$b^2 = (50.2)^2 - (30.4)^2 = 1595.88$$

$$b = \sqrt{1595.88} \approx 39.95$$

In summary, $A \approx 37.3°$, $B \approx 52.7°$, and
$b \approx 39.95$.

9. Find the measure of angle A. Because we have a
known opposite side, a known adjacent side, and
an unknown angle, use the tangent function.

$$\tan A = \frac{10.8}{24.7}$$

$$A = \tan^{-1}\left(\frac{10.8}{24.7}\right) \approx 23.6°$$

Find the measure of angle B. Because
$C = 90°$, $A + B = 90°$.
Thus, $B = 90° - A \approx 90° - 23.6° = 66.4°$.
Because we have a known opposite side, a
known adjacent side, and an unknown
hypotenuse, use the Pythagorean Theorem.

$$c^2 = a^2 + b^2 = (10.8)^2 + (24.7)^2 = 726.73$$

$$c = \sqrt{726.73} \approx 26.96$$

In summary, $A \approx 23.6°$, $B \approx 66.4°$, and
$c \approx 26.96$.

11. Find the measure of angle A. Because we have a known hypotenuse, a known adjacent side, and unknown angle, use the cosine function.

    $$\cos A = \frac{2}{7}$$

    $$A = \cos^{-1}\left(\frac{2}{7}\right) \approx 73.4°$$

    Find the measure of angle B. Because $C = 90°$, $A + B = 90°$.
    Thus, $B = 90° - A \approx 90° - 73.4° = 16.6°$. Because we have a known hypotenuse, a known adjacent side, and an unknown opposite side, use the Pythagorean Theorem.

    $$a^2 + b^2 = c^2$$
    $$a^2 + (2)^2 = (7)^2$$
    $$a^2 = (7)^2 - (2)^2 = 45$$
    $$a = \sqrt{45} \approx 6.71$$

    In summary, $A \approx 73.4°$, $B \approx 16.6°$, and $a \approx 6.71$.

13. We need the acute angle between ray OA and the north-south line through O. This angle measure $90° - 75° = 15°$. This angle is measured from the north side of the north-south line and lies east of the north-south line. Thus, the bearing from O and A is N 15° E.

15. The measurement of this angle is given to be 80°. The angle is measured from the south side of the north-south line and lies west of the north-south line. Thus, the bearing from O to C is S 80° W.

17. When the object is released $(t = 0)$, the object's distance, d, from its rest position is 6 centimeters down. Because it is down, d is negative: When $t = 0$, $d = -6$. Notice the greatest distance from rest position occurs at $t = 0$. Thus, we will use the equation with the cosine function, $y = a\cos\omega t$ to model the object's motion.

    Recall that $|a|$ is the maximum distance.

    Because the object's initial position is down, $a = -6$. The value of ω can be found using the formula for the period.

    $$period = \frac{2\pi}{\omega} = 4$$
    $$2\pi = 4\omega$$
    $$\omega = \frac{2\pi}{4} = \frac{\pi}{2}$$

Substitute these values into $d = a\cos\omega t$. The equation for the object's simple harmonic motion is $d = -6\cos\frac{\pi}{2}t$.

19. When the object is released $(t = 0)$, the object's distance, d, from its rest position is 0 inches: When $t = 0$, $d = 0$. Therefore, we will use the equation with the sine function, $y = a\sin\omega t$, to model the object's motion.

    Recall that $|a|$ is the maximum distance.

    Because the object's initial position is down, and has an amplitude of 3 inches, $a = -3$. The value of ω can be found using the formula for the period.

    $$period = \frac{2\pi}{\omega} = 1.5$$
    $$2\pi = 1.5\omega$$
    $$\omega = \frac{2\pi}{1.5} = \frac{4\pi}{3}$$

    Substitute these values into $d = a\sin\omega t$. The equation for the object's simple harmonic motion is $d = -3\sin\frac{4\pi}{3}t$.

21. We begin by identifying values for a and ω.

    $d = 5\cos\frac{\pi}{2}t$, $a = 5$ and $\omega = \frac{\pi}{2}$

    a. The maximum displacement from the rest position is the amplitude. Because $a = 5$, the maximum displacement is 5 inches.

    b. The frequency, f, is

    $$f = \frac{\omega}{2\pi} = \frac{\frac{\pi}{2}}{2\pi} = \frac{\pi}{2} \cdot \frac{1}{2\pi} = \frac{1}{4}.$$

    The frequency is $\frac{1}{4}$ inch per second.

    c. The time required for one cycle is the period.

    $$period = \frac{2\pi}{\omega} = \frac{2\pi}{\frac{\pi}{2}} = 2\pi \cdot \frac{2}{\pi} = 4$$

    The time required for one cycle is 4 seconds.

23. We begin by identifying values for a and ω.
    $d = -6\cos 2\pi t$, $a = -6$ and $\omega = 2\pi$

    a. The maximum displacement from the rest position is the amplitude. Because $a = -6$, the maximum displacement is 6 inches.

b.   The frequency, f, is
$$f = \frac{\omega}{2\pi} = \frac{2\pi}{2\pi} = 1.$$
The frequency is 1 inch per second.

c.   The time required for one cycle is the period.
$$\text{period} = \frac{2\pi}{\omega} = \frac{2\pi}{2\pi} = 1$$
The time required for one cycle is 1 second.

25.   We begin by identifying values for a and ω.
$$d = \frac{1}{2}\sin 2t,\ a = \frac{1}{2}\text{ and }\omega = 2$$

a.   The maximum displacement from the rest position is the amplitude.

Because $a = \frac{1}{2}$, the maximum

displacement is $\frac{1}{2}$ inch.

b.   The frequency, f, is
$$f = \frac{\omega}{2\pi} = \frac{2}{2\pi} = \frac{1}{\pi} \approx 0.32.$$
The frequency is approximately 0.32 cycle per second.

c.   The time required for one cycle is the period.
$$\text{period} = \frac{2\pi}{\omega} = \frac{2\pi}{2} = \pi \approx 3.14$$
The time required for one cycle is approximately 3.14 seconds.

27.   We begin by identifying values for a and ω.
$$d = -5\sin\frac{2\pi}{3}t,\ a = -5\text{ and }\omega = \frac{2\pi}{3}$$

a.   The maximum displacement from the rest position is the amplitude. Because $a = -5$, the maximum displacement is 5 inches.

b.   The frequency, f, is
$$f = \frac{\omega}{2\pi} = \frac{\frac{2\pi}{3}}{2\pi} = \frac{2\pi}{3} \cdot \frac{1}{2\pi} = \frac{1}{3}.$$
The frequency is $\frac{1}{3}$ cycle per second.

c.   The time required for one cycle is the period.
$$\text{period} = \frac{2\pi}{\omega} = \frac{2\pi}{\frac{2\pi}{3}} = 2\pi \cdot \frac{3}{2\pi} = 3$$
The time required for one cycle is 3 seconds.

29. $x = 500\tan 40° + 500\tan 25°$
$x \approx 653$

31. $x = 600\tan 28° - 600\tan 25°$
$x \approx 39$

33. $x = \dfrac{300}{\tan 34°} - \dfrac{300}{\tan 64°}$
$x \approx 298$

35. $x = \dfrac{400\tan 40°\tan 20°}{\tan 40° - \tan 20°}$
$x \approx 257$

37. $d = 4\cos\left(\pi t - \dfrac{\pi}{2}\right)$

$$d = 4\cos\left(\pi t - \frac{\pi}{2}\right)$$

a.   4 in.

b. $\dfrac{1}{2}$ in. per sec

c.   2 sec

d. $\dfrac{1}{2}$

39. $d = -2\sin\left(\dfrac{\pi t}{4} + \dfrac{\pi}{2}\right)$

$$d = -2\sin\left(\frac{\pi}{4}t + \frac{\pi}{2}\right)$$

a.   2 in.

b. $\dfrac{1}{8}$ in. per sec

   c.   8 sec

   d.   −2

41. Using a right triangle, we have a known angle, an unknown opposite side, a, and a known adjacent side. Therefore, use tangent function.

$$\tan 21.3° = \frac{a}{5280}$$
$$a = 5280 \tan 21.3° \approx 2059$$

The height of the tower is approximately 2059 feet.

43. Using a right triangle, we have a known angle, a known opposite side, and an unknown adjacent side, a. Therefore, use the tangent function.

$$\tan 23.7° = \frac{305}{a}$$
$$a = \frac{305}{\tan 23.7°} \approx 695$$

The ship is approximately 695 feet from the statue's base.

45. The angle of depression from the helicopter to point P is equal to the angle of elevation from point P to the helicopter. Using a right triangle, we have a known angle, a known opposite side, and an unknown adjacent side, d. Therefore, use the tangent function.

$$\tan 36° = \frac{1000}{d}$$
$$d = \frac{1000}{\tan 36°} \approx 1376$$

The island is approximately 1376 feet off the coast.

47. Using a right triangle, we have an unknown angle, A, a known opposite side, and a known hypotenuse. Therefore, use the sine function.

$$\sin A = \frac{6}{23}$$
$$A = \sin^{-1}\left(\frac{6}{23}\right) \approx 15.1°$$

The ramp makes an angle of approximately 15.1° with the ground.

49. Using the two right triangles, we have a known angle, an unknown opposite side, a in the smaller triangle, b in the larger triangle, and a known adjacent side in each triangle. Therefore, use the tangent function.

$$\tan 19.2° = \frac{a}{125}$$
$$a = 125 \tan 19.2° \approx 43.5$$
$$\tan 31.7° = \frac{b}{125}$$
$$b = 125 \tan 31.7° \approx 77.2$$

The balloon rises approximately 77.2 − 43.5 or 33.7 feet.

51. Using a right triangle, we have a known angle, a known hypotenuse, and unknown sides. To find the opposite side, a, use the sine function.

$$\sin 53° = \frac{a}{150}$$
$$a = 150 \sin 53° \approx 120$$

To find the adjacent side, b, use the cosine function.

$$\cos 53° = \frac{b}{150}$$
$$b = 150 \cos 53° \approx 90$$

The boat has traveled approximately 90 miles north and 120 miles east.

53. The bearing from the fire to the second ranger is N 28° E. Using a right triangle, we have a known angle, a known opposite side, and an unknown adjacent side, b. Therefore, use the tangent function.

$$\tan 28° = \frac{7}{b}$$
$$b = \frac{7}{\tan 28°} \approx 13.2$$

The first ranger is 13.2 miles from the fire, to the nearest tenth of a mile.

55. Using a right triangle, we have a known adjacent side, a known opposite side, and an unknown angle, A. Therefore, use the tangent function.

$$\tan A = \frac{1.5}{2}$$

$$A = \tan\left(\frac{1.5}{2}\right) \approx 37°$$

We need the acute angle between the ray that runs from your house through your location, and the north-south line through your house. This angle measures approximately $90° - 37° = 53°$. This angle is measured from the north side of the north-south line and lies west of the north-south line. Thus, the bearing from your house to you is N 53° W.

57. To find the jet's bearing from the control tower, consider a north-south line passing through the tower. The acute angle from this line to the ray on which the jet lies is $35° + \theta$. Because we are measuring the angle from the north side of the line and the jet is east of the tower, the jet's bearing from the tower is N $(35° + \theta)$ E. To find θ, use a right triangle and the tangent function.

$$\tan \theta = \frac{7}{5}$$

$$\theta = \tan^{-1}\left(\frac{7}{5}\right) \approx 54.5°$$

Thus, $35° + \theta = 35° + 54.5° = 89.5°$.
The jet's bearing from the control tower is N 89.5° E.

59. The frequency, f, is $f = \frac{\omega}{2\pi}$, so

$$\frac{1}{2} = \frac{\omega}{2\pi}$$

$$\omega = \frac{1}{2} \cdot 2\pi = \pi$$

Because the amplitude is 6 feet, $a = 6$. Thus, the equation for the object's simple harmonic motion is $d = 6\sin \pi t$.

61. The frequency, f, is $f = \frac{\omega}{2\pi}$, so

$$264 = \frac{\omega}{2\pi}$$

$$\omega = 264 \cdot 2\pi = 528\pi$$

Thus, the equation for the tuning fork's simple harmonic motion is $d = \sin 528\pi t$.

71. $y = -6e^{-0.09x}\cos 2\pi x$

10 complete oscillations occur.

73. Let d be the adjacent side to the 40° angle. Using the right triangles, we have a known angle and unknown sides in both triangles. Use the tangent function.

$$\tan 20° = \frac{h}{75 + d}$$

$$h = (75 + d)\tan 20°$$

Also, $\tan 40° = \frac{h}{d}$

$$h = d\tan 40°$$

Using the transitive property we have

$$(75 + d)\tan 20° = d\tan 40°$$

$$75\tan 20° + d\tan 20° = d\tan 40°$$

$$d\tan 40° - d\tan 20° = 75\tan 20°$$

$$d(\tan 40° - \tan 20°) = 75\tan 20°$$

$$d = \frac{75\tan 20°}{\tan 40° - \tan 20°}$$

Thus, $h = d\tan 40°$

$$= \frac{75\tan 20°}{\tan 40° - \tan 20°}\tan 40° \approx 48$$

The height of the building is approximately 48 feet.

Chapter 4 Review Exercises

1. The radian measure of a central angle is the length of the intercepted arc divided by the circle's radius.

$$\theta = \frac{27}{6} = 4.5 \text{ radians}$$

2. $15° = 15° \cdot \dfrac{\pi \text{ radians}}{180°} = \dfrac{15\pi}{180} \text{ radian}$

$$= \frac{\pi}{12} \text{ radian}$$

3. $120° = 120° \cdot \dfrac{\pi \text{ radians}}{180°} = \dfrac{120\pi}{180} \text{ radians}$

$$= \frac{2\pi}{3} \text{ radians}$$

4. $315° = 315° \cdot \dfrac{\pi \text{ radians}}{180°} = \dfrac{315\pi}{180} \text{ radians}$

$$= \frac{7\pi}{4} \text{ radians}$$

5. $\dfrac{5\pi}{3} \text{ radians} = \dfrac{5\pi}{3} \text{ radians} \cdot \dfrac{180°}{\pi \text{ radians}}$

$$= \frac{5 \cdot 180°}{3} = 300°$$

6. $\dfrac{7\pi}{5} \text{ radians} = \dfrac{7\pi}{5} \text{ radians} \cdot \dfrac{180°}{\pi \text{ radians}}$

$$= \frac{7 \cdot 180°}{5} = 252°$$

7. $-\dfrac{5\pi}{6} \text{ radians} = -\dfrac{5\pi}{6} \text{ radians} \cdot \dfrac{180°}{\pi \text{ radians}}$

$$= -\frac{5 \cdot 180°}{6} = -150°$$

8.

9.

10.

11.

12.

13. $400° - 360° = 40°$

14. $-445° + (2)360° = 275°$

15. $\dfrac{13\pi}{4} - 2\pi = \dfrac{13\pi}{4} - \dfrac{8\pi}{4} = \dfrac{5\pi}{4}$

16. $\dfrac{31\pi}{6} - (2)2\pi = \dfrac{31\pi}{6} - \dfrac{24\pi}{6} = \dfrac{7\pi}{6}$

17. $-\dfrac{8\pi}{3} + (2)2\pi = -\dfrac{8\pi}{3} + \dfrac{12\pi}{3} = \dfrac{4\pi}{3}$

18. $135° = 135° \cdot \dfrac{\pi \text{ radians}}{180°} = \dfrac{135 \cdot \pi}{180} \text{ radians}$

$$= \frac{3\pi}{4} \text{ radians}$$

$s = r\theta$

$$s = (10 \text{ ft})\left(\frac{3\pi}{4}\right) = \frac{15\pi}{2} \text{ ft} \approx 23.56 \text{ ft}$$

19. $\dfrac{10.3 \text{ revolutions}}{1 \text{ minute}} \cdot \dfrac{2\pi \text{ radians}}{1 \text{ revolution}}$

$= \dfrac{20.6\pi \text{ radians}}{1 \text{ minute}} = 20.6\pi$ radians per minute

20. Use $v = r\omega$ where v is the linear speed and ω is the angular speed in radians per minute.

$\omega = \dfrac{2250 \text{ revolutions}}{1 \text{ minute}} \cdot \dfrac{2\pi \text{ radians}}{1 \text{ revolution}}$

$= 4500\pi$ radians per minute

$v = 3 \text{ feet} \dfrac{4500\pi}{\text{minute}} = \dfrac{13,500\pi \text{ feet}}{\text{min}}$

$\approx 42,412$ ft per min

21. $P\left(-\dfrac{4}{5}, -\dfrac{3}{5}\right)$

$\sin t = y = -\dfrac{3}{5}$

$\cos t = x = -\dfrac{4}{5}$

$\tan t = \dfrac{y}{x} = \dfrac{-\frac{3}{5}}{-\frac{4}{5}} = \dfrac{3}{4}$

$\csc t = \dfrac{1}{y} = -\dfrac{5}{3}$

$\sec t = \dfrac{1}{x} = -\dfrac{5}{4}$

$\cot t = \dfrac{x}{y} = \dfrac{4}{3}$

22. $P\left(\dfrac{8}{17}, -\dfrac{15}{17}\right)$

$\sin t = y = -\dfrac{15}{17}$

$\cos t = x = \dfrac{8}{17}$

$\tan t = \dfrac{y}{x} = \dfrac{-\frac{15}{17}}{\frac{8}{17}} = -\dfrac{15}{8}$

$\csc t = \dfrac{1}{y} = -\dfrac{17}{15}$

$\sec t = \dfrac{1}{x} = \dfrac{17}{8}$

$\cot t = \dfrac{x}{y} = -\dfrac{8}{15}$

23. $\sec \dfrac{5\pi}{6} = \dfrac{1}{-\frac{\sqrt{3}}{2}} = -\dfrac{2\sqrt{3}}{3}$

24. $\tan \dfrac{4\pi}{3} = \dfrac{-\frac{\sqrt{3}}{2}}{-\frac{1}{2}} = \sqrt{3}$

25. $\sec \dfrac{\pi}{2}$ is undefined.

26. $\cot \pi$ is undefined.

27. $\sin t = \dfrac{2}{\sqrt{7}}, 0 \le t < \dfrac{\pi}{2}$

$\sin^2 t + \cos^2 t = 1$

$\left(\dfrac{2}{\sqrt{7}}\right)^2 + \cos^2 t = 1$

$\cos^2 t = 1 - \dfrac{4}{7}$

$\cos t = \sqrt{\dfrac{3}{7}} = \dfrac{\sqrt{21}}{7}$

Because $0 \le t < \dfrac{\pi}{2}$, $\cos t$ is positive.

$\tan t = \dfrac{\frac{2}{\sqrt{7}}}{\sqrt{\frac{3}{7}}} = \dfrac{2\sqrt{3}}{3}$

$\csc t = \dfrac{\sqrt{7}}{2}$

$\sec t = \dfrac{\sqrt{21}}{3}$

$\cot t = \dfrac{\sqrt{3}}{2}$

28. $\tan 4.7 \cot 4.7 = \tan 4.7 \left(\dfrac{1}{\tan 4.7}\right) = 1$

29. $\sin^2 \dfrac{\pi}{17} + \cos^2 \dfrac{\pi}{17} = 1$ because $\sin^2 t + \cos^2 t = 1.$

30. $\tan^2 1.4 - \sec^2 1.4 = -\left(\sec^2 1.4 - \tan^2 1.4\right)$
$= -1$

31. Use the Pythagorean Theorem to find the hypotenuse, c.

$$c^2 = a^2 + b^2$$

$$c = \sqrt{8^2 + 5^2} = \sqrt{64 + 25} = \sqrt{89}$$

$$\sin\theta = \frac{5}{\sqrt{89}} = \frac{5\sqrt{89}}{\sqrt{89}}$$

$$\cos\theta = \frac{8}{\sqrt{89}} = \frac{8\sqrt{89}}{\sqrt{89}}$$

$$\tan\theta = \frac{5}{8}$$

$$\csc\theta = \frac{\sqrt{89}}{5}$$

$$\sec\theta = \frac{\sqrt{89}}{8}$$

$$\cot\theta = \frac{3}{5}$$

32.
$$\sin\frac{\pi}{6} + \tan^2\frac{\pi}{3} = \frac{1}{2} - \left(\sqrt{3}\right)^2$$
$$= \frac{1}{2} - 3$$
$$= -\frac{5}{2}$$

33.
$$\cos^2\frac{\pi}{4} + \tan^2\frac{\pi}{4} = \left(\frac{\sqrt{2}}{2}\right)^2 - (1)^2$$
$$= \frac{1}{2} - 1$$
$$= -\frac{1}{2}$$

34.
$$4\cot\frac{\pi}{4} + \cos\frac{\pi}{3}\csc\frac{\pi}{6} = 4(1) + \left(\frac{1}{2}\right)(2)$$
$$= 4 + 1$$
$$= 5$$

35.
$$\cos\left(-\frac{\pi}{6}\right)\sin\left(-\frac{\pi}{4}\right) - \tan\frac{\pi}{4}$$
$$= \left(\frac{\sqrt{3}}{2}\right)\left(-\frac{\sqrt{2}}{2}\right) - 1$$
$$= -\frac{\sqrt{6}}{4} - 1$$

36. $\sin 70° = \cos(90° - 70°) = \cos 20°$

37. $\cos\dfrac{\pi}{2} = \sin\left(\dfrac{\pi}{2} - \dfrac{\pi}{2}\right) = \sin 0$

38.
$$\tan 23° = \frac{a}{100}$$
$$a = 100\tan 23°$$
$$a \approx 100(0.4245) \approx 42\,\text{mm}$$

39.
$$\sin 61° = \frac{20}{c}$$
$$c = \frac{20}{\sin 61°}$$
$$c \approx \frac{20}{0.8746} \approx 23\,\text{cm}$$

40.
$$\sin 48° = \frac{a}{50}$$
$$a = 50\sin 48°$$
$$a \approx 50(0.7431) \approx 37\,\text{in.}$$

41.
$$\sin\theta = \frac{y}{r} = \frac{1}{4}$$
$$x^2 + y^2 = r^2$$
$$x^2 + 1^2 = 4^2$$
$$x^2 = 15$$
$$x = \sqrt{15}$$
$$\tan\left(\frac{\pi}{2} - \theta\right) = \cot\theta = \frac{x}{y} = \frac{\sqrt{15}}{1} = \sqrt{15}$$

42.
$$\frac{1}{2}\,\text{mi.} = \frac{1}{2}\cdot 5280\,\text{ft} = 2640\,\text{ft}$$
$$\sin 17° = \frac{a}{2640}$$
$$a = 2640\cdot\sin 17°$$
$$a \approx 2640(0.2924) \approx 772$$
The hiker gains 772 feet of altitude.

43.
$$\tan 32° = \frac{d}{50}$$
$$d = 50\tan 32°$$
$$d \approx 50(0.6249) \approx 31$$
The distance across the lake is about 31 meters.

44. $\tan\theta = \dfrac{6}{4}$

Use a calculator in degree mode to find θ.

The display should show approximately 56. Thus, the angle of elevation of the sun is approximately 56°.

45.   We need values for x, y, and r. Because $P = (-1, -5)$ is a point on the terminal side of θ, $x = -1$ and $y = -5$. Furthermore,

$$r = \sqrt{(-1)^2 + (-5)^2}$$
$$= \sqrt{1 + 25} = \sqrt{26}$$

Now that we know x, y, and r, we can find the six trigonometric functions of θ.

$$\sin\theta = \frac{y}{r} = \frac{-5}{\sqrt{26}} = \frac{-5\sqrt{26}}{\sqrt{26}\cdot\sqrt{26}} = -\frac{5\sqrt{26}}{26}$$

$$\cos\theta = \frac{x}{r} = \frac{-1}{\sqrt{26}} = \frac{-1\sqrt{26}}{\sqrt{26}\cdot\sqrt{26}} = -\frac{\sqrt{26}}{26}$$

$$\tan\theta = \frac{y}{x} = \frac{-5}{-1} = 5$$

$$\csc\theta = \frac{r}{y} = \frac{\sqrt{26}}{-5} = -\frac{\sqrt{26}}{5}$$

$$\sec\theta = \frac{r}{x} = \frac{\sqrt{26}}{-1} = -\sqrt{26}$$

$$\cot\theta = \frac{x}{y} = \frac{-1}{-5} = \frac{1}{5}$$

46.   We need values for x, y, and r. Because $P = (0, -1)$ is a point on the terminal side of θ, $x = 0$ and $y = -1$. Furthermore,

$$r = \sqrt{x^2 + y^2} = \sqrt{0^2 + (-1)^2}$$
$$= \sqrt{0 + 1} = \sqrt{1} = 1$$

Now that we know x, y, and r, we can find the six trigonometric functions of θ.

$$\sin\theta = \frac{y}{r} = \frac{-1}{1} = -1$$

$$\cos\theta = \frac{x}{r} = \frac{0}{1} = 0$$

$$\tan\theta = \frac{y}{x} = \frac{-1}{0}, \text{ undefined}$$

$$\csc\theta = \frac{r}{y} = \frac{1}{-1} = -1$$

$$\sec\theta = \frac{r}{x} = \frac{1}{0}, \text{ undefined}$$

$$\cot\theta = \frac{x}{y} = \frac{0}{-1} = 0$$

47.   Because $\tan\theta > 0$, θ cannot lie in quadrant II and quadrant IV; the tangent function is negative in those two quadrants. Thus, with $\tan\theta > 0$, θ lies in quadrant I or quadrant III. We are also given that $\sec\theta > 0$. Because quadrant I is the only quadrant in which the tangent is positive and the secant is positive, we conclude that θ lies in quadrant I.

48.   Because $\tan\theta > 0$, θ cannot lie in quadrant II and quadrant IV; the tangent function is negative in those two quadrants. Thus, with $\tan\theta > 0$, θ lies in quadrant I or quadrant III. We are also given that $\cos\theta < 0$. Because quadrant III is the only quadrant in which the tangent is positive and the cosine is negative, we conclude that θ lies in quadrant III.

49.   Because the cosine is positive and the sine is negative, θ lies in quadrant IV. In quadrant IV, x is positive and y is negative. Thus,

$$\cos\theta = \frac{2}{5} = \frac{x}{r}, \; x = 2, r = 5. \text{ Furthermore,}$$

$$x^2 + y^2 = r^2$$
$$2^2 + y^2 = 5^2$$
$$y^2 = 25 - 4 = 21$$
$$y = -\sqrt{21}$$

Now that we know x, y, and r, we can find the six trigonometric functions of θ.

$$\sin\theta = \frac{y}{r} = \frac{-\sqrt{21}}{5} = -\frac{\sqrt{21}}{5}$$

$$\tan\theta = \frac{y}{x} = \frac{-\sqrt{21}}{2} = -\frac{\sqrt{21}}{2}$$

$$\csc\theta = \frac{r}{y} = \frac{5}{-\sqrt{21}} = -\frac{5\cdot\sqrt{21}}{\sqrt{21}\cdot\sqrt{21}} = -\frac{5\sqrt{21}}{21}$$

$$\sec\theta = \frac{r}{x} = \frac{5}{2}$$

$$\cot\theta = \frac{x}{y} = \frac{2}{-\sqrt{21}} = -\frac{2\sqrt{21}}{\sqrt{21}\cdot\sqrt{21}} = -\frac{2\sqrt{21}}{21}$$

50. Because the tangent is negative and the sine is positive, θ lies in quadrant II. In quadrant II x is negative and y is positive. Thus,

$$\tan\theta = -\frac{1}{3} = \frac{y}{x} = \frac{1}{-3}, \ x = -3, y = 1.$$

Furthermore,

$$r = \sqrt{x^2 + y^2} = \sqrt{(-3)^2 + 1^2} = \sqrt{9+1} = \sqrt{10}$$

Now that we know x, y, and r, we can find the six trigonometric functions of θ.

$$\sin\theta = \frac{y}{r} = \frac{1}{\sqrt{10}} = \frac{1 \cdot \sqrt{10}}{\sqrt{10} \cdot \sqrt{10}} = \frac{\sqrt{10}}{10}$$

$$\cos\theta = \frac{x}{r} = \frac{-3}{\sqrt{10}} = -\frac{3\sqrt{10}}{\sqrt{10} \cdot \sqrt{10}} = -\frac{3\sqrt{10}}{10}$$

$$\csc\theta = \frac{r}{y} = \frac{\sqrt{10}}{1} = \sqrt{10}$$

$$\sec\theta = \frac{r}{x} = \frac{\sqrt{10}}{-3} = -\frac{\sqrt{10}}{3}$$

$$\cot\theta = \frac{x}{y} = \frac{-3}{1} = -3$$

51. Because the cotangent is positive and the cosine is negative, θ lies in quadrant III. In quadrant III x and y are both negative. Thus,

$$\cot\theta = \frac{3}{1} = \frac{x}{y} = \frac{-3}{-1}, \ x = -3, y = -1.$$

Furthermore,

$$r = \sqrt{x^2 + y^2} = \sqrt{(-3)^2 + (-1)^2} = \sqrt{9+1} = \sqrt{10}$$

Now that we know x, y, and r, we can find the six trigonometric functions of θ.

$$\sin\theta = \frac{y}{r} = \frac{-1}{\sqrt{10}} = -\frac{\sqrt{10}}{10}$$

$$\cos\theta = \frac{x}{r} = \frac{-3}{\sqrt{10}} = -\frac{3\sqrt{10}}{10}$$

$$\tan\theta = \frac{y}{x} = \frac{-1}{-3} = \frac{1}{3}$$

$$\csc\theta = \frac{r}{y} = \frac{\sqrt{10}}{-1} = -\sqrt{10}$$

$$\sec\theta = \frac{r}{x} = \frac{\sqrt{10}}{-3} = -\frac{\sqrt{10}}{3}$$

52. Because $265°$ lies between $180°$ and $270°$, it is in quadrant III.

The reference angle is $\theta' = 265° - 180° = 85°$.

53. Because $\dfrac{5\pi}{8}$ lies between $\dfrac{\pi}{2} = \dfrac{4\pi}{8}$ and

$\pi = \dfrac{8\pi}{8}$, it is in quadrant II.

The reference angle is

$$\theta' = \pi - \frac{5\pi}{8} = \frac{8\pi}{8} - \frac{5\pi}{8} = \frac{3\pi}{8}.$$

54. Find the coterminal angle:

$$-410° + (2)360° = 310°$$

Find the reference angle: $360° - 310° = 50°$

55. Find the coterminal angle: $\dfrac{17\pi}{6} - 2\pi = \dfrac{5\pi}{6}$

Find the reference angle: $2\pi - \dfrac{5\pi}{6} = \dfrac{\pi}{6}$

56. Find the coterminal angle: $-\dfrac{11\pi}{3} + 4\pi = \dfrac{\pi}{3}$

Find the reference angle: $\dfrac{\pi}{3}$

57. $240°$ lies in quadrant III.
The reference angle is
$\theta' = 240° - 180° = 60°$.

$$\sin 60° = \frac{\sqrt{3}}{2}$$

In quadrant III, $\sin\theta < 0$, so

$$\sin 240° = -\sin 60° = -\frac{\sqrt{3}}{2}.$$

58. $120°$ lies in quadrant II.
The reference angle is
$\theta' = 180° - 120° = 60°$.

$$\tan 60° = \sqrt{3}$$

In quadrant II, $\tan\theta < 0$, so

$$\tan 120° = -\tan 60° = -\sqrt{3}.$$

59. $\frac{7\pi}{4}$ lies in quadrant IV.

The reference angle is

$$\theta' = 2\pi - \frac{7\pi}{4} = \frac{8\pi}{4} - \frac{7\pi}{4} = \frac{\pi}{4}.$$

$$\sec\frac{\pi}{4} = \sqrt{2}$$

In quadrant IV, $\sec\theta > 0$, so

$$\sec\frac{7\pi}{4} = \sec\frac{\pi}{4} = \sqrt{2}.$$

60. $\frac{11\pi}{6}$ lies in quadrant IV.

The reference angle is

$$\theta' = 2\pi - \frac{11\pi}{6} = \frac{12\pi}{6} - \frac{11\pi}{6} = \frac{\pi}{6}.$$

$$\cos\frac{\pi}{6} = \frac{\sqrt{3}}{2}$$

In quadrant IV, $\cos\theta > 0$, so

$$\cos\frac{11\pi}{6} = \cos\frac{\pi}{6} = \frac{\sqrt{3}}{2}.$$

61. $-210°$ lies in quadrant II.
The reference angle is
$$\theta' = 210° - 180° = 30°.$$

$$\cot 30° = \sqrt{3}$$

In quadrant II, $\cot\theta < 0$, so
$$\cot(-210°) = -\cot 30° = -\sqrt{3}.$$

62. $-\frac{2\pi}{3}$ lies in quadrant III.

The reference angle is

$$\theta' = \pi + \frac{-2\pi}{3} = \frac{3\pi}{3} - \frac{2\pi}{3} = \frac{\pi}{3}.$$

$$\csc\left(\frac{\pi}{3}\right) = \frac{2\sqrt{3}}{3}$$

In quadrant III, $\csc\theta < 0$, so

$$\csc\left(-\frac{2\pi}{3}\right) = -\csc\left(\frac{\pi}{3}\right) = -\frac{2\sqrt{3}}{3}.$$

63. $-\frac{\pi}{3}$ lies in quadrant IV.

The reference angle is

$$\theta' = \frac{\pi}{3}.$$

$$\sin\left(\frac{\pi}{3}\right) = \frac{\sqrt{3}}{2}$$

In quadrant IV, $\sin\theta < 0$, so

$$\sin\left(-\frac{\pi}{3}\right) = -\sin\left(\frac{\pi}{3}\right) = -\frac{\sqrt{3}}{2}.$$

64. $495°$ lies in quadrant II.
$495° - 360° = 135°$
The reference angle is
$$\theta' = 180° - 135° = 45°.$$

$$\sin 45° = \frac{\sqrt{2}}{2}$$

In quadrant II, $\sin\theta > 0$, so

$$\sin 495° = \sin 45° = \frac{\sqrt{2}}{2}.$$

65. $\frac{13\pi}{4}$ lies in quadrant III.

$$\frac{13\pi}{4} - 2\pi = \frac{13\pi}{4} - \frac{8\pi}{4} = \frac{5\pi}{4}$$

The reference angle is

$$\theta' = \frac{5\pi}{4} - \pi = \frac{5\pi}{4} - \frac{4\pi}{4} = \frac{\pi}{4}.$$

$$\tan\frac{\pi}{4} = 1$$

In quadrant III, $\tan\theta > 0$, so

$$\tan\frac{13\pi}{4} = \tan\frac{\pi}{4} = 1.$$

66.
$$\sin\frac{22\pi}{3} = \sin\left(\frac{22\pi}{3} - 6\pi\right)$$
$$= \sin\frac{4\pi}{3}$$
$$= -\sin\frac{\pi}{3}$$
$$= -\frac{\sqrt{3}}{2}$$

67.
$$\cos\left(-\frac{35\pi}{6}\right) = \cos\left(-\frac{35\pi}{6} + 6\pi\right)$$
$$= \cos\frac{\pi}{6}$$
$$= \frac{\sqrt{3}}{2}$$

68. The equation $y = 3\sin 4x$ is of the form $y = A\sin Bx$ with $A = 3$ and $B = 4$. The amplitude is $|A| = |3| = 3$. The period is $\frac{2\pi}{B} = \frac{2\pi}{4} = \frac{\pi}{2}$. The quarter-period is $\frac{\frac{\pi}{2}}{4} = \frac{\pi}{2} \cdot \frac{1}{4} = \frac{\pi}{8}$. The cycle begins at $x = 0$. Add quarter-periods to generate x-values for the key points.

$x = 0$

$x = 0 + \frac{\pi}{8} = \frac{\pi}{8}$

$x = \frac{\pi}{8} + \frac{\pi}{8} = \frac{\pi}{4}$

$x = \frac{\pi}{4} + \frac{\pi}{8} = \frac{3\pi}{8}$

$x = \frac{3\pi}{8} + \frac{\pi}{8} = \frac{\pi}{2}$

Evaluate the function at each value of x.

x	coordinates
0	$(0, 0)$
$\frac{\pi}{8}$	$\left(\frac{\pi}{8}, 3\right)$
$\frac{\pi}{4}$	$\left(\frac{\pi}{4}, 0\right)$
$\frac{3\pi}{8}$	$\left(\frac{3\pi}{8}, -3\right)$
$\frac{\pi}{2}$	$(2\pi, 0)$

Connect the five key points with a smooth curve and graph one complete cycle of the given function.

$y = 3 \sin 4x$

69. The equation $y = -2\cos 2x$ is of the form $y = A\cos Bx$ with $A = -2$ and $B = 2$. The amplitude is $|A| = |-2| = 2$. The period is $\frac{2\pi}{B} = \frac{2\pi}{2} = \pi$. The quarter-period is $\frac{\pi}{4}$. The cycle begins at $x = 0$. Add quarter-periods to generate x-values for the key points.

$x = 0$

$x = 0 + \frac{\pi}{4} = \frac{\pi}{4}$

$x = \frac{\pi}{4} + \frac{\pi}{4} = \frac{\pi}{2}$

$x = \frac{\pi}{2} + \frac{\pi}{4} = \frac{3\pi}{4}$

$x = \frac{3\pi}{4} + \frac{\pi}{4} = \pi$

Evaluate the function at each value of x.

x	coordinates
0	$(0, -2)$
$\frac{\pi}{4}$	$\left(\frac{\pi}{4}, 0\right)$
$\frac{\pi}{2}$	$\left(\frac{\pi}{2}, 2\right)$
$\frac{3\pi}{4}$	$\left(\frac{3\pi}{4}, 0\right)$
π	$(\pi, -2)$

Connect the five key points with a smooth curve and graph one complete cycle of the given function.

$y = -2 \cos 2x$

70. The equation $y = 2\cos\frac{1}{2}x$ is of the form

$y = A\cos Bx$ with $A = 2$ and $B = \frac{1}{2}$. The

amplitude is $|A| = |2| = 2$. The period is

$\frac{2\pi}{B} = \frac{2\pi}{\frac{1}{2}} = 2\pi \cdot 2 = 4\pi$. The quarter-period is

$\frac{4\pi}{4} = \pi$. The cycle begins at $x = 0$. Add quarter-periods to generate x-values for the key points.

$x = 0$
$x = 0 + \pi = \pi$
$x = \pi + \pi = 2\pi$
$x = 2\pi + \pi = 3\pi$
$x = 3\pi + \pi = 4\pi$

Evaluate the function at each value of x.

x	coordinates
0	$(0, 2)$
π	$(\pi, 0)$
2π	$(2\pi, -2)$
3π	$(3\pi, 0)$
4π	$(4\pi, 2)$

Connect the five key points with a smooth curve and graph one complete cycle of the given function.

$$y = 2\cos\frac{1}{2}x$$

71. The equation $y = \frac{1}{2}\sin\frac{\pi}{3}x$ is of the form

$y = A\sin Bx$ with $A = \frac{1}{2}$ and $B = \frac{\pi}{3}$. The

amplitude is $|A| = \left|\frac{1}{2}\right| = \frac{1}{2}$. The period is

$\frac{2\pi}{B} = \frac{2\pi}{\frac{\pi}{3}} = 2\pi \cdot \frac{3}{\pi} = 6$. The quarter-period is

$\frac{6}{4} = \frac{3}{2}$. The cycle begins at $x = 0$. Add quarter-periods to generate x-values for the key points.

$x = 0$
$x = 0 + \frac{3}{2} = \frac{3}{2}$
$x = \frac{3}{2} + \frac{3}{2} = 3$
$x = 3 + \frac{3}{2} = \frac{9}{2}$
$x = \frac{9}{2} + \frac{3}{2} = 6$

Evaluate the function at each value of x.

x	coordinates
0	$(0, 0)$
$\frac{3}{2}$	$\left(\frac{3}{2}, \frac{1}{2}\right)$
3	$(3, 0)$
$\frac{9}{2}$	$\left(\frac{9}{2}, -\frac{1}{2}\right)$
6	$(6, 0)$

Connect the five key points with a smooth curve and graph one complete cycle of the given function.

$$y = \frac{1}{2}\sin\frac{\pi}{3}x$$

72. The equation $y = -\sin \pi x$ is of the form $y = A \sin Bx$ with $A = -1$ and $B = \pi$. The amplitude is $|A| = |-1| = 1$. The period is $\frac{2\pi}{B} = \frac{2\pi}{\pi} = 2$. The quarter-period is $\frac{2}{4} = \frac{1}{2}$. The cycle begins at $x = 0$. Add quarter-periods to generate x-values for the key points.

$x = 0$

$x = 0 + \frac{1}{2} = \frac{1}{2}$

$x = \frac{1}{2} + \frac{1}{2} = 1$

$x = 1 + \frac{1}{2} = \frac{3}{2}$

$x = \frac{3}{2} + \frac{1}{2} = 2$

Evaluate the function at each value of x.

x	coordinates
0	$(0, 0)$
$\frac{1}{2}$	$\left(\frac{1}{2}, -1\right)$
1	$(1, 0)$
$\frac{3}{2}$	$\left(\frac{3}{2}, 1\right)$
2	$(2, 0)$

Connect the five key points with a smooth curve and graph one complete cycle of the given function.

$y = -\sin \pi x$

73. The equation $y = 3\cos\frac{x}{3}$ is of the form $y = A\cos Bx$ with $A = 3$ and $B = \frac{1}{3}$. The amplitude is $|A| = |3| = 3$. The period is $\frac{2\pi}{B} = \frac{2\pi}{\frac{1}{3}} = 2\pi \cdot 3 = 6\pi$. The quarter-period is $\frac{6\pi}{4} = \frac{3\pi}{2}$. The cycle begins at $x = 0$. Add quarter-periods to generate x-values for the key points.

$x = 0$

$x = 0 + \frac{3\pi}{2} = \frac{3\pi}{2}$

$x = \frac{3\pi}{2} + \frac{3\pi}{2} = 3\pi$

$x = 3\pi + \frac{3\pi}{2} = \frac{9\pi}{2}$

$x = \frac{9\pi}{2} + \frac{3\pi}{2} = 6\pi$

Evaluate the function at each value of x.

x	coordinates
0	$(0, 3)$
$\frac{3\pi}{2}$	$\left(\frac{3\pi}{2}, 0\right)$
3π	$(3\pi, -3)$
$\frac{9\pi}{2}$	$\left(\frac{9\pi}{2}, 0\right)$
6π	$(6\pi, 3)$

Connect the five key points with a smooth curve and graph one complete cycle of the given function.

$y = 3\cos\frac{x}{3}$

74. The equation $y = 2\sin(x - \pi)$ is of the form $y = A\sin(Bx - C)$ with $A = 2$, $B = 1$, and $C = \pi$. The amplitude is $|A| = |2| = 2$. The period is $\frac{2\pi}{B} = \frac{2\pi}{1} = 2\pi$. The phase shift is $\frac{C}{B} = \frac{\pi}{1} = \pi$. The quarter-period is $\frac{2\pi}{4} = \frac{\pi}{2}$. The cycle begins at $x = \pi$. Add quarter-periods to generate x-values for the key points.

$$x = \pi$$
$$x = \pi + \frac{\pi}{2} = \frac{3\pi}{2}$$
$$x = \frac{3\pi}{2} + \frac{\pi}{2} = 2\pi$$
$$x = 2\pi + \frac{\pi}{2} = \frac{5\pi}{2}$$
$$x = \frac{5\pi}{2} + \frac{\pi}{2} = 3\pi$$

Evaluate the function at each value of x.

x	coordinates
π	$(\pi, 0)$
$\frac{3\pi}{2}$	$\left(\frac{3\pi}{2}, 2\right)$
2π	$(2\pi, 0)$
$\frac{5\pi}{2}$	$\left(\frac{5\pi}{2}, -2\right)$
3π	$(3\pi, 0)$

Connect the five key points with a smooth curve and graph one complete cycle of the given function.

$y = 2 \sin (x - \pi)$

75. $y = -3\cos(x + \pi) = -3\cos(x - (-\pi))$

The equation $y = -3\cos(x - (-\pi))$ is of the form $y = A\cos(Bx - C)$ with $A = -3$,

$B = 1$, and $C = -\pi$. The amplitude is $|A| = |-3| = 3$.

The period is $\frac{2\pi}{B} = \frac{2\pi}{1} = 2\pi$. The phase shift is $\frac{C}{B} = \frac{-\pi}{1} = -\pi$. The quarter-period is $\frac{2\pi}{4} = \frac{\pi}{2}$. The cycle begins at $x = -\pi$. Add quarter-periods to generate x-values for the key points.

$$x = -\pi$$
$$x = -\pi + \frac{\pi}{2} = -\frac{\pi}{2}$$
$$x = -\frac{\pi}{2} + \frac{\pi}{2} = 0$$
$$x = 0 + \frac{\pi}{2} = \frac{\pi}{2}$$
$$x = \frac{\pi}{2} + \frac{\pi}{2} = \pi$$

Evaluate the function at each value of x.

x	coordinates
$-\pi$	$(-\pi, -3)$
$-\frac{\pi}{2}$	$\left(-\frac{\pi}{2}, 0\right)$
0	$(0, 3)$
$\frac{\pi}{2}$	$\left(\frac{\pi}{2}, 0\right)$
π	$(\pi, -3)$

Connect the five key points with a smooth curve and graph one complete cycle of the given function.

$y = -3 \cos (x + \pi)$

76. $y = \dfrac{3}{2}\cos\left(2x + \dfrac{\pi}{4}\right) = \dfrac{3}{2}\cos\left(2x - \left(-\dfrac{\pi}{4}\right)\right)$

The equation $y = \dfrac{3}{2}\cos\left(2x - \left(-\dfrac{\pi}{4}\right)\right)$ is of

the form $y = A\cos(Bx - C)$ with $A = \dfrac{3}{2}$,

$B = 2$, and $C = -\dfrac{\pi}{4}$. The amplitude is

$|A| = \left|\dfrac{3}{2}\right| = \dfrac{3}{2}$.

The period is $\dfrac{2\pi}{B} = \dfrac{2\pi}{2} = \pi$. The phase shift is

$\dfrac{C}{B} = \dfrac{-\frac{\pi}{4}}{2} = -\dfrac{\pi}{4} \cdot \dfrac{1}{2} = -\dfrac{\pi}{8}$. The quarter-period is

$\dfrac{\pi}{4}$. The cycle begins at $x = -\dfrac{\pi}{8}$. Add quarter-periods to generate x-values for the key points.

$x = -\dfrac{\pi}{8}$

$x = -\dfrac{\pi}{8} + \dfrac{\pi}{4} = \dfrac{\pi}{8}$

$x = \dfrac{\pi}{8} + \dfrac{\pi}{4} = \dfrac{3\pi}{8}$

$x = \dfrac{3\pi}{8} + \dfrac{\pi}{4} = \dfrac{5\pi}{8}$

$x = \dfrac{5\pi}{8} + \dfrac{\pi}{4} = \dfrac{7\pi}{8}$

Evaluate the function at each value of x.

x	coordinates
$-\dfrac{\pi}{8}$	$\left(-\dfrac{\pi}{8}, \dfrac{3}{2}\right)$
$\dfrac{\pi}{8}$	$\left(\dfrac{\pi}{8}, 0\right)$
$\dfrac{3\pi}{8}$	$\left(\dfrac{3\pi}{8}, -\dfrac{3}{2}\right)$
$\dfrac{5\pi}{8}$	$\left(\dfrac{5\pi}{8}, 0\right)$
$\dfrac{7\pi}{8}$	$\left(\dfrac{7\pi}{8}, \dfrac{3}{2}\right)$

Connect the five key points with a smooth curve and graph one complete cycle of the given function.

$y = \dfrac{3}{2}\cos\left(2x + \dfrac{\pi}{4}\right)$

77. $y = \dfrac{5}{2}\sin\left(2x + \dfrac{\pi}{2}\right) = \dfrac{5}{2}\sin\left(2x - \left(-\dfrac{\pi}{2}\right)\right)$

The equation $y = \dfrac{5}{2}\sin\left(2x - \left(-\dfrac{\pi}{2}\right)\right)$ is of

the form $y = A\sin(Bx - C)$ with $A = \dfrac{5}{2}$,

$B = 2$, and $C = -\dfrac{\pi}{2}$. The amplitude is

$|A| = \left|\dfrac{5}{2}\right| = \dfrac{5}{2}$.

The period is $\dfrac{2\pi}{B} = \dfrac{2\pi}{2} = \pi$. The phase shift is

$\dfrac{C}{B} = \dfrac{-\frac{\pi}{2}}{2} = -\dfrac{\pi}{2} \cdot \dfrac{1}{2} = -\dfrac{\pi}{4}$. The quarter-period is

$\dfrac{\pi}{4}$. The cycle begins at $x = -\dfrac{\pi}{4}$. Add quarter-periods to generate x-values for the key points.

$x = -\dfrac{\pi}{4}$

$x = -\dfrac{\pi}{4} + \dfrac{\pi}{4} = 0$

$x = 0 + \dfrac{\pi}{4} = \dfrac{\pi}{4}$

$x = \dfrac{\pi}{4} + \dfrac{\pi}{4} = \dfrac{\pi}{2}$

$x = \dfrac{\pi}{2} + \dfrac{\pi}{4} = \dfrac{3\pi}{4}$

Evaluate the function at each value of x.

x	coordinates
$-\dfrac{\pi}{4}$	$\left(-\dfrac{\pi}{4}, 0\right)$
0	$\left(0, \dfrac{5}{2}\right)$

$\dfrac{\pi}{4}$	$\left(\dfrac{\pi}{4},\,0\right)$
$\dfrac{\pi}{2}$	$\left(\dfrac{\pi}{2},\,-\dfrac{5}{2}\right)$
$\dfrac{3\pi}{4}$	$\left(\dfrac{3\pi}{4},\,0\right)$

Connect the five key points with a smooth curve and graph one complete cycle of the given function.

$$y = \frac{5}{2}\sin\left(2x + \frac{\pi}{2}\right)$$

78. The equation $y = -3\sin\left(\dfrac{\pi}{3}x - 3\pi\right)$ is of

the form $y = A\sin(Bx - C)$ with $A = -3$,

$B = \dfrac{\pi}{3}$, and $C = 3\pi$. The amplitude is

$|A| = |-3| = 3$.

The period is $\dfrac{2\pi}{B} = \dfrac{2\pi}{\frac{\pi}{3}} = 2\pi \cdot \dfrac{3}{\pi} = 6$. The phase

shift is $\dfrac{C}{B} = \dfrac{3\pi}{\frac{\pi}{3}} = 3\pi \cdot \dfrac{3}{\pi} = 9$. The quarter-period

is $\dfrac{6}{4} = \dfrac{3}{2}$. The cycle begins at $x = 9$. Add

quarter-periods to generate x-values for the key points.

$x = 9$

$x = 9 + \dfrac{3}{2} = \dfrac{21}{2}$

$x = \dfrac{21}{2} + \dfrac{3}{2} = 12$

$x = 12 + \dfrac{3}{2} = \dfrac{27}{2}$

$x = \dfrac{27}{2} + \dfrac{3}{2} = 15$

Evaluate the function at each value of x.

x	coordinates
9	$(9, 0)$
$\dfrac{21}{2}$	$\left(\dfrac{21}{2},\,-3\right)$
12	$(12, 0)$
$\dfrac{27}{2}$	$\left(\dfrac{27}{2},\,3\right)$
15	$(15, 0)$

Connect the five key points with a smooth curve and graph one complete cycle of the given function.

$$y = -3\sin\left(\frac{\pi}{3}x - 3\pi\right)$$

79. The graph of $y = \sin 2x + 1$ is the graph of $y = \sin 2x$ shifted one unit upward. The period

for both functions is $\dfrac{2\pi}{2} = \pi$. The quarter-

period is $\dfrac{\pi}{4}$. The cycle begins at $x = 0$. Add

quarter-periods to generate x-values for the key points.

$x = 0$

$x = 0 + \dfrac{\pi}{4} = \dfrac{\pi}{4}$

$x = \dfrac{\pi}{4} + \dfrac{\pi}{4} = \dfrac{\pi}{2}$

$x = \dfrac{\pi}{2} + \dfrac{\pi}{4} = \dfrac{3\pi}{4}$

$x = \dfrac{3\pi}{4} + \dfrac{\pi}{4} = \pi$

Evaluate the function at each value of x.

x	coordinates
0	$(0, 1)$
$\dfrac{\pi}{4}$	$\left(\dfrac{\pi}{4}, 2\right)$
$\dfrac{\pi}{2}$	$\left(\dfrac{\pi}{2}, 1\right)$
$\dfrac{3\pi}{4}$	$\left(\dfrac{3\pi}{4}, 0\right)$
π	$(\pi, 1)$

By connecting the points with a smooth curve we obtain one period of the graph.

$y = \sin 2x + 1$

80. The graph of $y = 2\cos\dfrac{1}{3}x - 2$ is the graph of

$y = 2\cos\dfrac{1}{3}x$ shifted two units downward. The

period for both functions is $\dfrac{2\pi}{\frac{1}{3}} = 2\pi \cdot 3 = 6\pi$.

The quarter-period is $\dfrac{6\pi}{4} = \dfrac{3\pi}{2}$. The cycle

begins at $x = 0$. Add quarter-periods to generate x-values for the key points.
$x = 0$

$x = 0 + \dfrac{3\pi}{2} = \dfrac{3\pi}{2}$

$x = \dfrac{3\pi}{2} + \dfrac{3\pi}{2} = 3\pi$

$x = 3\pi + \dfrac{3\pi}{2} = \dfrac{9\pi}{2}$

$x = \dfrac{9\pi}{2} + \dfrac{3\pi}{2} = 6\pi$

Evaluate the function at each value of x.

x	coordinates
0	$(0, 0)$
$\dfrac{3\pi}{2}$	$\left(\dfrac{3\pi}{2}, -2\right)$
3π	$(3\pi, -4)$
$\dfrac{9\pi}{2}$	$\left(\dfrac{9\pi}{2}, -2\right)$
6π	$(6\pi, 0)$

By connecting the points with a smooth curve we obtain one period of the graph.

$y = 2\cos\dfrac{1}{3}x - 2$

81. a. At midnight $x = 0$. Thus,

$y = 98.6 + 0.3\sin\left(\dfrac{\pi}{12} \cdot 0 - \dfrac{11\pi}{12}\right)$

$= 98.6 + 0.3\sin\left(-\dfrac{11\pi}{12}\right)$

$\approx 98.6 + 0.3(-0.2588) \approx 98.52$

The body temperature is about 98.52°F.

b. period: $\dfrac{2\pi}{B} = \dfrac{2\pi}{\frac{\pi}{12}} = 2\pi \cdot \dfrac{12}{\pi} = 24$ hours

c. Solve the equation

$\dfrac{\pi}{12}x - \dfrac{11\pi}{12} = \dfrac{\pi}{2}$

$\dfrac{\pi}{12}x = \dfrac{\pi}{2} + \dfrac{11\pi}{12} = \dfrac{6\pi}{12} + \dfrac{11\pi}{12} = \dfrac{17\pi}{12}$

$x = \dfrac{17\pi}{12} \cdot \dfrac{12}{\pi} = 17$

The body temperature is highest for $x = 17$.

$$y = 98.6 + 0.3\sin\left(\frac{\pi}{12} \cdot 17 - \frac{11\pi}{12}\right)$$

$$= 98.6 + 0.3\sin\frac{\pi}{2} = 98.6 + 0.3 = 98.9$$

17 hours after midnight, which is
5 P.M., the body temperature is 98.9°F.

d.   Solve the equation

$$\frac{\pi}{12}x - \frac{11\pi}{12} = \frac{3\pi}{2}$$

$$\frac{\pi}{12}x = \frac{3\pi}{2} + \frac{11\pi}{12} = \frac{18\pi}{12} + \frac{11\pi}{12} = \frac{29\pi}{12}$$

$$x = \frac{29\pi}{12} \cdot \frac{12}{\pi} = 29$$

The body temperature is lowest for $x = 29$.

$$y = 98.6 + 0.3\sin\left(\frac{\pi}{12} \cdot 29 - \frac{11\pi}{12}\right)$$

$$= 98.6 + 0.3\sin\left(\frac{3\pi}{2}\right)$$

$$= 98.6 + 0.3(-1) = 98.3°$$

29 hours after midnight or 5 hours after
midnight, at 5 A.M., the body temperature
is 98.3°F.

e.   The graph of

$$y = 98.6 + 0.3\sin\left(\frac{\pi}{12}x - \frac{11\pi}{12}\right) \text{ is of the}$$

form $y = D + A\sin(Bx - C)$ with $A = 0.3$,

$B = \frac{\pi}{12}$, $C = \frac{11\pi}{12}$, and $D = 98.6$. The

amplitude is $|A| = |0.3| = 0.3$. The
period from part (b) is 24. The quarter-

period is $\frac{24}{4} = 6$. The phase shift is

$$\frac{C}{B} = \frac{\frac{11\pi}{12}}{\frac{\pi}{12}} = \frac{11\pi}{12} \cdot \frac{12}{\pi} = 11. \text{ The cycle begins}$$

at $x = 11$. Add quarter-periods to generate
x-values for the key points.
$x = 11$
$x = 11 + 6 = 17$
$x = 17 + 6 = 23$
$x = 23 + 6 = 29$
$x = 29 + 6 = 35$
Evaluate the function at each value of x.
The key points are (11, 98.6), (17, 98.9),
(23, 98.6), (29, 98.3), (35, 98.6). Extend
the pattern to the left, and graph the

function for $0 \le x \le 24$.

Hours after midnight

82.   Solve the equations

$$2x = -\frac{\pi}{2} \quad \text{and} \quad 2x = \frac{\pi}{2}$$

$$x = \frac{-\frac{\pi}{2}}{2} \qquad\qquad x = \frac{\frac{\pi}{2}}{2}$$

$$x = -\frac{\pi}{4} \qquad\qquad x = \frac{\pi}{4}$$

Thus, two consecutive asymptotes occur at

$$x = -\frac{\pi}{4} \text{ and } x = \frac{\pi}{4}.$$

$$x\text{-intercept} = \frac{-\frac{\pi}{4} + \frac{\pi}{4}}{2} = \frac{0}{2} = 0$$

An x-intercept is 0 and the graph passes through
(0, 0). Because the coefficient of the tangent is
4, the points on the graph midway between an x-
intercept and the asymptotes have y-coordinates
of –4 and 4. Use the two consecutive

asymptotes. $x = -\frac{\pi}{4}$ and $x = \frac{\pi}{4}$, to graph one

full period of $y = 4\tan 2x$ from $-\frac{\pi}{4}$ to $\frac{\pi}{4}$.

Continue the pattern and extend the graph
another full period to the right.

$y = 4\tan 2x$

83. Solve the equations

$$\frac{\pi}{4}x = -\frac{\pi}{2} \quad \text{and} \quad \frac{\pi}{4}x = \frac{\pi}{2}$$

$$x = -\frac{\pi}{2} \cdot \frac{4}{\pi} \qquad x = \frac{\pi}{2} \cdot \frac{4}{\pi}$$

$$x = -2 \qquad x = 2$$

Thus, two consecutive asymptotes occur at $x = -2$ and $x = 2$.

$$x\text{-intercept} = \frac{-2+2}{2} = \frac{0}{2} = 0$$

An x-intercept is 0 and the graph passes through $(0, 0)$. Because the coefficient of the tangent is -2, the points on the graph midway between an x-intercept and the asymptotes have y-coordinates of 2 and -2. Use the two consecutive asymptotes, $x = -2$ and $x = 2$, to graph one full period of $y = -2\tan\frac{\pi}{4}x$ from -2 to 2. Continue the pattern and extend the graph another full period to the right.

$$y = -2\tan\frac{\pi}{4}x$$

84. Solve the equations

$$x + \pi = -\frac{\pi}{2} \quad \text{and} \quad x + \pi = \frac{\pi}{2}$$

$$x = -\frac{\pi}{2} - \pi \qquad x = \frac{\pi}{2} - \pi$$

$$x = -\frac{3\pi}{2} \qquad x = -\frac{\pi}{2}$$

Thus, two consecutive asymptotes occur at $x = -\frac{3\pi}{2}$ and $x = -\frac{\pi}{2}$.

$$x\text{-intercept} = \frac{-\frac{3\pi}{2} - \frac{\pi}{2}}{2} = \frac{-2\pi}{2} = -\pi$$

An x-intercept is $-\pi$ and the graph passes through $(-\pi, 0)$. Because the coefficient of the tangent is 1, the points on the graph midway between an x-intercept and the asymptotes have y-coordinates of -1 and 1. Use the two consecutive asymptotes, $x = -\frac{3\pi}{2}$ and $x = -\frac{\pi}{2}$, to graph one full period

of $y = \tan(x + \pi)$ from $-\frac{3\pi}{2}$ to $-\frac{\pi}{2}$. Continue the pattern and extend the graph another full period to the right.

$$y = \tan(x + \pi)$$

85. Solve the equations

$$x - \frac{\pi}{4} = -\frac{\pi}{2} \quad \text{and} \quad x - \frac{\pi}{4} = \frac{\pi}{2}$$

$$x = -\frac{\pi}{2} + \frac{\pi}{4} \qquad x = \frac{\pi}{2} + \frac{\pi}{4}$$

$$x = -\frac{\pi}{4} \qquad x = \frac{3\pi}{4}$$

Thus, two consecutive asymptotes occur at

$$x = -\frac{\pi}{4} \text{ and } x = -\frac{3\pi}{4}.$$

$$x\text{-intercept} = \frac{-\frac{\pi}{4} - \frac{3\pi}{4}}{2} = \frac{\frac{\pi}{2}}{2} = \frac{\pi}{4}$$

An x-intercept is $\frac{\pi}{4}$ and the graph passes

through $\left(\frac{\pi}{4}, 0\right)$. Because the coefficient of the

tangent is -1, the points on the graph midway between an x-intercept and the asymptotes have y-coordinates of 1 and -1. Use the two consecutive asymptotes,

$x = -\frac{\pi}{4}$ and $x = \frac{3\pi}{4}$, to graph one full period

of $y = -\tan\left(x - \frac{\pi}{4}\right)$ from $-\frac{\pi}{4}$ to $\frac{3\pi}{4}$.

Continue the pattern and extend the graph another full period to the right.

$$y = -\tan\left(x - \frac{\pi}{4}\right)$$

86. Solve the equations

$$3x = 0 \quad \text{and} \quad 3x = \pi$$

$$x = 0 \qquad\qquad x = \frac{\pi}{3}$$

Thus, two consecutive asymptotes occur at

$x = 0$ and $x = \dfrac{\pi}{3}$.

$$x\text{-intercept} = \frac{0 + \frac{\pi}{3}}{2} = \frac{\frac{\pi}{3}}{2} = \frac{\pi}{6}$$

An x-intercept is $\dfrac{\pi}{6}$ and the graph passes

through $\left(\dfrac{\pi}{6}, 0\right)$.

Because the coefficient of the tangent is 2, the points on the graph midway between an x-intercept and the asymptotes have y-coordinates of 2 and -2. Use the two consecutive

asymptotes, $x = 0$ and $x = \dfrac{\pi}{3}$, to graph one full

period of $y = 2\cot 3x$ from 0 to $\dfrac{\pi}{3}$. Continue

the pattern and extend the graph another full period to the right.

$$y = 2\cot 3x$$

87. Solve the equations

$$\frac{\pi}{2}x = 0 \quad \text{and} \quad \frac{\pi}{2}x = \pi$$

$$x = 0 \qquad\qquad x = \pi \cdot \frac{2}{\pi}$$

$$\qquad\qquad\qquad x = 2$$

Thus, two consecutive asymptotes occur at $x = 0$ and $x = 2$.

$$x\text{-intercept} = \frac{0 + 2}{2} = \frac{2}{2} = 1$$

An x-intercept is 1 and the graph passes through $(1, 0)$. Because the coefficient of the cotangent is

$-\dfrac{1}{2}$, the points on the graph midway between

an x-intercept and the asymptotes have y-

coordinates of $-\dfrac{1}{2}$ and $\dfrac{1}{2}$. Use the two

consecutive asymptotes, $x = 0$ and $x = 2$, to

graph one full period of $y = -\dfrac{1}{2}\cot\dfrac{\pi}{2}x$ from 0

to 2. Continue the pattern and extend the graph another full period to the right.

$$y = -\frac{1}{2}\cot\frac{\pi}{2}x$$

88. Solve the equations

$$x + \frac{\pi}{2} = 0 \qquad \text{and} \quad x + \frac{\pi}{2} = \pi$$

$$x = 0 - \frac{\pi}{2} \qquad\qquad x = \pi - \frac{\pi}{2}$$

$$x = -\frac{\pi}{2} \qquad\qquad x = \frac{\pi}{2}$$

Thus, two consecutive asymptotes occur at

$x = -\dfrac{\pi}{2}$ and $x = \dfrac{\pi}{2}$.

$$x\text{-intercept} = \frac{-\frac{\pi}{2} + \frac{\pi}{2}}{2} = \frac{0}{2} = 0$$

An x-intercept is 0 and the graph passes through $(0, 0)$. Because the coefficient of the cotangent is 2, the points on the graph midway between an x-intercept and the asymptotes have y-coordinates of 2 and -2. Use the two consecutive

asymptotes, $x = -\dfrac{\pi}{2}$ and $x = \dfrac{\pi}{2}$, to graph one

full period of $y = 2\cot\left(x + \dfrac{\pi}{2}\right)$ from $-\dfrac{\pi}{2}$ to

$\dfrac{\pi}{2}$. Continue the pattern and extend the graph

another full period to the right.

$$y = 2\cot\left(x + \frac{\pi}{2}\right)$$

89. Graph the reciprocal cosine function,
$y = 3\cos 2\pi x$. The equation is of the form
$y = A\cos Bx$ with $A = 3$ and $B = 2\pi$.

amplitude: $|A| = |3| = 3$

period: $\dfrac{2\pi}{B} = \dfrac{2\pi}{2\pi} = 1$

Use quarter-periods, $\dfrac{1}{4}$, to find x-values for the
five key points. Starting with $x = 0$, the x-values
are 0, $\dfrac{1}{4}$, $\dfrac{1}{2}$, $\dfrac{3}{4}$, 1. Evaluating the function at
each value of x, the key points are $(0, 3)$,
$\left(\dfrac{1}{4}, 0\right)$, $\left(\dfrac{1}{2}, -3\right)$, $\left(\dfrac{3}{4}, 0\right)$, $(1, 3)$ Use these key
points to graph $y = 3\cos 2\pi x$ from 0 to 1.
Extend the graph one cycle to the right. Use the
graph to obtain the graph of the reciprocal
function. Draw vertical asymptotes through the
x-intercepts, and use them as guides to graph
$y = 3\sec 2\pi x$.

$y = 3\sec 2\pi\, x$

90. Graph the reciprocal sine function,
$y = -2\sin \pi x$. The equation is of the form
$y = A\sin Bx$ with
$A = -2$ and $B = \pi$.
amplitude: $|A| = |-2| = 2$

period: $\dfrac{2\pi}{B} = \dfrac{2\pi}{\pi} = 2$

Use quarter-periods, $\dfrac{2}{4} = \dfrac{1}{2}$, to find
x-values for the five key points. Starting with
$x = 0$, the x-values are 0, $\dfrac{1}{2}$, 1, $\dfrac{3}{2}$, 2. Evaluating
the function at each value of x, the key points
are $(0, 0)$, $\left(\dfrac{1}{2}, -2\right)$, $(1, 0)$, $\left(\dfrac{3}{2}, 2\right)$, $(2, 0)$. Use
these key points to graph $y = -2\sin \pi x$ from 0
to 2. Extend the graph one cycle to the right. Use
the graph to obtain the graph of the reciprocal
function. Draw vertical asymptotes through the

x-intercepts, and use them as guides to graph
$y = -2\csc \pi x$.

$y = -2\csc \pi x$

91. Graph the reciprocal cosine function,
$y = 3\cos(x + \pi)$. The equation is of the form
$y = A\cos(Bx - C)$ with $A = 3$, $B = 1$, and
$C = -\pi$.
amplitude: $|A| = |3| = 3$

period: $\dfrac{2\pi}{B} = \dfrac{2\pi}{1} = 2\pi$

phase shift: $\dfrac{C}{B} = \dfrac{-\pi}{1} = -\pi$

Use quarter-periods, $\dfrac{2\pi}{4} = \dfrac{\pi}{2}$, to find
x-values for the five key points. Starting with

$x = -\pi$, the x-values are $-\pi$, $-\dfrac{\pi}{2}$, 0, $\dfrac{\pi}{2}$, π.
Evaluating the function at each value of x, the

key points are $(-\pi, 3)$, $\left(-\dfrac{\pi}{2}, 0\right)$, $(0, -3)$,

$\left(\dfrac{\pi}{2}, 0\right)$, $(\pi, 3)$. Use these key points to graph

$y = 3\cos(x + \pi)$ from $-\pi$ to π. Extend the
graph one cycle to the right. Use the graph to
obtain the graph of the reciprocal function. Draw
vertical asymptotes through the x-intercepts, and
use them as guides to graph $y = 3\sec(x + \pi)$.

$y = 3\sec(x + \pi)$

92. Graph the reciprocal sine function,

$y = \frac{5}{2}\sin(x - \pi)$. The equation is of the form

$y = A\sin(Bx - C)$ with $A = \frac{5}{2}$, $B = 1$, and

$C = \pi$.

amplitude: $|A| = \left|\frac{5}{2}\right| = \frac{5}{2}$

period: $\frac{2\pi}{B} = \frac{2\pi}{1} = 2\pi$

phase shift: $\frac{C}{B} = \frac{\pi}{1} = \pi$

Use quarter-periods, $\frac{2\pi}{4} = \frac{\pi}{2}$, to find

x-values for the five key points. Starting with

$x = \pi$, the x-values are $\pi, \frac{3\pi}{2}, 2\pi, \frac{5\pi}{2}, 3\pi$.

Evaluating the function at each value of x, the

key points are $(\pi, 0)$, $\left(\frac{3\pi}{2}, \frac{5}{2}\right)$, $(2\pi, 0)$,

$\left(\frac{5\pi}{2}, -\frac{5}{2}\right)$, $(3\pi, 0)$. Use these key points to

graph $y = \frac{5}{2}\sin(x - \pi)$ from π to 3π. Extend

the graph one cycle to the right. Use the graph to
obtain the graph of the reciprocal function. Draw
vertical asymptotes through the x-intercepts, and

use them as guides to graph $y = \frac{5}{2}\csc(x - \pi)$.

$y = \frac{5}{2}\csc(x - \pi)$

93. Let $\theta = \sin^{-1} 1$, then $\sin\theta = 1$.

The only angle in the interval $\left[-\frac{\pi}{2}, \frac{\pi}{2}\right]$ that

satisfies $\sin\theta = 1$ is $\frac{\pi}{2}$. Thus $\theta = \frac{\pi}{2}$, or

$\sin^{-1} 1 = \frac{\pi}{2}$.

94. Let $\theta = \cos^{-1} 1$, then $\cos\theta = 1$.

The only angle in the interval $[0, \pi]$ that

satisfies $\cos\theta = 1$ is 0. Thus $\theta = 0$, or

$\cos^{-1} 1 = 0$.

95. Let $\theta = \tan^{-1} 1$, then $\tan\theta = 1$.

The only angle in the interval $\left(-\frac{\pi}{2}, \frac{\pi}{2}\right)$ that

satisfies $\tan\theta = 1$ is $\frac{\pi}{4}$. Thus $\theta = \frac{\pi}{4}$, or

$\tan^{-1} 1 = \frac{\pi}{4}$.

96. Let $\theta = \sin^{-1}\left(-\frac{\sqrt{3}}{2}\right)$, then $\sin\theta = -\frac{\sqrt{3}}{2}$.

The only angle in the interval $\left(-\frac{\pi}{2}, \frac{\pi}{2}\right)$ that

satisfies $\sin\theta = -\frac{\sqrt{3}}{2}$ is $-\frac{\pi}{3}$. Thus $\theta = -\frac{\pi}{3}$, or

$\sin^{-1}\left(-\frac{\sqrt{3}}{2}\right) = -\frac{\pi}{3}$.

97. Let $\theta = \cos^{-1}\left(-\frac{1}{2}\right)$, then $\cos\theta = -\frac{1}{2}$.

The only angle in the interval $[0, \pi]$ that

satisfies $\cos\theta = -\frac{1}{2}$ is $\frac{2\pi}{3}$. Thus $\theta = \frac{2\pi}{3}$, or

$\cos^{-1}\left(-\frac{1}{2}\right) = \frac{2\pi}{3}$.

98. Let $\theta = \tan^{-1}\left(-\frac{\sqrt{3}}{3}\right)$, then $\tan\theta = -\frac{\sqrt{3}}{3}$.

The only angle in the interval $\left(-\frac{\pi}{2}, \frac{\pi}{2}\right)$ that

satisfies $\tan\theta = -\frac{\sqrt{3}}{3}$ is $-\frac{\pi}{6}$.

Thus $\theta = -\frac{\pi}{6}$, or $\tan^{-1}\left(-\frac{\sqrt{3}}{3}\right) = -\frac{\pi}{6}$.

99. Let $\theta = \sin^{-1}\dfrac{\sqrt{2}}{2}$, then $\sin\theta = \dfrac{\sqrt{2}}{2}$. The only

angle in the interval $\left[-\dfrac{\pi}{2}, \dfrac{\pi}{2}\right]$ that satisfies

$\sin\theta = \dfrac{\sqrt{2}}{2}$ is $\dfrac{\pi}{4}$.

Thus, $\cos\left(\sin^{-1}\dfrac{\sqrt{2}}{2}\right) = \cos\dfrac{\pi}{4} = \dfrac{\sqrt{2}}{2}$.

100. Let $\theta = \cos^{-1} 0$, then $\cos\theta = 0$. The only angle
in the interval $[0, \pi]$ that satisfies $\cos\theta = 0$ is

$\dfrac{\pi}{2}$. Thus, $\sin\left(\cos^{-1} 0\right) = \sin\dfrac{\pi}{2} = 1$.

101. Let $\theta = \sin^{-1}\left(-\dfrac{1}{2}\right)$, then $\sin\theta = -\dfrac{1}{2}$. The only

angle in the interval $\left[-\dfrac{\pi}{2}, \dfrac{\pi}{2}\right]$ that satisfies

$\sin\theta = -\dfrac{1}{2}$ is $-\dfrac{\pi}{6}$.

Thus, $\tan\left[\sin^{-1}\left(-\dfrac{1}{2}\right)\right] = \tan\left(-\dfrac{\pi}{6}\right) = -\dfrac{\sqrt{3}}{3}$.

102. Let $\theta = \cos^{-1}\left(-\dfrac{\sqrt{3}}{2}\right)$, then $\cos\theta = -\dfrac{\sqrt{3}}{2}$. The

only angle in the interval $[0, \pi]$ that satisfies

$\cos\theta = -\dfrac{\sqrt{3}}{2}$ is $\dfrac{5\pi}{6}$.

Thus, $\tan\left[\cos^{-1}\left(-\dfrac{\sqrt{3}}{2}\right)\right] = \tan\dfrac{5\pi}{6} = -\dfrac{\sqrt{3}}{3}$.

103. Let $\theta = \tan^{-1}\dfrac{\sqrt{3}}{3}$, then $\tan\theta = \dfrac{\sqrt{3}}{3}$.

The only angle in the interval $\left(-\dfrac{\pi}{2}, \dfrac{\pi}{2}\right)$ that

satisfies $\tan\theta = \dfrac{\sqrt{3}}{3}$ is $\dfrac{\pi}{6}$.

Thus $\csc\left(\tan^{-1}\dfrac{\sqrt{3}}{3}\right) = \csc\dfrac{\pi}{6} = 2$.

104. Let $\theta = \tan^{-1}\dfrac{3}{4}$, then $\tan\theta = \dfrac{3}{4}$.
Because $\tan\theta$ is positive, θ is in the first
quadrant.

$r^2 = x^2 + y^2$

$r^2 = 4^2 + 3^2$

$r^2 = 25$

$r = 5$

$\cos\left(\tan^{-1}\dfrac{3}{4}\right) = \cos\theta = \dfrac{x}{r} = \dfrac{4}{5}$

105. Let $\theta = \cos^{-1}\dfrac{3}{5}$, then $\cos\theta = \dfrac{3}{5}$.
Because $\cos\theta$ is positive, θ is in the first
quadrant.

$x^2 + y^2 = r^2$

$3^2 + y^2 = 5^2$

$y^2 = 25 - 9 = 16$

$y = \sqrt{16} = 4$

$\sin\left(\cos^{-1}\dfrac{3}{5}\right) = \sin\theta = \dfrac{y}{r} = \dfrac{4}{5}$

106. Let $\theta = \sin^{-1}\left(-\dfrac{3}{5}\right)$, then $\sin\theta = -\dfrac{3}{5}$.

Because $\sin\theta$ is negative, θ is in quadrant IV.

$$x^2 + (-3)^2 = 5^2$$
$$x^2 + y^2 = r^2$$
$$x^2 = 25 - 9 = 16$$
$$x = \sqrt{16} = 4$$
$$\tan\left[\sin^{-1}\left(-\dfrac{3}{5}\right)\right] = \tan\theta = \dfrac{y}{x} = -\dfrac{3}{4}$$

107. Let $\theta = \cos^{-1}\left(-\dfrac{4}{5}\right)$, then $\cos\theta = -\dfrac{4}{5}$.

Because $\cos\theta$ is negative, θ is in quadrant II.

$$x^2 + y^2 = r^2$$
$$(-4)^2 + y^2 = 5^2$$
$$y^2 = 25 - 16 = 9$$
$$y = \sqrt{9} = 3$$

Use the right triangle to find the exact value.

$$\tan\left[\cos^{-1}\left(-\dfrac{4}{5}\right)\right] = \tan\theta = -\dfrac{3}{4}$$

108. Let $\theta = \tan^{-1}\left(-\dfrac{1}{3}\right)$,

Because $\tan\theta$ is negative, θ is in quadrant IV and $x = 3$ and $y = -1$.

$$r^2 = x^2 + y^2$$
$$r^2 = 3^2 + (-1)^2$$
$$r^2 = 10$$
$$r = \sqrt{10}$$
$$\sin\left[\tan^{-1}\left(-\dfrac{4}{5}\right)\right] = \sin\theta = \dfrac{y}{r} = \dfrac{-1}{\sqrt{10}} = -\dfrac{\sqrt{10}}{10}$$

109. $x = \dfrac{\pi}{3}$, x is in $\left[-\dfrac{\pi}{2}, \dfrac{\pi}{2}\right]$, so $\sin^{-1}\left(\sin\dfrac{\pi}{3}\right) = \dfrac{\pi}{3}$

110. $x = \dfrac{2\pi}{3}$, x is not in $\left[-\dfrac{\pi}{2}, \dfrac{\pi}{2}\right]$. x is in the domain of $\sin x$, so

$$\sin^{-1}\left(\sin\dfrac{2\pi}{3}\right) = \sin^{-1}\dfrac{\sqrt{3}}{2} = \dfrac{\pi}{3}$$

111. $\sin^{-1}\left(\cos\dfrac{2\pi}{3}\right) = \sin^{-1}\left(-\dfrac{1}{2}\right)$

Let $\theta = \sin^{-1}\left(-\dfrac{1}{2}\right)$, then $\sin\theta = -\dfrac{1}{2}$. The only

angle in the interval $\left[-\dfrac{\pi}{2}, \dfrac{\pi}{2}\right]$ that satisfies

$\sin\theta = -\dfrac{1}{2}$ is $-\dfrac{\pi}{6}$. Thus, $\theta = -\dfrac{\pi}{6}$, or

$$\sin^{-1}\left(\cos\dfrac{2\pi}{3}\right) = \sin^{-1}\left(-\dfrac{1}{2}\right) = -\dfrac{\pi}{6}.$$

112. Let $\theta = \tan^{-1}\dfrac{x}{2}$, then $\tan\theta = \dfrac{x}{2}$.

$$r^2 = x^2 + 2^2$$
$$r^2 = x^2 + y^2$$
$$r = \sqrt{x^2 + 4}$$

Use the right triangle to write the algebraic expression.

$$\cos\left(\tan^{-1}\dfrac{x}{2}\right) = \cos\theta = \dfrac{2}{\sqrt{x^2 + 4}} = \dfrac{2\sqrt{x^2 + 4}}{x^2 + 4}$$

113. Let $\theta = \sin^{-1}\dfrac{1}{x}$, then $\sin\theta = \dfrac{1}{x}$.

$b = \sqrt{x^2 - 1}$

Use the Pythagorean theorem to find the third side, b.

$1^2 + b^2 = x^2$

$b^2 = x^2 - 1$

$b = \sqrt{x^2 - 1}$

Use the right triangle to write the algebraic expression.

$\sec\left(\sin^{-1}\dfrac{1}{x}\right) = \sec\theta = \dfrac{x}{\sqrt{x^2 - 1}} = \dfrac{x\sqrt{x^2 - 1}}{x^2 - 1}$

114. Find the measure of angle B. Because $C = 90°$, $A + B = 90°$. Thus,
$B = 90° - A = 90° - 22.3° = 67.7°$
We have a known angle, a known hypotenuse, and an unknown opposite side. Use the sine function.

$\sin 22.3° = \dfrac{a}{10}$

$a = 10\sin 22.3° \approx 3.79$

We have a known angle, a known hypotenuse, and an unknown adjacent side. Use the cosine function.

$\cos 22.3° = \dfrac{b}{10}$

$b = 10\cos 22.3° \approx 9.25$

In summary, $B = 67.7°$, $a \approx 3.79$, and $b \approx 9.25$.

115. Find the measure of angle A. Because $C = 90°$, $A + B = 90°$. Thus,
$A = 90° - B = 90° - 37.4° = 52.6°$
We have a known angle, a known opposite side, and an unknown adjacent side. Use the tangent function.

$\tan 37.4° = \dfrac{6}{a}$

$a = \dfrac{6}{\tan 37.4°} \approx 7.85$

We have a known angle, a known opposite side, and an unknown hypotenuse. Use the sine function.

$\sin 37.4° = \dfrac{6}{c}$

$c = \dfrac{6}{\sin 37.4°} \approx 9.88$

In summary, $A = 52.6°$, $a \approx 7.85$, and $c \approx 9.88$.

116. Find the measure of angle A. We have a known hypotenuse, a known opposite side, and an unknown angle. Use the sine function.

$\sin A = \dfrac{2}{7}$

$A = \sin^{-1}\left(\dfrac{2}{7}\right) \approx 16.6°$

Find the measure of angle B. Because $C = 90°$, $A + B = 90°$. Thus,
$B = 90° - A \approx 90° - 16.6° = 73.4°$
We have a known hypotenuse, a known opposite side, and an unknown adjacent side. Use the Pythagorean theorem.

$a^2 + b^2 = c^2$

$2^2 + b^2 = 7^2$

$b^2 = 7^2 - 2^2 = 45$

$b = \sqrt{45} \approx 6.71$

In summary, $A \approx 16.6°$, $B \approx 73.4°$, and $b \approx 6.71$.

117. Find the measure of angle A. We have a known opposite side, a known adjacent side, and an unknown angle. Use the tangent function.

$\tan A = \dfrac{1.4}{3.6}$

$A = \tan^{-1}\left(\dfrac{1.4}{3.6}\right) \approx 21.3°$

Find the measure of angle B. Because $C = 90°$, $A + B = 90°$. Thus,
$B = 90° - A \approx 90° - 21.3° = 68.7°$
We have a known opposite side, a known adjacent side, and an unknown hypotenuse.

Use the Pythagorean theorem.

$c^2 = a^2 + b^2 = (1.4)^2 + (3.6)^2 = 14.92$

$c = \sqrt{14.92} \approx 3.86$

In summary, $A \approx 21.3°$, $B \approx 68.7°$, and $c \approx 3.86$.

118. Using a right triangle, we have a known angle, an unknown opposite side, h, and a known adjacent side. Therefore, use the tangent function.

$$\tan 25.6° = \frac{h}{80}$$
$$h = 80 \tan 25.6°$$
$$\approx 38.3$$

The building is about 38 feet high.

119. Using a right triangle, we have a known angle, an unknown opposite side, h, and a known adjacent side. Therefore, use the tangent function.

$$\tan 40° = \frac{h}{60}$$
$$h = 60 \tan 40° \approx 50 \text{ yd}$$

The second building is 50 yds taller than the first. Total height = $40 + 50 = 90$ yd.

120. Using two right triangles, a smaller right triangle corresponding to the smaller angle of elevation drawn inside a larger right triangle corresponding to the larger angle of elevation, we have a known angle, a known opposite side, and an unknown adjacent side, d, in the smaller triangle. Therefore, use the tangent function.

$$\tan 68° = \frac{125}{d}$$
$$d = \frac{125}{\tan 68°} \approx 50.5$$

We now have a known angle, a known adjacent side, and an unknown opposite side, h, in the larger triangle. Again, use the tangent function.

$$\tan 71° = \frac{h}{50.5}$$
$$h = 50.5 \tan 71° \approx 146.7$$

The height of the antenna is $146.7 - 125$, or 21.7 ft, to the nearest tenth of a foot.

121. We need the acute angle between ray OA and the north-south line through O. This angle measures $90° - 55° = 35°$. This angle measured from the north side of the north-south line and lies east of the north-south line. Thus the bearing from O to A is N35°E.

122. We need the acute angle between ray OA and the north-south line through O. This angle measures $90° - 55° = 35°$. This angle measured from the south side of the north-south line and lies west of the north-south line. Thus the bearing from O to A is S35°W.

123. Using a right triangle, we have a known angle, a known adjacent side, and an unknown opposite side, d. Therefore, use the tangent function.

$$\tan 64° = \frac{d}{12}$$
$$d = 12 \tan 64° \approx 24.6$$

The ship is about 24.6 miles from the lighthouse.

124.

a. Using the figure,
$B = 58° + 32° = 90°$
Thus, use the Pythagorean Theorem to find the distance from city A to city C.
$$850^2 + 960^2 = b^2$$
$$b^2 = 722,500 + 921,600$$
$$b^2 = 1,644,100$$
$$b = \sqrt{1,644,100} \approx 1282.2$$

The distance from city A to city B is about 1282.2 miles.

b. Using the figure,
$$\tan A = \frac{\text{opposite}}{\text{adjacent}} = \frac{960}{850} \approx 1.1294$$
$$A \approx \tan^{-1}(1.1294) \approx 48°$$
$$180° - 58° - 48° = 74°$$

The bearing from city A to city C is S74°E.

125. $d = 20 \cos \dfrac{\pi}{4} t$

$a = 20$ and $\omega = \dfrac{\pi}{4}$

a. maximum displacement:
$|a| = |20| = 20 \text{ cm}$

b. $f = \dfrac{\omega}{2\pi} = \dfrac{\frac{\pi}{4}}{2\pi} = \dfrac{\pi}{4} \cdot \dfrac{1}{2\pi} = \dfrac{1}{8}$

frequency: $\dfrac{1}{8}$ cycle per second

c. period: $\dfrac{2\pi}{\omega} = \dfrac{2\pi}{\frac{\pi}{4}} = 2\pi \cdot \dfrac{4}{\pi} = 8$

The time required for one cycle is 8 seconds.

126. $d = \dfrac{1}{2}\sin 4t$

$a = \dfrac{1}{2}$ and $\omega = 4$

a. maximum displacement:

$|a| = \left|\dfrac{1}{2}\right| = \dfrac{1}{2}\,\text{cm}$

b. $f = \dfrac{\omega}{2\pi} = \dfrac{4}{2\pi} = \dfrac{2}{\pi} \approx 0.64$

frequency: 0.64 cycle per second

c. period: $\dfrac{2\pi}{\omega} = \dfrac{2\pi}{4} = \dfrac{\pi}{2} \approx 1.57$

The time required for one cycle is about 1.57 seconds.

127. Because the distance of the object from the rest position at $t = 0$ is a maximum, use the form $d = a\cos\omega t$. The period is $\dfrac{2\pi}{\omega}$ so,

$2 = \dfrac{2\pi}{\omega}$

$\omega = \dfrac{2\pi}{2} = \pi$

Because the amplitude is 30 inches, $|a| = 30$.

because the object starts below its rest position $a = -30$. the equation for the object's simple harmonic motion is $d = -30\cos\pi t$.

128. Because the distance of the object from the rest position at $t = 0$ is 0, use the form $d = a\sin\omega t$.

The period is $\dfrac{2\pi}{\omega}$ so

$5 = \dfrac{2\pi}{\omega}$

$\omega = \dfrac{2\pi}{5}$

Because the amplitude is $\dfrac{1}{4}$ inch, $|a| = \dfrac{1}{4}$. a is negative since the object begins pulled down. The equation for the object's simple harmonic motion is $d = -\dfrac{1}{4}\sin\dfrac{2\pi}{5}t$.

Chapter 4 Test

1. $135° = 135° \cdot \dfrac{\pi \text{ radians}}{180°}$

$= \dfrac{135\pi}{180}\text{ radians}$

$= \dfrac{3\pi}{4}\text{ radians}$

2. $75° = 75° \cdot \dfrac{\pi \text{ radians}}{180°} = \dfrac{75\pi}{180}\text{ radians}$

$= \dfrac{5\pi}{12}\text{ radians}$

$s = r\theta$

$s = 20\left(\dfrac{5\pi}{12}\right) = \dfrac{25\pi}{3}\text{ ft} \approx 26.18\text{ ft}$

3. **a.** $\dfrac{16\pi}{3} - 4\pi = \dfrac{16\pi}{3} - \dfrac{12\pi}{3} = \dfrac{4\pi}{3}$

b. $\dfrac{16\pi}{3}$ is coterminal with $\dfrac{4\pi}{3}$.

$\dfrac{4\pi}{3} - \pi = \dfrac{4\pi}{3} - \dfrac{3\pi}{3} = \dfrac{\pi}{3}$

4. $P = (-2, 5)$ is a point on the terminal side of θ, $x = -2$ and $y = 5$. Furthermore,

$r = \sqrt{x^2 + y^2} = \sqrt{(-2)^2 + (5)^2}$

$= \sqrt{4 + 25} = \sqrt{29}$

Use x, y, and r, to find the six trigonometric functions of θ.

$\sin\theta = \dfrac{y}{r} = \dfrac{5}{\sqrt{29}} = \dfrac{5\sqrt{29}}{\sqrt{29}\sqrt{29}} = \dfrac{5\sqrt{29}}{29}$

$\cos\theta = \dfrac{x}{r} = \dfrac{-2}{\sqrt{29}} = -\dfrac{2\sqrt{29}}{\sqrt{29}\sqrt{29}} = -\dfrac{2\sqrt{29}}{29}$

$\tan\theta = \dfrac{y}{x} = \dfrac{5}{-2} = -\dfrac{5}{2}$

$\csc\theta = \dfrac{r}{y} = \dfrac{\sqrt{29}}{5}$

$\sec\theta = \dfrac{r}{x} = \dfrac{\sqrt{29}}{-2} = -\dfrac{\sqrt{29}}{2}$

$\cot\theta = \dfrac{x}{y} = \dfrac{-2}{5} = -\dfrac{2}{5}$

5. Because $\cos\theta < 0$, θ cannot lie in quadrant I and quadrant IV; the cosine function is positive in those two quadrants. Thus, with $\cos\theta < 0$, θ lies in quadrant II or quadrant III. We are also given that $\cot\theta > 0$. Because quadrant III is the only quadrant in which the cosine is negative and the cotangent is positive, θ lies in quadrant III.

6. Because the cosine is positive and the tangent is negative, θ lies in quadrant IV. In quadrant IV x is positive and y is negative. Thus,

$$\cos\theta = \frac{1}{3} = \frac{x}{r}, \; x = 1, \; r = 3. \text{ Furthermore,}$$

$$x^2 + y^2 = r^3$$
$$1^2 + y^2 = 3^2$$
$$y^2 = 9 - 1 = 8$$
$$y = -\sqrt{8} = -2\sqrt{2}$$

Use x, y, and r, to find the six trigonometric functions of θ.

$$\sin\theta = \frac{y}{r} = \frac{-2\sqrt{2}}{3} = -\frac{2\sqrt{2}}{3}$$

$$\tan\theta = \frac{y}{x} = \frac{-2\sqrt{2}}{1} = -2\sqrt{2}$$

$$\csc\theta = \frac{r}{y} = \frac{3}{-2\sqrt{2}} = -\frac{3\sqrt{2}}{2\sqrt{2}\cdot\sqrt{2}} = -\frac{3\sqrt{2}}{4}$$

$$\sec\theta = \frac{r}{x} = \frac{3}{1} = 3$$

$$\cot\theta = \frac{x}{y} = \frac{1}{-2\sqrt{2}} = -\frac{1\cdot\sqrt{2}}{2\sqrt{2}\sqrt{2}} = -\frac{\sqrt{2}}{4}$$

7. $\tan\dfrac{\pi}{6}\cos\dfrac{\pi}{3} - \cos\dfrac{\pi}{2} = \dfrac{\sqrt{3}}{3}\cdot\dfrac{1}{2} - 0 = \dfrac{\sqrt{3}}{6}$

8. $300°$ lies in quadrant IV.
The reference angle is
$$\theta' = 360° - 300° = 60°$$
$$\tan 60° = \sqrt{3}$$
In quadrant IV, $\tan\theta < 0$, so
$$\tan 300° = -\tan 60 = -\sqrt{3}.$$

9. $\dfrac{7\pi}{4}$ lies in quadrant IV.
The reference angle is
$$\theta' = 2\pi - \frac{7\pi}{4} = \frac{8\pi}{4} - \frac{7\pi}{4} = \frac{\pi}{4}$$
$$\sin\frac{\pi}{4} = \frac{\sqrt{2}}{2}$$

In quadrant IV, $\sin\theta < 0$, so
$$\sin\frac{7\pi}{4} = -\sin\frac{\pi}{4} = -\frac{\sqrt{2}}{2}.$$

10. $\sec\dfrac{22\pi}{3} = \sec\dfrac{4\pi}{3} = -\sec\dfrac{\pi}{3}$

$$= \frac{1}{-\cos\dfrac{\pi}{3}} = \frac{1}{-\dfrac{1}{2}} = -2$$

11. $\cot\left(-\dfrac{8\pi}{3}\right) = \cot\left(\dfrac{4\pi}{3}\right) = \cot\dfrac{\pi}{3}$

$$= \frac{1}{\tan\dfrac{\pi}{3}} = \frac{1}{\sqrt{3}} = \frac{\sqrt{3}}{3}$$

12. $\tan\left(\dfrac{7\pi}{3} + n\pi\right) = \tan\dfrac{7\pi}{3} = \tan\dfrac{\pi}{3} = \sqrt{3}$

13. a. $\sin(-\theta) + \cos(-\theta) = -\sin(\theta) + \cos(\theta)$
$$= -a + b$$

   b. $\tan\theta - \sec\theta = \dfrac{\sin\theta}{\cos\theta} - \dfrac{1}{\cos\theta}$
$$= \frac{a}{b} - \frac{1}{b}$$
$$= \frac{a-1}{b}$$

14. The equation $y = 3\sin 2x$ is of the form $y = A\sin Bx$ with $A = 3$ and $B = 2$. The amplitude is $|A| = |3| = 3$. The period is $\dfrac{2\pi}{B} = \dfrac{2\pi}{2} = \pi$. The quarter-period is $\dfrac{\pi}{4}$.
The cycle begins at $x = 0$. Add quarter-periods to generate x-values for the key points.
$$x = 0$$
$$x = 0 + \frac{\pi}{4} = \frac{\pi}{4}$$
$$x = \frac{\pi}{4} + \frac{\pi}{4} = \frac{\pi}{2}$$
$$x = \frac{\pi}{2} + \frac{\pi}{4} = \frac{3\pi}{4}$$
$$x = \frac{3\pi}{4} + \frac{\pi}{4} = \pi$$
Evaluate the function at each value of x.

x	coordinates
0	$(0, 0)$
$\dfrac{\pi}{4}$	$\left(\dfrac{\pi}{4}, 3\right)$
$\dfrac{\pi}{2}$	$\left(\dfrac{\pi}{2}, 0\right)$
$\dfrac{3\pi}{4}$	$\left(\dfrac{3\pi}{4}, -3\right)$
π	$(\pi, 0)$

Connect the five key points with a smooth curve and graph one complete cycle of the given function.

$y = 3 \sin 2x$

15. The equation $y = -2\cos\left(x - \dfrac{\pi}{2}\right)$ is of the form

$y = A\cos(Bx - C)$ with $A = -2$, $B = 1$, and

$C = \dfrac{\pi}{2}$. The amplitude is $|A| = |-2| = 2$.

The period is $\dfrac{2\pi}{B} = \dfrac{2\pi}{1} = 2\pi$. The phase shift is

$\dfrac{C}{B} = \dfrac{\frac{\pi}{2}}{1} = \dfrac{\pi}{2}$. The quarter-period is $\dfrac{2\pi}{4} = \dfrac{\pi}{2}$.

The cycle begins at $x = \dfrac{\pi}{2}$. Add quarter-periods

to generate x-values for the key points.

$x = \dfrac{\pi}{2}$

$x = \dfrac{\pi}{2} + \dfrac{\pi}{2} = \pi$

$x = \pi + \dfrac{\pi}{2} = \dfrac{3\pi}{2}$

$x = \dfrac{3\pi}{2} + \dfrac{\pi}{2} = 2\pi$

$x = 2\pi + \dfrac{\pi}{2} = \dfrac{5\pi}{2}$

Evaluate the function at each value of x.

x	coordinates
$\dfrac{\pi}{2}$	$\left(\dfrac{\pi}{2}, -2\right)$
π	$(\pi, 0)$
$\dfrac{3\pi}{2}$	$\left(\dfrac{3\pi}{2}, 2\right)$
2π	$(2\pi, 0)$
$\dfrac{5\pi}{2}$	$\left(\dfrac{5\pi}{2}, -2\right)$

Connect the five key points with a smooth curve and graph one complete cycle of the given function.

$y = -2\cos\left(x - \dfrac{\pi}{2}\right)$

16. Solve the equations

$\dfrac{x}{2} = -\dfrac{\pi}{2}$ and $\dfrac{x}{2} = \dfrac{\pi}{2}$

$x = -\dfrac{\pi}{2} \cdot 2$ $x = \dfrac{\pi}{2} \cdot 2$

$x = -\pi$ $x = \pi$

Thus, two consecutive asymptotes occur at $x = -\pi$ and $x = \pi$.

$x\text{-intercept} = \dfrac{-\pi + \pi}{2} = \dfrac{0}{2} = 0$

An x-intercept is 0 and the graph passes through $(0, 0)$. Because the coefficient of the tangent is 2, the points on the graph midway between an x-intercept and the asymptotes have y-coordinates of -2 and 2. Use the two consecutive asymptotes, $x = -\pi$ and $x = \pi$, to graph one

full period of $y = 2\tan\dfrac{x}{2}$ from $-\pi$ to π.

$y = 2\tan\dfrac{x}{2}$

17. Graph the reciprocal sine function,
    $y = -\frac{1}{2} \sin \pi x$. The equation is of the form

    $y = A \sin Bx$ with $A = -\frac{1}{2}$ and $B = \pi$.

    amplitude: $|A| = \left| -\frac{1}{2} \right| = \frac{1}{2}$

    period: $\frac{2\pi}{B} = \frac{2\pi}{\pi} = 2$

    Use quarter-periods, $\frac{2}{4} = \frac{1}{2}$, to find x-values for
    the five key points. Starting with $x = 0$, the
    x-values are $0, \frac{1}{2}, 1, \frac{3}{2}, 2$. Evaluating the
    function at each value of x, the key points are

    $(0, 3), \left(\frac{1}{2}, -\frac{1}{2} \right), (1, 0), \left(\frac{3}{2}, \frac{1}{2} \right), (2, 0)$.

    Use these key points to graph $y = -\frac{1}{2} \sin \pi x$

    from 0 to 2. Use the graph to obtain the graph of
    the reciprocal function. Draw vertical
    asymptotes through the x-intercepts, and use
    them as guides to graph $y = -\frac{1}{2} \csc \pi x$.

    $y = -\frac{1}{2} \csc \pi x$

18. Let $\theta = \cos^{-1}\left(-\frac{1}{2} \right)$, then $\cos \theta = -\frac{1}{2}$. Because
    $\cos \theta$ is negative, θ is in quadrant II.
    $x^2 + y^2 = r^2$
    $(-1)^2 + y^2 = 2^2$
    $\quad y^2 = 4 - 1 = 3$
    $\quad\quad y = \sqrt{3}$
    $\tan \left[\cos^{-1}\left(-\frac{1}{2} \right) \right] = \tan \theta = \frac{y}{x} = \frac{\sqrt{3}}{-1} = -\sqrt{3}$

19. Let $\theta = \cos^{-1}\left(\frac{x}{3} \right)$, then $\cos \theta = \frac{x}{3}$. Because
    $\cos \theta$ is positive, θ is in quadrant I.

$x^2 + y^2 = r^2$
$x^2 + y^2 = 3^2$
$\quad y^2 = 9 - x^2$
$\quad\quad y = \sqrt{9 - x^2}$
$\sin \left[\cos^{-1}\left(\frac{x}{3} \right) \right] = \sin \theta = \frac{y}{r} = \frac{\sqrt{9 - x^2}}{3}$

20. Find the measure of angle B. Because
    $C = 90°$, $A + B = 90°$.
    Thus, $B = 90° - A = 90° - 21° = 69°$.
    We have a known angle, a known hypotenuse,
    and an unknown opposite side. Use the sine
    function.

    $\sin 21° = \frac{a}{13}$

    $\quad a = 13 \sin 21° \approx 4.7$
    We have a known angle, a known hypotenuse,
    and an unknown adjacent side. Use the cosine
    function.

    $\cos 21° = \frac{b}{13}$

    $\quad b = 13 \cos 21° \approx 12.1$
    In summary, $B = 69°$, $a \approx 4.7$, and $b \approx 12.1$.

21. Using a right triangle, we have a known angle,
    an unknown opposite side, h, and a known
    adjacent side. Therefore, use the tangent
    function.

    $\tan 37° = \frac{h}{30}$

    $\quad h = 30 \tan 37° \approx 23$
    The building is about 23 yards high.

22. Using a right triangle, we have a known
    hypotenuse, a known opposite side, and an
    unknown angle. Therefore, use the sine function.

    $\sin \theta = \frac{43}{73}$

    $\quad \theta = \sin^{-1}\left(\frac{43}{73} \right) \approx 36.1°$

    The rope makes an angle of about 36.1° with the
    pole.

23. We need the acute angle between ray OP and
    the north-south line through O. This angle
    measures $90° - 10°$. This angle is measured
    from the north side of the north-south line and
    lies west of the north-south line. Thus the
    bearing from O to P is N80°W.

24. $d = -6\cos \pi t$

$a = -6$ and $\omega = \pi$

    a. maximum displacement:
$|a| = |-6| = 6$ in.

    b. $f = \dfrac{\omega}{2\pi} = \dfrac{\pi}{2\pi} = \dfrac{1}{2}$

        frequency: $\dfrac{1}{2}$ cycle per second

    c. period $= \dfrac{2\pi}{\omega} = \dfrac{2\pi}{\pi} = 2$

        The time required for one cycle is 2 seconds.

25. Trigonometric functions are periodic.

Cumulative Review Exercises (Chapters P-4)

1. $x^2 = 18 + 3x$

$x^2 - 3x - 18 = 0$

$(x-6)(x+3) = 0$

$x - 6 = 0$ or $x + 3 = 0$

  $x = 6$ $x = -3$

The solution set is $\{-3, 6\}$.

2. $x^3 + 5x^2 - 4x - 20 = 0$

$x^2(x+5) - 4(x+5) = 0$

$(x^2 - 4)(x+5) = 0$

$(x-2)(x+2)(x+5) = 0$

$x - 2 = 0$ or $x + 2 = 0$ or $x + 5 = 0$

  $x = 2$ $x = -2$ $x = -5$

The solution set is $\{-5, -2, 2\}$.

3. $\log_2 x + \log_2 (x-2) = 3$

$\log_2 x(x-2) = 3$

$x(x-2) = 2^3$

$x^2 - 2x = 2^3$

$x^2 - 2x - 8 = 0$

$(x-4)(x+2) = 0$

$x - 4 = 0$ or $x + 2 = 0$

  $x = 4$ $x = -2$

$x = -2$ is extraneous

The solution set is $\{4\}$

4. $\sqrt{x-3} + 5 = x$

$\sqrt{x-3} = x - 5$

$\left(\sqrt{x-3}\right)^2 = (x-5)^2$

$x - 3 = x^2 - 10x + 25$

$x^2 - 11x + 28 = 0$

$(x-4)(x-7) = 0$

$x - 4 = 0$ or $x - 7 = 0$

  $x = 4$ $x = 7$

$\sqrt{4-3} + 5 = 4$

$\sqrt{1} + 5 = 4$

$1 + 5 = 4$ false

$x = 4$ is not a solution

$\sqrt{7-3} + 5 = 7$

$\sqrt{4} + 5 = 7$

$2 + 5 = 7$ true

The solution set is $\{7\}$.

5. $x^3 - 4x^2 + x + 6 = 0$

$p : \pm 1, \pm 2, \pm 3, \pm 6$

$q : \pm 1$

$\dfrac{p}{q} : \pm 1, \pm 2, \pm 3, \pm 6$

2	1	−4	1	6
		2	−4	−6
	1	−2	−3	0

$x^3 - 4x^2 + x + 6 = (x-2)\left(x^2 - 2x - 3\right)$

Thus,

$x^3 - 4x^2 + x + 6 = 0$

$(x-2)\left(x^2 - 2x - 3\right) = 0$

$(x-2)(x-3)(x+1) = 0$

$x - 2 = 0$ or $x - 3 = 0$ or $x + 1 = 0$

  $x = 2$ $x = 3$ $x = -1$

The solution set is $\{-1, 2, 3\}$

6. $|2x - 5| \le 11$

$-11 \le 2x - 5 \le 11$

$-6 \le 2x \le 16$

$-3 \le x \le 8$

The solution set is $\{x \mid -3 \le x \le 8\}$

7.
$$f(x) = \sqrt{x-6}$$
$$x = \sqrt{y-6}$$
$$x^2 = y-6$$
$$y = x^2 + 6$$
$$f^{-1}(x) = x^2 + 6$$

8.
$$4x^2 - \frac{14}{5}x - \frac{17}{25}$$
$$5x + 2\sqrt{20x^3 - 6x^2 - 9x + 10}$$
$$\underline{20x^3 + 8x^2}$$
$$-14x^2 - 9x$$
$$\underline{-14x^2 - \frac{28}{5}x}$$
$$-\frac{17}{5}x + 10$$
$$\underline{-\frac{17}{5}x - \frac{34}{25}}$$
$$\frac{284}{25}$$

The quotient is $4x^2 - \frac{14}{5}x - \frac{17}{25} + \frac{284}{125x+50}$.

9.
$$\log 25 + \log 40 = \log(25 \cdot 40)$$
$$= \log 1000$$
$$= \log 10^3$$
$$= 3$$

10. $\frac{14\pi}{9}$ radians $= \frac{14\pi}{9}$ radians $\cdot \frac{180°}{\pi \text{ radians}}$

$$= \frac{14 \cdot 180°}{9} = 280°$$

11. $3x^4 - 2x^3 + 5x^2 + x - 9 = 0$

The sign changes 3 times so the equation has at most 3 positive real roots;

$f(-x) = 3x^4 + 2x^3 + 5x^2 - x - 9$

The sign changes 1 time, so the equation has at most 1 negative real root.

12. $f(x) = \dfrac{x}{x^2 - 1}$

vertical asymptotes: $x^2 - 1 = 0$, $x = 1$ and $x = -1$

horizontal asymptote: $m = 1$ and $n = 2$ so $m < n$ and the x-axis is a horizontal asymptote.

x-intercept: $(0,0)$

$$f(x) = \frac{x}{x^2 - 1}$$

13. $(x-2)^2 + y^2 = 1$

The graph is a circle with center $(2,0)$ and $r = 1$.

$$(x-2)^2 + y^2 = 1$$

14. $y = (x-1)(x+2)^2$

x-intercepts: $(1,0)$ and $(-2,0)$

y-intercept: $y = (-1)(2)^2 = -4$

$(0,-4)$

$$y = (x-1)(x+2)^2$$

15. $y = \sin\left(2x + \dfrac{\pi}{2}\right) = \sin\left(2x - \left(-\dfrac{\pi}{2}\right)\right)$

The equation $y = \sin\left(2x - \left(-\dfrac{\pi}{2}\right)\right)$ is of the

form $y = A\sin(Bx - C)$ with $A = 1$, $B = 2$, and

$C = -\dfrac{\pi}{2}$. The amplitude is $|A| = |1| = 1$

The period is $\dfrac{2\pi}{B} = \dfrac{2\pi}{2} = \pi$. The phase shift is

$\dfrac{C}{B} = \dfrac{-\frac{\pi}{2}}{2} = -\dfrac{\pi}{2} \cdot \dfrac{1}{2} = -\dfrac{\pi}{4}$. The quarter-period is

$\dfrac{\pi}{4}$. The cycle begins at $x = -\dfrac{\pi}{4}$. Add quarter-

periods to generate x-values for the key points.

$x = -\dfrac{\pi}{4}$, $x = -\dfrac{\pi}{4} + \dfrac{\pi}{4} = 0$, $x = 0 + \dfrac{\pi}{4} = \dfrac{\pi}{4}$,

$x = \dfrac{\pi}{4} + \dfrac{\pi}{4} = \dfrac{\pi}{2}$, $x = \dfrac{\pi}{2} + \dfrac{\pi}{4} = \dfrac{3\pi}{4}$ To graph from 0 to π, evaluate the function at the last four key points and at $x = \pi$.

x	coordinates
0	$(0, 1)$
$\dfrac{\pi}{4}$	$\left(\dfrac{\pi}{4}, 0\right)$
$\dfrac{\pi}{2}$	$\left(\dfrac{\pi}{2}, -1\right)$
$\dfrac{3\pi}{4}$	$\left(\dfrac{3\pi}{4}, 0\right)$
π	$(\pi, 1)$

Connect the points with a smooth curve and extend the graph one cycle to the right to graph from 0 to 2π.

$y = \sin\left(2x + \dfrac{\pi}{2}\right)$

16. Solve the equations

$3x = -\dfrac{\pi}{2}$ and $3x = \dfrac{\pi}{2}$

$x = \dfrac{-\frac{\pi}{2}}{3}$ $x = \dfrac{\frac{\pi}{2}}{3}$

$x = -\dfrac{\pi}{6}$ $x = \dfrac{\pi}{6}$

Thus, two consecutive asymptotes occur at

$x = -\dfrac{\pi}{6}$ and $x = \dfrac{\pi}{6}$.

x-intercept $= \dfrac{-\frac{\pi}{6} + \frac{\pi}{6}}{2} = \dfrac{0}{2} = 0$

An x-intercept is 0 and the graph passes through $(0, 0)$. Because the coefficient of the tangent is 2, the points on the graph midway between an x-intercept and the asymptotes have y-coordinates of -2 and 2. Use the two consecutive asymptotes, $x = -\dfrac{\pi}{6}$ and $x = \dfrac{\pi}{6}$, to

graph one full period of $y = 2\tan 3x$ from $-\dfrac{\pi}{6}$ to $\dfrac{\pi}{6}$. Extend the pattern to the right to graph two complete cycles.

$y = 2\tan 3x$

17. $C(p) = 30,000 + 2500p$

$R(p) = 3125p$

$30,000 + 2500p = 3125p$

$30,000 = 625p$

$p = 48$

48 performances must be played for you to break even.

18. a.   Let t be the number of years after 1984. 2003 is 19 years after 1984.

$A = A_0 e^{kt}$

$A = 25000 e^{kt}$

$70500000 = 25000 e^{k(19)}$

$\dfrac{70500000}{25000} = e^{k(19)}$

$2820 = e^{k(19)}$

$\ln 2820 = \ln e^{k(19)}$

$\ln 2820 = 19k$

$\dfrac{\ln 2820}{19} = k$

$0.418 \approx k$

Thus, $A = 25000 e^{0.418t}$

b.
$$A = 25,000e^{0.418t}$$
$$150,000,000 = 25,000e^{0.418t}$$
$$\frac{150,000,000}{25,000} = e^{0.418t}$$
$$6000 = e^{0.418t}$$
$$\ln 6000 = \ln e^{0.418t}$$
$$\ln 6000 = 0.418t$$
$$\frac{\ln 6000}{0.418} = t$$
$$21 \approx t$$

150,000,000 cell phones will be sold in the United States 21 years after 1984, or 2005

19.
$$2200 = \frac{k}{3.5}$$
$$k = 7700$$
$$h = \frac{7700}{5} = 1540$$

The rate of heat loss is 1540 Btu per hour.

20. Using a right triangle, we have a known opposite side, a known adjacent side, and an unknown angle. Therefore, use the tangent function.
$$\tan \theta = \frac{200}{50} = 4$$
$$\theta = \tan^{-1}(4) \approx 76°$$

The angle of elevation is about 76°.

Chapter 5

Check Point Exercises

1. $\csc x \tan x = \dfrac{1}{\sin x} \cdot \dfrac{\sin x}{\cos x}$

$\qquad = \dfrac{1}{\cos x}$

$\qquad = \sec x$

We worked with the left side and arrived at the right side. Thus, the identity is verified.

2. $\cos x \cot x + \sin x = \cos x \cdot \dfrac{\cos x}{\sin x} + \sin x$

$\qquad = \dfrac{\cos^2 x}{\sin x} + \sin x$

$\qquad = \dfrac{\cos^2 x}{\sin x} + \sin x \cdot \dfrac{\sin x}{\sin x}$

$\qquad = \dfrac{\cos^2 x}{\sin x} + \dfrac{\sin^2 x}{\sin x}$

$\qquad = \dfrac{\cos^2 x + \sin^2 x}{\sin x}$

$\qquad = \dfrac{1}{\sin x}$

$\qquad = \csc x$

We worked with the left side and arrived at the right side. Thus, the identity is verified.

3. $\sin x - \sin x \cos^2 x = \sin x \left(1 - \cos^2 x\right)$

$\qquad = \sin x \cdot \sin^2 x$

$\qquad = \sin^3 x$

We worked with the left side and arrived at the right side. Thus, the identity is verified.

4. $\dfrac{1 + \cos \theta}{\sin \theta} = \dfrac{1}{\sin \theta} + \dfrac{\cos \theta}{\sin \theta}$

$\qquad = \csc \theta + \cot \theta$

We worked with the left side and arrived at the right side. Thus, the identity is verified.

5. $\dfrac{\sin x}{1 + \cos x} + \dfrac{1 + \cos x}{\sin x}$

$\quad = \dfrac{\sin x(\sin x)}{(1 + \cos x)\sin x} + \dfrac{(1 + \cos x)(1 + \cos x)}{\sin x(1 + \cos x)}$

$\quad = \dfrac{\sin^2 x}{(1 + \cos x)\sin x} + \dfrac{1 + 2\cos x + \cos^2 x}{(1 + \cos x)\sin x}$

$\quad = \dfrac{\sin^2 x + \cos^2 x + 2\cos x + 1}{(1 + \cos x)\sin x}$

$\quad = \dfrac{1 + 1 + 2\cos x}{(1 + \cos x)\sin x}$

$\quad = \dfrac{2 + 2\cos x}{(1 + \cos x)\sin x}$

$\quad = \dfrac{2(1 + \cos x)}{(1 + \cos x)\sin x}$

$\quad = \dfrac{2}{\sin x}$

$\quad = 2\csc x$

We worked with the left side and arrived at the right side. Thus, the identity is verified.

6. $\dfrac{\cos x}{1 + \sin x} = \dfrac{\cos x}{(1 + \sin x)} \cdot \dfrac{1 - \sin x}{1 - \sin x}$

$\qquad = \dfrac{\cos x(1 - \sin x)}{1 - \sin^2 x}$

$\qquad = \dfrac{\cos x(1 - \sin x)}{\cos^2 x}$

$\qquad = \dfrac{1 - \sin x}{\cos x}$

We worked with the left side and arrived at the right side. Thus, the identity is verified.

7. $\dfrac{\sin x}{1+\cos x} + \dfrac{1+\cos}{\sin x}$

$= \dfrac{\sin x(\sin x)}{(1+\cos x)\sin x} + \dfrac{(1+\cos x)(1+\cos x)}{\sin x(1+\cos x)}$

$= \dfrac{\sin^2 x}{(1+\cos x)\sin x} + \dfrac{1+2\cos x+\cos^2 x}{(1+\cos x)\sin x}$

$= \dfrac{\sin^2 x+\cos^2 x+2\cos x+1}{(1+\cos x)\sin x}$

$= \dfrac{1+1+2\cos x}{(1+\cos x)\sin x}$

$= \dfrac{2+2+\cos x}{(1+\cos x)\sin x}$

$= \dfrac{2(1+\cos x)}{(1+\cos x)\sin x}$

$= \dfrac{2}{\sin x}$

$= 2\csc x$

We worked with the left side and arrived at the right side. Thus, the identity is verified.

8. Left side:

$\dfrac{1}{1+\sin\theta} + \dfrac{1}{1-\sin\theta}$

$= \dfrac{1(1-\sin\theta)}{(1+\sin\theta)(1-\sin\theta)} + \dfrac{1(1+\sin\theta)}{(1-\sin\theta)(1+\sin\theta)}$

$= \dfrac{1-\sin\theta+1+\sin\theta}{(1+\sin\theta)(1-\sin\theta)}$

$= \dfrac{2}{(1+\sin\theta)(1-\sin\theta)}$

$= \dfrac{2}{1-\sin^2\theta}$

Right side:

$2+2\tan^2\theta = 2+2\left(\dfrac{\sin^2\theta}{\cos^2\theta}\right)$

$= \dfrac{2\cos^2\theta}{\cos^2\theta} + \dfrac{2\sin^2\theta}{\cos^2\theta}$

$= \dfrac{2\cos^2\theta+2\sin^2\theta}{\cos^2\theta}$

$= \dfrac{2}{\cos^2\theta} = \dfrac{2}{1-\sin^2\theta}$

The identity is verified because both sides are equal to $\dfrac{2}{1-\sin^2\theta}$.

Exercise Set 5.1

1. $\sin x \sec x = \sin x \cdot \dfrac{1}{\cos x}$

$= \dfrac{\sin x}{\cos x}$

$= \tan x$

3. $\tan(-x)\cdot\cos x = -\tan x \cdot \cos x$

$= -\dfrac{\sin x}{\cos x}\cdot\cos x$

$= -\sin x$

5. $\tan x \csc x \cos x = \dfrac{\sin x}{\cos x}\cdot\dfrac{1}{\sin x}\cos x$

$= 1$

7. $\sec x - \sec x \sin^2 x = \sec x(1-\sin^2 x)$

$= \dfrac{1}{\cos x}\cdot\cos^2 x$

$= \cos x$

9. $\cos^2 x - \sin^2 x = \left(1-\sin^2 x\right)-\sin^2 x$

$= 1-\sin^2 x-\sin^2 x$

$= 1-2\sin^2 x$

11. $\csc\theta - \sin\theta = \dfrac{1}{\sin\theta} - \sin\theta$

$= \dfrac{1}{\sin\theta} - \dfrac{\sin^2\theta}{\sin\theta}$

$= \dfrac{1-\sin^2\theta}{\sin\theta}$

$= \dfrac{\cos^2\theta}{\sin\theta}$

$= \dfrac{\cos\theta}{\sin\theta}\cdot\cos\theta$

$= \cot\theta\cos\theta$

13.
$$\frac{\tan\theta\cot\theta}{\csc\theta} = \frac{\dfrac{\sin\theta}{\cos\theta}\cdot\dfrac{\cos\theta}{\sin\theta}}{\dfrac{1}{\sin\theta}}$$

$$= \frac{1}{\dfrac{1}{\sin\theta}}$$

$$= 1 \div \frac{1}{\sin\theta}$$

$$= 1 \cdot \frac{\sin\theta}{1}$$

$$= \sin\theta$$

15. $\sin^2\theta(1+\cot^2\theta) = \sin^2\theta(\csc^2\theta)$

$$= \sin^2\theta\cdot\frac{1}{\sin^2\theta}$$

$$= 1$$

17.
$$\frac{1-\cos^2 t}{\cos t} = \frac{\sin^2 t}{\cos t}$$

$$= \sin t\cdot\frac{\sin t}{\cos t}$$

$$= \sin t\tan t$$

19.
$$\frac{\csc^2 t}{\cot t} = \frac{\dfrac{1}{\sin^2 t}}{\dfrac{\cos t}{\sin t}}$$

$$= \frac{1}{\sin^2 t}\div\frac{\cos t}{\sin t}$$

$$= \frac{1}{\sin^2 t}\cdot\frac{\sin t}{\cos t}$$

$$= \frac{1}{\sin t}\cdot\frac{1}{\cos t}$$

$$= \csc t\sec t$$

21.
$$\frac{\tan^2 t}{\sec t} = \frac{\sec^2 t-1}{\sec t}$$

$$= \frac{\sec^2 t}{\sec t} - \frac{1}{\sec t}$$

$$= \sec t - \cos t$$

23.
$$\frac{1-\cos\theta}{\sin\theta} = \frac{1}{\sin\theta} - \frac{\cos\theta}{\sin\theta}$$

$$= \csc\theta - \cot\theta$$

25.
$$\frac{\sin t}{\csc t} + \frac{\cos t}{\sec t} = \frac{\sin t}{\dfrac{1}{\sin t}} + \frac{\cos t}{\dfrac{1}{\cos t}}$$

$$= \sin t\div\frac{1}{\sin t} + \cos t\div\frac{1}{\cos t}$$

$$= \sin t\cdot\frac{\sin t}{1} + \cos t\cdot\frac{\cos t}{1}$$

$$= \sin^2 t + \cos^2 t$$

$$= 1$$

27.
$$\tan t + \frac{\cos t}{1+\sin t}$$

$$= \frac{\sin t}{\cos t} + \frac{\cos t}{1+\sin t}$$

$$= \frac{\sin t}{\cos t}\cdot\frac{1+\sin t}{1+\sin t} + \frac{\cos t}{1+\sin t}\cdot\frac{\cos t}{\cos t}$$

$$= \frac{\sin t+\sin^2 t}{\cos t(1+\sin t)} + \frac{\cos^2 t}{\cos t(1+\sin t)}$$

$$\frac{\sin t+\sin^2 t+\cos^2 t}{\cos t(1+\sin t)}$$

$$= \frac{1+\sin t}{\cos t(1+\sin t)}$$

$$= \frac{1}{\cos t}$$

$$= \sec t$$

29.
$$1-\frac{\sin^2 x}{1+\cos x} = 1-\frac{\sin^2 x}{1+\cos x}\cdot\frac{1-\cos x}{1-\cos x}$$

$$= 1-\frac{\sin^2 x(1-\cos x)}{1-\cos^2 x}$$

$$= 1-\frac{\sin^2 x(1-\cos x)}{\sin^2 x}$$

$$= 1-1+\cos x$$

$$= \cos x$$

31. $\dfrac{\cos x}{1-\sin x}+\dfrac{1-\sin x}{\cos x}$

$=\dfrac{\cos x}{1-\sin x}\cdot\dfrac{1+\sin x}{1+\sin x}+\dfrac{1-\sin x}{\cos x}$

$=\dfrac{\cos x(1+\sin x)}{1-\sin^2 x}+\dfrac{1-\sin x}{\cos x}$

$==\dfrac{\cos x(1+\sin x)}{\cos^2 x}+\dfrac{1-\sin x}{\cos x}$

$=\dfrac{1+\sin x}{\cos x}+\dfrac{1-\sin x}{\cos x}$

$=\dfrac{2}{\cos x}$

$=2\cdot\dfrac{1}{\cos x}$

$=2\sec x$

33. $\sec^2 x\csc^2 x=(1+\tan^2 x)\csc^2 x$

$=\csc^2 x+\tan^2 x\csc^2 x$

$=\csc^2 x+\dfrac{\sin^2 x}{\cos^2 x}\cdot\dfrac{1}{\sin^2 x}$

$=\csc^2 x+\dfrac{1}{\cos^2 x}$

$=\csc^2 x+\sec^2 x$

$=\sec^2 x+\csc^2 x$

35. $\dfrac{\sec x-\csc x}{\sec x+\csc x}=\dfrac{\dfrac{1}{\cos x}-\dfrac{1}{\sin x}}{\dfrac{1}{\cos x}+\dfrac{1}{\sin x}}$

$=\dfrac{\dfrac{1}{\cos x}-\dfrac{1}{\sin x}}{\dfrac{1}{\cos x}+\dfrac{1}{\sin x}}\cdot\dfrac{\sin x}{\sin x}$

$=\dfrac{\dfrac{\sin x}{\cos x}-1}{\dfrac{\sin x}{\cos x}+1}$

$=\dfrac{\tan x-1}{\tan x+1}$

37. $\dfrac{\sin^2 x-\cos^2 x}{\sin x+\cos x}=\dfrac{(\sin x+\cos x)(\sin x-\cos x)}{\sin x+\cos x}$

$=\sin x-\cos x$

39. $\tan^2 2x+\sin^2 2x+\cos^2 2x=\tan^2 2x+1$

$=\sec^2 2x$

41. $\dfrac{\tan 2\theta+\cot 2\theta}{\csc 2\theta}=\dfrac{\dfrac{\sin 2\theta}{\cos 2\theta}+\dfrac{\cos 2\theta}{\sin 2\theta}}{\dfrac{1}{\sin 2\theta}}$

$=\dfrac{\dfrac{\sin 2\theta}{\cos 2\theta}\cdot\dfrac{\sin 2\theta}{\sin 2\theta}+\dfrac{\cos 2\theta}{\sin 2\theta}\cdot\dfrac{\cos 2\theta}{\cos 2\theta}}{\dfrac{1}{\sin 2\theta}}$

$=\dfrac{\dfrac{\sin^2 2\theta+\cos 2\theta}{\cos 2\theta\sin 2\theta}}{\dfrac{1}{\sin 2\theta}}$

$=\dfrac{1}{\cos 2\theta\sin 2\theta}\div\dfrac{1}{\sin 2\theta}$

$=\dfrac{1}{\cos 2\theta\sin 2\theta}\cdot\dfrac{\sin 2\theta}{1}$

$=\dfrac{1}{\cos 2\theta}=\sec 2\theta$

43. $\dfrac{\tan x+\tan y}{1-\tan x\tan y}=\dfrac{\dfrac{\sin x}{\cos x}+\dfrac{\sin y}{\cos y}}{1-\dfrac{\sin x}{\cos y}\cdot\dfrac{\sin y}{\cos y}}\cdot\dfrac{\cos x\cos y}{\cos x\cos y}$

$=\dfrac{\sin x\cos y+\cos x\sin y}{\cos x\cos y-\sin x\sin y}$

45. Left side:

$$(\sec x - \tan x)^2 = \left(\frac{1}{\cos x} - \frac{\sin x}{\cos x} \right)^2$$

$$= \left(\frac{1 - \sin x}{\cos x} \right)^2$$

$$= \frac{(1 - \sin x)^2}{\cos^2 x}$$

Right side:

$$\frac{1 - \sin x}{1 + \sin x} = \frac{1 - \sin x}{1 + \sin x} \cdot \frac{1 - \sin x}{1 - \sin x}$$

$$= \frac{(1 - \sin x)^2}{1 - \sin^2 x}$$

$$= \frac{(1 - \sin x)^2}{\cos^2 x}$$

The identity is verified because both sides are equal to $\dfrac{(1 - \sin x)^2}{\cos^2 x}$.

47.
$$\frac{\tan t}{\sec t - 1} = \frac{\tan t}{\sec t - 1} \cdot \frac{\sec t + 1}{\sec t + 1}$$

$$= \frac{\tan t(\sec t + 1)}{\sec^2 t - 1}$$

$$= \frac{\tan t(\sec t + 1)}{\tan^2 t}$$

$$= \frac{\sec t + 1}{\tan t}$$

49. Left side:

$$\frac{1 + \cos t}{1 - \cos t} = \frac{1 + \cos t}{1 - \cos t} \cdot \frac{1 + \cos t}{1 + \cos t}$$

$$= \frac{(1 + \cos t)^2}{1 - \cos^2 t}$$

$$= \frac{(1 + \cos t)^2}{\sin^2 t}$$

Right side:

$$(\csc t + \cot t)^2 = \left(\frac{1}{\sin t} + \frac{\cos t}{\sin t} \right)^2$$

$$= \left(\frac{1 + \cos t}{\sin t} \right)^2$$

$$= \frac{(1 + \cos t)^2}{\sin^2 t}$$

The identity is verified because both sides are

equal to $\dfrac{(1 + \cos t)^2}{\sin^2 t}$.

51.
$$\cos^4 t - \sin^4 t = \left(\cos^2 t - \sin^2 t \right)\left(\cos^2 t + \sin^2 t \right)$$

$$= \left(\cos^2 t - \sin^2 t \right) \cdot 1$$

$$= 1 - \sin^2 t - \sin^2 t$$

$$= 1 - 2\sin^2 t$$

53.
$$\frac{\sin x - \cos x}{\sin x} + \frac{\cos x - \sin x}{\cos x}$$

$$= \frac{\sin x}{\sin x} - \frac{\cos x}{\sin x} + \frac{\cos x}{\cos x} - \frac{\sin x}{\cos x}$$

$$= 1 - \frac{\cos x}{\sin x} + 1 - \frac{\sin x}{\cos x}$$

$$= 2 - \frac{\cos x \cos x}{\sin x \cos x} - \frac{\sin x \sin x}{\sin x \cos x}$$

$$= 2 - \frac{\cos^2 x}{\sin x \cos x} - \frac{\sin^2 x}{\sin x \cos x}$$

$$= 2 - \frac{\cos^2 x + \sin^2 x}{\sin x \cos x}$$

$$= 2 - \frac{1}{\sin x \cos x}$$

$$= 2 - \sec x \csc x$$

55. $\left(\tan^2\theta+1\right)\left(\cos^2\theta+1\right)$

$= \tan^2\theta\cos^2\theta+\tan^2\theta+\cos^2\theta+1$

$= \dfrac{\sin^2\theta}{\cos^2\theta}\cdot\cos^2\theta+\tan^2\theta+\cos^2\theta+1$

$= \sin^2\theta+\tan^2\theta+\cos^2\theta+1$

$= \sin^2\theta+\cos^2\theta+\tan^2\theta+1$

$= 1+\tan^2\theta+1$

$= \tan^2\theta+2$

57. $(\cos\theta-\sin\theta)^2+(\cos\theta+\sin\theta)^2 = \cos^2\theta-2\cos\theta\sin\theta+\sin^2\theta+\cos^2\theta+2\cos\theta\sin\theta+\sin^2\theta$

$= \cos^2\theta+\sin^2\theta+\cos^2\theta+\sin^2\theta$

$= 1+1 = 2$

59. $\dfrac{\cos^2 x-\sin^2 x}{1-\tan^2 x} = \dfrac{\cos^2 x-\sin^2 x}{1-\dfrac{\sin^2 x}{\cos^2 x}} = \dfrac{\cos^2 x-\sin^2 x}{\dfrac{\cos^2 x-\sin^2 x}{\cos^2 x}}$

$= \dfrac{\cos^2 x-\sin^2 x}{1}\div\dfrac{\cos^2 x-\sin^2 x}{\cos^2 x}$

$= \dfrac{\cos^2 x-\sin^2 x}{1}\cdot\dfrac{\cos^2 x}{\cos^2 x-\sin^2 x}=\cos^2 x$

61. Conjecture: left side is equal to $\cos x$

$\dfrac{(\sec x+\tan x)(\sec x-\tan x)}{\sec x} = \dfrac{\sec^2 x-\tan^2 x}{\sec x}$

$= \dfrac{1}{\sec x}$

$= \cos x$

63. Conjecture: left side is equal to $2\sin x$

$\dfrac{\cos x+\cot x\sin x}{\cot x} = \dfrac{\cos x}{\cot x}+\dfrac{\cot x\sin x}{\cot x}$

$= \dfrac{\cos x}{\dfrac{\cos x}{\sin x}}+\dfrac{\cot x\sin x}{\cot x}$

$= \dfrac{\cos x\sin x}{\cos x}+\sin x$

$= \sin x+\sin x$

$= 2\sin x$

65. Conjecture: left side is equal to $2\sec x$

$\dfrac{1}{\sec x+\tan x}+\dfrac{1}{\sec x-\tan x} = \dfrac{\sec^2 x-\tan^2 x}{\sec x+\tan x}+\dfrac{\sec^2 x-\tan^2 x}{\sec x-\tan x}$

$= \dfrac{(\sec x+\tan x)(\sec x-\tan x)}{\sec x+\tan x}+\dfrac{(\sec x+\tan x)(\sec x-\tan x)}{\sec x-\tan x}$

$= \sec x-\tan x+\sec x+\tan x$

$= 2\sec x$

67.
$$\frac{\tan x + \cot x}{\csc x} = \frac{\dfrac{\sin x}{\cos x} + \dfrac{\cos x}{\sin x}}{\dfrac{1}{\sin x}}$$

$$= \left(\frac{\sin x}{\cos x} + \frac{\cos x}{\sin x}\right)\frac{\sin x}{1}$$

$$= \frac{\sin^2 x}{\cos x} + \frac{\sin x \cos x}{\sin x}$$

$$= \frac{1 - \cos^2 x}{\cos x} + \frac{\cos x}{1}$$

$$= \frac{1 - \cos^2 x}{\cos x} + \frac{\cos^2 x}{\cos x}$$

$$= \frac{1}{\cos x}$$

69.
$$\frac{\cos x}{1 + \sin x} + \tan x = \frac{\cos x}{1 + \sin x} \cdot \frac{\cos x}{\cos x} + \frac{\sin x}{\cos x} \cdot \frac{1 + \sin x}{1 + \sin x}$$

$$= \frac{\cos^2 x}{(1 + \sin x)(\cos x)} + \frac{\sin x + \sin^2 x}{(1 + \sin x)(\cos x)}$$

$$= \frac{\cos^2 x + \sin x + \sin^2 x}{(1 + \sin x)(\cos x)}$$

$$= \frac{\sin x + \cos^2 x + \sin^2 x}{(1 + \sin x)(\cos x)}$$

$$= \frac{\sin x + 1}{(1 + \sin x)(\cos x)}$$

$$= \frac{1}{\cos x}$$

71.
$$\frac{1}{1 - \cos x} - \frac{\cos x}{1 + \cos x} = \frac{1}{1 - \cos x} \cdot \frac{1 + \cos x}{1 + \cos x} - \frac{\cos x}{1 + \cos x} \cdot \frac{1 - \cos x}{1 - \cos x}$$

$$= \frac{1 + \cos x}{1 - \cos^2 x} - \frac{\cos x - \cos^2 x}{1 - \cos^2 x}$$

$$= \frac{1 + \cos x - \cos x + \cos^2 x}{1 - \cos^2 x}$$

$$= \frac{1 + \cos^2 x}{\sin^2 x}$$

$$= \frac{1}{\sin^2 x} + \frac{\cos^2 x}{\sin^2 x}$$

$$= \csc^2 x + \cot^2 x$$

$$= \csc^2 x + \csc^2 x - 1$$

$$= 2\csc^2 x - 1$$

73. $\dfrac{1}{\csc x - \sin x} = \dfrac{1}{\dfrac{1}{\sin x} - \sin x}$

$= \dfrac{1}{\dfrac{1}{\sin x} - \sin x}$

$= \dfrac{1}{\dfrac{1}{\sin x} - \dfrac{\sin^2 x}{\sin x}}$

$= \dfrac{1}{\dfrac{1 - \sin^2 x}{\sin x}}$

$= \dfrac{1}{\dfrac{\cos^2 x}{\sin x}}$

$= \dfrac{\sin x}{\cos^2 x}$

$= \dfrac{1}{\cos x} \cdot \dfrac{\sin x}{\cos x}$

$= \sec x \tan x$

79.

$\sec x(\sin x - \cos x) + 1 = \dfrac{1}{\cos x}(\sin x - \cos x) + 1$

$= \dfrac{\sin x}{\cos x} - \dfrac{\cos x}{\cos x} + 1$

$= \tan x - 1 + 1$

$= \tan x$

81.

The graphs do not coincide. Values for x may vary.

83.

The graphs do not coincide. Values for x may vary.

85.

$\dfrac{\sin x}{1 - \cos^2 x} = \dfrac{\sin x}{\sin^2 x} = \dfrac{1}{\sin x} = \csc x$

87.

The graphs do not coincide. Values for x may vary.

89.
$$\frac{\sin x - \cos x + 1}{\sin x + \cos x - 1}$$

$$= \frac{\sin x - \cos x + 1}{\sin x + \cos x - 1} \cdot \frac{\sin x - \cos x - 1}{\sin x - \cos x - 1}$$

$$= \frac{\sin^2 x - 2\cos x \sin x + \cos^2 x - 1}{\sin^2 x - 2\sin x - \cos^2 x + 1}$$

$$= \frac{\sin^2 x + \cos^2 x - 2\cos x \sin x - 1}{\sin x^2 - 2\sin x - (1 - \sin^2 x) + 1}$$

$$= \frac{1 - 2\cos x \sin x - 1}{\sin^2 x - 2\sin x + \sin x^2}$$

$$= \frac{-2\cos x \sin x}{2\sin^2 x - 2\sin x}$$

$$= \frac{-2\sin x \cos x}{2\sin x(\sin x - 1)}$$

$$= \frac{-\cos x}{\sin x - \cos x}$$

$$= \frac{-\cos x}{\sin x - 1} \cdot \frac{\sin x + 1}{\sin x + 1}$$

$$= \frac{-\cos x(\sin x + 1)}{\sin^2 x - 1}$$

$$= \frac{-\cos x(\sin x + 1)}{\cos^2 x - 1 - \cos^2 x}$$

$$= \frac{-\cos x(\sin x + 1)}{\cos^2 x}$$

$$= \frac{\sin x + 1}{\cos x}$$

Section 5.2

Check Point Exercises

1.
$$\cos 30° = \cos(90° - 60°)$$
$$= \cos 90° \cos 60° + \sin 90° \sin 60°$$
$$= 0 \cdot \frac{1}{2} + 1 \cdot \frac{\sqrt{3}}{2}$$
$$= 0 + \frac{\sqrt{3}}{2}$$
$$= \frac{\sqrt{3}}{2}$$

2.
$$\cos 70° \cos 40° + \sin 70° \sin 40°$$
$$= \cos(70 - 40°)$$
$$= \cos 30°$$
$$= \frac{\sqrt{3}}{2}$$

3.
$$\frac{\cos(\alpha - \beta)}{\cos \alpha \cos \beta} = \frac{\cos \alpha \cos \beta + \sin \alpha \sin \beta}{\cos \alpha \cos \beta}$$
$$= \frac{\cos \alpha}{\cos \alpha} \cdot \frac{\cos \beta}{\cos \beta} + \frac{\sin \alpha}{\cos \alpha} \cdot \frac{\sin \beta}{\cos \beta}$$
$$= 1 \cdot 1 + \tan \alpha \cdot \tan \beta$$
$$= 1 + \tan \alpha \tan \beta$$

We worked with the left side and arrived at the right side. Thus, the identity is verified.

4.
$$\sin \frac{5\pi}{12} = \sin\left(\frac{\pi}{6} + \frac{\pi}{4}\right)$$
$$= \sin \frac{\pi}{6} \cos \frac{\pi}{4} + \cos \frac{\pi}{6} \sin \frac{\pi}{4}$$
$$= \frac{1}{2} \cdot \frac{\sqrt{2}}{2} + \frac{\sqrt{3}}{2} \cdot \frac{\sqrt{2}}{2}$$
$$= \frac{\sqrt{2}}{4} + \frac{\sqrt{6}}{4}$$
$$= \frac{\sqrt{2} + \sqrt{6}}{4}$$

5. **a.** $\sin\alpha = \dfrac{4}{5} = \dfrac{y}{r}$

Find x:

$x^2 + y^2 = r^2$

$x^2 + 4^2 = 5^2$

$x^2 + 16 = 25$

$x^2 = 9$

Because α is in Quadrant II, x is negative.

$x = -\sqrt{9} = -3$

$\cos\alpha = \dfrac{x}{r} = \dfrac{-3}{5} = -\dfrac{3}{5}$

b. $\sin\beta = \dfrac{1}{2} = \dfrac{y}{r}$

Find x:

$x^2 + y^2 = r^2$

$x^2 + 1^2 = 2^2$

$x^2 + 1 = 4$

$x^2 = 3$

Because β is in Quadrant I, x is positive.

$x = \sqrt{3}$

$\cos\beta = \dfrac{x}{r} = \dfrac{\sqrt{3}}{2}$

c. $\cos(\alpha+\beta) = \cos\alpha\cos\beta - \sin\alpha\sin\beta$

$= -\dfrac{3}{5}\cdot\dfrac{\sqrt{3}}{2} - \dfrac{4}{5}\cdot\dfrac{1}{2}$

$= \dfrac{-3\sqrt{3}}{10} - \dfrac{4}{10}$

$= \dfrac{-3\sqrt{3}-4}{10}$

d. $\sin(\alpha+\beta) = \sin\alpha\cos\beta + \cos\alpha\sin\beta$

$= \dfrac{4}{5}\cdot\dfrac{\sqrt{3}}{2} + \dfrac{-3}{5}\cdot\dfrac{1}{2}$

$= \dfrac{4\sqrt{3}}{10} + \dfrac{-3}{10}$

$= \dfrac{4\sqrt{3}-3}{10}$

6. **a.** The graph appears to be the sine curve, $y = \sin x$.

It cycles through intercept, maximum, intercept, minimum and back to intercept. Thus, $y = \sin x$ also describes the graph.

b. $\cos\left(x+\dfrac{3\pi}{2}\right) = \cos x\cos\dfrac{3\pi}{2} - \sin x\sin\dfrac{3\pi}{2}$

$= \cos x\cdot 0 - \sin x\cdot(-1)$

$= \sin x$

This verifies our observation that

$y = \cos\left(x+\dfrac{3\pi}{2}\right)$ and $y = \sin x$ describe

the same graph.

7. $\tan(x+\pi) = \dfrac{\tan x + \tan\pi}{1 - \tan x\tan\pi}$

$= \dfrac{\tan x + 0}{1 - \tan x\cdot 0}$

$= \dfrac{\tan x}{1}$

$= \tan x$

Exercise Set 5.2

1. $\cos(45° - 30°) = \cos 45°\cos 30° + \sin 45°\sin 30°$

$= \dfrac{\sqrt{2}}{2}\cdot\dfrac{\sqrt{3}}{2} + \dfrac{\sqrt{2}}{2}\cdot\dfrac{1}{2}$

$= \dfrac{\sqrt{6}}{4} + \dfrac{\sqrt{2}}{4}$

$= \dfrac{\sqrt{6}+\sqrt{2}}{4}$

3. $\cos\left(\dfrac{3\pi}{4} - \dfrac{\pi}{6}\right) = \cos\dfrac{3\pi}{4}\cos\dfrac{\pi}{6} + \sin\dfrac{3\pi}{4}\sin\dfrac{\pi}{6}$

$= -\dfrac{\sqrt{2}}{2}\cdot\dfrac{\sqrt{3}}{2} + \dfrac{\sqrt{2}}{2}\cdot\dfrac{1}{2}$

$= -\dfrac{\sqrt{6}}{4} + \dfrac{\sqrt{2}}{4}$

$= \dfrac{\sqrt{2}-\sqrt{6}}{4}$

5. **a.** $\cos 50°\cos 20° + \sin 50°\sin 20°$

$= \cos\alpha\cos\beta + \sin\alpha\sin\beta$

Thus, $\alpha = 50°$ and $\beta = 20°$.

b. $\cos 50°\cos 20° + \sin 50°\sin 20°$

$= \cos(50° - 20°)$

$= \cos 30°$

c. $\cos 30° = \dfrac{\sqrt{3}}{2}$

7. **a.** $\cos\dfrac{5\pi}{12}\cos\dfrac{\pi}{12}+\sin\dfrac{5\pi}{12}\sin\dfrac{\pi}{12}$

$= \cos\alpha\cos\beta+\sin\alpha\sin\beta$

Thus, $\alpha=\dfrac{5\pi}{12}$ and $\beta=\dfrac{\pi}{12}$.

b. $\cos\dfrac{5\pi}{12}\cos\dfrac{\pi}{12}+\sin\dfrac{5\pi}{12}\sin\dfrac{\pi}{12}$

$=\cos\left(\dfrac{5\pi}{12}-\dfrac{\pi}{12}\right)$

$=\cos\dfrac{4\pi}{12}$

$=\cos\dfrac{\pi}{3}$

c. $\cos\dfrac{\pi}{3}=\dfrac{1}{2}$

9. $\dfrac{\cos(\alpha-\beta)}{\cos\alpha\sin\beta}=\dfrac{\cos\alpha\cos\beta-\sin\alpha\sin\beta}{\cos\alpha\sin\beta}$

$=\dfrac{\cos\alpha}{\cos\alpha}\cdot\dfrac{\cos\beta}{\sin\beta}-\dfrac{\sin\alpha}{\cos\alpha}\cdot\dfrac{\sin\beta}{\sin\beta}$

$=1\cdot\cot\beta+\tan\alpha\cdot1$

$=\tan\alpha+\cot\beta$

11. $\cos\left(x-\dfrac{\pi}{4}\right)=\cos x\cos\dfrac{\pi}{4}+\sin x\sin\dfrac{\pi}{4}$

$=\cos x\cdot\dfrac{\sqrt{2}}{2}+\sin x\cdot\dfrac{\sqrt{2}}{2}$

$=\dfrac{\sqrt{2}}{2}(\cos x+\sin x)$

13. $\sin(45°-30°)=\sin45°\cos30°-\cos45°\sin30°$

$=\dfrac{\sqrt{2}}{2}\cdot\dfrac{\sqrt{3}}{2}-\dfrac{\sqrt{2}}{2}\cdot\dfrac{1}{2}$

$=\dfrac{\sqrt{6}}{4}-\dfrac{\sqrt{2}}{4}$

$=\dfrac{\sqrt{6}-\sqrt{2}}{4}$

15. $\sin(105°)=\sin(60°+45°)$

$=\sin60°\cos45°+\cos60°\sin45°$

$=\dfrac{\sqrt{3}}{2}\cdot\dfrac{\sqrt{2}}{2}+\dfrac{1}{2}\cdot\dfrac{\sqrt{2}}{2}$

$=\dfrac{\sqrt{6}}{4}+\dfrac{\sqrt{2}}{4}$

$=\dfrac{\sqrt{6}+\sqrt{2}}{4}$

17. $\cos(135°+30°)=\cos135°\cos30°-\sin135°\sin30°$

$=\cos(90°+45°)\cos30°-\sin(90°+45°)\sin30°$

$=(\cos90°\cos45°-\sin90°\sin45°)\cos30°-(\sin90°\cos45°+\cos90°\sin45°)\sin30°$

$=\left(0\cdot\dfrac{\sqrt{2}}{2}-1\cdot\dfrac{\sqrt{2}}{2}\right)\dfrac{\sqrt{3}}{2}-\left(1\cdot\dfrac{\sqrt{2}}{2}+0\cdot\dfrac{\sqrt{2}}{2}\right)\dfrac{1}{2}$

$=\left(-\dfrac{\sqrt{2}}{2}\right)\dfrac{\sqrt{3}}{2}-\left(\dfrac{\sqrt{2}}{2}\right)\dfrac{1}{2}$

$=-\dfrac{\sqrt{6}}{4}-\dfrac{\sqrt{2}}{4}$

$=-\dfrac{\sqrt{6}+\sqrt{2}}{4}$

19. $\cos 75° = \cos(45° + 30°)$

$\qquad = \cos 45° \cos 30° - \sin 45° \sin 30°$

$\qquad = \dfrac{\sqrt{2}}{2} \cdot \dfrac{\sqrt{3}}{2} - \dfrac{\sqrt{2}}{2} \cdot \dfrac{1}{2}$

$\qquad = \dfrac{\sqrt{6}}{4} - \dfrac{\sqrt{2}}{4}$

$\qquad = \dfrac{\sqrt{6} - \sqrt{2}}{4}$

21. $\tan\left(\dfrac{\pi}{6} + \dfrac{\pi}{4}\right) = \dfrac{\tan\dfrac{\pi}{6} + \tan\dfrac{\pi}{4}}{1 - \tan\dfrac{\pi}{6} \tan\dfrac{\pi}{4}}$

$\qquad = \dfrac{\dfrac{\sqrt{3}}{3} + 1}{1 - \dfrac{\sqrt{3}}{3} \cdot 1}$

$\qquad = \dfrac{\dfrac{\sqrt{3}}{3} + \dfrac{3}{3}}{\dfrac{3}{3} - \dfrac{\sqrt{3}}{3}}$

$\qquad = \dfrac{\sqrt{3} + 3}{3 - \sqrt{3}}$

$\qquad = \dfrac{3 + \sqrt{3}}{3 - \sqrt{3}} \cdot \dfrac{3 + \sqrt{3}}{3 + \sqrt{3}}$

$\qquad = \dfrac{9 + 6\sqrt{3} + 3}{9 - 3}$

$\qquad = \dfrac{12 + 6\sqrt{3}}{6}$

$\qquad = 2 + \sqrt{3}$

23. $\tan\left(\dfrac{4\pi}{3} - \dfrac{\pi}{4}\right) = \dfrac{\tan\dfrac{4\pi}{3} - \tan\dfrac{\pi}{4}}{1 + \tan\dfrac{4\pi}{3} \tan\dfrac{\pi}{4}}$

$\qquad = \dfrac{\sqrt{3} - 1}{1 + \sqrt{3} \cdot 1}$

$\qquad = \dfrac{-1 + \sqrt{3}}{1 + \sqrt{3}}$

$\qquad = \dfrac{-1 + \sqrt{3}}{1 + \sqrt{3}} \cdot \dfrac{1 - \sqrt{3}}{1 - \sqrt{3}}$

$\qquad = \dfrac{-1 + 2\sqrt{3} - 3}{1 - 3}$

$\qquad = \dfrac{-4 + 2\sqrt{3}}{-2}$

$\qquad = 2 - \sqrt{3}$

25. $\sin 25° \cos 5° + \cos 25° \sin 5° = \sin(25° + 5°)$

$\qquad\qquad\qquad\qquad\qquad = \sin 30°$

$\qquad\qquad\qquad\qquad\qquad = \dfrac{1}{2}$

27. $\dfrac{\tan 10° + \tan 35°}{1 - \tan 10° \tan 35°} = \tan(10° + 35°)$

$\qquad\qquad\qquad\qquad = \tan 45°$

$\qquad\qquad\qquad\qquad = 1$

29. $\sin\dfrac{5\pi}{12} \cos\dfrac{\pi}{4} - \cos\dfrac{5\pi}{12} \sin\dfrac{\pi}{4} = \sin\left(\dfrac{5\pi}{12} - \dfrac{\pi}{4}\right)$

$\qquad\qquad\qquad\qquad\qquad = \sin\left(\dfrac{2\pi}{12}\right)$

$\qquad\qquad\qquad\qquad\qquad = \sin\left(\dfrac{\pi}{6}\right)$

$\qquad\qquad\qquad\qquad\qquad = \dfrac{1}{2}$

31. $\dfrac{\tan\frac{\pi}{5} - \tan\frac{\pi}{30}}{1 + \tan\frac{\pi}{5} \tan\frac{\pi}{30}} = \tan\left(\dfrac{\pi}{5} - \dfrac{\pi}{30}\right)$

$\qquad\qquad\qquad = \tan\left(\dfrac{5\pi}{30}\right) = \tan\left(\dfrac{\pi}{6}\right)$

$\qquad\qquad\qquad = \dfrac{\sqrt{3}}{3}$

33. $\sin\left(x+\dfrac{\pi}{2}\right)=\sin x\cos\dfrac{\pi}{2}+\cos x\sin\dfrac{\pi}{2}$

$\qquad\qquad = \sin x\cdot 0+\cos x\cdot 1$

$\qquad\qquad = \cos x$

35. $\cos\left(x-\dfrac{\pi}{2}\right)=\cos x\cos\dfrac{\pi}{2}+\sin x\sin\dfrac{\pi}{2}$

$\qquad\qquad = \cos x\cdot 0+\sin x\cdot 1$

$\qquad\qquad = \sin x$

37. $\tan(2\pi-x)=\dfrac{\tan 2\pi-\tan x}{1+\tan 2\pi\tan x}$

$\qquad\qquad = \dfrac{0-\tan x}{1+0\cdot\tan x}$

$\qquad\qquad = -\tan x$

39. $\sin(\alpha+\beta)+\sin(\alpha-\beta)$

$\qquad = \sin\alpha\cos\beta+\cos\alpha\sin\beta$

$\qquad +\sin\alpha\cos\beta-\cos\alpha\sin\beta$

$\qquad = 2\sin\alpha\cos\beta$

41. $\dfrac{\sin(\alpha-\beta)}{\cos\alpha\cos\beta}=\dfrac{\sin\alpha\cos\beta-\cos\alpha\sin\beta}{\cos\alpha\cos\beta}$

$\qquad\qquad = \dfrac{\sin\alpha\cos\beta}{\cos\alpha\cos\beta}-\dfrac{\cos\alpha\sin\beta}{\cos\alpha\cos\beta}$

$\qquad\qquad = \tan\alpha\cdot 1-1\cdot\tan\beta$

$\qquad\qquad = \tan\alpha-\tan\beta$

43. $\tan\left(\theta+\dfrac{\pi}{4}\right)=\dfrac{\tan\theta+\tan\frac{\pi}{4}}{1-\tan\theta\tan\frac{\pi}{4}}$

$\qquad\qquad = \dfrac{\tan\theta+1}{1-\tan\theta}$

$\qquad\qquad = \dfrac{\frac{\sin\theta}{\cos\theta}+\frac{\cos\theta}{\cos\theta}}{\frac{\cos\theta}{\cos\theta}-\frac{\sin\theta}{\cos\theta}}$

$\qquad\qquad = \dfrac{\frac{\sin\theta+\cos\theta}{\cos\theta}}{\frac{\cos\theta-\sin\theta}{\cos\theta}}$

$\qquad\qquad = \dfrac{\sin\theta+\cos\theta}{\cos\theta}\cdot\dfrac{\cos\theta}{\cos\theta-\sin\theta}$

$\qquad\qquad = \dfrac{\sin\theta+\cos\theta}{\cos\theta-\sin\theta}$

$\qquad\qquad = \dfrac{\cos\theta+\sin\theta}{\cos\theta-\sin\theta}$

45. $\cos(\alpha+\beta)\cos(\alpha-\beta)$

$\qquad = (\cos\alpha\cos\beta-\sin\alpha\sin\beta)$

$\qquad \cdot(\cos\alpha\cos\beta+\sin\alpha\sin\beta)$

$\qquad = \cos^2\alpha\cos^2\beta-\sin^2\alpha\sin^2\beta$

$\qquad = \left(1-\sin^2\alpha\right)\cos^2\beta-\sin^2\alpha\left(1-\cos^2\beta\right)$

$\qquad = \cos^2\beta-\sin^2\alpha\cos^2\beta$

$\qquad -\sin^2\alpha+\sin^2\alpha\cos^2\beta$

$\qquad = \cos^2\beta-\sin^2\alpha$

47. $\dfrac{\sin(\alpha+\beta)}{\sin(\alpha-\beta)}$

$\qquad = \dfrac{\sin\alpha\cos\beta+\cos\alpha\sin\beta}{\sin\alpha\cos\beta-\cos\alpha\sin\beta}$

$\qquad = \dfrac{\sin\alpha\cos\beta+\cos\alpha\sin\beta}{\sin\alpha\cos\beta-\cos\alpha\sin\beta}\cdot\dfrac{\frac{1}{\cos\alpha\cos\beta}}{\frac{1}{\cos\alpha\cos\beta}}$

$\qquad = \dfrac{\frac{\sin\alpha\cos\beta+\cos\alpha\sin\beta}{\cos\alpha\cos\beta}}{\frac{\sin\alpha\cos\beta-\cos\alpha\sin\beta}{\cos\alpha\cos\beta}}$

$\qquad = \dfrac{\frac{\sin\alpha\cos\beta}{\cos\alpha\cos\beta}+\frac{\cos\alpha\sin\beta}{\cos\alpha\cos\beta}}{\frac{\sin\alpha\cos\beta}{\cos\alpha\cos\beta}-\frac{\cos\alpha\sin\beta}{\cos\alpha\cos\beta}}$

$\qquad = \dfrac{\tan\alpha\cdot 1+1\cdot\tan\beta}{\tan\alpha\cdot 1-1\cdot\tan\beta}$

$\qquad = \dfrac{\tan\alpha+\tan\beta}{\tan\alpha-\tan\beta}$

49. $\dfrac{\cos(x+h)-\cos x}{h}$

$\qquad = \dfrac{\cos x\cos h-\sin x\sin h-\cos x}{h}$

$\qquad = \dfrac{\cos x\cos h-\cos x-\sin x\sin h}{h}$

$\qquad = \dfrac{\cos x(\cos h-1)-\sin x\sin h}{h}$

$\qquad = \cos x\cdot\dfrac{\cos h-1}{h}-\sin x\cdot\dfrac{\sin h}{h}$

51. $\sin 2\alpha = \sin(\alpha+\alpha)$

$\qquad\quad = \sin\alpha\cos\alpha+\cos\alpha\sin\alpha$

$\qquad\quad = 2\sin\alpha\cos\alpha$

53.
$$\tan 2\alpha = \tan(\alpha + \alpha)$$
$$= \frac{\tan \alpha + \tan \alpha}{1 - \tan \alpha \tan \alpha}$$
$$= \frac{2 \tan \alpha}{1 - \tan^2 \alpha}$$

55.
$$\tan(\alpha + \beta) = \frac{\sin(\alpha + \beta)}{\cos(\alpha + \beta)}$$
$$= \frac{\sin \alpha \cos \beta + \cos \alpha \sin \beta}{\cos \alpha \cos \beta - \sin \alpha \sin \beta}$$
$$= \frac{\sin \alpha \cos \beta + \cos \alpha \sin \beta}{\cos \alpha \cos \beta - \sin \alpha \sin \beta} \cdot \frac{\frac{1}{\cos\alpha \cos \beta}}{\frac{1}{\cos\alpha \cos \beta}}$$
$$= \frac{\frac{\sin\alpha \cos \beta + \cos\alpha \sin \beta}{\cos\alpha \cos \beta}}{\frac{\cos\alpha \cos \beta - \sin\alpha \sin \beta}{\cos\alpha \cos \beta}}$$
$$= \frac{\frac{\sin\alpha \cos \beta}{\cos\alpha \cos \beta} + \frac{\cos\alpha \sin \beta}{\cos\alpha \cos \beta}}{\frac{\cos\alpha \cos \beta}{\cos\alpha \cos \beta} - \frac{\sin\alpha \sin \beta}{\cos\alpha \cos \beta}}$$
$$= \frac{\tan \alpha + \tan \beta}{1 - \tan \alpha \tan \beta}$$

57.
$$\sin \alpha = \frac{3}{5} = \frac{y}{r}$$
$$x^2 + y^2 = r^2$$
$$x^2 + 3^2 = 5^2$$
$$x^2 + 9 = 25$$
$$x^2 = 16$$
Because α lies in quadrant I, x is positive.
$$x = 4$$
Thus, $\cos \alpha = \dfrac{x}{r} = \dfrac{4}{5}$, and
$$\tan \alpha = \frac{\sin \alpha}{\cos \alpha} = \frac{\frac{3}{5}}{\frac{4}{5}} = \frac{3}{4}.$$

$$\sin \beta = \frac{5}{13} = \frac{y}{r}$$
$$x^2 + y^2 = r^2$$
$$x^2 + 5^2 = 13^2$$
$$x^2 + 25 = 169$$
$$x^2 = 144$$

Because β lies in quadrant II, x is negative.
$$x = -12$$
Thus, $\cos \beta = \dfrac{x}{r} = \dfrac{-12}{13} = -\dfrac{12}{13}$, and
$$\tan \beta = \frac{\sin \beta}{\cos \beta} = \frac{\frac{5}{13}}{-\frac{12}{13}} = -\frac{5}{12}.$$

a. $\cos(\alpha + \beta) = \cos \alpha \cos \beta - \sin \alpha \sin \beta$
$$= \frac{4}{5} \cdot \left(-\frac{12}{13}\right) - \frac{3}{5} \cdot \frac{5}{13} = -\frac{63}{65}$$

b. $\sin(\alpha + \beta) = \sin \alpha \cos \beta + \cos \alpha \sin \beta$
$$= \frac{3}{5} \cdot \left(-\frac{12}{13}\right) + \frac{4}{5} \cdot \frac{5}{13} = -\frac{16}{65}$$

c. $\tan(\alpha + \beta) = \dfrac{\tan \alpha + \tan \beta}{1 - \tan \alpha \tan \beta}$
$$= \frac{\frac{3}{4} + \left(-\frac{5}{12}\right)}{1 - \frac{3}{4} \cdot \left(-\frac{5}{12}\right)} = \frac{\frac{4}{12}}{\frac{63}{48}} = \frac{16}{63}$$

59.
$$\tan \alpha = -\frac{3}{4} = \frac{3}{-4} = \frac{y}{x}$$
$$x^2 + y^2 = r^2$$
$$(-4)^2 + 3^2 = r^2$$
$$16 + 9 = r^2$$
$$25 = r^2$$
Because r is a distance, it is positive.
$$r = 5$$
Thus, $\cos \alpha = \dfrac{x}{r} = \dfrac{-4}{5} = -\dfrac{4}{5}$, and
$$\sin \alpha = \frac{y}{r} = \frac{3}{5}.$$

$$\cos \beta = \frac{1}{3} = \frac{x}{r}$$
$$x^2 + y^2 = r^2$$
$$1^2 + y^2 = 3^2$$
$$1 + y^2 = 9$$
$$y^2 = 8$$
Because β lies in quadrant I, y is positive.
$$y = \sqrt{8} = 2\sqrt{2}$$
Thus, $\sin \beta = \dfrac{y}{r} = \dfrac{2\sqrt{2}}{3}$, and
$$\tan \beta = \frac{\sin \beta}{\cos \beta} = \frac{\frac{2\sqrt{2}}{3}}{\frac{1}{3}} = 2\sqrt{2}.$$

a. $\cos(\alpha + \beta) = \cos\alpha\cos\beta - \sin\alpha\sin\beta$

$$= \left(-\frac{4}{5}\right)\cdot\frac{1}{3} - \frac{3}{5}\cdot\frac{2\sqrt{2}}{3}$$

$$= -\frac{4}{15} - \frac{6\sqrt{2}}{15}$$

$$= \frac{-4 - 6\sqrt{2}}{15}$$

$$= -\frac{4 + 6\sqrt{2}}{15}$$

b. $\sin(\alpha + \beta) = \sin\alpha\cos\beta + \cos\alpha\sin\beta$

$$= \frac{3}{5}\cdot\frac{1}{3} + \left(-\frac{4}{5}\right)\cdot\frac{2\sqrt{2}}{3}$$

$$= \frac{3}{15} - \frac{8\sqrt{2}}{15}$$

$$= \frac{3 - 8\sqrt{2}}{15}$$

c. $\tan(\alpha + \beta) = \dfrac{\tan\alpha + \tan\beta}{1 - \tan\alpha\tan\beta}$

$$= \frac{-\frac{3}{4} + 2\sqrt{2}}{1 - \left(-\frac{3}{4}\right)\left(2\sqrt{2}\right)}$$

$$= \frac{\frac{-3 + 8\sqrt{2}}{4}}{\frac{4 + 6\sqrt{2}}{4}}$$

$$= \frac{-3 + 8\sqrt{2}}{4 + 6\sqrt{2}}\cdot\frac{\left(4 - 6\sqrt{2}\right)}{\left(4 - 6\sqrt{2}\right)}$$

$$= \frac{-108 + 50\sqrt{2}}{-56}$$

$$= \frac{54 - 25\sqrt{2}}{28}$$

61. $\cos\alpha = \dfrac{8}{17} = \dfrac{x}{r}$

$$x^2 + y^2 = r^2$$
$$8^2 + y^2 = 17^2$$
$$64 + y^2 = 289$$
$$y^2 = 225$$

Because α lies in quadrant IV, y is negative.
$$y = -15$$

Thus, $\sin\alpha = \dfrac{y}{r} = \dfrac{-15}{17} = -\dfrac{15}{17}$, and

$$\tan\alpha = \frac{\sin\alpha}{\cos\alpha} = \frac{-\frac{15}{17}}{\frac{8}{17}} = -\frac{15}{8}.$$

$$\sin\beta = -\frac{1}{2} = \frac{-1}{2} = \frac{y}{r}$$
$$x^2 + y^2 = r^2$$
$$x^2 + (-1)^2 = 2^2$$
$$x^2 + 1 = 4$$
$$x^2 = 3$$

Because β lies in quadrant III, x is negative.

$$x = -\sqrt{3}$$

Thus, $\cos\beta = \dfrac{x}{r} = \dfrac{-\sqrt{3}}{2} = -\dfrac{\sqrt{3}}{2}$, and

$$\tan\beta = \frac{\sin\beta}{\cos\beta} = \frac{-\frac{1}{2}}{-\frac{\sqrt{3}}{2}} = \frac{1}{\sqrt{3}} = \frac{\sqrt{3}}{3}.$$

a. $\cos(\alpha + \beta) = \cos\alpha\cos\beta - \sin\alpha\sin\beta$

$$= \frac{8}{17}\cdot\left(-\frac{\sqrt{3}}{2}\right) - \left(-\frac{15}{17}\right)\cdot\left(-\frac{1}{2}\right)$$

$$= \frac{-8\sqrt{3} - 15}{34}$$

$$= -\frac{8\sqrt{3} + 15}{34}$$

b. $\sin(\alpha + \beta) = \sin\alpha\cos\beta + \cos\alpha\sin\beta$

$$= \left(-\frac{15}{17}\right)\cdot\left(-\frac{\sqrt{3}}{2}\right) + \frac{8}{17}\cdot\left(-\frac{1}{2}\right)$$

$$= \frac{15\sqrt{3} - 8}{34}$$

c.
$$\tan(\alpha + \beta) = \frac{\tan \alpha + \tan \beta}{1 - \tan \alpha \tan \beta}$$

$$= \frac{-\dfrac{15}{8} + \dfrac{\sqrt{3}}{3}}{1 - \left(-\dfrac{15}{8}\right)\left(\dfrac{\sqrt{3}}{3}\right)}$$

$$= \frac{\dfrac{-45 + 8\sqrt{3}}{24}}{\dfrac{24 + 15\sqrt{3}}{24}}$$

$$= \frac{-45 + 8\sqrt{3}}{24 + 15\sqrt{3}} \cdot \frac{24 - 15\sqrt{3}}{24 - 15\sqrt{3}}$$

$$= \frac{-1440 + 867\sqrt{3}}{-99}$$

$$= \frac{489 - 289\sqrt{3}}{33}$$

63. $\tan \alpha = \dfrac{3}{4} = \dfrac{y}{x}$

Because α lies in quadrant III, x and y are negative.

$r^2 = x^2 + y^2$

$r^2 = (-4)^2 + (-3)^2$

$r^2 = 25$

$r = 5$

$\sin \alpha = \dfrac{y}{r} = \dfrac{-3}{5} = -\dfrac{3}{5}$

$\cos \alpha = \dfrac{x}{r} = \dfrac{-4}{5} = -\dfrac{4}{5}$

$\cos \beta = \dfrac{1}{4} = \dfrac{x}{r}$

Because β lies in quadrant IV, y is negative.

$x^2 + y^2 = r^2$

$1^2 + y^2 = 4^2$

$y^2 = 15$

$y = -\sqrt{15}$

$\sin \beta = \dfrac{y}{r} = \dfrac{-\sqrt{15}}{4} = -\dfrac{\sqrt{15}}{4}$

$\tan \beta = \dfrac{y}{x} = \dfrac{-\sqrt{15}}{1} = -\sqrt{15}$

a. $\cos(\alpha + \beta) = \cos \alpha \cos \beta - \sin \alpha \sin \beta$

$$= -\frac{4}{5} \cdot \left(\frac{1}{4}\right) - \left(-\frac{3}{5}\right)\left(-\frac{\sqrt{15}}{4}\right)$$

$$= -\frac{4}{20} - \frac{3\sqrt{15}}{20}$$

$$= -\frac{4 + 3\sqrt{15}}{20}$$

b. $\sin(\alpha + \beta) = \sin \alpha \cos \beta + \cos \alpha \sin \beta$

$$= \left(-\frac{3}{5}\right)\left(\frac{1}{4}\right) + \left(-\frac{4}{5}\right)\left(-\frac{\sqrt{15}}{4}\right)$$

$$= -\frac{3}{20} + \frac{4\sqrt{15}}{20}$$

$$= \frac{-3 + 4\sqrt{15}}{20}$$

c. $\tan(\alpha + \beta) = \dfrac{\tan \alpha + \tan \beta}{1 - \tan \alpha \tan \beta}$

$$= \frac{\dfrac{3}{4} + \left(-\sqrt{15}\right)}{1 - \dfrac{3}{4}\left(-\sqrt{15}\right)}$$

$$= \frac{\dfrac{3}{4} - \dfrac{4\sqrt{15}}{4}}{\dfrac{4}{4} + \dfrac{3\sqrt{15}}{4}}$$

$$= \frac{3 - 4\sqrt{15}}{4 + 3\sqrt{15}}$$

$$= \frac{3 - 4\sqrt{15}}{4 + 3\sqrt{15}} \cdot \frac{4 - 3\sqrt{15}}{4 - 3\sqrt{15}}$$

$$= \frac{12 - 9\sqrt{15} - 16\sqrt{15} + 180}{16 - 135}$$

$$= \frac{192 - 25\sqrt{15}}{-119}$$

$$= \frac{-192 + 25\sqrt{15}}{119}$$

65. a. The graph appears to be the sine curve, $y = \sin x$. It cycles through intercept, maximum, minimum and back to intercept. Thus, $y = \sin x$ also describes the graph.

b. $\sin(\pi - x) = \sin \pi \cos x - \cos \pi \sin x$

$\qquad\qquad = 0 \cdot \cos x - (-1) \cdot \sin x$

$\qquad\qquad = \sin x$

This verifies our observation that $y = \sin (\pi - x)$ and $y = \sin x$ describe the same graph.

67. a. The graph appears to be 2 times the cosine curve, $y = 2 \cos x$. It cycles through maximum, intercept, minimum, intercept and back to maximum. Thus $y = 2 \cos x$ also describes the graph.

b.

$\sin\left(x + \dfrac{\pi}{2}\right) + \sin\left(\dfrac{\pi}{2} - x\right)$

$= \sin x \cos \dfrac{\pi}{2} + \cos x \sin \dfrac{\pi}{2} + \sin \dfrac{\pi}{2} \cos x$

$\quad - \cos \dfrac{\pi}{2} \sin x$

$= \sin x \cdot 0 + \cos x \cdot 1 + 1 \cdot \cos x - 0 \cdot \sin x$

$= \cos x + \cos x$

$= 2 \cos x$

This verifies our observation that

$y = \sin\left(x + \dfrac{\pi}{2}\right) + \sin\left(\dfrac{\pi}{2} - x\right)$ and

$y = 2\cos x$ describe the same graph.

69. $\cos(\alpha + \beta)\cos \beta + \sin(\alpha + \beta)\sin \beta$

$= \cos\left[(\alpha + \beta) - \beta\right]$

$= \cos \alpha$

71. $\dfrac{\sin(\alpha + \beta) - \sin(\alpha - \beta)}{\cos(\alpha + \beta) + \cos(\alpha - \beta)}$

$= \dfrac{(\sin \alpha \cos \beta + \cos \alpha \sin \beta) - (\sin \alpha \cos \beta - \cos \alpha \sin \beta)}{(\cos \alpha \cos \beta - \sin \alpha \sin \beta) + (\cos \alpha \cos \beta + \sin \alpha \sin \beta)}$

$= \dfrac{\sin \alpha \cos \beta + \cos \alpha \sin \beta - \sin \alpha \cos \beta + \cos \alpha \sin \beta}{\cos \alpha \cos \beta - \sin \alpha \sin \beta + \cos \alpha \cos \beta + \sin \alpha \sin \beta}$

$= \dfrac{\cos \alpha \sin \beta + \cos \alpha \sin \beta}{\cos \alpha \cos \beta + \cos \alpha \cos \beta}$

$= \dfrac{2 \cos \alpha \sin \beta}{2 \cos \alpha \cos \beta}$

$= \dfrac{\sin \beta}{\cos \beta}$

$= \tan \beta$

73. $\cos\left(\dfrac{\pi}{6} + \alpha\right)\cos\left(\dfrac{\pi}{6} - \alpha\right) - \sin\left(\dfrac{\pi}{6} + \alpha\right)\sin\left(\dfrac{\pi}{6} - \alpha\right)$

$= \cos\left[\left(\dfrac{\pi}{6} + \alpha\right) + \left(\dfrac{\pi}{6} - \alpha\right)\right]$

$= \cos\left[\dfrac{\pi}{6} + \alpha + \dfrac{\pi}{6} - \alpha\right]$

$= \cos \dfrac{\pi}{3}$

$= \dfrac{1}{2}$

75. Conjecture: the left side is equal to $\cos 3x$.

$$\cos 2x \cos 5x + \sin 2x \sin 5x$$
$$= \cos(2x - 5x)$$
$$= \cos(-3x)$$
$$= \cos 3x$$

77. Conjecture: the left side is equal to $\sin \dfrac{x}{2}$.

$$\sin \frac{5x}{2} \cos 2x - \cos \frac{5x}{2} \sin 2x$$
$$= \sin\left(\frac{5x}{2} - 2x\right)$$
$$= \sin\left(\frac{5x}{2} - \frac{4x}{2}\right)$$
$$= \sin \frac{x}{2}$$

79. $\tan \theta = \dfrac{3}{2} = \dfrac{y}{x}$

$$x^2 + y^2 = r^2$$
$$2^2 + 3^3 = r^2$$
$$4 + 9 = r^2$$
$$13 = r^2$$

Because r is a distance, it is positive.

$$r = \sqrt{13}$$

Thus, $\sin \theta = \dfrac{y}{r} = \dfrac{3}{\sqrt{13}}$

and $\cos \theta = \dfrac{x}{r} = \dfrac{2}{\sqrt{13}}$

$$\sqrt{13} \cos(t - \theta) = \sqrt{13}(\cos t \cos \theta + \sin t \sin \theta)$$
$$= \sqrt{13}\left(\cos t \cdot \frac{2}{\sqrt{13}} + \sin t \cdot \frac{3}{\sqrt{13}}\right) \text{F}$$
$$= \cos t \cdot 2 + \sin t \cdot 3$$
$$= 2 \cos t + 3 \sin t$$

or the equation $y = \sqrt{13} \cos(t - \theta)$, the

amplitude is $\left|\sqrt{13}\right| = \sqrt{13}$, and the period is

$$\frac{2\pi}{1} = 2\pi.$$

89.

$$\tan(\pi - x) = \frac{\tan \pi - \tan x}{1 + \tan \pi \tan x}$$
$$= \frac{0 - \tan x}{1 + 0 \cdot \tan x}$$
$$= \frac{-\tan x}{1}$$
$$= -\tan x$$

91.

The graphs do not coincide. Values for x may vary.

93.

$$\sin 1.2x \cos 0.8x + \cos 1.2x \sin 0.8x$$
$$\sin(1.2x + 0.8x)$$
$$\sin 2x$$

95. $\cos^{-1}\dfrac{1}{2}$

$x = 1$

$y = \sqrt{3}$

$r = 2$

$\sin^{-1}\dfrac{3}{5}$

$x = 4$

$y = 3$

$r = 5$

$\sin\left(\cos^{-1}\dfrac{1}{2}+\sin^{-1}\dfrac{3}{5}\right)$

$=\sin\cos^{-1}\dfrac{1}{2}\cos\sin^{-1}\dfrac{3}{5}$

$\quad +\cos\cos^{-1}\dfrac{1}{2}\sin\sin^{-1}\dfrac{3}{5}$

$=\dfrac{\sqrt{3}}{2}\cdot\dfrac{4}{5}+\dfrac{1}{2}\cdot\dfrac{3}{5}$

$=\dfrac{4\sqrt{3}+3}{10}$

97. $\tan^{-1}\dfrac{4}{3}$

$x = 3$

$y = 4$

$r = 5$

$\cos^{-1}\dfrac{5}{13}$

$x = 5$

$y = 12$

$r = 13$

$\cos\left(\tan^{-1}\dfrac{4}{3}+\cos^{-1}\dfrac{5}{13}\right)$

$=\cos\tan^{-1}\dfrac{4}{3}\cos\cos^{-1}\dfrac{5}{13}$

$\quad -\sin\tan^{-1}\dfrac{4}{3}\sin\cos^{-1}\dfrac{5}{13}$

$=\dfrac{3}{5}\cdot\dfrac{5}{13}-\dfrac{4}{5}\cdot\dfrac{12}{13}$

$=-\dfrac{33}{65}$

99. Let $\alpha=\sin^{-1}x$, where $-\dfrac{\pi}{2}\le\alpha\le\dfrac{\pi}{2}$. $\sin\alpha=x$

Because x is positive, $\sin\alpha$ is positive. Thus α is in quadrant I. Using a right triangle in quadrant I with $\sin\alpha=x$, the third side can be found using the Pythagorean Theorem.

$$a^2+x^2=1^2$$
$$a^2=1-x^2$$
$$a=\sqrt{1-x^2}$$

Thus $\cos\alpha=\dfrac{\sqrt{1-x^2}}{1}=\sqrt{1-x^2}$

Because y is positive, $\cos\beta$ is positive. Thus β is in quadrant I. Using a right triangle in quadrant I with $\cos\beta=y$, the third side can be found using the Pythagorean Theorem.

$$b^2+y^2=1^2$$
$$b^2=1-x^2$$
$$a=\sqrt{1-y^2}$$

Thus $\cos\alpha=\dfrac{\sqrt{1-y^2}}{1}=\sqrt{1-y^2}$

$\cos(\sin^{-1}x-\cos^{-1}y)=\cos(\alpha-\beta)$

$\qquad =\cos\alpha\cos\beta+\sin\alpha\sin\beta$

$\qquad =\sqrt{1-x^2}\,y+x\sqrt{1-y^2}$

$\qquad =y\sqrt{1-x^2}+x\sqrt{1-y^2}$

101. $\sin^{-1}$

$x=\sqrt{1-x^2}$

$y=x$

$r=1$

$\cos^{-1}y$

$x=y$

$y=\sqrt{1-y^2}$

$r=1$

$\tan(\sin^{-1} x + \cos^{-1} y)$

$= \dfrac{\tan \sin^{-1} x + \tan \cos^{-1} y}{1 - \tan \sin^{-1} x \cdot \tan \cos^{-1} y}$

$= \dfrac{\dfrac{x}{\sqrt{1-x^2}} + \dfrac{\sqrt{1-y^2}}{y}}{1 - \dfrac{x}{\sqrt{1-x^2}} \cdot \dfrac{\sqrt{1-y^2}}{y}}$

$= \dfrac{xy + \sqrt{1-y^2}\sqrt{1-x^2}}{y\sqrt{1-x^2} - x\sqrt{1-y^2}}$

Section 5.3

Check Point Exercises

1. $\sin\theta = \dfrac{4}{5} = \dfrac{y}{r}$

    Because θ lies in quadrant II, x is negative.

    $x^2 + y^2 = r^2$

    $x^2 + 4^2 = 5^2$

    $\quad x^2 = 5^2 - 4^2 = 9$

    $\quad\ x = -\sqrt{9} = -3$

    Now we use values for x, y, and r to find the required values.

    a. $\sin 2\theta = 2\sin\theta\cos\theta$

    $\qquad\qquad = 2\left(\dfrac{4}{5}\right)\left(-\dfrac{3}{5}\right) = -\dfrac{24}{25}$

    b. $\cos 2\theta = \cos^2\theta - \sin^2\theta$

    $\qquad\qquad = \left(-\dfrac{3}{5}\right)^2 - \left(\dfrac{4}{5}\right)^2 = \dfrac{9}{25} - \dfrac{16}{25}$

    $\qquad\qquad = -\dfrac{7}{25}$

    c. $\tan 2\theta = \dfrac{2\tan\theta}{1 - \tan^2\theta}$

    $\qquad\qquad = \dfrac{2\left(-\frac{4}{3}\right)}{1 - \left(-\frac{4}{3}\right)^2} = \dfrac{-\frac{8}{3}}{1 - \frac{16}{9}} = \dfrac{-\frac{8}{3}}{-\frac{7}{9}}$

    $\qquad\qquad = \left(-\dfrac{8}{3}\right)\left(-\dfrac{9}{7}\right) = \dfrac{24}{7}$

2. The given expression is the right side of the formula for $\cos 2\theta$ with $\theta = 15°$.

    $\cos^2 15° - \sin^2 15° = \cos(2 \cdot 15°)$

    $\qquad\qquad\qquad\qquad = \cos 30° = \dfrac{\sqrt{3}}{2}$

3. $\sin 3\theta = \sin(2\theta + \theta)$

    $\qquad = \sin 2\theta \cos\theta + \cos 2\theta \sin\theta$

    $\qquad = 2\sin\theta\cos\theta\cos\theta + (2\cos^2\theta - 1)\sin\theta$

    $\qquad = 2\sin\theta\cos^2\theta + 2\sin\theta\cos^2\theta - \sin\theta$

    $\qquad = 4\sin\theta\cos^2\theta - \sin\theta$

    $\qquad = 4\sin\theta(1 - \sin^2\theta) - \sin\theta$

    $\qquad = 4\sin\theta - 4\sin^3\theta - \sin\theta$

    $\qquad = 3\sin\theta - 4\sin^3\theta$

    By working with the left side and expressing it in a form identical to the right side, we have verified the identity.

4. $\sin^4 x = \left(\sin^2 x\right)^2$

    $\qquad = \left(\dfrac{1 - \cos 2x}{2}\right)^2$

    $\qquad = \dfrac{1 - 2\cos 2x + \cos^2 2x}{4}$

    $\qquad = \dfrac{1}{4} - \dfrac{1}{2}\cos 2x + \dfrac{1}{4}\cos^2 2x$

    $\qquad = \dfrac{1}{4} - \dfrac{1}{2}\cos 2x + \dfrac{1}{4}\left(\dfrac{1 + \cos 2(2x)}{2}\right)$

    $\qquad = \dfrac{1}{4} - \dfrac{1}{2}\cos 2x + \dfrac{1}{8} + \dfrac{1}{8}\cos 4x$

    $\qquad = \dfrac{3}{8} - \dfrac{1}{2}\cos 2x + \dfrac{1}{8}\cos 4x$

5. Because $105°$ lies in quadrant II, $\cos 105° < 0$.

    $\cos 105° = \cos\left(\dfrac{210°}{2}\right)$

    $\qquad\quad = -\sqrt{\dfrac{1 + \cos 210°}{2}}$

    $\qquad\quad = -\sqrt{\dfrac{1 - \frac{\sqrt{3}}{2}}{2}}$

    $\qquad\quad = -\sqrt{\dfrac{2 - \sqrt{3}}{4}}$

    $\qquad\quad = -\dfrac{\sqrt{2 - \sqrt{3}}}{2}$

6. $\dfrac{\sin 2\theta}{1+\cos 2\theta} = \dfrac{2\sin\theta\cos\theta}{1+\left(1-2\sin^2\theta\right)}$

$\qquad\qquad = \dfrac{2\sin\theta\cos\theta}{2-2\sin^2\theta}$

$\qquad\qquad = \dfrac{2\sin\theta\cos\theta}{2\left(1-\sin^2\theta\right)}$

$\qquad\qquad = \dfrac{2\sin\theta\cos\theta}{2\cos^2\theta}$

$\qquad\qquad = \dfrac{\sin\theta}{\cos\theta} = \tan\theta$

The right side simplifies to $\tan\theta$, the expression on the left side. Thus, the identity is verified.

7. $\dfrac{\sec\alpha}{\sec\alpha\csc\alpha + \csc\alpha} = \dfrac{\frac{1}{\cos\alpha}}{\frac{1}{\cos\alpha}\cdot\frac{1}{\sin\alpha}+\frac{1}{\sin\alpha}}$

$\qquad\qquad = \dfrac{\frac{1}{\cos\alpha}}{\frac{1}{\cos\alpha\sin\alpha}+\frac{\cos\alpha}{\cos\alpha\sin\alpha}}$

$\qquad\qquad = \dfrac{\frac{1}{\cos\alpha}}{\frac{1+\cos\alpha}{\cos\alpha\sin\alpha}}$

$\qquad\qquad = \dfrac{1}{\cos\alpha}\cdot\dfrac{\cos\alpha\sin\alpha}{1+\cos\alpha}$

$\qquad\qquad = \dfrac{\sin\alpha}{1+\cos\alpha}$

$\qquad\qquad = \tan\dfrac{\alpha}{2}$

We worked with the right side and arrived at the left side. Thus, the identity is verified.

Exercise Set 5.3

1. $\sin 2\theta = 2\sin\theta\cos\theta = 2\left(\dfrac{3}{5}\right)\left(\dfrac{4}{5}\right) = \dfrac{24}{25}$

3. $\tan 2\theta = \dfrac{2\tan\theta}{1-\tan^2\theta}$

$\qquad = \dfrac{2\left(\frac{3}{4}\right)}{1-\left(\frac{3}{4}\right)^2} = \dfrac{\frac{3}{2}}{1-\frac{9}{16}}$

$\qquad = \dfrac{\frac{3}{2}}{\frac{7}{16}} = \left(\dfrac{3}{2}\right)\left(\dfrac{16}{7}\right) = \dfrac{24}{7}$

Use this information to solve problem 5.

$\tan\alpha = \dfrac{7}{24} = \dfrac{y}{x}$

Because r is a distance it is positive.

$x^2 + y^2 = r^2$

$24^2 + 7^2 = r^2$

$576 + 49 = r^2$

$625 = r^2$

$r = 25$

$\sin\alpha = \dfrac{y}{r} = \dfrac{7}{25}$

$\cos\alpha = \dfrac{x}{r} = \dfrac{24}{25}$

5. $\cos 2\alpha = \cos^2\alpha - \sin^2\alpha$

$\qquad = \left(\dfrac{24}{25}\right)^2 - \left(\dfrac{7}{25}\right)^2 = \dfrac{576}{625} - \dfrac{49}{625}$

$\qquad = \dfrac{527}{625}$

7. $\sin\theta = \dfrac{15}{17} = \dfrac{y}{r}$

Because θ lies in quadrant II, x is negative.

$x^2 + y^2 = r^2$

$x^2 + 15^2 = 17^2$

$x^2 = 17^2 - 15^2 = 64$

$x = -\sqrt{64} = -8$

Now we use values for x, y, and r to find the required values.

a. $\sin 2\theta = 2\sin\theta\cos\theta$

$\qquad = 2\left(\dfrac{15}{17}\right)\left(-\dfrac{8}{17}\right) = -\dfrac{240}{289}$

b. $\cos 2\theta = \cos^2\theta - \sin^2\theta$

$\qquad = \left(-\dfrac{8}{17}\right)^2 - \left(\dfrac{15}{17}\right)^2 = \dfrac{64}{289} - \dfrac{225}{289}$

$\qquad = -\dfrac{161}{289}$

c. $\tan 2\theta = \dfrac{2\tan\theta}{1-\tan^2\theta}$

$\qquad = \dfrac{2\left(-\frac{15}{8}\right)}{1-\left(-\frac{15}{8}\right)^2} = \dfrac{-\frac{15}{4}}{1-\frac{225}{64}} = \dfrac{-\frac{15}{4}}{-\frac{161}{64}}$

$\qquad = \left(-\dfrac{15}{4}\right)\left(-\dfrac{64}{161}\right) = \dfrac{240}{161}$

9. $\cos\theta = \dfrac{24}{25} = \dfrac{x}{r}$

Because θ lies in quadrant IV, y is negative.

$x^2 + y^2 = r^2$

$24^2 + y^2 = 25^2$

$\qquad y^2 = 25^2 - 24^2 = 49$

$\qquad y = -\sqrt{49} = -7$

Now we use values for $x, y,$ and r to find the required values.

a. $\sin 2\theta = 2\sin\theta\cos\theta$

$\qquad = 2\left(-\dfrac{7}{25}\right)\left(\dfrac{24}{25}\right) = -\dfrac{336}{625}$

b. $\cos 2\theta = \cos^2\theta - \sin^2\theta$

$\qquad = \left(\dfrac{24}{25}\right)^2 - \left(-\dfrac{7}{25}\right)^2$

$\qquad = \dfrac{576}{625} - \dfrac{49}{625} = \dfrac{527}{625}$

c. $\tan 2\theta = \dfrac{2\tan\theta}{1-\tan^2\theta}$

$\qquad = \dfrac{2\left(-\frac{7}{24}\right)}{1-\left(-\frac{7}{24}\right)^2} = \dfrac{-\frac{7}{12}}{1-\frac{49}{576}} = \dfrac{-\frac{7}{12}}{\frac{527}{576}}$

$\qquad = \left(-\dfrac{7}{12}\right)\left(\dfrac{576}{527}\right) = -\dfrac{336}{527}$

11. $\cot\theta = 2 = \dfrac{-2}{-1} = \dfrac{x}{y}$

Because r is a distance, it is positive.

$r^2 = x^2 + y^2$

$r^2 = (-2)^2 + (-1)^2$

$r^2 = 5$

$\qquad r = \sqrt{5}$

Now we use values for $x, y,$ and r to find the required values.

a. $\sin 2\theta = 2\sin\theta\cos\theta$

$\qquad = 2\left(-\dfrac{1}{\sqrt5}\right)\left(-\dfrac{2}{\sqrt5}\right) = \dfrac{4}{5}$

b. $\cos 2\theta = \cos^2\theta - \sin^2\theta$

$\qquad = \left(-\dfrac{2}{\sqrt5}\right)^2 - \left(-\dfrac{1}{\sqrt5}\right)^2$

$\qquad = \dfrac{4}{5} - \dfrac{1}{5} = \dfrac{3}{5}$

c. $\tan 2\theta = \dfrac{2\tan\theta}{1-\tan^2\theta}$

$\qquad = \dfrac{2\left(\frac{1}{2}\right)}{1-\left(\frac{1}{2}\right)^2} = \dfrac{1}{1-\frac14} = \dfrac{1}{\frac34}$

$\qquad = (1)\left(\dfrac{4}{3}\right) = \dfrac{4}{3}$

13. $\sin\theta = -\dfrac{9}{41} = \dfrac{-9}{41} = \dfrac{y}{r}$

Because θ lies in quadrant III, x is negative.

$x^2 + y^2 = r^2$

$x^2 + (-9)^2 = 41^2$

$\qquad x^2 = 1600$

$\qquad x = -\sqrt{1600}$

$\qquad x = -40$

Now we use values for $x, y,$ and r to find the required values.

a. $\sin 2\theta = 2\sin\theta\cos\theta$

$\qquad = 2\left(-\dfrac{9}{41}\right)\left(-\dfrac{40}{41}\right) = \dfrac{720}{1681}$

b. $\cos 2\theta = \cos^2\theta - \sin^2\theta$

$\qquad = \left(-\dfrac{40}{41}\right)^2 - \left(-\dfrac{9}{41}\right)^2$

$\qquad = \dfrac{1600}{1681} - \dfrac{81}{1681}$

$\qquad = \dfrac{1519}{1681}$

c.
$$\tan 2\theta = \frac{2\tan\theta}{1-\tan^2\theta}$$
$$= \frac{2\left(\frac{9}{40}\right)}{1-\left(\frac{9}{40}\right)^2} = \frac{\frac{9}{20}}{1-\frac{81}{1600}} = \frac{\frac{9}{20}}{\frac{1519}{1600}}$$
$$= \left(\frac{9}{20}\right)\left(\frac{1600}{1519}\right) = \frac{720}{1519}$$

15. The given expression is the right side of the formula for $\sin 2\theta$ with $\theta = 15°$.
$$2\sin 15° \cos 15° = \sin(2\cdot 15°)$$
$$= \sin 30° = \frac{1}{2}$$

17. The given expression is the right side of the formula for $\cos 2\theta$ with $\theta = 75°$.
$$\cos^2 75° - \sin^2 75° = \cos(2\cdot 75°)$$
$$= \cos 150° = -\frac{\sqrt{3}}{2}$$

19. The given expression is the right side of the formula for $\cos 2\theta$ with $\theta = \frac{\pi}{8}$.
$$2\cos^2\frac{\pi}{8} - 1 = \cos\left(2\cdot\frac{\pi}{8}\right)$$
$$= \cos\frac{\pi}{4} = \frac{\sqrt{2}}{2}$$

21. The given expression is the right side of the formula for $\tan 2\theta$ with $\theta = \frac{\pi}{12}$.
$$\frac{2\tan\frac{\pi}{12}}{1-\tan^2\frac{\pi}{12}} = \tan\left(2\cdot\frac{\pi}{12}\right) = \tan\frac{\pi}{6} = \frac{\sqrt{3}}{3}$$

23.
$$\frac{2\tan\theta}{1+\tan^2\theta} = \frac{2\cdot\frac{\sin\theta}{\cos\theta}}{\frac{\cos^2\theta}{\cos^2\theta} + \frac{\sin^2\theta}{\cos^2\theta}}$$
$$= \frac{\frac{2\sin\theta}{\cos\theta}}{\frac{\cos^2\theta + \sin^2\theta}{\cos^2\theta}}$$
$$= \frac{\frac{2\sin\theta}{\cos\theta}}{\frac{1}{\cos^2\theta}}$$
$$= \frac{2\sin\theta}{\cos\theta}\cdot\frac{\cos^2\theta}{1}$$
$$= 2\sin\theta\cos\theta$$
$$= \sin 2\theta$$

25.
$$(\sin\theta + \cos\theta)^2 = \sin^2\theta + 2\sin\theta\cos\theta + \cos^2\theta$$
$$= \sin^2\theta + \cos^2\theta + 2\sin\theta\cos\theta$$
$$= 1 + 2\sin\theta\cos\theta$$
$$= 1 + \sin 2\theta$$

27.
$$\sin^2 x + \cos 2x = \sin^2 x + \cos^2 x - \sin^2 x$$
$$= \cos^2 x$$

29.
$$\frac{\sin 2x}{1-\cos 2x} = \frac{2\sin x\cos x}{1-\left(\cos^2 x - \sin^2 x\right)}$$
$$= \frac{2\sin x\cos x}{1-\cos^2 x + \sin^2 x}$$
$$= \frac{2\sin x\cos x}{\sin^2 + \sin^2 x}$$
$$= \frac{2\sin x\cos x}{2\sin^2 x}$$
$$= \frac{\cos x}{\sin x}$$
$$= \cot x$$

31.
$$\tan t\cos 2t = \frac{\sin t}{\cos t}\cdot\left(2\cos^2 t - 1\right)$$
$$= \frac{2\sin t\cos^2 t}{\cos t} - \frac{\sin t}{\cos t}$$
$$= 2\sin t\cos t - \tan t$$
$$= \sin 2t - \tan t$$

33.
$$\sin 4t = \sin(2t + 2t)$$
$$= \sin 2t\cos 2t + \cos 2t\sin 2t$$
$$= \cos 2t(\sin 2t + \sin 2t)$$
$$= \cos 2t\cdot 2\sin 2t$$
$$= \left(\cos^2 t - \sin^2 t\right)\cdot 2\cdot 2\sin t\cos t$$
$$= 4\sin t\cos^3 t - 4\sin^3 t\cos t$$

35. $6\sin^4 x$

$$= 6\left(\frac{1-\cos 2x}{2}\right)^2$$

$$= 6\left(\frac{1-2\cos 2x+\cos^2 2x}{4}\right)$$

$$= \frac{6-12\cos 2x+6\cos^2 2x}{4}$$

$$= \frac{3}{4}-3\cos 2x+\frac{3}{2}\cos^2 2x$$

$$= \frac{3}{4}-3\cos 2x+\frac{3}{2}\left(\frac{1+\cos 4x}{2}\right)$$

$$= \frac{3}{4}-3\cos 2x+\frac{3}{2}\left(\frac{1}{2}+\frac{\cos 4x}{2}\right)$$

$$= \frac{3}{4}-3\cos 2x+\frac{3}{4}+\frac{3}{4}\cos 4x$$

$$= \frac{9}{4}-3\cos 2x+\frac{3}{4}\cos 4x$$

37. $\sin^2 x\cos^2 x = \left(\frac{1-\cos 2x}{2}\right)\left(\frac{1+\cos 2x}{2}\right)$

$$= \frac{1-\cos^2 2x}{4}$$

$$= \frac{1}{4}-\frac{1}{4}\cos^2 2x$$

$$= \frac{1}{4}-\frac{1}{4}\left(\frac{1+\cos(2\cdot 2x)}{2}\right)$$

$$= \frac{1}{4}-\frac{1}{8}(1+\cos 4x)$$

$$= \frac{1}{4}-\frac{1}{8}-\frac{1}{8}\cos 4x$$

$$= \frac{1}{8}-\frac{1}{8}\cos 4x$$

39. Because $15°$ lies in quadrant I, $\sin 15° > 0$.

$$\sin 15° = \sin\frac{30°}{2}$$

$$= \sqrt{\frac{1-\cos 30°}{2}} = \sqrt{\frac{1-\frac{\sqrt{3}}{2}}{2}}$$

$$= \sqrt{\frac{2-\sqrt{3}}{4}} = \frac{\sqrt{2-\sqrt{3}}}{2}$$

41. Because $157.5°$ lies in quadrant II, $\cos 157.5° < 0$.

$$\cos 157.5° = \cos\frac{315°}{2} = -\sqrt{\frac{1+\cos 315°}{2}}$$

$$= -\sqrt{\frac{1+\frac{\sqrt{2}}{2}}{2}} = -\sqrt{\frac{2+\sqrt{2}}{4}}$$

$$= -\frac{\sqrt{2+\sqrt{2}}}{2}$$

43. Because $75°$ lies in quadrant I, $\tan 75° > 0$.

$$\tan 75° = \tan\frac{150°}{2} = \frac{1-\cos 150°}{\sin 150°}$$

$$= \frac{1-\left(-\frac{\sqrt{3}}{2}\right)}{\frac{1}{2}} = 2+\sqrt{3}$$

45. Because $\frac{7\pi}{8}$ lies in quadrant II, $\tan\frac{7\pi}{8} < 0$.

$$\tan\frac{7\pi}{8} = \tan\left(\frac{\frac{7\pi}{4}}{2}\right) = \frac{1-\cos\frac{7\pi}{4}}{\sin\frac{7\pi}{4}}$$

$$= \frac{1-\frac{\sqrt{2}}{2}}{-\frac{\sqrt{2}}{2}} = -\frac{2}{\sqrt{2}}+1$$

$$= -\sqrt{2}+1$$

47. $\sin\frac{\theta}{2} = \sqrt{\frac{1-\cos\theta}{2}}$

$$= \sqrt{\frac{1-\frac{4}{5}}{2}} = \sqrt{\frac{1}{10}}$$

$$= \frac{1}{\sqrt{10}} = \frac{\sqrt{10}}{10}$$

49. $\tan\frac{\theta}{2} = \frac{1-\cos\theta}{\sin\theta}$

$$= \frac{1-\frac{4}{5}}{\frac{3}{5}}$$

$$= \frac{1}{3}$$

Use this information to solve problem 51.

$\tan \alpha = \dfrac{7}{24} = \dfrac{y}{x}$

Because r is a distance, it is positive.

$r^2 = x^2 + y^2$

$r^2 = 24^2 + 7^2$

$r^2 = 625$

$r = 25$

$\sin \alpha = \dfrac{y}{r} = \dfrac{7}{25}$

$\cos \alpha = \dfrac{x}{r} = \dfrac{24}{25}$

$\sin \alpha = \dfrac{y}{r} = \dfrac{7}{25}, \quad \cos \alpha = \dfrac{x}{r} = \dfrac{24}{25}$

51. $\cos \dfrac{\alpha}{2} = \sqrt{\dfrac{1 + \cos \alpha}{2}} = \sqrt{\dfrac{1 + \frac{24}{25}}{2}} = \sqrt{\dfrac{49}{50}}$

$\qquad = \dfrac{7}{5\sqrt{2}} = \dfrac{7\sqrt{2}}{10}$

53. $2 \sin \dfrac{\theta}{2} \cos \dfrac{\theta}{2} = 2 \cdot \sqrt{\dfrac{1 - \cos \theta}{2}} \cdot \sqrt{\dfrac{1 + \cos \theta}{2}}$

$\qquad = 2 \sqrt{\dfrac{1 - \frac{4}{5}}{2}} \cdot \sqrt{\dfrac{1 + \frac{4}{5}}{2}}$

$\qquad = 2 \cdot \sqrt{\dfrac{1}{10}} \cdot \sqrt{\dfrac{9}{10}}$

$\qquad = 2 \cdot \dfrac{1}{\sqrt{10}} \cdot \dfrac{3}{\sqrt{10}}$

$\qquad = \dfrac{6}{10} = \dfrac{3}{5}$

55. $\tan \alpha = \dfrac{4}{3} = \dfrac{-4}{-3} = \dfrac{y}{x}$

Because r is a distance, it is positive.

$r^2 = x^2 + y^2$

$r^2 = (-4)^2 + (-3)^2$

$r^2 = 25$

$r = 5$

Because α lies in quadrant III, $\dfrac{\alpha}{2}$ lies in

quadrant II. Thus, $\sin \dfrac{\alpha}{2} > 0$, $\cos \dfrac{\alpha}{2} < 0$, and

$\tan \dfrac{\alpha}{2} < 0$.

a.

$\sin \dfrac{\alpha}{2} = \sqrt{\dfrac{1 - \cos \alpha}{2}} = \sqrt{\dfrac{1 - \left(-\dfrac{3}{5}\right)}{2}}$

$\qquad = \sqrt{\dfrac{\frac{8}{5}}{2}} = \sqrt{\dfrac{4}{5}} = \dfrac{2}{\sqrt{5}} = \dfrac{2\sqrt{5}}{5}$

b.

$\cos \dfrac{\alpha}{2} = -\sqrt{\dfrac{1 + \cos \alpha}{2}} = -\sqrt{\dfrac{1 + \left(-\dfrac{3}{5}\right)}{2}}$

$\qquad = -\sqrt{\dfrac{\frac{2}{5}}{2}} = -\sqrt{\dfrac{1}{5}} = -\dfrac{1}{\sqrt{5}} = -\dfrac{\sqrt{5}}{5}$

c.

$\tan \dfrac{\alpha}{2} = \dfrac{1 - \cos \alpha}{\sin \alpha} = \dfrac{1 - \left(-\dfrac{3}{5}\right)}{-\dfrac{4}{5}}$

$\qquad = \dfrac{\frac{8}{5}}{-\frac{4}{5}} = \dfrac{8}{-4} = -2$

57. $\sec\alpha = -\dfrac{13}{5} = \dfrac{13}{-5} = \dfrac{r}{x}$

Because α lies in quadrant II, y is positive.

$x^2 + y^2 = r^2$

$(-5)^2 + y^2 = (13)^2$

$\qquad y^2 = 144$

$\qquad\quad y = 12$

Because α lies in quadrant II, $\dfrac{\alpha}{2}$ lies in

quadrant I. Thus, $\sin\dfrac{\alpha}{2} > 0$, $\cos\dfrac{\alpha}{2} > 0$, and

$\tan\dfrac{\alpha}{2} > 0$.

a. $\sin\dfrac{\alpha}{2} = \sqrt{\dfrac{1-\cos\alpha}{2}} = \sqrt{\dfrac{1-\left(-\frac{5}{13}\right)}{2}}$

$\qquad = \sqrt{\dfrac{18}{26}} = \sqrt{\dfrac{9}{13}} = \dfrac{3}{\sqrt{13}}$

$\qquad = \dfrac{3\sqrt{13}}{13}$

b. $\cos\dfrac{\alpha}{2} = \sqrt{\dfrac{1+\cos\alpha}{2}} = \sqrt{\dfrac{1+\left(-\frac{5}{13}\right)}{2}}$

$\qquad = \sqrt{\dfrac{8}{26}} = \sqrt{\dfrac{4}{13}} = \dfrac{2}{\sqrt{13}}$

$\qquad = \dfrac{2\sqrt{13}}{13}$

c. $\tan\dfrac{\alpha}{2} = \dfrac{1-\cos\alpha}{\sin\alpha} = \dfrac{1-\left(-\frac{5}{13}\right)}{\frac{12}{13}}$

$\qquad = \dfrac{13+5}{12} = \dfrac{18}{12} = \dfrac{3}{2}$

59. $\sin^2\dfrac{\theta}{2} = \dfrac{1-\cos 2\left(\frac{\theta}{2}\right)}{2}$

$\qquad = \dfrac{1-\cos\theta}{2}\cdot\dfrac{\frac{1}{\cos\theta}}{\frac{1}{\cos\theta}}$

$\qquad = \dfrac{\frac{1-\cos\theta}{\cos\theta}}{\frac{2}{\cos\theta}}$

$\qquad = \dfrac{\frac{1}{\cos\theta}-\frac{\cos\theta}{\cos\theta}}{2\cdot\frac{1}{\cos\theta}}$

$\qquad = \dfrac{\sec\theta-1}{2\sec\theta}$

61. $\cos^2\dfrac{\theta}{2} = \dfrac{1+\cos 2\left(\frac{\theta}{2}\right)}{2}$

$\qquad = \dfrac{1+\cos\theta}{2}$

$\qquad = \dfrac{1+\cos\theta}{2}\cdot\dfrac{\frac{\sin\theta}{\cos\theta}}{\frac{\sin\theta}{\cos\theta}}$

$\qquad = \dfrac{\frac{\sin\theta}{\cos\theta}+\sin\theta}{2\cdot\frac{\sin\theta}{\cos\theta}}$

$\qquad = \dfrac{\tan\theta+\sin\theta}{2\tan\theta}$

$\qquad = \dfrac{\sin\theta+\tan\theta}{2\tan\theta}$

63. $\tan\dfrac{\alpha}{2} = \dfrac{\sin\alpha}{1+\cos\alpha}$

$\qquad = \dfrac{\sin\alpha}{1+\cos\alpha}\cdot\dfrac{\frac{1}{\cos\alpha}}{\frac{1}{\cos\alpha}}$

$\qquad = \dfrac{\frac{\sin\alpha}{\cos\alpha}}{\frac{1+\cos\alpha}{\cos\alpha}}$

$\qquad = \dfrac{\tan\alpha}{\frac{1}{\cos\alpha}+\frac{\cos\alpha}{\cos\alpha}}$

$\qquad = \dfrac{\tan\alpha}{\sec\alpha+1}$

65. $\dfrac{\sin x}{1-\cos x} = \dfrac{\sin x}{1-\cos x} \cdot \dfrac{\frac{1}{\sin x}}{\frac{1}{\sin x}}$

$= \dfrac{\frac{\sin x}{\sin x}}{\frac{1-\cos x}{\sin x}}$

$= \dfrac{1}{\tan\frac{x}{2}}$

$= \cot\dfrac{x}{2}$

67. $\tan\dfrac{x}{2} + \cot\dfrac{x}{2} = \dfrac{1-\cos x}{\sin x} + \dfrac{1}{\tan\frac{x}{2}}$

$= \dfrac{1-\cos x}{\sin x} + \dfrac{1}{\frac{\sin x}{1+\cos x}}$

$= \dfrac{1-\cos x}{\sin x} + \dfrac{1+\cos x}{\sin x}$

$= \dfrac{1-\cos x+1+\cos x}{\sin x}$

$= \dfrac{2}{\sin x} = 2\csc x$

69. Conjecture: The left side is equal to $\cos 2x$.

$\dfrac{\cot x - \tan x}{\cot x + \tan x} = \dfrac{\dfrac{\cos x}{\sin x} - \dfrac{\sin x}{\cos x}}{\dfrac{\cos x}{\sin x} + \dfrac{\sin x}{\cos x}}$

$= \dfrac{\dfrac{\cos x}{\sin x} \cdot \dfrac{\cos x}{\cos x} - \dfrac{\sin x}{\cos x} \cdot \dfrac{\sin x}{\sin x}}{\dfrac{\cos x}{\sin x} \cdot \dfrac{\cos x}{\cos x} + \dfrac{\sin x}{\cos x} \cdot \dfrac{\sin x}{\sin x}}$

$= \dfrac{\dfrac{\cos^2 x}{\sin x\cos x} - \dfrac{\sin^2 x}{\sin x\cos x}}{\dfrac{\cos^2 x}{\sin x\cos x} + \dfrac{\sin^2 x}{\sin x\cos x}}$

$= \dfrac{\cos^2 x - \sin^2 x}{\cos^2 x + \sin^2 x}$

$= \dfrac{\cos 2x}{1}$

$= \cos 2x$

71. Conjecture: The left side is equal to $\sin x + 1$.

$\left(\sin\dfrac{x}{2} + \cos\dfrac{x}{2}\right)^2 = \sin^2\dfrac{x}{2} + 2\sin\dfrac{x}{2}\cos\dfrac{x}{2} + \cos^2\dfrac{x}{2}$

$= 2\sin\dfrac{x}{2}\cos\dfrac{x}{2} + \sin^2\dfrac{x}{2} + \cos^2\dfrac{x}{2}$

$= \left[2\sin\dfrac{x}{2}\cos\dfrac{x}{2}\right] + \left[\sin^2\dfrac{x}{2} + \cos^2\dfrac{x}{2}\right]$

$= \sin\left(2\cdot\dfrac{x}{2}\right) + 1$

$= \sin x + 1$

73. Conjecture: The left side is equal to $\sec x$.

$\dfrac{\sin 2x}{\sin x} - \dfrac{\cos 2x}{\cos x} = \dfrac{2\sin x\cos x}{\sin x} - \dfrac{2\cos^2 x - 1}{\cos x}$

$= 2\cos x - \dfrac{2\cos^2 x}{\cos x} + \dfrac{1}{\cos x}$

$= 2\cos x - 2\cos x + \sec x$

$= \sec x$

75. Conjecture: The left side is equal to $2\csc 2x$.

$$\frac{\csc^2 x}{\cot x} = \frac{\dfrac{1}{\sin^2 x}}{\dfrac{\cos x}{\sin x}}$$

$$= \frac{1}{\sin^2 x} \cdot \frac{\sin x}{\cos x}$$

$$= \frac{1}{\sin x \cos x}$$

$$= \frac{2}{2\sin x \cos x}$$

$$= \frac{2}{\sin 2x}$$

$$= 2\csc 2x$$

77. Conjecture: The left side is equal to $\sin 3x$.

$$\sin x \left(4\cos^2 x - 1\right) = \sin x \left(2\cos^2 x + 2\cos^2 x - 1\right)$$

$$= \sin x \left(2\cos^2 x + \cos 2x\right)$$

$$= 2\sin x \cos^2 x + \sin x \cos 2x$$

$$= 2\sin x \cos x \cos x + \sin x \cos 2x$$

$$= \sin 2x \cos x + \sin x \cos 2x$$

$$= \sin(2x + x)$$

$$= \sin 3x$$

79. a.
$$\frac{v_o^2}{16}\sin\theta\cos\theta = \frac{v_o^2}{32} \cdot 2\sin\theta\cos\theta$$

$$= \frac{v_o^2}{32} \cdot \sin 2\theta$$

    b. $\sin\alpha$ is at a maximum in the interval $[0, 2\pi]$ when $\alpha = \dfrac{\pi}{2}$, so $\sin 2\theta$ is at a maximum when $2\theta = \dfrac{\pi}{2}$ or $\theta = \dfrac{\pi}{4}$.

81.
$$\theta = \frac{\pi}{4}$$

$$\sin\frac{\theta}{2} = \sqrt{\frac{1-\cos\theta}{2}}$$

$$= \sqrt{\frac{1-\cos\frac{\pi}{4}}{2}}$$

$$= \sqrt{\frac{1-\frac{\sqrt{2}}{2}}{2}}$$

$$= \sqrt{\frac{2-\sqrt{2}}{4}}$$

$$= \frac{\sqrt{2-\sqrt{2}}}{2}$$

$$\sin\frac{\theta}{2} = \frac{1}{M}$$

$$\frac{\sqrt{2-\sqrt{2}}}{2} = \frac{1}{M}$$

$$M = \frac{2}{\sqrt{2-\sqrt{2}}}$$

$$= \frac{2\sqrt{2-\sqrt{2}}}{2-\sqrt{2}}$$

$$= \frac{2\sqrt{2-\sqrt{2}}}{2-\sqrt{2}} \cdot \frac{2+\sqrt{2}}{2+\sqrt{2}}$$

$$= \frac{4\sqrt{2-\sqrt{2}} + 2\sqrt{2}\sqrt{2-\sqrt{2}}}{4-2}$$

$$= \frac{2\left(2\sqrt{2-\sqrt{2}} + \sqrt{2}\sqrt{2-\sqrt{2}}\right)}{2}$$

$$= 2\sqrt{2-\sqrt{2}} + \sqrt{2}\sqrt{2-\sqrt{2}}$$

$$= \sqrt{2-\sqrt{2}} \cdot \left(2+\sqrt{2}\right) \approx 2.6$$

95.

$$3 - 6\sin^2 x = 3 - 6\left(\frac{1-\cos 2x}{2}\right)$$

$$= 3 - 3(1 - \cos 2x)$$

$$= 3 - 3 + 3\cos 2x$$

$$= 3\cos 2x$$

97.

The graphs do not coincide.
Values for *x* may vary.

99.

a.   The graph appears to be the sum of 1 and 2 times the sine curve, $y = 1 + 2\sin x$. If you subtract 1 from the graph, it cycles through intercept, maximum, intercept, minimum, and back to intercept. Thus, $y = 1 + 2\sin x$ also describes the graph.

b. $$\frac{1 - 2\cos 2x}{2\sin x - 1} = \frac{1 - 2\left(1 - 2\sin^2 x\right)}{2\sin x - 1} = \frac{1 - 2 + 4\sin^2 x}{2\sin x - 1}$$

$$= \frac{4\sin^2 x - 1}{2\sin x - 1} = \frac{(2\sin x - 1)(2\sin x + 1)}{2\sin x - 1}$$

$$= 2\sin x + 1 = 1 + 2\sin x$$

This verifies our observation that $y = \dfrac{1 - 2\cos 2x}{2\sin x - 1}$ and $y = 1 + 2\sin x$ describe the same graph.

101.

a.   The graph appears to be the tangent of half the angle. It cycles from negative infinity through intercept to positive infinity. Thus, $y = \tan\dfrac{x}{2}$ also describes the graph.

b. $\tan\dfrac{x}{2} = \dfrac{1 - \cos x}{\sin x} = \dfrac{1}{\sin x} - \dfrac{\cos x}{\sin x} = \csc x - \cot x$

This verifies our observation that $y = \csc x - \cot x$ and $y = \tan\dfrac{x}{2}$ describe the same graph.

103. $\sin\left(2\sin^{-1}\dfrac{\sqrt{3}}{2}\right) = \sin\left(2 \cdot \dfrac{\pi}{3}\right)$

$$= \sin\dfrac{2\pi}{3}$$

$$= \dfrac{\sqrt{3}}{2}$$

105. $\cos^2\left[\dfrac{1}{2}\sin^{-1}\dfrac{3}{5}\right]$

Let $\theta = \sin^{-1}\dfrac{3}{5}$, then $\sin\theta = \dfrac{y}{r} = \dfrac{3}{5}$

Since θ is in quadrant I, x is positive.

$x^2 + y^2 = r^2$

$x^2 + 3^2 = 5^2$

$x^2 = 16$

$x = 4$

$\cos^2\left[\dfrac{1}{2}\sin^{-1}\dfrac{3}{5}\right] = \cos^2\left[\dfrac{1}{2}\theta\right]$

$$= \dfrac{1 + \cos\left(2\cdot\dfrac{1}{2}\theta\right)}{2}$$

$$= \dfrac{1 + \cos\theta}{2}$$

$$= \dfrac{1 + \dfrac{4}{5}}{2}$$

$$= \dfrac{1 + \dfrac{x}{r}}{2}$$

$$= \dfrac{9}{10}$$

107. Let $\alpha = \sin^{-1} x$ where $-\dfrac{\pi}{2} \le \alpha \le \dfrac{\pi}{2}$.

$\sin\alpha = x$

Because x is positive, $\sin\alpha$ is positive. Thus, α is in quadrant I. Using a right triangle in quadrant I with

$\sin\alpha = x = \dfrac{x}{1}$ the third side a can be found using the Pythagorean Theorem.

$a^2 + x^2 = 1^2$

$a^2 = 1 - x^2$

$a = \sqrt{1 - x^2}$

$\cos\alpha = \dfrac{\sqrt{1 - x^2}}{1} = \sqrt{1 - x^2}$

$\sin(2\sin^{-1} x) = \sin 2\alpha = 2x\sqrt{1 - x^2}$

Mid-Chapter 5 Check Point

1. $\cos x(\tan x + \cot x)$

$$= \cos x\left(\frac{\sin x}{\cos x} + \frac{\cos x}{\sin x}\right)$$

$$= \cos x\left(\frac{\sin x}{\cos x} \cdot \frac{\sin x}{\sin x} + \frac{\cos x}{\sin x} \cdot \frac{\cos x}{\cos x}\right)$$

$$= \cos x\left(\frac{\sin^2 x}{\sin x \cos x} + \frac{\cos^2 x}{\sin x \cos x}\right)$$

$$= \cos x\left(\frac{\sin^2 x + \cos^2 x}{\sin x \cos x}\right)$$

$$= \cos x\left(\frac{1}{\sin x \cos x}\right)$$

$$= \frac{\cos x}{\sin x \cos x}$$

$$= \frac{1}{\sin x}$$

$$= \csc x$$

2. $\dfrac{\sin(x+\pi)}{\cos\left(x+\dfrac{3\pi}{2}\right)} = \dfrac{-\sin x}{\cos\left((x+\pi)+\dfrac{\pi}{2}\right)}$

$$= \frac{-\sin x}{-\sin(x+\pi)}$$

$$= \frac{-\sin x}{\sin x}$$

$$= -1$$

$$= -\left(\sec^2 x - \tan^2 x\right)$$

$$= \tan^2 x - \sec^2 x$$

3. $(\sin\theta + \cos\theta)^2 + (\sin\theta - \cos\theta)^2$

$$= \sin^2\theta + 2\sin\theta\cos\theta + \cos^2\theta$$

$$\quad + \sin^2\theta - 2\sin\theta\cos\theta + \cos^2\theta$$

$$= \sin^2\theta + \cos^2\theta + \sin^2\theta + \cos^2\theta$$

$$= 1 + 1$$

$$= 2$$

4. $\dfrac{\sin t - 1}{\cos t} = \dfrac{\sin t - 1}{\cos t} \cdot \dfrac{\cot t}{\cot t}$

$$= \frac{\sin t \cot t - \cot t}{\cos t \cot t}$$

$$= \frac{\sin t \cdot \dfrac{\cos t}{\sin t} - \cot t}{\cos t \cot t}$$

$$= \frac{\cos t - \cot t}{\cos t \cot t}$$

5. $\dfrac{1 - \cos 2x}{\sin 2x} = \dfrac{1 - 2\cos^2 x - 1}{2\sin x \cos x}$

$$= \frac{2\cos^2 x}{2\sin x \cos x}$$

$$= \frac{\cos x}{\sin x}$$

$$= \tan x$$

6. $\sin\theta\cos\theta + \cos^2\theta$

$$= \cos\theta(\sin\theta + \cos\theta)$$

$$= \cos\theta(\sin\theta + \cos\theta) \cdot \frac{\csc\theta}{\csc\theta}$$

$$= \frac{\cos\theta(\sin\theta\csc\theta + \cos\theta\csc\theta)}{\csc\theta}$$

$$= \frac{\cos\theta\left(\sin\theta \cdot \dfrac{1}{\sin\theta} + \cos\theta \cdot \dfrac{1}{\sin\theta}\right)}{\csc\theta}$$

$$= \frac{\cos\theta(1 + \tan\theta)}{\csc\theta}$$

7. $\dfrac{\sin x}{\tan x} + \dfrac{\cos x}{\cot x} = \dfrac{\sin x}{\dfrac{\sin x}{\cos x}} + \dfrac{\cos x}{\dfrac{\cos x}{\sin x}}$

$$= \sin x \cdot \frac{\cos x}{\sin x} + \cos x \cdot \frac{\sin x}{\cos x}$$

$$= \cos x + \sin x$$

$$= \sin x + \cos x$$

8.
$$\sin^2 \frac{t}{2} = \left(\sin \frac{t}{2}\right)^2$$
$$= \left(\pm\sqrt{\frac{1-\cos t}{2}}\right)^2$$
$$= \frac{1-\cos t}{2}$$
$$= \frac{1-\cos t}{2} \cdot \frac{\tan t}{\tan t}$$
$$= \frac{\tan t - \cos t \tan t}{2\tan t}$$
$$= \frac{\tan t - \cos t \cdot \dfrac{\sin t}{\cos t}}{2\tan t}$$
$$= \frac{\tan t - \sin t}{2\tan t}$$

9.
$$\frac{1}{2}\left[\sin(\alpha+\beta)+\sin(\alpha-\beta)\right]$$
$$= \frac{1}{2}\left[\sin\alpha\cos\beta+\cos\alpha\sin\beta+ \right.$$
$$\left. \sin\alpha\cos\beta - \cos\alpha\sin\beta\right]$$
$$= \frac{1}{2}\left[2\sin\alpha\cos\beta\right]$$
$$= \sin\alpha\cos\beta$$

10.
$$\frac{1+\csc x}{\sec x}-\cot x = \frac{1+\dfrac{1}{\sin x}}{\dfrac{1}{\cos x}}-\frac{\cos x}{\sin x}$$
$$= \cos x\left(1+\frac{1}{\sin x}\right)-\frac{\cos x}{\sin x}$$
$$= \cos x+\frac{\cos x}{\sin x}-\frac{\cos x}{\sin x}$$
$$= \cos x$$

11.
$$\frac{\cot x-1}{\cot x+1} = \frac{\dfrac{\cot x}{\cot x}-\dfrac{1}{\cot x}}{\dfrac{\cot x}{\cot x}+\dfrac{1}{\cot x}}$$
$$= \frac{1-\tan x}{1+\tan x}$$

12.
$$2\sin^3\theta\cos\theta+2\sin\theta\cos^3\theta$$
$$= 2\sin\theta\cos\theta\left(\sin^2\theta+\cos^2\theta\right)$$
$$= 2\sin\theta\cos\theta$$
$$= \sin 2\theta$$

13.
$$\frac{\sin t+\cos t}{\sec t+\csc t} = \frac{\sin t+\cos t}{\dfrac{1}{\cos t}+\dfrac{1}{\sin t}}$$
$$= \frac{\sin t+\cos t}{\dfrac{1}{\cos t}\cdot\dfrac{\sin t}{\sin t}+\dfrac{1}{\sin t}\cdot\dfrac{\cos t}{\cos t}}$$
$$= \frac{\sin t+\cos t}{\dfrac{\sin t+\cos t}{\sin t\cos t}}$$
$$= (\sin t+\cos t)\frac{\sin t\cos t}{\sin t+\cos t}$$
$$= \sin t\cos t$$
$$= \sin t\frac{1}{\sec t}$$
$$= \frac{\sin t}{\sec t}$$

14.
$$\frac{\sec^2 x}{2-\sec^2 x} = \frac{\dfrac{\sec^2 x}{\sec^2 x}}{\dfrac{2}{\sec^2 x}-\dfrac{\sec^2 x}{\sec^2 x}}$$
$$= \frac{1}{2\cos^2 x-1}$$
$$= \frac{1}{\cos 2x}$$
$$= \sec 2x$$

15.
$$\tan(\alpha+\beta)\tan(\alpha-\beta)$$
$$= \tan(\alpha+\beta)\tan(\alpha-\beta)$$
$$= \frac{\tan\alpha+\tan\beta}{1-\tan\alpha\tan\beta}\cdot\frac{\tan\alpha-\tan\beta}{1+\tan\alpha\tan\beta}$$
$$= \frac{\tan^2\alpha-\tan^2\beta}{1-\tan^2\alpha\tan^2\beta}$$

16.
$$\frac{\sin\theta}{1-\cos\theta} = \frac{\sin\theta}{1-\cos\theta}\cdot\frac{1+\cos\theta}{1+\cos\theta}$$
$$= \frac{\sin\theta+\sin\theta\cos\theta}{1-\cos^2\theta}$$
$$= \frac{\sin\theta+\sin\theta\cos\theta}{\sin^2\theta}$$
$$= \frac{\sin\theta}{\sin^2\theta}+\frac{\sin\theta\cos\theta}{\sin^2\theta}$$
$$= \frac{1}{\sin\theta}+\frac{\cos\theta}{\sin\theta}$$
$$= \csc\theta+\cot\theta$$

17. $\dfrac{1}{\csc 2x} = \sin 2x$

$= 2\sin x \cos x$

$= 2\sin x \cos x \cdot \dfrac{\cos x}{\cos x}$

$= \dfrac{2\sin x \cos^2 x}{\cos x}$

$= \dfrac{2\sin x}{\cos x} \cdot \cos^2 x$

$= 2\tan x \cdot \dfrac{1}{\sec^2 x}$

$= \dfrac{2\tan x}{\sec^2 x}$

$= \dfrac{2\tan x}{1 + \tan^2 x}$

18. $\dfrac{\sec t - 1}{t \sec t} = \dfrac{\sec t - 1}{t \sec t} \cdot \dfrac{\cos t}{\cos t}$

$= \dfrac{\sec t \cos t - \cos t}{t \sec t \cos t}$

$= \dfrac{\dfrac{1}{\cos t} \cos t - \cos t}{t \dfrac{1}{\cos t} \cos t}$

$= \dfrac{1 - \cos t}{t}$

19. Use $\sin \alpha = \dfrac{3}{5} = \dfrac{y}{r}$ to find $\cos \alpha$ and $\tan \alpha$.

Because α is in Quadrant II, x is negative.

$x^2 + y^2 = r^2$

$x^2 + 3^2 = 5^2$

$x^2 = 16$

$x = -\sqrt{16}$

$x = -4$

Thus, $\cos \alpha = \dfrac{-4}{5} = -\dfrac{4}{5}$ and $\tan \alpha = \dfrac{-3}{4} = -\dfrac{3}{4}$.

Use $\cos \beta = \dfrac{-12}{13} = \dfrac{x}{r}$ to find $\sin \beta$ and $\tan \beta$.

Because β is in Quadrant III, x and y are negative.

$x^2 + y^2 = r^2$

$(-12)^2 + y^2 = 13^2$

$y^2 = 25$

$y = -\sqrt{25}$

$y = -5$

Thus, $\sin \beta = \dfrac{-5}{13} = -\dfrac{5}{13}$ and $\tan \beta = \dfrac{-5}{-12} = \dfrac{5}{12}$.

$\cos(\alpha - \beta) = \cos \alpha \cos \beta + \sin \alpha \sin \beta$

$= \left(-\dfrac{4}{5}\right)\left(-\dfrac{12}{13}\right) + \left(\dfrac{3}{5}\right)\left(-\dfrac{5}{13}\right)$

$= \dfrac{33}{65}$

20. In exercise 19 it was shown that

$\tan \alpha = -\dfrac{3}{4}$ and $\tan \beta = \dfrac{5}{12}$. Thus,

$\tan(\alpha + \beta) = \dfrac{\tan \alpha + \tan \beta}{1 - \tan \alpha \tan \beta}$

$= \dfrac{-\dfrac{3}{4} + \dfrac{5}{12}}{1 - \left(-\dfrac{3}{4}\right)\dfrac{5}{12}}$

$= -\dfrac{16}{63}$

21. In exercise 19 it was shown that

$\sin \alpha = \dfrac{3}{5}$ and $\cos \alpha = -\dfrac{4}{5}$. Thus,

$\sin 2\alpha = 2\sin \alpha \cos \alpha$

$= 2 \cdot \dfrac{3}{5}\left(-\dfrac{4}{5}\right)$

$= -\dfrac{24}{25}$

22. $\cos\beta = -\dfrac{12}{13}$.

Since β is in quadrant III, $\dfrac{\beta}{2}$ is in quadrant II.

The cosine is negative in quadrant II.

$$\cos\frac{\beta}{2} = -\sqrt{\frac{1+\cos\beta}{2}}$$

$$= -\sqrt{\frac{1+\left(-\dfrac{12}{13}\right)}{2}}$$

$$= -\sqrt{\frac{1}{26}}$$

$$= -\frac{1}{\sqrt{26}}$$

$$= -\frac{\sqrt{26}}{26}$$

23. $\sin\left(\dfrac{3\pi}{4} + \dfrac{5\pi}{6}\right)$

$$= \sin\frac{3\pi}{4}\cos\frac{5\pi}{6} + \cos\frac{3\pi}{4}\sin\frac{5\pi}{6}$$

$$= \left(\frac{\sqrt{2}}{2}\right)\left(-\frac{\sqrt{3}}{2}\right) + \left(-\frac{\sqrt{2}}{2}\right)\left(\frac{1}{2}\right)$$

$$= -\frac{\sqrt{6}}{4} - \frac{\sqrt{2}}{4}$$

$$= -\frac{\sqrt{6}+\sqrt{2}}{4}$$

24. $\cos^2 15° - \sin^2 15° = \cos(2\cdot 15°)$

$$= \cos 30°$$

$$= \frac{\sqrt{3}}{2}$$

25. $\cos\dfrac{5\pi}{12}\cos\dfrac{\pi}{12} + \sin\dfrac{5\pi}{12}\sin\dfrac{\pi}{12} = \cos\left(\dfrac{5\pi}{12} - \dfrac{\pi}{12}\right)$

$$= \cos\frac{4\pi}{12}$$

$$= \cos\frac{\pi}{3}$$

$$= \frac{1}{2}$$

26. $\tan 22.5° = \tan\dfrac{45°}{2}$

$$= \frac{\sin 45°}{1+\cos 45°}$$

$$= \frac{\dfrac{\sqrt{2}}{2}}{1+\dfrac{\sqrt{2}}{2}}$$

$$= \frac{\sqrt{2}}{2+\sqrt{2}}$$

$$= \frac{\sqrt{2}}{2+\sqrt{2}}\cdot\frac{2-\sqrt{2}}{2-\sqrt{2}}$$

$$= \frac{2\sqrt{2}-2}{4-2}$$

$$= \frac{2\sqrt{2}-2}{2}$$

$$= \sqrt{2}-1$$

Section 5.4

Check Point Exercises

1.　a.　$\sin 5x \sin 2x$

$$= \frac{1}{2}[\cos(5x-2x) - \cos(5x+2x)]$$

$$= \frac{1}{2}[\cos 3x - \cos 7x]$$

b.　$\cos 7x \cos x$

$$= \frac{1}{2}[\cos(7x-x) + \cos(7x+x)]$$

$$= \frac{1}{2}[\cos 6x + \cos 8x]$$

2.　a.　$\sin 7x + \sin 3x$

$$= 2\sin\left(\frac{7x+3x}{2}\right)\cos\left(\frac{7x-3x}{2}\right)$$

$$= 2\sin\left(\frac{10x}{2}\right)\cos\left(\frac{4x}{2}\right)$$

$$= 2\sin 5x \cos 2x$$

b.　$\cos 3x + \cos 2x$

$$= 2\cos\left(\frac{3x+2x}{2}\right)\cos\left(\frac{3x-2x}{2}\right)$$

$$= 2\cos\left(\frac{5x}{2}\right)\cos\left(\frac{x}{2}\right)$$

3.
$$\frac{\cos 3x - \cos x}{\sin 3x + \sin x} = \frac{-2\sin\left(\dfrac{3x+x}{2}\right)\sin\left(\dfrac{3x-2x}{2}\right)}{2\sin\dfrac{3x+x}{2}\cos\left(\dfrac{3x-x}{2}\right)}$$

$$= \frac{-2\sin 2x \sin x}{2\sin 2x \cos x}$$

$$= \frac{-\sin x}{\cos x}$$

$$= -\tan x$$

We worked with the left side and arrived at the right side. Thus, the identity is verified.

Exercise Set 5.4

1. The given formula can be used to change a <u>product</u> of two sines into the <u>difference</u> of two cosine expressions.

3. The given formula can be used to change a <u>product</u> of a sine and a cosine into the <u>sum</u> of two sine expressions.

5.
$$\sin 6x \sin 2x = \frac{1}{2}\left[\cos(6x-2x) - \cos(6x+2x)\right]$$

$$= \frac{1}{2}\left[\cos 4x - \cos 8x\right]$$

7.
$$\cos 7x \cos 3x = \frac{1}{2}\left[\cos(7x-3x) + \cos(7x+3x)\right]$$

$$= \frac{1}{2}\left[\cos 4x + \cos 10x\right]$$

9.
$$\sin x \cos 2x = \frac{1}{2}\left[\sin(x+2x) + \sin(x-2x)\right]$$

$$= \frac{1}{2}\left[\sin 3x + \sin(-x)\right]$$

$$= \frac{1}{2}\left[\sin 3x - \sin x\right]$$

11.
$$\cos\frac{3x}{2}\sin\frac{x}{2} = \frac{1}{2}\left[\sin\left(\frac{3x}{2}+\frac{x}{2}\right) - \sin\left(\frac{3x}{2}-\frac{x}{2}\right)\right]$$

$$= \frac{1}{2}\left[\sin\left(\frac{4x}{2}\right) - \sin\left(\frac{2x}{2}\right)\right]$$

$$= \frac{1}{2}\left[\sin 2x - \sin x\right]$$

13. The given formula can be used to change a <u>sum</u> of two sines into the <u>product</u> of a sine and a cosine expression.

15. The given formula can be used to change a <u>sum</u> of two cosines into the <u>product</u> of two cosine the expressions.

17.
$$\sin 6x + \sin 2x = 2\sin\left(\frac{6x+2x}{2}\right)\cos\left(\frac{6x-2x}{2}\right)$$

$$= 2\sin\left(\frac{8x}{2}\right)\cos\left(\frac{4x}{2}\right)$$

$$= 2\sin 4x \cos 2x$$

19.
$$\sin 7x - \sin 3x = 2\sin\left(\frac{7x-3x}{2}\right)\cos\left(\frac{7x+3x}{2}\right)$$

$$= 2\sin\left(\frac{4x}{2}\right)\cos\left(\frac{10x}{2}\right)$$

$$= 2\sin 2x \cos 5x$$

21.
$$\cos 4x + \cos 2x = 2\cos\left(\frac{4x+2x}{2}\right)\cos\left(\frac{4x-2x}{2}\right)$$

$$= 2\cos\left(\frac{6x}{2}\right)\cos\left(\frac{2x}{2}\right)$$

$$= 2\cos 3x \cos x$$

23.
$$\sin x + \sin 2x = 2\sin\left(\frac{x+2x}{2}\right)\cos\left(\frac{x-2x}{2}\right)$$

$$= 2\sin\left(\frac{3x}{2}\right)\cos\left(\frac{-x}{2}\right)$$

$$= 2\sin\frac{3x}{2}\cos\frac{x}{2}$$

25.
$$\cos\frac{3x}{2} + \cos\frac{x}{2} = 2\cos\left(\frac{\dfrac{3x}{2}+\dfrac{x}{2}}{2}\right)\cos\left(\frac{\dfrac{3x}{2}-\dfrac{x}{2}}{2}\right)$$

$$= 2\cos\left(\frac{4x}{4}\right)\cos\left(\frac{2x}{4}\right)$$

$$= 2\cos x \cos\frac{x}{2}$$

27. $\sin 75° + \sin 15°$

$= 2\sin\left(\dfrac{75° + 15°}{2}\right)\cos\left(\dfrac{75° - 15°}{2}\right)$

$= 2\sin(45°)\cos(30°)$

$= 2\left(\dfrac{\sqrt{2}}{2}\right)\left(\dfrac{\sqrt{3}}{2}\right)$

$= \dfrac{\sqrt{6}}{2}$

29. $\sin\dfrac{\pi}{12} - \sin\dfrac{5\pi}{12}$

$= 2\sin\left(\dfrac{\dfrac{\pi}{12} - \dfrac{5\pi}{12}}{2}\right)\cos\left(\dfrac{\dfrac{\pi}{12} + \dfrac{5\pi}{12}}{2}\right)$

$= 2\sin\left(-\dfrac{4\pi}{24}\right)\cos\left(\dfrac{6\pi}{24}\right)$

$= -2\sin\dfrac{\pi}{6}\cos\dfrac{\pi}{4}$

$= -2\left(\dfrac{1}{2}\right)\left(\dfrac{\sqrt{2}}{2}\right)$

$= -\dfrac{\sqrt{2}}{2}$

31. $\dfrac{\sin 3x - \sin x}{\cos 3x - \cos x} = \dfrac{2\sin\left(\dfrac{3x - x}{2}\right)\cos\left(\dfrac{3x + x}{2}\right)}{-2\sin\left(\dfrac{3x + x}{2}\right)\sin\left(\dfrac{3x - x}{2}\right)}$

$= \dfrac{2\sin\left(\dfrac{2x}{2}\right)\cos\left(\dfrac{4x}{2}\right)}{-2\sin\left(\dfrac{4x}{2}\right)\sin\left(\dfrac{2x}{2}\right)}$

$= \dfrac{2\sin x\cos 2x}{-2\sin 2x\sin x}$

$= -\dfrac{\cos 2x}{\sin 2x} = -\cot 2x$

33. $\dfrac{\sin 2x + \sin 4x}{\cos 2x + \cos 4x}$

$= \dfrac{2\sin\left(\dfrac{2x + 4x}{2}\right)\cos\left(\dfrac{2x - 4x}{2}\right)}{2\cos\left(\dfrac{2x + 4x}{2}\right)\cos\left(\dfrac{2x - 4x}{2}\right)}$

$= \dfrac{2\sin\left(\dfrac{6x}{2}\right)\cos\left(\dfrac{-2x}{2}\right)}{2\cos\left(\dfrac{6x}{2}\right)\cos\left(\dfrac{-2x}{2}\right)}$

$= \dfrac{2\sin 3x\cos(-x)}{2\cos 3x\cos(-x)}$

$= \dfrac{\sin 3x}{\cos 3x}$

$= \tan 3x$

35. $\dfrac{\sin x - \sin y}{\sin x + \sin y} = \dfrac{2\sin\left(\dfrac{x - y}{2}\right)\cos\left(\dfrac{x + y}{2}\right)}{2\sin\left(\dfrac{x + y}{2}\right)\cos\left(\dfrac{x - y}{2}\right)}$

$= \dfrac{\sin\left(\dfrac{x - y}{2}\right)}{\cos\left(\dfrac{x - y}{2}\right)} \cdot \dfrac{\cos\left(\dfrac{x + y}{2}\right)}{\sin\left(\dfrac{x + y}{2}\right)}$

$= \tan\dfrac{x - y}{2}\cot\dfrac{x + y}{2}$

37. $\dfrac{\sin x + \sin y}{\cos x + \cos y} = \dfrac{2\sin\left(\dfrac{x + y}{2}\right)\cos\left(\dfrac{x - y}{2}\right)}{2\cos\left(\dfrac{x + y}{2}\right)\cos\left(\dfrac{x - y}{2}\right)}$

$= \dfrac{\sin\left(\dfrac{x + y}{2}\right)}{\cos\left(\dfrac{x + y}{2}\right)}$

$= \tan\dfrac{x + y}{2}$

39. a. $y = \cos x$ also describes the graph.

b. $\dfrac{\sin x + \sin 3x}{2\sin 2x} = \dfrac{2\sin\left(\dfrac{x + 3x}{2}\right)\cos\left(\dfrac{x - 3x}{2}\right)}{2\sin 2x} = \dfrac{2\sin\left(\dfrac{4x}{2}\right)\cos\left(\dfrac{-2x}{2}\right)}{2\sin 2x}$

$= \dfrac{2\sin 2x\cos(-x)}{2\sin 2x} = \cos(-x) = \cos x$

41. a. $y = \tan 2x$ also describes the graph.

b. $\dfrac{\cos x - \cos 5x}{\sin x + \sin 5x} = \dfrac{-2\sin\left(\dfrac{x+5x}{2}\right)\sin\left(\dfrac{x-5x}{2}\right)}{2\sin\left(\dfrac{x+5x}{2}\right)\cos\left(\dfrac{x-5x}{2}\right)} = \dfrac{-2\sin\left(\dfrac{6x}{2}\right)\sin\left(\dfrac{-4x}{2}\right)}{2\sin\left(\dfrac{6x}{2}\right)\cos\left(\dfrac{-4x}{2}\right)}$

$= \dfrac{-2\sin 3x \sin(-2x)}{2\sin 3x \cos(-2x)} = \dfrac{-\sin(-2x)}{\cos 2x} = \dfrac{\sin 2x}{\cos 2x} = \tan 2x$

43. a. $y = -\cot 2x$ also describes the graph.

b. $\dfrac{\sin x - \sin 3x}{\cos x - \cos 3x} = \dfrac{2\sin\left(\dfrac{x-3x}{2}\right)\cos\left(\dfrac{x+3x}{2}\right)}{-2\sin\left(\dfrac{x+3x}{2}\right)\sin\left(\dfrac{x-3x}{2}\right)}$

$= \dfrac{2\sin(-x)\cos 2x}{-2\sin 2x \sin(-x)}$

$= \dfrac{\cos 2x}{-\sin 2x}$

$= -\cot 2x$

45. a. The low frequency is $l = 852$ cycles per second and the high frequency is $h = 1209$ cycles per second. The sound produced by touching 7 is described by $y = \sin 2\pi(852)t + \sin 2\pi(1209)t$, or

$y = \sin 1704\pi t + \sin 2418\pi t$.

b. $y = \sin 1704\pi t + \sin 2418\pi t$

$= 2\sin\left(\dfrac{1704\pi t + 2418\pi t}{2}\right) \cdot \cos\left(\dfrac{1704\pi t - 2418\pi t}{2}\right)$

$= 2\sin 2061\pi t \cdot \cos(-357\pi t)$

$= 2\sin 2061\pi t \cdot \cos 357\pi t$

53.

The graphs do not coincide.
Values for x may vary.

55.

$\sin x + \sin 3x = 2\sin\left(\dfrac{x+3x}{2}\right)\cos\left(\dfrac{x-3x}{2}\right)$

$= 2\sin 2x \cos(-x)$

$= 2\sin 2x \cos x$

We worked with the left side and arrived at the right side. Thus, the identity is verified.

57.

59. **a.**

Answers may vary.

b.

Answers may vary.

c.   When $x = \dfrac{\pi}{2}$,

$$\frac{\pi}{2} = 2\left(\frac{\sin\frac{\pi}{2}}{1} - \frac{\sin\left(2\cdot\frac{\pi}{2}\right)}{2} + \frac{\sin\left(3\cdot\frac{\pi}{2}\right)}{3} - \frac{\sin\left(4\cdot\frac{\pi}{2}\right)}{4} + \frac{\sin\left(5\cdot\frac{\pi}{2}\right)}{5} - \frac{\sin\left(6\cdot\frac{\pi}{2}\right)}{6} + \frac{\sin\left(7\cdot\frac{\pi}{2}\right)}{7} - \frac{\sin\left(8\cdot\frac{\pi}{2}\right)}{8} + \cdots \right)$$

$$= 2\left(1 - 0 + \left(-\frac{1}{3}\right) - 0 + \frac{1}{5} - 0 + \left(-\frac{1}{7}\right) + \cdots\right)$$

$$= 2 - \frac{2}{3} + \frac{2}{5} - \frac{2}{7} + \cdots$$

Multiplying both sides by 2 gives: $\pi = 4 - \dfrac{4}{3} + \dfrac{4}{5} - \dfrac{4}{7} + \cdots$

61.
$$\sin(\alpha + \beta) = \sin\alpha\cos\beta + \cos\alpha\sin\beta$$
$$\underline{-[\sin(\alpha - \beta) = \sin\alpha\cos\beta - \cos\alpha\sin\beta]}$$
$$\sin(\alpha + \beta) - \sin(\alpha - \beta) = 2\cos\alpha\sin\beta$$

Solve for $\cos\alpha\sin\beta$ by multiplying both sides by $\dfrac{1}{2}$: $\dfrac{1}{2}\big[\sin(\alpha + \beta) - \sin(\alpha - \beta)\big] = \cos\alpha\sin\beta$

63. $2\cos\dfrac{\alpha + \beta}{2}\cos\dfrac{\alpha - \beta}{2} = 2\cdot\dfrac{1}{2}\left[\cos\left(\dfrac{\alpha + \beta}{2} - \dfrac{\alpha - \beta}{2}\right) + \cos\left(\dfrac{\alpha + \beta}{2} + \dfrac{\alpha - \beta}{2}\right)\right]$

$$= \cos\left(\frac{2\beta}{2}\right) + \cos\left(\frac{2\alpha}{2}\right)$$

$$= \cos\beta + \cos\alpha$$

$$= \cos\alpha + \cos\beta$$

65.

$$\sin 2x + \sin 4x + \sin 6x = \sin 4x + (\sin 2x + \sin 6x)$$

$$= \sin 4x + 2\sin\left(\frac{2x+6x}{2}\right)\cos\left(\frac{2x-6x}{2}\right)$$

$$= \sin 4x + 2\sin\left(\frac{8x}{2}\right)\cos\left(\frac{-4x}{2}\right)$$

$$= \sin 4x + 2\sin 4x \cos(-2x)$$

$$= \sin 4x + 2\sin 4x \cos 2x$$

$$= \sin(2 \cdot 2x) + 2\sin 4x \cos 2x$$

$$= 2\sin 2x \cos 2x + 2\sin 4x \cos 2x$$

$$= 2\cos 2x(\sin 2x + \sin 4x)$$

$$= 2\cos 2x\left(2\sin\left(\frac{2x+4x}{2}\right)\cos\left(\frac{2x-4x}{2}\right)\right)$$

$$= 2\cos 2x \cdot 2\sin\left(\frac{6x}{2}\right)\cos\left(\frac{-2x}{2}\right)$$

$$= 2\cos 2x \cdot 2\sin 3x \cos(-x)$$

$$= 4\cos 2x \sin 3x \cos x$$

$$= 4\cos x \cos 2x \sin 3x$$

Section 5.5

Check Point Exercises

1.

$$5\sin x = 3\sin x + \sqrt{3}$$

$$5\sin x - 3\sin x = 3\sin x - 3\sin x + \sqrt{3}$$

$$2\sin x = \sqrt{3}$$

$$\sin x = \frac{\sqrt{3}}{2}$$

Because $\sin\dfrac{\pi}{3} = \dfrac{\sqrt{3}}{2}$, the solutions for $\sin x = \dfrac{\sqrt{3}}{2}$ in $[0, 2\pi)$ are

$$x = \frac{\pi}{3}$$

$$x = \pi - \frac{\pi}{3} = \frac{3\pi}{3} - \frac{\pi}{3} = \frac{2\pi}{3}.$$

Because the period of the sine function is 2π, the solutions are given by

$$x = \frac{\pi}{3} + 2n\pi \quad \text{or}$$

$$x = \frac{2\pi}{3} + 2n\pi$$

where n is any integer.

2.   The period of the tangent function is π. In the interval $[0, \pi)$, the only value for which the tangent function is

$\sqrt{3}$ is $\dfrac{\pi}{3}$. All the solutions to $\tan 2x = \sqrt{3}$ are given by

$$2x = \frac{\pi}{3} + n\pi$$

$$x = \frac{\pi}{6} + \frac{n\pi}{2}$$

where n is any integer. In the interval $[0, 2\pi)$, we obtain solutions as follows:

Let $n = 0$. $x = \dfrac{\pi}{6} + \dfrac{0\pi}{2}$

$$= \frac{\pi}{6}$$

Let $n = 1$. $x = \dfrac{\pi}{6} + \dfrac{1\pi}{2}$

$$= \frac{\pi}{6} + \frac{3\pi}{6} = \frac{2\pi}{3}$$

Let $n = 2$. $x = \dfrac{\pi}{6} + \dfrac{2\pi}{2}$

$$= \frac{\pi}{6} + \frac{6\pi}{6} = \frac{7\pi}{6}$$

Let $n = 3$. $x = \dfrac{\pi}{6} + \dfrac{3\pi}{2}$

$$= \frac{\pi}{6} + \frac{9\pi}{6} = \frac{5\pi}{3}$$

In the interval $[0, 2\pi)$, the solutions are $\dfrac{\pi}{6}, \dfrac{2\pi}{3}, \dfrac{7\pi}{6}$, and $\dfrac{5\pi}{3}$.

3.   The period of the sine function is 2π.

In the interval $[0, 2\pi)$, there are two values at which the sine function is $\dfrac{1}{2}$. One is $\dfrac{\pi}{6}$. The sine is positive in

quadrant II. Thus, the other value is $\pi - \dfrac{\pi}{6} = \dfrac{5\pi}{6}$. All the solutions to $\sin \dfrac{x}{3} = \dfrac{1}{2}$ are given by

$$\frac{x}{3} = \frac{\pi}{6} + 2n\pi$$

$$x = \frac{\pi}{2} + 6n\pi$$

or

$$\frac{x}{3} = \frac{5\pi}{6} + 2n\pi$$

$$x = \frac{5\pi}{2} + 6n\pi$$

where n is any integer. In the interval $[0, 2\pi)$, we obtain solutions as follows:

Let $n = 0$. $x = \dfrac{\pi}{2}$ or $x = \dfrac{5\pi}{2}$

If we let $n = 1$, we are adding 6π to each of these expressions. These values of x exceed 2π. Thus in the

interval $[0, 2\pi)$, the solution set is $\left\{ \dfrac{\pi}{2}, \dfrac{5\pi}{2} \right\}$

4.   The given equation is in quadratic form

$$2\sin x - 1 = 0 \qquad \text{or} \qquad \sin x - 1 = 0$$
$$2\sin x = 1 \qquad \qquad \qquad \sin x = 1$$
$$\sin x = \frac{1}{2}$$

$$2t^2 - 3t + 1 = 0 \text{ with } t = \sin x. \quad 2\sin^2 x - 3\sin x + 1 = 0$$
$$(2\sin x - 1)(\sin x - 1) = 0 \qquad x = \frac{\pi}{6} \qquad\qquad\qquad x = \frac{\pi}{2}$$

$$x = \pi - \frac{\pi}{6} = \frac{5\pi}{6}$$

The solutions in the interval $[0, 2\pi)$ are $\dfrac{\pi}{6}, \dfrac{\pi}{2}$, and $\dfrac{5\pi}{6}$.

5. $4\cos^2 x - 3 = 0$

$$\cos^2 x = \frac{3}{4}$$

$$\cos x = \pm\sqrt{\frac{3}{4}}$$

$$\cos x = \pm\frac{\sqrt{3}}{2}$$

$$\cos x = \frac{\sqrt{3}}{2} \qquad \text{or} \qquad \cos x = -\frac{\sqrt{3}}{2}$$
$$x = \frac{\pi}{6}, \frac{11\pi}{6} \qquad\qquad x = \frac{5\pi}{6}, \frac{7\pi}{6}$$

The solutions in the interval $[0, 2\pi)$ are $\dfrac{\pi}{6}, \dfrac{5\pi}{6}, \dfrac{7\pi}{6}$, and $\dfrac{11\pi}{6}$.

6. $$\sin x \tan x = \sin x$$
$$\sin x \tan x - \sin x = 0$$
$$\sin x(\tan x - 1) = 0$$
$$\sin x = 0 \qquad \text{or} \qquad \tan x - 1 = 0$$
$$x = 0 \quad x = \pi \qquad \tan x = 1$$
$$x = \frac{\pi}{4}$$
$$x = \pi + \frac{\pi}{4} = \frac{5\pi}{4}$$

The solutions in the interval $[0, 2\pi)$ are $0, \dfrac{\pi}{4}, \pi$, and $\dfrac{5\pi}{4}$.

7.
$$2\sin^2 x - 3\cos x = 0$$
$$2\left(1 - \cos^2 x\right) - 3\cos x = 0$$
$$2 - 2\cos^2 x - 3\cos x = 0$$
$$-2\cos^2 x - 3\cos x + 2 = 0$$
$$2\cos^2 x + 3\cos x - 2 = 0$$
$$\left(2\cos x - 1\right)\left(\cos x + 2\right) = 0$$
$$2\cos x - 1 = 0 \quad \text{or} \quad \cos x + 2 = 0$$

$$\cos x = \frac{1}{2} \qquad\qquad \cos x = -2$$

$$\qquad\qquad\qquad \cancel{\cos x = -2}$$

$$x = \frac{\pi}{3}, \frac{5\pi}{3} \qquad \text{This equation}$$
has no solution.

The solutions in the interval $[0, 2\pi)$ are $\frac{\pi}{3}$ and $\frac{5\pi}{3}$.

8.
$$\cos 2x + \sin x = 0$$
$$1 - 2\sin^2 x + \sin x = 0$$
$$-2\sin^2 x + \sin x + 1 = 0$$
$$2\sin^2 x - \sin x - 1 = 0$$
$$(2\sin x + 1)(\sin x - 1) = 0$$
$$2\sin x + 1 = 0 \qquad \text{or} \qquad \sin x - 1 = 0$$
$$2\sin x = -1 \qquad\qquad\qquad \sin x = 1$$

$$\sin x = -\frac{1}{2} \qquad\qquad\qquad x = \frac{\pi}{2}$$

$$x = \pi + \frac{\pi}{6} = \frac{7\pi}{6} \text{ or}$$
$$x = 2\pi - \frac{\pi}{6} = \frac{11\pi}{6}$$

The solutions in the interval $[0, 2\pi)$ are $\frac{\pi}{2}, \frac{7\pi}{6}$, and $\frac{11\pi}{6}$.

9.
$$\sin x \cos x = -\frac{1}{2}$$
$$2\sin x \cos x = -1$$
$$\sin 2x = -1$$

The period of the sine function is 2π. In the interval $[0, 2\pi)$, the sine function is -1 at $\frac{3\pi}{2}$. All the solutions to $\sin 2x$ are given by
$$2x = \frac{3\pi}{2} + 2n\pi$$
$$x = \frac{3\pi}{4} + n\pi,$$
where n is any integer. The solutions in the interval $[0, 2\pi)$ are obtained by letting $n = 0$ and $n = 1$. The solutions are $\frac{3\pi}{4}$ and $\frac{7\pi}{4}$.

10.
$$\cos x - \sin x = -1$$
$$(\cos x - \sin x)^2 = (-1)^2$$
$$\cos^2 x - 2\cos x \sin x + \sin^2 x = 1$$
$$\cos^2 x + \sin^2 x - 2\cos x \sin x = 1$$
$$1 - 2\cos x \sin x = 1$$
$$-2\cos x \sin x = 0$$
$$\cos x \sin x = 0$$

$$\cos x = 0 \quad \text{or} \quad \sin x = 0$$

$$x = \frac{\pi}{2} \qquad x = 0$$

$$x = \frac{3\pi}{2} \qquad x = \pi$$

We check these proposed solutions to see if any are extraneous.

Check 0: $\cos 0 - \sin 0 = -1$
$$1 - 0 = -1$$
$$1 = -1 \quad \text{False}$$

Check $\frac{\pi}{2}$: $\cos\frac{\pi}{2} - \sin\frac{\pi}{2} = -1$
$$0 - 1 = -1$$
$$-1 = -1 \quad \text{True}$$

Check π: $\cos\frac{\pi}{2} - \sin\frac{\pi}{2} = -1$
$$-1 - 0 = -1$$
$$-1 = -1 \quad \text{True}$$

Check $\frac{3\pi}{2}$: $\cos\frac{3\pi}{2} - \sin\frac{3\pi}{2} = -1$
$$0 - (-1) = -1$$
$$1 = -1 \quad \text{False}$$

The actual solutions in the interval $[0, 2\pi)$ are $\frac{\pi}{2}$ and π.

11. **a.** $\tan x = 3.1044$

Be sure calculator is in radian mode and find the inverse tangent of 3.1044. This gives the first quadrant reference angle.

$\theta = \tan^{-1} 3.1044 \approx 1.2592$

The tangent is positive in quadrants I and III thus,

$x \approx 1.2592 \quad \text{or} \quad x \approx \pi + 1.2592$

$\qquad\qquad\qquad\qquad x \approx 4.4008$

b. $\sin x = -0.2315$

Be sure calculator is in radian mode and find the inverse sine of $+0.2315$. This gives the first quadrant reference angle.

$\theta = \sin^{-1}(0.2315) \approx 0.2336$

The sine is negative in quadrants III and IV thus,

$x \approx \pi + 0.2336 \quad \text{or} \quad x \approx 2\pi - 1.2592$

$x \approx 3.3752 \qquad\qquad x \approx 6.0496$

12. $\cos^2 x + 5\cos x + 3 = 0$

Use the quadratic formula to solve for $\cos x$.

$$\cos x = \frac{-b \pm \sqrt{b^2 - 4ac}}{2a}$$

$$\cos x = \frac{-(5) \pm \sqrt{(5)^2 - 4(1)(3)}}{2(1)}$$

$$\cos x = \frac{-5 \pm \sqrt{13}}{2}$$

$\cos x \approx -0.6972$ or $\cos x \approx -4.3028$

~~$\cos x \approx -4.3028$~~

This equation

has no solution.

Be sure calculator is in radian mode and find the inverse cosine of $+0.6972$. This gives the first quadrant reference angle.

$\theta = \cos^{-1} 0.6972 \approx 0.7993$

The cosine is negative in quadrants II and III thus,

$x \approx \pi - 0.7993$ or $x \approx \pi + 0.7993$

$x \approx 2.3423$ $\qquad\qquad$ $x \approx 3.9409$

Exercise Set 5.5

1. $\cos\dfrac{\pi}{4} = \dfrac{\sqrt{2}}{2}$

   $\dfrac{\sqrt{2}}{2} = \dfrac{\sqrt{2}}{2}$ is true.

   Thus, $\dfrac{\pi}{4}$ is a solution.

3. $\sin\dfrac{\pi}{6} = \dfrac{\sqrt{3}}{2}$

   $\dfrac{1}{2} = \dfrac{\sqrt{3}}{2}$ is false.

   Thus, $\dfrac{\pi}{6}$ is not a solution.

5. $\cos\dfrac{2\pi}{3} = -\dfrac{1}{2}$

   $-\dfrac{1}{2} = -\dfrac{1}{2}$ is true.

   Thus, $\dfrac{2\pi}{3}$ is a solution.

7. $\tan\left(2 \cdot \dfrac{5\pi}{12}\right) = -\dfrac{\sqrt{3}}{3}$

   $\tan\dfrac{5\pi}{6} = -\dfrac{\sqrt{3}}{3}$

   $-\dfrac{\sqrt{3}}{3} = -\dfrac{\sqrt{3}}{3}$ is true.

   Thus, $\dfrac{5\pi}{12}$ is a solution.

9. $\cos\dfrac{\pi}{3} = \dfrac{\sqrt{3}}{2}$

   $\dfrac{1}{2} = \dfrac{\sqrt{3}}{2}$ is false.

   Thus, $\dfrac{\pi}{3}$ is not a solution.

11. $\sin x = \dfrac{\sqrt{3}}{2}$

Because $\sin\dfrac{\pi}{3} = \dfrac{\sqrt{3}}{2}$, the solutions

for $\sin x = \dfrac{\sqrt{3}}{2}$ in $[0, 2\pi)$ are

$x = \dfrac{\pi}{3}$

$x = \pi - \dfrac{\pi}{3} = \dfrac{3\pi}{3} - \dfrac{\pi}{3} = \dfrac{2\pi}{3}.$

Because the period of the sine function is 2π, the solutions are given by

$x = \dfrac{\pi}{3} + 2n\pi \quad$ or $\quad x = \dfrac{2\pi}{3} + 2n\pi$

where n is any integer.

13. $\tan x = 1$

Because $\tan\dfrac{\pi}{4} = 1$, the solution

for $\tan x = 1$ in $[0, \pi)$ is

$x = \dfrac{\pi}{4}.$

Because the period of the tangent function is π, the solutions are given by

$x = \dfrac{\pi}{4} + n\pi$

where n is any integer.

15. $\cos x = -\dfrac{1}{2}$

Because $\cos\dfrac{\pi}{3} = \dfrac{1}{2}$, the solutions

for $\cos x = -\dfrac{1}{2}$ in $[0, 2\pi)$ are

$x = \pi - \dfrac{\pi}{3} = \dfrac{3\pi}{3} - \dfrac{\pi}{3} = \dfrac{2\pi}{3}$

$x = \pi + \dfrac{\pi}{3} = \dfrac{3\pi}{3} + \dfrac{\pi}{3} = \dfrac{4\pi}{3}.$

Because the period of the cosine function is 2π, the solutions are given by

$x = \dfrac{2\pi}{3} + 2n\pi \quad$ or $\quad x = \dfrac{4\pi}{3} + 2n\pi$

where n is any integer.

17. $\tan x = 0$

Because $\tan 0 = 0$, the solution

for $\tan x = 0$ in $[0, \pi)$ is

$x = 0.$

Because the period of the tangent function is π, the solutions are given by

$x = 0 + n\pi = n\pi$

where n is any integer.

19. $2\cos x + \sqrt{3} = 0$

$2\cos x = -\sqrt{3}$

$\cos x = -\dfrac{\sqrt{3}}{2}$

Because $\cos\dfrac{\pi}{6} = \dfrac{\sqrt{3}}{2}$, the solutions

for $\cos x = -\dfrac{\sqrt{3}}{2}$ in $[0, 2\pi)$ are

$x = \pi - \dfrac{\pi}{6} = \dfrac{6\pi}{6} - \dfrac{\pi}{6} = \dfrac{5\pi}{6}$

$x = \pi + \dfrac{\pi}{6} = \dfrac{6\pi}{6} + \dfrac{\pi}{6} = \dfrac{7\pi}{6}.$

Because the period of the cosine function is 2π, the solutions are given by

$x = \dfrac{5\pi}{6} + 2n\pi \quad$ or $\quad x = \dfrac{7\pi}{6} + 2n\pi$

where n is any integer.

21. $\quad\quad 4\sin\theta - 1 = 2\sin\theta$

$4\sin\theta - 2\sin\theta = 1$

$2\sin\theta = 1$

$\sin\theta = \dfrac{1}{2}$

Because $\sin\dfrac{\pi}{6} = \dfrac{1}{2}$, the solutions

for $\sin\theta = \dfrac{1}{2}$ in $[0, 2\pi)$ are

$\theta = \dfrac{\pi}{6}$

$\theta = \pi - \dfrac{\pi}{6} = \dfrac{6\pi}{6} - \dfrac{\pi}{6} = \dfrac{5\pi}{6}.$

Because the period of the sine function is 2π, the solutions are given by

$\theta = \dfrac{\pi}{6} + 2n\pi \quad$ or $\quad \theta = \dfrac{5\pi}{6} + 2n\pi$

where n is any integer.

23.
$$3\sin\theta + 5 = -2\sin\theta$$
$$3\sin\theta + 2\sin\theta = -5$$
$$5\sin\theta = -5$$
$$\sin\theta = -1$$

Because $\sin\dfrac{\pi}{2} = 1$, the solutions

for $\sin\theta = -1$ in $[0, 2\pi)$ are

$$\theta = \pi + \frac{\pi}{2} = \frac{2\pi}{2} + \frac{\pi}{2} = \frac{3\pi}{2}$$
$$\theta = 2\pi - \frac{\pi}{2} = \frac{4\pi}{2} - \frac{\pi}{2} = \frac{3\pi}{2}.$$

Because the period of the sine function is 2π, the solutions are given by

$$\theta = \frac{3\pi}{2} + 2n\pi$$

where n is any integer.

25. The period of the sine function is 2π. In the

interval $[0, 2\pi)$, there are two values at which

the sine function is $\dfrac{\sqrt{3}}{2}$. One is $\dfrac{\pi}{3}$. The sine is

positive in quadrant II; thus, the other value is

$\pi - \dfrac{\pi}{3} = \dfrac{2\pi}{3}$. All the solutions to $\sin 2x = \dfrac{\sqrt{3}}{2}$

are given by

$$2x = \frac{\pi}{3} + 2n\pi \quad\text{or}\quad 2x = \frac{2\pi}{3} + 2n\pi$$
$$x = \frac{\pi}{6} + n\pi \qquad\qquad x = \frac{\pi}{3} + n\pi$$

Where n is any integer.
The solutions in the interval $[0, 2\pi)$ are
obtained by letting $n = 0$ and $n = 1$.

The solutions are $\dfrac{\pi}{6}, \dfrac{\pi}{3}, \dfrac{7\pi}{6}$, and $\dfrac{4\pi}{3}$.

27. The period of the cosine function is 2π. In the

interval $[0, 2\pi)$, there are two values at

which the cosine function is $-\dfrac{\sqrt{3}}{2}$. One is $\dfrac{5\pi}{6}$.

The cosine is negative in quadrant III; thus, the

other value is $2\pi - \dfrac{5\pi}{6} = \dfrac{7\pi}{6}$. All the solutions

to

$\cos 4x = -\dfrac{\sqrt{3}}{2}$ are given by

$$4x = \frac{5\pi}{6} + 2n\pi \quad\text{or}\quad 4x = \frac{7\pi}{6} + 2n\pi$$
$$x = \frac{5\pi}{24} + \frac{n\pi}{2} \qquad\qquad x = \frac{7\pi}{24} + \frac{n\pi}{2}$$

where n is any integer.
The solutions in the interval $[0, 2\pi)$ are
obtained by letting $n = 0$, $n = 1$, $n = 2$, and
$n = 3$.

The solutions are $\dfrac{5\pi}{24}, \dfrac{7\pi}{24}, \dfrac{17\pi}{24}, \dfrac{19\pi}{24},$

$\dfrac{29\pi}{24}, \dfrac{31\pi}{24}, \dfrac{41\pi}{24}$ and $\dfrac{43\pi}{24}.$

29. The period of the tangent function is π. In the

interval $[0, \pi)$, the only value for which the

tangent function is $\dfrac{\sqrt{3}}{3}$ is $\dfrac{\pi}{6}$.

All the solutions to $\tan 3x = \dfrac{\sqrt{3}}{3}$ are given by

$$3x = \frac{\pi}{6} + n\pi$$
$$x = \frac{\pi}{18} + \frac{n\pi}{3}$$

where n is any integer.
The solutions in the interval $[0, 2\pi)$ are
obtained by letting $n = 0$, $n = 1$, $n = 2$, $n = 3$, $n = 4$, and $n = 5$.
The solutions are

$\dfrac{\pi}{18}, \dfrac{7\pi}{18}, \dfrac{13\pi}{18}, \dfrac{19\pi}{18}, \dfrac{25\pi}{18},$ and $\dfrac{31\pi}{18}.$

31. The period of the tangent function is π. In the

interval $[0, \pi)$, the only value for which the

tangent function is $\sqrt{3}$ is $\dfrac{\pi}{3}$.

All the solutions to $\tan\dfrac{x}{2} = \sqrt{3}$ are given by

$$\frac{x}{2} = \frac{\pi}{3} + n\pi$$
$$x = \frac{2\pi}{3} + 2n\pi \quad\text{where } n \text{ is any integer. The}$$

solution in the interval $[0, 2\pi)$ is obtained by

letting $n = 0$. The only solution is $\dfrac{2\pi}{3}.$

33. The period of the sine function is 2π. In the interval $[0, 2\pi)$, the only value for which the sine function is -1 is $\dfrac{3\pi}{2}$.

All the solutions to $\sin\dfrac{2\theta}{3} = -1$ are given by

$$\frac{2\theta}{3} = \frac{3\pi}{2} + 2n\pi$$

$$\theta = \frac{9\pi}{4} + 3n\pi \quad \text{where } n \text{ is any integer. All}$$

values of θ exceed 2π or are less than zero. Thus, in the interval $[0, 2\pi)$ there is no solution.

35. The period of the secant function is 2π. In the interval $[0, 2\pi)$, there are two values at which the secant function is -2. One is $\dfrac{2\pi}{3}$. The secant is negative in quadrant III; thus, the other value is $2\pi - \dfrac{2\pi}{3} = \dfrac{4\pi}{3}$. All the solutions to

$\sec\dfrac{3\theta}{2} = -2$ are given by

$$\frac{3\theta}{2} = \frac{2\pi}{3} + 2n\pi \quad \text{or} \quad \frac{3\theta}{2} = \frac{4\pi}{3} + 2n\pi$$

$$\theta = \frac{4\pi}{9} + \frac{4n\pi}{3} \qquad \theta = \frac{8\pi}{9} + \frac{4n\pi}{3}$$

where n is any integer. The solutions in the interval $[0, 2\pi)$ are obtained by letting $n = 0$ and $n = 1$.

Since $\dfrac{20\pi}{9}$ is not in $[0, 2\pi)$, the solutions are

$$\frac{4\pi}{9}, \frac{8\pi}{9}, \text{ and } \frac{16\pi}{9}.$$

37. The period of the sine function is 2π. In the interval $[0, 2\pi)$, there are two values at which the sine function is $\dfrac{1}{2}$. One is $\dfrac{\pi}{6}$. The sine is positive in quadrant II; Thus, the other value is $\pi - \dfrac{\pi}{6} = \dfrac{5\pi}{6}$. All the solutions to

$\sin\left(2x + \dfrac{\pi}{6}\right) = \dfrac{1}{2}$ are given by

$$2x + \frac{\pi}{6} = \frac{\pi}{6} + 2n\pi$$

$$2x = 2n\pi$$

$$x = n\pi \qquad \text{or}$$

$$2x + \frac{\pi}{6} = \frac{5\pi}{6} + 2n\pi$$

$$2x = \frac{4\pi}{6} + 2n\pi$$

$$x = \frac{2\pi}{6} + n\pi$$

$$x = \frac{\pi}{3} + n\pi$$

where n is any integer. The solutions in the interval $[0, 2\pi)$ are obtained by letting $n = 0$ and $n = 1$.

The solutions are $0, \dfrac{\pi}{3}, \pi,$ and $\dfrac{4\pi}{3}$.

39.
$$2\sin^2 x - \sin x - 1 = 0$$
$$(2\sin x + 1)(\sin x - 1) = 0$$
$$2\sin x + 1 = 0 \qquad \text{or} \qquad \sin x - 1 = 0$$
$$2\sin x = -1 \qquad\qquad\qquad \sin x = 1$$
$$\sin x = -\frac{1}{2}$$
$$x = \frac{7\pi}{6} \quad x = \frac{11\pi}{6} \qquad\qquad x = \frac{\pi}{2}$$

The solutions in the interval $[0, 2\pi)$ are $\dfrac{\pi}{2}, \dfrac{7\pi}{6},$ and $\dfrac{11\pi}{6}$.

41. $2\cos^2 x + 3\cos x + 1 = 0$

$(2\cos x + 1)(\cos x + 1) = 0$

$2\cos x + 1 = 0$ or $\cos x + 1 = 0$

$\quad 2\cos x = -1$ $\cos x = -1$

$\quad\quad \cos x = -\dfrac{1}{2}$

$\quad x = \dfrac{2\pi}{3}$ $x = \dfrac{4\pi}{3}$ $x = \pi$

The solutions in the interval $[0, 2\pi)$ are $\dfrac{2\pi}{3}$, π,

and $\dfrac{4\pi}{3}$.

43. $\quad\quad 2\sin^2 x = \sin x + 3$

$\quad 2\sin^2 x - \sin x - 3 = 0$

$(2\sin x - 3)(\sin x + 1) = 0$

$2\sin x - 3 = 0$ or $\sin x + 1 = 0$

$\quad 2\sin x = 3$ $\sin x = -1$

$\quad\quad \sin x = \dfrac{3}{2}$ $x = \dfrac{3\pi}{2}$

$\sin x$ cannot be greater than 1.

The solution in the interval $[0, 2\pi)$ is $\dfrac{3\pi}{2}$.

45. $\quad\quad\quad \sin^2\theta - 1 = 0$

$(\sin\theta - 1)(\sin\theta + 1) = 0$

$\sin\theta - 1 = 0$ or $\sin\theta + 1 = 0$

$\quad \sin\theta = 1$ $\sin\theta = -1$

$\quad\quad \theta = \dfrac{\pi}{2}$ $\theta = \dfrac{3\pi}{2}$

The solutions in the interval $[0, 2\pi)$ are

$\dfrac{\pi}{2}$ and $\dfrac{3\pi}{2}$.

47. $\quad\quad\quad 4\cos^2 x - 1 = 0$

$(2\cos x + 1)(2\cos x - 1) = 1$

$2\cos x + 1 = 0$ or $2\cos x - 1 = 0$

$\quad \cos x = -\dfrac{1}{2}$ $\cos x = \dfrac{1}{2}$

$\quad x = \dfrac{2\pi}{3}, \dfrac{4\pi}{3}$ $x = \dfrac{\pi}{3}, \dfrac{5\pi}{3}$

The solutions in the interval $[0, 2\pi)$ are

$\dfrac{\pi}{3}, \dfrac{2\pi}{3}, \dfrac{4\pi}{3}$, and $\dfrac{5\pi}{3}$.

49. $9\tan^2 x - 3 = 0$

$\quad \tan^2 x = \dfrac{3}{9}$

$\quad \tan x = \pm\sqrt{\dfrac{3}{9}}$

$\quad \tan x = \pm\dfrac{\sqrt{3}}{3}$

$\tan x = \dfrac{\sqrt{3}}{3}$ or $\tan x = -\dfrac{\sqrt{3}}{3}$

$\quad x = \dfrac{\pi}{6}, \dfrac{7\pi}{6}$ $x = \dfrac{5\pi}{6}, \dfrac{11\pi}{6}$

The solutions in the interval $[0, 2\pi)$ are

$\dfrac{\pi}{6}, \dfrac{5\pi}{6}, \dfrac{7\pi}{6}$, and $\dfrac{11\pi}{6}$.

51. $\sec^2 x - 2 = 0$

$\quad \sec^2 x = 2$

$\quad \cos^2 x = \dfrac{1}{2}$

$\quad \cos x = \pm\sqrt{\dfrac{1}{2}}$

$\quad \cos x = \pm\dfrac{\sqrt{2}}{2}$

$\cos x = \dfrac{\sqrt{2}}{2}$ or $\cos x = -\dfrac{\sqrt{2}}{2}$

$\quad x = \dfrac{\pi}{4}, \dfrac{7\pi}{4}$ $x = \dfrac{3\pi}{4}, \dfrac{5\pi}{4}$

The solutions in the interval $[0, 2\pi)$ are

$\dfrac{\pi}{4}, \dfrac{3\pi}{4}, \dfrac{5\pi}{4}$, and $\dfrac{7\pi}{4}$.

53. $(\tan x - 1)(\cos x + 1) = 0$

$\tan x - 1 = 0$ or $\cos x + 1 = 0$

$\quad \tan x = 1$ $\cos x = -1$

$\quad x = \dfrac{\pi}{4}$ $x = \dfrac{5\pi}{4}$ $x = \pi$

The solutions in the interval $[0, 2\pi)$ are

$\dfrac{\pi}{4}, \pi$, and $\dfrac{5\pi}{4}$.

55. $\left(2\cos x + \sqrt{3}\right)(2\sin x + 1) = 0$

$2\cos x + \sqrt{3} = 0$ or $2\sin x + 1 = 0$

$\qquad 2\cos x = -\sqrt{3} \qquad\qquad 2\sin x = -1$

$\qquad\qquad \cos x = -\dfrac{\sqrt{3}}{2} \qquad\qquad \sin x = -\dfrac{1}{2}$

$x = \dfrac{5\pi}{6} \quad x = \dfrac{7\pi}{6} \qquad\qquad x = \dfrac{7\pi}{6} \quad x = \dfrac{11\pi}{6}$

The solutions in the interval $[0, 2\pi)$ are

$\dfrac{5\pi}{6}, \dfrac{7\pi}{6},$ and $\dfrac{11\pi}{6}.$

57. $\cot x(\tan x - 1) = 0$

$\cot x = 0$ or $\tan x - 1 = 0$

$\qquad\qquad\qquad\qquad \tan x = 1$

$x = \dfrac{\pi}{2} \quad x = \dfrac{3\pi}{2} \quad x = \dfrac{\pi}{4} \quad x = \dfrac{5\pi}{4}$

The solutions in the interval $[0, 2\pi)$ are

$\dfrac{\pi}{4}$ and $\dfrac{5\pi}{4}$ since tan is undefined for

$\dfrac{\pi}{2}$ and $\dfrac{3\pi}{2}.$

59. $\sin x + 2\sin x \cos x = 0$

$\sin x(1 + 2\cos x) = 0$

$\sin x = 0$ or $1 + 2\cos x = 0$

$\qquad\qquad\qquad\qquad 2\cos x = -1$

$\qquad\qquad\qquad\qquad \cos x = -\dfrac{1}{2}$

$x = 0 \quad x = \pi \quad x = \dfrac{2\pi}{3} \quad x = \dfrac{4\pi}{3}$

The solutions in the interval $[0, 2\pi)$ are

$0, \dfrac{2\pi}{3}, \pi,$ and $\dfrac{4\pi}{3}.$

61. $\tan^2 x \cos x = \tan^2 x$

$\tan^2 x \cos x - \tan^2 x = 0$

$\tan^2 x(\cos x - 1) = 0$

$\tan^2 x = 0$ or $\cos x - 1 = 0$

$\tan x = 0 \qquad\qquad\qquad \cos x = 1$

$\quad x = 0 \quad x = \pi \qquad\qquad x = 0$

The solutions in the interval $[0, 2\pi)$ are 0 and π.

63. $2\cos^2 x + \sin x - 1 = 0$

$2\left(1 - \sin^2 x\right) + \sin x - 1 = 0$

$2 - 2\sin^2 x + \sin x - 1 = 0$

$-2\sin^2 x + \sin x + 1 = 0$

$2\sin^2 x - \sin x - 1 = 0$

$(2\sin x + 1)(\sin x - 1) = 0$

$2\sin x + 1 = 0$ or $\sin x - 1 = 0$

$2\sin x = -1 \qquad\qquad \sin x = 1$

$\sin x = -\dfrac{1}{2}$

$x = \dfrac{7\pi}{6} \quad x = \dfrac{11\pi}{6} \qquad\qquad x = \dfrac{\pi}{2}$

The solutions in the interval $[0, 2\pi)$ are

$\dfrac{\pi}{2}, \dfrac{7\pi}{6},$ and $\dfrac{11\pi}{6}.$

65.
$\sin^2 x - 2\cos x - 2 = 0$

$1 - \cos^2 x - 2\cos x - 2 = 0$

$-\cos^2 x - 2\cos x - 1 = 0$

$\cos^2 x + 2\cos x + 1 = 0$

$(\cos x + 1)(\cos x + 1) = 0$

$\cos x + 1 = 0$

$\cos x = -1$

$x = \pi$

The solution in the interval $[0, 2\pi)$ is π.

67. $4\cos^2 x = 5 - 4\sin x$

$4\cos^2 x + 4\sin x - 5 = 0$

$4\left(1 - \sin^2 x\right) + 4\sin x - 5 = 0$

$4 - 4\sin^2 x + 4\sin x - 5 = 0$

$-4\sin^2 x + 4\sin x - 1 = 0$

$4\sin^2 x - 4\sin x + 1 = 0$

$(2\sin x - 1)(2\sin x - 1) = 0$

$2\sin x - 1 = 0$

$2\sin x = 1$

$\sin x = \dfrac{1}{2}$

$x = \dfrac{\pi}{6} \quad x = \dfrac{5\pi}{6}$

The solutions in the interval $[0, 2\pi)$ are

$\dfrac{\pi}{6}$ and $\dfrac{5\pi}{6}.$

69.
$$\sin 2x = \cos x$$
$$2\sin x \cos x = \cos x$$
$$2\sin x \cos x - \cos x = 0$$
$$\cos x (2\sin x - 1) = 0$$
$$\cos x = 0 \quad \text{or} \quad 2\sin x - 1 = 0$$
$$2\sin x = 1$$
$$\sin x = \frac{1}{2}$$
$$x = \frac{\pi}{2} \quad x = \frac{3\pi}{2} \qquad x = \frac{\pi}{6} \quad x = \frac{5\pi}{6}$$

The solutions in the interval $[0, 2\pi)$ are

$$\frac{\pi}{6}, \frac{\pi}{2}, \frac{5\pi}{6}, \text{and } \frac{3\pi}{2}.$$

71.
$$\cos 2x = \cos x$$
$$2\cos^2 x - 1 = \cos x$$
$$2\cos^2 x - 1 - \cos x = 0$$
$$2\cos^2 x - \cos x - 1 = 0$$
$$(2\cos x + 1)(\cos x - 1) = 0$$
$$2\cos x + 1 = 0 \qquad\qquad \text{or} \qquad \cos x - 1 = 0$$
$$2\cos x = -1 \qquad\qquad\qquad\qquad \cos x = 1$$
$$\cos x = -\frac{1}{2} \qquad\qquad\qquad\quad \cos x = 1$$
$$x = \frac{2\pi}{3} \quad x = \frac{4\pi}{3} \qquad\qquad\qquad x = 0$$

The solutions in the interval $[0, 2\pi)$ are

$$0, \frac{2\pi}{3}, \text{and } \frac{4\pi}{3}.$$

73.
$$\cos 2x + 5\cos x + 3 = 0$$
$$2\cos^2 x - 1 + 5\cos x + 3 = 0$$
$$2\cos^2 x + 5\cos x + 2 = 0$$
$$(2\cos x + 1)(\cos x + 2) = 0$$
$$2\cos x + 1 = 0 \quad \text{or} \quad \cos x + 2 = 0$$
$$2\cos x = -1 \qquad\qquad \cos x = -2$$
$$\cos x = -\frac{1}{2}$$
$$x = \frac{2\pi}{3} \quad x = \frac{4\pi}{3} \qquad \begin{array}{l}\cos x \text{ cannot} \\ \text{be less than } -1\end{array}$$

The solutions in the interval $[0, 2\pi)$ are

$$\frac{2\pi}{3} \text{ and } \frac{4\pi}{3}.$$

75.
$$\sin x \cos x = \frac{\sqrt{2}}{4}$$
$$2\sin x \cos x = \frac{\sqrt{2}}{2}$$
$$\sin 2x = \frac{\sqrt{2}}{2}$$

The period of the sine function is 2π. In the interval $[0, 2\pi)$, there are two values at which the sine function is $\frac{\sqrt{2}}{2}$. One is $\frac{\pi}{4}$. The sine is positive in quadrant II; thus, the other value is $\pi - \frac{\pi}{4} = \frac{3\pi}{4}$. All the solutions to $\sin 2x = \frac{\sqrt{2}}{2}$ are given by

$$2x = \frac{\pi}{4} + 2n\pi \quad \text{or} \quad 2x = \frac{3\pi}{4} + 2n\pi$$
$$x = \frac{\pi}{8} + n\pi \qquad\qquad x = \frac{3\pi}{8} + n\pi$$

where n is any integer.
The solutions in the interval $[0, 2\pi)$ are obtained by letting $n = 0$ and $n = 1$.

The solutions are $\frac{\pi}{8}, \frac{3\pi}{8}, \frac{9\pi}{8}, \text{and } \frac{11\pi}{8}$.

77.
$$\sin x + \cos x = 1$$
$$(\sin x + \cos x)^2 = 1^2$$
$$\sin^2 x + 2\sin x \cos x + \cos^2 x = 1$$
$$\sin^2 x + \cos^2 x + 2\sin x \cos x = 1$$
$$1 + 2\sin x \cos x = 1$$
$$2\sin x \cos x = 0$$
$$\sin x \cos x = 0$$

$$\sin x = 0 \quad \text{or} \quad \cos x = 0$$
$$x = 0 \qquad\qquad x = \frac{\pi}{2}$$
$$x = \pi \qquad\qquad x = \frac{3\pi}{2}$$

After checking these proposed solutions, the actual solutions in the interval $[0, 2\pi)$ are 0 and $\frac{\pi}{2}$.

79.

$$\sin\left(x+\frac{\pi}{4}\right)+\sin\left(x-\frac{\pi}{4}\right)=1$$

$$\frac{1}{2}\left[\sin\left(x+\frac{\pi}{4}\right)+\sin\left(x-\frac{\pi}{4}\right)\right]=1\cdot\frac{1}{2}$$

$$\sin x\cos\frac{\pi}{4}=\frac{1}{2}$$

$$\sin x\cdot\frac{\sqrt{2}}{2}=\frac{1}{2}$$

$$\sin x=\frac{1}{\sqrt{2}}$$

$$\sin x=\frac{\sqrt{2}}{2}$$

$$x=\frac{\pi}{4}\quad\text{or}\quad x=\frac{3\pi}{4}$$

The solutions in the interval $[0,2\pi)$ are
$\frac{\pi}{4}$ and $\frac{3\pi}{4}$.

81. $\sin 2x\cos x+\cos 2x\sin x=\dfrac{\sqrt{2}}{2}$

$$\sin(2x+x)=\frac{\sqrt{2}}{2}$$

$$\sin 3x=\frac{\sqrt{2}}{2}$$

The period of the sine function is 2π. In the interval $[0,2\pi)$, there are two values at which

the sine function is $\dfrac{\sqrt{2}}{2}$. One is $\dfrac{\pi}{4}$. The sine function is positive in quadrant II; thus, the other

value is $\pi-\dfrac{\pi}{4}=\dfrac{3\pi}{4}$. All the solutions to

$\sin 3x=\dfrac{\sqrt{2}}{2}$ are given by

$$3x=\frac{\pi}{4}+2n\pi\quad\text{or}\quad 3x=\frac{3\pi}{4}+2n\pi$$

$$x=\frac{\pi}{12}+\frac{2n\pi}{3}\qquad\qquad x=\frac{\pi}{4}+\frac{2n\pi}{3}$$

where n is any integer. The solutions in the interval $[0,2\pi)$ are obtained by letting $n=0$, n
$=1$, and $n=2$. The solutions are
$\dfrac{\pi}{12},\dfrac{\pi}{4},\dfrac{3\pi}{4},\dfrac{11\pi}{12},\dfrac{17\pi}{12}$, and $\dfrac{19\pi}{12}$.

83.

$$\tan x+\sec x=1$$

$$\tan x-1=-\sec x$$

$$(\tan x-1)^2=(-\sec x)^2$$

$$\tan^2 x-2\tan x+1=\sec^2 x$$

$$\tan^2 x-2\tan x+1=1+\tan^2 x$$

$$-2\tan x=0$$

$$\tan x=0$$

$$x=0\quad x=\pi$$

We check these proposed solutions to see if any are extraneous.

Check 0: $\tan 0\;+\;\sec 0\;\overset{?}{=}\;1$

$\qquad\qquad 0\;+\;1\qquad\overset{?}{=}\;1$ True

Check π : $\tan\pi\;+\;\sec\pi\;\overset{?}{=}\;1$

$\qquad\qquad 0\qquad+\;(-1)\quad\overset{?}{=}\;1$ False

The actual solution in the interval $[0,2\pi)$ is 0.

85. $\sin x=0.8246$

Be sure calculator is in radian mode and find the inverse sine of 0.8246. This gives the first quadrant reference angle.

$\theta=\sin^{-1}0.8246\approx 0.9695$

The sine is positive in quadrants I and II thus,

$x\approx 0.9695\quad\text{or}\quad x\approx\pi-0.9695$

$\qquad\qquad\qquad\qquad x\approx 2.1721$

87. $\cos x=-\dfrac{2}{5}$

Be sure calculator is in radian mode and find the inverse cosine of $+\dfrac{2}{5}$. This gives the first quadrant reference angle.

$\theta=\cos^{-1}\dfrac{2}{5}\approx 1.1593$

The cosine is negative in quadrants II and III thus,

$x\approx\pi-1.1593\quad\text{or}\quad x\approx\pi+1.1593$

$x\approx 1.9823\qquad\qquad\quad x\approx 4.3009$

89. $\tan x = -3$

Be sure calculator is in radian mode and find the inverse tangent of $+3$. This gives the first quadrant reference angle.

$\theta = \tan^{-1} 3 \approx 1.2490$

The tangent is negative in quadrants II and IV thus,

$x \approx \pi - 1.2490$ or $x \approx 2\pi - 1.2490$

$x \approx 1.8925$ $x \approx 5.0341$

91. $\cos^2 x - \cos x - 1 = 0$

Use the quadratic formula to solve for $\cos x$.

$\cos x = \dfrac{-b \pm \sqrt{b^2 - 4ac}}{2a}$

$\cos x = \dfrac{-(-1) \pm \sqrt{(-1)^2 - 4(1)(-1)}}{2(1)}$

$\cos x = \dfrac{1 \pm \sqrt{5}}{2}$

$\cos x \approx -0.6180$ or $\cos x \approx 1.6180$

$\cancel{\cos x \approx 1.6180}$

This equation

has no solution.

Be sure calculator is in radian mode and find the inverse cosine of $+0.6180$. This gives the first quadrant reference angle.

$\theta = \cos^{-1} 0.6180 \approx 0.9046$

The cosine is negative in quadrants II and III thus,

$x \approx \pi - 0.9046$ or $x \approx \pi + 0.9046$

$x \approx 2.2370$ $x \approx 4.0462$

93. $4\tan^2 x - 8\tan x + 3 = 0$

$(2\tan x - 1)(2\tan x - 3) = 0$

$2\tan x - 1 = 0$ or $2\tan x - 3 = 0$

$\tan x = \dfrac{1}{2}$ $\tan x = \dfrac{3}{2}$

$x \approx 0.4636,\ 3.6052$ $x \approx 0.9828,\ 4.1244$

95. $7\sin^2 x - 1 = 0$

$\sin^2 x = \dfrac{1}{7}$

$\sin x = \pm\sqrt{\dfrac{1}{7}}$

$\sin x = \pm\dfrac{\sqrt{7}}{7}$

$\sin x \approx 0.3780$ or $\sin x \approx -0.3780$

$x \approx 0.3876,\ 2.7540$ $x \approx 3.5292,\ 5.8956$

97. $2\cos 2x + 1 = 0$

$\cos 2x = -\dfrac{1}{2}$

The period of the cosine function is 2π. On the interval $[0, 2\pi)$ the cosine function equals $-\dfrac{1}{2}$ at $\dfrac{2\pi}{3}$ and $\dfrac{4\pi}{3}$. This means that $2x = \dfrac{2\pi}{3}$ or $2x = \dfrac{4\pi}{3}$. Because the period is 2π, all the solutions of the equation are given by

$2x = \dfrac{2\pi}{3} + 2n\pi$ or $2x = \dfrac{4\pi}{3} + 2n\pi$

$x = \dfrac{\pi}{3} + n\pi$ $x = \dfrac{2\pi}{3} + n\pi$

Use all values of n that result in x values on the interval $[0, 2\pi)$. Thus,

$x = \dfrac{\pi}{3},\ \dfrac{5\pi}{3}$ or $x = \dfrac{2\pi}{3},\ \dfrac{4\pi}{3}$

99. $\sin 2x + \sin x = 0$

$2\sin x \cos x + \sin x = 0$

$\sin x(2\cos x + 1) = 0$

$\sin x = 0$ or $2\cos x + 1 = 0$

$x = 0,\ \pi$ $\cos x = -\dfrac{1}{2}$

$x = \dfrac{2\pi}{3},\ \dfrac{4\pi}{3}$

Thus, $x = 0,\ \dfrac{2\pi}{3},\ \pi,$ and $\dfrac{4\pi}{3}$.

101. $3\cos x - 6\sqrt{3} = \cos x - 5\sqrt{3}$

$\qquad 2\cos x = \sqrt{3}$

$\qquad\quad \cos x = \dfrac{\sqrt{3}}{2}$

$\qquad\qquad x = \dfrac{\pi}{6}, \dfrac{11\pi}{6}$

103. $\tan x = -4.7143$

Be sure calculator is in radian mode and find the inverse tangent of $+4.7143$. This gives the first quadrant reference angle.

$\theta = \tan^{-1} 4.7143 \approx 1.3618$

The tangent is negative in quadrants II and IV thus,

$x \approx \pi - 1.3618 \quad$ or $\quad x \approx 2\pi - 1.3618$

$x \approx 1.7798 \qquad\qquad x \approx 4.9214$

105. $\qquad 2\sin^2 x = 3 - \sin x$

$\qquad 2\sin^2 x + \sin x - 3 = 0$

$\qquad (\sin x - 1)(2\sin x + 3) = 0$

$\sin x - 1 = 0 \quad$ or $\quad 2\sin x + 3 = 0$

$\quad \sin x = 1 \qquad\qquad \sin x = -\dfrac{3}{2}$

$\qquad x = \dfrac{\pi}{2} \qquad\quad \sin x = -\dfrac{3}{2}$

107. $\qquad \cos x \csc x = 2\cos x$

$\cos x \csc x - 2\cos x = 0$

$\qquad \cos x(\csc x - 2) = 0$

$\cos x = 0 \qquad$ or $\quad \csc x - 2 = 0$

$\sin x = \dfrac{1}{2} \qquad\qquad \csc x = 2$

$\qquad\qquad\qquad\qquad \sin x = \dfrac{1}{2}$

$x = \dfrac{\pi}{2}, \dfrac{3\pi}{2}$

$\qquad\qquad\qquad\qquad x = \dfrac{\pi}{6}, \dfrac{5\pi}{6}$

Thus, $x = \dfrac{\pi}{6}, \dfrac{\pi}{2}, \dfrac{5\pi}{6},$ and $\dfrac{3\pi}{2}$.

109. $5\cot^2 x - 15 = 0$

$\qquad \cot^2 x = 3$

$\qquad \tan^2 x = \dfrac{1}{3}$

$\qquad \tan x = \pm\sqrt{\dfrac{1}{3}}$

$\qquad \tan x = \pm\dfrac{\sqrt{3}}{3}$

$\tan x = \dfrac{\sqrt{3}}{3} \quad$ or $\quad \tan x = -\dfrac{\sqrt{3}}{3}$

$x = \dfrac{\pi}{6}, \dfrac{7\pi}{6} \qquad\qquad x = \dfrac{5\pi}{6}, \dfrac{11\pi}{6}$

Thus, $x = \dfrac{\pi}{6}, \dfrac{5\pi}{6}, \dfrac{7\pi}{6},$ and $\dfrac{11\pi}{6}$.

111. $\cos^2 x + 2\cos x - 2 = 0$

Use the quadratic formula to solve for $\cos x$.

$\cos x = \dfrac{-b \pm \sqrt{b^2 - 4ac}}{2a}$

$\cos x = \dfrac{-(2) \pm \sqrt{(2)^2 - 4(1)(-2)}}{2(1)}$

$\cos x = \dfrac{-2 \pm \sqrt{12}}{2}$

$\cos x = \dfrac{-2 \pm 2\sqrt{3}}{2}$

$\cos x = -1 \pm \sqrt{3}$

$\cos x \approx 0.7321 \quad$ or $\quad \cos x \approx -2.7321$

$\qquad\qquad\qquad\qquad \cos x \approx -2.7321$

$\qquad\qquad\qquad\qquad$ This equation

$\qquad\qquad\qquad\qquad$ has no solution.

Be sure calculator is in radian mode and find the inverse cosine of 0.7321. This gives the first quadrant reference angle.

$\theta = \cos^{-1} 0.7321 \approx 0.7495$

The cosine is positive in quadrants I and IV thus,

$x \approx 0.7495 \quad$ or $\quad x \approx 2\pi - 0.7495$

$\qquad\qquad\qquad\qquad x \approx 5.5337$

113.
$$5\sin x = 2\cos^2 x - 4$$
$$5\sin x = 2(1 - \sin^2 x) - 4$$
$$5\sin x = 2 - 2\sin^2 x - 4$$
$$2\sin^2 x + 5\sin x + 2 = 0$$
$$(2\sin x + 1)(\sin x + 2) = 0$$
$$2\sin x + 1 = 0 \qquad \text{or} \quad \sin x + 2 = 0$$
$$\sin x = -\frac{1}{2} \qquad\qquad \sin x = -2$$
$$\qquad\qquad\qquad \cancel{\sin x = -2}$$
$$x = \frac{7\pi}{6}, \ \frac{11\pi}{6}$$

115. $\quad 2\tan^2 x + 5\tan x + 3 = 0$
$$(\tan x + 1)(2\tan x + 3) = 0$$
$$\tan x + 1 = 0 \qquad \text{or} \quad 2\tan x + 3 = 0$$
$$\tan x = -1 \qquad\qquad \tan x = -\frac{3}{2}$$
$$x = \frac{3\pi}{4}, \ \frac{7\pi}{4} \qquad x \approx 2.1588, \ 5.3004$$

117.

$$f(x) = 3\cos x$$
$$g(x) = \cos x - 1$$

$$3\cos x = \cos x - 1$$
$$2\cos x = -1$$
$$\cos x = -\frac{1}{2}$$
$$x = \frac{2\pi}{3}, \ \frac{4\pi}{3}$$
$$\left(\frac{2\pi}{3}, -\frac{3}{2}\right), \left(\frac{4\pi}{3}, -\frac{3}{2}\right)$$

119.

$$f(x) = \cos 2x$$
$$g(x) = -2\sin x$$

$$\cos 2x = -2\sin x$$
$$1 - 2\sin^2 x = -2\sin x$$
$$-2\sin^2 x + 2\sin x + 1 = 0$$
$$2\sin^2 x - 2\sin x - 1 = 0$$
$$\sin x = \frac{-b \pm \sqrt{b^2 - 4ac}}{2a}$$
$$\sin x = \frac{-(-2) \pm \sqrt{(-2)^2 - 4(2)(-1)}}{2(2)}$$
$$\sin x = \frac{2 \pm \sqrt{12}}{4}$$
$$\sin x = \frac{2 \pm 2\sqrt{3}}{4}$$
$$\sin x = \frac{1 \pm \sqrt{3}}{2}$$
$$\sin x \approx -0.3660 \qquad \text{or} \qquad \sin x \approx 1.3660$$
$$\qquad\qquad\qquad\qquad\qquad \cancel{\sin x \approx 1.3660}$$
$$x \approx 3.5163, \ 5.9085 \qquad \text{This equation}$$
$$\qquad\qquad\qquad\qquad\qquad \text{has no solution.}$$
$$(3.5163, 0.7321), (5.9085, 0.7321)$$

121. $\quad |\cos x| = \dfrac{\sqrt{3}}{2}$
$$\cos x = \frac{\sqrt{3}}{2} \qquad \text{or} \quad \cos x = -\frac{\sqrt{3}}{2}$$
$$x = \frac{\pi}{6}, \ \frac{11\pi}{6} \qquad\qquad x = \frac{5\pi}{6}, \ \frac{7\pi}{6}$$

123.
$$10\cos^2 x + 3\sin x - 9 = 0$$
$$10(1 - \sin^2 x) + 3\sin x - 9 = 0$$
$$10 - 10\sin^2 x + 3\sin x - 9 = 0$$
$$-10\sin^2 x + 3\sin x + 1 = 0$$
$$10\sin^2 x - 3\sin x - 1 = 0$$
$$(2\sin x - 1)(5\sin x + 1) = 0$$
$$2\sin x - 1 = 0 \qquad \text{or} \quad 5\sin x + 1 = 0$$
$$\sin x = \frac{1}{2} \qquad\qquad \sin x = -\frac{1}{5}$$
$$x = \frac{\pi}{6}, \ \frac{5\pi}{6} \qquad x = 3.3430, \ 6.0818$$

125. $2\cos^3 x + \cos^2 x - 2\cos x - 1 = 0$

$\cos^2 x(2\cos x + 1) - 1(2\cos x + 1) = 0$

$(2\cos x + 1)(\cos^2 x - 1) = 0$

$(2\cos x + 1)(\cos x + 1)(\cos x - 1) = 0$

$\cos x = -\dfrac{1}{2}$ or $\cos x = -1$ or $\cos x = 1$

$x = 0, \ \dfrac{2\pi}{3}, \ \pi, \ \dfrac{4\pi}{3}$

127. 0.3649, 1.2059, 3.5064, 4.3475
This matches graph a.

129. Substitute $y = 0.3$ into the equation and solve for x:

$$0.3 = 0.6\sin\frac{2\pi}{5}x$$

$$\frac{0.3}{0.6} = \frac{0.6\sin\frac{2\pi}{5}x}{0.6}$$

$$\frac{1}{2} = \sin\frac{2\pi}{5}x$$

$$\sin\frac{2\pi}{5}x = \frac{1}{2}$$

The period of the sine function is 2π. In the interval $[0, 2\pi)$, there are two values at which the sine function is $\dfrac{1}{2}$. One is $\dfrac{\pi}{6}$. The sine is positive in quadrant II; thus, the other value is $\pi - \dfrac{\pi}{6} = \dfrac{5\pi}{6}$. All of the solutions to $\sin\dfrac{2\pi}{5}x = \dfrac{1}{2}$ are given by

$$\frac{2\pi}{5}x = \frac{\pi}{6} + 2n\pi$$

$$x = \frac{5}{12} + 5n$$

or

$$\frac{2\pi}{5}x = \frac{5\pi}{6} + 2n\pi$$

$$x = \frac{25}{12} + 5n$$

where n is any integer. In the interval $[0, 5]$ we obtain solutions when $n = 0$. The solutions are $\dfrac{5}{12}$ and $\dfrac{25}{12}$.

Therefore, we are inhaling at 0.3 liter per second at $x = \dfrac{5}{12} \approx 0.4$ second and at $x = \dfrac{25}{12} \approx 2.1$ seconds.

131. Substitute $y = 10.5$ into the equation and solve for x:

$$10.5 = 3\sin\left[\frac{2\pi}{365}(x - 79)\right] + 12$$

$$-1.5 = 3\sin\left[\frac{2\pi}{365}(x - 79)\right]$$

$$\frac{-1.5}{3} = \frac{3\sin\left[\frac{2\pi}{365}(x - 79)\right]}{3}$$

$$-\frac{1}{2} = \sin\left[\frac{2\pi}{365}(x - 79)\right]$$

$$\sin\left[\frac{2\pi}{365}(x - 79)\right] = -\frac{1}{2}$$

The period of the sine function is 2π. In the interval $[0, 2\pi)$, there are two values at which the sine function is $-\dfrac{1}{2}$. One is $\pi + \dfrac{\pi}{6} = \dfrac{7\pi}{6}$.

The other is $2\pi - \dfrac{\pi}{6} = \dfrac{11\pi}{6}$. All the solutions to $\sin\left[\dfrac{2\pi}{365}(x - 79)\right] = -\dfrac{1}{2}$ are given by

$$\frac{2\pi}{365}(x - 79) = \frac{7\pi}{6} + 2n\pi$$

$$x - 79 = \frac{2555}{12} + 365n$$

$$x = \frac{3503}{12} + 365n$$

or

$$\frac{2\pi}{365}(x - 79) = \frac{11\pi}{6} + 2n\pi$$

$$x - 79 = \frac{4015}{12} + 365n$$

$$x = \frac{4963}{12} + 365n$$

where n is any integer.
Substitute various integers for n in the two equations. In the interval $[0, 365]$ we obtain values of 49 and 292 days. Thus, Boston has 10.5 hours of daylight 49 and 292 days after January 1.

133. Substitute $d = 2$ into the equation and solve for t:

$$2 = -4\cos\frac{\pi}{3}t$$

$$\frac{2}{-4} = \frac{-4\cos\frac{\pi}{3}t}{-4}$$

$$-\frac{1}{2} = \cos\frac{\pi}{3}t$$

$$\cos\frac{\pi}{3}t = -\frac{1}{2}$$

The period of the cosine function is 2π. In the interval $[0, 2\pi)$, there are two values at which the cosine function is $-\frac{1}{2}$. One is $\frac{2\pi}{3}$. The cosine function is negative in quadrant III; thus, the other value is $2\pi - \frac{2\pi}{3} = \frac{4\pi}{3}$. All solutions to $\cos\frac{\pi}{3}t = -\frac{1}{2}$ are given by

$$\frac{\pi}{3}t = \frac{2\pi}{3} + 2n\pi$$

$$t = 2 + 6n$$

or

$$\frac{\pi}{3}t = \frac{4\pi}{3} + 2n\pi$$

$$t = 4 + 6n$$

where n is any nonnegative integer.

135. Substitute $v_0 = 90$ and $d = 170$, and solve for θ:

$$170 = \frac{90^2}{16}\sin\theta\cos\theta$$

$$\frac{136}{405} = \sin\theta\cos\theta$$

$$2 \cdot \frac{136}{405} = 2\sin\theta\cos\theta$$

$$\frac{272}{405} = \sin 2\theta$$

$$\sin 2\theta = \frac{272}{405}$$

The period of the sine function is $360°$. In the interval $[0, 360°]$, there are two values at which the sine function is $\frac{272}{405}$.

One is $\sin^{-1}\left(\frac{272}{405}\right) \approx 42.19°$. The sine function is positive in quadrant II; Thus, the other value is $180° - 42.19° = 137.81°$. All solutions to

$\sin 2\theta = \frac{272}{405}$ are given by

$$2\theta = 42.19° + 360°n$$

$$\theta = 21.095° + 180°n$$

or

$$2\theta = 137.81° + 360°n$$

$$\theta = 68.905° + 180°n$$

where n is any integer.

In the interval $[0, 90°)$ we obtain the solutions by letting $n = 0$. The solutions are approximately $21°$ and $69°$. Therefore, the angle of elevation should be $21°$ or $69°$.

147.

$$x = 1.37, \qquad x = 2.30$$
$$x = 3.98, \quad \text{or} \quad x = 4.91$$

149.

$$x = 0.37, 2.77$$

151.

$$x = 0, \qquad x = 1.57, \qquad x = 2.09,$$
$$x = 3.14, \quad x = 4.19, \quad \text{or} \quad x = 4.71$$

153. $2\cos x - 1 + 3\sec x = 0$

$$2\cos x - 1 = -3\sec x$$

$$2\cos x - 1 = \frac{-3}{\cos x}$$

$$\cos x \cdot (2\cos x - 1) = \frac{-3}{\cos x}$$

$$2\cos^2 x - \cos x = -3$$

$$2\cos^2 x - \cos x + 3 = 0$$

The equation is now in quadratic form $2t^2 - t + 3 = 0$. Use the quadratic formula to solve.

$$\cos x = \frac{-(-1)\pm\sqrt{(-1)^2-4(2)(3)}}{2(2)}$$

$$\cos x = \frac{1\pm\sqrt{1-24}}{4}$$

$$\cos x = \frac{1\pm\sqrt{-23}}{4}$$

Since $\dfrac{1\pm\sqrt{-23}}{4}$ are not real numbers, the equation has no solution.

155.

$$\sin x + 2\sin\frac{x}{2} = \cos\frac{x}{2}+1$$

$$\sin\left(2\cdot\frac{x}{2}\right)+2\sin\frac{x}{2} = \cos\frac{x}{2}+1$$

$$2\sin\frac{x}{2}\cos\frac{x}{2}+2\sin\frac{x}{2} = \cos\frac{x}{2}+1$$

$$2\sin\frac{x}{2}\cos\frac{x}{2}+2\sin\frac{x}{2}-\cos\frac{x}{2}-1=0$$

$$2\sin\frac{x}{2}\left(\cos\frac{x}{2}+1\right)-\left(\cos\frac{x}{2}+1\right)=0$$

$$\left(\cos\frac{x}{2}+1\right)\left(2\sin\frac{x}{2}-1\right)=0$$

$$\cos\frac{x}{2}+1=0 \quad\text{or}\quad 2\sin\frac{x}{2}-1=0$$

$$\cos\frac{x}{2}=-1 \qquad 2\sin\frac{x}{2}=1$$

$$\sin\frac{x}{2}=\frac{1}{2}$$

The period of the sine function and cosine function is 2π. In the interval $[0,2\pi)$, there are two values at which the sine function is $\dfrac{1}{2}$. One is $\dfrac{\pi}{6}$. The other is $\pi-\dfrac{\pi}{6}=\dfrac{5\pi}{6}$.

In the interval $[0,2\pi)$, the only value at which the cosine function is -1 is π. All of the solutions to $\cos\dfrac{x}{2}=-1$ are given by

$$\frac{x}{2}=\pi+2n\pi$$

$$x=2\pi+4n\pi$$

where n is any integer. All of the solutions to $\sin\dfrac{x}{2}=\dfrac{1}{2}$ are given by

$$\frac{x}{2}=\frac{\pi}{6}+2n\pi$$

$$x=\frac{\pi}{3}+4n\pi$$

or

$$\frac{x}{2}=\frac{5\pi}{6}+2n\pi$$

$$x=\frac{5\pi}{3}+4n\pi$$

where n is any integer.
The solutions in the interval $[0,2\pi)$, are obtained by letting $n=0$. The solutions are $\dfrac{\pi}{3}$ and $\dfrac{5\pi}{3}$.

Chapter 5 Review Exercises

1.
$$\sec x - \cos x = \frac{1}{\cos x}-\cos x$$
$$=\frac{1}{\cos x}-\frac{\cos x}{1}\cdot\frac{\cos x}{\cos x}$$
$$=\frac{1}{\cos x}-\frac{\cos^2 x}{\cos x}$$
$$=\frac{1-\cos^2 x}{\cos x}$$
$$=\frac{\sin^2 x}{\cos x}$$
$$=\frac{\sin x}{\cos x}\cdot\sin x$$
$$=\tan x\sin x$$

2.
$$\cos x + \sin x\tan x$$
$$=\frac{\cos x}{\cos x}\cos x+\sin x\cdot\frac{\sin x}{\cos x}$$
$$=\frac{\cos^2 x}{\cos x}+\frac{\sin^2 x}{\cos x}$$
$$=\frac{\cos^2 x+\sin^2 x}{\cos x}$$
$$=\frac{1}{\cos x}=\sec x$$

3.
$$\sin^2\theta(1+\cot^2\theta)=\sin^2\theta+\sin^2\theta\cot^2\theta$$
$$=\sin^2\theta+\sin^2\theta\cdot\frac{\cos^2\theta}{\sin^2\theta}$$
$$=\sin^2\theta+\cos^2\theta$$
$$=1$$

4. $(\sec\theta - 1)(\sec\theta + 1) = \sec^2\theta - 1$

$$= 1 + \tan^2\theta - 1$$

$$= \tan^2\theta$$

5. $\dfrac{1 - \tan x}{\sin x} = \dfrac{1}{\sin x} - \dfrac{\tan x}{\sin x}$

$$= \csc x - \frac{\sin x}{\cos x} \cdot \frac{1}{\sin x}$$

$$= \csc x - \frac{1}{\cos x}$$

$$= \csc x - \sec x$$

6. $\dfrac{1}{\sin t - 1} + \dfrac{1}{\sin t + 1}$

$$= \frac{1}{\sin t - 1} \cdot \frac{\sin t + 1}{\sin t + 1} + \frac{1}{\sin t + 1} \cdot \frac{\sin t - 1}{\sin t - 1}$$

$$= \frac{\sin t + 1}{\sin^2 t - 1} + \frac{\sin t - 1}{\sin^2 t - 1}$$

$$= \frac{\sin t + 1 + \sin t - 1}{\sin^2 t - 1}$$

$$= \frac{2\sin t}{\sin^2 t - 1}$$

$$= \frac{2\sin t}{-\cos^2 t}$$

$$= -2 \cdot \frac{\sin t}{\cos t} \cdot \frac{1}{\cos t}$$

$$= -2\tan t \sec t$$

7. $\dfrac{1 + \sin t}{\cos^2 t} = \dfrac{1}{\cos^2 t} + \dfrac{\sin t}{\cos^2 t}$

$$= \sec^2 t + \frac{\sin t}{\cos t} \cdot \frac{1}{\cos t}$$

$$= \tan^2 t + 1 + \tan t \sec t$$

8. $\dfrac{\cos x}{1 - \sin x} = \dfrac{\cos x}{1 - \sin x} \cdot \dfrac{1 + \sin x}{1 + \sin x}$

$$= \frac{\cos x(1 + \sin x)}{1 - \sin^2 x}$$

$$= \frac{\cos x(1 + \sin x)}{\cos^2 x}$$

$$= \frac{1 + \sin x}{\cos x}$$

9. $1 - \dfrac{\sin^2 x}{1 + \cos x} = 1 - \dfrac{1 - \cos^2 x}{1 + \cos x}$

$$= 1 - \frac{(1 + \cos x)(1 - \cos x)}{1 + \cos x}$$

$$= 1 - (1 - \cos x)$$

$$= 1 - 1 + \cos x$$

$$= \cos x$$

10. $(\tan\theta + \cot\theta)^2$

$$= \tan^2\theta + 2\tan\theta\cot\theta + \cot^2\theta$$

$$= \sec^2\theta - 1 + 2\frac{\sin\theta}{\cos\theta} \cdot \frac{\cos\theta}{\sin\theta} + \csc^2\theta - 1$$

$$= \sec^2\theta - 1 + 2 + \csc^2\theta - 1$$

$$= \sec^2\theta + \csc^2\theta$$

11. $\dfrac{1}{\sin\theta + \cos\theta} + \dfrac{1}{\sin\theta - \cos\theta}$

$$= \frac{\sin\theta - \cos\theta}{\sin\theta - \cos\theta} \cdot \frac{1}{\sin\theta + \cos\theta}$$

$$+ \frac{\sin\theta + \cos\theta}{\sin\theta + \cos\theta} \cdot \frac{1}{\sin\theta - \cos\theta}$$

$$= \frac{\sin\theta - \cos\theta}{\sin^2\theta - \cos^2\theta} + \frac{\sin\theta + \cos\theta}{\sin^2\theta - \cos^2\theta}$$

$$= \frac{2\sin\theta}{\sin^2\theta - \cos^2\theta}$$

$$= \frac{2\sin\theta}{\sin^2\theta - \cos^2\theta} \cdot \frac{\sin^2\theta + \cos^2\theta}{\sin^2\theta + \cos^2\theta}$$

$$= \frac{2\sin\theta \cdot 1}{\sin^4\theta - \cos^4\theta}$$

$$= \frac{2\sin\theta}{\sin^4\theta - \cos^4\theta}$$

12.
$$\frac{\cos t}{\cot t - 5\cos t} = \frac{\cos t}{\cot t - 5\cos t} \cdot \frac{\frac{1}{\cos t}}{\frac{1}{\cos t}}$$

$$= \frac{\frac{\cos t}{\cos t}}{\frac{\cot t - 5\cos t}{\cos t}}$$

$$= \frac{1}{\frac{\cot t}{\cos t} - 5}$$

$$= \frac{1}{\frac{\frac{\cos t}{\sin t}}{\cos t} - 5}$$

$$= \frac{1}{\frac{\cos t}{\sin t} \cdot \frac{1}{\cos t} - 5}$$

$$= \frac{1}{\frac{1}{\sin t} - 5}$$

$$= \frac{1}{\csc t - 5}$$

13.
$$\frac{1-\cos t}{1+\cos t} = \frac{1-\cos t}{1+\cos t} \cdot \frac{1-\cos t}{1-\cos t}$$

$$= \frac{(1-\cos t)^2}{1-\cos^2 t}$$

$$= \frac{(1-\cos t)^2}{\sin^2 t}$$

$$= \left(\frac{1-\cos t}{\sin t}\right)^2$$

$$= \left(\frac{1}{\sin t} - \frac{\cos t}{\sin t}\right)^2$$

$$= (\csc t - \cot t)^2$$

14. $\cos(45° + 30°)$

$= \cos 45° \cos 30° - \sin 45° \sin 30°$

$$= \frac{\sqrt{2}}{2} \cdot \frac{\sqrt{3}}{2} - \frac{\sqrt{2}}{2} \cdot \frac{1}{2}$$

$$= \frac{\sqrt{6}}{4} - \frac{\sqrt{2}}{4}$$

$$= \frac{\sqrt{6} - \sqrt{2}}{4}$$

15. $\sin 195° = \sin(135° + 60°)$

$= \sin 135° \cos 60° + \cos 135° \sin 60°$

$$= \frac{\sqrt{2}}{2} \cdot \frac{1}{2} + \left(-\frac{\sqrt{2}}{2}\right) \cdot \frac{\sqrt{3}}{2}$$

$$= \frac{\sqrt{2}}{4} - \frac{\sqrt{6}}{4}$$

$$= \frac{\sqrt{2} - \sqrt{6}}{4}$$

16. $\tan\left(\dfrac{4\pi}{3} - \dfrac{\pi}{4}\right) = \dfrac{\tan\frac{4\pi}{3} - \tan\frac{\pi}{4}}{1 + \tan\frac{4\pi}{3} \cdot \tan\frac{\pi}{4}} = \dfrac{\sqrt{3} - 1}{1 + \sqrt{3} \cdot (1)}$

$$= \frac{(\sqrt{3}-1)(1-\sqrt{3})}{(1+\sqrt{3})(1-\sqrt{3})} = \frac{-(1-\sqrt{3})^2}{1-3}$$

$$= \frac{-(1 - 2\sqrt{3} + 3)}{-2} = \frac{1 - 2\sqrt{3} + 3}{2}$$

$$= \frac{4 - 2\sqrt{3}}{2} = \frac{2(2-\sqrt{3})}{2} = 2 - \sqrt{3}$$

17. $\tan\dfrac{5\pi}{12} = \tan\left(\dfrac{2\pi}{12} + \dfrac{3\pi}{12}\right)$

$$= \tan\left(\frac{\pi}{6} + \frac{\pi}{4}\right)$$

$$= \frac{\tan\frac{\pi}{6} + \tan\frac{\pi}{4}}{1 - \tan\frac{\pi}{6}\tan\frac{\pi}{4}}$$

$$= \frac{\frac{\sqrt{3}}{3} + 1}{1 - \frac{\sqrt{3}}{3} \cdot 1} = \frac{\frac{\sqrt{3}}{3} + 1}{1 - \frac{\sqrt{3}}{3}} \cdot \frac{\left(1 + \frac{\sqrt{3}}{3}\right)}{\left(1 + \frac{\sqrt{3}}{3}\right)}$$

$$= \frac{\frac{2\sqrt{3}}{3} + 1 + \frac{1}{3}}{1 - \frac{1}{3}} = \frac{\frac{2\sqrt{3}}{3} + \frac{4}{3}}{\frac{2}{3}}$$

$$= \left(\frac{2\sqrt{3}}{3} + \frac{4}{3}\right) \cdot \frac{3}{2} = \sqrt{3} + 2$$

18. $\cos 65° \cos 5° + \sin 65° \sin 5°$

$= \cos(65° - 5°)$

$= \cos 60°$

$$= \frac{1}{2}$$

19. $\sin 80° \cos 50° - \cos 80° \sin 50°$
$= \sin(80° - 50°)$
$= \sin 30°$
$= \dfrac{1}{2}$

20. $\sin\left(x + \dfrac{\pi}{6}\right) - \cos\left(x + \dfrac{\pi}{3}\right)$
$= \sin x \cos \dfrac{\pi}{6} + \cos x \sin \dfrac{\pi}{6}$
$\qquad - \left(\cos x \cos \dfrac{\pi}{3} - \sin x \sin \dfrac{\pi}{3}\right)$
$= \sin x \cdot \dfrac{\sqrt{3}}{2} + \cos x \cdot \dfrac{1}{2}$
$\qquad - \left(\cos x \cdot \dfrac{1}{2} - \sin x \cdot \dfrac{\sqrt{3}}{2}\right)$
$= 2 \cdot \dfrac{\sqrt{3}}{2} \cdot \sin x$
$= \sqrt{3} \sin x$

21. $\tan\left(x + \dfrac{3\pi}{4}\right) = \dfrac{\tan x + \tan \frac{3\pi}{4}}{1 - \tan x \tan \frac{3\pi}{4}}$
$= \dfrac{\tan x + (-1)}{1 - \tan x(-1)}$
$= \dfrac{\tan x - 1}{1 + \tan x}$

22. $\sec(\alpha + \beta) = \dfrac{1}{\cos(\alpha + \beta)}$
$= \dfrac{1}{\cos \alpha \cos \beta - \sin \alpha \sin \beta}$
$= \dfrac{1}{\cos \alpha \cos \beta - \sin \alpha \sin \beta} \cdot \dfrac{\frac{1}{\cos \alpha \cos \beta}}{\frac{1}{\cos \alpha \cos \beta}}$
$= \dfrac{\frac{1}{\cos \alpha \cos \beta}}{\frac{\cos \alpha \cos \beta - \sin \alpha \sin \beta}{\cos \alpha \cos \beta}}$
$= \dfrac{\frac{1}{\cos \alpha} \cdot \frac{1}{\cos \beta}}{\frac{\cos \alpha \cos \beta}{\cos \alpha \cos \beta} - \frac{\sin \alpha \sin \beta}{\cos \alpha \cos \beta}}$
$= \dfrac{\sec \alpha \sec \beta}{1 - \frac{\sin \alpha \sin \beta}{\cos \alpha \cos \beta}}$
$= \dfrac{\sec \alpha \sec \beta}{1 - \tan \alpha \tan \beta}$

23. $\dfrac{\cos(\alpha - \beta)}{\cos \alpha \cos \beta} = \dfrac{\cos \alpha \cos \beta + \sin \alpha \sin \beta}{\cos \alpha \cos \beta}$
$= \dfrac{\cos \alpha \cos \beta}{\cos \alpha \cos \beta} + \dfrac{\sin \alpha \sin \beta}{\cos \alpha \cos \beta}$
$= 1 + \tan \alpha \tan \beta$

24. $\cos^4 t - \sin^4 t = \left(\cos^2 t - \sin^2 t\right)\left(\cos^2 t + \sin^2 t\right)$
$= (\cos 2t) \cdot (1)$
$= \cos 2t$

25. $\sin t - \cos 2t = \sin t - \left(1 - 2\sin^2 t\right)$
$= \sin t - 1 + 2\sin^2 t$
$= 2\sin^2 t + \sin t - 1$
$= (2\sin t - 1)(\sin t + 1)$

26. $\dfrac{\sin 2\theta - \sin \theta}{\cos 2\theta + \cos \theta} = \dfrac{2\sin \theta \cos \theta - \sin \theta}{2\cos^2 \theta - 1 + \cos \theta}$
$= \dfrac{\sin \theta(2\cos \theta - 1)}{2\cos^2 \theta + \cos \theta - 1}$
$= \dfrac{\sin \theta(2\cos \theta - 1)}{(2\cos \theta - 1)(\cos \theta + 1)}$
$= \dfrac{\sin \theta}{\cos \theta + 1}$
$= \dfrac{\sin \theta}{\cos \theta + 1} \cdot \dfrac{\cos \theta - 1}{\cos \theta - 1}$
$= \dfrac{\sin \theta(\cos \theta - 1)}{\cos^2 \theta - 1}$
$= \dfrac{\sin \theta(\cos \theta - 1)}{-\sin^2 \theta}$
$= \dfrac{-(\cos \theta - 1)}{\sin \theta}$
$= \dfrac{1 - \cos \theta}{\sin \theta}$

27. $\dfrac{\sin 2\theta}{1 - \sin^2 \theta} = \dfrac{2\sin \theta \cos \theta}{\cos^2 \theta}$
$= \dfrac{2\sin \theta}{\cos \theta} \cdot \dfrac{\cos \theta}{\cos \theta}$
$= 2\tan \theta$

28. $2\sin t \cos t \sec 2t = \sin 2t \cdot \sec 2t$
$= \sin 2t \cdot \dfrac{1}{\cos 2t}$
$= \dfrac{\sin 2t}{\cos 2t}$
$= \tan 2t$

29.
$$\cos 4t = \cos(2 \cdot 2t)$$
$$= 1 - 2\sin^2 2t$$
$$= 1 - 2(\sin 2t)^2$$
$$= 1 - 2 \cdot (2\sin t \cos t)^2$$
$$= 1 - 2 \cdot 4\sin^2 t \cos^2 t$$
$$= 1 - 8\sin^2 t \cos^2 t$$

30. $\tan\dfrac{x}{2}(1+\cos x) = \dfrac{\sin x}{1+\cos x} \cdot (1+\cos x) = \sin x$

31.
$$\tan\frac{x}{2} = \frac{1-\cos x}{\sin x}$$
$$= \frac{1-\cos x}{\sin x} \cdot \frac{\frac{1}{\cos x}}{\frac{1}{\cos x}}$$
$$= \frac{\frac{1-\cos x}{\cos x}}{\frac{\sin x}{\cos x}}$$
$$= \frac{\frac{1}{\cos x} - \frac{\cos x}{\cos x}}{\tan x}$$
$$= \frac{\sec x - 1}{\tan x}$$

32. a. The graph appears to be the cosine curve, $y = \cos x$. It cycles through maximum, intercept, minimum, intercept and back to maximum. Thus, $y = \cos x$ also describes the graph.

b.
$$\sin\left(x - \frac{3\pi}{2}\right) = \sin x \cos\frac{3\pi}{2} - \cos x \sin\frac{3\pi}{2}$$
$$= \sin x \cdot 0 - \cos x \cdot (-1)$$
$$= \cos x$$

33. a. The graph appears to be the negative of the sine curve, $y = -\sin x$. It cycles through intercept, minimum, intercept, maximum and back to intercept. Thus, $y = -\sin x$ also describes the graph.

b.
$$\cos\left(x + \frac{\pi}{2}\right) = \cos x \cos\frac{\pi}{2} - \sin x \sin\frac{\pi}{2}$$
$$= \cos x \cdot 0 - \sin x \cdot 1$$
$$= -\sin x$$

34. a. The graph appears to be the tangent curve, $y = \tan x$. It cycles through intercept to positive infinity, then from negative infinity through the intercept. Thus, $y = \tan x$ also describes the graph.

b.
$$y = \frac{\tan x - 1}{1 - \cot x}$$
$$= \frac{\frac{\sin x}{\cos x} - 1}{1 - \frac{\cos x}{\sin x}}$$
$$= \frac{\frac{\sin x - \cos x}{\cos x}}{\frac{\sin x - \cos x}{\sin x}}$$
$$= \frac{\sin x - \cos x}{\cos x} \cdot \frac{\sin x}{\sin x - \cos x}$$
$$= \frac{\sin x}{\cos x}$$
$$= \tan x$$

35. $\sin\alpha = \dfrac{3}{5} = \dfrac{y}{r}$

Because α lies in quadrant I, x is positive.
$$x^2 + 3^2 = 5^2$$
$$x^2 = 5^2 - 3^2 = 16$$
$$x = \sqrt{16} = 4$$

Thus, $\cos\alpha = \dfrac{x}{r} = \dfrac{4}{5}$, and $\tan\alpha = \dfrac{y}{x} = \dfrac{3}{4}$.

$\sin\beta = \dfrac{12}{13} = \dfrac{y}{r}$

Because β lies in quadrant II, x is negative.
$$x^2 + 12^2 = 13^2$$
$$x^2 = 13^2 - 12^2 = 25$$
$$x = -\sqrt{25} = -5$$

Thus, $\cos\beta = \dfrac{x}{r} = \dfrac{-5}{13} = -\dfrac{5}{13}$, and

$\tan\beta = \dfrac{y}{x} = \dfrac{12}{-5} = -\dfrac{12}{5}$.

a. $\sin(\alpha+\beta) = \sin\alpha\cos\beta + \cos\alpha\sin\beta$
$$= \frac{3}{5}\cdot\left(-\frac{5}{13}\right) + \frac{4}{5}\cdot\frac{12}{13} = \frac{33}{65}$$

b. $\cos(\alpha-\beta) = \cos\alpha\cos\beta + \sin\alpha\sin\beta$
$$= \frac{4}{5}\cdot\left(-\frac{5}{13}\right) + \frac{3}{5}\cdot\frac{12}{13} = \frac{16}{65}$$

c. $\tan(\alpha + \beta) = \dfrac{\tan \alpha + \tan \beta}{1 - \tan \alpha \tan \beta}$

$= \dfrac{\frac{3}{4} + \left(-\frac{12}{5}\right)}{1 - \frac{3}{4}\left(-\frac{12}{5}\right)}$

$= \dfrac{-\frac{33}{20}}{1 + \frac{36}{20}} = \dfrac{-\frac{33}{20}}{\frac{56}{20}}$

$= -\dfrac{33}{56}$

d. $\sin 2\alpha = 2 \sin \alpha \cos \alpha = 2 \cdot \dfrac{3}{5} \cdot \dfrac{4}{5} = \dfrac{24}{25}$

e. $\cos \dfrac{\beta}{2} = \sqrt{\dfrac{1 + \cos \beta}{2}} = \sqrt{\dfrac{1 - \frac{5}{13}}{2}}$

$= \sqrt{\dfrac{8}{26}} = \sqrt{\dfrac{4}{13}} = \dfrac{2}{\sqrt{13}} = \dfrac{2\sqrt{13}}{13}$

36. $\tan \alpha = \dfrac{4}{3} = \dfrac{-4}{-3} = \dfrac{y}{x}$

Because r is a distance, it is positive.

$r^2 = (-4)^2 + (-3)^2 = 25$

$r = \sqrt{25} = 5$

Thus, $\sin \alpha = \dfrac{y}{r} = \dfrac{-4}{5} = -\dfrac{4}{5}$, and

$\cos \alpha = \dfrac{x}{r} = \dfrac{-3}{5} = -\dfrac{3}{5}$.

$\tan \beta = \dfrac{5}{12} = \dfrac{y}{x}$

Because r is a distance, it is positive.

$r^2 = 5^2 + 12^2 = 169$

$r = \sqrt{169} = 13$

Thus, $\sin \beta = \dfrac{y}{r} = \dfrac{5}{13}$, and $\cos \beta = \dfrac{x}{r} = \dfrac{12}{13}$.

a. $\sin(\alpha + \beta) = \sin \alpha \cos \beta + \cos \alpha \sin \beta$

$= -\dfrac{4}{5} \cdot \dfrac{12}{13} + \left(-\dfrac{3}{5}\right) \cdot \dfrac{5}{13}$

$= -\dfrac{63}{65}$

b. $\cos(\alpha - \beta) = \cos \alpha \cos \beta + \sin \alpha \sin \beta$

$= -\dfrac{3}{5} \cdot \dfrac{12}{13} + \left(-\dfrac{4}{5}\right) \cdot \dfrac{5}{13}$

$= -\dfrac{56}{65}$

c. $\tan(\alpha + \beta) = \dfrac{\tan \alpha + \tan \beta}{1 - \tan \alpha \tan \beta}$

$= \dfrac{\frac{4}{3} + \frac{5}{12}}{1 - \frac{4}{3} \cdot \frac{5}{12}} = \dfrac{\frac{21}{12}}{1 - \frac{20}{36}} = \dfrac{\frac{21}{12}}{\frac{16}{36}}$

$= \dfrac{21}{12} \cdot \dfrac{36}{16} = \dfrac{63}{16}$

d. $\sin 2\alpha = 2 \sin \alpha \sin \alpha$

$= 2\left(-\dfrac{4}{5}\right)\left(-\dfrac{4}{5}\right) = \dfrac{24}{25}$

e. $\cos \dfrac{\beta}{2} = \sqrt{\dfrac{1 + \cos \beta}{2}} = \sqrt{\dfrac{1 + \frac{12}{13}}{2}}$

$= \sqrt{\dfrac{25}{26}} = \dfrac{5}{\sqrt{26}} = \dfrac{5\sqrt{26}}{26}$

37. $\tan \alpha = -3 = \dfrac{3}{-1} = \dfrac{y}{x}$

Because r is a distance, it is positive.

$r^2 = 3^2 + (-1)^2$

$r^2 = 10$

$r = \sqrt{10}$

$\sin \alpha = \dfrac{3}{\sqrt{10}} = \dfrac{3\sqrt{10}}{10}$

$\cos \alpha = \dfrac{-1}{\sqrt{10}} = -\dfrac{\sqrt{10}}{10}$

$\cot \beta = -3 = \dfrac{3}{-1} = \dfrac{x}{y}$

Because r is a distance, it is positive.

$r^2 = 3^2 + (-1)^2$

$r^2 = 10$

$r = \sqrt{10}$

$\sin \beta = \dfrac{-1}{\sqrt{10}} = -\dfrac{\sqrt{10}}{10}$

$\cos \beta = \dfrac{3}{\sqrt{10}} = \dfrac{3\sqrt{10}}{10}$

a.

$$\sin(\alpha + \beta) = \sin\alpha\cos\beta + \cos\alpha\sin\beta$$

$$= \frac{3\sqrt{10}}{10}\cdot\frac{3\sqrt{10}}{10} + \left(-\frac{\sqrt{10}}{10}\right)\left(-\frac{\sqrt{10}}{10}\right)$$

$$= \frac{90}{100} + \frac{10}{100}$$

$$= \frac{100}{100}$$

$$= 1$$

b.

$$\cos(\alpha - \beta) = \cos\alpha\cos\beta + \sin\alpha\sin\beta$$

$$= \left(-\frac{\sqrt{10}}{10}\right)\left(\frac{3\sqrt{10}}{10}\right) + \frac{3\sqrt{10}}{10}\left(\frac{-\sqrt{10}}{10}\right)$$

$$= -\frac{60}{100}$$

$$= -\frac{3}{5}$$

c.

$$\tan(\alpha + \beta) = \frac{\tan\alpha + \tan\beta}{1 - \tan\alpha\tan\beta}$$

$$= \frac{-3 + \left(\frac{-1}{3}\right)}{1 - (-3)\left(-\frac{1}{3}\right)}$$

$$= \frac{-\frac{10}{3}}{0}$$

Since this value is undefined, the tangent function is undefined at $\alpha + \beta$.

d.

$$\sin 2\alpha = 2\sin\alpha\cos\alpha$$

$$= 2\left(\frac{3\sqrt{10}}{10}\right)\left(\frac{-\sqrt{10}}{10}\right)$$

$$= -\frac{3}{5}$$

e.

$$\cos\frac{\beta}{2} = \sqrt{\frac{1 + \cos\beta}{2}}$$

$$= \sqrt{\frac{1 + \frac{3\sqrt{10}}{10}}{2}}$$

$$= \sqrt{\frac{10 + 3\sqrt{10}}{20}}$$

$$= \frac{\sqrt{10 + 3\sqrt{10}}}{2\sqrt{5}}$$

38.

$$\sin\alpha = -\frac{1}{3} = \frac{-1}{3} = \frac{y}{r}$$

Because α is in quadrant II, x is negative.

$$x^2 + (-1)^2 = 3^2$$

$$x^2 + 1 = 9$$

$$x^2 = 8$$

$$x = -\sqrt{8} = -2\sqrt{2}$$

$$\cos\alpha = \frac{-2\sqrt{2}}{3}$$

$$\tan\alpha = \frac{-1}{-2\sqrt{2}} = \frac{\sqrt{2}}{4}$$

$$\cos\beta = -\frac{1}{3} = \frac{-1}{3} = \frac{x}{r}$$

Because β is in quadrant III, y is negative.

$$(-1)^2 + y^2 = 3^2$$

$$y^2 = 8$$

$$y = -\sqrt{8} = -2\sqrt{2}$$

$$\sin\beta = \frac{-2\sqrt{2}}{3}$$

$$\tan\beta = \frac{-2\sqrt{2}}{-1} = 2\sqrt{2}$$

a.

$$\sin(\alpha + \beta)$$

$$= \sin\alpha\cos\beta + \cos\alpha\sin\beta$$

$$= -\frac{1}{3}\cdot-\frac{1}{3} + \left(-\frac{2\sqrt{2}}{3}\right)\left(-\frac{2\sqrt{2}}{3}\right)$$

$$= \frac{9}{9} = 1$$

b.

$$\cos(\alpha - \beta)$$

$$= \cos\alpha\cos\beta + \sin\alpha\sin\beta$$

$$= -\frac{2\sqrt{2}}{3}\cdot\left(-\frac{1}{3}\right) + \left(-\frac{1}{3}\right)\cdot\left(-\frac{2\sqrt{2}}{3}\right)$$

$$= \frac{4\sqrt{2}}{9}$$

c. $\tan(\alpha + \beta) = \dfrac{\tan \alpha + \tan \beta}{1 - \tan \alpha \tan B}$

$= \dfrac{\frac{\sqrt{2}}{4} + 2\sqrt{2}}{1 - \left(\frac{\sqrt{2}}{4}\right)\left(2\sqrt{2}\right)}$

$= \dfrac{\frac{9\sqrt{2}}{4}}{0}$

Since this value is undefined, the tangent function is undefined at $\alpha + \beta$.

d. $\sin 2\alpha = 2 \sin \alpha \cos \alpha$

$= 2\left(-\dfrac{1}{3}\right)\left(-\dfrac{2\sqrt{2}}{3}\right) = \dfrac{4\sqrt{2}}{9}$

e. $\cos \dfrac{\beta}{2} = -\sqrt{\dfrac{1 + \cos \beta}{2}}$

$= -\sqrt{\dfrac{1 + \left(-\frac{1}{3}\right)}{2}}$

$= -\sqrt{\dfrac{\frac{2}{3}}{2}} = -\sqrt{\dfrac{1}{3}}$

$= -\dfrac{1}{\sqrt{3}}$

$= -\dfrac{\sqrt{3}}{3}$

39. The given expression is the right side of the formula for $\cos 2\theta$ with $\theta = 15°$.

$\cos^2 15° - \sin^2 15° = \cos(2 \cdot 15°)$

$= \cos 30°$

$= \dfrac{\sqrt{3}}{2}$

40. The given expression is the right side of the formula for $\tan 2\theta$ with $\theta = \dfrac{5\pi}{12}$.

$\dfrac{2 \tan \frac{5\pi}{12}}{1 - \tan^2 \frac{5\pi}{12}} = \tan\left(2 \cdot \dfrac{5\pi}{12}\right)$

$= \tan \dfrac{5\pi}{6}$

$= -\dfrac{\sqrt{3}}{3}$

41. Because $22.5°$ lies in quadrant I, $\sin 22.5° > 0$.

$\sin 22.5° = \sin \dfrac{45°}{2}$

$= \sqrt{\dfrac{1 - \cos 45°}{2}} = \sqrt{\dfrac{1 - \frac{\sqrt{2}}{2}}{2}}$

$= \sqrt{\dfrac{2 - \sqrt{2}}{4}} = \dfrac{\sqrt{2 - \sqrt{2}}}{2}$

42. Because $\dfrac{\pi}{12}$ lies in quadrant I, $\tan \dfrac{\pi}{12} > 0$.

$\tan \dfrac{\pi}{12} = \tan \dfrac{\frac{\pi}{6}}{2}$

$= \dfrac{1 - \cos \frac{\pi}{6}}{\sin \frac{\pi}{6}} = \dfrac{1 - \frac{\sqrt{3}}{2}}{\frac{1}{2}}$

$= 2 - \sqrt{3}$

43. $\sin 6x \sin 4x$

$= \dfrac{1}{2}\left[\cos(6x - 4x) - \cos(6x + 4x)\right]$

$= \dfrac{1}{2}\left[\cos 2x - \cos 10x\right]$

44. $\sin 7x \cos 3x$

$= \dfrac{1}{2}\left[\sin(7x + 3x) + \sin(7x - 3x)\right]$

$= \dfrac{1}{2}\left[\sin 10x + \sin 4x\right]$

45. $\sin 2x - \sin 4x$

$= 2 \sin\left(\dfrac{2x - 4x}{2}\right) \cos\left(\dfrac{2x + 4x}{2}\right)$

$= 2 \sin(-x) \cos 3x$

$= -2 \sin x \cos 3x$

46. $\cos 75° + \cos 15°$

$= 2 \cos\left(\dfrac{75° + 15°}{2}\right) \cos\left(\dfrac{75° - 15°}{2}\right)$

$= 2 \cos 45° \cos 30°$

$= 2\left(\dfrac{\sqrt{2}}{2}\right)\left(\dfrac{\sqrt{3}}{2}\right) = \dfrac{\sqrt{6}}{2}$

47.

$$\frac{\cos 3x + \cos 5x}{\cos 3x - \cos 5x} = \frac{2\cos\left(\frac{3x+5x}{2}\right)\cos\left(\frac{3x-5x}{2}\right)}{-2\sin\left(\frac{3x+5x}{2}\right)\sin\left(\frac{3x-5x}{2}\right)}$$

$$= \frac{2\cos\left(\frac{8x}{2}\right)\cos\left(\frac{-2x}{2}\right)}{-2\sin\left(\frac{8x}{2}\right)\sin\left(\frac{-2x}{2}\right)}$$

$$= \frac{2\cos 4x\cos(-x)}{-2\sin 4x\sin(-x)}$$

$$= \frac{2\cos 4x\cos x}{2\sin 4x\sin x}$$

$$= \frac{\cos 4x}{\sin 4x}\cdot\frac{\cos x}{\sin x}$$

$$= \cot 4x \cot x$$

$$= \cot x \cot 4x$$

48.

$$\frac{\sin 2x + \sin 6x}{\sin 2x - \sin 6x} = \frac{2\sin\left(\frac{2x+6x}{2}\right)\cos\left(\frac{2x-6x}{2}\right)}{2\sin\left(\frac{2x-6x}{2}\right)\cos\left(\frac{2x+6x}{2}\right)}$$

$$= \frac{2\sin\left(\frac{8x}{2}\right)\cos\left(\frac{-4x}{2}\right)}{2\sin\left(\frac{-4x}{2}\right)\cos\left(\frac{8x}{2}\right)}$$

$$= \frac{\sin 4x\cos(-2x)}{\sin(-2x)\cos 4x}$$

$$= -\frac{\sin 4x\cos 2x}{\sin 2x\cos 4x}$$

$$= -\frac{\sin 4x}{\cos 4x}\cdot\frac{\cos 2x}{\sin 2x}$$

$$= -\tan 4x \cot 2x$$

49. a. The graph appears to be the cotangent curve, $y = \cot x$. It cycles from positive infinity through the intercept to negative infinity. Thus, $y = \cot x$ also describes the graph.

b.

$$\frac{\cos 3x + \cos x}{\sin 3x - \sin x} = \frac{2\cos\left(\frac{3x+x}{2}\right)\cos\left(\frac{3x-x}{2}\right)}{2\sin\left(\frac{3x-x}{2}\right)\cos\left(\frac{3x+x}{2}\right)}$$

$$= \frac{2\cos\left(\frac{4x}{2}\right)\cos\left(\frac{2x}{2}\right)}{2\sin\left(\frac{2x}{2}\right)\cos\left(\frac{4x}{2}\right)}$$

$$= \frac{2\cos 2x\cos x}{2\sin x\cos 2x}$$

$$= \frac{\cos x}{\sin x}$$

$$= \cot x$$

This verifies our observation that $y = \dfrac{\cos 3x + \cos x}{\sin 3x - \sin x}$ and $y = \cot x$ describe the same graph.

50. $\cos x = -\dfrac{1}{2}$

Because $\cos\dfrac{\pi}{3} = \dfrac{1}{2}$, the solutions for

$\cos x = -\dfrac{1}{2}$ in $[0, 2\pi)$ are $x = \pi - \dfrac{\pi}{3} = \dfrac{2\pi}{3}$

$x = \pi + \dfrac{\pi}{3} = \dfrac{4\pi}{3}$. Because the period of the cosine function is 2π, the solutions are given

by $x = \dfrac{2\pi}{3} + 2n\pi$ or $x = \dfrac{4\pi}{3} + 2n\pi$

where n is any integer.

51. $\sin x = \dfrac{\sqrt{2}}{2}$

Because $\sin\dfrac{\pi}{4} = \dfrac{\sqrt{2}}{2}$, the solutions for

$\sin x = \dfrac{\sqrt{2}}{2}$ in $[0, 2\pi)$ are $x = \dfrac{\pi}{4}$

$x = \pi - \dfrac{\pi}{4} = \dfrac{3\pi}{4}$. Because the period of the cosine function is 2π, the solutions are given by

$x = \dfrac{\pi}{4} + 2n\pi$ or $x = \dfrac{3\pi}{4} + 2n\pi$

where n is any integer.

52. $2\sin x + 1 = 0$

$2\sin x = -1$

$\sin x = -\dfrac{1}{2}$

Because $\sin\dfrac{\pi}{6} = \dfrac{1}{2}$, the solutions for

$\sin x = -\dfrac{1}{2}$ in $[0, 2\pi)$ are

$x = \pi + \dfrac{\pi}{6} = \dfrac{7\pi}{6}$

$x = 2\pi - \dfrac{\pi}{6} = \dfrac{11\pi}{6}$.

Because the period of the sine function is 2π the solutions are given by

$x = \dfrac{7\pi}{6} + 2n\pi$ or $x = \dfrac{11\pi}{6} + 2n\pi$

where n is any integer.

53. $\sqrt{3}\tan x - 1 = 0$

$\sqrt{3}\tan x = 1$

$\tan x = \dfrac{1}{\sqrt{3}}$

Because $\tan\dfrac{\pi}{6} = \dfrac{1}{\sqrt{3}}$, the solution for

$\tan x = \dfrac{1}{\sqrt{3}}$ in $[0, \pi)$ is $x = \dfrac{\pi}{6}$.

Because the period of the tangent function is π, the solutions are given by

$x = \dfrac{\pi}{6} + n\pi$ where n is any integer.

54. The period of the cosine function is 2π. In the interval $[0, 2\pi)$, the only value at which the cosine function is -1 is π. All the solutions to $\cos 2x = -1$ are given by

$2x = \pi + 2n\pi$

$x = \dfrac{\pi}{2} + n\pi$ where n is any integer.

The solutions in the interval $[0, 2\pi)$ are obtained by letting $n = 0$ and $n = 1$.

The solutions are $\dfrac{\pi}{2}$ and $\dfrac{3\pi}{2}$.

55. The period of the sine function is 2π. In the interval $[0, 2\pi)$, the only value at which the

sine function is 1 is $\dfrac{\pi}{2}$. All the solutions to

$\sin 3x = 1$ are given by

$3x = \dfrac{\pi}{2} + 2n\pi$

$x = \dfrac{\pi}{6} + \dfrac{2n\pi}{3}$

where n is any integer. The solutions in the interval $[0, 2\pi)$ are obtained by letting $n = 0$, $n = 1$, and $n = 2$.

The solutions are $\dfrac{\pi}{6}, \dfrac{5\pi}{6}$, and $\dfrac{9\pi}{6}$.

56. The period of the tangent function is π. In the interval $[0, \pi)$, the only value for which the

tangent function is -1 is $\dfrac{3\pi}{4}$. All the solutions

to $\tan\dfrac{x}{2} = -1$ are given by

$\dfrac{x}{2} = \dfrac{3\pi}{4} + n\pi$

$x = \dfrac{3\pi}{2} + 2n\pi$

where n is any integer. The solution in the interval $[0, 2\pi)$ is obtained by letting $n = 0$.

The solution is $\dfrac{3\pi}{2}$.

57. $\tan x = 2\cos x\tan x$

$\tan x - 2\cos x\tan x = 0$

$\tan x(1 - 2\cos x) = 0$

$\tan x = 0 \quad$ or $\quad 1 - 2\cos x = 0$

$x = 0 \ x = \pi \qquad\qquad -2\cos x = -1$

$\cos x = \dfrac{1}{2}$

$x = \dfrac{\pi}{3} \quad x = \dfrac{5\pi}{3}$

The solutions in the interval $[0, 2\pi)$ are 0,

$\dfrac{\pi}{3}, \pi$, and $\dfrac{5\pi}{3}$.

58. The given equation is in quadratic form
$t^2 - 2t = 3$ with $t = \cos x$.

$$\cos^2 x - 2\cos x = 3$$
$$\cos^2 x - 2\cos x - 3 = 0$$
$$(\cos x + 1)(\cos x - 3) = 0$$
$$\cos x + 1 = 0 \quad \text{or} \quad \cos x - 3 = 0$$
$$\cos x = -1 \qquad\qquad \cos x = 3$$
$$x = \pi \qquad\qquad \cos x \text{ cannot be}$$
$$\text{greater than } 1.$$

The solution in the interval $[0, 2\pi)$ is π.

59. $2\cos^2 x - \sin x = 1$

$$2\left(1 - \sin^2 x\right) - \sin x = 1$$
$$2 - 2\sin^2 x - \sin x - 1 = 0$$
$$-2\sin^2 x - \sin x + 1 = 0$$
$$2\sin^2 x + \sin x - 1 = 0$$
$$(2\sin x - 1)(\sin x + 1) = 0$$
$$2\sin x - 1 = 0 \quad \text{or} \quad \sin x + 1 = 0$$
$$2\sin x = 1 \qquad\qquad \sin x = -1$$
$$\sin x = \frac{1}{2} \qquad\qquad x = \frac{3\pi}{2}$$
$$x = \frac{\pi}{6}, \frac{5\pi}{6}$$

The solutions in the interval $[0, 2\pi)$ are
$$\frac{\pi}{6}, \frac{5\pi}{6}, \text{ and } \frac{3\pi}{2}.$$

60. The given equation is in quadratic form
$4t^2 = 1$ with $t = \sin x$.

$$4\sin^2 x = 1$$
$$4\sin^2 x - 1 = 0$$
$$(2\sin x - 1)(2\sin x + 1) = 0$$
$$2\sin x - 1 = 0 \quad \text{or} \quad 2\sin x + 1 = 0$$
$$2\sin x = 1 \qquad\qquad 2\sin x = -1$$
$$\sin x = \frac{1}{2} \qquad\qquad \sin x = -\frac{1}{2}$$
$$x = \frac{\pi}{6} \quad x = \frac{5\pi}{6} \qquad x = \frac{7\pi}{6} \quad x = \frac{11\pi}{6}$$

The solutions in the interval $[0, 2\pi)$ are
$$\frac{\pi}{6}, \frac{5\pi}{6}, \frac{7\pi}{6}, \text{ and } \frac{11\pi}{6}.$$

61. $\cos 2x - \sin x = 1$

$$2\cos^2 x - 1 - \sin x = 1$$
$$2\left(1 - \sin^2 x\right) - \sin x - 2 = 0$$
$$2 - 2\sin^2 x - \sin x - 2 = 0$$
$$-2\sin^2 x - \sin x = 0$$
$$2\sin^2 x + \sin x = 0$$
$$\sin x\left(2\sin x + 1\right) = 0$$
$$\sin x = 0 \qquad\qquad 2\sin x + 1 = 0$$
$$x = 0, \pi \qquad\qquad \sin x = -\frac{1}{2}$$
$$x = \frac{7\pi}{6}, \frac{11\pi}{6}$$

The solutions in the interval $[0, 2\pi)$ are
$$0, \pi, \frac{7\pi}{6}, \text{ and } \frac{11\pi}{6}..$$

62. $\sin 2x = \sqrt{3}\sin x$

$$2\sin x\cos x = \sqrt{3}\sin x$$
$$2\sin x\cos x - \sqrt{3}\sin x = 0$$
$$\sin x\left(2\cos x - \sqrt{3}\right) = 0$$
$$\sin x = 0 \quad \text{or} \quad 2\cos x - \sqrt{3} = 0$$
$$x = 0 \;\; x = \pi \qquad 2\cos x = \sqrt{3}$$
$$\cos x = \frac{\sqrt{3}}{2}$$
$$x = \frac{\pi}{6} \qquad x = \frac{11\pi}{6}$$

The solutions in the interval $[0, 2\pi)$ are 0,
$$\frac{\pi}{6}, \pi, \text{ and } \frac{11\pi}{6}.$$

63. $\sin x = \tan x$

$$\sin x = \frac{\sin x}{\cos x}$$
$$\sin x \cdot \cos x = \sin x$$
$$\sin x\cos x - \sin x = 0$$
$$\sin x(\cos x - 1) = 0$$
$$\sin x = 0 \quad \text{or} \quad \cos x - 1 = 0$$
$$x = 0 \;\; x = \pi \qquad \cos x = 1$$
$$x = 0$$

The solutions in the interval $[0, 2\pi)$ are 0 and π.

64. $\sin x = -0.6031$

Be sure calculator is in radian mode and find the inverse sine of $+0.6031$. This gives the first quadrant reference angle.

$\theta = \sin^{-1}(0.6031) \approx 0.6474$

The sine is negative in quadrants III and IV thus,

$x \approx \pi + 0.6474$ or $x \approx 2\pi - 0.6474$

$x \approx 3.7890$ $x \approx 5.6358$

65. $5\cos^2 x - 3 = 0$

$\cos^2 x = \dfrac{3}{5}$

$\cos x = \pm\sqrt{\dfrac{3}{5}}$

$\cos x = \pm\dfrac{\sqrt{15}}{5}$

$\cos x \approx 0.7746$ or $\cos x \approx -0.7746$

$x \approx 0.6847,\ 5.5985$ $x \approx 2.4569,\ 3.8263$

66. $1 + \tan^2 x = 4\tan x - 2$

$\tan^2 x - 4\tan x + 3 = 0$

$(\tan x - 1)(\tan x - 3) = 0$

$\tan x = 1$ or $\tan x = 3$

$x = \dfrac{\pi}{4}, \dfrac{5\pi}{4}$ $x \approx 1.2490,\ 4.3906$

67. $2\sin^2 x + \sin x - 2 = 0$

$\sin x = \dfrac{-b \pm \sqrt{b^2 - 4ac}}{2a}$

$\sin x = \dfrac{-(1) \pm \sqrt{(1)^2 - 4(2)(-2)}}{2(2)}$

$\sin x = \dfrac{-1 \pm \sqrt{17}}{4}$

$\sin x = 0.7808$ or $\sin x = -1.2808$

$x = 0.8959,\ 2.2457$ $\cancel{\sin x = -1.2808}$

68. Substitute $d = -3$ into the equation and solve for t:

$-3 = -6\cos\dfrac{\pi}{2}t$

$\dfrac{-3}{-6} = \dfrac{-6\cos\frac{\pi}{2}t}{-6}$

$\dfrac{1}{2} = \cos\dfrac{\pi}{2}t$

$\cos\dfrac{\pi}{2}t = \dfrac{1}{2}$

The period of the cosine function is 2π. In the interval $[0, 2\pi)$, there are two values at which the cosine function is $\dfrac{1}{2}$. One is $\dfrac{\pi}{3}$. The cosine function is positive in quadrant IV. Thus, the other value is $2\pi - \dfrac{\pi}{3} = \dfrac{5\pi}{3}$.

All solutions to $\cos\dfrac{\pi}{2}t = \dfrac{1}{2}$ are given by

$\dfrac{\pi}{2}t = \dfrac{\pi}{3} + 2n\pi$

$\dfrac{\pi}{2}t = \dfrac{5\pi}{3} + 2n\pi$

$t = \dfrac{2}{3} + 4n$ or

$t = \dfrac{10}{3} + 4n$

where n is any integer.

69. Substitute $v_0 = 90$ and $d = 100$, and solve for θ:

$100 = \dfrac{90^2}{16}\sin\theta\cos\theta$

$\dfrac{16}{81} = \sin\theta\cos\theta$

$2\cdot\dfrac{16}{81} = 2\sin\theta\cos\theta$

$\dfrac{32}{81} = \sin 2\theta$

$\sin 2\theta = \dfrac{32}{81}$

The period of the sine function is $360°$. In the interval $[0, 360°)$, there are two values at which the sine function is $\dfrac{32}{81}$. One is $\sin^{-1}\left(\dfrac{32}{81}\right) \approx 23.27°$. The sine function is positive in quadrant II. Thus, the other value is $180° - 23.27° = 156.73°$. All solutions to $\sin 2\theta = \dfrac{32}{81}$ are given by

$2\theta = 23.27° + 360°n$

$\theta = 11.635° + 180°n$

or

$2\theta = 156.73° + 360°n$

$\theta = 78.365° + 180°n$

where n is any integer.

In the interval $[0, 90°)$ we obtain the solutions by letting $n = 0$. The solutions are approximately $12°$ and $78°$. Therefore, the angle of elevation should be $12°$ or $78°$.

Chapter 5 Test

For problems 1–4: $\sin \alpha = \dfrac{4}{5} = \dfrac{y}{r}$

Because α lies in quadrant II, x is negative.

$x^2 + 4^2 = 5^2$

$\quad x^2 = 5^2 - 4^2 = 9$

$\quad\quad x = -\sqrt{9} = -3$

Thus, $\cos \alpha = \dfrac{x}{r} = \dfrac{-3}{5} = -\dfrac{3}{5}$, and

$\tan \alpha = \dfrac{y}{x} = \dfrac{4}{-3} = -\dfrac{4}{3}$.

$\cos \beta = \dfrac{5}{13} = \dfrac{x}{r}$

Because β lies in quadrant I, y is positive.

$5^2 + y^2 = 13^2$

$\quad y^2 = 13^2 - 5^2 = 144$

$\quad\quad y = \sqrt{144} = 12$

Thus, $\sin \beta = \dfrac{y}{r} = \dfrac{12}{13}$, and $\tan \beta = \dfrac{y}{x} = \dfrac{12}{5}$.

1. $\cos(\alpha + \beta) = \cos \alpha \cos \beta - \sin \alpha \sin \beta$

$\quad = -\dfrac{3}{5} \cdot \dfrac{5}{13} - \dfrac{4}{5} \cdot \dfrac{12}{13} = -\dfrac{63}{65}$

2. $\tan(\alpha - \beta) = \dfrac{\tan \alpha - \tan \beta}{1 + \tan \alpha \tan \beta}$

$\quad = \dfrac{-\frac{4}{3} - \frac{12}{5}}{1 + \left(-\frac{4}{3}\right) \cdot \frac{12}{5}} = \dfrac{-\frac{56}{15}}{-\frac{33}{15}} = \dfrac{56}{33}$

3. $\sin 2\alpha = 2 \sin \alpha \cos \alpha = 2\left(\dfrac{4}{5}\right)\left(-\dfrac{3}{5}\right) = -\dfrac{24}{25}$

4. $\cos \dfrac{\beta}{2} = \sqrt{\dfrac{1 + \cos \beta}{2}} = \sqrt{\dfrac{1 + \frac{5}{13}}{2}} = \sqrt{\dfrac{18}{26}}$

$\quad = \dfrac{3\sqrt{2}}{\sqrt{26}} = \dfrac{3\sqrt{52}}{26} = \dfrac{3 \cdot 2\sqrt{13}}{26}$

$\quad = \dfrac{3\sqrt{13}}{13}$

5. $\sin 105° = \sin(135° - 30°)$

$\quad = \sin 135° \cos 30° - \cos 135° \sin 30°$

$\quad = \dfrac{\sqrt{2}}{2} \cdot \dfrac{\sqrt{3}}{2} - \left(-\dfrac{\sqrt{2}}{2}\right) \cdot \dfrac{1}{2}$

$\quad = \dfrac{\sqrt{6}}{4} + \dfrac{\sqrt{2}}{4} = \dfrac{\sqrt{6} + \sqrt{2}}{4}$

6. $\cos x \csc x = \cos x \cdot \dfrac{1}{\sin x} = \dfrac{\cos x}{\sin x} = \cot x$

7. $\dfrac{\sec x}{\cot x + \tan x} = \dfrac{\frac{1}{\cos x}}{\frac{\cos x}{\sin x} + \frac{\sin x}{\cos x}}$

$\quad = \dfrac{\frac{1}{\cos x}}{\frac{\cos x}{\sin x} \cdot \frac{\cos x}{\cos x} + \frac{\sin x}{\cos x} \cdot \frac{\sin x}{\sin x}}$

$\quad = \dfrac{\frac{1}{\cos x}}{\frac{\cos^2 x + \sin^2 x}{\sin x \cos x}} = \dfrac{\frac{1}{\cos x}}{\frac{1}{\sin x \cos x}}$

$\quad = \dfrac{1}{\cos x} \cdot \dfrac{\sin x \cos x}{1}$

$\quad = \sin x$

8. $1 - \dfrac{\cos^2 x}{1 + \sin x} = 1 - \dfrac{\left(1 - \sin^2 x\right)}{1 + \sin x}$

$\quad = 1 - \dfrac{(1 + \sin x)(1 - \sin x)}{1 + \sin x}$

$\quad = 1 - (1 - \sin x)$

$\quad = \sin x$

9. $\cos\left(\theta + \dfrac{\pi}{2}\right) = \cos \theta \cos \dfrac{\pi}{2} - \sin \theta \sin \dfrac{\pi}{2}$

$\quad = \cos \theta \cdot 0 - \sin \theta \cdot 1$

$\quad = -\sin \theta$

10. $\dfrac{\sin(\alpha - \beta)}{\sin \alpha \cos \beta} = \dfrac{\sin \alpha \cos \beta - \cos \alpha \sin \beta}{\sin \alpha \cos \beta}$

$\quad = \dfrac{\sin \alpha \cos \beta}{\sin \alpha \cos \beta} - \dfrac{\cos \alpha \sin \beta}{\sin \alpha \cos \beta}$

$\quad = 1 - \cot \alpha \tan \beta$

11. $\sin t \cos t(\tan t + \cot t) = \sin t \cos t\left(\dfrac{\sin t}{\cos t} + \dfrac{\cos t}{\sin t}\right)$

$\quad = \dfrac{\sin^2 t \cos t}{\cos t} + \dfrac{\sin t \cos^2 t}{\sin t}$

$\quad = \sin^2 t + \cos^2 t$

$\quad = 1$

12. The period of the sine function is 2π. In the interval $[0, 2\pi)$, there are two values at which the sine function is $-\dfrac{1}{2}$. One is $\pi + \dfrac{\pi}{6} = \dfrac{7\pi}{6}$.

The other is $2\pi - \dfrac{\pi}{6} = \dfrac{11\pi}{6}$. All the solutions to $\sin 3x = -\dfrac{1}{2}$ are given by $3x = \dfrac{7\pi}{6} + 2n\pi$

$$x = \dfrac{7\pi}{18} + \dfrac{2n\pi}{3}$$

or

$$3x = \dfrac{11\pi}{6} + 2n\pi$$

$$x = \dfrac{11\pi}{18} + \dfrac{2n\pi}{3}$$

where n is any integer. The solutions in the interval $[0, 2\pi)$ are obtained by letting $n = 0$, $n = 1$, and $n = 2$.

The solutions are $\dfrac{7\pi}{18}, \dfrac{11\pi}{18}, \dfrac{19\pi}{18}, \dfrac{23\pi}{18},$

$\dfrac{31\pi}{18},$ and $\dfrac{35\pi}{18}$.

13. $\sin 2x + \cos x = 0$

$2\sin x \cos x + \cos x = 0$

$\cos x(2\sin x + 1) = 0$

$\cos x = 0$ or $2\sin x + 1 = 0$

$x = \dfrac{\pi}{2}$ $x = \dfrac{3\pi}{2}$ $2\sin x = -1$

$$\sin x = -\dfrac{1}{2}$$

$$x = \dfrac{7\pi}{6} \quad x = \dfrac{11\pi}{6}$$

The solutions in the interval $[0, 2\pi)$ are $\dfrac{\pi}{2}$,

$\dfrac{7\pi}{6}, \dfrac{3\pi}{2},$ and $\dfrac{11\pi}{6}$.

14. $2\cos^2 x - 3\cos x + 1 = 0$

$(2\cos x - 1)(\cos x - 1) = 0$

$2\cos x - 1 = 0$ or $\cos x - 1 = 0$

$2\cos x = 1$ $\cos x = 1$

$\cos x = \dfrac{1}{2}$ $x = 0$

$x = \dfrac{\pi}{3}$ $x = \dfrac{5\pi}{3}$

The solutions in the interval $[0, 2\pi)$ are

$0, \dfrac{\pi}{3},$ and $\dfrac{5\pi}{3}$.

15. $2\sin^2 x + \cos x = 1$

$2\left(1 - \cos^2 x\right) + \cos x - 1 = 0$

$2 - 2\cos^2 x + \cos x - 1 = 0$

$-2\cos^2 x + \cos x + 1 = 0$

$2\cos^2 x - \cos x - 1 = 0$

$(2\cos x + 1)(\cos x - 1) = 0$

$2\cos x + 1 = 0$ or $\cos x - 1 = 0$

$2\cos x = -1$ $\cos x = 1$

$\cos x = -\dfrac{1}{2}$ $x = 0$

$x = \dfrac{2\pi}{3}$ $x = \dfrac{4\pi}{3}$

The solutions in the interval $[0, 2\pi)$ are

$0, \dfrac{2\pi}{3},$ and $\dfrac{4\pi}{3}$.

16. $\cos x = -0.8092$

Be sure calculator is in radian mode and find the inverse cosine of $+0.8092$. This gives the first quadrant reference angle.

$\theta = \cos^{-1}(0.8092) \approx 0.6280$

The cosine is negative in quadrants II and III thus,

$x \approx \pi - 0.6280$ or $x \approx \pi + 0.6280$

$x \approx 2.5136$ $x \approx 3.7696$

17.
$$\tan x \sec x = 3 \tan x$$
$$\tan x \sec x - 3 \tan x = 0$$
$$\tan x (\sec x - 3) = 0$$
$$\tan x = 0 \quad \text{or} \quad \sec x - 3 = 0$$
$$\sec x = 3$$
$$x = 0, \ \pi$$
$$\cos x = \frac{1}{3}$$
$$x \approx 1.2310, \ 5.0522$$

18. $\tan^2 x - 3 \tan x - 2 = 0$
$$\tan x = \frac{-b \pm \sqrt{b^2 - 4ac}}{2a}$$
$$\tan x = \frac{-(-3) \pm \sqrt{(-3)^2 - 4(1)(-2)}}{2(1)}$$
$$\tan x = \frac{3 \pm \sqrt{17}}{2}$$
$$\tan x \approx 3.5616 \quad \text{or} \quad \tan x \approx -0.5616$$
$$x \approx 1.2971, \ 4.4387 \qquad x \approx 2.6299, \ 5.7715$$

Cumulative Review Exercises (Chapters P–5)

1. $x^3 + x^2 - x + 15 = 0$

The possible rational zeros are: $\pm 1, \pm 3, \pm 5, \pm 15$.
Synthetic division shows that -3 is a zero:

$$
\begin{array}{r|rrrr}
-3 & 1 & 1 & -1 & 15 \\
   &   & -3 & 6 & -15 \\
\hline
   & 1 & -2 & 5 & 0
\end{array}
$$

The quotient is $x^2 - 2x + 5$. The remaining zeros are found using the quadratic formula:
$$x = \frac{-(-2) \pm \sqrt{(-2)^2 - 4(1)(5)}}{2(1)}$$
$$= \frac{2 \pm \sqrt{4 - 20}}{2}$$
$$= \frac{2 \pm \sqrt{-16}}{2}$$
$$= \frac{2 \pm 4i}{2}$$
$$= 1 \pm 2i$$
All solutions are: -3, $1 + 2i$ and $1 - 2i$.

2.
$$11^{x-1} = 125$$
$$\log 11^{x-1} = \log 125$$
$$(x-1)\log 11 = \log 125$$
$$x - 1 = \frac{\log 125}{\log 11}$$
$$x = \frac{\log 125}{\log 11} + 1$$
or $x \approx 3.01$

3. $x^2 + 2x - 8 > 0$

$(x - 2)(x + 4) > 0$

zero points are $x = 2$ and $x = -4$.

Test Interval	Representative Number	Substitute into $x^2 + 2x - 8 > 0$	Conclusion
$(-\infty, -4)$	-5	$(-5)^2 + 2(-5) - 8 = 25 - 10 - 8 = 7 > 0$	$(-\infty, -4)$ belongs to the solution set.
$(-4, 2)$	0	$0^2 + 2(0) - 8 = -8 > 0$	$(-4, 2)$ does not belong to the solution set.
$(2, \infty)$	3	$3^2 + 2(3) - 8 = 9 + 6 - 8 = 7 > 0$	$(2, \infty)$ belongs to the solution set.

The solution intervals are $(-\infty, -4) \cup (2, \infty)$.

4. $\cos 2x + 3 = 5\cos x$

$2\cos^2 x - 1 + 3 = 5\cos x$

$2\cos^2 x - 5\cos x + 2 = 0$

$(2\cos x - 1)(\cos x - 2) = 0$

$2\cos x - 1 = 0 \quad \text{or} \quad \cos x - 2 = 0$

$2\cos x = 1 \qquad \cos x = 2$

$\cos x = \dfrac{1}{2} \qquad$ cos x cannot be greater than 1.

$x = \dfrac{\pi}{3} \quad x = \dfrac{5\pi}{3}$

The solutions in the interval $[0, 2\pi)$ are

$\dfrac{\pi}{3}$ and $\dfrac{5\pi}{3}$.

5. $\tan x + \sec^2 x = 3$

$\tan x + 1 + \tan^2 x = 3$

$\tan^2 x + \tan x - 2 = 0$

$(\tan x - 1)(\tan x + 2) = 0$

$\tan x - 1 = 0 \quad \text{or} \quad \tan x + 2 = 0$

$\tan x = 1 \qquad \tan x = -2$

$x = \dfrac{\pi}{4}, \dfrac{5\pi}{4} \qquad x \approx 2.0344, \ 5.1760$

6.

$y = \sqrt{x + 2} - 1$

Shift the graph of $y = \sqrt{x}$ left 2 units and down 1 unit.

7.

$(x - 1)^2 + (y + 2)^2 = 9$

8.

$y + 2 = \dfrac{1}{3}(x - 1)$

9.

$y = 3 \cos 2x$

10.

$y = 2 \sin \dfrac{x}{2} + 1$

11.

$f(x) = (x-1)^2 (x-3)$

12. $f(x) = x^2 + 3x - 1$

$\dfrac{f(a+h) - f(a)}{h}$

$= \dfrac{(a+h)^2 + 3(a+h) - 1 - \left(a^2 + 3a - 1\right)}{h}$

$= \dfrac{a^2 + 2ah + h^2 + 3a + 3h - 1 - a^2 - 3a + 1}{h}$

$= \dfrac{2ah + h^2 + 3h}{h}$

$= 2a + h + 3$

13. $\sin 225° = \sin(180° + 45°)$

$= \sin 180° \cos 45° + \cos 180° \sin 45°$

$= 0 \cdot \dfrac{\sqrt{2}}{2} + (-1) \cdot \dfrac{\sqrt{2}}{2}$

$= -\dfrac{\sqrt{2}}{2}$

14. $\sec^4 x - \sec^2 x$

$= \sec^2 x \cdot \sec^2 x - \sec^2 x$

$= \left(1 + \tan^2 x\right)\left(1 + \tan^2 x\right) - \left(1 + \tan^2 x\right)$

$= 1 + 2\tan^2 x + \tan^4 x - 1 - \tan^2 x$

$= \tan^4 x + \tan^2 x$

We worked with the left side and arrived at the right side. Thus, the identity is verified.

15. $320° \times \dfrac{\pi}{180°} = \dfrac{16}{9}\pi$ or 5.59 radians

16.

$A = Pe^{rt}$

$3P = Pe^{0.0575t}$

$3 = e^{0.0575t}$

$\ln 3 = \ln e^{0.0575t}$

$\ln 3 = 0.0575t$

$\dfrac{\ln 3}{0.0575} = t$

$t \approx 19.1$ years

17.

$f(x) = \dfrac{2x+1}{x-3}$

$y = \dfrac{2x+1}{x-3}$

$x = \dfrac{2y+1}{y-3}$

$x(y-3) = 2y+1$

$xy - 3x = 2y+1$

$xy - 2y = 3x+1$

$y(x-2) = 3x+1$

$y = \dfrac{3x+1}{x-2}$

$f^{-1}(x) = \dfrac{3x+1}{x-2}$

18. The third angle is:
     $B = 180° - 90° - 23° = 67°$.

     Since $\sin\theta = \dfrac{\text{opposite}}{\text{hypotenuse}}$,

     $\sin A = \sin 23° = \dfrac{12}{c}$

     $c = \dfrac{12}{\sin 23°} \approx 30.71$ and

     $\sin B = \sin 67° = \dfrac{b}{30.71}$

     $b = 30.71 \cdot \sin 67° \approx 28.27$
     The angles are 90°, 23°, and 67°.
     The sides are 12, 30.71, and 28.27.

19. $8.5 = \dfrac{12}{150} \cdot a$

     where a is the adult dose.

     $a = \dfrac{(8.5) \cdot 150}{12}$

     $\quad = 106.25$ mg

     $a \approx 106$ mg

20.. Let h be the height of the flagpole. Then

     $\tan 53° = \dfrac{h}{12}$

     $\quad h = 12 \cdot \tan 53°$

     $\quad h \approx 15.9$ feet

Chapter 6

Section 6.1

Check Point Exercises

1. Begin by finding B, the third angle of the triangle.

$$A + B + C = 180°$$
$$64° + B + 82° = 180°$$
$$146° + B = 180°$$
$$B = 34°$$

In this problem, we are given c and C: $c = 14$ and $C = 82°$. Thus, Use the ratio $\dfrac{c}{\sin C}$, or $\dfrac{14}{\sin 82°}$, to find the other two sides.

Use the Law of Sines to find a.

$$\frac{a}{\sin A} = \frac{c}{\sin C}$$
$$\frac{a}{\sin 64°} = \frac{14}{\sin 82°}$$
$$a = \frac{14 \sin 64°}{\sin 82°}$$
$$a \approx 13 \text{ centimeters}$$

Use the Law of Sines again, this time to find b.

$$\frac{b}{\sin B} = \frac{c}{\sin C}$$
$$\frac{b}{\sin 34°} = \frac{14}{\sin 82°}$$
$$b = \frac{14 \sin 34°}{\sin 82°}$$
$$b \approx 8 \text{ centimeters}$$

The solution is $B = 34°$, $a \approx 13$ centimeters, and $b \approx 8$ centimeters.

2. Begin by finding B.

$$A + B + C = 180°$$
$$40° + B + 22.5° = 180°$$
$$62.5° + B = 180°$$
$$B = 117.5°$$

In this problem, we are given that $b = 12$ and we find that $B = 117.5°$. Thus, Use the ratio $\dfrac{b}{\sin B}$, or $\dfrac{12}{\sin 117.5°}$, to find the other two sides.

Use the Law of Sines to find a.

$$\frac{a}{\sin A} = \frac{b}{\sin B}$$
$$\frac{a}{\sin 40°} = \frac{12}{\sin 117.5°}$$
$$a = \frac{12 \sin 40°}{\sin 117.5°} \approx 9$$

Use the Law of Sines again, this time to find c.

$$\frac{c}{\sin C} = \frac{b}{\sin B}$$
$$\frac{c}{\sin 22.5°} = \frac{12}{\sin 117.5°}$$
$$c = \frac{12 \sin 22.5°}{\sin 117.5°} \approx 5$$

The solution is $B = 117.5°$, $a \approx 9$, and $c \approx 5$.

3. The known ratio is $\dfrac{a}{\sin A}$, or $\dfrac{33}{\sin 57°}$. Because side b is given, Use the Law of Sines to find angle B.

$$\frac{a}{\sin A} = \frac{b}{\sin B}$$
$$\frac{33}{\sin 57°} = \frac{26}{\sin B}$$
$$33 \sin B = 26 \sin 57°$$
$$\sin B = \frac{26 \sin 57°}{33} \approx 0.6608$$
$$\sin B \approx 0.6608$$
$$B \approx 41°$$

$180° - 41° = 139°$ also has this sine value, but, the sum of $57°$ and $139°$ exceeds $180°$, so B cannot have this value.

$C = 180° - B - A = 180° - 41° - 57° = 82°$. Use the law of sines to find C.

$$\frac{a}{\sin A} = \frac{c}{\sin C}$$
$$\frac{33}{\sin 57°} = \frac{c}{\sin 82°}$$
$$c = \frac{33 \sin 82°}{\sin 57°}$$
$$c \approx 39$$

Thus, $B \approx 41°$, $C \approx 82°$, $c \approx 39$.

4. The known ratio is $\dfrac{a}{\sin A}$, or $\dfrac{10}{\sin 50°}$. Because side b is given, Use the Law of Sines to find angle B.

$$\frac{a}{\sin A}=\frac{b}{\sin B}$$

$$\frac{10}{\sin 50^\circ}=\frac{20}{\sin B}$$

$$10\sin B = 20\sin 50^\circ$$

$$\sin B = \frac{20\sin 50^\circ}{10}\approx 1.53$$

Because the sine can never exceed 1, there is no angle B for which $\sin B \approx 1.53$. There is no triangle with the given measurements.

5. The known ratio is $\dfrac{a}{\sin A}$, or $\dfrac{12}{\sin 35^\circ}$. Because side b is given, Use the Law of Sines to find angle B.

$$\frac{a}{\sin A}=\frac{b}{\sin B}$$

$$\frac{12}{\sin 35^\circ}=\frac{16}{\sin B}$$

$$12\sin B = 16\sin 35^\circ$$

$$\sin B = \frac{16\sin 35^\circ}{12}\approx 0.7648$$

There are two angles possible:
$B_1 \approx 50^\circ$, $B_2 \approx 180^\circ - 50^\circ = 130^\circ$

There are two triangles:
$C_1 = 180^\circ - A - B_1 \approx 180^\circ - 35^\circ - 50^\circ = 95^\circ$
$C_2 = 180^\circ - A - B_2 \approx 180^\circ - 35^\circ - 130^\circ = 15^\circ$

Use the Law of Sines to find c_1 and c_2.

$$\frac{c_1}{\sin C_1}=\frac{a}{\sin A}$$

$$\frac{c_1}{\sin 95^\circ}=\frac{12}{\sin 35^\circ}$$

$$c_1 = \frac{12\sin 95^\circ}{\sin 35^\circ}\approx 21$$

$$\frac{c_2}{\sin C_2}=\frac{a}{\sin A}$$

$$\frac{c_2}{\sin 15^\circ}=\frac{12}{\sin 35^\circ}$$

$$c_2 = \frac{12\sin 15^\circ}{\sin 35^\circ}\approx 5$$

In one triangle, the solution is $B_1 \approx 50^\circ$, $C_1 \approx 95^\circ$, and $c_1 \approx 21$. In the other triangle, $B_2 \approx 130^\circ$, $C_2 \approx 15^\circ$, and $c_2 \approx 5$.

6. The area of the triangle is half the product of the lengths of the two sides times the sine of the included angle.

$$\text{Area} = \frac{1}{2}(8)(12)(\sin 135^\circ)\approx 34$$

The area of the triangle is approximately 34 square meters.

7.

Using a north-south line, the interior angles are found as follows:
$A = 90^\circ - 35^\circ = 55^\circ$

$B = 90^\circ - 49^\circ = 41^\circ$

Find angle C using a 180° angle sum in the triangle.
$C = 180^\circ - A - B = 180^\circ - 55^\circ - 41^\circ = 84^\circ$

The ratio $\dfrac{c}{\sin C}$, or $\dfrac{13}{\sin 84^\circ}$ is now known. Use this ratio and the Law of Sines to find a.

$$\frac{a}{\sin A}=\frac{c}{\sin C}$$

$$\frac{a}{\sin 55^\circ}=\frac{13}{\sin 84^\circ}$$

$$a = \frac{13\sin 55^\circ}{\sin 84^\circ}\approx 11$$

The fire is approximately 11 miles from station B.

Exercise Set 6.1

1. Begin by finding B.
$$A + B + C = 180^\circ$$
$$42^\circ + B + 96^\circ = 180^\circ$$
$$138^\circ + B = 180^\circ$$
$$B = 42^\circ$$

Use the ratio $\dfrac{c}{\sin C}$, or $\dfrac{12}{\sin 96^\circ}$, to find the other two sides. Use the Law of Sines to find a.

$$\frac{a}{\sin A} = \frac{c}{\sin C}$$

$$\frac{a}{\sin 42°} = \frac{12}{\sin 96°}$$

$$a = \frac{12 \sin 42°}{\sin 96°}$$

$$a \approx 8.1$$

Use the Law of Sines again, this time to find b.

$$\frac{b}{\sin B} = \frac{c}{\sin C}$$

$$\frac{b}{\sin 42°} = \frac{12}{\sin 96°}$$

$$b = \frac{12 \sin 42°}{\sin 96°}$$

$$b \approx 8.1$$

The solution is $B = 42°$, $a \approx 8.1$, and $b \approx 8.1$.

3. Begin by finding A.

$$A + B + C = 180°$$

$$A + 54° + 82° = 180°$$

$$A + 136° = 180°$$

$$A = 44°$$

Use the ratio $\dfrac{a}{\sin A}$, or $\dfrac{16}{\sin 44°}$, to find the other two sides. Use the Law of Sines to find b.

$$\frac{b}{\sin B} = \frac{a}{\sin A}$$

$$\frac{b}{\sin 54°} = \frac{16}{\sin 44°}$$

$$b = \frac{16 \sin 54°}{\sin 44°}$$

$$b \approx 18.6$$

Use the Law of Sines again, this time to find c.

$$\frac{c}{\sin C} = \frac{a}{\sin A}$$

$$\frac{c}{\sin 82°} = \frac{16}{\sin 44°}$$

$$c = \frac{16 \sin 82°}{\sin 44°}$$

$$c \approx 22.8$$

The solution is $A = 44°$, $b \approx 18.6$, and $c \approx 22.8$.

5. Begin by finding C.

$$A + B + C = 180°$$

$$48° + 37° + C = 180°$$

$$85° + C = 180°$$

$$C = 95°$$

Use the ratio $\dfrac{a}{\sin A}$, or $\dfrac{100}{\sin 48°}$, to find the other two sides. Use the Law of Sines to find b.

$$\frac{b}{\sin B} = \frac{a}{\sin A}$$

$$\frac{b}{\sin 37°} = \frac{100}{\sin 48°}$$

$$b = \frac{100 \sin 37°}{\sin 48°}$$

$$b \approx 81.0$$

Use the Law of Sines again, this time to find c.

$$\frac{c}{\sin C} = \frac{a}{\sin A}$$

$$\frac{c}{\sin 95°} = \frac{100}{\sin 48°}$$

$$c = \frac{100 \sin 95°}{\sin 48°}$$

$$c \approx 134.1$$

The solution is $C = 95°$, $b \approx 81.0$, and $c \approx 134.1$.

7. Begin by finding B.

$$A + B + C = 180°$$

$$38° + B + 102° = 180°$$

$$B + 140° = 180°$$

$$B = 40°$$

Use the ratio $\dfrac{a}{\sin A}$, or $\dfrac{20}{\sin 38°}$, to find the other two sides. Use the Law of Sines to find b.

$$\frac{b}{\sin B} = \frac{a}{\sin A}$$

$$\frac{b}{\sin 40°} = \frac{20}{\sin 38°}$$

$$b = \frac{20 \sin 40°}{\sin 38°}$$

$$b \approx 20.9$$

Use the Law of Sines again, this time to find c.

$$\frac{c}{\sin C} = \frac{a}{\sin A}$$

$$\frac{c}{\sin 102°} = \frac{20}{\sin 38°}$$

$$c = \frac{20 \sin 102°}{\sin 38°}$$

$$c \approx 31.8$$

The solution is $B = 40°$, $b \approx 20.9$, and $c \approx 31.8$.

9.   Begin by finding C.

$$A + B + C = 180°$$

$$44° + 25° + C = 180°$$

$$69° + C = 180°$$

$$C = 111°$$

Use the ratio $\dfrac{a}{\sin A}$, or $\dfrac{12}{\sin 44°}$, to find the other two sides. Use the Law of Sines to find b.

$$\frac{b}{\sin B} = \frac{a}{\sin A}$$

$$\frac{b}{\sin 25°} = \frac{12}{\sin 44°}$$

$$b = \frac{12 \sin 25°}{\sin 44°}$$

$$b \approx 7.3$$

Use the Law of Sines again, this time to find c.

$$\frac{c}{\sin C} = \frac{a}{\sin A}$$

$$\frac{c}{\sin 111°} = \frac{12}{\sin 44°}$$

$$c = \frac{12 \sin 111°}{\sin 44°}$$

$$c \approx 16.1$$

The solution is $C = 111°$, $b \approx 7.3$, and $c \approx 16.1$.

11.   Begin by finding A.

$$A + B + C = 180°$$

$$A + 85° + 15° = 180°$$

$$A + 100° = 180°$$

$$A = 80°$$

Use the ratio $\dfrac{b}{\sin B}$, or $\dfrac{40}{\sin 85°}$, to find the other two sides. Use the Law of Sines to find a.

$$\frac{a}{\sin A} = \frac{b}{\sin B}$$

$$\frac{a}{\sin 80°} = \frac{40}{\sin 85°}$$

$$a = \frac{40 \sin 80°}{\sin 85°}$$

$$a \approx 39.5$$

Use the Law of Sines again, this time to find c.

$$\frac{c}{\sin C} = \frac{b}{\sin B}$$

$$\frac{c}{\sin 15°} = \frac{40}{\sin 85°}$$

$$c = \frac{40 \sin 15°}{\sin 85°}$$

$$c \approx 10.4$$

The solution is $A = 80°$, $a \approx 39.5$, and $c \approx 10.4$.

13.   Begin by finding B.

$$A + B + C = 180°$$

$$115° + B + 35° = 180°$$

$$B + 150° = 180°$$

$$B = 30°$$

Use the ratio $\dfrac{c}{\sin C}$, or $\dfrac{200}{\sin 35°}$, to find the other two sides. Use the Law of Sines to find a.

$$\frac{a}{\sin A} = \frac{c}{\sin C}$$

$$\frac{a}{\sin 115°} = \frac{200}{\sin 35°}$$

$$a = \frac{200 \sin 115°}{\sin 35°}$$

$$a \approx 316.0$$

Use the Law of Sines again, this time to find b.

$$\frac{b}{\sin B} = \frac{c}{\sin C}$$

$$\frac{b}{\sin 30°} = \frac{200}{\sin 35°}$$

$$b = \frac{200 \sin 30°}{\sin 35°}$$

$$b \approx 174.3$$

The solution is $B = 30°$, $a \approx 316.0$, and $b \approx 174.3$.

15. Begin by finding C.

$$A + B + C = 180°$$
$$65° + 65° + C = 180°$$
$$130° + C = 180°$$
$$C = 50°$$

Use the ratio $\dfrac{c}{\sin C}$, or $\dfrac{6}{\sin 50°}$, to find the other two sides. Use the Law of Sines to find a.

$$\frac{a}{\sin A} = \frac{c}{\sin C}$$
$$\frac{a}{\sin 65°} = \frac{6}{\sin 50°}$$
$$a = \frac{6\sin 65°}{\sin 50°}$$
$$a \approx 7.1$$

Use the Law of Sines to find angle B.

$$\frac{b}{\sin B} = \frac{c}{\sin C}$$
$$\frac{b}{\sin 65°} = \frac{6}{\sin 50°}$$
$$b = \frac{6\sin 65°}{\sin 50°}$$
$$b \approx 7.1$$

The solution is $C = 50°$, $a \approx 7.1$, and $b \approx 7.1$.

17. The known ratio is $\dfrac{a}{\sin A}$, or $\dfrac{20}{\sin 40°}$.
Use the Law of Sines to find angle B.

$$\frac{a}{\sin A} = \frac{b}{\sin B}$$
$$\frac{20}{\sin 40°} = \frac{15}{\sin B}$$
$$20\sin B = 15\sin 40°$$
$$\sin B = \frac{15\sin 40°}{20}$$
$$\sin B \approx 0.4821$$

There are two angles possible:
$B_1 \approx 29°$, $B_2 \approx 180° - 29° = 151°$

B_2 is impossible, since $40° + 151° = 191°$.

We find C using B_1 and the given information $A = 40°$.
$$C = 180° - B_1 - A \approx 180° - 29° - 40° = 111°$$
Use the Law of Sines to find side c.

$$\frac{c}{\sin C} = \frac{a}{\sin A}$$
$$\frac{c}{\sin 111°} = \frac{20}{\sin 40°}$$
$$c = \frac{20\sin 111°}{\sin 40°} \approx 29.0$$

There is one triangle and the solution is
B_1 (or B) $\approx 29°$, $C \approx 111°$, and $c \approx 29.0$.

19. The known ratio is $\dfrac{a}{\sin A}$, or $\dfrac{10}{\sin 63°}$.
Use the Law of Sines to find angle C.

$$\frac{a}{\sin A} = \frac{c}{\sin C}$$
$$\frac{10}{\sin 63°} = \frac{8.9}{\sin C}$$
$$10\sin C = 8.9\sin 63°$$
$$\sin C = \frac{8.9\sin 63°}{10}$$
$$\sin C \approx 0.7930$$

There are two angles possible:
$C_1 \approx 52°$, $C_2 \approx 180° - 52° = 128°$

C_2 is impossible, since $63° + 128° = 191°$.

We find B using C_1 and the given information $A = 63°$.
$$B = 180° - C_1 - A \approx 180° - 52° - 63° = 65°$$
Use the Law of Sines to find side b.

$$\frac{b}{\sin B} = \frac{a}{\sin A}$$
$$\frac{b}{\sin 65°} = \frac{10}{\sin 63°}$$
$$b = \frac{10\sin 65°}{\sin 63°} \approx 10.2$$

There is one triangle and the solution is
C_1 (or C) $\approx 52°$, $B \approx 65°$, and $b \approx 10.2$.

21. The known ratio is $\dfrac{a}{\sin A}$, or $\dfrac{42.1}{\sin 112°}$.

Use the Law of Sines to find angle C.

$$\frac{a}{\sin A} = \frac{c}{\sin C}$$

$$\frac{42.1}{\sin 112°} = \frac{37}{\sin C}$$

$$42.1\sin C = 37\sin 112°$$

$$\sin C = \frac{37\sin 112°}{42.1}$$

$$\sin C \approx 0.8149$$

There are two angles possible:

$C_1 \approx 55°$, $C_2 \approx 180° - 55° = 125°$

C_2 is impossible, since $112° + 125° = 237°$.

We find B using C_1 and the given information $A = 112°$.

$B = 180° - C_1 - A \approx 180° - 55° - 112° = 13°$

Use the Law of Sines to find b.

$$\frac{b}{\sin B} = \frac{a}{\sin A}$$

$$\frac{b}{\sin 13°} = \frac{42.1}{\sin 112°}$$

$$b = \frac{42.1\sin 13°}{\sin 112°} \approx 10.2$$

There is one triangle and the solution is
C_1 (or C) $\approx 55°$, $B \approx 13°$, and $b \approx 10.2$.

23. The known ratio is $\dfrac{a}{\sin A}$, or $\dfrac{10}{\sin 30°}$.

Use the Law of Sines to find angle B.

$$\frac{a}{\sin A} = \frac{b}{\sin B}$$

$$\frac{10}{\sin 30°} = \frac{40}{\sin B}$$

$$10\sin B = 40\sin 30°$$

$$\sin B = \frac{40\sin 30°}{10} = 2$$

Because the sine can never exceed 1, there is no angle B for which $\sin B = 2$. There is no triangle with the given measurements.

25. The known ratio is $\dfrac{a}{\sin A}$, or $\dfrac{16}{\sin 60°}$.

Use the Law of Sines to find angle B.

$$\frac{a}{\sin A} = \frac{b}{\sin B}$$

$$\frac{16}{\sin 60°} = \frac{18}{\sin B}$$

$$16\sin B = 18\sin 60°$$

$$\sin B = \frac{18\sin 60°}{16}$$

$$\sin B \approx 0.9743$$

There are two angles possible:

$B_1 \approx 77°$, $B_2 \approx 180° - 77° = 103°$

There are two triangles:

$C_1 = 180° - B_1 - A \approx 180° - 77° - 60° = 43°$

$C_2 = 180° - B_2 - A \approx 180° - 103° - 60° = 17°$ Use the Law of Sines to find c_1 and c_2.

$$\frac{c_1}{\sin C_1} = \frac{a}{\sin A}$$

$$\frac{c_1}{\sin 43°} = \frac{16}{\sin 60°}$$

$$c_1 = \frac{16\sin 43°}{\sin 60°} \approx 12.6$$

$$\frac{c_2}{\sin C_2} = \frac{a}{\sin A}$$

$$\frac{c_2}{\sin 17°} = \frac{16}{\sin 60°}$$

$$c_2 = \frac{16\sin 17°}{\sin 60°} \approx 5.4$$

In one triangle, the solution is
$B_1 \approx 77°$, $C_1 \approx 43°$, and $c_1 \approx 12.6$.
In the other triangle,
$B_2 \approx 103°$, $C_2 \approx 17°$, and $c_2 \approx 5.4$.

27. The known ratio is $\dfrac{a}{\sin A}$, or $\dfrac{12}{\sin 37°}$.

Use the Law of Sines to find angle B.

$$\frac{a}{\sin A} = \frac{b}{\sin B}$$

$$\frac{12}{\sin 37°} = \frac{16.1}{\sin B}$$

$$12\sin B = 16.1\sin 37°$$

$$\sin B = \frac{16.1\sin 37°}{12}$$

$$\sin B \approx 0.8074$$

There are two angles possible:
$B_1 \approx 54°$, $B_2 \approx 180° - 54° = 126°$

There are two triangles:

$$C_1 = 180° - B_1 - A \approx 180° - 54° - 37° = 89°$$
$$C_2 = 180° - B_2 - A \approx 180° - 126° - 37° = 17°$$ Use the Law of Sines to find c_1 and c_2.

$$\frac{c_1}{\sin C_1} = \frac{a}{\sin A}$$

$$\frac{c_1}{\sin 89°} = \frac{12}{\sin 37°}$$

$$c_1 = \frac{12 \sin 89°}{\sin 37°} \approx 19.9$$

$$\frac{c_2}{\sin C_2} = \frac{a}{\sin A}$$

$$\frac{c_2}{\sin 17°} = \frac{12}{\sin 37°}$$

$$c_2 = \frac{12 \sin 17°}{\sin 37°} \approx 5.8$$

In one triangle, the solution is
$B_1 \approx 54°$, $C_1 \approx 89°$, and $c_1 \approx 19.9$.
In the other triangle,
$B_2 \approx 126°$, $C_2 \approx 17°$, and $c_2 \approx 5.8$.

29. The known ratio is $\dfrac{a}{\sin A}$, or $\dfrac{22}{\sin 58°}$.
Use the Law of Sines to find angle C.

$$\frac{a}{\sin A} = \frac{c}{\sin C}$$

$$\frac{22}{\sin 58°} = \frac{24.1}{\sin C}$$

$$22 \sin C = 24.1 \sin 58°$$

$$\sin C = \frac{24.1 \sin 58°}{22}$$

$$\sin C \approx 0.9290$$

There are two angles possible:
$C_1 \approx 68°$, $C_2 \approx 180° - 68° = 112°$

There are two triangles:

$$B_1 = 180° - C_1 - A \approx 180° - 68° - 58° = 54°$$
$$B_2 = 180° - C_2 - A \approx 180° - 112° - 58° = 10°$$ Use the Law of Sines to find b_1 and b_2.

$$\frac{b_1}{\sin B_1} = \frac{a}{\sin A}$$

$$\frac{b_1}{\sin 54°} = \frac{22}{\sin 58°}$$

$$b_1 = \frac{22 \sin 54°}{\sin 58°} \approx 21.0$$

$$\frac{b_2}{\sin B_2} = \frac{a}{\sin A}$$

$$\frac{b_2}{\sin 10°} = \frac{22}{\sin 58°}$$

$$b_2 = \frac{22 \sin 10°}{\sin 58°} \approx 4.5$$

In one triangle, the solution is
$C_1 \approx 68°$, $B_1 \approx 54°$, and $b_1 \approx 21.0$.
In the other triangle,
$C_2 \approx 112°$, $B_2 \approx 10°$, and $b_2 \approx 4.5$.

31. The known ratio is $\dfrac{a}{\sin A}$, or $\dfrac{9.3}{\sin 18°}$.
Use the Law of Sines to find angle B.

$$\frac{a}{\sin A} = \frac{b}{\sin B}$$

$$\frac{9.3}{\sin 18°} = \frac{41}{\sin B}$$

$$9.3 \sin B = 41 \sin 18°$$

$$\sin B = \frac{41 \sin 18°}{9.3} \approx 1.36$$

Because the sine can never exceed 1, there is no angle B for which $\sin B = 1.36$. There is no triangle with the given measurements.

33. Area $= \dfrac{1}{2} bc \sin A = \dfrac{1}{2}(20)(40)(\sin 48°) \approx 297$
The area of the triangle is approximately 297 square feet.

35. Area $= \dfrac{1}{2} ac \sin B = \dfrac{1}{2}(3)(6)(\sin 36°) \approx 5$
The area of the triangle is approximately 5 square yards.

37. Area $= \dfrac{1}{2} ab \sin C = \dfrac{1}{2}(4)(6)(\sin 124°) \approx 10$
The area of the triangle is approximately 10 square meters.

39. $\angle ABC = 180° - 67° = 113°$

$\angle ACB = 180° - 43° - 113° = 24°$

Use the law of sines to find $\overline{BC}$.

$$\frac{\overline{BC}}{\sin 43°} = \frac{312}{\sin 24°}$$

$$\overline{BC} = \frac{312 \sin 43°}{\sin 24°}$$

$$\overline{BC} \approx 523.1$$

Use the law of sines to find h.

$$\frac{h}{\sin 67°} = \frac{523.1}{\sin 90°}$$

$$h = \frac{523.1 \sin 67°}{\sin 90°}$$

$$h \approx 481.5$$

41. Begin by finding the six angles inside the two triangles. Then use the law of sines.

$$\frac{a}{\sin 4°} = \frac{\dfrac{450 \sin 145°}{\sin 34°}}{\sin 30°}$$

$$a \approx 64.4$$

43.

$$\frac{a}{\sin A} = \frac{b}{\sin B}$$

$$\frac{300}{\sin 2\theta} = \frac{200}{\sin \theta}$$

$$200 \sin 2\theta = 300 \sin \theta$$

$$400 \sin \theta \cos \theta = 300 \sin \theta$$

$$\cos \theta = \frac{300 \sin \theta}{400 \sin \theta}$$

$$\cos \theta = \frac{3}{4}$$

$$\theta \approx 41°$$

$$2\theta \approx 82°$$

$$A \approx 82°, B \approx 41°, C \approx 57°, c \approx 255.7$$

45.

$$A = \frac{1}{2}bh$$

$$= \frac{1}{2}(5)(4)$$

$$= 10$$

47.

Using a north-south line, the interior angles are found as follows:

$A = 90° - 25° = 65°$

$B = 90° - 56° = 34°$

Find angle C using a 180° angle sum in the triangle.

$C = 180° - A - B = 180° - 65° - 34° = 81°$

The ratio $\dfrac{c}{\sin C}$, or $\dfrac{10}{\sin 81°}$, is now known. Use this ratio and the Law of Sines to find b and a.

$$\frac{b}{\sin B} = \frac{c}{\sin C}$$

$$\frac{b}{\sin 34°} = \frac{10}{\sin 81°}$$

$$b = \frac{10 \sin 34°}{\sin 81°} \approx 6$$

Station A is about 6 miles from the fire.

$$\frac{a}{\sin A} = \frac{c}{\sin C}$$

$$\frac{a}{\sin 65°} = \frac{10}{\sin 81°}$$

$$a = \frac{10 \sin 65°}{\sin 81°} \approx 9$$

Station B is about 9 miles from the fire.

49.

$c = 1200$ yards

Using the figure,
$$C = 180° - A - B = 180° - 85° - 76° = 19°$$

The ratio $\dfrac{c}{\sin C}$, or $\dfrac{1200}{\sin 19°}$, is now known. Use this ratio and the Law of Sines to find a and b.

$$\frac{a}{\sin A} = \frac{c}{\sin C}$$

$$\frac{a}{\sin 85°} = \frac{1200}{\sin 19°}$$

$$a = \frac{1200 \sin 85°}{\sin 19°} \approx 3672$$

$$\frac{b}{\sin B} = \frac{c}{\sin C}$$

$$\frac{b}{\sin 76°} = \frac{1200}{\sin 19°}$$

$$b = \frac{1200 \sin 76°}{\sin 19°} \approx 3576$$

The platform is about 3672 yards from one end of the beach and 3576 yards from the other.

51. According to the figure,
$$C = 180° - A - B = 180° - 84.7° - 50° = 45.3°$$ The
ratio $\dfrac{c}{\sin C}$, or $\dfrac{171}{\sin 45.3°}$, is now known. Use this ratio and the Law of Sines to find b.

$$\frac{b}{\sin B} = \frac{c}{\sin C}$$

$$\frac{b}{\sin 50°} = \frac{171}{\sin 45.3°}$$

$$b = \frac{171 \sin 50°}{\sin 45.3°} \approx 184$$

The distance is about 184 feet.

53. The ratio $\dfrac{b}{\sin B}$, or $\dfrac{562}{\sin 85.3°}$, is known.

Use this ratio, the figure, and the Law of Sines to find c.

$$\frac{c}{\sin C} = \frac{b}{\sin B}$$

$$\frac{c}{\sin 5.7°} = \frac{562}{\sin 85.3°}$$

$$c = \frac{562 \sin 5.7°}{\sin 85.3°} \approx 56$$

The toss was about 56 feet.

55.

$A \quad c = 20$ feet $\quad B$

Using the figure,
$$B = 90° - 8° = 82°$$

$$C = 180° - A - B = 180° - 62° - 82° = 36°$$

The ratio $\dfrac{c}{\sin C}$, or $\dfrac{20}{\sin 36°}$, is now known. Use this ratio and the Law of Sines to find a.

$$\frac{a}{\sin A} = \frac{c}{\sin C}$$

$$\frac{a}{\sin 62°} = \frac{20}{\sin 36°}$$

$$a = \frac{20 \sin 62°}{\sin 36°} \approx 30$$

The length of the pole is about 30 feet.

57. a. Using the figure and the measurements shown,

$$B = 180° - 44° = 136°$$

$$C = 180° - B - A = 180° - 136° - 37° = 7°$$

The ratio $\dfrac{c}{\sin C}$, or $\dfrac{100}{\sin 7°}$, is now known.

Use this ratio and the Law of Sines to find a.

$$\frac{a}{\sin A} = \frac{c}{\sin C}$$

$$\frac{a}{\sin 37°} = \frac{100}{\sin 7°}$$

$$a = \frac{100 \sin 37°}{\sin 7°} \approx 494$$

To the nearest foot, $a = 494$ feet.

Let $a = 494$ be the hypotenuse of the right triangle. Then if h represents the height of the tree,

$$\frac{h}{\sin 44°} = \frac{494}{\sin 90°}$$

$$h = \frac{494 \sin 44°}{\sin 90°} \approx 343$$

A typical redwood tree is about 343 feet.

59.

Using the figure,

$$B = 90° - 62° = 28°$$

The known ratio is $\dfrac{b}{\sin B}$, or $\dfrac{5}{\sin 28°}$.

Use the Law of Sines to find angle C.

$$\frac{b}{\sin B} = \frac{c}{\sin C}$$

$$\frac{5}{\sin 28°} = \frac{7}{\sin C}$$

$$5 \sin C = 7 \sin 28°$$

$$\sin C = \frac{7 \sin 28°}{5} \approx 0.6573$$

There are two angles possible:

$$C_1 \approx 41°, \; C_2 \approx 180° - 41° = 139°$$

There are two triangles:

$$A_1 = 180° - C_1 - B \approx 180° - 41° - 28° = 111°$$

$$A_2 = 180° - C_2 - B \approx 180° - 139° - 28° = 13°$$ Use

the Law of Sines to find a_1 and a_2.

$$\frac{a_1}{\sin A_1} = \frac{b}{\sin B}$$

$$\frac{a_1}{\sin 111°} = \frac{5}{\sin 28°}$$

$$a_1 = \frac{5 \sin 111°}{\sin 28°} \approx 9.9$$

$$\frac{a_2}{\sin A_2} = \frac{b}{\sin B}$$

$$\frac{a_2}{\sin 13°} = \frac{5}{\sin 28°}$$

$$a_2 = \frac{5 \sin 13°}{\sin 28°} \approx 2.4$$

The boat is either 9.9 miles or 2.4 miles from lighthouse B, to the nearest tenth of a mile.

71. No. Explanations may vary.

73.

Using the figure,

$$A = 180° - 150° = 30°$$

Using the Law of Sines we have,

$$\frac{d}{\sin A} = \frac{36}{\sin 90°}$$

$$\frac{d}{\sin 30°} = \frac{36}{\sin 90°}$$

$$d = \frac{36 \sin 30°}{\sin 90°} = 18$$

$$CC' = 18 + 5 + 18 = 41$$

The wingspan CC' is 41 feet.

Section 6.2

Check Point Exercises

1. Apply the three-step procedure for solving a SAS triangle. Use the Law of Cosines to find the side opposite the given angle. Thus, we will find a.

$$a^2 = b^2 + c^2 - 2bc\cos A$$
$$a^2 = 7^2 + 8^2 - 2(7)(8)\cos 120°$$
$$= 49 + 64 - 112(-0.5)$$
$$= 169$$
$$a = \sqrt{169} = 13$$

Use the Law of Sines to find the angle opposite the shorter of the two sides. Thus, we will find acute angle B.

$$\frac{b}{\sin B} = \frac{a}{\sin A}$$
$$\frac{7}{\sin B} = \frac{13}{\sin 120°}$$
$$13\sin B = 7\sin 120°$$
$$\sin B = \frac{7\sin 120°}{13} \approx 0.4663$$
$$B \approx 28°$$

Find the third angle.
$$C = 180° - A - B \approx 180° - 120° - 28° = 32°$$
The solution is $a = 13, B \approx 28°,$ and $C \approx 32°$.

2. Apply the three-step procedure for solving a SSS triangle. Use the Law of Cosines to find the angle opposite the longest side. Thus, we will find angle B.

$$b^2 = a^2 + c^2 - 2ac\cos B$$
$$2ac\cos B = a^2 + c^2 - b^2$$
$$\cos B = \frac{a^2 + c^2 - b^2}{2ac}$$
$$\cos B = \frac{8^2 + 5^2 - 10^2}{2 \cdot 8 \cdot 5} = -\frac{11}{80}$$
$$\cos^{-1}\left(\frac{11}{80}\right) \approx 82.1°$$

B is obtuse, since $\cos B$ is negative.
$B \approx 180° - 82.1° = 97.9°$
Use the Law of Sines to find either of the two remaining acute angles. We will find angle A.

$$\frac{a}{\sin A} = \frac{b}{\sin B}$$
$$\frac{8}{\sin A} = \frac{10}{\sin 97.9°}$$
$$10\sin A = 8\sin 97.9°$$
$$\sin A = \frac{8\sin 97.9°}{10} \approx 0.7924$$
$$A \approx 52.4°$$

Find the third angle.
$$C = 180° - A - B \approx 180° - 52.4° - 97.9°$$
$$= 29.7°$$
The solution is $B \approx 97.9°, A \approx 52.4°,$ and $C \approx 29.7°$

3. The plane flying 400 miles per hour travels $400 \cdot 2 = 800$ miles in 2 hours. Similarly, the other plane travels 700 miles.

Use the figure and the Law of Cosines to find a in this SAS situation.

$$a^2 = b^2 + c^2 - 2bc\cos A$$
$$a^2 = 700^2 + 800^2 - 2(700)(800)\cos 75°$$
$$\approx 840,123$$
$$a \approx \sqrt{840,123} \approx 917$$

After 2 hours, the planes are approximately 917 miles apart.

4. Begin by calculating one-half the perimeter:

$$s = \frac{1}{2}(a + b + c) = \frac{1}{2}(6 + 16 + 18) = 20$$

Use Heron's formula to find the area.
$$\text{Area} = \sqrt{s(s-a)(s-b)(s-c)}$$
$$= \sqrt{20(20-6)(20-16)(20-18)}$$
$$= \sqrt{2240} \approx 47$$

The area of the triangle is approximately 47 square meters.

Exercise Set 6.2

1. Apply the three-step procedure for solving a SAS triangle. Use the Law of Cosines to find the side opposite the given angle.
    Thus, we will find a.
    $$a^2 = b^2 + c^2 - 2bc \cos A$$
    $$a^2 = 4^2 + 8^2 - 2(4)(8) \cos 46°$$
    $$a^2 = 16 + 64 - 64(\cos 46°)$$
    $$a^2 \approx 35.54$$
    $$a \approx \sqrt{35.54} \approx 6.0$$
    Use the Law of Sines to find the angle opposite the shorter of the two given sides. Thus, we will find acute angle B.
    $$\frac{b}{\sin B} = \frac{a}{\sin A}$$
    $$\frac{4}{\sin B} = \frac{\sqrt{35.54}}{\sin 46°}$$
    $$\sqrt{35.54} \sin B = 4 \sin 46°$$
    $$\sin B = \frac{4 \sin 46°}{\sqrt{35.54}} \approx 0.4827$$
    $$B \approx 29°$$
    Find the third angle.
    $$C = 180° - A - B \approx 180° - 46° - 29° = 105°$$
    The solution is $a \approx 6.0, B \approx 29°$, and $C \approx 105°$.

3. Apply the three-step procedure for solving a SAS triangle. Use the Law of Cosines to find the side opposite the given angle.
    Thus, we will find c.
    $$c^2 = a^2 + b^2 - 2ab \cos C$$
    $$c^2 = 6^2 + 4^2 - 2(6)(4) \cos 96°$$
    $$c^2 = 36 + 16 - 48(\cos 96°)$$
    $$c^2 \approx 57.02$$
    $$c \approx \sqrt{57.02} \approx 7.6$$
    Use the Law of Sines to find the angle opposite the shorter of the two given sides. Thus, we will find acute angle B.
    $$\frac{b}{\sin B} = \frac{c}{\sin C}$$
    $$\frac{4}{\sin B} = \frac{\sqrt{57.02}}{\sin 96°}$$
    $$\sqrt{57.02} \sin B = 4 \sin 96°$$
    $$\sin B = \frac{4 \sin 96°}{\sqrt{57.02}} \approx 0.5268$$
    $$B \approx 32°$$
    Find the third angle.

$$A = 180° - B - C \approx 180° - 32° - 96° = 52°$$
The solution is $c \approx 7.6, A \approx 52°$, and $B \approx 32°$.

5. Apply the three-step procedure for solving a SSS triangle. Use the Law of Cosines to find the angle opposite the longest side. Since two sides have length 8, we can begin by finding angle B or C.
    $$b^2 = a^2 + c^2 - 2ac \cos B$$
    $$\cos B = \frac{a^2 + c^2 - b^2}{2ac}$$
    $$\cos B = \frac{6^2 + 8^2 - 8^2}{2 \cdot 6 \cdot 8} = \frac{36}{96} = \frac{3}{8}$$
    $$B \approx 68°$$
    Use the Law of Sines to find either of the two remaining acute angles. We will find angle A.
    $$\frac{a}{\sin A} = \frac{b}{\sin B}$$
    $$\frac{6}{\sin A} = \frac{8}{\sin 68°}$$
    $$8 \sin A = 6 \sin 68°$$
    $$\sin A = \frac{6 \sin 68°}{8} \approx 0.6954$$
    $$A \approx 44°$$
    Find the third angle.
    $$C = 180° - B - A \approx 180° - 68° - 44° = 68°$$
    The solution is $A \approx 44°, B \approx 68°$, and $C \approx 68°$.

7. Apply the three-step procedure for solving a SSS triangle. Use the Law of Cosines to find the angle opposite the longest side. Thus, we will find angle A
    $$a^2 = b^2 + c^2 - 2bc \cos A$$
    $$\cos A = \frac{b^2 + c^2 - a^2}{2bc}$$
    $$\cos A = \frac{4^2 + 3^2 - 6^2}{2 \cdot 4 \cdot 3} = -\frac{11}{24}$$
    A is obtuse, since $\cos A$ is negative.
    $$\cos^{-1}\left(\frac{11}{24}\right) \approx 63°$$
    $$A \approx 180° - 63° = 117°$$
    Use the Law of Sines to find either of the two remaining acute angles. We will find angle B.

$$\frac{b}{\sin B} = \frac{a}{\sin A}$$

$$\frac{4}{\sin B} = \frac{6}{\sin 117^\circ}$$

$$6\sin B = 4\sin 117^\circ$$

$$\sin B = \frac{4\sin 117^\circ}{6} \approx 0.5940$$

$$B \approx 36^\circ$$

Find the third angle.

$$C = 180^\circ - B - A \approx 180^\circ - 36^\circ - 117^\circ = 27^\circ$$

The solution is $A \approx 117^\circ, B \approx 36^\circ,$ and $C \approx 27^\circ$.

9. Apply the three-step procedure for solving a SAS triangle. Use the Law of Cosines to find the side opposite the given angle. Thus, we will find c.

$$c^2 = a^2 + b^2 - 2ab\cos C$$

$$c^2 = 5^2 + 7^2 - 2(5)(7)\cos 42^\circ$$

$$c^2 = 25 + 49 - 70(\cos 42^\circ)$$

$$c^2 \approx 21.98$$

$$c \approx \sqrt{21.98} \approx 4.7$$

Use the Law of Sines to find the angle opposite the shorter of the two given sides. Thus, we will find acute angle A.

$$\frac{a}{\sin A} = \frac{c}{\sin C}$$

$$\frac{5}{\sin A} = \frac{\sqrt{21.98}}{\sin 42^\circ}$$

$$\sqrt{21.98}\sin A = 5\sin 42^\circ$$

$$\sin A = \frac{5\sin 42^\circ}{\sqrt{21.98}} \approx 0.7136$$

$$A \approx 46^\circ$$

Find the third angle.

$$B = 180^\circ - C - A \approx 180^\circ - 42^\circ - 46^\circ = 92^\circ$$

The solution is $c \approx 4.7, A \approx 46^\circ,$ and $B \approx 92^\circ$.

11. Apply the three-step procedure for solving a SAS triangle. Use the Law of Cosines to find the side opposite the given angle. Thus, we will find a.

$$a^2 = b^2 + c^2 - 2bc\cos A$$

$$a^2 = 5^2 + 3^2 - 2(5)(3)\cos 102^\circ$$

$$a^2 = 25 + 9 - 30(\cos 102^\circ)$$

$$a^2 \approx 40.24$$

$$a \approx \sqrt{40.24} \approx 6.3$$

Use the Law of Sines to find the angle opposite the shorter of the two given sides. Thus, we will

find acute angle C.

$$\frac{c}{\sin C} = \frac{a}{\sin A}$$

$$\frac{3}{\sin C} = \frac{\sqrt{40.24}}{\sin 102^\circ}$$

$$\sqrt{40.24}\sin C = 3\sin 102^\circ$$

$$\sin C = \frac{3\sin 102^\circ}{\sqrt{40.24}} \approx 0.4626$$

$$C \approx 28^\circ$$

Find the third angle.

$$B = 180^\circ - C - A \approx 180^\circ - 28^\circ - 102^\circ = 50^\circ$$

The solution is $a \approx 6.3, C \approx 28^\circ,$ and $B \approx 50^\circ$.

13. Apply the three-step procedure for solving a SAS triangle. Use the Law of Cosines to find the side opposite the given angle. Thus, we will find b.

$$b^2 = a^2 + c^2 - 2ac\cos B$$

$$b^2 = 6^2 + 5^2 - 2(6)(5)\cos 50^\circ$$

$$b^2 = 36 + 25 - 60(\cos 50^\circ)$$

$$b^2 \approx 22.43$$

$$b \approx \sqrt{22.43} \approx 4.7$$

Use the Law of Sines to find the angle opposite the shorter of the two given sides. Thus, we will find acute angle C.

$$\frac{c}{\sin C} = \frac{b}{\sin B}$$

$$\frac{5}{\sin C} = \frac{\sqrt{22.43}}{\sin 50^\circ}$$

$$\sqrt{22.43}\sin C = 5\sin 50^\circ$$

$$\sin C = \frac{5\sin 50^\circ}{\sqrt{22.43}} \approx 0.8087$$

$$C \approx 54^\circ$$

Find the third angle.

$$A = 180^\circ - C - B \approx 180^\circ - 54^\circ - 50^\circ = 76^\circ$$

The solution is $b \approx 4.7, C \approx 54^\circ,$ and $A \approx 76^\circ$.

15. Apply the three-step procedure for solving a SAS triangle. Use the Law of Cosines to find the side opposite the given angle. Thus, we will find b.

$$b^2 = a^2 + c^2 - 2ac\cos 90°$$
$$b^2 = 5^2 + 2^2 - 2(5)(2)\cos 90°$$
$$b^2 = 25 + 4 - 20\cos 90°$$
$$b^2 = 29$$
$$b = \sqrt{29} \approx 5.4$$

(use exact value of b from previous step) Use the Law of Sines to find the angle opposite the shorter of the two given sides. Thus, we will find acute angle C.

$$\frac{c}{\sin C} = \frac{b}{\sin B}$$
$$\frac{2}{\sin C} = \frac{\sqrt{29}}{\sin 90°}$$
$$\sqrt{29}\sin C = 2\sin 90°$$
$$\sin C = \frac{2\sin 90°}{\sqrt{29}} \approx 0.3714$$
$$C \approx 22°$$

Find the third angle.
$$A = 180° - C - B \approx 180° - 22° - 90° = 68°$$
The solution is $b \approx 5.4, C \approx 22°,$ and $A \approx 68°$.

17. Apply the three-step procedure for solving a SSS triangle. Use the Law of Cosines to find the angle opposite the longest side. Thus, we will find C.

$$c^2 = a^2 + b^2 - 2ab\cos C$$
$$\cos C = \frac{a^2 + b^2 - c^2}{2ab}$$
$$\cos C = \frac{5^2 + 7^2 - 10^2}{2 \cdot 5 \cdot 7} = -\frac{13}{35}$$

C is obtuse, since $\cos C$ is negative.

$$\cos^{-1}\left(\frac{13}{35}\right) \approx 68°$$

$$C \approx 180° - 68° = 112°$$

Use the Law of Sines to find either of the two remaining angles. We will find angle A.

$$\frac{a}{\sin A} = \frac{c}{\sin C}$$
$$\frac{5}{\sin A} = \frac{10}{\sin 112°}$$
$$10\sin A = 5\sin 112°$$
$$\sin A = \frac{5\sin 112°}{10} \approx 0.4636$$
$$A \approx 28°$$

Find the third angle.
$$B = 180° - C - A \approx 180° - 112° - 28° = 40°$$
The solution is $C \approx 112°, A \approx 28°,$ and $B \approx 40°$.

19. Apply the three-step procedure for solving a SSS triangle. Use the Law of Cosines to find the angle opposite the longest side. Thus, we will find B.

$$b^2 = a^2 + c^2 - 2ac\cos B$$
$$\cos B = \frac{a^2 + c^2 - b^2}{2ac}$$
$$\cos B = \frac{3^2 + 8^2 - 9^2}{2 \cdot 3 \cdot 8} = -\frac{1}{6}$$

B is obtuse, since $\cos B$ is negative.

$$\cos^{-1}\left(\frac{1}{6}\right) \approx 80°$$

$$B \approx 180° - 80° = 100°$$

Use the Law of Sines to find either of the two remaining angles. We will find angle A.

$$\frac{a}{\sin A} = \frac{b}{\sin B}$$
$$\frac{3}{\sin A} = \frac{9}{\sin 100°}$$
$$9\sin A = 3\sin 100°$$
$$\sin A = \frac{3\sin 100°}{9} \approx 0.3283$$
$$A \approx 19°$$

Find the third angle.
$$C = 180° - B - A \approx 180° - 100° - 19° = 61°$$
The solution is $B \approx 100°, A \approx 19°,$ and $C \approx 61°$.

21. Apply the three-step procedure for solving a SSS triangle. Use the Law of Cosines to find any of the three angles, since each side has the same measure.

$$a^2 = b^2 + c^2 - 2bc\cos A$$
$$\cos A = \frac{b^2 + c^2 - a^2}{2bc}$$
$$\cos A = \frac{3^2 + 3^2 - 3^2}{2 \cdot 3 \cdot 3} = \frac{1}{2}$$
$$A = 60°$$

Use the Law of Sines to find either of the two remaining angles. We will find angle B.

$$\frac{b}{\sin B} = \frac{a}{\sin A}$$

$$\frac{3}{\sin B} = \frac{3}{\sin 60°}$$

$$3\sin B = 3\sin 60°$$

$$\sin B = \sin 60°$$

$$B = 60°$$

Find the third angle.

$$C = 180° - A - B = 180° - 60° - 60° = 60°$$

The solution is $A = 60°, B = 60°$, and $C = 60°$.

23. Apply the three-step procedure for solving a SSS triangle. Use the Law of Cosines to find the angle opposite the longest side. Thus, we will find A.

$$a^2 = b^2 + c^2 - 2bc\cos A$$

$$\cos A = \frac{b^2 + c^2 - a^2}{2bc}$$

$$\cos A = \frac{22^2 + 50^2 - 63^2}{2 \cdot 22 \cdot 50} = -\frac{985}{2200}$$

$$A \approx 117°$$

Use the Law of Sines to find either of the two remaining angles. We will find angle B.

$$\frac{b}{\sin B} = \frac{a}{\sin A}$$

$$\frac{22}{\sin B} = \frac{63}{\sin 117°}$$

$$63\sin B = 22\sin 117°$$

$$\sin B = \frac{22\sin 117°}{63}$$

$$B = 18°$$

Find the third angle.

$$C = 180° - A - B = 180° - 117° - 18° = 45°$$

The solution is $A = 117°, B = 18°$, and $C = 45°$.

25. $s = \frac{1}{2}(a + b + c) = \frac{1}{2}(4 + 4 + 2) = 5$

$$\begin{aligned}
\text{Area} &= \sqrt{s(s-a)(s-b)(s-c)} \\
&= \sqrt{5(5-4)(5-4)(5-2)} \\
&= \sqrt{15} \approx 4
\end{aligned}$$

The area of the triangle is approximately 4 square feet.

27. $s = \frac{1}{2}(a + b + c) = \frac{1}{2}(14 + 12 + 4) = 15$

$$\begin{aligned}
\text{Area} &= \sqrt{s(s-a)(s-b)(s-c)} \\
&= \sqrt{15(15-14)(15-12)(15-4)} \\
&= \sqrt{495} \approx 22
\end{aligned}$$

The area of the triangle is approximately 22 square meters.

29. $s = \frac{1}{2}(a + b + c) = \frac{1}{2}(11 + 9 + 7) = 13.5$

$$\begin{aligned}
\text{Area} &= \sqrt{s(s-a)(s-b)(s-c)} \\
&= \sqrt{13.5(13.5-11)(13.5-9)(13.5-7)} \\
&= \sqrt{987.1875} \approx 31
\end{aligned}$$

The area of the triangle is approximately 31 square yards.

31. $C = 180° - 15° - 35° = 130°$

$$c^2 = b^2 + c^2 - 2bc\cos C$$

$$c^2 = 8^2 + 13^2 - 2(8)(13)\cos 130°$$

$$c^2 \approx 366.6998$$

$$c \approx 19.1$$

Use the law of sines to find the solution is $A \approx 31°, B \approx 19°, C \approx 130°$, and $c \approx 19.1..$

33. Use the given radii to determine that $a = 7.5, b = 8.5$, and $c = 9.0$.

$$c^2 = a^2 + b^2 - 2ab\cos C$$

$$9^2 = 7.5^2 + 8.5^2 - 2(7.5)(8.5)\cos C$$

$$\cos C \approx 0.3725$$

$$C \approx 68°$$

Use the law of sines to find the solution is $A \approx 51°, B \approx 61°$, and $C \approx 68°$.

35. Use the distance formula to determine that $a = \sqrt{61} \approx 7.8, b = \sqrt{10} \approx 3.2$, and $c = 5$.

$$a^2 = b^2 + c^2 - 2bc\cos A$$

$$\sqrt{61}^2 = \sqrt{10}^2 + 5^2 - 2\left(\sqrt{10}\right)(5)\cos A$$

$$\cos A \approx -0.8222$$

$$A \approx 145°$$

Use the law of sines to find the solution is $A \approx 145°, B \approx 13°$, and $C \approx 22°$.

37. Use the law of cosines.
$$c^2 = a^2 + b^2 - 2ab\cos C$$
$$5.78^2 = 2.9^2 + 3.0^2 - 2(2.9)(3.0)\cos\theta$$
$$\cos\theta \approx -0.9194$$
$$\theta \approx 157°$$
This dinosaur was an efficient walker.

39. Let b = the distance between the ships after three hours.
After three hours, the ship traveling 14 miles per hour has gone $3 \cdot 14$ or 42 miles. Similarly, the ship traveling 10 miles per hour has gone 30 miles.

Using the figure,
$$B = 180° - 75° + 12° = 117°$$
$$b^2 = a^2 + c^2 - 2ac\cos B$$
$$b^2 = 30^2 + 42^2 - 2(30)(42)\cos 117° \approx 3808$$
$$b \approx 61.7$$
After three hours, the ships will be about 61.7 miles apart.

41. Let b = the distance across the lake.
$$b^2 = a^2 + c^2 - 2ac\cos B$$
$$b^2 = 160^2 + 140^2 - 2(160)(140)\cos 80°$$
$$\approx 37,421$$
$$b \approx \sqrt{37,421} \approx 193$$
The distance across the lake is about 193 yards.

43. Assume that Island B is due east of Island A. Let A = angle at Island A.
$$a^2 = b^2 + c^2 - 2bc\cos A$$
$$\cos A = \frac{b^2 + c^2 - a^2}{2bc}$$
$$\cos A = \frac{5^2 + 6^2 - 7^2}{2 \cdot 5 \cdot 6} = \frac{1}{5}$$
$$A \approx 78°$$
Since $90° - 78° = 12°$, you should navigate on a bearing of N12°E.

45. a. Using the figure,
$$B = 90° - 40° = 50°$$
$$b^2 = a^2 + c^2 - 2ac\cos B$$
$$b^2 = 13.5^2 + 25^2 - 2(13.5)(25)\cos 50°$$
$$\approx 373$$
$$b \approx \sqrt{373} \approx 19.3$$
You are about 19.3 miles from the pier.

b.
$$\frac{a}{\sin A} = \frac{b}{\sin B}$$
$$\frac{13.5}{\sin A} = \frac{\sqrt{373}}{\sin 50°}$$
$$\sqrt{373}\sin A = 13.5\sin 50°$$
$$\sin A = \frac{13.5\sin 50°}{\sqrt{373}} \approx 0.5355$$
$$A \approx 32°$$
Since $90° - 32° = 58°$, the original bearing could have been S58°E.

47.

In the figure, b = the guy wire anchored downhill, e = the guy wire anchored uphill.
$$B = 90° + 7° = 97°$$
$$E = 90° - 7° = 83°$$
$$b^2 = a^2 + c^2 - 2ac\cos B$$
$$b^2 = 400^2 + 80^2 - 2(400)(80)\cos 97°$$
$$\approx 174,200$$
$$b \approx \sqrt{174,200} \approx 417.4$$
$$e^2 = d^2 + f^2 - 2df\cos E$$
$$e^2 = 400^2 + 80^2 - 2(400)(80)\cos 83°$$
$$\approx 158,600$$
$$e \approx \sqrt{158.600} \approx 398.2$$
The guy wire anchored downhill is about 417.4 feet long. The one anchored uphill is about 398.2 feet long.

49.

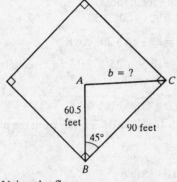

Using the figure,

$B = 90° \div 2 = 45°$ (using symmetry)

$b^2 = a^2 + c^2 - 2ac \cos B$

$b^2 = 90^2 + 60.5^2 - 2(90)(60.5) \cos 45°$

≈ 4060

$b \approx \sqrt{4060} \approx 63.7$

It is about 63.7 feet from the pitcher's mound to first base.

51. First, find the area using Heron's formula.

$s = \dfrac{1}{2}(a+b+c) = \dfrac{1}{2}(240+300+420) = 480$ Are

$a = \sqrt{s(s-a)(s-b)(s-c)}$

$= \sqrt{480(480-240)(480-300)(480-420)}$

$= \sqrt{1,244,160,000} \approx 35,272.65$

Now multiply by the price per square foot.

$(35,272.65)(3.50) \approx 123,454$

The cost is $123,454, to the nearest dollar.

61. $A \approx 29°, B \approx 87°, C \approx 64°, a \approx 11.6, b \approx 23.9$

Section 6.3

Check Point Exercises

1. a. $(r, \theta) = (3, 315°)$

Because $315°$ is a positive angle, draw $\theta = 315°$ counterclockwise from the polar axis. Because $r > 0$, plot the point by going out 3 units on the terminal side of θ.

b. $(r, \theta) = (-2, \pi)$

Because π is a positive angle, draw $\theta = \pi$ counterclockwise from the polar axis. Because $r < 0$, plot the point by going out 2 units along the ray opposite the terminal side of θ.

c. $(r, \theta) = \left(-1, -\dfrac{\pi}{2}\right)$

Because $-\dfrac{\pi}{2}$ is a negative angle, draw

$\theta = -\dfrac{\pi}{2}$ clockwise from the polar axis.

Because $r < 0$, plot the point by going out one unit along the ray opposite the terminal side of θ.

2. a. Add 2π to the angle and do not change r.

$\left(5, \dfrac{\pi}{4}\right) = \left(5, \dfrac{\pi}{4} + 2\pi\right) = \left(5, \dfrac{\pi}{4} + \dfrac{8\pi}{4}\right)$

$= \left(5, \dfrac{9\pi}{4}\right)$

b. Add π to the angle and replace r by $-r$.

$\left(5, \dfrac{\pi}{4}\right) = \left(-5, \dfrac{\pi}{4} + \pi\right) = \left(-5, \dfrac{\pi}{4} + \dfrac{4\pi}{4}\right)$

$= \left(-5, \dfrac{5\pi}{4}\right)$

c. Subtract 2π from the angle and do not change r.

$$\left(5, \frac{\pi}{4}\right) = \left(5, \frac{\pi}{4} - 2\pi\right) = \left(5, \frac{\pi}{4} - \frac{8\pi}{4}\right)$$

$$= \left(5, -\frac{7\pi}{4}\right)$$

3. a. $(r, \theta) = (3, \pi)$

$x = r\cos\theta = 3\cos\pi = 3(-1) = -3$

$y = r\sin\theta = 3\sin\pi = 3(0) = 0$

The rectangular coordinates of $(3, \pi)$ are $(-3, 0)$.

b. $(r, \theta) = \left(-10, \dfrac{\pi}{6}\right)$

$x = r\cos\theta = -10\cos\dfrac{\pi}{6} = -10\left(\dfrac{\sqrt{3}}{2}\right)$

$\quad = -5\sqrt{3}$

$y = r\sin\theta = -10\sin\dfrac{\pi}{6} = -10\left(\dfrac{1}{2}\right) = -5$

The rectangular coordinates of $\left(-10, \dfrac{\pi}{6}\right)$

are $\left(-5\sqrt{3}, -5\right)$.

4.

$r = \sqrt{x^2 + y^2} = \sqrt{1^2 + \left(-\sqrt{3}\right)^2}$

$\quad = \sqrt{1+3} = \sqrt{4} = 2$

$\tan\theta = \dfrac{y}{x} = \dfrac{-\sqrt{3}}{1} = -\sqrt{3}$

Because $\tan\dfrac{\pi}{3} = \sqrt{3}$ and θ lies in quadrant IV,

$\theta = 2\pi - \dfrac{\pi}{3} = \dfrac{6\pi}{3} - \dfrac{\pi}{3} = \dfrac{5\pi}{3}$

The polar coordinates of $\left(1, -\sqrt{3}\right)$ are

$(r, \theta) = \left(2, \dfrac{5\pi}{3}\right)$

5.

$r = \sqrt{x^2 + y^2} = \sqrt{(0)^2 + (-4)^2} = \sqrt{16} = 4$

The point $(0, -4)$ is on the negative y-axis. Thus,

$\theta = \dfrac{3\pi}{2}$. Polar coordinates of $(0, -4)$ are

$\left(4, \dfrac{3\pi}{2}\right)$.

6. a. $3x - y = 6$

$3r\cos\theta - r\sin\theta = 6$

$r(3\cos\theta - \sin\theta) = 6$

$$r = \frac{6}{3\cos\theta - \sin\theta}$$

b. $x^2 + (y+1)^2 = 1$

$\left(r\cos\theta\right)^2 + (r\sin\theta + 1)^2 = 1$

$r^2\cos^2\theta + r^2\sin^2\theta + 2r\sin\theta + 1 = 1$

$r^2 + 2r\sin\theta = 0$

$r\left(r + 2\sin\theta\right) = 0$

$r = 0 \quad$ or $\quad r + 2\sin\theta = 0$

$r = -2\sin\theta$

7. a. Use $r^2 = x^2 + y^2$ to convert to a rectangular equation.

$r = 4$

$r^2 = 16$

$x^2 + y^2 = 16$

The rectangular equation for $r = 4$ is

$x^2 + y^2 = 16$.

b. Use $\tan\theta = \dfrac{y}{x}$ to convert to a rectangular equation in x and y.

$$\theta = \frac{3\pi}{4}$$

$$\tan\theta = \tan\frac{3\pi}{4}$$

$$\tan\theta = -1$$

$$\frac{y}{x} = -1$$

$$y = -x$$

The rectangular equation for $\theta = \dfrac{3\pi}{4}$ is $y = -x$.

c. $\qquad r = -2\sec\theta$

$$r = \frac{-2}{\cos\theta}$$

$$r\cos\theta = -2$$

$$x = -2$$

$$r = 10\sin\theta$$

$$r^2 = 10r\sin\theta$$

$$x^2 + y^2 = 10y$$

d.

$$x^2 + y^2 - 10y = 0$$

$$x^2 + y^2 - 10y + 25 = 25$$

$$x^2 + (y-5)^2 = 25$$

Exercise Set 6.3

1. $225°$ is in the third quadrant.
C

3. $\dfrac{5\pi}{4} = 225°$ is in the third quadrant. Since r is negative, the point lies along the ray opposite the terminal side of θ, in the first quadrant.
A

5. $\pi = 180°$ lies on the negative x-axis.
B

7. $-135°$ is measured clockwise $135°$ from the positive x-axis. The point lies in the third quadrant.
C

9. $-\dfrac{3\pi}{4} = -135°$ is measured clockwise $135°$ from the positive x-axis. Since r is negative, the point lies along the ray opposite the terminal side of θ, in the first quadrant.
A

11. Draw $\theta = 45°$ counterclockwise, since θ is positive, from the polar axis. Go out 2 units on the terminal side of θ, since $r > 0$.

13. Draw $\theta = 90°$ counterclockwise, since θ is positive, from the polar axis. Go out 3 units on the terminal side of θ, since $r > 0$.

15. Draw $\theta = \dfrac{4\pi}{3} = 240°$ counterclockwise, since θ is positive, from polar axis. Go out 3 units on the terminal side of θ, since $r > 0$.

17. Draw $\theta = \pi = 180°$ counterclockwise, since θ is positive, from the polar axis. Go one unit out on the ray opposite the terminal side of θ, since $r < 0$.

19. Draw $\theta = -\dfrac{\pi}{2} = -90°$ clockwise, since θ is positive, from the polar axis. Go 2 units out on the ray opposite the terminal side of θ, since $r < 0$.

21. Draw $\theta = \dfrac{\pi}{6} = 30°$ counterclockwise, since θ is positive, from the polar axis. Go 5 units out on the terminal side of θ, since $r > 0$.

   a. Add 2π to the angle and do not change r.
   $$\left(5, \frac{\pi}{6}\right) = \left(5, \frac{\pi}{6} + 2\pi\right) = \left(5, \frac{13\pi}{6}\right)$$

   b. Add π to the angle and replace r by $-r$.
   $$\left(5, \frac{\pi}{6}\right) = \left(-5, \frac{\pi}{6} + \pi\right) = \left(-5, \frac{7\pi}{6}\right)$$

   c. Subtract 2π from the angle and do not change r.
   $$\left(5, \frac{\pi}{6}\right) = \left(5, \frac{\pi}{6} - 2\pi\right) = \left(5, -\frac{11\pi}{6}\right)$$

23. Draw $\theta = \dfrac{3\pi}{4} = 135°$ counterclockwise, since θ is positive, from the polar axis. Go out 10 units on the terminal side of θ, since $r > 0$.

   a. Add 2π to the angle and do not change r.
   $$\left(10, \frac{3\pi}{4}\right) = \left(10, \frac{3\pi}{4} + 2\pi\right) = \left(10, \frac{11\pi}{4}\right)$$

   b. Add π to the angle and replace r by $-r$.
   $$\left(10, \frac{3\pi}{4}\right) = \left(-10, \frac{3\pi}{4} + \pi\right) = \left(-10, \frac{7\pi}{4}\right)$$

   c. Subtract 2π from the angle and do not change r.
   $$\left(10, \frac{3\pi}{4}\right) = \left(10, \frac{3\pi}{4} - 2\pi\right) = \left(10, \frac{-5\pi}{4}\right)$$

25. Draw $\theta = \dfrac{\pi}{2} = 90°$ counterclockwise, since θ is positive, from the polar axis. Go 4 units out on the terminal side of θ, since $r > 0$.

a. Add 2π to the angle and do not change r.
$$\left(4, \frac{\pi}{2}\right) = \left(4, \frac{\pi}{2} + 2\pi\right) = \left(4, \frac{5\pi}{2}\right)$$

b. Add π to the angle and replace r by $-r$.
$$\left(4, \frac{\pi}{2}\right) = \left(-4, \frac{\pi}{2} + \pi\right) = \left(-4, \frac{3\pi}{2}\right)$$

c. Subtract 2π from the angle and do not change r.
$$\left(4, \frac{\pi}{2}\right) = \left(4, \frac{\pi}{2} - 2\pi\right) = \left(4, -\frac{3\pi}{2}\right)$$

27. a, b, d

29. b, d

31. a, b

33. The rectangular coordinates of $(4, 90°)$ are $(0, 4)$.

35. $x = r\cos\theta = 2\cos\frac{\pi}{3} = 2\left(\frac{1}{2}\right) = 1$

$y = r\sin\theta = 2\sin\frac{\pi}{3} = 2\left(\frac{\sqrt{3}}{2}\right) = \sqrt{3}$

The rectangular coordinates of $\left(2, \frac{\pi}{3}\right)$ are $\left(1, \sqrt{3}\right)$.

37. $x = r\cos\theta = -4\cos\frac{\pi}{2} = -4 \cdot 0 = 0$

$y = r\sin\theta = -4\sin\frac{\pi}{2} = -4(1) = -4$

The rectangular coordinates of $\left(-4, \frac{\pi}{2}\right)$ are $(0, -4)$.

39. $x = r\cos\theta = 7.4\cos 2.5 \approx 7.4(-0.80) \approx -5.9$

$y = r\sin\theta = 7.4\sin 2.5 \approx 7.4(0.60) \approx 4.4$

The rectangular coordinates of $(7.4, 2.5)$ are approximately $(-5.9, 4.4)$.

41. $r = \sqrt{x^2 + y^2} = \sqrt{(-2)^2 + 2^2}$
$$= \sqrt{4+4} = \sqrt{8} = 2\sqrt{2}$$

$\tan\theta = \frac{y}{x} = \frac{2}{-2} = -1$

Because $\tan\theta = -1$ and θ lies in quadrant II,

$\theta = \frac{3\pi}{4}$.

The polar coordinates of $(-2, 2)$ are

$(r, \theta) = \left(\sqrt{8}, \frac{3\pi}{4}\right)$.

43. $r = \sqrt{x^2 + y^2} = \sqrt{(2)^2 + \left(-2\sqrt{3}\right)^2}$
$$= \sqrt{4+12} = \sqrt{16} = 4$$

$\tan\theta = \frac{y}{x} = \frac{-2\sqrt{3}}{2} = -\sqrt{3}$

Because $\tan\frac{\pi}{3} = \sqrt{3}$ and θ lies in quadrant

IV, $\theta = 2\pi - \frac{\pi}{3} = \frac{5\pi}{3}$.

The polar coordinates of $\left(2, -2\sqrt{3}\right)$ are

$(r, \theta) = \left(4, \frac{5\pi}{3}\right)$.

45. $r = \sqrt{x^2 + y^2} = \sqrt{\left(-\sqrt{3}\right)^2 + (-1)^2}$
$$= \sqrt{3+1} = \sqrt{4} = 2$$

$\tan\theta = \frac{y}{x} = \frac{-1}{-\sqrt{3}} = \frac{1}{\sqrt{3}}$

Because $\tan\frac{\pi}{6} = \frac{1}{\sqrt{3}}$ and θ lies in quadrant III,

$\theta = \pi + \frac{\pi}{6} = \frac{7\pi}{6}$.

The polar coordinates of $\left(-\sqrt{3}, -1\right)$ are

$(r, \theta) = \left(2, \frac{7\pi}{6}\right)$.

47. $r = \sqrt{x^2 + y^2} = \sqrt{(5)^2 + (0)^2} = \sqrt{25} = 5$

$\tan\theta = \dfrac{y}{x} = \dfrac{0}{5} = 0$

Because $\tan 0 = 0$ and θ lies on the polar axis, $\theta = 0$.

The polar coordinates of (5, 0) are

$(r, \theta) = (5, 0)$.

49. $3x + y = 7$

$3r\cos\theta + r\sin\theta = 7$

$r(3\cos\theta + \sin\theta) = 7$

$$r = \frac{7}{3\cos\theta + \sin\theta}$$

51. $x = 7$

$r\cos\theta = 7$

$r = \dfrac{7}{\cos\theta}$

53. $x^2 + y^2 = 9$

$r^2 = 9$

$r = 3$

55. $(x - 2)^2 + y^2 = 4$

$(r\cos\theta - 2)^2 + (r\sin\theta)^2 = 4$

$r^2\cos^2\theta - 4r\cos\theta + 4 + r^2\sin^2\theta^2 = 4$

$r^2 - 4r\cos\theta = 0$

$r^2 = 4r\cos\theta$

$r = 4\cos\theta$

57. $y^2 = 6x$

$(r\sin\theta)^2 = 6r\cos\theta$

$r^2\sin^2\theta = 6r\cos\theta$

$r\sin^2\theta = 6\cos\theta$

$r = \dfrac{6\cos\theta}{\sin^2\theta}$

59. $r = 8$

$r^2 = 64$

$x^2 + y^2 = 64$

$x^2 + y^2 = 64$

61. $\theta = \dfrac{\pi}{2}$

$\tan\theta = \tan\dfrac{\pi}{2}$

$\tan\theta$ is undefined

$\dfrac{y}{x}$ is undefined

$x = 0$

$x = 0$

63. $r\sin\theta = 3$

$y = 3$

$y = 3$

65.
$$r = 4\csc\theta$$
$$r = \frac{4}{\sin\theta}$$
$$r\sin\theta = 4$$
$$y = 4$$

$$y = 4$$

67.
$$r = \sin\theta$$
$$r \cdot r = r \cdot \sin\theta$$
$$r^2 = r\sin\theta$$
$$x^2 + y^2 = y$$

$$x^2 + y^2 = y$$

69.
$$r = 12\cos\theta$$
$$r^2 = 12r\cos\theta$$
$$x^2 + y^2 = 12x$$
$$x^2 - 12x + y^2 = 0$$
$$x^2 - 12x + 36 + y^2 = 36$$
$$\left(x - 6\right)^2 + y^2 = 36$$

$$(x - 6)^2 + y^2 = 36$$

71.
$$r = 6\cos\theta + 4\sin\theta$$
$$r \cdot r = r(6\cos\theta + 4\sin\theta)$$
$$r^2 = 6r\cos\theta + 4r\sin\theta$$
$$x^2 + y^2 = 6x + 4y$$

$$x^2 + y^2 = 6x + 4y$$

73.
$$r^2\sin 2\theta = 2$$
$$r^2(2\sin\theta\cos\theta) = 2$$
$$2r\sin\theta\, r\cos\theta = 2$$
$$2yx = 2$$
$$xy = 1$$
$$y = \frac{1}{x}$$

$$y = \frac{1}{x}$$

75.
$$r = a\sec\theta$$
$$r = \frac{a}{\cos\theta}$$
$$r\cos\theta = a$$
$$x = a$$

This is the equation of a vertical line.

77.
$$r = a\sin\theta$$
$$r^2 = ar\sin\theta$$
$$x^2 + y^2 = ay$$
$$x^2 + y^2 - ay = 0$$
$$x^2 + y^2 - ay + \frac{a^2}{4} = \frac{a^2}{4}$$
$$x^2 + \left(y - \frac{a}{2}\right)^2 = \left(\frac{a}{2}\right)^2$$

This is the equation of a circle of radius $\frac{a}{2}$

centered at $\left(0, \frac{a}{2}\right)$.

79.
$$r\sin\left(\theta - \frac{\pi}{4}\right) = 2$$
$$r\left(\sin\theta\cos\frac{\pi}{4} - \cos\theta\sin\frac{\pi}{4}\right) = 2$$
$$r\sin\theta \cdot \frac{\sqrt{2}}{2} - r\cos\theta \cdot \frac{\sqrt{2}}{2} = 2$$
$$y \cdot \frac{\sqrt{2}}{2} - x \cdot \frac{\sqrt{2}}{2} = 2$$
$$y = x + 2\sqrt{2}$$

$y = x + 2\sqrt{2}$ has slope of 1 and y-intercept of $2\sqrt{2}$.

81. $x_1 = r\cos\theta = 2\cos\frac{2\pi}{3} = -1$

$y_1 = r\sin\theta = 2\sin\frac{2\pi}{3} = \sqrt{3}$

$\left(-1, \sqrt{3}\right)$

$x_2 = r\cos\theta = 4\cos\frac{\pi}{6} = 2\sqrt{3}$

$y_2 = r\sin\theta = 4\sin\frac{\pi}{6} = 2$

$\left(2\sqrt{3}, 2\right)$

$d = \sqrt{\left(x_2 - x_1\right)^2 + \left(y_2 - y_1\right)^2}$

$d = \sqrt{\left(2\sqrt{3} + 1\right)^2 + \left(2 - \sqrt{3}\right)^2}$

$d = 2\sqrt{5}$

83. The angle is measured counterclockwise from the polar axis.

$\theta = \frac{2}{3}(360°) = 240°$ or $\frac{4\pi}{3}$.

The distance from the inner circle's center to the outer circle is
$r = 6 + 3(3) = 6 + 9 = 15$

The polar coordinates are $(r, \theta) = \left(15, \frac{4\pi}{3}\right)$.

85. $(6.3, 50°)$ represents a sailing speed of 6.3 knots at an angle of 50° to the wind.

87. Out of the four points in this 10-knot-wind situation, you would recommend a sailing angle of 105°. A sailing speed of 7.5 knots is achieved at this angle.

97.
```
P▶Rx(4,2π/3)
                -2
P▶Ry(4,2π/3)
      3.464101615
```

To three decimal places, the rectangular coordinates are $(-2, 3.464)$.

99.
```
P▶Rx(-4,1.088)
     -1.857030778
P▶Ry(-4,1.088)
     -3.542800684
■
```

To three decimal places, the rectangular coordinates are $(-1.857, -3.543)$.

101.
```
R▶Pr(√(5),2)
                3
R▶Pθ(√(5),2)
      .7297276562
```

To three decimal places, the polar coordinates are $(r, \theta) = (3, 0.730)$.

103. Use the distance formula for rectangular coordinates, $d = \sqrt{(x_2 - x_1)^2 + (y_2 - y_1)^2}$.

Let $x_1 = r_1 \cos\theta_1, y_1 = r_1 \sin\theta_1$,

$\quad\quad x_2 = r_2 \cos\theta_2, y_2 = r_2 \sin\theta_2$

$$d = \sqrt{\left(r_2\cos\theta_2 - r_1\cos\theta_1\right)^2 + \left(r_2\sin\theta_2 - r_1\sin\theta_1\right)^2}$$

$$= \sqrt{r_2^2\cos^2\theta_2 - 2r_1r_2\cos\theta_1\cos\theta_2 + r_1^2\cos^2\theta_1 + r_2^2\sin^2\theta_2 - 2r_1r_2\sin\theta_1\sin\theta_2 + r_1^2\sin^2\theta_1}$$

$$= \sqrt{r_2^2\left(\cos^2\theta_2 + \sin^2\theta_2\right) + r_1^2\left(\cos^2\theta_1 + \sin^2\theta_1\right) - 2r_1r_2\left(\cos\theta_1\cos\theta_2 + \sin\theta_1\sin\theta_2\right)}$$

$$= \sqrt{r_2^2(1) + r_1^2(1) - 2r_1r_2\left(\cos(\theta_2 - \theta_1)\right)}$$

$$= \sqrt{r_1^2 + r_2^2 - 2r_1r_2\cos(\theta_2 - \theta_1)}$$

Section 6.4

Check Point Exercises

1. Construct a partial table of coordinates using multiples of $\dfrac{\pi}{6}$. Then plot the points and join them with a smooth curve.

$r = 4\sin\theta$

θ	r	(r, θ)
0	$4\sin 0 = 4 \cdot 0 = 0$	$(0, 0)$
$\dfrac{\pi}{6}$	$4\sin\dfrac{\pi}{6} = 4 \cdot \dfrac{1}{2} = 2$	$\left(2, \dfrac{\pi}{6}\right)$
$\dfrac{\pi}{3}$	$4\sin\dfrac{\pi}{3} = 4 \cdot \dfrac{\sqrt{3}}{2} = 2\sqrt{3}$	$\left(2\sqrt{3}, \dfrac{\pi}{3}\right)$
$\dfrac{\pi}{2}$	$4\sin\dfrac{\pi}{2} = 4 \cdot 1 = 4$	$\left(4, \dfrac{\pi}{2}\right)$
$\dfrac{2\pi}{3}$	$4\sin\dfrac{2\pi}{3} = 4 \cdot \dfrac{\sqrt{3}}{2} = 2\sqrt{3}$	$\left(2\sqrt{3}, \dfrac{2\pi}{3}\right)$
$\dfrac{5\pi}{6}$	$4\sin\dfrac{5\pi}{6} = 4 \cdot \dfrac{1}{2} = 2$	$\left(2, \dfrac{5\pi}{6}\right)$
π	$4\sin\pi = 4 \cdot 0 = 0$	$(0, \pi)$

$r = 4\sin\theta$

2.   **Polar Axis:** Replace θ by $-\theta$ in $r = 1 + \cos\theta$.

$$r = 1 + \cos(-\theta)$$
$$r = 1 + \cos\theta$$

Because the polar equation does not change when θ is replaced by $-\theta$, the graph is symmetric with respect to the polar axis.

The Line $\theta = \dfrac{\pi}{2}$**:** Replace (r, θ) by $(-r, -\theta)$ in $r = 1 + \cos\theta$.

$$-r = 1 + \cos(-\theta)$$
$$-r = 1 + \cos\theta$$
$$r = -1 - \cos\theta$$

Because the polar equation changes when (r, θ) is replaced by $(-r, -\theta)$, the equation fails the symmetry test.

The graph may or may not be symmetric with respect to the line $\theta = \dfrac{\pi}{2}$.

The Pole: Replace r by $-r$ in $r = 1 + \cos\theta$.

$$-r = 1 + \cos\theta$$
$$r = -1 - \cos\theta$$

Because the polar equation changes when r is replaced by $-r$, the equation fails the symmetry test. The graph may or may not be symmetric with respect to the pole.

Because the period of the cosine function is 2π, and the graph is symmetric with respect to the polar axis, begin by finding vales of r for values of θ from 0 to π. then graph $r = 1 + \cos\theta$ for these values and reflect the graph about the polar axis.

θ	0	$\dfrac{\pi}{6}$	$\dfrac{\pi}{3}$	$\dfrac{\pi}{2}$	$\dfrac{2\pi}{3}$	$\dfrac{5\pi}{6}$	π
r	2	1.87	1.5	1	0.5	0.13	0

$r = 1 + \cos\theta$

3. $r = 1 - 2\sin\theta$
Check for symmetry:

Polar Axis	The Line $\theta = \dfrac{\pi}{2}$	The Pole
$r = 1 - 2\sin(-\theta)$	$-r = 1 - 2\sin(-\theta)$	$-r = 1 - 2\sin\theta$
$r = 1 - 2(-\sin\theta)$	$-r = 1 + 2\sin\theta$	
$r = 1 + 2\sin\theta$	$r = -1 - 2\sin\theta$	$r = -1 + 2\sin\theta$

There may be no symmetry, since each equation is not equivalent to $r = 1 - 2\sin\theta$. Because the period of the sine function is 2π, we need not consider values of θ beyond 2π.

θ	0	$\dfrac{\pi}{6}$	$\dfrac{\pi}{3}$	$\dfrac{\pi}{2}$	$\dfrac{2\pi}{3}$	$\dfrac{5\pi}{6}$	π	$\dfrac{7\pi}{6}$	$\dfrac{4\pi}{3}$	$\dfrac{3\pi}{2}$	$\dfrac{5\pi}{6}$	$\dfrac{11\pi}{6}$	2π
r	1	0	-0.73	-1	-0.73	0	1	2	2.73	3	2.73	2	1

$r = 1 - 2\sin\theta$

4. $r = 3\cos 2\theta$
Check for symmetry:

Polar Axis	The Line $\theta = \dfrac{\pi}{2}$	The Pole
$r = 3\cos 2(-\theta)$	$-r = 3\cos 2(-\theta)$	$-r = 3\cos 2\theta$
	$-r = 3\cos 2\theta$	
$r = 3\cos 2\theta$	$r = -3\cos 2\theta$	$r = -3\cos 2\theta$

The graph has symmetry with respect to the polar axis. The graph may or may not be symmetric with respect to the line $\theta = \dfrac{\pi}{2}$ or the pole.

Since the graph is symmetric with respect to the polar axis, calculate values of r for θ from 0 to π. Then, graph $r = 3\cos 2\theta$ for these values and reflect the graph about the polar axis.

θ	0	$\dfrac{\pi}{6}$	$\dfrac{\pi}{3}$	$\dfrac{\pi}{2}$	$\dfrac{2\pi}{3}$	$\dfrac{5\pi}{6}$	π
r	3	1.5	-1.5	-3	-1.5	1.5	3

$r = 3\cos 2\theta$

5. $r^2 = 4\cos 2\theta$

Check for symmetry:

Polar Axis	The Line $\theta = \dfrac{\pi}{2}$	The Pole
$r^2 = 4\cos 2(-\theta)$	$(-r)^2 = 4\cos 2(-\theta)$	$(-r)^2 = 4\cos 2\theta$
$r^2 = 4\cos(-2\theta)$	$r^2 = 4\cos(-2\theta)$	
$r^2 = 4\cos 2\theta$	$r^2 = 4\cos 2\theta$	$r^2 = 4\cos 2\theta$

The graph has symmetry with respect to the polar axis, the line $\theta = \dfrac{\pi}{2}$, and the pole.

Calculate values of r for θ from 0 to $\dfrac{\pi}{2}$, and use symmetry to obtain the graph.

θ	0	$\dfrac{\pi}{6}$	$\dfrac{\pi}{4}$	$\dfrac{\pi}{3}$	$\dfrac{\pi}{2}$
r	± 2	± 1.41	0	undef.	undef.

Use symmetry to obtain the graph.

$r^2 = 4\cos 2\theta$

Exercise Set 6.4

1. heart-shaped limaçon or cardiod

$\dfrac{a}{b} = 1$

$r = 0$ when $\theta = \dfrac{\pi}{2}$

The polar equation is $r = 1 - \sin\theta$.

3. circle

$r = 2$ when $\theta = 0$

The polar equation is $r = 2\cos\theta$.

5. rose curve

3 petals $\Rightarrow n = 3$

The polar equation is $r = 3\sin 3\theta$.

523

7. a. $r = \sin\theta$

         Replace θ with $-\theta$.

         $r = \sin(-\theta)$

         $r = -\sin\theta$

         The graph may or may not have symmetry with respect to the polar axis.

    b. $r = \sin\theta$

         Replace (r, θ) with $(-r, -\theta)$.

         $-r = \sin(-\theta)$

         $-r = -\sin\theta$

         $r = \sin\theta$

         The graph has symmetry with respect to the line $\theta = \dfrac{\pi}{2}$.

    c. $r = \sin\theta$

         Replace r with $-r$.

         $-r = \sin\theta$

         $r = -\sin\theta$

         The graph may or may not have symmetry about the pole.

9. a. $r = 4 + 3\cos\theta$

         Replace θ with $-\theta$.

         $r = 4 + 3\cos(-\theta)$

         $r = 4 + 3\cos\theta$

         The graph has symmetry with respect to the polar axis.

    b. $r = 4 + 3\cos\theta$

         Replace (r, θ) with $(-r, -\theta)$.

         $-r = 4 + 3\cos(-\theta)$

         $-r = 4 + 3\cos\theta$

         $r = -4 - 3\cos\theta$

         The graph may or may not have symmetry with respect to the line $\theta = \dfrac{\pi}{2}$.

    c. $r = 4 + 3\cos\theta$

         Replace r with $-r$.

         $-r = 4 + 3\cos\theta$

         $r = -4 - 3\cos\theta$

         The graph may or may not have symmetry about the pole.

11. a. $r^2 = 16\cos 2\theta$

         Replace θ with $-\theta$.

         $r^2 = 16\cos 2(-\theta)$

         $r^2 = 16\cos(-2\theta)$

         $r^2 = 16\cos 2\theta$

         The graph has symmetry with respect to the polar axis.

    b. $r^2 = 16\cos 2\theta$

         Replace (r, θ) with $(-r, -\theta)$.

         $(-r)^2 = 16\cos 2(-\theta)$

         $r^2 = 16\cos 2\theta$

         The graph has symmetry with respect to the line $\theta = \dfrac{\pi}{2}$.

c. $r^2 = 16\cos 2\theta$

   Replace r with $-r$.

   $(-r)^2 = 16\cos 2\theta$

   $r^2 = 16\cos 2\theta$

   The graph has symmetry about the pole.

13. $r = 2\cos\theta$

   Check for symmetry:

Polar Axis	The Line $\theta = \dfrac{\pi}{2}$	The Pole
$r = 2\cos(-\theta)$	$-r = 2\cos(-\theta)$	$-r = 2\cos\theta$
	$-r = 2\cos\theta$	
$r = 2\cos\theta$	$r = -2\cos\theta$	$r = -2\cos\theta$

The graph is symmetric with respect to the polar axis. The graph may or may not be symmetric with respect to the line $\theta = \dfrac{\pi}{2}$ or the pole.

Calculate values of r for θ from 0 to π and use symmetry to obtain the graph.

θ	0	$\dfrac{\pi}{6}$	$\dfrac{\pi}{3}$	$\dfrac{\pi}{2}$
r	2	1.73	1	0

$r = 2\cos\theta$

Notice that there are no points in quadrants II or III. Because the cosine is negative in quadrants II and III, r is negative here. This places the points in quadrants IV and I respectively.

15. $r = 1 - \sin\theta$

   Check for symmetry:

Polar Axis	The Line $\theta = \dfrac{\pi}{2}$	The Pole
$r = 1 - \sin(-\theta)$	$-r = 1 - \sin(-\theta)$	$-r = 1 - \sin\theta$
	$-r = 1 + \sin\theta$	
$r = 1 + \sin\theta$	$r = -1 - \sin\theta$	$r = -1 + \sin\theta$

There may be no symmetry since each equation is not equivalent to $r = 1 - \sin\theta$. Because the period of the sine function is 2π, we need not consider values of θ beyond 2π.

θ	0	$\dfrac{\pi}{6}$	$\dfrac{\pi}{3}$	$\dfrac{\pi}{2}$	$\dfrac{2\pi}{3}$	$\dfrac{5\pi}{6}$	π	$\dfrac{7\pi}{6}$	$\dfrac{4\pi}{3}$	$\dfrac{3\pi}{2}$	$\dfrac{5\pi}{6}$	$\dfrac{11\pi}{6}$	2π
r	1	0.5	0.13	0	0.13	0.5	1	1.5	1.87	2	1.87	1.5	1

$r = 1 - \sin\theta$

17. $r = 2 + 2\cos\theta$
Check for symmetry:

Polar Axis	The Line $\theta = \dfrac{\pi}{2}$	The Pole
$r = 2 + 2\cos(-\theta)$	$-r = 2 + 2\cos(-\theta)$	$-r = 2 + 2\cos\theta$
	$-r = 2 + 2\cos\theta$	
$r = 2 + 2\cos\theta$	$r = -2 - 2\cos\theta$	$r = -2 - 2\cos\theta$

The graph is symmetric with respect to the polar axis. The graph may or may not be symmetric with respect to

the line $\theta = \dfrac{\pi}{2}$ or the pole.

Calculate values of r for θ from 0 to π and use symmetry to obtain the graph.

θ	0	$\dfrac{\pi}{6}$	$\dfrac{\pi}{3}$	$\dfrac{\pi}{2}$	$\dfrac{2\pi}{3}$	$\dfrac{5\pi}{6}$	π
r	4	3.73	3	2	1	0.27	0

$r = 2 + 2\cos\theta$

19. $r = 2 + \cos\theta$
Check for symmetry:

Polar Axis	The Line $\theta = \dfrac{\pi}{2}$	The Pole
$r = 2 + \cos(-\theta)$	$-r = 2 + \cos(-\theta)$	$-r = 2 + \cos\theta$
	$-r = 2 + \cos\theta$	
$r = 2 + \cos\theta$	$r = -2 - \cos\theta$	$r = -2 - \cos\theta$

The graph is symmetric with respect to the polar axis. The graph may or may not be symmetric with respect to

the line $\theta = \dfrac{\pi}{2}$ or the pole.

Calculate values of r for θ from 0 to π and use symmetry to obtain the graph.

θ	0	$\frac{\pi}{6}$	$\frac{\pi}{3}$	$\frac{\pi}{2}$	$\frac{2\pi}{3}$	$\frac{5\pi}{6}$	π
r	3	2.87	2.5	2	1.5	1.13	1

$r = 2 + \cos\theta$

21. $r = 1 + 2\cos\theta$

Check for symmetry:

Polar Axis	The Line $\theta = \frac{\pi}{2}$	The Pole
$r = 1 + 2\cos(-\theta)$	$-r = 1 + 2\cos(-\theta)$	$-r = 1 + 2\cos\theta$
	$-r = 1 + 2\cos\theta$	
$r = 1 + 2\cos\theta$	$r = -1 - 2\cos\theta$	$r = -1 - 2\cos\theta$

The graph is symmetric with respect to the polar axis. The graph may or may not be symmetric with respect to the line $\theta = \frac{\pi}{2}$ or the pole.

Calculate values of r for θ from 0 to π and use symmetry to obtain the graph.

θ	0	$\frac{\pi}{6}$	$\frac{\pi}{3}$	$\frac{\pi}{2}$	$\frac{2\pi}{3}$	$\frac{5\pi}{6}$	π
r	3	2.73	2	1	0	-0.73	-1

$r = 1 + 2\cos\theta$

23. $r = 2 - 3\sin\theta$

Check for symmetry:

Polar Axis	The Line $\theta = \dfrac{\pi}{2}$	The Pole
$r = 2 - 3\sin(-\theta)$	$-r = 2 - 3\sin(-\theta)$	$-r = 2 - 3\sin\theta$
	$-r = 2 + 3\sin\theta$	
$r = 2 + 3\sin\theta$	$r = -2 - 3\sin\theta$	$r = -2 + 3\sin\theta$

There may be no symmetry since each equation is not equivalent to $r = 2 - 3\sin\theta$. Because the period of the sine function is 2π, we need not consider values of θ beyond 2π.

θ	0	$\dfrac{\pi}{6}$	$\dfrac{\pi}{3}$	$\dfrac{\pi}{2}$	$\dfrac{2\pi}{3}$	$\dfrac{5\pi}{6}$	π	$\dfrac{7\pi}{6}$	$\dfrac{4\pi}{3}$	$\dfrac{3\pi}{2}$	$\dfrac{5\pi}{6}$	$\dfrac{11\pi}{6}$	2π
r	2	0.5	−0.60	−1	−0.60	0.5	2	3.5	4.6	5	4.6	3.5	2

$r = 2 - 3\sin\theta$

25. $r = 2\cos 2\theta$

Check for symmetry:

Polar Axis	The Line $\theta = \dfrac{\pi}{2}$	The Pole
$r = 2\cos 2(-\theta)$	$-r = 2\cos 2(-\theta)$	$-r = 2\cos 2\theta$
$r = 2\cos(-2\theta)$	$-r = 2\cos(-2\theta)$	
	$-r = 2\cos 2\theta$	
$r = 2\cos 2\theta$	$r = -2\cos 2\theta$	$r = -2\cos 2\theta$

The graph is symmetric with respect to the polar axis. The graph may or may not be symmetric with respect to the line $\theta = \dfrac{\pi}{2}$ or the pole.

Calculate values of r for θ from 0 to π and use symmetry to obtain the graph.

θ	0	$\dfrac{\pi}{6}$	$\dfrac{\pi}{3}$	$\dfrac{\pi}{2}$	$\dfrac{2\pi}{3}$	$\dfrac{5\pi}{6}$	π
r	2	1	−1	−2	−1	1	2

$r = 2\cos 2\theta$

27. $r = 4\sin 3\theta$
      Check for symmetry:

Polar Axis	The Line $\theta = \dfrac{\pi}{2}$	The Pole
$r = 4\sin 3(-\theta)$ $r = 4\sin(-3\theta)$	$-r = 4\sin 3(-\theta)$ $-r = 4\sin(-3\theta)$ $-r = -4\sin 3\theta$	$-r = 4\sin 3\theta$
$r = -4\sin 3\theta$	$r = 4\sin 3\theta$	$r = -4\sin 3\theta$

The graph is symmetric with respect to the line $\theta = \dfrac{\pi}{2}$. The graph may or may not be symmetric with respect to the polar axis or the poles.

Calculate values of r for θ from 0 to $\dfrac{\pi}{2}$ and for θ from π to $\dfrac{3\pi}{2}$. Then, use symmetry to obtain the graph.

θ	0	$\dfrac{\pi}{6}$	$\dfrac{\pi}{4}$	$\dfrac{\pi}{3}$	$\dfrac{\pi}{2}$	π	$\dfrac{7\pi}{6}$	$\dfrac{5\pi}{4}$	$\dfrac{4\pi}{3}$	$\dfrac{3\pi}{2}$
r	0	4	2.83	0	-4	0	-4	-2.83	0	4

$r = 4\sin 3\theta$

29. $r^2 = 9\cos 2\theta$
Check for symmetry:

Polar Axis	The Line $\theta = \dfrac{\pi}{2}$	The Pole
$r^2 = 9\cos 2(-\theta)$	$(-r)^2 = 9\cos 2(-\theta)$	$(-r)^2 = 9\cos 2\theta$
$r^2 = 9\cos(-2\theta)$	$r^2 = 9\cos(-2\theta)$	
$r^2 = 9\cos 2\theta$	$r^2 = 9\cos 2\theta$	$r^2 = 9\cos 2\theta$

The graph is symmetric with respect to the polar axis, the line $\theta = \dfrac{\pi}{2}$, and the pole.

Note that since $\cos 2\theta$ is negative for $\dfrac{\pi}{4} < \theta < \dfrac{3\pi}{4}$, there is no graph there.

Calculate values of r for θ from 0 to $\dfrac{\pi}{4}$ and use symmetry to obtain the graph.

θ	0	$\dfrac{\pi}{6}$	$\dfrac{\pi}{4}$
r	± 3	± 2.12	0

$r^2 = 9\cos 2\theta$

31. $r = 1 - 3\sin\theta$
Check for symmetry:

Polar Axis	The Line $\theta = \dfrac{\pi}{2}$	The Pole
$r = 1 - 3\sin(-\theta)$	$-r = 1 - 3\sin(-\theta)$	$-r = 1 - 3\sin\theta$
	$-r = 1 + 3\sin\theta$	
$r = 1 + 3\sin\theta$	$r = -1 - 3\sin\theta$	$r = -1 + 3\sin\theta$

There may be no symmetry. Since each equation is not equivalent to $r = 1 - 3\sin\theta$. Because the period of the sine function is 2π, we need not consider values of θ beyond 2π.

θ	0	$\dfrac{\pi}{6}$	$\dfrac{\pi}{3}$	$\dfrac{\pi}{2}$	$\dfrac{2\pi}{3}$	$\dfrac{5\pi}{6}$	π	$\dfrac{7\pi}{6}$	$\dfrac{4\pi}{3}$	$\dfrac{3\pi}{2}$	$\dfrac{5\pi}{6}$	$\dfrac{11\pi}{6}$	2π
r	1	-0.5	-1.6	-2	-1.6	-0.5	1	2.5	3.6	4	3.6	2.5	1

$r = 1 - 3\sin\theta$

33. $r\cos\theta = -3$

$$r = \frac{-3}{\cos\theta} = -3\sec\theta$$

Check for symmetry:

Polar Axis	The Line $\theta = \dfrac{\pi}{2}$	The Pole
$r = -3\sec(-\theta)$	$-r = -3\sec(-\theta)$	$-r = -3\sec\theta$
	$-r = -3\sec\theta$	
$r = -3\sec\theta$	$r = 3\sec\theta$	$r = 3\sec\theta$

The graph is symmetric with respect to the polar axis. The graph may or may not be symmetric with respect to the line $\theta = \dfrac{\pi}{2}$ or the pole.

Calculate values of r for θ from 0 to π. Then, use symmetry to obtain the graph.

θ	0	$\dfrac{\pi}{6}$	$\dfrac{\pi}{3}$	$\dfrac{\pi}{2}$	$\dfrac{2\pi}{3}$	$\dfrac{5\pi}{6}$	π
r	−3	−3.46	−6	Undef.	6	3.46	3

Note that since $\sec\theta$ is undefined when $\theta = \dfrac{\pi}{2}$ and $\theta = \dfrac{3\pi}{2}$, r increases without bound as θ approaches these angles. $r\cos\theta = -3$ is equivalent to $x = -3$.

$r\cos\theta = -3$

35. $r = \cos\dfrac{\theta}{2}$

Symmetrical about the polar axis: yes

Symmetrical about the line $\theta = \dfrac{\pi}{2}$: yes

Symmetrical about the pole: yes

$$r = \cos\dfrac{\theta}{2}$$

37. $r = \sin\theta + \cos\theta$

Symmetrical about the polar axis: maybe

Symmetrical about the line $\theta = \dfrac{\pi}{2}$: maybe

Symmetrical about the pole: maybe

$$r = \sin\theta + \cos\theta$$

39. $r = \dfrac{1}{1 - \cos\theta}$

Symmetrical about the polar axis: yes

Symmetrical about the line $\theta = \dfrac{\pi}{2}$: maybe

Symmetrical about the pole: maybe

$$r = \dfrac{1}{1 - \cos\theta}$$

41. $r = \sin\theta\cos^2\theta$

Symmetrical about the polar axis: maybe

Symmetrical about the line $\theta = \dfrac{\pi}{2}$: yes

Symmetrical about the pole: maybe

$$r = \sin\theta\cos^2\theta$$

43. $r = 2 + 3\sin 2\theta$

Symmetrical about the polar axis: maybe

Symmetrical about the line $\theta = \dfrac{\pi}{2}$: maybe

Symmetrical about the pole: yes

$$r = 2 + 3\sin 2\theta$$

45. Using the graph, sailing at a 60° angle to the wind gives a speed of about 6 knots (to the nearest knot).

47. Using the graph, sailing at a 90° angle to the wind gives a speed of about 8 knots (to the nearest knot).

49. It appears that an angle of 90° gives a maximum speed of about $7\dfrac{1}{2}$ knots.

59.

61.

63.

65.

67.

69.

71.

73.

75.

77. If $\theta \max = 2\pi$, the graph is drawn once.

79. θ step $= 0.1$

81. θ step $= 0.1$

83. As n increases, $\sin n\theta$ increases its number of loops. If n is odd, there are n loops and $\theta \max = \pi$ traces the graph once, while if n is even, there are $2n$ loops and $\theta \max = 2\pi$ traces the graph once.

85. There are n small petals and n large petals for each value of n. For odd values of n, the small petals are inside the large petals. For even n, they are between the large petals.

87. $\theta \min = 0$, $\theta \max = 2\pi$ $\theta \min = 0$, $\theta \max = 4\pi$ $\theta \min = 0$, $\theta \max = 8\pi$

89.

$r_1 = 4 \cos 2\theta$

$r_2 = 4 \cos 2\left(\theta - \frac{\pi}{4}\right)$

The graph of r_2 is the graph of r_1 rotated $\frac{\pi}{4}$ or $45°$.

Mid-Chapter 6 Check Point

1. $C = 180° - 32° - 41° = 107°$

Use the Law of Sines to find b.

$$\frac{a}{\sin A} = \frac{b}{\sin B}$$

$$\frac{20}{\sin 32°} = \frac{b}{\sin 41°}$$

$$b = \frac{20 \sin 41°}{\sin 32°}$$

$$b \approx 24.8$$

Use the Law of Sines to find c.

$$\frac{a}{\sin A} = \frac{c}{\sin C}$$

$$\frac{20}{\sin 32°} = \frac{c}{\sin 107°}$$

$$c = \frac{20 \sin 107°}{\sin 32°}$$

$$c \approx 36.1$$

The solution is $C = 107°$, $b \approx 24.8$, and $c \approx 36.1$.

2. Use the Law of Sines to find B.

$$\frac{a}{\sin A} = \frac{b}{\sin B}$$

$$\frac{63}{\sin 42°} = \frac{57}{\sin B}$$

$$\sin B = \frac{57 \sin 42°}{63}$$

$$\sin B \approx 0.6054$$

There are two angles possible:

$B_1 \approx 37°$, $B_2 \approx 180° - 37° = 143°$

B_2 is impossible, since $42° + 143° = 185°$.

$C = 180° - B_1 - A \approx 180° - 37° - 42° = 101°$

Use the Law of Sines to find c.

$$\frac{c}{\sin C} = \frac{a}{\sin A}$$

$$\frac{c}{\sin 101°} = \frac{63}{\sin 42°}$$

$$c = \frac{63 \sin 101°}{\sin 42°}$$

$$c \approx 92.4$$

There is one triangle and the solution is B_1 (or B) $\approx 37°$, $C \approx 101°$, and $c \approx 92.4$.

3. Use the Law of Sines to find angle B.

$$\frac{a}{\sin A} = \frac{b}{\sin B}$$

$$\frac{6}{\sin 65°} = \frac{7}{\sin B}$$

$$\sin B = \frac{7 \sin 65°}{6}$$

$$\sin B \approx 1.0574$$

The sine can never exceed 1. There is no triangle with the given measurements.

4. Use the Law of Cosines to find b.

$$b^2 = a^2 + c^2 - 2ac\cos B$$

$$b^2 = 10^2 + 16^2 - 2(10)(16)\cos 110°$$

$$b^2 \approx 465.4464$$

$$b \approx 21.6$$

Use the Law of Sines to find A.

$$\frac{b}{\sin B} = \frac{a}{\sin A}$$

$$\frac{21.6}{\sin 110°} = \frac{10}{\sin A}$$

$$\sin A = \frac{10\sin 110°}{21.6}$$

$$\sin A \approx 0.4350$$

$$A \approx 26°$$

Find the third angle.

$$C = 180° - A - B \approx 180° - 26° - 110° = 44°$$

The solution is $A \approx 26°$, $C \approx 44°$, and $b \approx 21.6$.

5. Use the Law of Sines to find angle A.

$$\frac{a}{\sin A} = \frac{c}{\sin C}$$

$$\frac{16}{\sin A} = \frac{13}{\sin 42°}$$

$$\sin A = \frac{16\sin 42°}{13}$$

$$\sin A \approx 0.8235$$

There are two angles possible:

$$A_1 \approx 55°, \; A_2 \approx 180° - 55° = 125°$$

There are two triangles:

$$B_1 = 180° - C - A_1 \approx 180° - 42° - 55° = 83°$$

$$B_2 = 180° - C - A_2 \approx 180° - 42° - 125° = 13°$$

Use the Law of Sines to find b_1 and b_2.

$$\frac{b_1}{\sin B_1} = \frac{c}{\sin C}$$

$$\frac{b_1}{\sin 83°} = \frac{13}{\sin 42°}$$

$$b_1 = \frac{13\sin 83°}{\sin 42°} \approx 19.3$$

$$\frac{b_2}{\sin B_2} = \frac{c}{\sin C}$$

$$\frac{b_2}{\sin 13°} = \frac{13}{\sin 42°}$$

$$b_2 = \frac{13\sin 13°}{\sin 42°} \approx 4.4$$

In one triangle, the solution is
$A_1 \approx 55°$, $B_1 \approx 83°$, $b_1 \approx 19.3$.
In the other triangle,
$A_2 \approx 125°$, $B_2 \approx 13°$, $b_2 \approx 4.4$.

6. Use the Law of Cosines to find the angle opposite the longest side.
Thus, find angle C.

$$c^2 = a^2 + b^2 - 2ab\cos C$$

$$\cos C = \frac{a^2 + b^2 - c^2}{2ab}$$

$$\cos C = \frac{5^2 + 7.2^2 - 10.1^2}{2 \cdot 5 \cdot 7.2}$$

$$\cos C \approx -0.3496$$

$$C \approx 110°$$

Use the Law of Sines to find angle A.

$$\frac{a}{\sin A} = \frac{c}{\sin C}$$

$$\frac{5}{\sin A} = \frac{10.1}{\sin 110°}$$

$$\sin A = \frac{5\sin 110°}{10.1}$$

$$\sin A \approx 0.4652$$

$$A \approx 28°$$

Find the third angle.

$$B = 180° - A - C = 180° - 28° - 110° = 42°$$

The solution is $A \approx 28°$, $B \approx 42°$, and $C \approx 110°$

7. The area of the triangle is half the product of the lengths of the two sides times the sine of the included angle.

$$\text{Area} = \frac{1}{2}(5)(7)(\sin 36°) \approx 10$$

The area of the triangle is approximately 10 square feet.

8. Begin by calculating one-half the perimeter:

$$s = \frac{1}{2}(a + b + c) = \frac{1}{2}(7 + 9 + 12) = 14$$

Use Heron's formula to find the area.

$$\begin{aligned} \text{Area} &= \sqrt{s(s-a)(s-b)(s-c)} \\ &= \sqrt{14(14-7)(14-9)(14-12)} \\ &= \sqrt{980} \approx 31 \end{aligned}$$

The area of the triangle is approximately 31 square meters.

9. The first train traveled 100 miles, the second train traveled 80 miles.
Use the Law of Cosines to find the distance.

$$c^2 = a^2 + b^2 - 2ab\cos C$$

$$c^2 = 100^2 + 80^2 - 2(100)(80)\cos 110°$$

$$c^2 \approx 21872.32229$$

$$c \approx 148$$

The two trains are 148 miles apart.

10. Let the fire be at point C.

$$A = 90° - 56° = 34°$$

$$B = 90° - 23° = 67°$$

$$C = 180° - 34° - 67° = 79°$$

Use the law of sines to find b.

$$\frac{b}{\sin B} = \frac{c}{\sin C}$$

$$\frac{b}{\sin 67°} = \frac{16}{\sin 79°}$$

$$b = \frac{16\sin 67°}{\sin 79°}$$

$$b \approx 15.0$$

The fire is 15.0 miles from station A

11. Let point A be where the angle of elevation is 66°.

Let point B be where the angle of elevation is 50°.

Let point C be at the top of the tree.

$$C = 180° - A - B = 180° - 66° - 50° = 64°$$

Use the law of sines to find a.

$$\frac{a}{\sin A} = \frac{c}{\sin C}$$

$$\frac{a}{\sin 66°} = \frac{420}{\sin 64°}$$

$$a = \frac{420\sin 66°}{\sin 64°}$$

$$a \approx 427$$

The height of the tree, h, is given by

$$h = a\sin B$$

$$h = 427\sin 50°$$

$$h \approx 327$$

The tree is 327 feet tall.

12. $x = r\cos\theta = -3\cos\dfrac{5\pi}{4} = \dfrac{3\sqrt{2}}{2}$

$y = r\sin\theta = -3\sin\dfrac{5\pi}{4} = -\dfrac{3\sqrt{2}}{2}$

Ordered pair: $\left(\dfrac{3\sqrt{2}}{2}, -\dfrac{3\sqrt{2}}{2}\right)$

13. $x = r\cos\theta = 6\cos\left(-\dfrac{\pi}{2}\right) = 0$

$y = r\sin\theta = 6\sin\left(-\dfrac{\pi}{2}\right) = -6$

Ordered pair: $(0, -6)$

14. $r = \sqrt{x^2 + y^2} = \sqrt{2^2 + \left(-2\sqrt{3}\right)^2} = 4$

$\tan\theta = \dfrac{y}{x} = \dfrac{-2\sqrt{3}}{2} = -\sqrt{3}$

Because θ lies in quadrant IV,

$\theta = 2\pi - \dfrac{\pi}{3} = \dfrac{5\pi}{3}$

Polar coordinates: $\left(4, \dfrac{5\pi}{3}\right)$

15. $r = \sqrt{x^2 + y^2} = \sqrt{(-6)^2 + 0^2} = 6$

$\tan\theta = \dfrac{y}{x} = \dfrac{0}{-6} = 0$

$\theta = \pi$

Polar coordinates: $(6, \pi)$

16.

a. $\left(4, \dfrac{11\pi}{4}\right)$

b. $\left(-4, \dfrac{7\pi}{4}\right)$

c. $\left(4, \dfrac{5\pi}{4}\right)$

17.

a. $\left(\dfrac{5}{2}, \dfrac{5\pi}{2}\right)$

b. $\left(-\dfrac{5}{2}, \dfrac{3\pi}{2}\right)$

c. $\left(\dfrac{5}{2}, -\dfrac{3\pi}{2}\right)$

18.
$$5x - y = 7$$
$$5r\cos\theta - r\sin\theta = 7$$
$$r(5\cos\theta - \sin\theta) = 7$$
$$r = \dfrac{7}{5\cos\theta - \sin\theta}$$

19.
$$y = -7$$
$$r\sin\theta = -7$$
$$r = \dfrac{-7}{\sin\theta}$$
$$r = -7\csc\theta$$

20.
$$(x+1)^2 + y^2 = 1$$
$$(r\cos\theta + 1)^2 + (r\sin\theta)^2 = 1$$
$$r^2\cos^2\theta + 2r\cos\theta + 1 + r^2\sin^2\theta^2 = 1$$
$$r^2 + 2r\cos\theta = 0$$
$$r^2 = -2r\cos\theta$$
$$r = -2\cos\theta$$

21.
$$r = 6$$
$$r^2 = 36$$
$$x^2 + y^2 = 36$$

22.
$$\theta = \dfrac{\pi}{3}$$
$$\tan\theta = \tan\dfrac{\pi}{3}$$
$$\tan\theta = \sqrt{3}$$
$$\dfrac{y}{x} = \sqrt{3}$$
$$y = \sqrt{3}x$$

23.
$$r = -3\csc\theta$$
$$r = \dfrac{-3}{\sin\theta}$$
$$r\sin\theta = -3$$
$$y = -3$$

24.
$$r = -10\cos\theta$$
$$r^2 = -10r\cos\theta$$
$$x^2 + y^2 = -10x$$
$$x^2 + 10x + y^2 = 0$$
$$x^2 + 10x + 25 + y^2 = 25$$
$$(x+5)^2 + y^2 = 25$$

$r = -10\cos\theta$

25.
$$r = 4\sin\theta\sec^2\theta$$
$$r = \frac{4\sin\theta}{\cos^2\theta}$$
$$r\cos^2\theta = 4\sin\theta$$
$$r^2\cos^2\theta = 4r\sin\theta$$
$$x^2 = 4y$$
$$y = \frac{1}{4}x^2$$

$r = 4\sin\theta\sec^2\theta$

26. $r = 1 - 4\cos\theta$

a. Replace θ with $-\theta$.
$$r = 1 - 4\cos(-\theta)$$
$$r = 1 - 4\cos\theta$$
The graph is symmetric with respect to the polar axis.

b. Replace (r,θ) with $(-r,-\theta)$.
$$-r = 1 - 4\cos(-\theta)$$
$$r = -1 + 4\cos\theta$$
The graph may or may not be symmetric with respect to the line $\theta = \dfrac{\pi}{2}$.

c. Replace r with $-r$.
$$-r = 1 - 4\cos\theta$$
$$r = -1 + 4\cos\theta$$
The graph may or may not be symmetric with respect to the polar axis.

27. $r^2 = 4\cos 2\theta$

a. Replace θ with $-\theta$.
$$r^2 = 4\cos(-2\theta)$$
$$r^2 = 4\cos 2\theta$$
The graph is symmetric with respect to the polar axis.

b. Replace (r,θ) with $(-r,-\theta)$.
$$(-r)^2 = 4\cos(-2\theta)$$
$$r^2 = 4\cos 2\theta$$
The graph is symmetric with respect to the line $\theta = \dfrac{\pi}{2}$.

c. Replace r with $-r$.
$$(-r)^2 = 4\cos 2\theta$$
$$r^2 = 4\cos 2\theta$$
The graph is symmetric with respect to the polar axis.

28.

$r = -4 \sin \theta$

29.

$r = 2 - 2 \cos \theta$

30.

$r = 2 - 4 \cos \theta$

31.

$r = 2 \sin 3\theta$

32.

$r^2 = 16 \sin 2\theta$

Section 6.5

Check Point Exercises

1. **a.** $z = 2 + 3i$ corresponds to the point $(2, 3)$. Plot the complex number by moving two units to the right on the real axis and 3 units up parallel to the imaginary axis.

b. $z = -3 - 5i$ corresponds to the point $(-3, -5)$. Plot the complex number by moving three units to the left on the real axis and five units down parallel to the imaginary axis.

c. Because $z = -4 = -4 + 0i$, this complex number corresponds to the point $(-4, 0)$. Plot the complex number by moving four units to the left on the real axis.

d. Because $z = -i = 0 - i$, this complex number corresponds to the point $(0, -1)$. Plot the complex number by moving one unit down on the imaginary axis.

2 a. $z = 5 + 12i$
$a = 5, b = 12$
$|z| = \sqrt{5^2 + 12^2} = \sqrt{25 + 144} = \sqrt{169} = 13$

b. $z = 2 - 3i$
$a = 2, b = -3$
$|z| = \sqrt{2^2 + (-3)^2} = \sqrt{4 + 9} = \sqrt{13}$

3. $z = -1 - \sqrt{3}i$ corresponds to the point $\left(-1, -\sqrt{3}\right)$.

Use $r = \sqrt{a^2 + b^2}$ with $a = -1$ and $b = -\sqrt{3}$ to find r.

$r = \sqrt{a^2 + b^2} = \sqrt{(-1)^2 + \left(-\sqrt{3}\right)^2}$
$= \sqrt{1 + 3} = \sqrt{4} = 2$

Use

$\tan\theta = \dfrac{b}{a}$ with $a = -1$ and $b = -\sqrt{3}$ to find θ.

$\tan\theta = \dfrac{b}{a} = \dfrac{-\sqrt{3}}{-1} = \sqrt{3}$

Because $\tan\dfrac{\pi}{3} = \sqrt{3}$ and θ lies in

quadrant III, $\theta = \pi + \dfrac{\pi}{3} = \dfrac{3\pi}{3} + \dfrac{\pi}{3} = \dfrac{4\pi}{3}$.

The polar form of $z = -1 - \sqrt{3}i$ is

$z = r(\cos\theta + i\sin\theta) = 2\left(\cos\dfrac{4\pi}{3} + i\sin\dfrac{4\pi}{3}\right)$.

4. The complex number $z = 4(\cos 30° + i\sin 30°)$ is in polar form, with $r = 4$ and $\theta = 30°$. We use exact values for $\cos 30°$ and $\sin 30°$ to write the number in rectangular form.

$4(\cos 30° + i\sin 30°) = 4\left(\dfrac{\sqrt{3}}{2} + i\dfrac{1}{2}\right) = 2\sqrt{3} + 2i$

The rectangular form of $z = 4(\cos 30° + i\sin 30°)$ is $z = 2\sqrt{3} + 2i$.

5. $z_1 z_2 = [6(\cos 40° + i\sin 40°)][5(\cos 20° + i\sin 20°)] = (6 \cdot 5)[(\cos(40° + 20°) + i\sin(40° + 20°)]$
$= 30(\cos 60° + i\sin 60°)$

6. $\dfrac{z_1}{z_2} = \dfrac{50\left(\cos\dfrac{4\pi}{3} + i\sin\dfrac{4\pi}{3}\right)}{5\left(\cos\dfrac{\pi}{3} + i\sin\dfrac{\pi}{3}\right)} = \dfrac{50}{5}\left[\cos\left(\dfrac{4\pi}{3} - \dfrac{\pi}{3}\right) + i\sin\left(\dfrac{4\pi}{3} - \dfrac{\pi}{3}\right)\right] = 10(\cos\pi + i\sin\pi)$

7. $\left[2(\cos 30° + i\sin 30°)\right]^5 = 2^5\left[\cos(5\cdot 30°) + i\sin(5\cdot 30°)\right] = 32(\cos 150° + i\sin 150°) = 32\left(-\dfrac{\sqrt{3}}{2} + i\dfrac{1}{2}\right)$

$$= -16\sqrt{3} + 16i$$

8. Write $1 + i$ in $r(\cos\theta + i\sin\theta)$ form.

$$r = \sqrt{a^2 + b^2} = \sqrt{1^2 + 1^2} = \sqrt{2}$$

$$\tan\theta = \frac{b}{a} = \frac{1}{1} = 1 \text{ and } \theta = \frac{\pi}{4}$$

$$1 + i = r(\cos\theta + i\sin\theta) = \sqrt{2}\left(\cos\frac{\pi}{4} + i\sin\frac{\pi}{4}\right)$$

Use DeMoivre's Theorem to raise $1 + i$ to the fourth power.

$$(1+i)^4 = \left[\sqrt{2}\left(\cos\frac{\pi}{4} + i\sin\frac{\pi}{4}\right)\right]^4 = \left(\sqrt{2}\right)^4\left[\cos\left(4\cdot\frac{\pi}{4}\right) + i\sin\left(4\cdot\frac{\pi}{4}\right)\right] = 4(\cos\pi + i\sin\pi) = 4(-1 + 0i) = -4$$

9. From DeMoivre's Theorem for finding complex roots, the fourth roots of $16(\cos 60° + i\sin 60°)$ are

$$z_k = \sqrt[4]{16}\left[\cos\left(\frac{60° + 360°k}{4}\right) + i\sin\left(\frac{60° + 360°k}{4}\right)\right], \; k = 0, 1, 2, 3.$$

Substitute 0, 1, 2, and 3 for k in the above expression for z_k.

$$z_0 = \sqrt[4]{16}\left[\cos\left(\frac{60° + 360°\cdot 0}{4}\right) + i\sin\left(\frac{60° + 360°\cdot 0}{4}\right)\right] = \sqrt[4]{16}\left[\cos\frac{60°}{4} + i\sin\frac{60°}{4}\right] = 2(\cos 15° + i\sin 15°)$$

$$z_1 = \sqrt[4]{16}\left[\cos\left(\frac{60° + 360°\cdot 1}{4}\right) + i\sin\left(\frac{60° + 360°\cdot 1}{4}\right)\right] = \sqrt[4]{16}\left[\cos\frac{420°}{4} + i\sin\frac{420°}{4}\right] = 2(\cos 105° + i\sin 105°)$$

$$z_2 = \sqrt[4]{16}\left[\cos\left(\frac{60° + 360°\cdot 2}{4}\right) + i\sin\left(\frac{60° + 360°\cdot 2}{4}\right)\right] = \sqrt[4]{16}\left[\cos\frac{780°}{4} + i\sin\frac{780°}{4}\right] = 2(\cos 195° + i\sin 195°)$$

$$z_3 = \sqrt[4]{16}\left[\cos\left(\frac{60° + 360°\cdot 3}{4}\right) + i\sin\left(\frac{60° + 360°\cdot 3}{4}\right)\right] = \sqrt[4]{16}\left[\cos\frac{1140°}{4} + i\sin\frac{1140°}{4}\right] = 2(\cos 285° + i\sin 285°)$$

10. First, write 27 in polar form. $27 = r(\cos\theta + i\sin\theta) = 27(\cos 0 + i\sin 0)$. From DeMoivre's theorem for finding complex roots, the cube roots of 27 are

$$z_k = \sqrt[3]{27}\left[\cos\left(\frac{0 + 2\pi k}{3}\right) + i\sin\left(\frac{0 + 2\pi k}{3}\right)\right], \; k = 0, 1, 2.$$

$$z_0 = \sqrt[3]{27}\left[\cos\left(\frac{0 + 2\pi\cdot 0}{3}\right) + i\sin\left(\frac{0 + 2\pi\cdot 0}{3}\right)\right] = 3(\cos 0 + i\sin 0) = 3(1 + i\cdot 0) = 3$$

$$z_1 = \sqrt[3]{27}\left[\cos\left(\frac{0 + 2\pi\cdot 1}{3}\right) + i\sin\left(\frac{0 + 2\pi\cdot 1}{3}\right)\right] = 3\left(\cos\frac{2\pi}{3} + i\sin\frac{2\pi}{3}\right) = 3\left(-\frac{1}{2} + i\cdot\frac{\sqrt{3}}{2}\right) = -\frac{3}{2} + \frac{3\sqrt{3}}{2}i$$

$$z_2 = \sqrt[3]{27}\left[\cos\left(\frac{0 + 2\pi\cdot 2}{3}\right) + i\sin\left(\frac{0 + 2\pi\cdot 2}{3}\right)\right] = 3\left(\cos\frac{4\pi}{3} + i\sin\frac{4\pi}{3}\right) = 3\left(-\frac{1}{2} + i\cdot\left(-\frac{\sqrt{3}}{2}\right)\right) = -\frac{3}{2} - \frac{3\sqrt{3}}{2}i$$

Exercise Set 6.5

1. Because $z = 4i = 0 + 4i$, this complex number corresponds to the point $(0, 4)$.

    With $a = 0$ and $b = 4$,
    $$|z| = \sqrt{0^2 + 4^2} = \sqrt{16} = 4.$$

3. Because $z = 3 = 3 + 0i$, this complex number corresponds to the point $(3, 0)$.

    With $a = 3$ and $b = 0$,
    $$|z| = \sqrt{3^2 + 0^2} = \sqrt{9} = 3.$$

5. $z = 3 + 2i$ corresponds to the point $(3, 2)$.

    With $a = 3$ and $b = 2$,
    $$|z| = \sqrt{3^2 + 2^2} = \sqrt{9 + 4} = \sqrt{13}.$$

7. $z = 3 - i$ corresponds to the point $(3, -1)$.

    With $a = 3$ and $b = -1$,
    $$|z| = \sqrt{3^2 + (-1)^2} = \sqrt{9 + 1} = \sqrt{10}.$$

9. $z = -3 + 4i$ corresponds to the point $(-3, 4)$.

    With $a = -3$ and $b = 4$,
    $$|z| = \sqrt{(-3)^2 + 4^2} = \sqrt{9 + 16} = \sqrt{25} = 5.$$

11. $z = 2 + 2i$ corresponds to the point $(2, 2)$.

    Use $r = \sqrt{a^2 + b^2}$ and $\tan\theta = \dfrac{b}{a}$, with $a = 2$ and $b = 2$, to find r and θ.

    $$r = \sqrt{2^2 + 2^2} = \sqrt{4 + 4} = \sqrt{8} = 2\sqrt{2}$$

    $$\tan\theta = \frac{2}{2} = 1$$

    Because $\tan\dfrac{\pi}{4} = 1$ and θ lies in quadrant I, $\theta = \dfrac{\pi}{4}$.

    $$z = 2 + 2i = r(\cos\theta + i\sin\theta)$$
    $$= 2\sqrt{2}\left(\cos\frac{\pi}{4} + i\sin\frac{\pi}{4}\right)$$
    $$\text{or } 2\sqrt{2}(\cos 45° + i\sin 45°)$$

13. $z = -1 - i$ corresponds to the point $(-1, -1)$.

Use $r = \sqrt{a^2 + b^2}$ and $\tan\theta = \dfrac{b}{a}$, with $a = -1$ and $b = -1$, to find r and θ.

$r = \sqrt{(-1)^2 + (-1)^2} = \sqrt{1+1} = \sqrt{2}$

$\tan\theta = \dfrac{-1}{-1} = 1$

Because $\tan\dfrac{\pi}{4} = 1$ and θ lies in quadrant III, $\theta = \pi + \dfrac{\pi}{4} = \dfrac{5\pi}{4}$.

$z = -1 - i = r(\cos\theta + i\sin\theta)$

$\quad = \sqrt{2}\left(\cos\dfrac{5\pi}{4} + i\sin\dfrac{5\pi}{4}\right)$

or $\sqrt{2}(\cos 225° + i\sin 225°)$

15. $z = -4i$ corresponds to the point $(0, -4)$.

Use $r = \sqrt{a^2 + b^2}$ and $\tan\theta = \dfrac{b}{a}$, with $a = 0$ and $b = -4$, to find r and θ.

$r = \sqrt{0^2 + (-4)^2} = \sqrt{16} = 4$

$\tan\theta = \dfrac{-4}{0}$ is undefined.

Because $\tan\dfrac{\pi}{2}$ is undefined and θ lies on the negative y-axis, $\theta = \dfrac{\pi}{2} + \pi = \dfrac{3\pi}{2}$.

$z = -4i = r(\cos\theta + i\sin\theta)$

$\quad = 4\left(\cos\dfrac{3\pi}{2} + i\sin\dfrac{3\pi}{2}\right)$

or $4(\cos 270° + i\sin 270°)$

17. $z = 2\sqrt{3} - 2i$ corresponds to the point $\left(2\sqrt{3}, -2\right)$.

Use $r = \sqrt{a^2 + b^2}$ and $\tan\theta = \dfrac{b}{a}$, with $a = 2\sqrt{3}$ and $b = -2$, to find r and θ.

$r = \sqrt{\left(2\sqrt{3}\right)^2 + (-2)^2} = \sqrt{12+4} = \sqrt{16} = 4$

$\tan\theta = \dfrac{-2}{2\sqrt{3}} = -\dfrac{1}{\sqrt{3}}$

Because $\tan\dfrac{\pi}{6} = \dfrac{1}{\sqrt{3}}$ and θ lies in quadrant IV, $\theta = 2\pi - \dfrac{\pi}{6} = \dfrac{11\pi}{6}$.

$z = 2\sqrt{3} - 2i = r(\cos\theta + i\sin\theta)$

$\quad = 4\left(\cos\dfrac{11\pi}{6} + i\sin\dfrac{11\pi}{6}\right)$

or $4(\cos 330° + i\sin 330°)$

19. $z = -3$ corresponds to the point $(-3, 0)$.

Use $r = \sqrt{a^2 + b^2}$ and $\tan\theta = \dfrac{b}{a}$, with

$a = -3$ and $b = 0$, to find r and θ.

$r = \sqrt{(-3)^2 + 0^2} = \sqrt{9} = 3$

$\tan\theta = \dfrac{0}{-3} = 0$

Because $\tan 0 = 0$ and θ lies on the negative
x-axis, $\theta = 0 + \pi = \pi$.

$z = -3 = r(\cos\theta + i\sin\theta)$

$\quad = 3\left(\cos\pi + i\sin\pi\right)$

$\quad$ or $3(\cos 180° + i\sin 180°)$

21. $z = -3\sqrt{2} - 3\sqrt{3}i$ corresponds to the point
$\left(-3\sqrt{2}, -3\sqrt{3}\right)$.

Use $r = \sqrt{a^2 + b^2}$ and $\tan\theta = \dfrac{b}{a}$, with

$a = -3\sqrt{2}$ and $b = -3\sqrt{3}$, to find r and θ.

$r = \sqrt{\left(-3\sqrt{2}\right)^2 + \left(-3\sqrt{3}\right)^2} = \sqrt{18 + 27}$

$\quad = \sqrt{45} = 3\sqrt{5}$

$\tan\theta = \dfrac{-3\sqrt{3}}{-3\sqrt{2}} = \dfrac{\sqrt{3}}{\sqrt{2}} = \dfrac{\sqrt{6}}{2}$

Because θ lies in quadrant III,

$\theta = 180° + \tan^{-1}\left(\dfrac{\sqrt{6}}{2}\right) \approx 180° + 50.8°$

$\quad = 230.8°$

$z = -3\sqrt{2} - 3\sqrt{3}i = r(\cos\theta + i\sin\theta)$

$\quad \approx 3\sqrt{5}(\cos 230.8° + i\sin 230.8°)$

23. $z = -3 + 4i$ corresponds to the point $(-3, 4)$.

Use $r = \sqrt{a^2 + b^2}$ and $\tan\theta = \dfrac{b}{a}$, with

$a = -3$ and $b = 4$, to find r and θ.

$r = \sqrt{(-3)^2 + (4)^2} = \sqrt{9 + 16} = \sqrt{25} = 5$

$\tan\theta = \dfrac{4}{-3} = -\dfrac{4}{3}$

Because θ lies in quadrant II,

$\theta = 180° - \tan^{-1}\left(\dfrac{4}{3}\right) \approx 180° - 53.1° = 126.9°$.

$z = -3 + 4i = r(\cos\theta + i\sin\theta)$

$\quad \approx 5(\cos 126.9° + i\sin 126.9°)$

25. $z = 2 - \sqrt{3}i$ corresponds to the point $\left(2, -\sqrt{3}\right)$.

Use $r = \sqrt{a^2 + b^2}$ and $\tan\theta = \dfrac{b}{a}$, with

$a = 2$ and $b = -\sqrt{3}$, to find r and θ.

$r = \sqrt{2^2 + \left(-\sqrt{3}\right)^2} = \sqrt{4 + 3} = \sqrt{7}$

$\tan\theta = \dfrac{-\sqrt{3}}{2} = -\dfrac{\sqrt{3}}{2}$

Because θ lies in quadrant IV,

$\theta = 360° - \tan^{-1}\left(\dfrac{\sqrt{3}}{2}\right) \approx 360° - 40.9° = 319.1°$

$z = 2 - \sqrt{3}i = r(\cos\theta + i\sin\theta)$

$\quad \approx \sqrt{7}(\cos 319.1° + i\sin 319.1°)$

27. $6(\cos 30° + i \sin 30°) = 6\left(\dfrac{\sqrt{3}}{2} + i\dfrac{1}{2}\right)$

$$= 3\sqrt{3} + 3i$$

The rectangular form of

$z = 6(\cos 30° + i \sin 30°)$ is $z = 3\sqrt{3} + 3i$.

29. $4(\cos 240° + i \sin 240°) = 4\left(-\dfrac{1}{2} + i\left(-\dfrac{\sqrt{3}}{2}\right)\right)$

$$= -2 - 2\sqrt{3}i$$

The rectangular form of

$z = 4(\cos 240° + i \sin 240°)$ is $z = -2 - 2\sqrt{3}i$.

31. $8\left(\cos\dfrac{7\pi}{4} + i\sin\dfrac{7\pi}{4}\right) = 8\left(\dfrac{\sqrt{2}}{2} + i\left(-\dfrac{\sqrt{2}}{2}\right)\right)$

$$= 4\sqrt{2} - 4\sqrt{2}i$$

The rectangular form of

$8\left(\cos\dfrac{7\pi}{4} + i\sin\dfrac{7\pi}{4}\right)$ is $z = 4\sqrt{2} - 4\sqrt{2}i$.

33. $5\left(\cos\dfrac{\pi}{2} + i\sin\dfrac{\pi}{2}\right) = 5\big(0 + i(1)\big)$

$$= 5i$$

The rectangular form of

$z = 5\left(\cos\dfrac{\pi}{2} + i\sin\dfrac{\pi}{2}\right)$ is $z = 5i$.

35. $20\big(\cos 205° + i\sin 205°\big)$

$\approx 20\big(-0.91 + i(-0.42)\big) = -18.2 - 8.4i$

The rectangular form of

$z = 20\big(\cos 205° + i\sin 205°\big)$ is $z \approx -18.2 - 8.5i$.

37. $z_1 z_2$

$= \big[6(\cos 20° + i\sin 20°)\big]\big[5(\cos 50° + i\sin 50°)\big]$

$= (6 \cdot 5)\big[\cos(20° + 50°) + i\sin(20° + 50°)\big]$

$= 30(\cos 70° + i\sin 70°)$

39. $z_1 z_2 = \left[3\left(\cos\dfrac{\pi}{5} + i\sin\dfrac{\pi}{5}\right)\right]\left[4\left(\cos\dfrac{\pi}{10} + i\sin\dfrac{\pi}{10}\right)\right] = (3 \cdot 4)\left[\cos\left(\dfrac{\pi}{5} + \dfrac{\pi}{10}\right) + i\sin\left(\dfrac{\pi}{5} + \dfrac{\pi}{10}\right)\right]$

$= 12\left(\cos\dfrac{3\pi}{10} + i\sin\dfrac{3\pi}{10}\right)$

41. $z_1 z_2 = \left[\cos\dfrac{\pi}{4} + i\sin\dfrac{\pi}{4}\right]\left[\cos\dfrac{\pi}{3} + i\sin\dfrac{\pi}{3}\right] = \cos\left(\dfrac{\pi}{4} + \dfrac{\pi}{3}\right) + i\sin\left(\dfrac{\pi}{4} + \dfrac{\pi}{3}\right) = \cos\left(\dfrac{3\pi}{12} + \dfrac{4\pi}{12}\right) + i\sin\left(\dfrac{3\pi}{12} + \dfrac{4\pi}{12}\right)$

$= \cos\dfrac{7\pi}{12} + i\sin\dfrac{7\pi}{12}$

43. Begin by converting $z_1 = 1 + i$ and $z_2 = -1 + i$ to polar form.

For z_1: $a = 1$ and $b = 1$

$r = \sqrt{a^2 + b^2} = \sqrt{1^2 + 1^2} = \sqrt{2}$

$\tan\theta = \dfrac{b}{a} = \dfrac{1}{1} = 1$ and $\theta = \dfrac{\pi}{4}$.

$z_1 = r(\cos\theta + i\sin\theta) = \sqrt{2}\left(\cos\dfrac{\pi}{4} + i\sin\dfrac{\pi}{4}\right)$

For z_2: $a = -1$ and $b = 1$

$r = \sqrt{a^2 + b^2} = \sqrt{(-1)^2 + 1^2} = \sqrt{2}$

$\tan\theta = \dfrac{b}{a} = \dfrac{1}{-1} = -1$

Because $\tan\dfrac{\pi}{4}=1$ and θ lies in quadrant II, $\theta=\pi-\dfrac{\pi}{4}=\dfrac{3\pi}{4}$.

$z_2=r(\cos\theta+i\sin\theta)=\sqrt{2}\left(\cos\dfrac{3\pi}{4}+i\sin\dfrac{3\pi}{4}\right)$

Now, find the product.

$z_1z_2=(1+i)(-1+i)$

$\quad=\left[\sqrt{2}\left(\cos\dfrac{\pi}{4}+i\sin\dfrac{\pi}{4}\right)\right]\left[\sqrt{2}\left(\cos\dfrac{3\pi}{4}+i\sin\dfrac{3\pi}{4}\right)\right]=\left(\sqrt{2}\cdot\sqrt{2}\right)\left[\cos\left(\dfrac{\pi}{4}+\dfrac{3\pi}{4}\right)+i\sin\left(\dfrac{\pi}{4}+\dfrac{3\pi}{4}\right)\right]$

$\quad=2\left(\cos\pi+i\sin\pi\right)$

45. $\dfrac{z_1}{z_2}=\dfrac{20(\cos75°+i\sin75°)}{4(\cos25°+i\sin25°)}=\dfrac{20}{4}\left[\cos(75°-25°)+i\sin(75°-25°)\right]$

$\qquad=5(\cos50°+i\sin50°)$

47. $\dfrac{z_1}{z_2}=\dfrac{3\left(\cos\dfrac{\pi}{5}+i\sin\dfrac{\pi}{5}\right)}{4\left(\cos\dfrac{\pi}{10}+i\sin\dfrac{\pi}{10}\right)}=\dfrac{3}{4}\left[\cos\left(\dfrac{\pi}{5}-\dfrac{\pi}{10}\right)+i\sin\left(\dfrac{\pi}{5}-\dfrac{\pi}{10}\right)\right]=\dfrac{3}{4}\left(\cos\dfrac{\pi}{10}+i\sin\dfrac{\pi}{10}\right)$

49. $\dfrac{z_1}{z_2}=\dfrac{\cos80°+i\sin80°}{\cos200°+i\sin200°}=\cos(80°-200°)+i\sin(80°-200°)=\cos(-120°)+i\sin(-120°)$

$\qquad=\cos240°+i\sin240°$

51. Begin by converting $z_1=2+2i$ and $z_2=1+i$ to polar form.

For z_1: $a=2$ and $b=2$

$r=\sqrt{a^2+b^2}=\sqrt{2^2+2^2}=\sqrt{8}=2\sqrt{2}$

$\tan\theta=\dfrac{b}{a}=\dfrac{2}{2}=1$ and $\theta=\dfrac{\pi}{4}$

$z_1=r(\cos\theta+i\sin\theta)=2\sqrt{2}\left(\cos\dfrac{\pi}{4}+i\sin\dfrac{\pi}{4}\right)$

For z_2: $a=1$ and $b=1$

$r=\sqrt{a^2+b^2}=\sqrt{1^2+1^2}=\sqrt{2}$

$\tan\theta=\dfrac{b}{a}=\dfrac{1}{1}=1$ and $\theta=\dfrac{\pi}{4}$

$z_2=r(\cos\theta+i\sin\theta)=\sqrt{2}\left(\cos\dfrac{\pi}{4}+i\sin\dfrac{\pi}{4}\right).$

Now, find the quotient.

$\dfrac{z_1}{z_2}=\dfrac{2+2i}{1+i}=\dfrac{2\sqrt{2}\left(\cos\dfrac{\pi}{4}+i\sin\dfrac{\pi}{4}\right)}{\sqrt{2}\left(\cos\dfrac{\pi}{4}+i\sin\dfrac{\pi}{4}\right)}=2\left[\cos\left(\dfrac{\pi}{4}-\dfrac{\pi}{4}\right)+i\sin\left(\dfrac{\pi}{4}-\dfrac{\pi}{4}\right)\right]=2(\cos0+i\sin0)$

53. $\left[4(\cos 15° + i\sin 15°)\right]^3 = (4)^3\left[\cos(3\cdot 15°) + i\sin(3\cdot 15°)\right] = 64(\cos 45° + i\sin 45°) = 64\left(\dfrac{\sqrt{2}}{2} + i\dfrac{\sqrt{2}}{2}\right)$

$$= 32\sqrt{2} + 32\sqrt{2}i$$

55. $\left[2(\cos 80° + i\sin 80°)\right]^3 = (2)^3\left[\cos(3\cdot 80°) + i\sin(3\cdot 80°)\right] = 8(\cos 240° + i\sin 240°)$

$$= 8\left(-\dfrac{1}{2} + i\left(-\dfrac{\sqrt{3}}{2}\right)\right) = -4 - 4\sqrt{3}i$$

57. $\left[\dfrac{1}{2}\left(\cos\dfrac{\pi}{12} + i\sin\dfrac{\pi}{12}\right)\right]^6 = \left(\dfrac{1}{2}\right)^6\left[\cos\left(6\cdot\dfrac{\pi}{12}\right) + i\sin\left(6\cdot\dfrac{\pi}{12}\right)\right] = \dfrac{1}{64}\left(\cos\dfrac{\pi}{2} + i\sin\dfrac{\pi}{2}\right) = \dfrac{1}{64}(0 + i) = \dfrac{1}{64}i$

59. $\left[\sqrt{2}\left(\cos\dfrac{5\pi}{6} + i\sin\dfrac{5\pi}{6}\right)\right]^4 = \left(\sqrt{2}\right)^4\left[\cos\left(4\cdot\dfrac{5\pi}{6}\right) + i\sin\left(4\cdot\dfrac{5\pi}{6}\right)\right]$

$$= 4\left(\cos\dfrac{20\pi}{6} + i\sin\dfrac{20\pi}{6}\right) = 4\left(\cos\dfrac{4\pi}{3} + i\sin\dfrac{4\pi}{3}\right)$$

$$= 4\left(-\dfrac{1}{2} + i\left(-\dfrac{\sqrt{3}}{2}\right)\right) = -2 - 2\sqrt{3}i$$

61. Write $1 + i$ in $r(\cos\theta + i\sin\theta)$ form.

$r = \sqrt{a^2 + b^2} = \sqrt{1^2 + 1^2} = \sqrt{2}$

$\tan\theta = \dfrac{b}{a} = \dfrac{1}{1} = 1$ and $\theta = \dfrac{\pi}{4}$

$1 + i = r(\cos\theta + i\sin\theta) = \sqrt{2}\left(\cos\dfrac{\pi}{4} + i\sin\dfrac{\pi}{4}\right)$

Use DeMoivre's Theorem to raise $1 + i$ to the fifth power.

$(1+i)^5 = \left[\sqrt{2}\left(\cos\dfrac{\pi}{4} + i\sin\dfrac{\pi}{4}\right)\right]^5 = \left(\sqrt{2}\right)^5\left[\cos\left(5\cdot\dfrac{\pi}{4}\right) + i\sin\left(5\cdot\dfrac{\pi}{4}\right)\right]$

$$= 4\sqrt{2}\left(\cos\dfrac{5\pi}{4} + i\sin\dfrac{5\pi}{4}\right) = 4\sqrt{2}\left(-\dfrac{\sqrt{2}}{2} + i\left(-\dfrac{\sqrt{2}}{2}\right)\right) = -4 - 4i$$

63. Write $\sqrt{3} - i$ in $r(\cos\theta + i\sin\theta)$ form.

$r = \sqrt{a^2 + b^2} = \sqrt{\left(\sqrt{3}\right)^2 + \left(-1\right)^2} = \sqrt{4} = 2$

$\tan\theta = \dfrac{b}{a} = \dfrac{-1}{\sqrt{3}} = -\dfrac{1}{\sqrt{3}}$

Because $\tan 30° = \dfrac{1}{\sqrt{3}}$ and θ lies in quadrant IV, $\theta = 360° - 30° = 330°$.

$\sqrt{3} - i = r(\cos\theta + i\sin\theta) = 2(\cos 330° + i\sin 330°)$

Use DeMoivre's Theorem to raise $\sqrt{3}-i$ to the sixth power.

$$(\sqrt{3}-i)^6 = \left[2(\cos 330° + i \sin 330°)\right]^6 = (2)^6 \left[\cos(6 \cdot 330°) + i \sin(6 \cdot 330°)\right]$$

$$= 64(\cos 1980° + i \sin 1980°) = 64(\cos 180° + i \sin 180°)$$

$$= 64(-1 + 0i) = -64$$

65. $9(\cos 30° + i \sin 30°)$

$$z_k = \sqrt[2]{9}\left[\cos\left(\frac{30° + 360°k}{2}\right) + i \sin\left(\frac{30° + 360°k}{2}\right)\right], \ k = 0,1$$

$$z_0 = \sqrt{9}\left[\cos\left(\frac{30° + 360° \cdot 0}{2}\right) + i \sin\left(\frac{30° + 360° \cdot 0}{2}\right)\right] = \sqrt{9}\left[\cos\left(\frac{30°}{2}\right) + i \sin\left(\frac{30°}{2}\right)\right] = 3(\cos 15° + i \sin 15°)$$

$$z_1 = \sqrt{9}\left[\cos\left(\frac{30° + 360° \cdot 1}{2}\right) + i \sin\left(\frac{30° + 360° \cdot 1}{2}\right)\right] = \sqrt{9}\left[\cos\left(\frac{390°}{2}\right) + i \sin\left(\frac{390°}{2}\right)\right] = 3(\cos 195° + i \sin 195°)$$

67. $8(\cos 210° + i \sin 210°)$

$$z_k = \sqrt[3]{8}\left[\cos\left(\frac{210° + 360°k}{3}\right) + i \sin\left(\frac{210° + 360°k}{3}\right)\right], \ k = 0,1,2$$

$$z_0 = \sqrt[3]{8}\left[\cos\left(\frac{210° + 360° \cdot 0}{3}\right) + i \sin\left(\frac{210° + 360° \cdot 0}{3}\right)\right] = \sqrt[3]{8}\left[\cos\left(\frac{210°}{3}\right) + i \sin\left(\frac{210°}{3}\right)\right]$$

$$= 2(\cos 70° + i \sin 70°)$$

$$z_1 = \sqrt[3]{8}\left[\cos\left(\frac{210° + 360° \cdot 1}{3}\right) + i \sin\left(\frac{210° + 360° \cdot 1}{3}\right)\right] = \sqrt[3]{8}\left[\cos\left(\frac{570°}{3}\right) + i \sin\left(\frac{570°}{3}\right)\right]$$

$$= 2(\cos 190° + i \sin 190°)$$

$$z_2 = \sqrt[3]{8}\left[\cos\left(\frac{210° + 360° \cdot 2}{3}\right) + i \sin\left(\frac{210° + 360° \cdot 2}{3}\right)\right] = \sqrt[3]{8}\left[\cos\left(\frac{930°}{3}\right) + i \sin\left(\frac{930°}{3}\right)\right]$$

$$= 2(\cos 310° + i \sin 310°)$$

69. $81\left(\cos\dfrac{4\pi}{3}+i\sin\dfrac{4\pi}{3}\right)$

$z_k = \sqrt[4]{81}\left[\cos\left(\dfrac{\frac{4\pi}{3}+2\pi k}{4}\right)+i\sin\left(\dfrac{\frac{4\pi}{3}+2\pi k}{4}\right)\right], \ k=0,1,2,3$

$z_0 = \sqrt[4]{81}\left[\cos\left(\dfrac{\frac{4\pi}{3}+2\pi\cdot 0}{4}\right)+i\sin\left(\dfrac{\frac{4\pi}{3}+2\pi\cdot 0}{4}\right)\right] = \sqrt[4]{81}\left(\cos\dfrac{\pi}{3}+i\sin\dfrac{\pi}{3}\right) = 3\left(\dfrac{1}{2}+i\dfrac{\sqrt{3}}{2}\right) = \dfrac{3}{2}+\dfrac{3\sqrt{3}}{2}i$

$z_1 = \sqrt[4]{81}\left[\cos\left(\dfrac{\frac{4\pi}{3}+2\pi\cdot 1}{4}\right)+i\sin\left(\dfrac{\frac{4\pi}{3}+2\pi\cdot 1}{4}\right)\right] = \sqrt[4]{81}\left(\cos\dfrac{5\pi}{6}+i\sin\dfrac{5\pi}{6}\right) = 3\left(-\dfrac{\sqrt{3}}{2}+i\dfrac{1}{2}\right) = -\dfrac{3\sqrt{3}}{2}+\dfrac{3}{2}i$

$z_2 = \sqrt[4]{81}\left[\cos\left(\dfrac{\frac{4\pi}{3}+2\pi\cdot 2}{4}\right)+i\sin\left(\dfrac{\frac{4\pi}{3}+2\pi\cdot 2}{4}\right)\right] = \sqrt[4]{81}\left(\cos\dfrac{4\pi}{3}+i\sin\dfrac{4\pi}{3}\right)$

$\quad = 3\left(-\dfrac{1}{2}+i\left(-\dfrac{\sqrt{3}}{2}\right)\right) = -\dfrac{3}{2}-\dfrac{3\sqrt{3}}{2}i$

$z_3 = \sqrt[4]{81}\left[\cos\left(\dfrac{\frac{4\pi}{3}+2\pi\cdot 3}{4}\right)+i\sin\left(\dfrac{\frac{4\pi}{3}+2\pi\cdot 3}{4}\right)\right] = \sqrt[4]{81}\left(\cos\dfrac{11\pi}{6}+i\sin\dfrac{11\pi}{6}\right)$

$\quad = 3\left(\dfrac{\sqrt{3}}{2}+i\left(-\dfrac{1}{2}\right)\right) = \dfrac{3\sqrt{3}}{2}-\dfrac{3}{2}i$

71. $32 = 32(\cos 0°+i\sin 0°)$

$z_k = \sqrt[5]{32}\left[\cos\left(\dfrac{0°+360°k}{5}\right)+i\sin\left(\dfrac{0°+360°k}{5}\right)\right], \ k=0,1,2,3,4$

$z_0 = \sqrt[5]{32}\left[\cos\left(\dfrac{0°+360°\cdot 0}{5}\right)+i\sin\left(\dfrac{0°+360°\cdot 0}{5}\right)\right] = \sqrt[5]{32}\left(\cos 0°+i\sin 0°\right) = 2(1+0i) = 2$

$z_1 = \sqrt[5]{32}\left[\cos\left(\dfrac{0°+360°\cdot 1}{5}\right)+i\sin\left(\dfrac{0°+360°\cdot 1}{5}\right)\right] = \sqrt[5]{32}\left(\cos 72°+i\sin 72°\right) \approx 2(0.31+i(0.95))$

$\quad \approx 0.6+1.9i$

$z_2 = \sqrt[5]{32}\left[\cos\left(\dfrac{0°+360°\cdot 2}{5}\right)+i\sin\left(\dfrac{0°+360°\cdot 2}{5}\right)\right] = \sqrt[5]{32}\left(\cos 144°+i\sin 144°\right) \approx 2(-0.81+i(0.59))$

$\quad \approx -1.6+1.2i$

$z_3 = \sqrt[5]{32}\left[\cos\left(\dfrac{0°+360°\cdot 3}{5}\right)+i\sin\left(\dfrac{0°+360°\cdot 3}{5}\right)\right] = \sqrt[5]{32}\left(\cos 216°+i\sin 216°\right) \approx 2(-0.81+i(-0.59))$

$\quad \approx -1.6-1.2i$

$z_4 = \sqrt[5]{32}\left[\cos\left(\dfrac{0°+360°\cdot 4}{5}\right)+i\sin\left(\dfrac{0°+360°\cdot 4}{5}\right)\right] = \sqrt[5]{32}\left(\cos 288°+i\sin 288°\right) \approx 2(0.31+i(-0.95))$

$\quad \approx 0.6-1.9i$

73. $1 = 1(\cos 0° + i\sin 0°)$

$$z_k = \sqrt[3]{1}\left[\cos\left(\frac{0° + 360°k}{3}\right) + i\sin\left(\frac{0° + 360°k}{3}\right)\right], \; k = 0, 1, 2$$

$$z_0 = \sqrt[3]{1}\left[\cos\left(\frac{0° + 360°\cdot 0}{3}\right) + i\sin\left(\frac{0° + 360°\cdot 0}{3}\right)\right] = \sqrt[3]{1}\left(\cos 0° + i\sin 0°\right) = 1(1 + 0i) = 1$$

$$z_1 = \sqrt[3]{1}\left[\cos\left(\frac{0° + 360°\cdot 1}{3}\right) + i\sin\left(\frac{0° + 360°\cdot 1}{3}\right)\right] = \sqrt[3]{1}\left(\cos 120° + i\sin 120°\right) = 1\left(-\frac{1}{2} + i\frac{\sqrt{3}}{2}\right) = -\frac{1}{2} + \frac{\sqrt{3}}{2}i$$

$$z_2 = \sqrt[3]{1}\left[\cos\left(\frac{0° + 360°\cdot 2}{3}\right) + i\sin\left(\frac{0° + 360°\cdot 2}{3}\right)\right] = \sqrt[3]{1}\left(\cos 240° + i\sin 240°\right) = 1\left(-\frac{1}{2} + i\left(-\frac{\sqrt{3}}{2}\right)\right)$$

$$= -\frac{1}{2} - \frac{\sqrt{3}}{2}i$$

75. $1 + i = \sqrt{2}\left(\cos 45° + i\sin 45°\right)$

$$z_k = \sqrt[4]{\sqrt{2}}\left[\cos\left(\frac{45° + 360°k}{4}\right) + i\sin\left(\frac{45° + 360°k}{4}\right)\right], \; k = 0, 1, 2, 3$$

$$z_0 = \sqrt[4]{\sqrt{2}}\left[\cos\left(\frac{45° + 360°\cdot 0}{4}\right) + i\sin\left(\frac{45° + 360°\cdot 0}{4}\right)\right] = \sqrt[4]{\sqrt{2}}\left(\cos 11.25° + i\sin 11.25°\right) \approx 1.1 + 0.2i$$

$$z_1 = \sqrt[4]{\sqrt{2}}\left[\cos\left(\frac{45° + 360°\cdot 1}{4}\right) + i\sin\left(\frac{45° + 360°\cdot 1}{4}\right)\right] = \sqrt[4]{\sqrt{2}}\left(\cos 101.25° + i\sin 101.25°\right) \approx -0.2 + 1.1i$$

$$z_2 = \sqrt[4]{\sqrt{2}}\left[\cos\left(\frac{45° + 360°\cdot 2}{4}\right) + i\sin\left(\frac{45° + 360°\cdot 2}{4}\right)\right] = \sqrt[4]{\sqrt{2}}\left(\cos 191.25° + i\sin 191.25°\right) \approx -1.1 - 0.2i$$

$$z_3 = \sqrt[4]{\sqrt{2}}\left[\cos\left(\frac{45° + 360°\cdot 3}{4}\right) + i\sin\left(\frac{45° + 360°\cdot 3}{4}\right)\right] = \sqrt[4]{\sqrt{2}}\left(\cos 281.25° + i\sin 281.25°\right) \approx 0.2 - 1.1i$$

77. $i\left(2 + 2i\right)\left(-\sqrt{3} + i\right)$

$$= \left[1\left(\cos 90° + i\sin 90°\right)\right]\left[2\sqrt{2}\left(\cos 45° + i\sin 45°\right)\right]\left[2\left(\cos 150° + i\sin 150°\right)\right]$$

$$= 4\sqrt{2}\left(\cos 285° + i\sin 285°\right)$$

$$\approx 1.4641 - 5.4641i$$

79. $\dfrac{\left(1 + \sqrt{3}i\right)\left(1 - i\right)}{2\sqrt{3} - 2i}$

$$= \frac{\left[2\left(\cos 60° + i\sin 60°\right)\right]\left[\sqrt{2}\left(\cos 315° + i\sin 315°\right)\right]}{\left[4\left(\cos 330° + i\sin 330°\right)\right]}$$

$$= \frac{\sqrt{2}}{2}\left(\cos 45° + i\sin 45°\right)$$

$$= \frac{1}{2} + \frac{1}{2}i$$

81. $x^6 - 1 = 0$

$$x^6 = 1$$
$$x = \sqrt[6]{1}$$
$$x = \sqrt[6]{1 + 0i}$$
$$x = \sqrt[6]{\cos 0^\circ + i \sin 0^\circ}$$

$$z_k = \sqrt[6]{1}\left[\cos\left(\frac{0^\circ + 360^\circ \cdot k}{6}\right) + i\sin\left(\frac{0^\circ + 360^\circ \cdot k}{6}\right)\right],\ k = 0,1,2,3,4,5$$

$$z_0 = \sqrt[6]{1}\left[\cos\left(\frac{0^\circ + 360^\circ \cdot 0}{6}\right) + i\sin\left(\frac{0^\circ + 360^\circ \cdot 0}{6}\right)\right] = \cos 0^\circ + i\sin 0^\circ = 1 + 0i = 1$$

$$z_1 = \sqrt[6]{1}\left[\cos\left(\frac{0^\circ + 360^\circ \cdot 1}{6}\right) + i\sin\left(\frac{0^\circ + 360^\circ \cdot 1}{6}\right)\right] = \cos 60^\circ + i\sin 60^\circ = \frac{1}{2} + \frac{\sqrt{3}}{2}i$$

$$z_2 = \sqrt[6]{1}\left[\cos\left(\frac{0^\circ + 360^\circ \cdot 2}{6}\right) + i\sin\left(\frac{0^\circ + 360^\circ \cdot 2}{6}\right)\right] = \cos 120^\circ + i\sin 120^\circ = -\frac{1}{2} + \frac{\sqrt{3}}{2}i$$

$$z_3 = \sqrt[6]{1}\left[\cos\left(\frac{0^\circ + 360^\circ \cdot 3}{6}\right) + i\sin\left(\frac{0^\circ + 360^\circ \cdot 3}{6}\right)\right] = \cos 180^\circ + i\sin 180^\circ = -1 + 0i = -1$$

$$z_4 = \sqrt[6]{1}\left[\cos\left(\frac{0^\circ + 360^\circ \cdot 4}{6}\right) + i\sin\left(\frac{0^\circ + 360^\circ \cdot 4}{6}\right)\right] = \cos 240^\circ + i\sin 240^\circ = -\frac{1}{2} + i\left(-\frac{\sqrt{3}}{2}\right) = -\frac{1}{2} - \frac{\sqrt{3}}{2}i$$

$$z_5 = \sqrt[6]{1}\left[\cos\left(\frac{0^\circ + 360^\circ \cdot 5}{6}\right) + i\sin\left(\frac{0^\circ + 360^\circ \cdot 5}{6}\right)\right] = \cos 300^\circ + i\sin 300^\circ = \frac{1}{2} + i\left(-\frac{\sqrt{3}}{2}\right) = \frac{1}{2} - \frac{\sqrt{3}}{2}i$$

83. $x^4 + 16i = 0$

$$x^4 = -16i$$
$$x = \sqrt[4]{-16i}$$
$$x = \sqrt[4]{0 - 16i}$$
$$x = \sqrt[4]{16\left(\cos 270^\circ + i\sin 270^\circ\right)}$$

$$z_k = \sqrt[4]{16}\left[\cos\left(\frac{270^\circ + 360^\circ k}{4}\right) + i\sin\left(\frac{270^\circ + 360^\circ k}{4}\right)\right],\ k = 0,1,2,3$$

$$z_0 = \sqrt[4]{16}\left[\cos\left(\frac{270^\circ + 360^\circ \cdot 0}{4}\right) + i\sin\left(\frac{270^\circ + 360^\circ \cdot 0}{4}\right)\right] = 2\left(\cos 67.5^\circ + i\sin 67.5^\circ\right) \approx 0.7654 + 1.8478i$$

$$z_1 = \sqrt[4]{16}\left[\cos\left(\frac{270^\circ + 360^\circ \cdot 1}{4}\right) + i\sin\left(\frac{270^\circ + 360^\circ \cdot 1}{4}\right)\right] = 2\left(\cos 157.5^\circ + i\sin 157.5^\circ\right) \approx -1.8478 + 0.7654i$$

$$z_2 = \sqrt[4]{16}\left[\cos\left(\frac{270^\circ + 360^\circ \cdot 2}{4}\right) + i\sin\left(\frac{270^\circ + 360^\circ \cdot 2}{4}\right)\right] = 2\left(\cos 247.5^\circ + i\sin 247.5^\circ\right) \approx -0.7654 - 1.8478i$$

$$z_3 = \sqrt[4]{16}\left[\cos\left(\frac{270^\circ + 360^\circ \cdot 3}{4}\right) + i\sin\left(\frac{270^\circ + 360^\circ \cdot 3}{4}\right)\right] = 2\left(\cos 337.5^\circ + i\sin 337.5^\circ\right) \approx 1.8478 - 0.7654i$$

85. $x^3 - \left(1 + \sqrt{3}i\right) = 0$

$$x^3 = 1 + \sqrt{3}i$$

$$x = \sqrt[3]{1 + \sqrt{3}i}$$

$$x = \sqrt[3]{2(\cos 60° + i\sin 60°)}$$

$$z_k = \sqrt[3]{2}\left[\cos\left(\frac{60° + 360°k}{3}\right) + i\sin\left(\frac{60° + 360°k}{3}\right)\right], \ k = 0, 1, 2$$

$$z_0 = \sqrt[3]{2}\left[\cos\left(\frac{60° + 360° \cdot 0}{3}\right) + i\sin\left(\frac{60° + 360° \cdot 0}{3}\right)\right] = \sqrt[3]{2}\left(\cos 20° + i\sin 20°\right) \approx 1.1839 + 0.4309i$$

$$z_1 = \sqrt[3]{2}\left[\cos\left(\frac{60° + 360° \cdot 1}{3}\right) + i\sin\left(\frac{60° + 360° \cdot 1}{3}\right)\right] = \sqrt[3]{2}\left(\cos 140° + i\sin 140°\right) \approx -0.9652 + 0.8099i$$

$$z_2 = \sqrt[3]{2}\left[\cos\left(\frac{60° + 360° \cdot 2}{3}\right) + i\sin\left(\frac{60° + 360° \cdot 2}{3}\right)\right] = \sqrt[3]{2}\left(\cos 260° + i\sin 260°\right) \approx -0.2188 - 1.2408i$$

87. $e^{\frac{\pi i}{4}} = \cos\frac{\pi}{4} + i\sin\frac{\pi}{4}$

$$= \frac{\sqrt{2}}{2} + \frac{\sqrt{2}}{2}i$$

89. $-e^{-\pi i} = -1\left(\cos(-\pi) + i\sin(-\pi)\right)$

$$= -(-1) - i(0)$$

$$= 1 + 0i$$

91. $z = i$

    a. $\quad z_1 = z = i$

$$z_2 = z^2 + z = (i)^2 + i = -1 + i$$

$$z_3 = \left(z^2 + z\right)^2 + z = z_2^2 + z = (-1+i)^2 + i = -i$$

$$z_4 = \left[\left(z^2 + z\right)^2 + z\right]^2 + z = z_3^2 + z = (-i)^2 + i = -1 + i$$

$$z_5 = z_4^2 + z = (-1+i)^2 + i = -i$$

$$z_6 = z_5^2 + z = (-i)^2 + i = -1 + i$$

    b. $\quad |-1+i| = \sqrt{(-1)^2 + 1^2} = \sqrt{2}$

$$|i| = \sqrt{0^2 + 1^2} = 1$$

The absolute values of the terms in the sequence are 1 and $\sqrt{2}$.

Choose a complex number with absolute value less than 1, and another with absolute value greater than $\sqrt{2}$. Complex numbers may vary.

107. $1 = 1\left(\cos 0° + i \sin 0°\right)$

$$z_k = \sqrt[4]{1}\left[\cos\left(\frac{0° + 360°k}{4}\right) + i\sin\left(\frac{0° + 360°k}{4}\right)\right], \; k = 0, 1, 2, 3$$

$$z_0 = \sqrt[4]{1}\left[\cos\left(\frac{0° + 360° \cdot 0}{4}\right) + i\sin\left(\frac{0° + 360° \cdot 0}{4}\right)\right] = \sqrt[4]{1}\left(\cos 0° + i\sin 0\right) = 1(1 + 0i) = 1$$

$$z_1 = \sqrt[4]{1}\left[\cos\left(\frac{0° + 360° \cdot 1}{4}\right) + i\sin\left(\frac{0° + 360° \cdot 1}{4}\right)\right] = \sqrt[4]{1}\left(\cos 90° + i\sin 90°\right) = 1(0 + i(1)) = i$$

$$z_2 = \sqrt[4]{1}\left[\cos\left(\frac{0° + 360° \cdot 2}{4}\right) + i\sin\left(\frac{0° + 360° \cdot 2}{4}\right)\right] = \sqrt[4]{1}\left(\cos 180° + i\sin 180°\right) = 1(-1 + 0i) = -1$$

$$z_3 = \sqrt[4]{1}\left[\cos\left(\frac{0° + 360° \cdot 3}{4}\right) + i\sin\left(\frac{0° + 360° \cdot 3}{4}\right)\right] = \sqrt[4]{1}\left(\cos 270° + i\sin 270°\right) = 1(0 + i(-1)) = -i$$

Section 6.6

Check Point Exercises

1. First, we show that **u** and **v** have the same magnitude.

$$\|\mathbf{u}\| = \sqrt{\left(x_2 - x_1\right)^2 + \left(y_2 - y_1\right)^2}$$
$$= \sqrt{\left(-2 - (-5)\right)^2 + \left(6 - 2\right)^2}$$
$$= \sqrt{3^2 + 4^2}$$
$$= \sqrt{9 + 16}$$
$$= \sqrt{25}$$
$$= 5$$

$$\|\mathbf{v}\| = \sqrt{\left(x_2 - x_1\right)^2 + \left(y_2 - y_1\right)^2}$$
$$= \sqrt{\left(5 - 2\right)^2 + \left(6 - 2\right)^2}$$
$$= \sqrt{3^2 + 4^2}$$
$$= \sqrt{9 + 16}$$
$$= \sqrt{25}$$
$$= 5$$

Thus, **u** and **v** have the same magnitude:
$\|\mathbf{u}\| = \|\mathbf{v}\|$.

Next, we show that **u** and **v** have the same direction. the line on which **u** lies has slope

$$m = \frac{y_2 - y_1}{x_2 - x_1} = \frac{6 - 2}{-2 - (-5)} = \frac{4}{3}.$$

The line on which **v** lies has slope

$$m = \frac{y_2 - y_1}{x_2 - x_1} = \frac{6 - 2}{5 - 2} = \frac{4}{3}.$$

Because **u** and **v** are both directed toward

the upper right on lines having the same slope, $\dfrac{4}{3}$,

they have the same direction. Thus, **u** and **v** have the same magnitude and direction, and **u** = **v**.

2. For the given vector $\mathbf{v} = 3\mathbf{i} - 3\mathbf{j}$, $a = 3$ and $b = -3$. The vector's initial point is the origin, $(0, 0)$. The vector's terminal point is $(a, b) = (3, -3)$. We sketch the vector by drawing an arrow from $(0, 0)$ to $(3, -3)$.

We determine the magnitude of the vector by using the distance formula. Thus, the magnitude is

$$\|\mathbf{v}\| = \sqrt{a^2 + b^2}$$
$$= \sqrt{3^2 + (-3)^2}$$
$$= \sqrt{9 + 9}$$
$$= \sqrt{18}$$
$$= 3\sqrt{2}.$$

3. We identify the values for the variables in the formula.

$$P_1 = (-1, 3) \quad P_2 = (2, 7)$$

$$\begin{array}{cc} \uparrow\ \uparrow & \uparrow\ \uparrow \\ x_1\ y_1 & x_2\ y_2 \end{array}$$

Using these values, we write **v** in terms of **i** and **j** as follows:

$$\mathbf{v} = (x_2 - x_1)\mathbf{i} + (y_2 - y_1)\mathbf{j}$$
$$= (2 - (-1))\mathbf{i} + (7 - 3)\mathbf{j}$$
$$= 3\mathbf{i} + 4\mathbf{j}$$

4.　a.　$\mathbf{v} + \mathbf{w} = (7\mathbf{i} + 3\mathbf{j}) + (4\mathbf{i} - 5\mathbf{j})$
$$= (7 + 4)\mathbf{i} + (3 - 5)\mathbf{j}$$
$$= 11\mathbf{i} - 2\mathbf{j}$$

　　b.　$\mathbf{v} - \mathbf{w} = (7\mathbf{i} + 3\mathbf{j}) - (4\mathbf{i} - 5\mathbf{j})$
$$= (7 - 4)\mathbf{i} + (3 - (-5))\mathbf{j}$$
$$= 3\mathbf{i} + 8\mathbf{j}$$

5.　a.　$8\mathbf{v} = 8(7\mathbf{i} + 10\mathbf{j})$
$$= (8\,?\,7)\mathbf{i} + (8\,?\,10)\mathbf{j}$$
$$= 56\mathbf{i} + 80\mathbf{j}$$

　　b.　$-5\mathbf{v} = -5(7\mathbf{i} + 10\mathbf{j})$
$$= (-5\,?\,7)\mathbf{i} + (-5\,?\,10)\mathbf{j}$$
$$= -35\mathbf{i} - 50\mathbf{j}$$

6.　$6\mathbf{v} - 3\mathbf{w} = 6(7\mathbf{i} + 3\mathbf{j}) - 3(4\mathbf{i} - 5\mathbf{j})$
$$= 42\mathbf{i} + 18\mathbf{j} - 12\mathbf{i} + 15\mathbf{j}$$
$$= (42 - 12)\mathbf{i} + (18 + 15)\mathbf{j}$$
$$= 30\mathbf{i} + 33\mathbf{j}$$

7.   First, find the magnitude of **v**.

$$\|\mathbf{v}\| = \sqrt{a^2 + b^2}$$
$$= \sqrt{4^2 + (-3)^2}$$
$$= \sqrt{16 + 9}$$
$$= \sqrt{25}$$
$$= 5$$

A unit vector in the same direction as **v** is

$$\frac{\mathbf{v}}{\|\mathbf{v}\|} = \frac{4\mathbf{i} - 3\mathbf{j}}{5} = \frac{4}{5}\mathbf{i} - \frac{3}{5}\mathbf{j}$$

Now, we must verify that the magnitude of the

vector is 1. The magnitude of $\frac{4}{5}\mathbf{i} - \frac{3}{5}\mathbf{j}$ is

$$\sqrt{\left(\frac{4}{5}\right)^2 + \left(-\frac{3}{5}\right)^2} = \sqrt{\frac{16}{25} + \frac{9}{25}} = \sqrt{\frac{25}{25}} = 1.$$

8. $60 \cos 45° \, \mathbf{i} + 60 \sin 45° \, \mathbf{j}$

$$= 60 \cdot \frac{\sqrt{2}}{2}\mathbf{i} + 60 \cdot \frac{\sqrt{2}}{2}\mathbf{j}$$
$$= 30\sqrt{2}\mathbf{i} + 30\sqrt{2}\mathbf{j}$$

9.   We need to find $\|\mathbf{F}\|$ and θ.

Use the Law of Cosines to find the magnitude of **F**.

$\|\mathbf{F}\|^2 = 60^2 + 30^2 - 2(60)(30)\cos 130° \approx 6814$ The

$$\|\mathbf{F}\| \approx \sqrt{6814} \approx 82.5$$

magnitude of the resultant force is about 82.5 pounds.

To find θ, the direction of the resultant force, we use the Law of Sines.

$$\frac{82.5}{\sin 130°} = \frac{30}{\sin \theta}$$
$$82.5 \sin \theta = 30 \sin 130°$$
$$\sin \theta = \frac{30 \sin 130°}{82.5}$$
$$\theta = \sin^{-1}\left(\frac{30 \sin 130°}{82.5}\right) \approx 16.2°$$

The two given forces are equivalent to a single force of about 82.5 pounds in the direction of approximately 16.2° relative to the 60-pound force.

Exercise Set 6.6

1.   a. $\|\mathbf{u}\| = \sqrt{(x_2 - x_1)^2 + (y_2 - y_1)^2}$

$$= \sqrt{(4 - (-1))^2 + (6 - 2)^2}$$
$$= \sqrt{5^2 + 4^2}$$
$$= \sqrt{25 + 16}$$
$$= \sqrt{41}$$

   b. $\|\mathbf{v}\| = \sqrt{(x_2 - x_1)^2 + (y_2 - y_1)^2}$

$$= \sqrt{(5 - 0)^2 + (4 - 0)^2}$$
$$= \sqrt{5^2 + 4^2}$$
$$= \sqrt{25 + 16}$$
$$= \sqrt{41}$$

   c.   Since $\|\mathbf{u}\| = \|\mathbf{v}\|$, and **u** and **v** have the same direction, we can conclude that **u** = **v**.

3.   a. $\|\mathbf{u}\| = \sqrt{(x_2 - x_1)^2 + (y_2 - y_1)^2}$

$$= \sqrt{(5 - (-1))^2 + (1 - 1)^2}$$
$$= \sqrt{6^2 + 0^2}$$
$$= \sqrt{36 + 0}$$
$$= \sqrt{36}$$
$$= 6$$

   b. $\|\mathbf{v}\| = \sqrt{(x_2 - x_1)^2 + (y_2 - y_1)^2}$

$$= \sqrt{(4 - (-2))^2 + (-1 - (-1))^2}$$
$$= \sqrt{6^2 + 0^2}$$
$$= \sqrt{36 + 0}$$
$$= \sqrt{36}$$
$$= 6$$

   c.   Since $\|\mathbf{u}\| = \|\mathbf{v}\|$, and **u** and **v** have the same direction, we can conclude that **u** = **v**.

5.

$$\|\mathbf{v}\| = \sqrt{3^2 + 1^2} = \sqrt{9+1} = \sqrt{10}$$

7.

$$\|\mathbf{v}\| = \sqrt{1^2 + (-1)^2} = \sqrt{1+1} = \sqrt{2}$$

9.

$$\|\mathbf{v}\| = \sqrt{(-6)^2 + (-2)^2}$$
$$= \sqrt{36+4}$$
$$= \sqrt{40}$$
$$= 2\sqrt{10}$$

11.

$$\|\mathbf{v}\| = \sqrt{(-4)^2 + 0^2} = \sqrt{16+0} = \sqrt{16} = 4$$

13. $\mathbf{v} = (x_2 - x_1)\mathbf{i} + (y_2 - y_1)\mathbf{j}$
$\mathbf{v} = (6-(-4))\mathbf{i} + (2-(-4))\mathbf{j} = 10\mathbf{i} + 6\mathbf{j}$

15. $\mathbf{v} = (x_2 - x_1)\mathbf{i} + (y_2 - y_1)\mathbf{j}$
$\mathbf{v} = (-2-(-8))\mathbf{i} + (3-6)\mathbf{j} = 6\mathbf{i} - 3\mathbf{j}$

17. $\mathbf{v} = (x_2 - x_1)\mathbf{i} + (y_2 - y_1)\mathbf{j}$
$\mathbf{v} = (-7-(-1))\mathbf{i} + (-7-7)\mathbf{j} = -6\mathbf{i} - 14\mathbf{j}$

19. $\mathbf{v} = (x_2 - x_1)\mathbf{i} + (y_2 - y_1)\mathbf{j}$
$\mathbf{v} = (6-(-3))\mathbf{i} + (4-4)\mathbf{j} = 9\mathbf{i} + 0\mathbf{j} = 9\mathbf{i}$

21. $\mathbf{u} + \mathbf{v} = (2\mathbf{i} - 5\mathbf{j}) + (-3\mathbf{i} + 7\mathbf{j})$
$= (2-3)\mathbf{i} + (-5+7)\mathbf{j}$
$= -\mathbf{i} + 2\mathbf{j}$

23. $\mathbf{u} - \mathbf{v} = (2\mathbf{i} - 5\mathbf{j}) - (-3\mathbf{i} + 7\mathbf{j})$
$= 2\mathbf{i} - 5\mathbf{j} + 3\mathbf{i} - 7\mathbf{j}$
$= (2+3)\mathbf{i} + (-5-7)\mathbf{j}$
$= 5\mathbf{i} - 12\mathbf{j}$

25. $\mathbf{v} - \mathbf{u} = (-3\mathbf{i} + 7\mathbf{j}) - (2\mathbf{i} - 5\mathbf{j})$
$= -3\mathbf{i} + 7\mathbf{j} - 2\mathbf{i} + 5\mathbf{j}$
$= (-3-2)\mathbf{i} + (7+5)\mathbf{j}$
$= -5\mathbf{i} + 12\mathbf{j}$

27. $5\mathbf{v} = 5(-3\mathbf{i} + 7\mathbf{j}) = -15\mathbf{i} + 35\mathbf{j}$

29. $-4\mathbf{w} = -4(-\mathbf{i} - 6\mathbf{j}) = 4\mathbf{i} + 24\mathbf{j}$

31. $3\mathbf{w} + 2\mathbf{v} = 3(-\mathbf{i} - 6\mathbf{j}) + 2(-3\mathbf{i} + 7\mathbf{j})$
$= -3\mathbf{i} - 18\mathbf{j} - 6\mathbf{i} + 14\mathbf{j}$
$= (-3-6)\mathbf{i} + (-18+14)\mathbf{j}$
$= -9\mathbf{i} - 4\mathbf{j}$

33. $3\mathbf{v} - 4\mathbf{w} = 3(-3\mathbf{i} + 7\mathbf{j}) - 4(-\mathbf{i} - 6\mathbf{j})$
$= -9\mathbf{i} + 21\mathbf{j} + 4\mathbf{i} + 24\mathbf{j}$
$= (-9+4)\mathbf{i} + (21+24)\mathbf{j}$
$= -5\mathbf{i} + 45\mathbf{j}$

35. $\|2\mathbf{u}\| = \|2(2\mathbf{i} - 5\mathbf{j})\|$
$= \|4\mathbf{i} - 10\mathbf{j}\|$
$= \sqrt{4^2 + (-10)^2}$
$= \sqrt{16+100}$
$= \sqrt{116}$
$= 2\sqrt{29}$

37. $\|\mathbf{w} - \mathbf{u}\| = \|(-\mathbf{i} - 6\mathbf{j}) - (2\mathbf{i} - 5\mathbf{j})\|$

$\qquad = \|-\mathbf{i} - 6\mathbf{j} - 2\mathbf{i} + 5\mathbf{j}\|$

$\qquad = \|(-1 - 2)\mathbf{i} + (-6 + 5)\mathbf{j}\|$

$\qquad = \|-3\mathbf{i} - \mathbf{j}\|$

$\qquad = \sqrt{(-3)^2 + (-1)^2}$

$\qquad = \sqrt{9 + 1}$

$\qquad = \sqrt{10}$

39. $\dfrac{\mathbf{v}}{\|\mathbf{v}\|} = \dfrac{6\mathbf{i}}{\sqrt{6^2 + 0^2}} = \dfrac{6\mathbf{i}}{\sqrt{36}} = \dfrac{6\mathbf{i}}{6} = \mathbf{i}$

41. $\dfrac{\mathbf{v}}{\|\mathbf{v}\|} = \dfrac{3\mathbf{i} - 4\mathbf{j}}{\sqrt{3^2 + (-4)^2}}$

$\qquad = \dfrac{3\mathbf{i} - 4\mathbf{j}}{\sqrt{9 + 16}}$

$\qquad = \dfrac{3\mathbf{i} - 4\mathbf{j}}{\sqrt{25}}$

$\qquad = \dfrac{3\mathbf{i} - 4\mathbf{j}}{5}$

$\qquad = \dfrac{3}{5}\mathbf{i} - \dfrac{4}{5}\mathbf{j}$

43.

$\dfrac{\mathbf{v}}{\|\mathbf{v}\|} = \dfrac{3\mathbf{i} - 2\mathbf{j}}{\sqrt{3^2 + (-2)^2}}$

$\qquad = \dfrac{3\mathbf{i} - 2\mathbf{j}}{\sqrt{9 + 4}}$

$\qquad = \dfrac{3\mathbf{i} - 2\mathbf{j}}{\sqrt{13}}$

$\qquad = \dfrac{3}{\sqrt{13}}\mathbf{i} - \dfrac{2}{\sqrt{13}}\mathbf{j}$

45. $\dfrac{\mathbf{v}}{\|\mathbf{v}\|} = \dfrac{\mathbf{i} + \mathbf{j}}{\sqrt{1^2 + 1^2}}$

$\qquad = \dfrac{\mathbf{i} + \mathbf{j}}{\sqrt{2}}$

$\qquad = \dfrac{\mathbf{i}}{\sqrt{2}} + \dfrac{\mathbf{j}}{\sqrt{2}}$

$\qquad = \dfrac{\sqrt{2}}{2}\mathbf{i} + \dfrac{\sqrt{2}}{2}\mathbf{j}$

47. $\mathbf{v} = \|\mathbf{v}\|\cos\theta\,\mathbf{i} + \|\mathbf{v}\|\sin\theta\,\mathbf{j}$

$\qquad = 6\cos 30°\,\mathbf{i} + 6\sin 30°\,\mathbf{j}$

$\qquad = 6\left(\dfrac{\sqrt{3}}{2}\right)\mathbf{i} + 6\left(\dfrac{1}{2}\right)\mathbf{j}$

$\qquad = 3\sqrt{3}\mathbf{i} + 3\mathbf{j}$

49. $\mathbf{v} = \|\mathbf{v}\|\cos\theta\,\mathbf{i} + \|\mathbf{v}\|\sin\theta\,\mathbf{j}$

$\qquad = 12\cos 225°\,\mathbf{i} + 12\sin 225°\,\mathbf{j}$

$\qquad = 12\left(-\dfrac{\sqrt{2}}{2}\right)\mathbf{i} + 12\left(-\dfrac{\sqrt{2}}{2}\right)\mathbf{j}$

$\qquad = -6\sqrt{2}\mathbf{i} - 6\sqrt{2}\mathbf{j}$

51. $\mathbf{v} = \|\mathbf{v}\|\cos\theta\,\mathbf{i} + \|\mathbf{v}\|\sin\theta\,\mathbf{j}$

$\qquad = \dfrac{1}{2}\cos 113°\,\mathbf{i} + \dfrac{1}{2}\sin 113°\,\mathbf{j}$

$\qquad \approx \dfrac{1}{2}(-0.39)\mathbf{i} + \dfrac{1}{2}(0.92)\mathbf{j}$

$\qquad \approx -0.20\mathbf{i} + 0.46\mathbf{j}$

53. $4\mathbf{u} - (2\mathbf{v} - \mathbf{w}) = 4(-2\mathbf{i} + 3\mathbf{j}) - \left[2(6\mathbf{i} - \mathbf{j}) - (-3\mathbf{i})\right]$

$\qquad = -8\mathbf{i} + 12\mathbf{j} - \left[12\mathbf{i} - 2\mathbf{j} + 3\mathbf{i}\right]$

$\qquad = -8\mathbf{i} + 12\mathbf{j} - 12\mathbf{i} + 2\mathbf{j} - 3\mathbf{i})$

$\qquad = -23\mathbf{i} + 14\mathbf{j}$

55. $\|\mathbf{u} + \mathbf{v}\|^2 - \|\mathbf{u} - \mathbf{v}\|^2$

$\qquad = \|-2\mathbf{i} + 3\mathbf{j} + 6\mathbf{i} - \mathbf{j}\|^2 - \|-2\mathbf{i} + 3\mathbf{j} - (6\mathbf{i} - \mathbf{j})\|^2$

$\qquad = \|4\mathbf{i} + 2\mathbf{j}\|^2 - \|-8\mathbf{i} + 4\mathbf{j}\|^2$

$\qquad = \left(\sqrt{4^2 + 2^2}\right)^2 - \left(\sqrt{(-8)^2 + 4^2}\right)^2$

$\qquad = 16 + 4 - (64 + 16)$

$\qquad = 20 - 80$

$\qquad = -60$

57. $\mathbf{u}+\mathbf{v}=\mathbf{v}+\mathbf{u}$

$$\left(a_1\mathbf{i}+b_1\mathbf{j}\right)+\left(a_2\mathbf{i}+b_2\mathbf{j}\right)=\left(a_2\mathbf{i}+b_2\mathbf{j}\right)+\left(a_1\mathbf{i}+b_1\mathbf{j}\right)$$

$$\left(a_1+a_2\right)\mathbf{i}+\left(b_1+b_2\right)\mathbf{j}=\left(a_1+a_2\right)\mathbf{i}+\left(b_1+b_2\right)\mathbf{j}$$

This demonstrates the commutative property of vectors.

59. $c(\mathbf{u}+\mathbf{v})=c\mathbf{u}+c\mathbf{v}$

$$c\left(\left(a_1\mathbf{i}+b_1\mathbf{j}\right)+\left(a_2\mathbf{i}+b_2\mathbf{j}\right)\right)=c\left(a_1\mathbf{i}+b_1\mathbf{j}\right)+c\left(a_2\mathbf{i}+b_2\mathbf{j}\right)$$

$$\left(ca_1+ca_2\right)\mathbf{i}+\left(cb_1+cb_2\right)\mathbf{j}=\left(ca_1+ca_2\right)\mathbf{i}+\left(cb_1+cb_2\right)\mathbf{j}$$

This demonstrates a distributive property of vectors.

61. $\|\mathbf{v}\|=\sqrt{(-10)^2+15^2}=\sqrt{325}\approx18.03$

$\theta=\tan^{-1}\left(\dfrac{15}{-10}\right)\approx123.7°$

63. $\mathbf{v}=\left(4\mathbf{i}-2\mathbf{j}\right)-\left(4\mathbf{i}-8\mathbf{j}\right)=6\mathbf{j}$

$\|\mathbf{v}\|=6$

$\theta=90°$

65. $\mathbf{v}=\|\mathbf{v}\|\cos\theta\mathbf{i}+\|\mathbf{v}\|\sin\theta\mathbf{j}$

$=44\cos30°\mathbf{i}+44\sin30°\mathbf{j}$

$=44\left(\dfrac{\sqrt{3}}{2}\right)\mathbf{i}+44\left(\dfrac{1}{2}\right)\mathbf{j}$

$=22\sqrt{3}\mathbf{i}+22\mathbf{j}$

67. $\mathbf{v}=\|\mathbf{v}\|\cos\theta\mathbf{i}+\|\mathbf{v}\|\sin\theta\mathbf{j}$

$=150\cos8°\mathbf{i}+150\sin8°\mathbf{j}$

$\approx148.5\mathbf{i}+20.9\mathbf{j}$

69. $\mathbf{v}=\|\mathbf{v}\|\cos\theta\mathbf{i}+\|\mathbf{v}\|\sin\theta\mathbf{j}$

$=1.5\cos25°\mathbf{i}+1.5\sin25°\mathbf{j}$

$\approx1.4\mathbf{i}+0.6\mathbf{j}$

The length of the shadow is

$\left|1.4\right|=1.4$ inches.

71. $\mathbf{F}_1=\|\mathbf{F}_1\|\cos\theta\mathbf{i}+\|\mathbf{F}_1\|\sin\theta\,\mathbf{j}$

$=70\cos326°\mathbf{i}+70\sin326°\mathbf{j}$

$=58\mathbf{i}-39.1\mathbf{j}$

$\mathbf{F}_2=\|\mathbf{F}_2\|\cos\theta\mathbf{i}+\|\mathbf{F}_2\|\sin\theta\,\mathbf{j}$

$=50\cos18°\mathbf{i}+50\sin18°\mathbf{j}$

$=47.6\mathbf{i}+15.5\mathbf{j}$

$\mathbf{F}=\mathbf{F}_1+\mathbf{F}_2=(58\mathbf{i}-39.1\mathbf{j})+(47.6\mathbf{i}+15.5\mathbf{j})$

$=105.6\mathbf{i}-23.6\,\mathbf{j}$

$\|F\|=\sqrt{105.6^2+(-23.6)^2}=108.2$ pounds

$\cos\theta=\dfrac{a}{\|F\|}$

$\theta=\cos^{-1}\dfrac{105.6}{108.2}=12.6°,90-12.6=\text{S}77.4°\text{E}$

73. $\mathbf{F}_1=1610\cos125°\,\mathbf{i}+1610\sin125°\,\mathbf{j}$

$=-923.46\mathbf{i}+1318.83\mathbf{j}$

$\mathbf{F}_2=1250\cos215°\,\mathbf{i}+1250\sin215°\,\mathbf{j}$

$=-1023.94\mathbf{i}-716.97\mathbf{j}$

$\mathbf{F}=(-923.46-1023.94)\,\mathbf{i}+(1318.83-716.97)\mathbf{j}$

$=-1947.40\mathbf{i}+601.86\mathbf{j}$

$\|\mathbf{F}\|=\sqrt{(-1947.40)^2+601.86^2}\approx2038.28$

2038 kilograms

$\cos\theta=\dfrac{-1947.40}{2038.28}$

$\theta=162.8°$

75. $F_1 = 70\cos 326^\circ \mathbf{i} + 70\sin 326^0 \mathbf{j}$

$= -100\mathbf{j}$

To find the length of the BC: $\cos 18^\circ = \dfrac{a}{100}$

$a \approx 95$

$F_2 = 95\cos 2888^0 + 95\sin 288^0$

$= 29.4\mathbf{i} - 90.4\mathbf{j}$

$F = F_1 - F_2 = (-100\mathbf{j}) - (29.4\mathbf{i} - 90.4\mathbf{j})$

$= -29.4\,\mathbf{i} - 9.6\,\mathbf{j}$

$\sqrt{(-29.4)^2 + (-9.6)^2} \approx 30.9$

The force required to pull the weight is 30.9 pounds.

77. a. 335 lb

    b. 3484 lb

79. a. $F_1 + F_2 = (3 + 6)\mathbf{i} + (-5 + 2)\mathbf{j} = 9\mathbf{i} - 3\mathbf{j}$

    b. $-9\mathbf{i} + 3\mathbf{j}$

81. a. $F_1 = -3\mathbf{i}$ $(-3, 0)$
$F_2 = -\mathbf{i} + 4\mathbf{j}$ $(-1, 4)$
$F_3 = 4\mathbf{i} - 2\mathbf{i}$ $(4, -2)$
$F_4 = -4\mathbf{j}$ $(0, -4)$
$F_1 + F_2 + F_2 + F_2 = (-3 - 1 + 4)\mathbf{i}$
$+ (4 - 2 - 4)\mathbf{j} = -2\mathbf{j}$

    b. $2\mathbf{j}$

83. a. $v = 180\cos 40^\circ \mathbf{i} + 180\sin 40^\circ \mathbf{j}$
$= 137.88\mathbf{i} + 115.7\mathbf{j}$
$w = 40\cos 0^\circ \mathbf{i} + 40\sin 0^0 \mathbf{j}$
$= 40\mathbf{i}$

    b. $v + w = (137.88 + 40)\mathbf{i} + 115.7\mathbf{j}$
$= 177.88\mathbf{i} + 115.7\mathbf{j}$

    c. $\sqrt{177.88^2 + 115.7^2} \approx 212$ mph

    d. $\cos\theta = \dfrac{177.88}{212}$

$\theta = 33^\circ$

$90^\circ - 33^\circ = \text{N}57^\circ\text{E}$

85. $v = 320\cos 20^\circ \mathbf{i} + 320\sin 20^\circ \mathbf{j}$
$= 300.7\mathbf{i} + 109.5\mathbf{j}$
$w = 370\cos 30^\circ \mathbf{i} + 370\sin 30^0 \mathbf{j}$
$= 320.4\mathbf{i} + 185\mathbf{j}$
$w - v = (320.4 - 300.7)\mathbf{i}$
$+ (115.7 - 109.5)\mathbf{j}$

$= 19.7\mathbf{i} + 75.6\mathbf{j}$

$\sqrt{19.7^2 + 75.6^2} \approx 78$ mph

$\cos\theta = \dfrac{19.7}{78}$

$\theta = 75.4^\circ$

105. $\dfrac{v}{\|v\|} = \dfrac{a\mathbf{i} + b\mathbf{j}}{\|a\mathbf{i} + b\mathbf{j}\|} = \dfrac{a\mathbf{i} + b\mathbf{j}}{\sqrt{a^2 + b^2}}$

$= \dfrac{a}{\sqrt{a^2 + b^2}}\mathbf{i} + \dfrac{b}{\sqrt{a^2 + b^2}}\mathbf{j}$

$\left\|\dfrac{v}{\|v\|}\right\|^2 = \left(\dfrac{a}{\sqrt{a^2 + b^2}}\right)^2 + \left(\dfrac{b}{\sqrt{a^2 + b^2}}\right)^2$

$= \dfrac{a^2}{a^2 + b^2} + \dfrac{b^2}{a^2 + b^2} = \dfrac{a^2 + b^2}{a^2 + b^2} = 1$

$\left\|\dfrac{v}{\|v\|}\right\| = 1$

Since $\left\|\dfrac{v}{\|v\|}\right\|$ is 1, $\left\|\dfrac{v}{\|v\|}\right\|$ is a unit vector.

107.

To find the magnitude of $\mathbf{F}$, we use the Law of Cosines.

$\|\mathbf{F}\|^2 = 2500^2 + 2000^2 - 2(2500)(2000)\cos 140^\circ$

$\approx 17,910,444.4$

$\|\mathbf{F}\| \approx \sqrt{17,910,444.4} \approx 4232.1$

To find the compass direction of the resultant force, use the Law of Sines.

$$\frac{4232.1}{\sin 140°} = \frac{2000°}{\sin \theta}$$

$$4232.1 \sin \theta = 2000 \sin 140°$$

$$\sin \theta = \frac{2000 \sin 140°}{4232.1}$$

$$\theta = \sin^{-1}\left(\frac{2000 \sin 140°}{4232.1}\right)$$

$$\theta \approx 17.7°$$

The compass direction of the resultant force is $55° + 17.7° = 72.7°$.

Section 6.7

Check Point Exercises

1. **a.** $\mathbf{v \cdot w} = 7(2) + (-4)(-1) = 14 + 4 = 18$

   b. $\mathbf{w \cdot v} = 2(7) + (-1)(-4) = 14 + 4 = 18$

   c. $\mathbf{w \cdot w} = 2(2) + (-1)(-1) = 4 + 1 = 5 \cdot$

2. $\cos \theta = \dfrac{\mathbf{v \cdot w}}{\|\mathbf{v}\|\;\|\mathbf{w}\|}$

   $= \dfrac{(4\mathbf{i} - 3\mathbf{j}) \cdot (\mathbf{i} + 2\mathbf{j})}{\sqrt{4^2 + (-3)^2}\sqrt{1^2 + 2^2}}$

   $= \dfrac{4(1) + (-3)(2)}{\sqrt{25}\sqrt{5}}$

   $= \dfrac{2}{\sqrt{125}}$

   The angle θ between the vector is

   $\theta = \cos^{-1}\left(-\dfrac{2}{\sqrt{125}}\right) \approx 100.3°$.

3. $\mathbf{v \cdot w} = (6\mathbf{i} - 3\mathbf{j}) \cdot (\mathbf{i} + 2\mathbf{j})$

   $= 6(1) + (-3)(2) = 6 - 6 = 0$

   The dot product is zero. Thus, the given vectors are orthogonal.

4. $\text{proj}_{\mathbf{w}}\mathbf{v} = \dfrac{\mathbf{v \cdot w}}{\|\mathbf{w}\|^2}\mathbf{w}$

   $= \dfrac{(2\mathbf{i} - 5\mathbf{j}) \cdot (\mathbf{i} - \mathbf{j})}{\left(\sqrt{1^2 + (-1)^2}\right)^2}\mathbf{w}$

   $= \dfrac{2(1) + (-5)(-1)}{\left(\sqrt{2}\right)^2}\mathbf{w}$

   $= \dfrac{7}{2}\mathbf{w}$

   $= \dfrac{7}{2}(\mathbf{i} - \mathbf{j})$

   $= \dfrac{7}{2}\mathbf{i} - \dfrac{7}{2}\mathbf{j}$

5. $\mathbf{v}_1 = \text{proj}_{\mathbf{w}}\mathbf{v} = \dfrac{7}{2}\mathbf{i} - \dfrac{7}{2}\mathbf{j}$

   $\mathbf{v}_2 = \mathbf{v} - \mathbf{v}_1$

   $= (2\mathbf{i} - 5\mathbf{j}) - \left(\dfrac{7}{2}\mathbf{i} - \dfrac{7}{2}\mathbf{j}\right)$

   $= -\dfrac{3}{2}\mathbf{i} - \dfrac{3}{2}\mathbf{j}$

6. $W = \|\mathbf{F}\|\,\|\overrightarrow{AB}\|\cos \theta = (20)(150)\cos 30°$

   ≈ 2598

   The work done is approximately 2598 foot-pounds.

Exercise Set 6.7

1. $\mathbf{v \cdot w} = 3(1) + 1(3) = 3 + 3 = 6$
   $\mathbf{v \cdot v} = 3(3) + 1(1) = 9 + 1 = 10$

3. $\mathbf{v \cdot w} = 5(-2) + (-4)(-1) = -10 + 4 = -6$
   $\mathbf{v \cdot v} = 5(5) + (-4)(-4) = 25 + 16 = 41$

5. $\mathbf{v \cdot w} = -6(-10) + (-5)(-8) = 60 + 40 = 100$
   $\mathbf{v \cdot v} = -6(-6) + (-5)(-5) = 36 + 25 = 61$

7. $\mathbf{v \cdot w} = 5(0) + 0(1) = 0 + 0 = 0$
   $\mathbf{v \cdot v} = 5(5) + 0(0) = 25 + 0 = 25$

9. $\mathbf{v} \cdot (\mathbf{v} + \mathbf{w}) = (2\mathbf{i} - \mathbf{j})[(3\mathbf{i} + \mathbf{j}) + (\mathbf{i} + 4\mathbf{j})]$

$\qquad\qquad = (2\mathbf{i} - \mathbf{j})[(3 + 1)\mathbf{i} + (1 + 4)\mathbf{j})]$

$\qquad\qquad = (2\mathbf{i} - \mathbf{j})(4\mathbf{i} + 5\mathbf{j})$

$\qquad\qquad = 2(4) + (-1)(5)$

$\qquad\qquad = 8 - 5$

$\qquad\qquad = 3$

11. $\mathbf{u} \cdot \mathbf{v} + \mathbf{u} \cdot \mathbf{w}$

$\qquad = (2\mathbf{i} - \mathbf{j}) \cdot (3\mathbf{i} + \mathbf{j}) + (2\mathbf{i} - \mathbf{j})(\mathbf{i} + 4\mathbf{j})$

$\qquad = (2)(3) + (-1)(1) + 2(1) + (-1)(4)$

$\qquad = 6 - 1 + 2 - 4$

$\qquad = 3$

13. $(4\mathbf{u}) \cdot \mathbf{v}$

$\qquad = [(4(2\mathbf{i} - \mathbf{j})] \cdot (3\mathbf{i} + \mathbf{j})$

$\qquad = (8\mathbf{i} - 4\mathbf{j}) \cdot (3\mathbf{i} + \mathbf{j})$

$\qquad = (8)(3) + (-4)(1)$

$\qquad = 24 - 4$

$\qquad = 20$

15. $4(\mathbf{u} \cdot \mathbf{v})$

$\qquad = 4[(2\mathbf{i} - \mathbf{j}) \cdot (3\mathbf{i} + \mathbf{j})]$

$\qquad = 4[2(3) + (-1)1]$

$\qquad = 4[6 - 1]$

$\qquad = 4[5]$

$\qquad = 20$

17. $\cos\theta \dfrac{\mathbf{v} \cdot \mathbf{w}}{\|\mathbf{v}\| \ \|\mathbf{w}\|}$

$\qquad = \dfrac{(2\mathbf{i} - \mathbf{j}) \cdot (3\mathbf{i} + 4\mathbf{j})}{\sqrt{2^2 + (-1)^2} \sqrt{3^2 + 4^2}}$

$\qquad = \dfrac{2(3) + (-1)(4)}{\sqrt{5}\sqrt{25}}$

$\qquad = \dfrac{6 - 4}{\sqrt{125}}$

$\qquad = \dfrac{2}{\sqrt{125}}$

The angle θ between the vectors is

$\theta = \cos^{-1}\left(\dfrac{2}{\sqrt{125}}\right) \approx 79.7°.$

19. $\cos\theta \dfrac{\mathbf{v} \cdot \mathbf{w}}{\|\mathbf{v}\| \ \|\mathbf{w}\|}$

$\qquad = \dfrac{(-3\mathbf{i} + 2\mathbf{j}) \cdot (4\mathbf{i} - \mathbf{j})}{\sqrt{(-3)^2 + 2^2} \sqrt{4^2 + (-1)^2}}$

$\qquad = \dfrac{-3(4) + 2(-1)}{\sqrt{13}\sqrt{17}}$

$\qquad = \dfrac{-14}{\sqrt{221}}$

The angle θ between the vectors is

$\theta = \cos^{-1}\left(-\dfrac{14}{\sqrt{221}}\right) \approx 160.3°.$

21. $\cos\theta \dfrac{\mathbf{v} \cdot \mathbf{w}}{\|\mathbf{v}\| \ \|\mathbf{w}\|}$

$\qquad = \dfrac{(6\mathbf{i} + 0\mathbf{j}) \cdot (5\mathbf{i} + 4\mathbf{j})}{\sqrt{6^2 + 0^2} \sqrt{5^2 + 4^2}}$

$\qquad = \dfrac{6(5) + 0(4)}{\sqrt{36}\sqrt{41}}$

$\qquad = \dfrac{30}{\sqrt{1476}}$

The angle θ between the vectors is

$\theta = \cos^{-1}\left(\dfrac{30}{\sqrt{1476}}\right) \approx 38.7°.$

23. $\mathbf{v} \cdot \mathbf{w} = (\mathbf{i} + \mathbf{j}) \cdot (\mathbf{i} - \mathbf{j}) = (1)(1) + 1(-1) = 1 - 1 = 0$
The dot product is zero. Thus, the given vectors are orthogonal.

25. $\mathbf{v} \cdot \mathbf{w} = (2\mathbf{i} + 8\mathbf{j}) \cdot (4\mathbf{i} - \mathbf{j})$

$\qquad\qquad = 2(4) + (8)(-1)$

$\qquad\qquad = 8 - 8$

$\qquad\qquad = 0$

The dot product is zero. Thus, the given vectors are orthogonal.

27. $\mathbf{v} \cdot \mathbf{w} = (2\mathbf{i} - 2\mathbf{j}) \cdot (-\mathbf{i} + \mathbf{j})$

$\qquad\qquad = 2(-1) + (-2)(1)$

$\qquad\qquad = -2 - 2$

$\qquad\qquad = -4$

The dot product is not zero. Thus, the given vectors are not orthogonal.

29. $\mathbf{v} \cdot \mathbf{w} = (3\mathbf{i} + 0\mathbf{j}) \cdot (-4\mathbf{i} + 0\mathbf{j})$
$= 3(-4) + 0(0)$
$= -12 + 0$
$= -12$

The dot product is not zero. Thus, the given vectors are not orthogonal.

31. $\mathbf{v} \cdot \mathbf{w} = (3\mathbf{i} + 0\mathbf{j}) \cdot (0\mathbf{i} - 4\mathbf{j})$
$= 3(0) + (0)(-4)$
$= 0 + 0$
$= 0$

The dot product is zero. Thus, the given vectors are orthogonal.

33. $\text{proj}_{\mathbf{w}} \mathbf{v} = \dfrac{\mathbf{v} \cdot \mathbf{w}}{\| \mathbf{w} \|^2} \mathbf{w}$
$= \dfrac{(3\mathbf{i} - 2\mathbf{j}) \cdot (\mathbf{i} - \mathbf{j})}{\left(\sqrt{1^2 + (-1)^2} \right)^2} \mathbf{w}$
$= \dfrac{3(1) + (-2)(-1)}{\left(\sqrt{2} \right)^2}$
$= \dfrac{5}{2} \mathbf{w}$
$= \dfrac{5}{2}(\mathbf{i} - \mathbf{j})$
$= \dfrac{5}{2}\mathbf{i} - \dfrac{5}{2}\mathbf{j}$

$\mathbf{v}_1 = \text{proj}_{\mathbf{w}} \mathbf{v} = \dfrac{5}{2}\mathbf{i} - \dfrac{5}{2}\mathbf{j}$

$\mathbf{v}_2 = \mathbf{v} - \mathbf{v}_1 = (3\mathbf{i} - 2\mathbf{j}) - \left(\dfrac{5}{2}\mathbf{i} - \dfrac{5}{2}\mathbf{j} \right)$
$= \dfrac{1}{2}\mathbf{i} + \dfrac{1}{2}\mathbf{j}$

35. $\text{proj}_{\mathbf{w}} \mathbf{v} = \dfrac{\mathbf{v} \cdot \mathbf{w}}{\| \mathbf{w} \|} \mathbf{w}$
$= \dfrac{(\mathbf{i} + 3\mathbf{j}) \cdot (-2\mathbf{i} + 5\mathbf{j})}{\sqrt{1^2 + (-1)^2}} \mathbf{w}$
$= \dfrac{1(-2) + 3(5)}{\left(\sqrt{(-2)^2 + 5^2} \right)^2} \mathbf{w}$
$= \dfrac{13}{\left(\sqrt{29} \right)^2} \mathbf{w}$
$= \dfrac{13}{29} \mathbf{w}$
$= \dfrac{13}{29}(-2\mathbf{i} + 5\mathbf{j})$
$= \dfrac{-26}{29}\mathbf{i} + \dfrac{65}{29}\mathbf{j}$

$\mathbf{v}_1 = \text{proj}_{\mathbf{w}} \mathbf{v} = -\dfrac{26}{29}\mathbf{i} + \dfrac{65}{29}\mathbf{j}$

$\mathbf{v}_2 = \mathbf{v} - \mathbf{v}_1$
$= (\mathbf{i} + 3\mathbf{j}) - \left(-\dfrac{26}{29}\mathbf{i} + \dfrac{65}{29}\mathbf{j} \right)$
$= \dfrac{55}{29}\mathbf{i} + \dfrac{22}{29}\mathbf{j}$

37. $\text{proj}_{\mathbf{w}} \mathbf{v} = \dfrac{\mathbf{v} \cdot \mathbf{w}}{\| \mathbf{w} \|^2} \mathbf{w}$
$= \dfrac{(\mathbf{i} + 2\mathbf{j}) \cdot (3\mathbf{i} + 6\mathbf{j})}{\left(\sqrt{3^2 + 6^2} \right)^2} \mathbf{w}$
$= \dfrac{1(3) + 2(6)}{\sqrt{45}}$
$= \dfrac{15}{45} \mathbf{w}$
$= \dfrac{1}{3} \mathbf{w}$
$= \dfrac{1}{3}(3\mathbf{i} + 6\mathbf{j})$
$= \mathbf{i} + 2\mathbf{j}$

$\mathbf{v}_1 = \text{proj}_{\mathbf{w}} \mathbf{v} = \mathbf{i} + 2\mathbf{j}$

$\mathbf{v}_2 = \mathbf{v} - \mathbf{v}_1$
$= (\mathbf{i} + 2\mathbf{j}) - (\mathbf{i} + 2\mathbf{j})$
$= 0\mathbf{i} + 0\mathbf{j}$
$= \mathbf{0}$

39. $5\mathbf{u} \cdot (3\mathbf{v} - 4\mathbf{w}) = 15\mathbf{u} \cdot \mathbf{v} - 20\mathbf{u} \cdot \mathbf{w}$

$$= 15\big[(-1)(3) + (1)(-2)\big] - 20\big[(-1)(0) + (1)(-5)\big]$$

$$= 15\big[-5\big] - 20\big[-5\big]$$

$$= 25$$

41. $\operatorname{proj}_{\mathbf{u}}(\mathbf{v} + \mathbf{w}) = \dfrac{(\mathbf{v} + \mathbf{w}) \cdot \mathbf{u}}{\|u\|^2}\mathbf{u}$

$$= \frac{(3\mathbf{i} - 2\mathbf{j} - 5\mathbf{j}) \cdot (-\mathbf{i} + \mathbf{j})}{\|-\mathbf{i} + \mathbf{j}\|^2}(-\mathbf{i} + \mathbf{j})$$

$$= \frac{(3\mathbf{i} - 7\mathbf{j}) \cdot (-\mathbf{i} + \mathbf{j})}{\left(\sqrt{(-1)^2 + 1^2}\right)^2}(-\mathbf{i} + \mathbf{j})$$

$$= \frac{-3 - 7}{2}(-\mathbf{i} + \mathbf{j})$$

$$= -5(-\mathbf{i} + \mathbf{j})$$

$$= 5\mathbf{i} - 5\mathbf{j}$$

43. $\cos\theta = \dfrac{\mathbf{v} \cdot \mathbf{w}}{\|\mathbf{v}\|\|\mathbf{w}\|}$

$$\cos\theta = \frac{\left(2\cos\dfrac{4\pi}{3}\right)\left(3\cos\dfrac{3\pi}{2}\right) + \left(2\sin\dfrac{4\pi}{3}\right)\left(3\sin\dfrac{3\pi}{2}\right)}{\sqrt{\left(2\cos\dfrac{4\pi}{3}\right)^2 + \left(2\sin\dfrac{4\pi}{3}\right)^2}\sqrt{\left(3\cos\dfrac{3\pi}{2}\right)^2 + \left(3\sin\dfrac{3\pi}{2}\right)^2}}$$

$$\cos\theta = \frac{3\sqrt{3}}{6}$$

$$\cos\theta = \frac{\sqrt{3}}{2}$$

$$\theta = 30°$$

45. $\cos\theta = \dfrac{\mathbf{v} \cdot \mathbf{w}}{\|\mathbf{v}\|\|\mathbf{w}\|}$

$$\cos\theta = \frac{(3)(6) + (-5)(-10)}{\sqrt{(3)^2 + (-5)^2}\sqrt{(6)^2 + (-10)^2}}$$

$$\cos\theta = \frac{68}{68}$$

$$\cos\theta = 1$$

$$\theta = 0°$$

The vectors are parallel.

$v \cdot w = 68$

$v \cdot w \neq 0$

The vectors are not orthogonal.

47. $\cos\theta = \dfrac{\mathbf{v}\cdot\mathbf{w}}{\|\mathbf{v}\|\|\mathbf{w}\|}$

$\cos\theta = \dfrac{(3)(6)+(-5)(10)}{\sqrt{(3)^2+(-5)^2}\sqrt{(6)^2+(10)^2}}$

$\cos\theta = \dfrac{-32}{68}$

$\theta \approx 118°$

The vectors are not parallel.

$\mathbf{v}\cdot\mathbf{w} = -32$

$\mathbf{v}\cdot\mathbf{w} \neq 0$

The vectors are not orthogonal.

49. $\mathbf{v}\cdot\mathbf{w} = (3)(6)+(-5)\left(\dfrac{18}{5}\right)=0$

The vectors are orthogonal.

51. $\mathbf{v}\cdot\mathbf{w} = (240\mathbf{i}+300\mathbf{j})\cdot(2.90\mathbf{i}+3.07\mathbf{j})$

$\quad = 240(2.90)+300(3.07)$

$\quad = 696+921$

$\quad = 1617$

$\mathbf{v}\cdot\mathbf{w} = 1617$ means \$1617 in revenue was generated on Monday by the sale of 240 gallons of regular gas at \$2.90 per gallon and 300 gallons of premium gas at \$3.07 per gallon.

53. Since the car is pushed along a level road, the angle between the force and the direction of motion is $\theta = 0$. The work done

$W = \|\mathbf{F}\|\|\overrightarrow{AB}\|\cos\theta$

$\quad = (95)(80)\cos 0°$

$\quad = 7600.$

The work done is 7600 foot-pounds.

55. $W = \|\mathbf{F}\|\|\overrightarrow{AB}\|\cos\theta$

$\quad = (40)(100)\cos 32°$

$\quad \approx 3392$

The work done is approximately 3392 foot-pounds.

57. $w = \mathbf{F}\cdot\overrightarrow{AB}$

$\quad = 60(20)\cos(38°-12°)$

$\quad = 1200\cos 26°$

$\quad \approx 1079$ foot-pounds

59. $w = \mathbf{F}\cdot\overrightarrow{AB}$

$\quad = (3,2)\cdot[(10,20)-(4,9)]$

$\quad = (3,2)\cdot(6,11)$

$\quad = 18+22$

$\quad = 40$ foot-pounds

61. $w = \mathbf{F}\cdot\overrightarrow{AB}$

$\quad = (4\cos 50°, 4\sin 50°)\cdot[(8,10)-(3,7)]$

$\quad = (4\cos 50°, 4\sin 50°)\cdot(5,3)$

$\quad = 20\cos 50° + 12\sin 50°$

$\quad \approx 22.05$ foot-pounds

63. a. $\cos 30°\,\mathbf{i} + \sin 30°\,\mathbf{j} = \dfrac{\sqrt{3}}{2}\mathbf{i}+\dfrac{1}{2}\mathbf{j}$

b. $\text{proj}_{\mathbf{u}}\mathbf{F} = \dfrac{(0,-700)\cdot\left(\dfrac{\sqrt{3}}{2},\dfrac{1}{2}\right)}{\|\mathbf{u}\|^2}\left(\dfrac{\sqrt{3}}{2},\dfrac{1}{2}\right)$

$\quad = -350\left(\dfrac{\sqrt{3}}{2},\dfrac{1}{2}\right) = -175\sqrt{3}\mathbf{i}-175\mathbf{j}$

c. $\sqrt{(-175\sqrt{3})^2+(-175)^2}$

$\quad = \sqrt{122,500} = 350$

A force of 350 pounds is required to keep the boat from rolling down the ramp.

75. $\mathbf{u}\cdot\mathbf{v} = (a_1\mathbf{i}+b_1\mathbf{j})\cdot(a_2\mathbf{i}+b_2\mathbf{j})$

$\quad = a_1 a_2 + b_1 b_2$

$\quad = a_2 a_1 + b_2 b_1$

$\quad = (a_2\mathbf{i}+b_2\mathbf{j})\cdot(a_1\mathbf{i}+b_1\mathbf{j})$

$\quad = \mathbf{v}\cdot\mathbf{u}$

Thus $\mathbf{u}\cdot\mathbf{v} = \mathbf{v}\cdot\mathbf{u}$.

77. $\mathbf{u} \cdot (\mathbf{v} + \mathbf{w}) = (a_1\mathbf{i} + b_1\mathbf{j}) \cdot [(a_2\mathbf{i} + b_2\mathbf{j}) + (a_3\mathbf{i} + a_3\mathbf{j})]$

$\quad\quad\quad\quad\quad = (a_1\mathbf{i} + b_1\mathbf{j}) \cdot [(a_2 + a_3)\mathbf{i} + (b_2 + b_3)\mathbf{j}]$

$\quad\quad\quad\quad\quad = a_1(a_2 + a_3) + b_1(b_2 + b_3)$

$\quad\quad\quad\quad\quad = a_1a_2 + a_1a_3 + b_1b_2 + b_1b_3$

$\quad\quad\quad\quad\quad = a_1a_2 + b_1b_2 + a_1a_3 + b_1b_3$

$\quad\quad\quad\quad\quad = (a_1\mathbf{i} + b_1\mathbf{j}) \cdot (a_2\mathbf{i} + b_2\mathbf{j}) + (a_1\mathbf{i} + b_1\mathbf{j}) \cdot (a_3\mathbf{i} + b_3\mathbf{j})$

$\quad\quad\quad\quad\quad = \mathbf{u} \cdot \mathbf{v} + \mathbf{u} \cdot \mathbf{w}$

79. Let $\mathbf{v} = 15\mathbf{i} - 3\mathbf{j}$ and $\mathbf{w} = -4\mathbf{i} + b\mathbf{j}$. The vectors $\mathbf{v}$ and $\mathbf{w}$ are orthogonal if $\mathbf{u} \cdot \mathbf{w} = 0$.

$\mathbf{v} \cdot \mathbf{w} = (15\mathbf{i} - 3\mathbf{j}) \cdot (-4\mathbf{i} + b\mathbf{j}) = 15(-4) + (-3)b = -60 - 3b$

$\mathbf{v} \cdot \mathbf{w} = 0$ if $-60 - 3b = 0$. Solving the equation for b, we find $b = -20$.

81. We know that $\text{proj}_{\mathbf{w}}\mathbf{v} = \dfrac{\mathbf{v} \cdot \mathbf{w}}{\|\mathbf{w}\|^2}\mathbf{w}$ If the projection of $\mathbf{v}$ onto $\mathbf{w}$ is $\mathbf{v}$, then $\mathbf{v} = \dfrac{\mathbf{v} \cdot \mathbf{w}}{\|\mathbf{w}\|^2}\mathbf{w}$.

Since $\dfrac{\mathbf{v} \cdot \mathbf{w}}{\|\mathbf{w}\|^2}$ is a scalar for all $\mathbf{v}$ and $\mathbf{w}$, let $k = \dfrac{\mathbf{v} \cdot \mathbf{w}}{\|\mathbf{w}\|^2}$. Substituting, we have $\mathbf{v} = k\mathbf{w}$.

When one vector can be expressed as a scalar multiple of another, the vectors have the same direction. Thus, the projection of $\mathbf{v}$ onto $\mathbf{w}$ is $\mathbf{v}$ only if $\mathbf{v}$ and $\mathbf{w}$ have the same direction. Thus, any two vectors, $\mathbf{v}$ and $\mathbf{w}$, having the same direction will satisfy the condition that the projection of $\mathbf{v}$ onto $\mathbf{w}$ is $\mathbf{v}$.

Chapter 6 Review Exercises

1. Begin by finding C.

$A + B + C = 180°$

$70° + 55° + C = 180°$

$125° + C = 180°$

$C = 55°$

Use the ratio $\dfrac{a}{\sin A}$, or $\dfrac{12}{\sin 70°}$, to find the other two sides. Use the Law of Sines to find b.

$\dfrac{b}{\sin B} = \dfrac{a}{\sin A}$

$\dfrac{b}{\sin 55°} = \dfrac{12}{\sin 70°}$

$b = \dfrac{12\sin 55°}{\sin 70°} \approx 10.5$

Use the Law of Sines again, this time to find c.

$\dfrac{c}{\sin C} = \dfrac{a}{\sin A}$

$\dfrac{c}{\sin 55°} = \dfrac{12}{\sin 70°}$

$c = \dfrac{12\sin 55°}{\sin 70°} \approx 10.5$

The solution is $C = 55°$, $b \approx 10.5$, $c \approx 10.5$.

2. Begin by finding A.

$A + B + C = 180°$

$A + 107° + 30° = 180°$

$A + 137° = 180°$

$A = 43°$

Use the ratio $\dfrac{c}{\sin C}$, or $\dfrac{126}{\sin 30°}$, to find the other two sides. Use the Law of Sines to find a.

$\dfrac{a}{\sin A} = \dfrac{c}{\sin C}$

$\dfrac{a}{\sin 43°} = \dfrac{126}{\sin 30°}$

$a = \dfrac{126\sin 43°}{\sin 30°} \approx 171.9$

Use the Law of Sines again, this time to find b.

$\dfrac{b}{\sin B} = \dfrac{c}{\sin C}$

$\dfrac{b}{\sin 107°} = \dfrac{126}{\sin 30°}$

$b = \dfrac{126\sin 107°}{\sin 30°} \approx 241.0$

The solution is $A = 43°$, $a \approx 171.9$, and $b \approx 241.0$.

3. Apply the three-step procedure for solving a SAS triangle. Use the Law of Cosines to find the side opposite the given angle. Thus, we will find b.

$$b^2 = a^2 + c^2 - 2ac \cos B$$

$$b^2 = 17^2 + 12^2 - 2(17)(12) \cos 66°$$

$$b^2 = 289 + 144 - 408(\cos 66°)$$

$$b^2 \approx 267.05$$

$$b \approx \sqrt{267.05} \approx 16.3$$

Use the Law of Sines to find the angle opposite the shorter of the two given sides. Thus, we will find acute angle C.

$$\frac{c}{\sin C} = \frac{b}{\sin B}$$

$$\frac{12}{\sin C} = \frac{\sqrt{267.05}}{\sin 66°}$$

$$\sqrt{267.05} \sin C = 12 \sin 66°$$

$$\sin C = \frac{12 \sin 66°}{\sqrt{267.05}} \approx 0.6708$$

$$C \approx 42°$$

$$A = 180° - B - C = 180° - 66° - 42° = 72°$$

The solution is $b \approx 16.3$, $A \approx 72°$, and $C \approx 42°$.

4. Apply the three-step procedure for solving a SSS triangle. Use the Law of Cosines to find the angle opposite the longest side. Thus, we will find angle C.

$$c^2 = a^2 + b^2 - 2ab \cos C$$

$$\cos C = \frac{a^2 + b^2 - c^2}{2ab}$$

$$= \frac{117^2 + 66^2 - 142^2}{2 \cdot 117 \cdot 66} \approx -0.1372$$

C is obtuse because $\cos C$ is negative.

$$\cos^{-1}(0.1372) \approx 82°$$

$$C \approx 180° - 82° = 98°$$

Use the Law of Sines to find either of the two remaining acute angles. We will find angle A.

$$\frac{a}{\sin A} = \frac{c}{\sin C}$$

$$\frac{117}{\sin A} = \frac{142}{\sin 98°}$$

$$142 \sin A = 117 \sin 98°$$

$$\sin A = \frac{117 \sin 98°}{142} \approx 0.8159$$

$$A \approx 55°$$

$$B = 180° - A - C \approx 180° - 55° - 98° = 27°$$

The solution is $C \approx 98°$, $A \approx 55°$, and $B \approx 27°$.

5. Begin by finding C.

$$A + B + C = 180°$$

$$35° + 25° + C = 180°$$

$$60° + C = 180°$$

$$C = 120°$$

Use the ratio $\dfrac{c}{\sin C}$, or $\dfrac{68}{\sin 120°}$, to find the other two sides. Use the Law of Sines to find a.

$$\frac{a}{\sin A} = \frac{c}{\sin C}$$

$$\frac{a}{\sin 35°} = \frac{68}{\sin 120°}$$

$$a = \frac{68 \sin 35°}{\sin 120°} \approx 45.0$$

Use the Law of Sines again, this time to find b.

$$\frac{b}{\sin B} = \frac{c}{\sin C}$$

$$\frac{b}{\sin 25°} = \frac{68°}{\sin 120°}$$

$$b = \frac{68 \sin 25°}{\sin 120°} \approx 33.2$$

The solution is
$C = 120°$, $a \approx 45.0$, and $b \approx 33.2$.

6. The known ratio is $\dfrac{a}{\sin A}$, or $\dfrac{20}{\sin 39°}$. Because side b is given, we used the Law of Sines to find angle B.

$$\frac{b}{\sin B} = \frac{a}{\sin A}$$

$$\frac{26}{\sin B} = \frac{20}{\sin 39°}$$

$$\sin B = \frac{26 \sin 39°}{20} \approx 0.8181$$

$$B_1 \approx 55°,\ B_2 \approx 180° - 55° = 125°$$

$$C_1 = 180° - A - B_1 \approx 180° - 39° - 55° = 86°$$

$$C_2 = 180° - A - B_2 \approx 180° - 39° - 125° = 16°$$

Use the Law of Sines to find c_1 and c_2.

$$\frac{c_1}{\sin C_1} = \frac{a}{\sin A}$$

$$\frac{c_1}{\sin 86°} = \frac{20}{\sin 39°}$$

$$c_1 = \frac{20 \sin 86°}{\sin 39°} \approx 31.7$$

$$\frac{c_2}{\sin C_2} = \frac{a}{\sin A}$$

$$\frac{c_2}{\sin 16°} = \frac{20}{\sin 39°}$$

$$c_2 = \frac{20 \sin 16°}{\sin 39°} \approx 8.8$$

There are two triangles. In one triangle, the solution is $B_1 \approx 55°$, $C_1 \approx 86°$, and $c_1 \approx 31.7$. In the other triangle, $B_2 \approx 125°$, $C_2 \approx 16°$, and $c_2 \approx 8.8$.

7. The known ration is $\dfrac{c}{\sin C}$, or $\dfrac{1}{\sin 50°}$. Because side a is given, we used the Law of Sines to find angle A.

$$\frac{a}{\sin A} = \frac{c}{\sin C}$$

$$\frac{3}{\sin A} = \frac{1}{\sin 50°}$$

$$\sin A = \frac{3 \sin 50°}{1} \approx 2.30$$

Because the sine can never exceed 1, there is no triangle with the given measurements.

8. Apply the three-step procedure for solving a SAS triangle. Use the Law of Cosines to find the side opposite the given angle. Thus, we will find a.

$$a^2 = b^2 + c^2 - 2bc \cos A \qquad \text{Us}$$

$$a^2 = (11.2)^2 + (48.2)^2 - 2(11.2)(48.2)\cos 162°$$

$$\approx 3475.5$$

$$a \approx \sqrt{3475.5} \approx 59.0$$

e the Law of Sines to find the angle opposite the shorter of the two given sides. Thus, we will find acute angle B.

$$\frac{b}{\sin B} = \frac{a}{\sin A}$$

$$\frac{11.2}{\sin B} = \frac{\sqrt{3475.5}}{\sin 162°}$$

$$\sin B = \frac{11.2 \sin 162°}{\sqrt{3475.5}} \approx 0.0587$$

$$B \approx 3°$$

$$C = 180° - A - B \approx 180° - 162° - 3° = 15°$$

The solution is $a \approx 59.0$, $B \approx 3°$, and $C \approx 15°$.

9. Apply the three-step procedure for solving a SSS triangle. Use the Law of Cosines to find the angle opposite the longest side. Thus, we will find angle B.

$$\cos B = \frac{a^2 + c^2 - b^2}{2ac}$$

$$\cos B = \frac{(26.1)^2 + (36.5)^2 - (40.2)^2}{2 \cdot 26.1 \cdot 36.5}$$

$$\approx 0.2086$$

$$B \approx 78°$$

Use the Law of Sines to find either of the two remaining acute angles. We will find angle A.

$$\frac{a}{\sin A} = \frac{b}{\sin B}$$

$$\frac{26.1}{\sin A} = \frac{40.2}{\sin 78°}$$

$$\sin A = \frac{26.1 \sin 78°}{40.2} \approx 0.6351$$

$$A \approx 39°$$

$$C = 180° - A - B \approx 180° - 39° - 78° = 63°$$

The solution is $B \approx 78°$, $A \approx 39°$, and $C \approx 63°$.

10. The known ratio is $\dfrac{a}{\sin A}$, or $\dfrac{6}{\sin 40°}$. Because side b is given, we used the Law of Sines to find angle B.

$$\frac{b}{\sin B} = \frac{a}{\sin A}$$

$$\frac{4}{\sin B} = \frac{6}{\sin 40°}$$

$$\sin B = \frac{4\sin 40°}{6} \approx 0.4285$$

$B_1 \approx 25°$, $B_2 \approx 180° - 25° = 155°$

B_2 is impossible, since $40° + 155° = 195°$.

$C = 180° - A - B_1 \approx 180° - 40° - 25° = 115°$

Use the Law of Sines to find c.

$$\frac{c}{\sin C} = \frac{a}{\sin A}$$

$$\frac{c}{\sin 115°} = \frac{6}{\sin 40°}$$

$$c = \frac{6\sin 115°}{\sin 40°} \approx 8.5$$

The solution is B_1 (or B) $\approx 25°$, $C \approx 115°$, and $c \approx 8.5$.

11. The known ratio is $\dfrac{b}{\sin B}$, or $\dfrac{8.7}{\sin 37°}$. Because side a is given, we use the Law of Sines to find angle A.

$$\frac{a}{\sin A} = \frac{b}{\sin B}$$

$$\frac{12.4}{\sin A} = \frac{8.7}{\sin 37°}$$

$$\sin A = \frac{12.4\sin 37°}{8.7} \approx 0.8578$$

$A_1 \approx 59°$, $A_2 \approx 180° - 59° = 121°$

$C_1 = 180° - A_1 - B$
$\quad \approx 180° - 59° - 37° - 84°$

$C_2 = 180° - A_2 - B$
$\quad \approx 180° - 121° - 37° = 22°$

Use the Law of Sines to find c_1 and c_2.

$$\frac{c_1}{\sin C_1} = \frac{b}{\sin B}$$

$$\frac{c_1}{\sin 84°} = \frac{8.7}{\sin 37°}$$

$$c_1 = \frac{8.7\sin 84°}{\sin 37°} \approx 14.4$$

$$\frac{c_2}{\sin C_2} = \frac{b}{\sin B}$$

$$\frac{c_2}{\sin 22°} = \frac{8.7}{\sin 37°}$$

$$c_2 = \frac{8.7\sin 22°}{\sin 37°} \approx 5.4$$

There are two triangles. In one triangle, the solution is $A_1 \approx 59°$, $C_1 \approx 84°$, and $c_1 \approx 14.4$. In the other triangle, $A_2 \approx 121°$, $C_2 \approx 22°$, and $c_2 \approx 5.4$.

12. The known ratio is $\dfrac{a}{\sin A}$, or $\dfrac{54.3}{\sin 23°}$. Because side b is given, we used the Law of Sines to find angle B.

$$\frac{b}{\sin B} = \frac{a}{\sin A}$$

$$\frac{22.1}{\sin B} = \frac{54.3}{\sin 23°}$$

$$\sin B = \frac{22.1\sin 23°}{54.3} \approx 0.1590$$

$B_1 \approx 9°$, $B_2 \approx 180° - 9° = 171°$

B_2 is impossible, since $23° + 171° = 194°$.

$C = 180° - A - B_1 \approx 180° - 23° - 9° = 148°$

Use the Law of Sines to find c.

$$\frac{c}{\sin C} = \frac{a}{\sin A}$$

$$\frac{c}{\sin 148°} = \frac{54.3}{\sin 23°}$$

$$c = \frac{54.3\sin 148°}{\sin 23°} \approx 73.6$$

The solution is B_1 (or B) $\approx 9°$, $C \approx 148°$, and $c \approx 73.6$.

13. $\text{Area} = \dfrac{1}{2}ab\sin C$

$\qquad\quad = \dfrac{1}{2}(4)(6)\sin 42°$

$\qquad\quad \approx 8$

The area of the triangle is approximately 8 square feet.

14. $\text{Area} = \dfrac{1}{2}bc\sin A$

$= \dfrac{1}{2}(4)(5)\sin 22°$

≈ 4

The area of the triangle is approximately 4 square feet.

15.

$s = \dfrac{1}{2}(a+b+c) = \dfrac{1}{2}(2+4+5) = \dfrac{11}{2}$

$\text{Area} = \sqrt{s(s-a)(s-b)(s-c)}$

$= \sqrt{\dfrac{11}{2}\left(\dfrac{11}{2}-2\right)\left(\dfrac{11}{2}-4\right)\left(\dfrac{11}{2}-5\right)}$

$= \sqrt{\dfrac{231}{16}} \approx 4$

The area of the triangle is approximately 4 square meters.

16. $s = \dfrac{1}{2}(a+b+c) = \dfrac{1}{2}(2+2+2) = 3$

$\text{Area} = \sqrt{s(s-a)(s-b)(s-c)}$

$= \sqrt{3(3-2)(3-2)(3-2)}$

$= \sqrt{3} \approx 2$

The area of the triangle is approximately 2 square meters.

17.

Using the figure,

$C = 180° - 60° - 60° = 60°$

Use the Law of Sines to find a.

$\dfrac{a}{\sin 60°} = \dfrac{35}{\sin 60°}$

$a = 35$

The length of the roof is 35 feet.

18. One car travels 60 miles per hour for 30 minutes (half an hour), or $60\left(\dfrac{1}{2}\right) = 30$ miles. Similarly, the other car travels 25 miles.

Using the figure,

$b^2 = a^2 + c^2 - 2ac\cos B$ The

$= 25^2 + 30^2 - 2(25)(30)\cos 80° \approx 1264.53$

$b \approx \sqrt{1264.53} \approx 35.6$

cars will be about 35.6 miles apart.

19. The first plane travels 325 miles per hour for 2 hours, or $325 \cdot 2 = 650$ miles. Similarly, the other plane travels $300 \cdot 2 = 600$ miles.

Using the figure,

$A = 180° - 66.5° - 26.5° = 87°$

Use the Law of Cosines to find a.

$a^2 = b^2 + c^2 - 2bc\cos A$

$= 600^2 + 650^2 - 2(600)(650)\cos 87°$

$\approx 741,678$

$a \approx \sqrt{741,678} \approx 861$

The planes are about 861 miles apart.

20.

Using the figure,

$C = 180° - A - B = 180° - 55° - 46° = 79°$

Use the Law of Sines to find b.

$$\frac{b}{\sin B} = \frac{a}{\sin A}$$

$$\frac{b}{\sin 46°} = \frac{460}{\sin 55°}$$

$$b = \frac{460 \sin 46°}{\sin 55°} \approx 404$$

Use the Law of Sines again, this time to find c.

$$\frac{c}{\sin C} = \frac{a}{\sin A}$$

$$\frac{c}{\sin 79°} = \frac{460}{\sin 55°}$$

$$c = \frac{460 \sin 79°}{\sin 55°} \approx 551$$

The lengths are about 404 feet and 551 feet.

21. $s = \frac{1}{2}(a+b+c) = \frac{1}{2}(260+320+450) = 515$

$$\text{Area} = \sqrt{s(s-a)(s-b)(s-c)}$$

$$= \sqrt{515(515-260)(515-320)(515-450)}$$

$$= \sqrt{1,664,544,375} \approx 40,798.83$$

$$\text{cost} \approx (5.25)(40,798.83) \approx 214,194$$

The cost is approximately $214,194.

22. Draw $\theta = 60°$ counterclockwise, since, θ is positive, from the polar axis. Go 4 units out on the terminal side of θ, since $r > 0$.

$$x = r\cos\theta = 4\cos 60° = 4\left(\frac{1}{2}\right) = 2$$

$$y = r\sin\theta = 4\sin 60° = 4\left(\frac{\sqrt{3}}{2}\right) = 2\sqrt{3}$$

The rectangular coordinates of $(4, 60°)$ are $\left(2, 2\sqrt{3}\right)$.

23. Draw $\theta = 150°$ counterclockwise, since θ is positive, from the polar axis. Go 3 units out on the terminal side of θ, since $r > 0$.

$$x = r\cos\theta = 3\cos 150° = 3\left(-\frac{\sqrt{3}}{2}\right) = -\frac{3\sqrt{3}}{2}$$

$$y = r\sin\theta = 3\sin 150° = 3\left(\frac{1}{2}\right) = \frac{3}{2}$$

The rectangular coordinates of $(3, 150°)$ are $\left(-\frac{3\sqrt{3}}{2}, \frac{3}{2}\right)$.

24. Draw $\theta = \frac{4\pi}{3} = 240°$ counterclockwise, since θ is positive, from the polar axis. Go 4 units out opposite the terminal side of θ, since $r < 0$.

$$x = r\cos\theta = -4\cos\frac{4\pi}{3} = -4\left(-\frac{1}{2}\right) = 2$$

$$y = r\sin\theta = -4\sin\frac{4\pi}{3} = -4\left(-\frac{\sqrt{3}}{2}\right) = 2\sqrt{3}$$

The rectangular coordinates of $\left(-4, \frac{4\pi}{3}\right)$ are $\left(2, 2\sqrt{3}\right)$.

25. Draw $\theta = \dfrac{5\pi}{4} = 225°$ counterclockwise, since θ is positive from the polar axis. Go 2 units out opposite the terminal side of θ, since $r < 0$.

$$x = r\cos\theta = -2\cos\dfrac{5\pi}{4} = -2\left(-\dfrac{\sqrt{2}}{2}\right) = \sqrt{2}$$

$$y = r\sin\theta = -2\sin\dfrac{5\pi}{4} = -2\left(-\dfrac{\sqrt{2}}{2}\right) = \sqrt{2}$$

The rectangular coordinates of $\left(-2, \dfrac{5\pi}{4}\right)$ are $\left(\sqrt{2}, \sqrt{2}\right)$.

26. Draw $\theta = -\dfrac{\pi}{2} = -90°$ clockwise, since θ is negative, from the polar axis. Go 4 units out opposite the terminal side of θ, since $r < 0$.

$$x = r\cos\theta = -4\cos\left(-\dfrac{\pi}{2}\right) = -4(0) = 0$$

$$y = r\sin\theta = -4\sin\left(-\dfrac{\pi}{2}\right) = -4(-1) = 4$$

The rectangular coordinates of $\left(-4, -\dfrac{\pi}{2}\right)$ are $(0, 4)$.

27. Draw $\theta = -\dfrac{\pi}{4} = -45°$ clockwise, since θ is negative, from the polar axis. Plot the point out 2 units opposite the terminal side of θ, since $r < 0$.

$$x = r\cos\theta = -2\cos\left(-\dfrac{\pi}{4}\right) = -2\left(\dfrac{\sqrt{2}}{2}\right) = -\sqrt{2}$$

$$y = r\sin\theta = -2\sin\left(-\dfrac{\pi}{4}\right) = -2\left(-\dfrac{\sqrt{2}}{2}\right) = \sqrt{2}$$

The rectangular coordinates of $\left(-2, -\dfrac{\pi}{4}\right)$ are $\left(-\sqrt{2}, \sqrt{2}\right)$.

28. Draw $\theta = \dfrac{\pi}{6} = 30°$ counterclockwise, since θ is positive, from the polar axis. Go out 3 units on the terminal side of θ, since $r > 0$.

a. $\left(3, \dfrac{\pi}{6}\right) = \left(3, \dfrac{\pi}{6} + 2\pi\right) = \left(3, \dfrac{13\pi}{6}\right)$

b. $\left(3, \dfrac{\pi}{6}\right) = \left(-3, \dfrac{\pi}{6} + \pi\right) = \left(-3, \dfrac{7\pi}{6}\right)$

c. $\left(3, \dfrac{\pi}{6}\right) = \left(3, \dfrac{\pi}{6} - 2\pi\right) = \left(3, -\dfrac{11\pi}{6}\right)$

29. Draw $\theta = \dfrac{2\pi}{3} = 120°$ counterclockwise,

since θ is positive, from the polar axis.
Go out 3 units on the terminal side of θ,
since $r > 0$.

a. $\left(2, \dfrac{2\pi}{3}\right) = \left(2, \dfrac{2\pi}{3} + 2\pi\right) = \left(2, \dfrac{8\pi}{3}\right)$

b. $\left(2, \dfrac{2\pi}{3}\right) = \left(-2, \dfrac{2\pi}{3} + \pi\right) = \left(-2, \dfrac{5\pi}{3}\right)$

c. $\left(2, \dfrac{2\pi}{3}\right) = \left(2, \dfrac{2\pi}{3} - 2\pi\right) = \left(2, -\dfrac{4\pi}{3}\right)$

30.

Draw $\theta = \dfrac{\pi}{2} = 90°$ counterclockwise,

since θ is positive, from the polar axis.
Go out 3.5 units on the terminal side of
θ, since $r > 0$.

a. $\left(3, \dfrac{\pi}{2} + 2\pi\right) = \left(3, \dfrac{5\pi}{2}\right)$

b. $\left(-3.5, \dfrac{\pi}{2} + \pi\right) = \left(-3.5, \dfrac{3\pi}{2}\right)$

c. $\left(3.5, \dfrac{\pi}{2} - 2\pi\right) = \left(3.5, -\dfrac{3\pi}{2}\right)$

31. $(-4, 4)$

$r = \sqrt{(-4)^2 + (-4)^2} = \sqrt{16 + 16} = \sqrt{32} = 4\sqrt{2}$

$\tan\theta = \dfrac{4}{-4} = -1$

Because $\tan\dfrac{\pi}{4} = 1$ and θ lies in quadrant II,

$\theta = \pi - \dfrac{\pi}{4} = \dfrac{3\pi}{4}$.

The polar coordinates of $(-4,4)$ are $\left(4\sqrt{2}, \dfrac{3\pi}{4}\right)$.

32. $(3, -3)$

$r = \sqrt{3^2 + (-3)^2} = \sqrt{9 + 9} = \sqrt{18} = 3\sqrt{2}$

$\tan\theta = \dfrac{-3}{3} = -1$

Because $\tan\dfrac{\pi}{4} = 1$, and θ lies in

quadrant IV, $\theta = 2\pi - \dfrac{\pi}{4} = \dfrac{7\pi}{4}$.

The polar coordinates of $(3, -3)$ are $\left(3\sqrt{2}, \dfrac{7\pi}{4}\right)$.

33. $(5, 12)$

$r = \sqrt{5^2 + 12^2} = \sqrt{25 + 144} = \sqrt{169} = 13$

$\tan\theta = \dfrac{12}{5}$

Because $\tan^{-1}\left(\dfrac{12}{5}\right) \approx 67°$ and θ lies in

quadrant I, $\theta \approx 67°$.
The polar coordinates of $(5, 12)$ are
approximately $(13, 67°)$.

34. $(-3, 4)$

$r = \sqrt{(-3)^2 + 4^2} = \sqrt{9 + 16} = \sqrt{25} = 5$

$\tan\theta = \dfrac{4}{-3} = -\dfrac{4}{3}$

Because $\tan^{-1}\left(\dfrac{4}{3}\right) \approx 53°$ and θ lies in quadrant

II, $\theta \approx 180° - 53° = 127°$. The polar coordinates
of $(-3, 4)$ are $(5, 127°)$.

35. $(0,-5)$

$r = \sqrt{0^2 + (-5)^2} = \sqrt{25} = 5$

$\tan\theta = \dfrac{-5}{0}$ is undefined

Because $\tan\dfrac{\pi}{2}$ is undefined and θ lies on the

negative y-axis, $\theta = \dfrac{\pi}{2} + \pi = \dfrac{3\pi}{2}$. The polar

coordinates of $(0,-5)$ are $\left(5, \dfrac{3\pi}{2}\right)$.

36. $(1,0)$

$r = \sqrt{1^2 + 0^2} = \sqrt{1} = 1$

$\tan\theta = \dfrac{0}{1} = 0$

Because $\tan 0 = 0$ and θ lies on the positive x-axis, $\theta = 0$.
The polar coordinates of $(1,0)$ are $(1,0)$.

37.
$$2x + 3y = 8$$
$$2r\cos\theta + 3r\sin\theta = 8$$
$$r(2\cos\theta + 3\sin\theta) = 8$$
$$r = \frac{8}{2\cos\theta + 3\sin\theta}$$

38. $x^2 + y^2 = 100$

$r^2 = 100$

$r = 10$

39.
$$(x-6)^2 + y^2 = 36$$
$$(r\cos\theta - 6)^2 + (r\sin\theta)^2 = 36$$
$$r^2\cos^2\theta - 12r\cos\theta + 36 + r^2\sin^2\theta = 36$$
$$r^2 - 12r\cos\theta = 0$$
$$r^2 = 12r\cos\theta$$
$$r = 12\cos\theta$$

40.
$$r = 3$$
$$r^2 = 3^2$$
$$x^2 + y^2 = 9$$

41.
$$\theta = \frac{3\pi}{4}$$
$$\tan\theta = \tan\frac{3\pi}{4}$$
$$\frac{x}{y} = -1$$
$$x = -y$$

42. $r\cos\theta = -1$

$x = -1$

43. $r = 5\csc\theta$

$r = \dfrac{5}{\sin\theta}$

$r\sin\theta = 5$

$y = 5$

44. $r = 3\cos\theta$

$r \cdot r = r \cdot 3\cos\theta$

$r^2 = 3r\cos\theta$

$x^2 + y^2 = 3x$

$x^2 - 3x + y^2 = 0$

$x^2 - 3x + \dfrac{9}{4} + y^2 = \dfrac{9}{4}$

$\left(x - \dfrac{3}{2}\right)^2 + y^2 = \dfrac{9}{4}$

$r = 3\cos\theta$

45. $4r\cos\theta + r\sin\theta = 8$

$4x + y = 8$

$y = -4x + 8$

$4r\cos\theta + r\sin\theta = 8$

46. $r^2\sin 2\theta = -2$

$r^2(2\sin\theta\cos\theta) = -2$

$2r\sin\theta\, r\cos\theta = -2$

$2yx = -2$

$y = \dfrac{-2}{2x}$

$y = -\dfrac{1}{x}$

$r^2\sin 2\theta = -2$

47. $r = 5 + 3\cos\theta$

a. $r = 5 + 3\cos(-\theta)$

$r = 5 + 3\cos\theta$

The graph has symmetry about the polar axis.

b. $-r = 5 + 3\cos(-\theta)$

$-r = 5 + 3\cos\theta$

$r = -5 - 3\cos\theta$

The graph may or may not have symmetry

with respect to the line $\theta = \dfrac{\pi}{2}$.

c. $-r = 5 + 3\cos\theta$

$r = -5 - 3\cos\theta$

The graph may or may not have symmetry with respect to the pole.

48. $r = 3\sin\theta$

    a. $r = 3\sin(-\theta)$

        $r = -3\sin\theta$

        The graph may or may not have symmetry with respect to the polar axis.

    b. $-r = 3\sin(-\theta)$

        $-r = -3\sin\theta$

        $r = 3\sin\theta$

        The graph has symmetry with respect to

        line $\theta = \dfrac{\pi}{2}$.

    c. $-r = 3\sin\theta$

        $r = -3\sin\theta$

        The graph may or may not have symmetry with respect to the pole.

49. $r^2 = 9\cos 2\theta$

    a. $r^2 = 9\cos 2(-\theta)$

        $r^2 = 9\cos(-2\theta)$

        $r^2 = 9\cos 2\theta$

        The graph has symmetry with respect to the polar axis.

    b. $(-r)^2 = 9\cos 2(-\theta)$

        $r^2 = 9\cos(-2\theta)$

        $r^2 = 9\cos 2\theta$

        The graph has symmetry with respect to the

        line $\theta = \dfrac{\pi}{2}$.

    c. $(-r)^2 = 9\cos 2\theta$

        $r^2 = 9\cos 2\theta$

        The graph has symmetry with respect to the pole.

50. $r = 3\cos\theta$

    Check for symmetry:

Polar Axis	The Line $\theta = \dfrac{\pi}{2}$	The Pole
$r = 3\cos(-\theta)$	$-r = 3\cos(-\theta)$	
	$-r = 3\cos\theta$	
$r = 3\cos\theta$	$r = -3\cos\theta$	

The graph has symmetry with respect to the polar axis. The graph may or may not be symmetric with respect to the line $\theta = \dfrac{\pi}{2}$ or the pole. Calculate values of r for θ from 0 to π and use symmetry to obtain the graph.

θ	0	$\dfrac{\pi}{6}$	$\dfrac{\pi}{3}$	$\dfrac{\pi}{2}$	$\dfrac{2\pi}{3}$	$\dfrac{5\pi}{6}$	π
r	3	2.6	1.5	0	−1.5	−2.6	−3

Use symmetry to obtain the graph.

$r = 3\cos\theta$

Notice that there are no points in quadrants II or III. Because the cosine is negative in quadrants II and III, r is negative here. This places the points in quadrants IV and I respectively.

51. $r = 2 + 2\sin\theta$
Check for symmetry:

Polar Axis	The Line $\theta = \dfrac{\pi}{2}$	The Pole
$r = 2 + 2\sin(-\theta)$	$-r = 2 + 2\sin(-\theta)$	$-r = 2 + 2\sin\theta$
	$-r = 2 - 2\sin\theta$	
$r = 2 - 2\sin\theta$	$r = -2 + 2\sin\theta$	$r = -2 - 2\sin\theta$

There may be no symmetry, since each equation is not equivalent to $r = 2 + 2\sin\theta$. Calculate values of r for θ from 0 to 2π.

θ	0	$\dfrac{\pi}{6}$	$\dfrac{\pi}{3}$	$\dfrac{\pi}{2}$	$\dfrac{2\pi}{3}$	$\dfrac{5\pi}{6}$	π	$\dfrac{7\pi}{6}$	$\dfrac{4\pi}{3}$	$\dfrac{3\pi}{2}$	$\dfrac{5\pi}{3}$	$\dfrac{11\pi}{6}$	2π
r	2	3	3.73	4	3.73	3	2	1	0.27	0	0.27	1	2

$r = 2 + 2\sin\theta$

52. $r = \sin 2\theta$
Check for symmetry:

Polar Axis	The Line $\theta = \dfrac{\pi}{2}$	The Pole
$r = \sin 2(-\theta)$	$-r = \sin 2(-\theta)$	$-r = \sin 2\theta$
$r = \sin(-2\theta)$	$-r = \sin(-2\theta)$	
	$-r = -\sin 2\theta$	
$r = -\sin 2\theta$	$r = \sin 2\theta$	$r = -\sin 2\theta$

The graph has symmetry with respect to the line $\theta = \dfrac{\pi}{2}$. The graph may or may not be symmetric with respect to the polar axis or the pole. Calculate values of r for θ from 0 to $\dfrac{\pi}{2}$ and for θ from π to $\dfrac{3\pi}{2}$. Then, use symmetry to obtain the graph.

θ	0	$\dfrac{\pi}{6}$	$\dfrac{\pi}{4}$	$\dfrac{\pi}{3}$	$\dfrac{\pi}{2}$	π	$\dfrac{7\pi}{6}$	$\dfrac{5\pi}{4}$	$\dfrac{4\pi}{3}$	$\dfrac{3\pi}{2}$
r	0	0.87	1	0.87	0	0	0.87	1	0.87	0

$r = \sin 2\theta$

53. $r = 2 + \cos\theta$

Check for symmetry:

Polar Axis	The Line $\theta = \dfrac{\pi}{2}$	The Pole
$r = 2 + \cos(-\theta)$	$-r = 2 + \cos(-\theta)$	$-r = 2 + \cos\theta$
	$-r = 2 + \cos\theta$	
$r = 2 + \cos\theta$	$r = -2 - \cos\theta$	$r = -2 - \cos\theta$

The graph is symmetric with respect to the polar axis. The graph may or may not be symmetric with respect to

the line $\theta = \dfrac{\pi}{2}$ or the pole. Calculate values of r for θ from 0 to π and use symmetry to obtain the graph.

θ	0	$\dfrac{\pi}{6}$	$\dfrac{\pi}{3}$	$\dfrac{\pi}{2}$	$\dfrac{2\pi}{3}$	$\dfrac{5\pi}{6}$	π
r	3	2.87	2.5	2	1.5	1.13	1

$r = 2 + \cos\theta$

54. $r = 1 + 3\sin\theta$

Check for symmetry:

Polar Axis	The Line $\theta = \dfrac{\pi}{2}$	The Pole
$r = 1 + 3\sin(-\theta)$	$-r = 1 + 3\sin(-\theta)$	$-r = 1 + 3\sin\theta$
	$-r = 1 - 3\sin\theta$	
$r = 1 - 3\sin\theta$	$r = -1 + 3\sin\theta$	$r = -1 - 3\sin\theta$

There may be no symmetry, since each equation is not equivalent to $r = 1 + 3\sin\theta$. Calculate values of r for θ from 0 to 2π.

θ	0	$\dfrac{\pi}{6}$	$\dfrac{\pi}{3}$	$\dfrac{\pi}{2}$	$\dfrac{2\pi}{3}$	$\dfrac{5\pi}{6}$	π	$\dfrac{7\pi}{6}$	$\dfrac{4\pi}{3}$	$\dfrac{3\pi}{2}$	$\dfrac{5\pi}{3}$	$\dfrac{11\pi}{6}$	2π
r	1	2.5	3.6	4	3.6	2.5	1	-0.5	-1.6	-2	-1.6	-0.5	1

$r = 1 + 3 \sin\theta$

55. $r = 1 - 2\cos\theta$

Check for symmetry:

Polar Axis	The Line $\theta = \dfrac{\pi}{2}$	The Pole
$r = 1 - 2\cos(-\theta)$	$-r = 1 - 2\cos(-\theta)$	$-r = 1 - 2\cos\theta$
	$-r = 1 - 2\cos\theta$	
$r = 1 - 2\cos\theta$	$r = -1 + 2\cos\theta$	$r = -1 + 2\cos\theta$

The graph is symmetric with respect to the polar axis. The graph may or may not be symmetric with respect to the line $\theta = \dfrac{\pi}{2}$ or the pole. Calculate values of r for θ from 0 to π and use symmetry to obtain the graph.

θ	0	$\dfrac{\pi}{6}$	$\dfrac{\pi}{3}$	$\dfrac{\pi}{2}$	$\dfrac{2\pi}{3}$	$\dfrac{5\pi}{6}$	π
r	-1	-0.73	0	1	2	2.73	3

$r = 1 - 2\cos\theta$

56. $r^2 = \cos 2\theta$

Check for symmetry:

Polar Axis	The Line $\theta = \dfrac{\pi}{2}$	The Pole
$r^2 = \cos 2(-\theta)$	$(-r)^2 = \cos 2(-\theta)$	$(-r)^2 = \cos 2\theta$
$r^2 = \cos(-2\theta)$	$r^2 = \cos(-2\theta)$	
$r^2 = \cos 2\theta$	$r^2 = \cos 2\theta$	$r^2 = \cos 2\theta$

The graph has symmetry with respect to the polar axis, the line $\theta = \dfrac{\pi}{2}$, and the pole.

Calculate values of r for θ from 0 to $\dfrac{\pi}{2}$ and use symmetry to obtain the graph.

θ	0	$\dfrac{\pi}{6}$	$\dfrac{\pi}{4}$	$\dfrac{\pi}{3}$	$\dfrac{\pi}{2}$
r	± 1	± 0.71	0	undef	undef

$r^2 = \cos 2\theta$

57. $z = 1 - i$ corresponds to the point $(1, -1)$.

Use $r = \sqrt{a^2 + b^2}$ and $\tan\theta = \dfrac{b}{a}$, with $a = 1$ and $b = -1$, to find r and θ.

$r = \sqrt{1^2 + (-1)^2} = \sqrt{1+1} = \sqrt{2}$

$\tan\theta = \dfrac{-1}{1} = -1$

Because $\tan\dfrac{\pi}{4} = 1$ and θ lies in quadrant IV,

$\theta = 2\pi - \dfrac{\pi}{4} = \dfrac{7\pi}{4}$.

$z = 1 - i = r(\cos\theta + i\sin\theta)$

$\quad = \sqrt{2}\left(\cos\dfrac{7\pi}{4} + i\sin\dfrac{7\pi}{4}\right)$

or $\sqrt{2}(\cos 315° + i\sin 315°)$

58. $z = -2\sqrt{3} + 2i$ corresponds to the point $(-2\sqrt{3},\ 2)$.

Use $r = \sqrt{a^2 + b^2}$ and $\tan\theta = \dfrac{b}{a}$, with $a = -2\sqrt{3}$ and $b = 2$, to find r and θ.

$r = \sqrt{\left(-2\sqrt{3}\right)^2 + 2^2} = \sqrt{12 + 4} = \sqrt{16} = 4$

$\tan\theta = \dfrac{2}{-2\sqrt{3}} = -\dfrac{1}{\sqrt{3}}$

Because $\tan 30° = \dfrac{1}{\sqrt{3}}$ and θ lies in quadrant II,

$\theta = 180° - 30° = 150°$.

$z = -2\sqrt{3} + 2i$

$\quad = r(\cos\theta + i\sin\theta)$

$\quad = 4(\cos 150° + i\sin 150°)$

or $4\left(\cos\dfrac{5\pi}{6} + i\sin\dfrac{5\pi}{6}\right)$

59. $z = -3 - 4i$ corresponds to the point $(-3, -4)$.

Use $r = \sqrt{a^2 + b^2}$ and $\tan\theta = \dfrac{b}{a}$, with

$a = -3$ and $b = -4$, to find r and θ.

$r = \sqrt{(-3)^2 + (-4)^2} = \sqrt{9 + 16} = \sqrt{25} = 5$

$\tan\theta = \dfrac{-4}{-3} = \dfrac{4}{3}$

Because $\tan^{-1}\left(\dfrac{4}{3}\right) \approx 53°$ and θ lies in quadrant

III, $\theta \approx 180° + 53° = 233°$.

$z = -3 - 4i = r(\cos\theta + i\sin\theta)$

$\approx 5(\cos 233° + i\sin 233°)$

60. $z = -5i = 0 - 5i$ corresponds to the point $(0, -5)$.

Use $r = \sqrt{a^2 + b^2}$ and $\tan\theta = \dfrac{b}{a}$, with $a = 0$

and $b = -5$, to find r and θ.

$r = \sqrt{0^2 + (-5)^2} = \sqrt{25} = 5$

$\tan\theta = \dfrac{-5}{0}$ is undefined

Because $\tan\dfrac{\pi}{2}$ is undefined and θ lies on the

negative y-axis, $\theta = \dfrac{\pi}{2} + \pi = \dfrac{3\pi}{2}$.

$z = -5i = r(\cos\theta + i\sin\theta) = 5\left(\cos\dfrac{3\pi}{2} + i\sin\dfrac{3\pi}{2}\right)$

or $5(\cos 270° + i\sin 270°)$

61. $8(\cos 60° + i\sin 60°) = 8\left(\dfrac{1}{2} + i\dfrac{\sqrt{3}}{2}\right) = 4 + 4\sqrt{3}i$

The rectangular form of $z = 8(\cos 60° + i\sin 60°)$ is $z = 4 + 4\sqrt{3}i$.

62. $4(\cos 210° + i\sin 210°) = 4\left(-\dfrac{\sqrt{3}}{2} + i\left(-\dfrac{1}{2}\right)\right) = -2\sqrt{3} - 2i$

The rectangular form of $z = 4(\cos 210° + i\sin 210°)$ is $z = -2\sqrt{3} - 2i$.

63. $6\left(\cos\dfrac{2\pi}{3} + i\sin\dfrac{2\pi}{3}\right) = 6\left(-\dfrac{1}{2} + i\dfrac{\sqrt{3}}{2}\right) = -3 + 3\sqrt{3}i$

The rectangular form of $z = 6\left(\cos\dfrac{2\pi}{3} + i\sin\dfrac{2\pi}{3}\right)$ is $z = -3 + 3\sqrt{3}i$.

64. $0.6(\cos 100° + i\sin 100°) \approx 0.6\left(-0.17 + i(0.98)\right) \approx -0.1 + 0.6i$

The rectangular form of $z = 0.6(\cos 100° + i\sin 100°)$ is $z \approx -0.1 + 0.6i$.

65. $z_1 z_2 = \left[3(\cos 40° + i \sin 40°)\right]\left[5\left(\cos 70° + i \sin 70°\right)\right]$

$\qquad = (3 \cdot 5)\left[\cos(40° + 70°) + i \sin(40° + 70°)\right]$

$\qquad = 15(\cos 110° + i \sin 110°)$

66. $z_1 z_2 = \left[\cos 210° + i \sin 210°\right]\left[\cos 55° + i \sin 55°\right]$

$\qquad = \cos\left(210° + 55°\right) + i \sin(210° + 55°)$

$\qquad = \cos 265° + i \sin 265°$

67. $z_1 z_2 = \left[4\left(\cos\dfrac{3\pi}{7} + i \sin\dfrac{3\pi}{7}\right)\right]\left[10\left(\cos\dfrac{4\pi}{7} + i\dfrac{4\pi}{7}\right)\right]$

$\qquad = (4 \cdot 10)\left[\cos\left(\dfrac{3\pi}{7} + \dfrac{4\pi}{7}\right) + i \sin\left(\dfrac{3\pi}{7} + \dfrac{4\pi}{7}\right)\right]$

$\qquad = 40(\cos \pi + i \sin \pi)$

68. $\dfrac{z_1}{z_2} = \dfrac{10(\cos 10° + i \sin 10°)}{5(\cos 5° + i \sin 5°)} = \dfrac{10}{5}\left[\cos(10° - 5°) + i \sin(10° - 5°)\right] = 2(\cos 5° + i \sin 5°)$

69. $\dfrac{z_1}{z_2} = \dfrac{5\left(\cos\dfrac{4\pi}{3} + i \sin\dfrac{4\pi}{3}\right)}{10\left(\cos\dfrac{\pi}{3} + i \sin\dfrac{\pi}{3}\right)} = \dfrac{5}{10}\left[\cos\left(\dfrac{4\pi}{3} - \dfrac{\pi}{3}\right) + i \sin\left(\dfrac{4\pi}{3} - \dfrac{\pi}{3}\right)\right] = \dfrac{1}{2}(\cos \pi + i \sin \pi)$

70. $\dfrac{z_1}{z_2} = \dfrac{2\left(\cos\dfrac{5\pi}{3} + i \sin\dfrac{5\pi}{3}\right)}{\cos\dfrac{\pi}{2} + i \sin\dfrac{\pi}{2}} = 2\left[\cos\left(\dfrac{5\pi}{3} - \dfrac{\pi}{2}\right) + i \sin\left(\dfrac{5\pi}{3} - \dfrac{\pi}{2}\right)\right]$

$\qquad = 2\left[\cos\left(\dfrac{10\pi}{6} - \dfrac{3\pi}{6}\right) + i \sin\left(\dfrac{10\pi}{6} - \dfrac{3\pi}{6}\right)\right] = 2\left(\cos\dfrac{7\pi}{6} + i \sin\dfrac{7\pi}{6}\right)$

71. $\left[2(\cos 20° + i \sin 20°)\right]^3 = (2)^3\left[\cos(3 \cdot 20°) + i \sin(3 \cdot 20°)\right] = 8(\cos 60° + i \sin 60°)$

$\qquad = 8\left(\dfrac{1}{2} + i\dfrac{\sqrt{3}}{2}\right) = 4 + 4\sqrt{3}i$

72. $\left[4(\cos 50° + i \sin 50°)\right]^3 = (4)^3\left[\cos(3 \cdot 50°) + i \sin(3 \cdot 50°)\right] = 64(\cos 150° + i \sin 150°) = 64\left(-\dfrac{\sqrt{3}}{2} + i\dfrac{1}{2}\right)$

$\qquad = -32\sqrt{3} + 32i$

73. $\left[\dfrac{1}{2}\left(\cos\dfrac{\pi}{14} + i \sin\dfrac{\pi}{14}\right)\right]^7 = \left(\dfrac{1}{2}\right)^7\left[\cos\left(7 \cdot \dfrac{\pi}{14}\right) + i \sin\left(7 \cdot \dfrac{\pi}{14}\right)\right] = \dfrac{1}{128}\left(\cos\dfrac{\pi}{2} + i \sin\dfrac{\pi}{2}\right)$

$\qquad = \dfrac{1}{128}(0 + i1) = \dfrac{1}{128}i$

74. Write $1 - \sqrt{3}i$ in $r(\cos\theta + i\sin\theta)$ form.

$$r = \sqrt{a^2 + b^2} = \sqrt{1^2 + \left(-\sqrt{3}\right)^2} = \sqrt{1+3} = 2$$

$$\tan\theta = \frac{b}{a} = \frac{-\sqrt{3}}{1} = -\sqrt{3}$$

Because $\tan 60° = \sqrt{3}$ and θ lies in quadrant IV, $\theta = 360° - 60° = 300°$.

$1 - \sqrt{3}i = r(\cos\theta + i\sin\theta) = 2(\cos 300° + i\sin 300°)$

Use DeMoivre's Theorem to raise $1 - \sqrt{3}i$ to the seventh power.

$$\left(1 - \sqrt{3}i\right)^7 = \left[2(\cos 300° + i\sin 300°)\right]^7$$

$$= (2)^7 \left[\cos(7\cdot 300°) + i\sin(7\cdot 300°)\right]$$

$$= 128(\cos 2100° + i\sin 2100°)$$

$$= 128(\cos 300° + i\sin 300°)$$

$$= 128\left(\frac{1}{2} + i\left(-\frac{\sqrt{3}}{2}\right)\right)$$

$$= 64 - 64\sqrt{3}i$$

75. Write $-2 - 2i$ in $r(\cos\theta + i\sin\theta)$ form.

$$r = \sqrt{a^2 + b^2} = \sqrt{(-2)^2 + (-2)^2} = \sqrt{4+4} = 2\sqrt{2}$$

$$\tan\theta = \frac{b}{a} = \frac{-2}{-2} = 1$$

Because $\tan\frac{\pi}{4} = 1$ and θ lies in quadrant III, $\theta = \pi + \frac{\pi}{4} = \frac{5\pi}{4}$.

$$-2 - 2i = r(\cos\theta + i\sin\theta) = 2\sqrt{2}\left(\cos\frac{5\pi}{4} + i\sin\frac{5\pi}{4}\right)$$

Use DeMoivre's Theorem to raise $-2 - 2i$ to the fifth power.

$$(-2 - 2i)^5 = \left[2\sqrt{2}\left(\cos\frac{5\pi}{4} + i\sin\frac{5\pi}{4}\right)\right]^5$$

$$= \left(2\sqrt{2}\right)^5 \left[\cos\left(5\cdot\frac{5\pi}{4}\right) + i\sin\left(5\cdot\frac{5\pi}{4}\right)\right]$$

$$= 128\sqrt{2}\left(\cos\frac{25\pi}{4} + i\sin\frac{25\pi}{4}\right)$$

$$= 128\sqrt{2}\left(\cos\frac{\pi}{4} + i\sin\frac{\pi}{4}\right)$$

$$= 128\sqrt{2}\left(\frac{\sqrt{2}}{2} + i\frac{\sqrt{2}}{2}\right)$$

$$= 128 + 128i$$

76. $49(\cos 50° + i\sin 50°)$

$$z_k = \sqrt[2]{49}\left[\cos\left(\frac{50° + 360°k}{2}\right) + i\sin\left(\frac{50° + 360°k}{2}\right)\right],\ k = 0,1$$

$$z_0 = \sqrt{49}\left[\cos\left(\frac{50° + 360°\cdot 0}{2}\right) + i\sin\left(\frac{50° + 360°\cdot 0}{2}\right)\right] = \sqrt{49}\left[\cos\left(\frac{50°}{2}\right) + i\sin\left(\frac{50°}{2}\right)\right]$$

$$= 7(\cos 25° + i\sin 25°)$$

$$z_1 = \sqrt{49}\left[\cos\left(\frac{50° + 360°\cdot 1}{2}\right) + i\sin\left(\frac{50° + 360°\cdot 1}{2}\right)\right] = \sqrt{49}\left[\cos\left(\frac{410°}{2}\right) + i\sin\left(\frac{410°}{2}\right)\right]$$

$$= 7(\cos 205° + i\sin 205°)$$

77. $125(\cos 165° + i\sin 165°)$

$$z_k = \sqrt[3]{125}\left[\cos\left(\frac{165° + 360°k}{3}\right) + i\sin\left(\frac{165° + 360°k}{3}\right)\right],\ k = 0,1,2$$

$$z_0 = \sqrt[3]{125}\left[\cos\left(\frac{165° + 360°\cdot 0}{3}\right) + i\sin\left(\frac{165° + 360°\cdot 0}{3}\right)\right] = \sqrt[3]{125}\left[\cos\left(\frac{165°}{3}\right) + i\sin\left(\frac{165°}{3}\right)\right]$$

$$= 5(\cos 55° + i\sin 55°)$$

$$z_1 = \sqrt[3]{125}\left[\cos\left(\frac{165° + 360°\cdot 1}{3}\right) + i\sin\left(\frac{165° + 360°\cdot 1}{3}\right)\right] = \sqrt[3]{125}\left[\cos\left(\frac{525°}{3}\right) + i\sin\left(\frac{525°}{3}\right)\right]$$

$$= 5(\cos 175° + i\sin 175°)$$

$$z_2 = \sqrt[3]{125}\left[\cos\left(\frac{165° + 360°\cdot 2}{3}\right) + i\sin\left(\frac{165° + 360°\cdot 2}{3}\right)\right] = \sqrt[3]{125}\left[\cos\left(\frac{885°}{3}\right) + i\sin\left(\frac{885°}{3}\right)\right]$$

$$= 5(\cos 295° + i\sin 295°)$$

78. $16\left(\cos\frac{2\pi}{3} + i\sin\frac{2\pi}{3}\right)$

$$z_k = \sqrt[4]{16}\left[\cos\left(\frac{\frac{2\pi}{3} + 2\pi k}{4}\right) + i\sin\left(\frac{\frac{2\pi}{3} + 2\pi k}{4}\right)\right],\ k = 0,1,2,3$$

$$z_0 = \sqrt[4]{16}\left[\cos\left(\frac{\frac{2\pi}{3} + 2\pi\cdot 0}{4}\right) + i\sin\left(\frac{\frac{2\pi}{3} + 2\pi\cdot 0}{4}\right)\right] = \sqrt[4]{16}\left[\cos\left(\frac{\pi}{6}\right) + i\sin\left(\frac{\pi}{6}\right)\right] = 2\left(\frac{\sqrt{3}}{2} + i\frac{1}{2}\right) = \sqrt{3} + i$$

$$z_1 = \sqrt[4]{16}\left[\cos\left(\frac{\frac{2\pi}{3} + 2\pi\cdot 1}{4}\right) + i\sin\left(\frac{\frac{2\pi}{3} + 2\pi\cdot 1}{4}\right)\right] = \sqrt[4]{16}\left(\cos\frac{2\pi}{3} + i\sin\frac{2\pi}{3}\right) = 2\left(-\frac{1}{2} + i\frac{\sqrt{3}}{2}\right) = -1 + \sqrt{3}i$$

$$z_2 = \sqrt[4]{16}\left[\cos\left(\frac{\frac{2\pi}{3} + 2\pi\cdot 2}{4}\right) + i\sin\left(\frac{\frac{2\pi}{3} + 2\pi\cdot 2}{4}\right)\right] = \sqrt[4]{16}\left(\cos\frac{7\pi}{6} + i\sin\frac{7\pi}{6}\right) = 2\left(-\frac{\sqrt{3}}{2} + i\left(-\frac{1}{2}\right)\right) = -\sqrt{3} - i$$

$$z_3 = \sqrt[4]{16}\left[\cos\left(\frac{\frac{2\pi}{3} + 2\pi\cdot 3}{4}\right) + i\sin\left(\frac{\frac{2\pi}{3} + 2\pi\cdot 3}{4}\right)\right] = \sqrt[4]{16}\left(\cos\frac{5\pi}{3} + i\sin\frac{5\pi}{3}\right) = 2\left(\frac{1}{2} + i\left(-\frac{\sqrt{3}}{2}\right)\right) = 1 - \sqrt{3}i$$

79. $8i = 8(\cos 90° + i\sin 90°)$

$$z_k = \sqrt[3]{8}\left[\cos\left(\frac{90° + 360°k}{3}\right) + i\sin\left(\frac{90° + 360°k}{3}\right)\right],\ k = 0,1,2$$

$$z_0 = \sqrt[3]{8}\left[\cos\left(\frac{90° + 360°\cdot 0}{3}\right) + i\sin\left(\frac{90° + 360°\cdot 0}{3}\right)\right] = \sqrt[3]{8}(\cos 30° + i\sin 30°) = 2\left(\frac{\sqrt{3}}{2} + i\frac{1}{2}\right) = \sqrt{3} + i$$

$$z_1 = \sqrt[3]{8}\left[\cos\left(\frac{90° + 360°\cdot 1}{3}\right) + i\sin\left(\frac{90° + 360°\cdot 1}{3}\right)\right] = \sqrt[3]{8}(\cos 150° + i\sin 150°) = 2\left(-\frac{\sqrt{3}}{2} + i\frac{1}{2}\right) = -\sqrt{3} + i$$

$$z_2 = \sqrt[3]{8}\left[\cos\left(\frac{90° + 360°\cdot 2}{3}\right) + i\sin\left(\frac{90° + 360°\cdot 2}{3}\right)\right] = \sqrt[3]{8}(\cos 270° + i\sin 270°) = 2(0 + i(-1)) = -2i$$

80. $-1 = \cos 180° + i\sin 180°$

$$z_k = \sqrt[3]{1}\left[\cos\left(\frac{180° + 360°k}{3}\right) + i\sin\left(\frac{180° + 360°k}{3}\right)\right],\ k = 0,1,2$$

$$z_0 = \sqrt[3]{1}\left[\cos\left(\frac{180° + 360°\cdot 0}{3}\right) + i\sin\left(\frac{180° + 360°\cdot 0}{3}\right)\right] = \sqrt[3]{1}(\cos 60° + i\sin 60°) = 1\left(\frac{1}{2} + i\frac{\sqrt{3}}{2}\right) = \frac{1}{2} + \frac{\sqrt{3}}{2}i$$

$$z_1 = \sqrt[3]{1}\left[\cos\left(\frac{180° + 360°\cdot 1}{3}\right) + i\sin\left(\frac{180° + 360°\cdot 1}{3}\right)\right] = \sqrt[3]{1}(\cos 180° + i\sin 180°) = 1(-1 + i0) = -1$$

$$z_2 = \sqrt[3]{1}\left[\cos\left(\frac{180° + 360°\cdot 2}{3}\right) + i\left(\frac{180° + 360°\cdot 2}{3}\right)\right] = \sqrt[3]{1}(\cos 300° + i\sin 300°) = 1\left(\frac{1}{2} + i\left(-\frac{\sqrt{3}}{2}\right)\right) = \frac{1}{2} - \frac{\sqrt{3}}{2}i$$

81. $-1 - i = \sqrt{2}(\cos 225° + i\sin 225°)$

$$z_k = \sqrt[5]{\sqrt{2}}\left[\cos\left(\frac{225° + 360°k}{5}\right) + i\sin\left(\frac{225° + 360°k}{5}\right)\right],\ k = 0,1,2,3,4$$

$$z_0 = \sqrt[5]{\sqrt{2}}\left[\cos\left(\frac{225° + 360°\cdot 0}{5}\right) + i\sin\left(\frac{225° + 360°\cdot 0}{5}\right)\right] = \sqrt[5]{\sqrt{2}}(\cos 45° + i\sin 45°) = \sqrt[5]{\sqrt{2}}\left(\frac{\sqrt{2}}{2} + i\frac{\sqrt{2}}{2}\right)$$

$$= \frac{\sqrt[5]{8}}{2} + \frac{\sqrt[5]{8}}{2}i$$

$$z_1 = \sqrt[5]{\sqrt{2}}\left[\cos\left(\frac{225° + 360°\cdot 1}{5}\right) + i\sin\left(\frac{225° + 360°\cdot 1}{5}\right)\right] = \sqrt[5]{\sqrt{2}}(\cos 117° + i\sin 117°) \approx -0.49 + 0.95i$$

$$z_2 = \sqrt[5]{\sqrt{2}}\left[\cos\left(\frac{225° + 360°\cdot 2}{5}\right) + i\sin\left(\frac{225° + 360°\cdot 2}{5}\right)\right] = \sqrt[5]{\sqrt{2}}(\cos 189° + i\sin 189°) \approx -1.06 - 0.17i$$

$$z_3 = \sqrt[5]{\sqrt{2}}\left[\cos\left(\frac{225° + 360°\cdot 3}{5}\right) + i\sin\left(\frac{225° + 360°\cdot 3}{5}\right)\right] = \sqrt[5]{\sqrt{2}}(\cos 261° + i\sin 261°) \approx -0.17 - 1.06i$$

$$z_4 = \sqrt[5]{\sqrt{2}}\left[\cos\left(\frac{225° + 360°\cdot 4}{5}\right) + i\sin\left(\frac{225° + 360°\cdot 4}{5}\right)\right] = \sqrt[5]{\sqrt{2}}(\cos 333° + i\sin 333°) \approx 0.95 - 0.49i$$

82.

$$\|\mathbf{v}\| = \sqrt{a^2 + b^2}$$
$$= \sqrt{(-3)^2 + (-4)^2}$$
$$= \sqrt{9 + 16}$$
$$= \sqrt{25}$$
$$= 5$$

83.

$$\|\mathbf{v}\| = \sqrt{a^2 + b^2}$$
$$= \sqrt{5^2 + (-2)^2}$$
$$= \sqrt{25 + 4}$$
$$= \sqrt{29}$$

84.

$$\|\mathbf{v}\| = \sqrt{a^2 + b^2}$$
$$= \sqrt{0^2 + (-3)^2}$$
$$= \sqrt{0 + 9}$$
$$= \sqrt{9}$$
$$= 3$$

85. $\mathbf{v} = (x_2 - x_1)\mathbf{i} + (y_2 - y_1)\mathbf{j}$
$$= (5 - 2)\mathbf{i} + [-3 - (-1)]\mathbf{j}$$
$$= 3\mathbf{i} - 2\mathbf{j}$$

86. $\mathbf{v} = (x_2 - x_1)\mathbf{i} + (y_2 - y_1)\mathbf{j}$
$$= [-2 - (-3)\mathbf{i}] + (-2 - 0)\mathbf{j}$$
$$= \mathbf{i} - 2\mathbf{j}$$

87. $\mathbf{v} + \mathbf{w} = (\mathbf{i} - 5\mathbf{j}) + (-2\mathbf{i} + 7\mathbf{j})$
$$= [1 + (-2)]\mathbf{i} + [-5 + 7]\mathbf{j}$$
$$= -\mathbf{i} + 2\mathbf{j}$$

88. $\mathbf{w} - \mathbf{v} = (-2\mathbf{i} + 7\mathbf{j}) - (\mathbf{i} - 5\mathbf{j})$
$$= (-2 - 1)\mathbf{i} + [7 - (-5)]\mathbf{j}$$
$$= -3\mathbf{i} + 12\mathbf{j}$$

89. $6\mathbf{v} - 3\mathbf{w} = 6(\mathbf{i} - 5\mathbf{j}) - 3(-2\mathbf{i} + 7\mathbf{j})$
$$= 6\mathbf{i} - 30\mathbf{j} + 6\mathbf{i} - 21\mathbf{j}$$
$$= 12\mathbf{i} - 51\mathbf{j}$$

90. $\|-2\mathbf{v}\| = |-2| \|\mathbf{v}\|$
$$= 2\|\mathbf{v}\|$$
$$= 2\sqrt{a^2 + b^2}$$
$$= 2\sqrt{1^2 + (-5)^2}$$
$$= 2\sqrt{1 + 25}$$
$$= 2\sqrt{26}$$

91. First, find the magnitude of $\mathbf{v}$.
$$\|\mathbf{v}\| = \sqrt{a^2 + b^2}$$
$$= \sqrt{8^2 + (-6)^2}$$
$$= \sqrt{64 + 36}$$
$$= \sqrt{100}$$
$$= 10$$
A unit vector in the same direction as $\mathbf{v}$ is
$$\frac{\mathbf{v}}{\|\mathbf{v}\|} = \frac{8\mathbf{i} - 6\mathbf{j}}{10} = \frac{4}{5}\mathbf{i} - \frac{3}{5}\mathbf{j}.$$

92. First, find the magnitude of $\mathbf{v}$.
$$\|\mathbf{v}\| = \sqrt{a^2 + b^2} = \sqrt{(-1)^2 + (2)^2} = \sqrt{1 + 4} = \sqrt{5}$$ A
unit vector in the same direction as $\mathbf{v}$ is
$$\frac{\mathbf{v}}{\|\mathbf{v}\|} = \frac{-\mathbf{i} + 2\mathbf{j}}{\sqrt{5}} = -\frac{1}{\sqrt{5}}\mathbf{i} + \frac{2}{\sqrt{5}}\mathbf{j}.$$

93. $\mathbf{v} = \|\mathbf{v}\|\cos\theta\,\mathbf{i} + \|\mathbf{v}\|\sin\theta\,\mathbf{j}$

$= 12\cos 60°\mathbf{i} + 12\sin 60°\mathbf{j}$

$= 12\left(\dfrac{1}{2}\right)\mathbf{i} + 12\left(\dfrac{\sqrt{3}}{2}\right)\mathbf{j}$

$= 6\mathbf{i} + 6\sqrt{3}\mathbf{j}$

94. $\mathbf{F}_1 = 100\cos 65°\,\mathbf{i} + 100\sin 65°\,\mathbf{j}$

$= 42.3\mathbf{i} + 90.6\mathbf{j}$

$\mathbf{F}_2 = 200\cos 10°\mathbf{i} + 200\sin 10°\mathbf{j}$

$= 197\mathbf{i} + 34.7\mathbf{j}$

$\mathbf{F}_1 + \mathbf{F}_2 = (42.3 + 197)\mathbf{i} + (90.6 + 34.7)\mathbf{j}$

$= 239.3\mathbf{i} + 125.3\mathbf{j}$

$\sqrt{239.3^2 + 125.3^2} \approx 270$ pounds

$\cos\theta = \dfrac{239.3}{270}$

$\theta = 27.6°$

95. $\mathbf{v} = 15\cos 25°\,\mathbf{i} + 15\sin 25°\,\mathbf{j} = 13.6\mathbf{i} + 6.3\mathbf{j}$

$\mathbf{w} = 4\cos 270°\,\mathbf{i} + 4\sin 270°\,\mathbf{j} = -4\mathbf{j}$

a. $13.6\mathbf{i} + (6.3 - 4)\mathbf{j} = 13.6\mathbf{i} + 2.3\mathbf{j}$

b. $\sqrt{13.6^2 + 2.3^2} \approx 14$ mph

c. $\cos\theta = \dfrac{13.6}{14}; \theta = 13.7°$

96. $\mathbf{v}\cdot(\mathbf{v} + \mathbf{w}) = (5\mathbf{i} + 2\mathbf{j})[(\mathbf{i} - \mathbf{j}) + (3\mathbf{i} - 7\mathbf{j})]$

$= (5\mathbf{i} + 2\mathbf{j})\cdot[4\mathbf{i} - 8\mathbf{j}]$

$= 5(4) + 2(-8)$

$= 20 - 16$

$= 4$

97. $\mathbf{v}\cdot\mathbf{w} = (2\mathbf{i} + 3\mathbf{j})\cdot(7\mathbf{i} - 4\mathbf{j}) = 2(7) + 3(-4) = 2$

$\cos\theta = \dfrac{2}{\sqrt{2^2 + 3^2}\sqrt{7^2 + (-4)^2}}$

$= \dfrac{2}{\sqrt{13}\sqrt{65}}$

$= \dfrac{2}{\sqrt{845}}$

The angle θ between the vectors is

$\theta = \cos^{-1}\left(\dfrac{2}{\sqrt{845}}\right) \approx 86.1°.$

98. $\mathbf{v}\cdot\mathbf{w} = (2\mathbf{i} + 4\mathbf{j})\cdot(6\mathbf{i} - 11\mathbf{j}) = 2(6) + 4(-11)$

$= 12 - 44$

$= -32$

$\cos\theta = \dfrac{-32}{\sqrt{2^2 + 4^2}\sqrt{6^2 + (-11)^2}}$

$= \dfrac{-32}{\sqrt{20}\sqrt{157}}$

$= \dfrac{-32}{\sqrt{3140}}$

The angle θ between the vectors is

$\theta = \cos^{-1}\left(-\dfrac{32}{\sqrt{3140}}\right) \approx 124.8°.$

99. $\mathbf{v}\cdot\mathbf{w} = (2\mathbf{i} + \mathbf{j})\cdot(\mathbf{i} - \mathbf{j}) = 2(1) + 1(-1)$

$= 2 - 1 = 1$

$\cos\theta = \dfrac{1}{\sqrt{2^2 + 1^2}\sqrt{1^2 + (-1)^2}}$

$= \dfrac{1}{\sqrt{5}\sqrt{2}}$

$= \dfrac{1}{\sqrt{10}}$

The angle θ between the vectors is

$\theta = \cos^{-1}\left(\dfrac{1}{\sqrt{10}}\right) \approx 71.6°.$

100. $\mathbf{v} \cdot \mathbf{w} = (12\mathbf{i} - 8\mathbf{j}) \cdot (2\mathbf{i} + 3\mathbf{j})$

$\qquad = 12(2) + (-8)(3)$

$\qquad = 24 - 24$

$\qquad = 0$

The dot product is zero. Thus, the given vectors are orthogonal.

101. $\mathbf{v} \cdot \mathbf{w} = (\mathbf{i} + 3\mathbf{j}) \cdot (-3\mathbf{i} - \mathbf{j})$

$\qquad = 1(-3) + 3(-1)$

$\qquad = -3 - 3$

$\qquad = -6$

The dot product is not zero. Thus, the given vectors are not orthogonal.

102. $\text{proj}_{\mathbf{w}} \mathbf{v} = \dfrac{\mathbf{v} \cdot \mathbf{w}}{\| \mathbf{w} \|^2} \mathbf{w}$

$\qquad = \dfrac{(-2\mathbf{i} + 5\mathbf{j}) \cdot (5\mathbf{i} + 4\mathbf{j})}{\left(\sqrt{5^2 + 4^2} \right)^2} \mathbf{w}$

$\qquad = \dfrac{-2(5) + 5(4)}{\left(\sqrt{41} \right)^2} \mathbf{w}$

$\qquad = \dfrac{10}{41} (5\mathbf{i} + 4\mathbf{j})$

$\qquad = \dfrac{50}{41} \mathbf{i} + \dfrac{40}{41} \mathbf{j}$

$\mathbf{v}_1 = \text{proj}_{\mathbf{w}} \mathbf{v} = \dfrac{50}{41} \mathbf{i} + \dfrac{40}{41} \mathbf{j}$

$\mathbf{v}_2 = \mathbf{v} - \mathbf{v}_1 = (-2\mathbf{i} + 5\mathbf{j}) - \left(\dfrac{50}{41} \mathbf{i} + \dfrac{40}{41} \mathbf{j} \right)$

$\qquad = -\dfrac{132}{41} \mathbf{i} + \dfrac{165}{41} \mathbf{j}$

103. $\text{proj}_{\mathbf{W}}\mathbf{v} = \dfrac{\mathbf{v}\cdot\mathbf{w}}{\|\mathbf{w}\|^2}\mathbf{w}$

$$= \dfrac{(-\mathbf{i}+2\mathbf{j})\cdot(3\mathbf{i}-\mathbf{j})}{\left(\sqrt{3^2+(-1)^2}\right)^2}\mathbf{w}$$

$$= \dfrac{-1(3)+2(-1)}{\left(\sqrt{10}\right)^2}\mathbf{w}$$

$$= \dfrac{-5}{10}\mathbf{w}$$

$$= -\dfrac{1}{2}(3\mathbf{i}-1\mathbf{j})$$

$$= \dfrac{-3}{2}\mathbf{i}+\dfrac{1}{2}\mathbf{j}$$

$$\mathbf{v}_1 = \text{proj}_{\mathbf{W}}\mathbf{v} = \dfrac{-3}{2}\mathbf{i}+\dfrac{1}{2}\mathbf{j}$$

$$\mathbf{v}_2 = \mathbf{v}-\mathbf{v}_1 = (-\mathbf{i}+2\mathbf{j})-\left(\dfrac{-3}{2}\mathbf{i}+\dfrac{1}{2}\mathbf{j}\right)$$

$$= \dfrac{1}{2}\mathbf{i}+\dfrac{3}{2}\mathbf{j}$$

104. $\mathbf{W} = \|\mathbf{F}\|\,\|\overrightarrow{AB}\|\cos\theta$

$$= (30)(50)\cos 42°$$

$$\approx 1115$$

The work done is approximately 1115 foot-pounds.

Chapter 6 Test

1. The known ratio is $\dfrac{a}{\sin A}$, or $\dfrac{4.8}{\sin 34°}$. Because angle B is given, we use the Law of Sines to find

side b $\qquad \dfrac{b}{\sin B} = \dfrac{a}{\sin A}$

$$\dfrac{b}{\sin 68°} = \dfrac{4.8}{\sin 34°}$$

$$b = \dfrac{4.8\sin 68°}{\sin 34°} \approx 8.0$$

2. Use the Law of Cosines to find c.

$$c^2 = a^2 + b^2 - 2ab\cos C$$

$$c^2 = 5^2 + 6^2 - 2(5)(6)\cos 68°$$

$$= 61 - 60\cos 68°$$

$$\approx 38.52$$

$$c \approx \sqrt{38.52} \approx 6.2$$

3. $s = \dfrac{1}{2}(a+b+c) = \dfrac{1}{2}(17+45+32) = 47$

$$\text{Area} = \sqrt{s(s-a)(s-b)(s-c)}$$

$$= \sqrt{47(47-17)(47-45)(47-32)}$$

$$= \sqrt{42,300} \approx 206$$

The area of the triangle is approximately 206 square inches.

4. Draw $\theta = \dfrac{5\pi}{4} = 225°$ counterclockwise, since θ is positive, from the polar axis. Go 4 units out on the terminal side of θ, since $r > 0$.

Ordered pairs may vary.

5. $(1, -1)$

$$r = \sqrt{1^2+(-1)^2} = \sqrt{1+1} = \sqrt{2}$$

$$\tan\theta = \dfrac{-1}{1} = -1$$

Because $\tan\dfrac{\pi}{4} = 1$ and θ lies in quadrant IV,

$$\theta = 2\pi - \dfrac{\pi}{4} = \dfrac{7\pi}{4}.$$

The polar coordinated of $(1, -1)$ are

$$(r, \theta) = \left(\sqrt{2}, \dfrac{7\pi}{4}\right).$$

6.
$$x^2 + (y+8)^2 = 64$$
$$(r\cos\theta)^2 + (r\sin\theta + 8)^2 = 64$$
$$r^2\cos^2\theta + r^2\sin^2\theta + 16r\sin\theta + 64 = 64$$
$$r^2 + 16r\sin\theta = 0$$
$$r^2 = -16r\sin\theta$$
$$r = -16\sin\theta$$

7.
$$r = -4\sec\theta$$
$$r = \frac{-4}{\cos\theta}$$
$$r\cos\theta = -4$$
$$x = -4$$

8. $r = 1 + \sin\theta$

Check for symmetry:

Polar Axis	The Line $\theta = \dfrac{\pi}{2}$	The Pole
$r = 1 + \sin(-\theta)$	$-r = 1 + \sin(-\theta)$	$-r = 1 + \sin\theta$
	$-r = 1 - \sin\theta$	
$r = 1 - \sin\theta$	$r = -1 + \sin\theta$	$r = -1 - \sin\theta$

There may be no symmetry, since each equation is not equivalent to $r = 1 + \sin\theta$.
Calculate values of r for θ from 0 to 2π.

θ	0	$\dfrac{\pi}{6}$	$\dfrac{\pi}{3}$	$\dfrac{\pi}{2}$	$\dfrac{2\pi}{3}$	$\dfrac{5\pi}{6}$	π	$\dfrac{7\pi}{6}$	$\dfrac{4\pi}{3}$	$\dfrac{3\pi}{2}$	$\dfrac{5\pi}{3}$	$\dfrac{11\pi}{6}$	2π
r	1	1.5	1.87	2	1.87	1.5	1	0.5	0.13	0	0.13	0.5	1

$r = 1 + \sin\theta$

9. $r = 1 + 3\cos\theta$
     Check for symmetry:

Polar Axis	The Line $\theta = \dfrac{\pi}{2}$	The Pole
$r = 1 + 3\cos(-\theta)$	$-r = 1 + 3\cos(-\theta)$	$-r = 1 + 3\cos\theta$
	$-r = 1 + 3\cos\theta$	
$r = 1 + 3\cos\theta$	$r = -1 - 3\cos\theta$	$r = -1 - 3\cos\theta$

The graph has symmetry with respect to the polar axis. The graph may or may not be symmetric with respect to the line $\theta = \dfrac{\pi}{2}$ or the pole. Calculate values of r for θ from 0 to π and use symmetry to complete the graph.

θ	0	$\dfrac{\pi}{6}$	$\dfrac{\pi}{3}$	$\dfrac{\pi}{2}$	$\dfrac{2\pi}{3}$	$\dfrac{5\pi}{6}$	π
r	4	3.6	2.5	1	-0.5	-1.6	-2

$r = 1 + 3\cos\theta$

10.   Use $r = \sqrt{a^2 + b^2}$ and $\tan\theta = \dfrac{b}{a}$, with $a = -\sqrt{3}$ and $b = 1$, to find r and θ.

$$r = \sqrt{\left(-\sqrt{3}\right)^2 + (1)^2} = \sqrt{3 + 1} = \sqrt{4} = 2$$

$$\tan\theta = \frac{1}{-\sqrt{3}} = -\frac{1}{\sqrt{3}}$$

Because $\tan 30° = \dfrac{1}{\sqrt{3}}$ and θ lies in quadrant II, $\theta = 180° - 30° = 150°$.

The polar form of $z = -\sqrt{3} + i$ is $z = r(\cos\theta + i\sin\theta) = 2(\cos 150° + i\sin 150°)$ or $2\left(\cos\dfrac{5\pi}{6} + i\sin\dfrac{5\pi}{6}\right)$.

11. $5(\cos 15° + i\sin 15°) \cdot 10(\cos 5° + i\sin 5°) = (5 \cdot 10)\left[\cos(15° + 5°) + i\sin(15° + 5°)\right]$
                                   $= 50(\cos 20° + i\sin 20°)$

12. $\dfrac{2\left(\cos\dfrac{\pi}{2} + i\sin\dfrac{\pi}{2}\right)}{4\left(\cos\dfrac{\pi}{3} + i\sin\dfrac{\pi}{3}\right)} = \dfrac{2}{4}\left[\cos\left(\dfrac{\pi}{2} - \dfrac{\pi}{3}\right) + i\sin\left(\dfrac{\pi}{2} - \dfrac{\pi}{3}\right)\right] = \dfrac{2}{4}\left[\cos\left(\dfrac{3\pi}{6} - \dfrac{2\pi}{6}\right) + i\sin\left(\dfrac{3\pi}{6} - \dfrac{2\pi}{6}\right)\right]$

$$= \dfrac{1}{2}\left(\cos\dfrac{\pi}{6} + i\sin\dfrac{\pi}{6}\right)$$

13. $\left[2(\cos 10° + i\sin 10°)\right]^5 = (2)^5\left[\cos(5\cdot 10°) + i\sin(5\cdot 10°)\right] = 32(\cos 50° + i\sin 50°)$

14. $27 = 27(\cos 0° + i\sin 0°)$

$$z_k = \sqrt[3]{27}\left[\cos\left(\frac{0° + 360°k}{3}\right) + i\sin\left(\frac{0° + 360°k}{3}\right)\right], \; k = 0, 1, 2$$

$$z_0 = \sqrt[3]{27}\left[\cos\left(\frac{0° + 360°\cdot 0}{3}\right) + i\sin\left(\frac{0° + 360°\cdot 0}{3}\right)\right] = \sqrt[3]{27}(\cos 0° + i\sin 0°) = 3(1 + 0i) = 3$$

$$z_1 = \sqrt[3]{27}\left[\cos\left(\frac{0° + 360°\cdot 1}{3}\right) + i\sin\left(\frac{0° + 360°\cdot 1}{3}\right)\right] = \sqrt[3]{27}\left(\cos 120° + i\sin 120°\right) = 3\left(-\frac{1}{2} + i\frac{\sqrt{3}}{2}\right) = -\frac{3}{2} + \frac{3\sqrt{3}}{2}i$$

$$z_2 = \sqrt[3]{27}\left[\cos\left(\frac{0° + 360°\cdot 2}{3}\right) + i\sin\left(\frac{0° + 360°\cdot 2}{3}\right)\right] = \sqrt[3]{27}(\cos 240° + i\sin 240°) = 3\left(-\frac{1}{2} - \frac{\sqrt{3}}{2}i\right) = -\frac{3}{2} - \frac{3\sqrt{3}}{2}i$$

15. a. $\mathbf{v} = \left(x_2 - x_1\right)\mathbf{i} + \left(y_2 - y_1\right)\mathbf{j}$

　　　$\mathbf{v} = [-1 - (-2)]\mathbf{i} + (5 - 3)\mathbf{j} = \mathbf{i} + 2\mathbf{j}$

　b. $\|\mathbf{v}\| = \sqrt{a^2 + b^2} = \sqrt{1^2 + 2^2} = \sqrt{1 + 4} = \sqrt{5}$

16. $3\mathbf{v} - 4\mathbf{w} = 3(-5\mathbf{i} + 2\mathbf{j}) - 4(2\mathbf{i} - 4\mathbf{j}) = -15\mathbf{i} + 6\mathbf{j} - 8\mathbf{i} + 16\mathbf{j}$

　　　　　　　　$= (-15 - 8)\mathbf{i} + (6 + 16)\mathbf{j} = -23\mathbf{i} + 22\mathbf{j}$

17. $\mathbf{v}\cdot\mathbf{w} = (-5\mathbf{i} + 2\mathbf{j})\cdot(2\mathbf{i} - 4\mathbf{j}) = -5(2) + 2(-4) = -10 - 8 = -18$

18.
$$\cos\theta = \frac{\mathbf{v}\cdot\mathbf{w}}{\|\mathbf{v}\|\|\mathbf{w}\|}\mathbf{w}$$

$$= \frac{(-5\mathbf{i} + 2\mathbf{j})\cdot(2\mathbf{i} - 4\mathbf{j})}{\sqrt{(-5)^2 + 2^2}\sqrt{2^2 + (-4)^2}}$$

$$= \frac{-5(2) + 2(-4)}{\sqrt{29}\sqrt{20}}$$

$$= -\frac{18}{\sqrt{580}}$$

The angle θ between the vectors is

$$\theta = \cos^{-1}\left(-\frac{18}{\sqrt{580}}\right) \approx 138°.$$

19.
$$\text{proj}_{\mathbf{W}}\mathbf{v} = \frac{\mathbf{v}\cdot\mathbf{w}}{\|\mathbf{w}\|^2}\mathbf{w}$$

$$= \frac{(-5\mathbf{i} + 2\mathbf{j})\cdot(2\mathbf{i} - 4\mathbf{j})}{\left(\sqrt{2^2 + (-4)^2}\right)^2}\mathbf{w}$$

$$= \frac{-5(2) + 2(-4)}{\left(\sqrt{20}\right)^2}\mathbf{w}$$

$$= -\frac{18}{20}\mathbf{w}$$

$$= -\frac{9}{10}(2\mathbf{i} - 4\mathbf{j})$$

$$= -\frac{9}{5}\mathbf{i} + \frac{18}{5}\mathbf{j}$$

20.

Using the figure,
$B = 90° - 50° = 40°$
$A = 90° - 40° = 50°$
$C = 180° - B - A = 180° - 40° - 50° = 90°$
Use the Law of Sines to find b.

$$\frac{b}{\sin B} = \frac{c}{\sin C}$$

$$\frac{b}{\sin 40°} = \frac{1.6}{\sin 90°}$$

$$b = \frac{1.6 \sin 40°}{\sin 90°} \approx 1.0$$

The fire is about 1.0 mile from the station.

21. $\mathbf{F_1} = 250 \cos 30° \ \mathbf{i} + 250 \sin 30° \ \mathbf{j}$
$= 216.5\mathbf{i} + 125\mathbf{j}$

$\mathbf{F_2} = 150 \cos 315° \ \mathbf{i} + 150 \sin 315° \ \mathbf{j}$
$= 106\mathbf{i} - 106\mathbf{j}$

$\mathbf{F_1} + \mathbf{F_2} = (216.5 + 106)\mathbf{i} + (125 - 106)\mathbf{j}$
$= 322.5\mathbf{i} + 19\mathbf{j}$

$\| \mathbf{F_1} + \mathbf{F_2} \| = \sqrt{322.5^2 + 19^2} \approx 323$ pounds

$\cos\theta = \frac{322.5}{323} = 3.4°$

22. $W = \| \mathbf{F} \| \| \overrightarrow{AB} \| \cos\theta$

$= (40)(60)\cos 35° \approx 1966$

The work done is approximately 1966 foot-pounds.

Cumulative Review Exercises (Chapters P–6)

1. $x^4 - x^3 - x^2 - x - 2 = 0$

$\frac{p}{q} : \ \pm\frac{2}{1}, \ \pm\frac{1}{1}$

-1	1	-1	-1	-1	-2
		-1	2	-1	2
	1	-2	1	-2	0

$x^4 - x^3 - x^2 - x - 2 = 0$

$(x+1)(x^3 - 2x^2 + x - 2) = 0$

$(x+1)[x^2(x-2) + 1(x-2)] = 0$

$(x+1)(x-2)(x^2+1) = 0$

$x + 1 = 0 \quad x - 2 = 0 \quad x^2 + 1 = 0$

$x = -1 \qquad x = 2 \qquad x^2 = -1$

$\qquad\qquad\qquad\qquad\qquad x = \pm i$

The solution set is $\{-1, \ 2 \ i, \ -i\}$.

2. $2\sin^2\theta - 3\sin\theta + 1 = 0, \ 0 \le \theta < 2\pi$

$(2\sin\theta - 1)(\sin\theta - 1) = 0$

$2\sin\theta - 1 = 0 \quad$ or $\quad \sin\theta - 1 = 0$

$2\sin\theta = 1 \qquad\qquad \sin\theta = 1$

$\sin\theta = \frac{1}{2}$

The solutions in the interval $\left[0, \ 2\pi\right)$ are

$\frac{\pi}{6}, \frac{5\pi}{6}$, and $\frac{\pi}{2}$.

3. Begin by solving the related quadratic equation. Thus, we will solve $x^2 + 2x + 3 = 11$.

$$x^2 + 2x + 3 = 11$$
$$x^2 + 2x - 8 = 0$$
$$(x+4)(x-2) = 0$$
$$x + 4 = 0 \quad \text{or} \quad x - 2 = 0$$
$$x = -4 \quad \text{or} \quad x = 2$$

The boundary points are –4 and 2. The boundary points divide the number line into three test intervals, namely $(-\infty, -4)$, $(-4, 2)$, and $(2, \infty)$. Take one representative number within each test interval and substitute that number into the original inequality.

Test Interval	Representative Number	Substitute into $x^2 + 2x + 3 > 11$	Conclusion
$(-\infty, -4)$	–5	$(-5)^2 + 2(-5) + 3 > 11$ $18 > 11$ True	$(-\infty, -4)$ belongs to the solution set.
$(-4, -2)$	0	$0^2 + 2(0) + 3 > 11$ $3 > 11$ False	$(-4, -2)$ does not belong to the solution set.
$(2, \infty)$	3	$3^2 + 2(3) + 3 > 11$ $18 > 11$ True	$(2, \infty)$ belongs to the solution set.

The solution set is $\left\{ x \mid x < -4 \text{ or } x > 2 \right\}$.

4. $\sin\theta\cos\theta = -\dfrac{1}{2}$

$$\frac{\sin 2\theta}{2} = -\frac{1}{2}$$
$$\sin 2\theta = -1$$

The period of the sine function is 2π. In the interval $[0, 2\pi)$, the only value for which the sine function is –1 is $\dfrac{3\pi}{2}$. This means that $2\theta = \dfrac{3\pi}{2}$. Since the period is 2π, all the solutions to $\sin 2\theta = -1$ are given by

$$2\theta = \frac{3\pi}{2} + 2n\pi$$
$$\theta = \frac{3\pi}{4} + n\pi$$

where n is any integer.
The solution in the interval $[0, 2\pi)$ is obtained by letting $n = 0$ and $n = 1$. The solutions are $\dfrac{3\pi}{4}$ and $\dfrac{7\pi}{4}$.

5. The equation $y = 3\sin(2x - \pi)$ is of the form $y = A\sin(Bx - C)$ with $A = 3$, $B = 2$, and $C = \pi$. The amplitude is $|A| = |3| = 3$. The period is $\dfrac{2\pi}{B} = \dfrac{2\pi}{2} = \pi$. The phase shift is $\dfrac{C}{B} = \dfrac{\pi}{2}$. The quarter-period is $\dfrac{\pi}{4}$. The cycle begins at $x = \dfrac{\pi}{2}$. Add quarter-periods to generate x-values for the key points.

$$x = \frac{\pi}{2}$$
$$x = \frac{\pi}{2} + \frac{\pi}{4} = \frac{3\pi}{4}$$
$$x = \frac{3\pi}{4} + \frac{\pi}{4} = \pi$$
$$x = \pi + \frac{\pi}{4} = \frac{5\pi}{4}$$
$$x = \frac{5\pi}{4} + \frac{\pi}{4} = \frac{3\pi}{2}$$

We evaluate the function at each value of x.

x	$y = 3\sin(2x - \pi)$	coordinates
$\dfrac{\pi}{2}$	$y = 3\sin\left(2\cdot\dfrac{\pi}{2} - \pi\right)$ $= 3\sin(\pi - \pi)$ $= 3\sin 0 = 3\cdot 0 = 0$	$\left(\dfrac{\pi}{2}, 0\right)$
$\dfrac{3\pi}{4}$	$y = 3\sin\left(2\cdot\dfrac{3\pi}{4} - \pi\right)$ $= 3\sin\left(\dfrac{3\pi}{2} - \pi\right)$ $= 3\sin\dfrac{\pi}{2} = 3\cdot 1 = 3$	$\left(\dfrac{3\pi}{4}, 3\right)$
π	$y = 3\sin(2\cdot\pi - \pi)$ $= 3\sin(2\pi - \pi)$ $= 3\sin\pi = 3\cdot 0 = 0$	$(\pi, 0)$
$\dfrac{5\pi}{4}$	$y = 3\sin\left(2\cdot\dfrac{5\pi}{4} - \pi\right)$ $= 3\sin\left(\dfrac{5\pi}{2} - \pi\right)$ $= 3\sin\dfrac{3\pi}{2}$ $= 3(-1) = -3$	$\left(\dfrac{5\pi}{4}, -3\right)$
$\dfrac{3\pi}{2}$	$y = 3\sin\left(2\cdot\dfrac{3\pi}{2} - \pi\right)$ $= 3\sin(3\pi - \pi)$ $= 3\sin 2\pi = 3\cdot 0 = 0$	$\left(\dfrac{3\pi}{2}, 0\right)$

Connect the five points with a smooth curve and graph one complete cycle of the given function.

6.   The equation $y = -4\cos\pi x$ is of the form

   $y = A\cos Bx$ with $A = -4$, and $B = \pi$. Thus, the

   amplitude is $|A| = |-4| = 4$.

   The period is $\dfrac{2\pi}{B} = \dfrac{2\pi}{\pi} = 2$.

   Find the x-values for the five key points by

   dividing the period, 2, by 4, $\dfrac{\text{period}}{4} = \dfrac{2}{4} = \dfrac{1}{2}$,

   then by adding quarter- periods to the value of x
   where the cycle begins, $x = 0$. The five x-values
   are

$x = 0$

$x = 0 + \dfrac{1}{2} = \dfrac{1}{2}$

$x = \dfrac{1}{2} + \dfrac{1}{2} = 1$

$x = 1 + \dfrac{1}{2} = \dfrac{3}{2}$

$x = \dfrac{3}{2} + \dfrac{1}{2} = 2$

We evaluate the function at each value of x.

x	$y = -4\cos\pi x$	coordinates
0	$y = -4\cos(\pi\cdot 0)$ $= -4\cos 0$ $= -4\cdot 1 = -4$	$(0, -4)$
$\dfrac{1}{2}$	$y = -4\cos\left(\pi\cdot\dfrac{1}{2}\right)$ $= -4\cos\dfrac{\pi}{2}$ $= -4\cdot 0 = 0$	$\left(\dfrac{1}{2}, 0\right)$
1	$y = -4\cos(\pi\cdot 1)$ $= -4\cos\pi$ $= -4\cdot(-1) = 4$	$(1, 4)$
$\dfrac{3}{2}$	$y = -4\cos\left(\pi\cdot\dfrac{3}{2}\right)$ $= -4\cos\dfrac{3\pi}{2}$ $= -4\cdot 0 = 0$	$\left(\dfrac{3}{2}, 0\right)$
2	$y = -4\cos(\pi\cdot 2)$ $= -4\cos 2\pi$ $= -4\cdot 1 = -4$	$(2, -4)$

Connect the five key points with a smooth curve and graph one complete cycle of the given function.

7. $\sin\theta\csc\theta - \cos^2\theta = \sin\theta\left(\dfrac{1}{\sin\theta}\right) - \cos^2\theta$

   $= 1 - \cos^2\theta$

   $= \sin^2\theta$

SSM: Precalculus

8. $\cos\left(\theta+\dfrac{3\pi}{2}\right)=\cos\theta\cos\dfrac{3\pi}{2}-\sin\theta\sin\dfrac{3\pi}{2}$

$\qquad\qquad = \cos\theta(0)-\sin\theta(-1)$

$\qquad\qquad = \sin\theta$

9. $2x+4y-8=0$

$\qquad 4y=-2x+8$

$\qquad \dfrac{4y}{4}=\dfrac{-2x+8}{4}$

$\qquad y=-\dfrac{1}{2}x+2$

The slope is $-\dfrac{1}{2}$, and the *y*-intercept is 2.

10. $2\sin\dfrac{\pi}{3}-3\tan\dfrac{\pi}{6}=2\left(\dfrac{\sqrt{3}}{2}\right)-3\left(\dfrac{1}{\sqrt{3}}\right)$

$\qquad\qquad\qquad = \sqrt{3}-\dfrac{3}{\sqrt{3}}$

$\qquad\qquad\qquad = \sqrt{3}-\sqrt{3}$

$\qquad\qquad\qquad = 0$

11. Let $\theta=\tan^{-1}\left(\dfrac{1}{2}\right)$, then $\tan\theta=\dfrac{1}{2}$. Because

$\tan\theta$ is positive, θ is in the first quadrant. Use the Pythagorean Theorem to find *r*.

$r=\sqrt{1^2+2^2}=\sqrt{1+4}=\sqrt{5}$

Use the right triangle to find the exact value.

$\sin\left(\tan^{-1}\dfrac{1}{2}\right)=\sin\theta=\dfrac{1}{\sqrt{5}}=\dfrac{\sqrt{5}}{5}$

12. $f(x)=\sqrt{5-x}$

$\quad 5-x\ge 0$

$\quad -x\ge -5$

$\quad x\le 5$

The domain of the function is $\{x\,|\,x\le 5\}$.

13. $\qquad\qquad g(x)=\dfrac{x-3}{x^2-9}$

$\qquad\qquad x^2-9=0$

$\qquad (x-3)(x+3)=0$

$\quad x-3=0\quad\text{or}\quad x+3=0$

$\qquad x=3\qquad\qquad x=-3$

The domain of the function is

$\{x\,|\,x\ne 3\text{ and }x\ne -3\}$.

14. $s(t)=-16t^2+48t+8$

$\qquad = -16\left(t^2-3t-\dfrac{1}{2}\right)$

$\qquad = -16\left(t^2-3t+\dfrac{9}{4}-\dfrac{1}{2}-\dfrac{9}{4}\right)$

$\qquad = -16\left[\left(t-\dfrac{3}{2}\right)^2-\dfrac{1}{2}-\dfrac{9}{4}\right]$

$\qquad = -16\left(t-\dfrac{3}{2}\right)^2+44$

The ball reaches its maximum height after the first 1.5 seconds. The maximum height is 44 feet.

15. $d=4\sin 5t$ is of the form $d=a\sin\omega t$ with $a=4$ and $\omega=5$.

a. $|\,a\,|=|\,4\,|=4$

The maximum displacement is 4 meters.

b. $f=\dfrac{\omega}{2\pi}=\dfrac{5}{2\pi}$

The frequency is $\dfrac{5}{2\pi}$ cycle per second.

c. $\text{period}=\dfrac{2\pi}{\omega}=\dfrac{2\pi}{5}$

$\dfrac{2\pi}{5}$ seconds are required for one cycle.

16. Because $22.5°$ lies in quadrant I, $\cos 22.5° > 0$.

$$\cos 22.5° = \cos \frac{45°}{2}$$

$$= \sqrt{\frac{1 + \cos 45°}{2}}$$

$$= \sqrt{\frac{1 + \frac{\sqrt{2}}{2}}{2}}$$

$$= \sqrt{\frac{2 + \sqrt{2}}{4}}$$

$$= \frac{\sqrt{2 + \sqrt{2}}}{2}$$

17. **a.** $3\mathbf{v} - \mathbf{w} = 3(2\mathbf{i} + 7\mathbf{j}) - (\mathbf{i} - 2\mathbf{j})$

$$= 6\mathbf{i} + 21\mathbf{j} - \mathbf{i} + 2\mathbf{j}$$

$$= 5\mathbf{i} + 23\mathbf{j}$$

     b. $\mathbf{v} \cdot \mathbf{w} = (2\mathbf{i} + 7\mathbf{j}) \cdot (\mathbf{i} - 2\mathbf{j})$

$$= 2(1) + 7(-2) = 2 - 14$$

$$= -12$$

18. $\dfrac{1}{2} \log_b x - \log_b (x^2 + 1)$

$$= \log_b x^{1/2} - \log_b (x^2 + 1)$$

$$= \log_b \sqrt{x} - \log_b (x^2 + 1)$$

$$= \log_b \frac{\sqrt{x}}{x^2 + 1}$$

19. $(4, -1)$ and $(-8, 5)$

$$m = \frac{5 - (-1)}{-8 - 4} = \frac{6}{-12} = -\frac{1}{2}$$

$$y - (-1) = -\frac{1}{2}(x - 4)$$

$$y + 1 = -\frac{1}{2}x + 2$$

$$y = -\frac{1}{2}x + 1$$

20. $L = A\left(1 - e^{-kt}\right)$

     a. $20 = 300\left(1 - e^{-k(5)}\right)$

$$20 = 300 - 300e^{-5k}$$

$$300e^{-5k} = 280$$

$$e^{-5k} = \frac{14}{15}$$

$$\ln\left(e^{-5k}\right) = \ln\left(\frac{14}{15}\right)$$

$$-5k = \ln\left(\frac{14}{15}\right)$$

$$k = -\frac{\ln\left(\frac{14}{15}\right)}{5} \approx 0.014$$

     b. $L = 300\left(1 - e^{-0.014(20)}\right) \approx 73$

After 20 minutes, the student will have learned approximately 73 words.

$$260 = 300\left(1 - e^{-0.014t}\right)$$

$$\frac{13}{15} = 1 - e^{-0.014t}$$

$$-\frac{2}{15} = -e^{-0.014t}$$

$$\frac{2}{15} = e^{-0.014t}$$

$$\ln\left(\frac{2}{15}\right) = \ln\left(e^{-0.014t}\right)$$

$$\ln\left(\frac{2}{15}\right) = -0.014t$$

$$t = -\frac{\ln\left(\frac{2}{15}\right)}{0.014} \approx 144$$

It will take about 144 minutes.

Chapter 7

Section 7.1

Check Point Exercises

1. a.
$$2x = 3y = -4$$
$$2(1) - 3(2) = -4$$
$$2 - 6 = -4$$
$$-4 = -4 \text{ true}$$
$$2x + y = 4$$
$$2(1) + 2 = 4$$
$$2 + 2 = 4$$
$$4 = 4 \text{ true}$$
$(1, 2)$ is a solution of the system.

b.
$$2x = 3y = -4$$
$$2(7) - 3(6) = -4$$
$$14 - 18 = -4$$
$$-4 = -4 \text{ true}$$
$$2x + y = 4$$
$$2(7) + 6 = 4$$
$$14 + 6 = 4$$
$$20 = 4 \text{ false}$$
$(7, 6)$ is not a solution of the system.

2.
$$3x + 2y = 4$$
$$2x + y = 1$$
Solve $2x + y = 1$ for y.
$$2x + y = 1$$
$$y = 1 - 2x$$
Substitute $1 - 2x$ for y in the other equation and solve.
$$3x + 2\overbrace{(1 - 2x)}^{y} = 4$$
$$3x + 2 - 4x = 4$$
$$-x = 2$$
$$x = -2$$
Back-substitute the obtained value:
$$3x + 2y = 4$$
$$3(-2) + 2y = 4$$
$$-6 + 2y = 4$$
$$2y = 10$$
$$y = 5$$
Checking these values in both equations shows that $(-2, 5)$ is the solution of the system.

3. Rewrite one or both equations:
$$4x + 5y = 3 \xrightarrow{\text{No change}} 4x + 5y = 3$$
$$2x - 3y = 7 \xrightarrow{\text{Mult. by } -2} \underline{-4x + 6y = -14}$$
$$11y = -11$$
$$y = -1$$
Back-substitute into either equation:
$$4x + 5y = 3$$
$$4x + 5(-1) = 3$$
$$4x - 5 = 3$$
$$4x = 8$$
$$x = 2$$
Checking confirms the solution set is $\{(2, -1)\}$.

4. Rewrite both equations in the form $Ax + By = C$:
$$2x = 9 + 3y \rightarrow 2x - 3y = 9$$
$$4y = 8 - 3x \rightarrow 3x + 4y = 8$$
Rewrite with opposite coefficients, then add and solve:
$$2x - 3y = 9 \xrightarrow{\text{Mult. by } 4} 8x - 12y = 36$$
$$3x + 4y = 8 \xrightarrow{\text{Mult. by } 3} \underline{9x + 12y = 24}$$
$$17x = 60$$
$$x = \frac{60}{17}$$
Back-substitute into either equation:
$$4y = 8 - 3x$$
$$4y = 8 - 3\left(\frac{60}{17}\right)$$
$$4y = -\frac{44}{17}$$
$$y = -\frac{11}{17}$$
Checking confirms the solution is $\left(\frac{60}{17}, -\frac{11}{17}\right)$.

5. Rewrite with a pair of opposite coefficients, then add:

$$5x - 2y = 4 \xrightarrow{\text{Mult. by 2}} 10x - 4y = 8$$

$$-10x + 4y = 7 \xrightarrow{\text{No change}} \underline{-10x + 4y = 7}$$

$$0 = 15$$

The statement $0 = 15$ is false which indicates that the system has no solution. The solution set is the empty set, $\varnothing$.

6. Substitute $4y - 8$ for x in the other equation:

$$5\overbrace{(4y - 8)}^{x} - 20y = -40$$

$$20y - 40 - 20y = -40$$

$$-40 = -40$$

The statement $-40 = -40$ is true which indicates that the system has infinitely many solutions.

The solution set is $\{(x, y) \mid x = 4y - 8\}$ or

$\{(x, y) \mid 5x - 20y = -40\}$.

7. x = liters of 18% acid
y = liters of 45% acid

$$x + y = 12$$

$$0.18x + 0.45y = 0.36(12)$$

$$y = 12 - x$$

$$0.18x + 0.45(12 - x) = 4.32$$

$$0.18x + 5.4 - 0.45x = 4.32$$

$$-0.27x = -1.08$$

$$x = 4$$

$$y = 12 - 4 = 8$$

Mix 4 liters of 18% acid and 8 liters of 45% acid.

8. x = velocity of the boat
y = velocity of the current

Velocity	Time	Distance
$x + y$	2	$2(x + y)$
$x - y$	3	$3(x - y)$

$$2(x + y) = 84$$

$$3(x - y) = 84$$

$$x + y = 42$$

$$x - y = 29$$

$$2x = 70$$

$$x = 35$$

$$x + y = 42$$

$$35 + y = 42$$

$$y = 7$$

Velocity of the boat is 35 mph and the current is 7 mph.

9. **a.** $C(x) = 300,000 + 30x$

b. $R(x) = 80x$

c. $R(x) = C(x)$

$$80x = 300,000 + 30x$$

$$50x = 300,000$$

$$x = 6000$$

$$C(6000) = 300,000 + 30(6000) = 480,000$$

Break even point (6000, 480000)
The company will need to make 6000 pairs of shoes and earn \$480,000 to break even.

Exercise Set 7.1

1. $x + 3y = 11$
$2 + 3(3) = 11$
$2 + 9 = 11$
$11 = 11$ true
$x - 5y = -13$
$2 - 5(3) = -13$
$2 - 15 = -13$
$-13 = -13$ true
(2, 3) is a solution.

3.
$$2x + 3y = 17$$
$$2(2) + 3(5) = 17$$
$$4 + 15 = 17$$
$$19 = 17 \text{ false}$$
$(2, 5)$ is not a solution.

5. $x + y = 4$
$$y = 3x$$
Substitute the expression $3x$ for y in the first equation and solve for x.
$$x + 3x = 4$$
$$4x = 4$$
$$x = 1$$
Substitute 1 for x in the second equation.
$$y = 3(1) = 3$$
The solution set is $\{(1, 3)\}$.

7. $x + 3y = 8$
$$y = 2x - 9$$
Substitute the expression $2x - 9$ for y in the first equation and solve for x.
$$x + 3(2x - 9) = 8$$
$$x + 6x - 27 = 8$$
$$7x = 35$$
$$x = 5$$
Substitute 5 for x in the second equation.
$$y = 2(5) - 9 = 10 - 9 = 1$$
The solution set is $\{(5, 1)\}$.

9. $x = 4y - 2$
$$x = 6y + 8$$
Substitute the expression $4y - 2$ for x in the second equation and solve for y.
$$4y - 2 = 6y + 8$$
$$-10 = 2y$$
$$-5 = y$$
Substitute -5 for y in the equation $x = 4y - 2$.
$$x = 4(-5) - 2 = -22$$
The solution set is $\{(-22, -5)\}$.

11. $5x + 2y = 0$
$$x - 3y = 0$$
Solve the second equation for x.
$$x = 3y$$
Substitute the expression $3y$ for x in the first equation and solve for y.
$$5(3y) + 2y = 0$$
$$15y + 2y = 0$$
$$17y = 0$$
$$y = 0$$
Substitute 0 for y in the equation $x = 3y$
$$y = 3(0) = 0$$
The solution set is $\{(0, 0)\}$.

13. $2x + 5y = -4$
$$3x - y = 11$$
Solve the second equation for y.
$$-y = -3x + 11$$
$$y = 3x - 11$$
Substitute the expression $3x - 11$ for y in the first equation and solve for x.
$$2x + 5(3x - 11) = -4$$
$$2x + 15x - 55 = -4$$
$$17x = 51$$
$$x = 3$$
Substitute 3 for x in the equation $y = 3x - 11$.
$$y = 3(3) - 11 = 9 - 11 = -2$$
The solution set is $\{(3, -2)\}$.

15. $2x - 3y = 8 - 2x$
$$2x + 4y = x + 3y + 14$$
Solve the second equation for y.
$$y = -2x + 14$$
Substitute the expression $-2x + 14$ for y in the first equation and solve for x.
$$2x - 3(-2x + 14) = 8 - 2x$$
$$2x + 6x - 42 = 8 - 2x$$
$$8x - 42 = 8 - 2x$$
$$10x = 50$$
$$x = 5$$
Substitute 5 for x in the equation $y = -2x + 14$.
$$y = -2(5) + 14 = -10 + 14 = 4$$
The solution set is $\{(5, 4)\}$.

17. $y = \dfrac{1}{3}x + \dfrac{2}{3}$

       $y = \dfrac{5}{7}x - 2$

Substitute the expression $y = \dfrac{1}{3}x + \dfrac{2}{3}$ for y in the second equation and solve for x.
$$\frac{1}{3}x + \frac{2}{3} = \frac{5}{7}x - 2$$
$$7x + 14 = 15x - 42$$
$$56 = 8x$$
$$7 = x$$
Substitute 7 for x in the equation $y = \dfrac{1}{3}x + \dfrac{2}{3}$ and solve for y.
$$y = \frac{1}{3}(7) + \frac{2}{3} = \frac{7}{3} + \frac{2}{3} = \frac{9}{3} = 3$$
The solution set is $\{(7, 3)\}$.

19. Eliminate y by adding the equations.

$$x + y = 1$$
$$\underline{x - y = 3}$$
$$2x = 4$$
$$x = 2$$

Substitute 2 for x in the first equation.

$$2 + y = 1$$
$$y = -1$$

The solution set is $\{(2, -1)\}$.

21. Eliminate y by adding the equations.

$$2x + 3y = 6$$
$$\underline{2x - 3y = 6}$$
$$4x = 12$$
$$x = 3$$

Substitute 3 for x in the first equation.

$$2(3) + 3y = 6$$
$$6 + 3y = 6$$
$$3y = 0$$
$$y = 0$$

The solution set is $\{(3, 0)\}$.

23.

$$x + 2y = 2$$
$$-4x + 3y = 25$$

Eliminate x by multiplying the first equation by 4 and adding the resulting equations.

$$4x + 8y = 8$$
$$\underline{-4x + 3y = 25}$$
$$11y = 33$$
$$y = 3$$

Substitute 3 for y in the first equation.

$$x + 2(3) = 2$$
$$x + 6 = 2$$
$$x = -4$$

The solution set is $\{(-4, 3)\}$.

25.

$$4x + 3y = 15$$
$$2x - 5y = 1$$

Eliminate x by multiplying the second equation by -2 and adding the resulting equations.

$$4x + 3y = 15$$
$$\underline{-4x + 10y = -2}$$
$$13y = 13$$
$$y = 1$$

Substitute 1 for y in the second equation.

$$2x - 5(1) = 1$$
$$2x = 6$$
$$x = 3$$

The solution set is $\{(3, 1)\}$.

27.

$$3x - 4y = 11$$
$$2x + 3y = -4$$

Eliminate x by multiplying the first equation by 2 and the second equation by -3. Add the resulting equations.

$$6x - 8y = 22$$
$$\underline{-6x - 9y = 12}$$
$$-17y = 34$$
$$y = -2$$

Substitute -2 for y in the second equation.

$$2x + 3(-2) = -4$$
$$2x - 6 = -4$$
$$2x = 2$$
$$x = 1$$

The solution set is $\{(1, -2)\}$.

29.

$$3x = 4y + 1$$
$$3y = 1 - 4x$$

Arrange the system so that variable terms appear on the left and constants appear on the right.

$$3x - 4y = 1$$
$$4x + 3y = 1$$

Eliminate y by multiplying the first equation by 3 and the second equation by 4. Add the resulting equations.

$$9x - 12y = 3$$
$$\underline{16x + 12y = 4}$$
$$25x = 7$$
$$x = \frac{7}{25}$$

Substitute $\frac{7}{25}$ for x in the second equation.

$$3y = 1 - 4\left(\frac{7}{25}\right)$$
$$3y = \frac{-3}{25}$$
$$y = \frac{-1}{25}$$

The solution set is $\left\{\left(\frac{7}{25}, -\frac{1}{25}\right)\right\}$.

31. The substitution method is used here to solve the system.
$$x = 9 - 2y$$
$$x + 2y = 13$$
Substitute the expression $9 - 2y$ for x in the second equation and solve for y.
$$9 - 2y + 2y = 13$$
$$9 = 13$$
The false statement $9 = 13$ indicates that the system has no solution.
The solution set is the empty set, $\varnothing$.

33. The substitution method is used here to solve the system.
$$y = 3x - 5$$
$$21x - 35 = 7y$$
Substitute the expression $3x - 5$ for y in the second equation and solve for x.
$$21x - 35 = 7(3x - 5)$$
$$21x - 35 = 21x - 35$$
$$-35 = -35$$
This true statement indicates that the system has infinitely many solutions.
The solution set is $\left\{ (x, y) \mid y = 3x - 5 \right\}$

35. The elimination method is used here to solve the system.
$$3x - 2y = -5$$
$$4x + y = 8$$
Eliminate y by multiplying the second equation by 2 and adding the resulting equations.
$$3x - 2y = -5$$
$$\underline{8x + 2y = 16}$$
$$11x = 11$$
$$x = 1$$
Substitute 1 for x in the second equation.
$$4(1) + y = 8$$
$$y = 4$$
The solution set is $\{(1, 4)\}$.

37. The elimination method is used here to solve the system.
$$x + 3y = 2$$
$$3x + 9y = 6$$
Eliminate x by multiplying the first equation by -3 and adding the resulting equations.
$$-3x - 9y = -6$$
$$\underline{3x + 9y = 6}$$
$$0 = 0$$
This true statement indicates that the system has infinitely many solutions.
The solution set is $\left\{ (x, y) \mid x + 3y = 2 \right\}$.

39. First multiply each term in the first equation by 4 to eliminate the fractions.
$$\frac{x}{4} - \frac{y}{4} = -1$$
$$x - y = -4$$
Multiply the first equation by -1 and add to the second equation and solve for y.
$$-x + y = 4$$
$$\underline{x + 4y = -9}$$
$$5y = -5$$
$$y = -1$$
Substitute -1 for y in the equation $x - y = -4$ and solve for x.
$$x - (-1) = -4$$
$$x + 1 = -4$$
$$x = -5$$
The solution set is $\{(-5, -1)\}$.

41. Rearrange the equations to get in the standard form.
$$2x - 3y = 4$$
$$4x + 5y = 3$$
Multiply the first equation by -2 and add to the second equation. Solve for y.
$$-4x + 6y = -8$$
$$\underline{4x + 5y = 3}$$
$$11y = -5$$
$$y = -\frac{5}{11}$$

Multiply the first equation by 5 and the second equation by 3 and add the equations. Solve for x.

$$10x - 15y = 20$$
$$12x + 15y = 9$$
$$22x = 29$$
$$x = \frac{29}{22}$$

The solution set is $\left\{ \left(\frac{29}{22}, -\frac{5}{11} \right) \right\}$.

43. Add the equations to eliminate y.

$$x + y = 7$$
$$\underline{x - y = -1}$$
$$2x = 6$$
$$x = 3$$

Substitute 3 for x in the first equation.

$$3 + y = 7$$
$$y = 4$$

The numbers are 3 and 4.

45. $3x - y = 1$
       $x + 2y = 12$

Eliminate y by multiplying the first equation by 2 and adding the resulting equations.

$$6x - 2y = 2$$
$$\underline{x + 2y = 12}$$
$$7x = 14$$
$$x = 2$$

Substitute 2 for x in the first equation.

$$3(2) - y = 1$$
$$6 - y = 1$$
$$-y = -5$$
$$y = 5$$

The numbers are 2 and 5.

47. $\dfrac{x+2}{2} - \dfrac{y+4}{3} = 3$

       $\dfrac{x+y}{5} = \dfrac{x-y}{2} - \dfrac{5}{2}$

Start by multiplying each equation by its LCD and simplifying to clear the fractions.

$$\frac{x+2}{2} - \frac{y+4}{3} = 3$$

$$\frac{x+y}{5} = \frac{x-y}{2} - \frac{5}{2}$$

Start by multiplying each equation by its LCD and simplifying to clear the fractions.

$$6\left(\frac{x+2}{2} - \frac{y+4}{3} \right) = 6(3)$$
$$3(x+2) - 2(y+4) = 18$$
$$3x + 6 - 2y - 8 = 18$$
$$3x - 2y = 20$$

$$10\left(\frac{x+y}{5} \right) = 10\left(\frac{x-y}{2} - \frac{5}{2} \right)$$
$$2(x+y) = 5(x-y) - 5(5)$$
$$2x + 2y = 5x - 5y - 25$$
$$3x - 7y = 25$$

We now need to solve the equivalent system of equations:

$$3x - 2y = 20$$
$$3x - 7y = 25$$

Subtract the two equations:

$$3x - 2y = 20$$
$$\underline{-(3x - 7y = 25)}$$
$$5y = -5$$
$$y = -1$$

Back-substitute this value for y and solve for x.

$$3x - 2y = 20$$
$$3x - 2(-1) = 20$$
$$3x + 2 = 20$$
$$3x = 18$$
$$x = 6$$

The solution is $(6, -1)$.

49. $5ax + 4y = 17$
       $ax + 7y = 22$

Multiply the second equation by -5 and add the equations.

$$5ax + 4y = 17$$
$$\underline{-5ax - 35y = -110}$$
$$-31y = -93$$
$$y = 3$$

Back-substitute into one of the original equations to solve for x.

$$ax + 7y = 22$$
$$ax + 7(3) = 22$$
$$ax + 21 = 22$$
$$ax = 1$$
$$x = \frac{1}{a}$$

The solution is $\left(\frac{1}{a}, 3 \right)$.

51. $f(-2) = 11 \rightarrow -2m + b = 11$

$f(3) = -9 \rightarrow 3m + b = -9$

We need to solve the resulting system of equations:

$-2m + b = 11$

$3m + b = -9$

Subtract the two equations:

$-2m + b = 11$

$\underline{3m + b = -9}$

$-5m = 20$

$m = -4$

Back-substitute into one of the original equations to solve for b.

$-2m + b = 11$

$-2(-4) + b = 11$

$8 + b = 11$

$b = 3$

Therefore, $m = -4$ and $b = 3$.

53. The solution to a system of linear equations is the point of intersection of the graphs of the equations in the system. If $(6, 2)$ is a solution, then we need to find the lines that intersect at that point.
Looking at the graph, we see that the graphs of $x + 3y = 12$ and $x - y = 4$ intersect at the point $(6, 2)$. Therefore, the desired system of equations is

$x + 3y = 12$ or $y = -\dfrac{1}{3}x + 4$

$x - y = 4$ $y = x - 4$

55. Let x = gallons of 5% wine.
Let y = gallons of 9% wine.

$x + y = 200$

$0.05x + 0.09y = 0.07(200)$

or

$x + y = 200$

$0.05x + 0.09y = 14$

Solve the first equation for x.

$x + y = 200$

$x = 200 - y$

Substitute this expression for x in the second equation.

$0.05(200 - y) + 0.09y = 14$

$10 - 0.05y + 0.09y = 14$

$0.04y = 4$

$y = 100$

Back-substitute and solve for x.

$x = 200 - y$

$= 200 - 100$

$= 100$

The wine company should mix 100 gallons of the 5% California wine with 100 gallons of the 9% French wine.

57. Let x = grams of 18-karat gold.
Let y = grams of 12-karat gold.

$x + y = 300$

$0.75x + 0.5y = 0.58(300)$

or

$x + y = 300$

$0.75x + 0.5y = 174$

Solve the first equation for x.

$x = 300 - y$

Substitute this result for x into the second equation and solve for y.

$0.75(300 - y) + 0.5y = 174$

$225 - 0.75 + 0.5y = 174$

$-0.25y = -51$

$y = 204$

Back-substitute to solve for x.

$x = 300 - y = 300 - 204 = 96$

You would need 96 grams of 18-karat gold and 204 grams of 12-karat gold.

59. Let x = pounds of cheaper candy.
Let y = pounds of more expensive candy.

$x + y = 75$

$1.6x + 2.1y = 1.9(75)$

or

$x + y = 75$

$1.6x + 2.1y = 142.5$

Multiply the first equation by -1.6 and add the two equations.

$-1.6x - 1.6y = -120$

$\underline{1.6x + 2.1y = 142.5}$

$0.5y = 22.5$

$y = 45$

Back-substitute to solve for x.

$x + 45 = 75$

$x = 30$

The manager should mix 30 pounds of the cheaper candy and 45 pounds of the more expensive candy.

61. x = velocity of the plane
y = velocity of the wind

Velocity	Time	Distance
$x + y$	5	$5(x + y)$
$x - y$	8	$8(x - y)$

$5(x + y) = 800 \rightarrow x + y = 160$
$8(x - y) = 800 \rightarrow x - y = 100$
$$\overline{\quad 2x = 260}$$
$$x = 130$$

$x + y = 160$
$130 + y = 160$
$y = 30$

Velocity of the plane is 130 mph and the wind is 30 mph.

63. x = velocity of the boat
y = velocity of the current

Velocity	Time	Distance
$x + y$	2	$2(x + y)$
$x - y$	4	$4(x - y)$

$2(x + y) = 16 \rightarrow x + y = 8$
$4(x - y) = 16 \rightarrow x - y = 4$
$$\overline{\quad 2x = 12}$$
$$x = 6$$

$x + y = 8$
$6 + y = 8$
$y = 2$

Velocity of the boat is 6 mph and the current is 2 mph.

65. x = velocity of the boat
y = velocity of the current

Velocity	Time	Distance
$x + y$	4	$4(x + y)$
$x - y$	6	$6(x - y)$

$4(x + y) = 24 \rightarrow x + y = 6$
$6(x - y) = \frac{3}{4}(24) \rightarrow x - y = 3$
$$\overline{\quad 2x = 9}$$
$$x = 4.5$$

$x + y = 6$
$4.5 + y = 6$
$y = 1.5$

Velocity of the boat is 4.5 mph and the current is 1.5 mph.

67. At the break-even point, $R(x) = C(x)$.
$$10000 + 30x = 50x$$
$$10000 = 20x$$
$$10000 = 20x$$
$$500 = x$$
Five hundred radios must be produced and sold to break-even.

69. $R(x) = 50x$
$R(200) = 50(200) = 10000$
$C(x) = 10000 + 30x$
$C(200) = 10000 + 30(200)$
$\qquad = 10000 + 6000 = 16000$
$R(200) - C(200) = 10000 - 16000$
$$= -6000$$
This means that if 200 radios are produced and sold the company will lose $6,000.

71. a. $P(x) = R(x) - C(x)$
$\qquad = 50x - (10000 + 30x)$
$\qquad = 50x - 10000 - 30x$
$\qquad = 20x - 10000$
$\qquad P(x) = 20x - 10000$

b. $P(10000) = 20(10000) - 10000$
$\qquad\qquad = 200000 - 10000 = 190000$
If 10,0000 radios are produced and sold the profit will be $190,000.

73. a. The cost function is:
$\qquad C(x) = 18,000 + 20x$

b. The revenue function is:
$\qquad R(x) = 80x$

c. At the break-even point, $R(x) = C(x)$.
$\qquad 80x = 18000 + 20x$
$\qquad 60x = 18000$
$\qquad x = 300$
$\qquad R(x) = 80x$
$\qquad R(300) = 80(300)$
$\qquad\qquad = 24,000$
When approximately 300 canoes are produced the company will break-even with cost and revenue at $24,000.

75.   **a.**   The cost function is:
$$C(x) = 30000 + 2500x$$

     b.   The revenue function is: $R(x) = 3125x$

     c.   At the break-even point, $R(x) = C(x)$.
$$3125x = 30000 + 2500x$$
$$625x = 30000$$
$$x = 48$$
After 48 sold out performances, the investor will break-even. ($150,000)

77.   **a.** $N_d = -5p + 750$
$$= -5(120) + 750$$
$$= -600 + 750$$
$$= 150$$
$$N_s = 2.5(120) = 300$$
If the price of the televisions is $120, 150 sets can be sold and 300 sets can be supplied.

     b.   To find the price at which supply and demand are equal, we set the two equations equal to each other and solve for p.
$$-5p + 750 = 2.5p$$
$$750 = 7.5p$$
$$\frac{750}{7.5} = p$$
$$100 = p$$
$$N = 2.5(100) = 250.$$
Supply and demand will be equal if the price of the televisions is $100. At that price, 250 sets can be supplied and sold.

79.   Solve $-x + y = 16$ for y
$$-x + y = 16$$
$$y = x + 16$$
Substitute for y in the other equation:
$$13x + 12\overbrace{(x+16)}^{y} = 992$$
$$13x + 12x + 192 = 992$$
$$25x = 800$$
$$x = 32$$
Substitute $x = 32$ into either equation to find y.
$$y = x + 16$$
$$y = 32 + 16$$
$$y = 48$$
The percentages will both be 48% 32 years after 1988, or 2020.

81.   **a.** $y = 0.04x + 5.48$

     b. $y = 0.17x + 1.84$

     c.   To find the year when the costs will be the same, we set the two equations equal to each other and solve for x.
$$0.04x + 5.48 = 0.17x + 1.84$$
$$-0.13x = -3.64$$
$$x = 28$$
The costs will be the same 28 years after 2000, or 2028.
$$y = 0.17x + 1.84$$
$$y = 0.17(28) + 1.84$$
$$y = 6.6$$
The cost of each program in 2028 will be 6.6% of the GDP. After that year, Medicare will have the greater cost.

83.   **a.** $m = \dfrac{25.3 - 38}{17 - 0} = \dfrac{-12.7}{17} \approx -0.75$
From the point $(0, 38)$ we have that the y-intercept is $b = 38$. Therefore, the equation of the line is $y = -0.75x + 38$.

     b. $m = \dfrac{23 - 40}{17 - 0} = \dfrac{-17}{17} = -1$
From the point $(0, 40)$ we have that the y-intercept is $b = 40$. Therefore, the equation of the line is $y = -x + 40$.

     c.   To find the year when cigarette use is the same, we set the two equations equal to each other and solve for x.
$$-0.75x + 38 = -x + 40$$
$$0.25x + 38 = 40$$
$$0.25x = 2$$
$$x = \frac{2}{0.25} = 8$$
$$y = -(8) + 40 = 32$$
Cigarette use was the same for African Americans and Hispanics in 1993 (8 years after 1985). At that time, 32% of each group used cigarettes.

85. $x + 2y = 1980$

$\quad\quad 2x + y = 2670$

Multiply the first equation by –2 and add to the second equation. Solve for y.

$-2x - 4y = -3960$

$\quad\ 2x + y = 2670$

$\quad\quad -3y = -1290$

$\quad\quad\quad y = 430$

Substitute 430 for y in the second equation and solve for x.

$2x + 430 = 2670$

$\quad\quad 2x = 2240$

$\quad\quad\ x = 1120$

There are 1120 calories in a pan pizza and 430 calories in a beef burrito.

87. $x + y = 300 + 241$ or $x + y = 541$

$\quad\quad 2x + 3y = 1257$

Multiply the first equation by -2 and add to the second equation. Solve for y.

$-2x - 2y = -1082$

$\quad\ 2x + 3y = 1257$

$\quad\quad\quad y = 175$

Substitute 175 for y in the first equation and solve for x.

$x + 175 = 541$

$\quad\quad x = 366$

There are 366 mg in scrambled eggs and 175 mg in a Double Beef Whooper.

89. $\quad\quad x + y = 200$

$\quad 100x + 80y = 17000$

Multiply the first equation by –100 and add to the second equation. Solve for y.

$-100x - 100y = -20000$

$\quad 100x + 80y = 17000$

$\quad\quad\quad -20y = -3000$

$\quad\quad\quad\quad\ y = 150$

Substitute 150 for y in the first equation and solve for x.

$x + 150 = 200$

$\quad\quad x = 50$

There are 50 rooms with kitchenettes and 150 rooms without.

91. $\quad\quad 2x + 2y = 360$

$\quad 20x + 8(2y) = 3280$

Multiply the first equation by −10 and add to the second equation. Solve for y.

$-20x - 20y = -3600$

$\quad 20x + 16y = 3280$

$\quad\quad\quad -4y = -320$

$\quad\quad\quad\quad y = 80$

Substitute 80 for y in the first equation and solve for x.

$2x + 2(80) = 360$

$\quad 2x + 160 = 360$

$\quad\quad\quad 2x = 200$

$\quad\quad\quad\ x = 100$

The lot is 100 feet long and 80 feet wide.

93. $\quad\quad x + 2y = 180$

$\quad (2x - 30) + y = 180$

Rewrite the second equation in standard form.

$x + 2y = 180$

$2x + y = 210$

Multiply the first equation by −2 and add the equations.

$-2x - 4y = -360$

$\underline{\quad 2x + y = 210\quad}$

$\quad\quad -3y = -150$

$\quad\quad\quad y = 50$

Back-substitute to solve for x.

$\quad x + 2y = 180$

$x + 2(50) = 180$

$\quad x + 100 = 180$

$\quad\quad\quad x = 80$

The three interior angles measure 80°, 50°, and 50°.

107. x = first lucky number
y = second lucky number
$3x + 6y = 12$
$x + 2y = 5$
Eliminate x by multiplying the second equation by -3 and adding the resulting equations.

$$3x + 6y = 12$$
$$\underline{-3x - 6y = -15}$$
$$0 = -3$$

The false statement $0 = -3$ indicates that the system has no solution. Therefore, the twin who always lies is talking.

Section 7.2

Check Point Exercises

1.
$$x - 2y + 3z = 22$$
$$-1 - 2(-4) + 3(5) = 22$$
$$-1 + 8 + 15 = 22$$
$$22 = 22 \text{ true}$$
$$2x - 3y - z = 5$$
$$2(-1) - 3(-4) - 5 = 5$$
$$-2 + 12 - 5 = 5$$
$$5 = 5 \text{ true}$$
$$3x + y - 5z = -32$$
$$3(-1) - 4 - 5(5) = -32$$
$$-3 - 4 - 25 = -32$$
$$-32 = -32 \text{ true}$$
$(-1, -4, 5)$ is a solution of the system.

2.
$$x + 4y - z = 20$$
$$3x + 2y + z = 8$$
$$2x - 3y + 2z = -16$$
Eliminate z from Equations 1 and 2 by adding Equation 1 and Equation 2.
$$x + 4y - z = 20$$
$$\underline{3x + 2y + z = 8}$$
$$4x + 6y = 28 \text{ Equation 4}$$
Eliminate z from Equations 2 and 3 by multiplying Equation 2 by -2 and adding the resulting equation to Equation 3.
$$-6x - 4y - 2z = -16$$
$$\underline{2x - 3y + 2z = -16}$$
$$-4x - 7y = -32 \text{ Equation 5}$$
Solve Equations 4 and 5 for x and y by adding Equation 4 and Equation 5.

$$4x + 6y = 28$$
$$\underline{-4x - 7y = -32}$$
$$-y = -4$$
$$y = 4$$
Substitute 4 for y in Equation 4 and solve for x.
$$4x + 6(4) = 28$$
$$4x + 24 = 28$$
$$4x = 4$$
$$x = 1$$
Substitute 1 for x and 4 for y in Equation 2 and solve for z.
$$3(1) + 2(4) + z = 8$$
$$3 + 8 + z = 8$$
$$11 + z = 8$$
$$z = -3$$
The solution set is $\{(1, 4, -3)\}$.

3.
$$2y - z = 7$$
$$x + 2y + z = 17$$
$$2x - 3y + 2z = -1$$
Eliminate x and z from Equations 2 and 3 by multiplying Equation 2 by -2 and adding the resulting equation to Equation 3.
$$-2x - 4y - 2z = -34$$
$$\underline{2x - 3y + 2z = -1}$$
$$-7y = -35$$
$$y = 5$$
Substitute 5 for y in Equation 1 and solve for z.
$$2(5) - z = 7$$
$$10 - z = 7$$
$$-z = -3$$
$$z = 3$$
Substitute 5 for y and 3 for z in Equation 2 and solve for x.
$$x + 2(5) + 3 = 17$$
$$x + 10 + 3 = 17$$
$$x + 13 = 17$$
$$x = 4$$
The solution set is $\{(4, 5, 3)\}$.

4. $(1, 4), (2, 1), (3, 4)$

$y = ax^2 + bx + c$

Substitute 1 for x and 4 for y in

$y = ax^2 + bx + c$.

$4 = a(1)^2 + b(1) + c$

$4 = a + b + c$ Equation 1

Substitute 2 for x and 1 for y in

$y = ax^2 + bx + c$.

$1 = a(2)^2 + b(2) + c$

$1 = 4a + 2b + c$ Equation 2

Substitute 3 for x and 4 for y in

$y = ax^2 + bx + c$.

$4 = a(3)^2 + b(3) + c$

$4 = 9a + 3b + c$ Equation 3

Eliminate c from Equations 1 and 2 by multiplying Equation 2 by -1 and adding the resulting equation to Equation 1.

$4 = a + b + c$

$\underline{-1 = -4a - 2b - c}$

$3 = -3a - b$ Equation 4

Eliminate c from Equation 2 and 3 by multiplying Equation 3 by -1 and adding the resulting equation to Equation 2.

$1 = 4a + 2b + c$

$\underline{-4 = -9a - 3b - c}$

$-3 = -5a - b$ Equation 5

Solve Equations 4 and 5 for a and b by multiplying Equation 5 by -1 and adding the resulting equation to Equation 4.

$3 = -3a - b$

$\underline{3 = 5a + b}$

$6 = 2a$

$a = 3$

Substitute 3 for a in Equation 4 and solve for b.

$3 = -3(3) - b$

$3 = -9 - b$

$12 = -b$

$b = -12$

Substitute 3 for a and -12 for b in Equation 1 and solve for c.

$4 = 3 - 12 + c$

$4 = -9 + c$

$c = 13$

Substituting 3 for a, -12 for b, and 13 for c in the quadratic equation $y = ax^2 + bx + c$ gives

$y = 3x^2 - 12x + 13$.

Exercise Set 7.2

1. $x + y + z = 4$

$2 - 1 + 3 = 4$

$4 = 4$ true

$x - 2y - z = 1$

$2(2) - 2(-1) - 3 = 1$

$4 + 2 - 3 = 1$

$1 = 1$ true

$2x - y - 2z = -1$

$2(2) - (-1) - 2(3) = -1$

$4 + 1 - 6 = -1$

$-1 = -1$ false

$(2, -1, 3)$ is a solution.

3. $x - 2y = 2$

$4 - 2(1) = 2$

$4 - 2 = 2$

$2 = 2$ true

$2x + 3y = 11$

$2(4) + 3(1) = 11$

$8 + 3 = 11$

$11 = 11$ true

$y - 4z = -7$

$1 - 4(2) = -7$

$1 - 8 = -7$

$-7 = -7$ true

$(4, 1, 2)$ is a solution.

5. $x + y + 2z = 11$

$x + y + 3z = 14$

$x + 2y - z = 5$

Eliminate x and y from Equations 1 and 2 by multiplying Equation 2 by -1 and adding the resulting equation to Equation 1.

$-x - y - 3z = -14$

$\underline{x + y + 2z = 11}$

$-z = -3$

$z = 3$

Substitute 3 for z in Equations 1 and 3.

$x + y + 2(3) = 11$

$x + 2y - (3) = 5$

Simplify:

$x + y = 5$ Equation 4

$x + 2y = 8$ Equation 5

Solve Equations 4 and 5 for x and y by multiplying Equation 5 by -1 and adding the resulting equation to Equation 4.

$$x + y = 5$$
$$\underline{-x - 2y = -8}$$
$$-y = -3$$
$$y = 3$$

Substitute 3 for z and 3 for y in Equation 2 and solve for x.
$$x + 3 + 3(3) = 14$$
$$x + 12 = 14$$
$$x = 2$$
The solution set is $\{(2, 3, 3)\}$.

7.
$$4x - y + 2z = 11$$
$$x + 2y - z = -1$$
$$2x + 2y - 3z = -1$$

Eliminate y from Equation 1 and 2 by multiplying Equation 1 by 2 and adding the resulting equation to Equation 2 and 3.
$$8x - 2y + 4z = 22$$
$$\underline{x + 2y - z = -1}$$
$$9x + 3z = 21 \quad \text{Equation 4}$$

Eliminate y from Equations 1 and 3 by multiplying Equation 1 by 2 and adding the resulting equation to Equation 3.
$$8x - 2y + 4z = 22$$
$$\underline{2x + 2y - 3z = -1}$$
$$10x + z = 21 \quad \text{Equation 5}$$

Solve Equations 4 and 5 for x and z by multiplying Equation 5 by -3 and adding the resulting equation to Equation 4.
$$9x + 3z = 21$$
$$\underline{-30x - 3z = -63}$$
$$-21x = -42$$
$$x = 2$$

Substitute 2 for x in Equation 5 and solve for z. $10(2) + z = 21$
$$20 + z = 21$$
$$z = 1$$

Substitute 2 for x and 1 for z in Equation 2 and solve for y.
$$2 + 2y - 1 = -1$$
$$2y + 1 = -1$$
$$2y = -2$$
$$y = -1$$
The solution set is $\{(2, -1, 1)\}$.

9.
$$3x + 2y - 3z = -2$$
$$2x - 5y + 2z = -2$$
$$4x - 3y + 4z = 10$$

Eliminate z from Equations 1 and 2 by multiplying Equation 1 by 2 and Equation 2 by 3. Add the resulting equations.
$$6x + 4y - 6z = -4$$
$$\underline{6x - 15y + 6z = -6}$$
$$12x - 11y = -10 \quad \text{Equation 4}$$

Eliminate z from Equations 2 and 3 by multiplying Equation 2 by -2.
$$-4x + 10y - 4z = 4$$
$$\underline{4x - 3y + 4z = 10}$$
$$7y = 14 \quad \text{Equation 5}$$
Solve Equation 5 for y
$$7y = 14$$
$$y = 2$$

Solve for x by substituting 7 for y in Equation 4.
$$12x - 11y = -10$$
$$12x - 11(2) = -10$$
$$12x - 22 = -10$$
$$12x = 12$$
$$x = 1$$

Substitute 2 for y and 1 for x in Equation 2 and solve for z.
$$2x - 5y + 2z = -2$$
$$2(1) - 5(2) + 2z = -2$$
$$2 - 10 + 2z = -2$$
$$2z = 6$$
$$z = 3$$
The solution set is $\{(1, 2, 3)\}$.

11.
$$2x - 4y + 3z = 17$$
$$x + 2y - z = 0$$
$$4x - y - z = 6$$

Eliminate z from Equations 1 and 2 by multiplying Equation 2 by 3 and adding the resulting equation to Equation 1.
$$2x - 4y + 3z = 17$$
$$\underline{3x + 6y - 3z = 0}$$
$$5x + 2y = 17 \quad \text{Equation 4}$$

Eliminate z from Equations 2 and 3 by multiplying Equation 2 by -1 and adding the resulting equation to Equation 3.
$$-x - 2y + z = 0$$
$$\underline{4x - y - z = 6}$$
$$3x - 3y = 6 \quad \text{Equation 5}$$

Solve Equations 4 and 5 for x and y by multiplying Equation 5 by $\dfrac{2}{3}$ and adding the resulting equation to Equation 4.

$$5x + 2y = 17$$
$$\underline{2x - 2y = 4}$$
$$7x = 21$$
$$x = 3$$

Substitute 3 for x in Equation 4 and solve for y.

$$5(3) + 2y = 17$$
$$15 + 2y = 17$$
$$2y = 2$$
$$y = 1$$

Substitute 3 for x and 1 for y in Equation 2 and solve for z.

$$3 + 2(1) - z = 0$$
$$3 + 2 - z = 0$$
$$5 - z = 0$$
$$5 = z$$

The solution set is $\{(3, 1, 5)\}$.

13.
$$2x + y = 2$$
$$x + y - z = 4$$
$$3x + 2y + z = 0$$

Eliminate z from Equations 2 and 3 by adding Equation 2 and Equation 3.

$$x + y - z = 4$$
$$\underline{3x + 2y + z = 0}$$
$$4x + 3y = 4 \quad \text{Equation 4}$$

Solve Equations 1 and 4 for x and y by multiplying Equation 1 by -3 and adding the resulting equation to Equation 4.

$$-6x - 3y = -6$$
$$\underline{4x + 3y = 4}$$
$$-2x = -2$$
$$x = 1$$

Substitute 1 for x in Equation 1 and solve for y.

$$2(1) + y = 2$$
$$2 + y = 2$$
$$y = 0$$

Substitute 1 for x and 0 for y in Equation 2 and solve for z.

$$1 + 0 - z = 4$$
$$1 - z = 4$$
$$-z = 3$$
$$z = -3$$

The solution set is $\{(1, 0, -3)\}$.

15.
$$x + y = -4$$
$$y - z = 1$$
$$2x + y + 3z = -21$$

Eliminate y from Equations 1 and 2 by multiplying Equation 1 by -1 and adding the resulting equation to Equation 2.

$$-x - y = 4$$
$$\underline{y - z = 1}$$
$$-x - z = 5 \quad \text{Equation 4}$$

Eliminate y from Equations 2 and 3 by multiplying Equation 2 by -1 and adding the resulting equation to Equation 3.

$$-y + z = -1$$
$$\underline{2x + y + 3z = -21}$$
$$2x + 4z = -22 \quad \text{Equation 5}$$

Solve Equations 4 and 5 for x and z by multiplying Equation 4 by 2 and adding the resulting equation to Equation 5.

$$-2x - 2z = 10$$
$$\underline{2x + 4z = -22}$$
$$2z = -12$$
$$z = -6$$

Substitute -6 for z in Equation 2 and solve for y.

$$y - (-6) = 1$$
$$y + 6 = 1$$
$$y = -5$$

Substitute -5 for y in Equation 1 and solve for x

$$x + (-5) = -4$$
$$x = 1$$

The solution set is $\{(1, -5, -6)\}$.

17.
$$3(2x + y) + 5z = -1$$
$$2(x - 3y + 4z) = -9$$
$$4(1 + x) = -3(z - 3y)$$

Simplify each equation.

$$6x + 3y + 5z = -1 \quad \text{Equation 4}$$
$$2x - 6y + 8z = -9 \quad \text{Equation 5}$$
$$4 + 4x = -3z + 9y$$
$$4x - 9y + 3z = -4 \quad \text{Equation 6}$$

Eliminate x from Equations 4 and 5 by multiplying Equation 5 by -3 and adding the resulting equation to Equation 4.

$$-6x + 3y + 5z = -1$$
$$\underline{-6x + 18y - 24z = 27}$$
$$21y - 19z = 26 \quad \text{Equation 7}$$

Eliminate x from Equations 5 and 6 by multiplying Equation 5 by -2 and adding the resulting equation to Equation 6.

$-4x + 12y - 16z = 18$

$\underline{4x - 9y + 3z = -4}$

$3y - 13z = 14$ Equation 8

Solve Equations 7 and 8 for y and z by multiplying Equation 8 by -7 and adding the resulting equation to Equation 7.

$21y - 19z = 26$

$\underline{-21y + 91z = -98}$

$72z = -72$

$z = -1$

Substitute -1 for z in Equation 8 and solve for y.

$3y - 13(-1) = 14$

$3y + 13 = 14$

$3y = 1$

$y = \dfrac{1}{3}$

Substitute $\dfrac{1}{3}$ for y and -1 for z in Equation 5 and solve for x.

$2x - 6\left(\dfrac{1}{3}\right) + 8(-1) = -9$

$2x - 2 - 8 = -9$

$2x - 10 = -9$

$2x = 1$

$x = \dfrac{1}{2}$

The solution set is $\left\{\left(\dfrac{1}{2}, \dfrac{1}{3}, -1\right)\right\}$.

19. $(-1, 6),\ (1, 4),\ (2, 9)$

$y = ax^2 + bx + c$

Substitute -1 for x and 6 for y in

$y = ax^2 + bx + c$.

$6 = a(-1)^2 + b(-1) + c$

$6 = a - b + c$ Equation 1

Substitute 1 for x and 4 for y in $y = ax^2 + bx + c$.

$4 = a(1)^2 + b(1) + c$

$4 = a + b + c$ Equation 2

Substitute 2 for x and 9 for y in

$y = ax^2 + bx + c$.

$9 = a(2)^2 + b(2) + c$

$9 = 4a + 2b + c$ Equation 3

Eliminate b from Equations 1 and 2 by adding Equation 1 and Equation 2.

$6 = a - b + c$

$\underline{4 = a + b + c}$

$10 = 2a + 2c$ Equation 4

Eliminate b from Equations 1 and 3 by multiplying Equation 1 by 2 and adding the resulting equation to Equation 3.

$12 = 2a - 2b + 2c$

$\underline{9 = 4a + 2b + c}$

$21 = 6a + 3c$ Equation 5

Solve Equations 4 and 5 for a and c by multiplying Equation 4 by -3 and adding the resulting equation to Equation 5.

$-30 = -6a - 6c$

$\underline{21 = 6a + 3c}$

$-9 = -3c$

$c = 3$

Substitute 3 for c in Equation 4 and solve for a.

$10 = 2a + 2(3)$

$10 = 2a + 6$

$4 = 2a$

$a = 2$

Substitute 2 for a and 3 for c in Equation 2 and solve for b.

$4 = 2 + b + 3$

$4 = b + 5$

$b = -1$

Substituting 2 for a, -1 for b, and 3 for c in the quadratic equation $y = ax^2 + bx + c$ gives

$y = 2x^2 - x + 3$.

21. $(-1, -4),\ (1, -2),\ (2, 5)$

Substitute -1 for x and -4 for y in

$y = ax^2 + bx + c$.

$-4 = a(-1)^2 + b(-1) + c$

$-4 = a - b + c$ Equation 1

Substitute 1 for x and -2 for y in

$y = ax^2 + bx + c$.

$-2 = a(1)^2 + b(1) + c$

$-2 = a + b + c$ Equation 2

Substitute 2 for x and 5 for y in $y = ax^2 + bx + c$.

$5 = a(2)^2 + b(2) + c$

$5 = 4a + 2b + c$ Equation 3

Eliminate a and b from Equations 1 and 2 by multiplying Equation 1 by -1 and adding the resulting equation to Equation 2.

$4 = -a + b - c$

$\underline{-2 = a + b + c}$

$2 = 2b$

$b = 1$

Eliminate c from Equations 1 and 3 by multiplying Equation 1 by -1 and adding the resulting equation to Equation 3.

$4 = -a + b - c$

$\underline{5 = 4a + 2b + c}$

$9 = 3a + 3b$ Equation 4

Substitute 1 for b in Equation 4 and solve for a.

$9 = 3a + 3(1)$

$9 = 3a + 3$

$6 = 3a$

$a = 2$

Substitute 2 for a and 1 for b in Equation 2 and solve for c.

$-2 = 2 + 1 + c$

$-2 = c + 3$

$c = -5$

Substituting 2 for a, 1 for b, and -5 for c in quadratic equation $y = ax^2 + bx + c$ gives

$y = 2x^2 + x - 5$.

23. $x + y + z = 16$

$2x + 3y + 4z = 46$

$5x - y = 31$

Eliminate z from Equations 1 and 2 by multiplying Equation 1 by -4 and adding the resulting equation to Equation 2.

$-4x - 4y - 4z = -64$

$\underline{2x + 3y + 4z = 46}$

$-2x - y = -18$ Equation 4

Solve Equations 3 and 4 for x and y by multiplying Equation 4 by -1 and adding the resulting equation to Equation 3.

$5x - y = 31$

$\underline{2x + y = 18}$

$7x = 49$

$x = 7$

Substitute 7 for x in Equation 3 and solve for y.

$5(7) - y = 31$

$35 - y = 31$

$-y = -4$

$y = 4$

Substitute 7 for x and 4 for y in Equation 1 and solve for z.

$7 + 4 + z = 16$

$z + 11 = 16$

$z = 5$

The numbers are 7, 4 and 5.

25.

$$\frac{x+2}{6} - \frac{y+4}{3} + \frac{z}{2} = 0$$

$$6\left(\frac{x+2}{6} - \frac{y+4}{3} + \frac{z}{2}\right) = 6(0)$$

$$(x+2) - 2(y+4) + 3z = 0$$

$$x + 2 - 2y - 8 + 3z = 0$$

$$x - 2y + 3z = 6$$

$$\frac{x+1}{2} + \frac{y-1}{2} - \frac{z}{4} = \frac{9}{2}$$

$$4\left(\frac{x+1}{2} + \frac{y-1}{2} - \frac{z}{4}\right) = 4\left(\frac{9}{2}\right)$$

$$2(x+1) + 2(y-1) - z = 18$$

$$2x + 2 + 2y - 2 - z = 18$$

$$2x + 2y - z = 18$$

$$\frac{x-5}{4} + \frac{y+1}{3} + \frac{z-2}{2} = \frac{19}{4}$$

$$12\left(\frac{x-5}{4} + \frac{y+1}{3} + \frac{z-2}{2}\right) = 12\left(\frac{19}{4}\right)$$

$$3(x-5) + 4(y+1) + 6(z-2) = 57$$

$$3x - 15 + 4y + 4 + 6z - 12 = 57$$

$$3x + 4y + 6z = 80$$

We need to solve the equivalent system:

$x - 2y + 3z = 6$

$2x + 2y - z = 18$

$3x + 4y + 6z = 80$

Add the first two equations together.

$x - 2y + 3z = 6$

$\underline{2x + 2y - z = 18}$

$3x + 2z = 24$

Multiply the second equation by -2 and add it to the third equation.

$$-4x - 4y + 2z = -36$$
$$\underline{3x + 4y + 6z = 80}$$
$$-x + 8z = 44$$

Using the two reduced equations, we solve the system

$$3x + 2z = 24$$
$$-x + 8z = 44$$

Multiply the second equation by 3 and add the equations.

$$3x + 2z = 24$$
$$\underline{-3x + 24z = 132}$$
$$26z = 156$$
$$z = 6$$

Back-substitute to find x.

$$-x + 8(6) = 44$$
$$-x + 48 = 44$$
$$-x = -4$$
$$x = 4$$

Back substitute to find y.

$$x - 2y + 3z = 6$$
$$4 - 2y + 3(6) = 6$$
$$-2y = -16$$
$$y = 8$$

The solution is $(4, 8, 6)$.

27. Selected points may vary, but the equation will be the same.

$$y = ax^2 + bx + c$$

Use the points $(2, -2)$, $(4, 1)$, and $(6, -2)$ to get the system

$$4a + 2b + c = -2$$
$$16a + 4b + c = 1$$
$$36a + 6b + c = -2$$

Multiply the first equation by -1 and add to the second equation.

$$-4a - 2b - c = 2$$
$$\underline{16a + 4b + c = 1}$$
$$12a + 2b = 3$$

Multiply the first equation by -1 and add to the third equation.

$$-4a - 2b - c = 2$$
$$\underline{36a + 6b + c = -2}$$
$$32a + 4b = 0$$

Using the two reduced equations, we get the system

$$12a + 2b = 3$$
$$32a + 4b = 0$$

Multiply the first equation by -2 and add to the second equation.

$$-24a - 4b = -6$$
$$\underline{32a + 4b = 0}$$
$$8a = -6$$
$$a = -\frac{3}{4}$$

Back-substitute to solve for b.

$$12a + 2b = 3$$
$$12\left(-\frac{3}{4}\right) + 2b = 3$$
$$-9 + 2b = 3$$
$$2b = 12$$
$$b = 6$$

Back-substitute to solve for c.

$$4a + 2b + c = -2$$
$$4\left(-\frac{3}{4}\right) + 2(6) + c = -2$$
$$-3 + 12 + c = -2$$
$$c = -11$$

The equation is:

$$y = -\frac{3}{4}x^2 + 6x - 11$$

29.
$$ax - by - 2cz = 21$$
$$ax + by + cz = 0$$
$$2ax - by + cz = 14$$

Add the first two equations.

$$ax - by - 2cz = 21$$
$$\underline{ax + by + cz = 0}$$
$$2ax - cz = 21$$

Multiply the first equation by -1 and add to the third equation.

$$-ax + by + 2cz = -21$$
$$\underline{2ax - by + cz = 14}$$
$$ax + 3cz = -7$$

Use the two reduced equations to get the following system:

$$2ax - cz = 21$$
$$ax + 3cz = -7$$

Multiply the second equation by -2 and add the equations.
$$2ax - cz = 21$$
$$\underline{-2ax - 6cz = 14}$$
$$-7cz = 35$$
$$z = -\frac{5}{c}$$

Back-substitute to solve for x.
$$ax + 3cz = -7$$
$$ax + 3c\left(-\frac{5}{c}\right) = -7$$
$$ax - 15 = -7$$
$$ax = 8$$
$$x = \frac{8}{a}$$

Back-substitute to solve for y.
$$ax + by + cz = 0$$
$$a\left(\frac{8}{a}\right) + by + c\left(-\frac{5}{c}\right) = 0$$
$$8 + by - 5 = 0$$
$$by = -3$$
$$y = -\frac{3}{b}$$

The solution is $\left(\frac{8}{a}, -\frac{3}{b}, -\frac{5}{c}\right)$.

31. **a.** 2000: $(0, 2.5)$
2002: $(2, 4.1)$
2003: $(3, 3.5)$

b. $y = ax^2 + bx + c$
$$a(0)^2 + b(0) + c = 2.5$$
$$c = 2.5 \quad \text{Equation 1}$$
$$y = ax^2 + bx + c$$
$$a(2)^2 + b(2) + c = 4.1$$
$$4a + 2b + c = 4.1 \quad \text{Equation 2}$$
$$y = ax^2 + bx + c$$
$$a(3)^2 + b(3) + c = 3.5$$
$$9a + 3b + c = 3.5 \quad \text{Equation 3}$$
System:
$$c = 2.5$$
$$4a + 2b + c = 4.1$$
$$9a + 3b + c = 3.5$$

c. Substitute $c = 2.5$ into equation 2
$$4a + 2b + 2.5 = 4.1$$
$$4a + 2b = 1.6 \quad \text{Equation 4}$$
Substitute $c = 2.5$ into equation 2
$$9a + 3b + 2.5 = 3.5$$
$$9a + 3b = 1 \quad \text{Equation 5}$$
Solve the system of two equations using equations 4 and 5.
$$4a + 2b = 1.6 \quad \text{Mult. by 3} \rightarrow \quad 12a + 6b = 4.8$$
$$9a + 3b = 1 \quad \text{Mult. by } -2 \rightarrow \quad \underline{-18a - 6b = -2}$$
$$-6a = 2.8$$
$$a \approx -0.4667$$
$$a \approx -0.47$$

Use back-substitution to find b.
$$4a + 2b = 1.6$$
$$4(-0.4667) + 2b = 1.6$$
$$b \approx 1.73$$
The equation that models steroid use by U.S. high school seniors x years after 2000 is $y = -0.47x^2 + 1.73x + 2.5$.

33. **a.** Substitute the values for x and y into the quadratic form.
$$224 = a(1)^2 + b(1) + c$$
$$a + b + c = 224$$

$$176 = a(3)^2 + b(3) + c$$
$$9a + 3b + c = 176$$

$$104 = a(4)^2 + b(4) + c$$
$$16a + 4b + c = 104$$

Multiply the first equation by -1 and add to both the second and the third equations to obtain 2 new equations with 2 variables.
$$-a - b - c = -224$$
$$9a + 3b + c = 176$$
$$8a + 2b = -48$$

$$-a - b - c = -224$$
$$16a + 4b + c = 104$$
$$15a + 3b = -120$$
Use the two new equations to solve for a and b. Multiply the first equation by -3 and the second equation by 2 and add the results together. Solve for a. Substitute that value in $8a + 2b = -48$ and solve for b.

$-24a - 6b = 144$

$30a + 6b = -240$

$6a = -96$

$a = -16$

$8(-16) + 2b = -48$

$-128 + 2b = -48$

$2b = 80$

$b = 40$

Substitute -16 for a and 40 for b into the equation $a + b + c = 224$ and solve for c.

$-16 + 40 + c = 224$

$c = 200$

The equation is $y = -16x^2 + 40x + 200$.

b. $y = -16(5)^2 + 40(5) + 200 = 0$

The ball hit the ground after 5 seconds.

35. $x + y + z = 244$

$x - y = 4$

$y - z = 48$

Multiply the second equation by -1 and add to the first equation.

$x + y + z = 244$

$\underline{-x + y = -4}$

$2y + z = 240$

Add this new equation to equation to the third equation and solve for y.

$y - z = 48$

$\underline{2y + z = 240}$

$3y = 288$

$y = 96$

Substitute 96 for y in the equation $x - y = 4$ and solve for x.

$x - 96 = 4$

$x = 100$

Substitute 96 for y into the equation $y - z = 48$ and solve for z.

$96 - z = 48$

$-z = -48$

$z = 48$

Andrew Carnegie's fortune is worth \$100 billion in today's money. Cornelius Vanderbilt's fortune is worth \$96 billion and Bill Gates is worth \$48 billion.

37. x = number of \$8 tickets sold

y = number of \$10 tickets sold

z = number of \$12 tickets sold

From the given conditions we have the following system of equations.

$x + y + z = 400$

$8x + 10y + 12z = 3700$

$x + y = 7z$ or $x + y - 7z = 0$

Eliminate z from Equations 1 and 2 multiplying Equation 1 by -12 and adding the resulting equation to Equation 2.

$-12x - 12y - 12z = -4800$

$\underline{8x + 10y + 12z = 3700}$

$-4x - 2y = -1100$ Equation 4

Eliminate z from Equations 1 and 3 by multiplying Equation 1 by 7 and adding the resulting equation to Equation 3.

$7x + 7y + 7z = 2800$

$\underline{x + y - 7z = 0}$

$8x + 8y = 2800$ Equation 5

Solve Equations 4 and 5 for x and y by multiplying Equation 4 by 2 and adding the resulting equation to Equation 5.

$-8x - 4y = -2200$

$\underline{8x + 8y = 2800}$

$4y = 600$

$y = 150$

Substitute 150 for y in Equation 5 and solve for x.

$8x + 8(150) = 2800$

$8x = 2800 - 1200$

$8x = 1600$

$x = 200$

Substitute 200 for x and 150 for y in Equation 1 and solve for z.

$200 + 150 + z = 400$

$350 + z = 400$

$z = 50$

The number of \$8 tickets sold was 200.

The number of \$10 tickets sold was 150.

The number of \$12 tickets sold was 50.

39. x = amount of money invested at 10%
y = amount of money invested at 12%
z = amount of money invested at 15%

$$x + y + z = 6700$$
$$0.08x + 0.10y + 0.12z = 716$$
$$z = x + y + 300$$

Arrange Equation 3 so that variable terms appear on the left and constants appear on the right.

$$-x - y + z = 300 \quad \text{Equation 4}$$

Eliminate x and y from Equations 1 and 4 by adding Equations 1 and 4.

$$x + y + z = 6700$$
$$\underline{-x - y + z = 300}$$
$$2z = 7000$$
$$z = 3500$$

Substitute 3500 for z in Equation 1 and Equation 2 and simplify.

$$x + y + 3500 = 6700$$
$$x + y = 3200 \quad \text{Equation 5}$$
$$0.08x + 0.10y + 0.12(3500) = 716$$
$$0.08x + 0.10y + 420 = 716 \qquad \text{S}$$
$$0.08x + 10y = 296 \quad \text{Equation 6}$$

olve Equations 5 and 6 for x and y by multiplying Equation 5 by -0.10 and adding the resulting equation to Equation 6.

$$-0.10x - 0.10y = -320$$
$$\underline{0.08x + 0.10y = 296}$$
$$-0.02x = 24$$
$$x = 1200$$

Substitute 1200 for x and 3,500 for z in Equation 1 and solve for y.

$$1200 + y + 3500 = 6700$$
$$y + 4700 = 6700$$
$$y = 2000$$

The person invested $1200 at 8%, $2000 at 10%, and $3500 at 12%.

41. $x + y + z = 180$
$$2x - 5 + z = 180$$
$$2x + z = 185$$

$$2x + 5 + y = 180$$
$$2x + y = 175$$

Multiply the second equation by -1 and add to the first equation. Use the new equation and the third equation to solve for x and z.

$$-2x - z = -185$$
$$x + y + z = 180$$
$$-x + y = -5$$

Multiply the new equation by -1.

$$x - y = 5$$
$$2x + y = 175$$
$$3x = 180$$
$$x = 60$$

$$60 - y = 5$$
$$-y = -55$$
$$y = 55$$

Substitute 60 for x and 55 for y in the first equation and solve for z.

$$60 + 55 + z = 180$$
$$z = 65$$

49. x = number of triangles
y = number of rectangles
z = number of pentagons

$$x + y + z = 40$$
$$3x + 4y + 5z = 153$$
$$2y + 5z = 72$$

Eliminate x from Equations 1 and 2 by multiplying Equation 1 by -3 and adding the resulting equation to Equation 2.

$$-3x - 3y - 3z = -120$$
$$\underline{3x + 4y + 5z = 153}$$
$$y + 2z = 33 \qquad \text{Equation 4}$$

Solve for z by multiplying Equation 4 by -2 and adding the resulting equation to Equation 3.

$$2y + 5z = 72$$
$$\underline{-2y - 4z = -66}$$
$$z = 6$$

Substitute 6 for z in Equation 4 and solve for y.

$$y + 2(6) = 33$$
$$y + 12 = 33$$
$$y = 21$$

Substitute 21 for y and 6 for z in Equation 1 and solve for x.

$$x + 21 + 6 = 40$$
$$x + 27 = 40$$
$$x = 13$$

The painting has 13 triangles, 21 rectangles, and 6 pentagons.

Section 7.3

Check Point Exercises

1. $\dfrac{5x-1}{(x-3)(x+4)} = \dfrac{A}{x-3} + \dfrac{B}{x+4}$

   Multiply both sides of the equation by the least common denominator $(x-3)(x+4)$ and divide out common factors.

   $5x-1 = A(x+4) + B(x-3)$

   $5x-1 = Ax + 4A + Bx - 3B$

   $5x-1 = (A+B)x + 4A - 3B$

   Equate coefficients of like powers of x and equate constant terms.

   $A + B = 5$

   $4A - 3B = -1$

   Solving the above system for A and B we find
   $A = 2$ and $B = 3$.

   $\dfrac{5x-1}{(x-3)(x+4)} = \dfrac{2}{x-3} + \dfrac{3}{x+4}$

2. $\dfrac{x+2}{x(x-1)^2} = \dfrac{A}{x} + \dfrac{B}{x-1} + \dfrac{C}{(x-1)^2}$

   Multiply both sides of the equation by the least common denominator $x(x-1)^2$ and divide out common factors.

   $x+2 = A(x-1)^2 + Bx(x-1) + Cx$

   $x+2 = A\left(x^2 - 2x + 1\right) + Bx^2 - Bx + Cx$

   $x+2 = Ax^2 - 2Ax + A + Bx^2 - Bx + Cx$

   $x+2 = Ax^2 + Bx^2 - 2Ax - Bx + Cx + A$

   $x+2 = (A+B)x^2 + (-2A - B + C)x + A$

   Equate coefficients of like powers of x and equate constant terms.

   $A + B = 0$

   $-2A - B + C = 1$

   $A = 2$

   Since $A = 2$, we find that $B = -2$ and $C = 3$ by substitution.

   $\dfrac{x+2}{x(x-1)^2} = \dfrac{2}{x} - \dfrac{2}{x-1} + \dfrac{3}{(x-1)^2}$

3. $\dfrac{8x^2 + 12x - 20}{(x+3)\left(x^2 + x + 2\right)} = \dfrac{A}{x+3} + \dfrac{Bx+C}{x^2 + x + 2}$

   Multiply both sides of the equation by the least common denominator $(x+3)\left(x^2 + x + 2\right)$ and divide out common factors.

   $8x^2 + 12x - 20 = A\left(x^2 + x + 2\right) + (Bx + C)(x + 3)$

   $8x^2 + 12x - 20 = Ax^2 + Ax + 2A + Bx^2 + 3Bx + Cx + 3C$

   $8x^2 + 12x - 20 = Ax^2 + Bx^2 + Ax + 3Bx + Cx + 2A + 3C$

   $8x^2 + 12x - 20 = (A+B)x^2 + (A + 3B + C)x + 2A + 3C$

   Equate coefficients of like powers of x and equate constant terms.

$$A + B = 8$$
$$A + 3B + C = 12$$
$$2A + 3C = -20$$

Solving the above system for A, B, and C we find $A = 2$, $B = 6$, and $C = -8$.

$$\frac{8x^2 + 12x - 20}{(x+3)(x^2+x+2)} = \frac{2}{x+3} + \frac{6x-8}{x^2+x+2}$$

4. $\quad \dfrac{2x^3 + x + 3}{(x^2+1)^2} = \dfrac{Ax+B}{x^2+1} + \dfrac{Cx+D}{(x^2+1)^2}$

Multiply both sides of the equation by the common denominator $(x^2+1)^2$ and divide out common factors.

$$2x^3 + x + 3 = (Ax+B)(x^2+1) + Cx + D$$
$$2x^3 + x + 3 = Ax^3 + Bx^2 + Ax + B + Cx + D$$
$$2x^3 + x + 3 = Ax^3 + Bx^2 + Ax + Cx + B + D$$
$$2x^3 + x + 3 = Ax^3 + Bx^2 + (A+C)x + B + D$$

Equate coefficients of like powers of x and equate constant terms.

$$A = 2$$
$$B = 0$$
$$A + C = 1$$
$$B + D = 3$$

Since $A = 2$ and $B = 0$ we find that $C = -1$ and $D = 3$ by substitution.

$$\frac{2x^3 + x + 3}{(x^2+1)^2} = \frac{2x}{x^2+1} + \frac{-x+3}{(x^2+1)^2} = \frac{2x}{x^2+1} - \frac{x-3}{(x^2+1)^2}$$

Exercise Set 7.3

1. $\quad \dfrac{11x - 10}{(x-2)(x+1)} = \dfrac{A}{x-2} + \dfrac{B}{x+1}$

3. $\quad \dfrac{6x^2 - 14x - 27}{(x+2)(x-3)^2} = \dfrac{A}{x+2} + \dfrac{B}{x-3} + \dfrac{C}{(x-3)^2}$

5. $\quad \dfrac{5x^2 - 6x + 7}{(x-1)(x^2+1)} = \dfrac{A}{x-1} + \dfrac{Bx+C}{x^2+1}$

7. $\quad \dfrac{x^3 + x^2}{(x^2+4)^2} = \dfrac{Ax+B}{x^2+4} + \dfrac{Cx+D}{(x^2+4)^2}$

9. $\quad \dfrac{x}{(x-3)(x-2)} = \dfrac{A}{x-3} + \dfrac{B}{x-2}$

Multiply both sides of the equation by the least common denominator $(x-3)(x-2)$ and divide out common factors.

$$x = A(x-2) + B(x-3)$$
$$x = Ax - 2A + Bx - 3B$$
$$x = Ax + Bx - 2A - 3B$$
$$x = (A+B)x - (2A+3B)$$

Equate coefficients of like powers of x, and equate constant terms.

$$A + B = 1$$
$$2A + 3B = 0$$

Solving the above system for A and B, we find $A = 3$ and $B = -2$.

$$\frac{x}{(x-3)(x-2)} = \frac{3}{x-3} - \frac{2}{x-2}$$

11. $\dfrac{3x+50}{(x-9)(x+2)} = \dfrac{A}{x-9} + \dfrac{B}{x+2}$

Multiply both sides of the equation by the least common denominator $(x-9)(x+2)$ and divide out common factors.

$3x+50 = A(x+2) + B(x-9)$

$3x+50 = Ax + 2A + Bx - 9B$

$3x+50 = Ax + Bx + 2A - 9B$

$3x+50 = (A+B)x + (2A-9B)$

Equate coefficients of like powers of x, and equate constant terms.

$A+B=3$

$2A-9B=50$

Solving the above system for A and B, we find $A = 7$ and $B = -4$.

$\dfrac{3x+50}{(x-9)(x+2)} = \dfrac{7}{x-9} - \dfrac{4}{x+2}$

13. $\dfrac{7x-4}{x^2-x-12} = \dfrac{7x-4}{(x-4)(x+3)} = \dfrac{A}{x-4} + \dfrac{B}{x+3}$

Multiply both sides of the last equation by the least common denominator $(x-4)(x-3)$ and divide out common factors.

$7x-4 = A(x+3) + B(x-4)$

$7x-4 = Ax + 3A + Bx - 4B$

$7x-4 = Ax + Bx + 3A - 4B$

$7x-4 = (A+B)x + (3A-4B)$

Equate coefficients of like powers of x, and equate constant terms.

$A+B=7$

$3A-4B=-4$

Solving the above system for A and B, we find $A = \dfrac{24}{7}$ and $B = \dfrac{25}{7}$.

$\dfrac{7x-4}{x^2-x-12} = \dfrac{24}{7(x-4)} + \dfrac{25}{7(x+3)}$

15. $\dfrac{4}{(2x+1)(x-3)} = \dfrac{A}{2x+1} + \dfrac{B}{x-3}$

Multiply both sides of the equation by the least common denominator $(2x+1)(x-3)$ and divide out common factors.

$4 = A(x-3) + B(2x+1)$

$4 = Ax - A3 + B2x + B$

$4 = (A+2B)x + (-3A+B)$

Equate coefficients of like powers of x and equate the constant terms. Solve for A and B.

$A + 2B = 0$

$-3A + B = 4$

$3A + 6B = 0$

$-3A + B = 4$

$7B = 4$

$B = \dfrac{4}{7}$

$A + 2B = 0$

$6A - 2B = -8$

$7A = -8$

$A = -\dfrac{8}{7}$

$\dfrac{4}{(2x+1)(x-3)} = \dfrac{-8}{7(2x+1)} + \dfrac{4}{7(x-3)}$

17. $\dfrac{4x^2+13x-9}{x(x-1)(x+3)} = \dfrac{A}{x} + \dfrac{B}{x-3} + \dfrac{C}{x+3}$

Multiply both sides of the equation by the least common denominator $x(x-1)(x+3)$ and divide out common factors.

$4x^2+13x-9 = A(x\text{-}1)(x+3) + Bx(x+3) + Cx(x-1)$

$4x^2+13x-9 = A(x^2+2x-3) + Bx^2+3Bx+Cx^2-Cx$

$4x^2+13x-9 = Ax^2+2Ax-3A+Bx^2+3Bx+Cx^2-Cx$

$4x^2+13x-9 = Ax^2+Bx^2+Cx^2+2Ax+3Bx-Cx-3A$

$4x^2+13x-9 = (A+B+C)x^2+(2A+3B-C)x-3A$

Equate coefficients of like powers of x, and equate constant terms.

$\quad A+B+C = 4$

$2A+3B-C = 13$

$\qquad\quad -3A = -9$

Solving the above system for A, B, and C, we find $A = 3$ and $B = 2$, and $C = -1$.

$\dfrac{4x^2+13x-9}{x(x-1)(x+3)} = \dfrac{3}{x} + \dfrac{2}{x-1} - \dfrac{1}{x+3}$

19. $\dfrac{4x^2-7x-3}{x^3-x} = \dfrac{4x^2-7x-3}{x(x+1)(x-1)} = \dfrac{A}{x} + \dfrac{B}{x+1} + \dfrac{C}{x-1}$

Multiply both sides of the last equation by the least common denominator $x(x+1)(x-1)$ and divide out common factors.

$4x^2-7x-3 = A(x+1)(x-1) + Bx(x-1) + Cx(x+1)$

$4x^2-7x-3 = A(x^2-1) + Bx^2-Bx+Cx^2+Cx$

$4x^2-7x-3 = Ax^2-A+Bx^2-Bx+Cx^2+Cx$

$4x^2-7x-3 = Ax^2+Bx^2+Cx^2-Bx+Cx-A$

$4x^2-7x-3 = (A+B+C)x^2+(-B+C)x-A$

Equate coefficients of like powers of x, and equate constant terms.

$A+B+C = 4$

$\quad -B+C = -7$

$\qquad\quad -A = -3$

Solving the above system for A, B, and C, we find $A = 3$ and $B = 4$, and $C = -3$.

$\dfrac{4x^2-7x-3}{x^3-x} = \dfrac{3}{x} + \dfrac{4}{x+1} - \dfrac{3}{x-1}$

21. $\dfrac{6x-11}{(x-1)^2} = \dfrac{A}{x-1} + \dfrac{B}{(x-1)^2}$

Multiply both sides of the equation by the least common denominator $(x-1)^2$ and divide out common factors.

$6x - 11 = A(x-1) + B$

$6x - 11 = Ax - A + B$

Equate coefficients of like powers of x, and equate constant terms.

$\quad A = 6$

$-A + B = -11$

Since $A = 6$, we find that $B = -5$ by substitution. $\dfrac{6x-11}{(x-1)^2} = \dfrac{6}{x-1} - \dfrac{5}{(x-1)^2}$

23. $\dfrac{x^2 - 6x + 3}{(x-2)^3} = \dfrac{A}{x-2} + \dfrac{B}{(x-2)^2} + \dfrac{C}{(x-2)^3}$

Multiply both sides of the equation by the least common denominator $(x-2)^3$ and divide out common factors.

$x^2 - 6x + 3 = A(x-2)^2 + B(x-2) + C$

$x^2 - 6x + 3 = A(x^2 - 4x + 4) + Bx - 2B + C$

$x^2 - 6x + 3 = Ax^2 - 4Ax + 4A + Bx - 2B + C$

$x^2 - 6x + 3 = Ax^2 - 4Ax + Bx + 4A - 2B + C$

$x^2 - 6x + 3 = Ax^2 + (-4A + B)x + 4A - 2B + C$

Equate coefficients of like powers of x, and equate constant terms.

$A = 1$

$-4A + B = -6$

$4A - 2B + C = 3$

Since $A = 1$, we find that $B = -2$ and $C = -5$ by substitution. $\dfrac{x^2 - 6x + 3}{(x-2)^3} = \dfrac{1}{x-2} - \dfrac{2}{(x-2)^2} - \dfrac{5}{(x-2)^3}$.

25. $\dfrac{x^2 + 2x + 7}{x(x-1)^2} = \dfrac{A}{x} + \dfrac{B}{x-1} + \dfrac{C}{(x-1)^2}$

Multiply both sides of the equation by the least common denominator $x(x-1)^2$ and divide out common factors.

$x^2 + 2x + 7 = A(x-1)^2 + Bx(x-1) + Cx$

$x^2 + 2x + 7 = A(x^2 - 2x + 1) + Bx^2 - Bx + Cx$

$x^2 + 2x + 7 = Ax^2 - 2Ax + A + Bx^2 - Bx + Cx$

$x^2 + 2x + 7 = Ax^2 + Bx^2 - 2Ax - Bx + Cx + A$

$x^2 + 2x + 7 = (A + B)x^2 + (-2A - B + C)x + A$

$A + B = 1$

$-2A - B + C = 2$

$A = 7$

Since $A = 7$, we find that $B = -6$ and $C = 10$ by substitution. $\dfrac{x^2 + 2x + 7}{x(x-1)^2} = \dfrac{7}{x} - \dfrac{6}{x-1} + \dfrac{10}{(x-1)^2}$

27. $\dfrac{x^2}{(x+1)(x-1)^2} = \dfrac{A}{x+1} + \dfrac{B}{x-1} + \dfrac{C}{(x-1)^2}$

Multiply both sides of the equation by the least common denominator $(x+1)(x-1)^2$ and divide out common factors.

$x^2 = A(x-1)^2 + B(x+1)(x-1) + C(x+1)$

$x^2 = x^2 A - 2xA + A + Bx^2 - B + Cx + C$

$x^2 = (A + B)x^2 + (-2A + C)x + (A - B + C)$

Equate coefficients of like powers of x, and equate constant terms.

$A + B = 1$

$-2A + C = 0$

$A - B + C = 0$

Solving the above system for A, B, and C, we find $A = \dfrac{1}{4}$, $B = \dfrac{3}{4}$, and $C = \dfrac{1}{2}$.

$\dfrac{x^2}{(x+1)(x-1)^2} = \dfrac{1}{4(x+1)} + \dfrac{3}{4(x-1)} + \dfrac{1}{2(x-1)^2}$

29. $\dfrac{5x^2 - 6x + 7}{(x-1)(x^2+1)} = \dfrac{A}{x-1} + \dfrac{Bx+C}{x^2+1}$

Multiply both sides of the equation by the least common denominator $(x-1)(x^2+1)$ and divide out common factors.

$5x^2 - 6x + 7 = A(x^2+1) + (Bx+C)(x-1)$

$5x^2 - 6x + 7 = Ax^2 + A + Bx^2 - Bx + Cx - C$

$5x^2 - 6x + 7 = Ax^2 + Bx^2 - Bx + Cx + A - C$

$5x^2 - 6x + 7 = (A+B)x^2 + (-B+C)x + A - C$

Equate coefficients of like powers of x, and equate constant terms.

$A + B = 5$
$-B + C = -6$
$A - C = 7$

Solving the above system for A, B, and C, we find $A = 3$, $B = 2$, and $C = -4$.

$\dfrac{5x^2 - 6x + 7}{(x-1)(x^2+1)} = \dfrac{3}{x-1} + \dfrac{2x-4}{x^2+1}$

31. $\dfrac{5x^2 + 6x + 3}{(x+1)(x^2+2x+2)} = \dfrac{A}{x+1} + \dfrac{Bx+C}{x^2+2x+2}$

Multiply both sides of the equation by the least common denominator $(x+1)(x^2+2x+2)$ and divide out common factors.

$5x^2 + 6x + 3 = A(x^2+2x+2) + (Bx+C)(x+1)$

$5x^2 + 6x + 3 = Ax^2 + 2Ax + 2A + Bx^2 + Bx + Cx + C$

$5x^2 + 6x + 3 = Ax^2 + Bx^2 + 2Ax + Bx + Cx + 2A + C$

$5x^2 + 6x + 3 = (A+B)x^2 + (2A+B+C)x + 2A + C$

Equate coefficients of like powers of x, and equate constant terms.

$A + B = 5$
$2A + B + C = 6$
$2A + C = 3$

Solving the above system for A, B, and C, we find $A = 2$, $B = 3$, and $C = -1$.

$\dfrac{5x^2 + 6x + 3}{(x+1)(x^2+2x+2)} = \dfrac{2}{x+1} + \dfrac{3x-1}{x^2+2x+2}$

33. $\dfrac{x+4}{x^2(x^2+4)} = \dfrac{A}{x} + \dfrac{B}{x^2} + \dfrac{Cx+D}{x^2+4}$

Multiply both sides of the equation by the least common denominator $x^2(x^2+4)$ and divide out common factors.

$x + 4 = Ax(x^2+4) + B(x^2+4) + (Cx+D)x^2$

$x + 4 = Ax^3 + 4Ax + Bx^2 + 4B + Cx^3 + Dx^2$

$x + 4 = (A+C)x^3 + (B+D)x^2 + 4Ax + 4B$

Equate coefficients of like powers of x, and equate constant terms

$A + C = 0$

$B + D = 0$

$4A = 1$

$4B = 4$

Solving the above system for A, B, and C, we find $A = \dfrac{1}{4}$, $B = 1$, $C = -\dfrac{1}{4}$, and $D = -1$.

$\dfrac{x+4}{x^2(x^2+4)} = \dfrac{1}{4x} + \dfrac{1}{x^2} + \dfrac{-1x-4}{4\left(x^2+4\right)}$

35. $\dfrac{6x^2-x+1}{x^3+x^2+x+1}=\dfrac{6x^2-x+1}{(x+1)(x^2+1)}=\dfrac{A}{x+1}+\dfrac{Bx+C}{x^2+1}$

Multiply both sides of the last equation by the least common denominator $(x+1)(x^2+1)$ and divide out common factors.

$6x^2-x+1=A(x^2+1)+(Bx+C)(x+1)$

$6x^2-x+1=Ax^2+A+Bx^2+Bx+Cx+C$

$6x^2-x+1=Ax^2+Bx^2+Bx+Cx+A+C$

$6x^2-x+1=(A+B)x^2+(B+C)x+A+C$

Equate coefficients of like powers of x, and equate constant terms.

$A+B=6$
$B+C=-1$
$A+C=1$

Solving the above system for A, B, and C, we find $A=4$, $B=2$, and $C=-3$.

$\dfrac{6x^2-x+1}{x^3+x^2+x+1}=\dfrac{4}{x+1}+\dfrac{2x-3}{x^2+1}$

37. $\dfrac{x^3+x^2+2}{\left(x^2+2\right)^2}=\dfrac{Ax+B}{x^2+2}+\dfrac{Cx+D}{\left(x^2+2\right)^2}$

Multiply both sides of the last equation by the least common denominator $(x^2+2)^2$ and divide out common factors.

$x^3+x^2+2=\left(Ax+B\right)\left(x^2+2\right)+Cx+D$

$x^3+x^2+2=Ax^3+Bx^2+2Ax+2B+Cx+D$

$x^3+x^2+2=Ax^3+Bx^2+2Ax+Cx+2B+D$

$x^3+x^2+2=Ax^3+Bx^2+\left(2A+C\right)x+\left(2B+D\right)$

Equate coefficients of like powers of x, and equate constant terms.

$A=1$
$B=1$
$2A+C=0$
$2B+D=2$

Since $A=1$ and $B=1$, we find that $C=-2$ and $D=0$ by substitution.

$\dfrac{x^3+x^2+2}{\left(x^2+2\right)^2}=\dfrac{x+1}{x^2+2}-\dfrac{2x}{\left(x^2+2\right)^2}$

39. $\dfrac{x^3-4x^2+9x-5}{(x^2-2x+3)^2}=\dfrac{Ax+B}{x^2-2x+3}+\dfrac{Cx+D}{(x^2-2x+3)^2}$

Multiply both sides of the equation by the least common denominator $(x^2-2x+3)^2$ and divide out common factors.

$x^3-4x^2+9x-5=(Ax+B)(x^2-2x+3)+Cx+D$

$x^3-4x^2+9x-5=Ax^3-2Ax^2+3Ax+Bx^2-2Bx+3B+Cx+D$

$x^3-4x^2+9x-5=Ax^3-2Ax^2+Bx^2+3Ax-2Bx+Cx+3B+D$

$x^3-4x^2+9x-5=Ax^3+(-2A+B)x^2+(3A-2B+C)x+3B+D$

Equate coefficients of like powers of x, and equate constant terms.

$$A = 1$$
$$-2A + B = -4$$
$$3A - 2B + C = 9$$
$$3B + D = -5$$

Since $A = 1$, we find that $B = -2$, $C = 2$, and $D = 1$ by substitution.

$$\frac{x^3 - 4x^2 + 9x - 5}{\left(x^2 - 2x + 3\right)^2} = \frac{x - 2}{x^2 - 2x + 3} + \frac{2x + 1}{\left(x^2 - 2x + 3\right)^2}$$

41. $\dfrac{4x^2 + 3x + 14}{x^3 - 8} = \dfrac{4x^2 + 3x + 14}{\left(x - 2\right)\left(x^2 + 2x + 4\right)} = \dfrac{A}{x - 2} + \dfrac{Bx + C}{x^2 + 2x + 4}$

Multiply both sides of the last equation by the least common denominator $(x - 2)(x^2 + 2x + 4)$ and divide out common factors.

$$4x^2 + 3x + 14 = A\left(x^2 + 2x + 4\right) + \left(Bx + C\right)\left(x - 2\right)$$

$$4x^2 + 3x + 14 = A^2 + 2Ax + 4A + Bx^2 - 2Bx + Cx - 2C$$

$$4x^2 + 3x + 14 = Ax^2 + Bx^2 + 2Ax - 2Bx + Cx + 4A - 2C$$

$$4x^2 + 3x + 14 = \left(A + B\right)x^2 + \left(2A - 2B + C\right)x + \left(4A - 2C\right)$$

Equate coefficients of like powers of x, and equate constant terms.

$$A + B = 4$$
$$2A - 2B + C = 3$$
$$4A - 2C = 14$$

Solving the above system for A, B, and C, we find $A = 3$, $B = 1$, and $C = -1$.

$$\frac{4x^2 + 3x + 4}{x^3 - 8} = \frac{3}{x - 2} + \frac{x - 1}{x^2 + 2x + 4}$$

43.   Divide $x^5 + 2$ by $x^2 - 1$.

$$
\begin{array}{r}
x^3 + x \\
x^2 - 1 \overline{\smash{)}\, x^5 + 2} \\
\underline{x^5 - x^3} \\
x^3 \\
\underline{x^3 - x} \\
x + 2
\end{array}
$$

$$\frac{x^5 + 2}{x^2 - 1} = x^3 + x + \frac{x + 2}{x^2 - 1}$$

Decompose $\dfrac{x + 2}{x^2 - 1}$.

$$\frac{x + 2}{x^2 - 1} = \frac{x + 2}{(x + 1)(x - 1)} = \frac{A}{x + 1} + \frac{B}{x - 1}$$

$$(x + 1)(x - 1)\frac{x + 2}{(x + 1)(x - 1)} = (x + 1)(x - 1)\left(\frac{A}{x + 1} + \frac{B}{x - 1}\right)$$

$$x + 2 = (x - 1)A + (x + 1)B$$

$$x + 2 = Ax - A + Bx + B$$

$$x + 2 = (A + B)x + (-A + B)$$

Equate coefficients:

$$A + B = 1$$
$$-A + B = 2$$

Solving this system results in $A = -\dfrac{1}{2}$ and $B = \dfrac{3}{2}$.

$$\frac{x^5 + 2}{x^2 - 1} = x^3 + x + \frac{-\dfrac{1}{2}}{x + 1} + \frac{\dfrac{3}{2}}{x - 1} \quad \text{or} \quad x^3 + x + \frac{-1}{2(x+1)} + \frac{3}{2(x-1)}$$

45. Divide $x^4 - x^2 + 2$ by $x^3 - x^2$.

$$
\begin{array}{r}
x + 1 \\
x^3 - x^2 \overline{\smash{\big)}\, x^4 - x^2 + 2} \\
\underline{x^4 - x^3} \\
x^3 - x^2 \\
\underline{x^3 - x^2} \\
2
\end{array}
$$

$$\frac{x^4 - x^2 + 2}{x^3 - x^2} = x + 1 + \frac{2}{x^3 - x^2}$$

Decompose $\dfrac{2}{x^3 - x^2}$.

$$\frac{2}{x^3 - x^2} = \frac{2}{x^2(x - 1)} = \frac{A}{x} + \frac{B}{x^2} + \frac{C}{x - 1}$$

$$x^2(x-1)\frac{2}{x^2(x-1)} = x^2(x-1)\left(\frac{A}{x} + \frac{B}{x^2} + \frac{C}{x-1}\right)$$

$$2 = x(x-1)A + (x-1)B + x^2 C$$
$$2 = Ax^2 - Ax + Bx - B + Cx^2$$
$$2 = (A + C)x^2 + (-A + B)x + (-B)$$

Equate coefficients:

$$A + C = 0$$
$$-A + B = 0$$
$$-B = 2$$

Solving this system results in $A = -2$, $B = -2$, and $C = 2$.

$$\frac{x^4 - x^2 + 2}{x^3 - x^2} = x + 1 + \frac{-2}{x} + \frac{-2}{x^2} + \frac{2}{x - 1}$$

47. $\dfrac{1}{x^2 - c^2} = \dfrac{1}{(x+c)(x-c)} = \dfrac{A}{x+c} + \dfrac{B}{x-c}$

$$(x+c)(x-c)\dfrac{1}{(x+c)(x-c)} = (x+c)(x-c)\left(\dfrac{A}{x+c} + \dfrac{B}{x-c}\right)$$

$$1 = (x-c)A + (x+c)B$$

$$1 = Ax - Ac + Bx + Bc$$

$$1 = (A+B)x + (-Ac + Bc)$$

Equate coefficients:

$$A + B = 0$$

$$-Ac + Bc = 1$$

Solving this system results in $A = \dfrac{-1}{2c}$ and $B = \dfrac{1}{2c}$.

$$\dfrac{1}{x^2 - c^2} = \dfrac{\frac{-1}{2c}}{x+c} + \dfrac{\frac{1}{2c}}{x-c}$$

49. $\dfrac{ax+b}{(x-c)^2} = \dfrac{D}{x-c} + \dfrac{E}{(x-c)^2}$

$$\dfrac{ax+b}{(x-c)^2} = \dfrac{D}{x-c} + \dfrac{E}{(x-c)^2}$$

$$(x-c)^2 \dfrac{ax+b}{(x-c)^2} = (x-c)^2 \left(\dfrac{D}{x-c} + \dfrac{E}{(x-c)^2}\right)$$

$$ax + b = (x-c)D + E$$

$$ax + b = Dx - Dc + E$$

$$ax + b = (D)x + (-Dc + E)$$

Equate coefficients:

$$D = a$$

$$-Dc + E = b$$

Solving this system results in $D = a$ and $E = ac + b$.

$$\dfrac{ax+b}{(x-c)^2} = \dfrac{a}{x-c} + \dfrac{ac+b}{(x-c)^2}$$

51. $\dfrac{1}{x(x+1)} = \dfrac{A}{x} + \dfrac{B}{x+1}$

Multiply both sides of the equation by the least common denominator $x(x+1)$ and divide out common factors.

$1 = A(x+1) + Bx$

$1 = Ax + A + Bx$

$1 = Ax + Bx + A$

$1 = (A+B)x + A$

Equate coefficients of like powers of x, and equate constant terms.

$A + B = 0$

$\quad A = 1$

Since $A = 1$ we find that $B = -1$ by substitution.

$$\frac{1}{x(x+1)} = \frac{1}{x} - \frac{1}{x+1}$$

$$\frac{1}{1\cdot 2} + \frac{1}{2\cdot 3} + \frac{1}{3\cdot 4} + \cdots + \frac{1}{99\cdot 100} = \left(\frac{1}{1} - \frac{1}{2}\right) + \left(\frac{1}{2} - \frac{1}{3}\right) + \left(\frac{1}{3} - \frac{1}{4}\right) + \cdots \left(\frac{1}{99} - \frac{1}{100}\right)$$

$$= \frac{1}{1} - \frac{1}{100}$$

$$= \frac{99}{100}$$

61. $\dfrac{4x^2 + 5x - 9}{x^3 - 6x - 9} = \dfrac{4x^2 + 5x - 9}{(x-3)(x^2 + 3x + 3)} = \dfrac{A}{x-3} + \dfrac{Bx + C}{x^2 + 3x + 3}$

Multiply both sides of the last equation by the common denominator $(x-3)(x^2 + 3x + 3)$ and divide out common factors.

$4x^2 + 5x - 9 = A(x^2 + 3x + 3) + (Bx + C)(x - 3)$

$4x^2 + 5x - 9 = Ax^2 + 3Ax + 3A + Bx^2 - 3Bx + Cx - 3C$

$4x^2 + 5x - 9 = Ax^2 + Bx^2 + 3Ax - 3Bx + Cx + 3A - 3C$

$4x^2 + 5x - 9 = (A+B)x^2 + (3A - 3B + C)x + 3A - 3C$

Equate coefficients of like powers of x and equate constant terms.

$\quad A + B = 4$

$3A - 3B + C = 5$

$\quad 3A - 3C = -9$

Solving the above system for A, B, and C, we find $A = 2$, and $B = 2$, and $C = 5$.

$$\frac{4x^2 + 5x - 9}{x^3 - 6x - 9} = \frac{2}{x-3} + \frac{2x + 5}{x^2 + 3x + 3}$$

Section 7.4

Check Point Exercises

1. $x^2 = y - 1$

    $4x - y = -1$

    Solve the first equation for y.

    $y = x^2 + 1$

    Substitute the expression $x^2 + 1$ for y in the second equation and solve for x.

    $4x - (x^2 + 1) = -1$

    $4x - x^2 - 1 = -1$

    $x^2 - 4x = 0$

    $x(x - 4) = 0$

    $x = 0$ or $x - 4 = 0$

    $x = 4$

    If $x = 0$, $y = (0)^2 + 1 = 1$.

    If $x = 4$, $y = (4)^2 + 1 = 17$.

    The solution set is $\{(0, 1), (4, 17)\}$.

2. $x + 2y = 0$

    $(x - 1)^2 + (y - 1)^2 = 5$

    Solve the first equation for x.

    $x = -2y$

    Substitute the expression $-2y$ for x in the second equation and solve for y.

    $(-2y - 1)^2 + (y - 1)^2 = 5$

    $4y^2 + 4y + 1 + y^2 - 2y + 1 = 5$

    $5y^2 + 2y - 3 = 0$

    $(5y - 3)(y + 1) = 0$

    $5y - 3 = 0$ or $y + 1 = 0$

    $y = \dfrac{3}{5}$ or $y = -1$

    If $y = \dfrac{3}{5}$, $x = -2\left(\dfrac{3}{5}\right) = -\dfrac{6}{5}$.

    If $y = -1$, $x = -2(-1) = 2$.

    The solution set is $\left\{\left(-\dfrac{6}{5}, \dfrac{3}{5}\right), (2, -1)\right\}$.

3. $3x^2 + 2y^2 = 35$

    $4x^2 + 3y^2 = 48$

    Eliminate the y^2-term by multiplying the first equation by -3 and the second equation by 2. Add the resulting equations.

    $-9x^2 - 6y = -105$

    $\underline{8x^2 + 6y^2 = 96}$

    $-x^2 = -9$

    $x^2 = 9$

    $x = \pm 3$

    If $x = 3$,

    $3(3)^2 + 2y^2 = 35$

    $y^2 = 4$

    $y = \pm 2$

    If $x = -3$,

    $3(-3)^2 + 2y^2 = 35$

    $y^2 = 4$

    $y = \pm 2$

    The solution set is $\{(3, 2), (3, -2), (-3, 2), (-3, -2)\}$.

4. $y = x^2 + 5$

    $x^2 + y^2 = 25$

    Arrange the first equation so that variable terms appear on the left, and constants appear on the right. Add the resulting equations to eliminate the x^2-terms and solve for y.

    $-x^2 + y = 5$

    $\underline{x^2 + y^2 = 25}$

    $y^2 + y = 30$

    $y^2 + y - 30 = 0$

    $(y + 6)(y - 5) = 0$

    $y + 6 = 0$ or $y - 5 = 0$

    $y = -6$ or $y = 5$

    If $y = -6$,

    $x^2 + (-6)^2 = 25$

    $x^2 = -11$

    no real solution

    If $y = 5$,

    $x^2 + (5)^2 = 25$

    $x^2 = 0$

    $x = 0$

    The solution set is $\{(0, 5)\}$.

5. $2x + 2y = 20$

$\quad xy = 21$

Solve the second equation for x.

$$x = \frac{21}{7}$$

Substitute the expression $\dfrac{21}{y}$ for x in the first

equation and solve for y.

$$2\left(\frac{21}{y}\right) + 2y = 20$$

$$\frac{42}{y} + 2y = 20$$

$$y^2 - 10y + 21 = 0$$

$$(y - 7)(y - 3) = 0$$

$$y - 7 = 0 \quad \text{or} \quad y - 3 = 0$$

$$y = 7 \quad \text{or} \quad\quad y = 3$$

If $y = 7$, $x = \dfrac{21}{7} = 3$.

If $y = 3$, $x = \dfrac{21}{3} = 7$.

The dimensions are 7 feet by 3 feet.

Exercise Set 7.4

1. $x + y = 2$

$\quad y = x^2 - 4$

Solve the first equation for y. $y = 2 - x$.

Substitute the expression $2 - x$ for y in the
second equation and solve for x.

$$2 - x = x^2 - 4$$

$$x^2 + x - 6 = 0$$

$$(x + 3)(x - 2) = 0$$

$$x + 3 = 0 \quad \text{or} \quad x - 2 = 0$$

$$x = -3 \quad \text{or} \quad\quad x = 2$$

If $x = -3$, $y = 2 - (-3) = 5$.

If $x = 2$, $y = 2 - 2 = 0$.

The solution set is $\{(-3, 5), (2, 0)\}$.

3. $x + y = 2$

$\quad y = x^2 - 4x + 4$

Substitute the expression $x^2 - 4x + 4$ for y in the
first equation and solve for x.

$$x + x^2 - 4x + 4 = 2$$

$$x^2 - 3x + 2 = 0$$

$$(x - 1)(x - 2) = 0$$

$$x - 1 = 0 \quad x - 2 = 0$$

$$x = 1 \quad\quad x = 2$$

Substitute $x = 1$ and then $x = 2$ into the
equation $x + y = 2$ and solve for each value
of y.

$$1 + y = 2 \quad 2 + y = 2$$

$$y = 1 \quad\quad\quad y = 0$$

The solution set is $\{(1, 1), (2, 0)\}$.

5. $y = x^2 - 4x - 10$

$\quad y = -x^2 - 2x + 14$

Substitute the expression $x^2 - 4x - 10$ for y in
the second equation and solve for x.

$$x^2 - 4x - 10 = -x^2 - 2x + 14$$

$$2x^2 - 2x - 24 = 0$$

$$x^2 - x - 12 = 0$$

$$(x - 4)(x + 3) = 0$$

$$x - 4 = 0 \quad \text{or} \quad x + 3 = 0$$

$$x = 4 \quad \text{or} \quad x = -3$$

If $x = 4$, $y = (4)^2 - 4(4) - 10 = -10$.

If $x = -3$, $y = (-3)^2 - 4(-3) - 10 = 11$.

The solution set is $\{(4, -10), (-3, 11)\}$.

7. $x^2 + y^2 = 25$

$\quad x - y = 1$

Solve the second equation for y. $y = x - 1$
Substitute the expression $x - 1$ for y in the first
equation and solve for x.

$$x^2 + (x - 1)^2 = 25$$

$$x^2 + x^2 - 2x + 1 = 25$$

$$2x^2 - 2x - 24 = 0$$

$$x^2 - x - 12 = 0$$

$$(x - 4)(x + 3) = 0$$

$$x - 4 = 0 \quad \text{or} \quad x + 3 = 0$$

$$x = 4 \quad \text{or} \quad x = -3$$

If $x = 4$, $y = 4 - 1 = 3$.

If $x = -3$, $y = -3 - 1 = -4$.

The solution set is $\{(4, 3), (-3, -4)\}$.

9. $xy = 6$
$2x - y = 1$
Solve the first equation for y.

$$y = \frac{6}{x}$$

Substitute the expression $\dfrac{6}{x}$ for y in the second

equation and solve for x.

$$2x - \frac{6}{x} = 1$$

$$2x^2 - 6 = x$$

$$2x^2 - x - 6 = 0$$

$$(2x + 3)(x - 2) = 0$$

$$2x + 3 = 0 \quad \text{or} \quad x - 2 = 0$$

$$x = -\frac{3}{2} \quad \text{or} \quad x = 2$$

If $x = -\dfrac{3}{2}$, $y = \dfrac{6}{-\frac{3}{2}} = -4$.

If $x = 2$, $y = \dfrac{6}{2} = 3$.

The solution set is $\left\{ \left(-\dfrac{3}{2}, -4 \right), (2, 3) \right\}$.

11. $y^2 = x^2 - 9$
$2y = x - 3$
Solve the second equation for y.

$$y = \frac{x - 3}{2}$$

Substitute the expression $\dfrac{x - 3}{2}$ for y in the

first equation and solve for x.

$$\left(\frac{x - 3}{2} \right)^2 = x^2 - 9$$

$$\frac{x^2 - 6x + 9}{4} = x^2 - 9$$

$$x^2 - 6x + 9 = 4x^2 - 36$$

$$3x^2 + 6x - 45 = 0$$

$$x^2 + 2x - 15 = 0$$

$$(x + 5)(x - 3) = 0$$

$$x + 5 = 0 \quad \text{or} \quad x - 3 = 0$$

$$x = -5 \quad \text{or} \quad x = 3$$

If $x = -5$, $y = \dfrac{-5 - 3}{2} = -4$.

If $x = 3$, $y = \dfrac{3 - 3}{2} = 0$.

The solution set is $\{(-5, -4), (3, 0)\}$.

13. $xy = 3$
$x^2 + y^2 = 10$
Solve the second equation for y.

$$y = \frac{3}{x}$$

Substitute the expression $\dfrac{3}{x}$ for y in the second

equation and solve for x.

$$x^2 + \left(\frac{3}{x} \right)^2 = 10$$

$$x^2 + \frac{9}{x^2} - 10 = 0$$

$$x^4 - 10x^2 + 9 = 0$$

$$\left(x^2 - 9 \right)\left(x^2 - 1 \right) = 0$$

$$(x - 3)(x + 3)(x - 1)(x + 1) = 0$$

$$x - 3 = 0 \quad \text{or} \quad x + 3 = 0 \quad \text{or} \quad x - 1 = 0 \quad \text{or} \quad x + 1 = 0$$

$$x = 3 \quad \text{or} \quad x = -3 \quad \text{or} \quad x = 1 \quad \text{or} \quad x = -1$$

If $x = 3$, $y = \dfrac{3}{3} = 1$.

If $x = -3$, $y = \dfrac{3}{-3} = -1$.

If $x = 1$, $y = \dfrac{3}{1} = 3$.

If $x = -1$, $y = \dfrac{3}{-1} = -3$.

The solution set is

$$\{(3, 1), (-3, -1), (1, 3), (-1, -3)\}.$$

15.
$$x + y = 1$$
$$x^2 + xy - y^2 = -5$$

Solve the first equation for y. $y = 1 - x$

Substitute the expression $1 - x$ for y in the second equation and solve for x.

$$x^2 + x(1-x) - (1-x)^2 = -5$$
$$x^2 + x - x^2 - (1 - 2x + x^2) = -5$$
$$x - 1 + 2x - x^2 = -5$$
$$x^2 - 3x - 4 = 0$$
$$(x-4)(x+1) = 0$$
$$x - 4 = 0 \quad \text{or} \quad x + 1 = 0$$
$$x = 4 \quad \text{or} \quad x = -1$$

If $x = 4$, $y = 1 - 4 = -3$.

If $x = -1$, $y = 1 - (-1) = 2$.

The solution set is $\{(4, -3), (-1, 2)\}$.

17.
$$x + y = 1$$
$$(x-1)^2 + (y+2)^2 = 10$$

Solve the first equation for y.

$$y = 1 - x$$

Substitute the expression $1 - x$ for y in the second equation and solve for x.

$$(x-1)^2 + (1 - x + 2)^2 = 10$$
$$(x-1)^2 + (3-x)^2 = 10$$
$$x^2 - 2x + 1 + 9 - 6x + x^2 - 10 = 0$$
$$2x^2 - 8x = 0$$
$$x^2 - 4x = 0$$
$$x(x-4) = 0$$
$$x = 0 \quad \text{or} \quad x - 4 = 0$$
$$x = 4$$

If $x = 0$, $y = 1 - 0 = 1$.

If $x = 4$, $y = 1 - 4 = -3$.

The solution set is $\{(0,1), (4,-3)\}$.

19. Eliminate the y^2–terms by adding the equations.

$$x^2 + y^2 = 13$$
$$\underline{x^2 - y^2 = 5}$$
$$2x^2 = 18$$
$$x^2 = 9$$
$$x = \pm 3$$

If $x = 3$,

$$(3)^2 + y^2 = 13$$
$$y^2 = 4$$
$$y = \pm 2$$

If $x = -3$,

$$(-3)^2 + y^2 = 13$$
$$y^2 = 4$$
$$y = \pm 2$$

The solution set is
$\{(3, 2), (3, -2), (-3, 2), (-3, -2)\}$.

21.
$$x^2 - 4y^2 = -7$$
$$3x^2 + y^2 = 31$$

Eliminate the x^2–terms by multiplying the first equation by -3 and adding the resulting equations.

$$-3x^2 + 12y^2 = 21$$
$$\underline{3x^2 + y^2 = 31}$$
$$13y^2 = 52$$
$$y^2 = 4$$
$$y = \pm 2$$

If $y = 2$,

$$x^2 - 4(2)^2 = -7$$
$$x^2 = 9$$
$$x = \pm 3$$

If $y = -2$,

$$x^2 - 4(-2)^2 = -7$$
$$x^2 = 9$$
$$x = \pm 3$$

The solution set is
$\{(3,2), (3,-2), (-3,2), (-3,-2)\}$.

23. Arrange the equations so that variable terms appear on the left and constants appear on the right.

$$3x^2 + 4y^2 = 16$$
$$2x^2 - 3y^2 = 5$$

Eliminate the y^2–terms by multiplying the first equation by 3 and the second equation by 4. Add the resulting equations.

$$9x^2 + 12y^2 = 48$$
$$\underline{8x^2 - 12y^2 = 20}$$
$$17x^2 = 68$$
$$x^2 = 4$$
$$x = \pm 2$$

If $x = 2$,
$$3(2)^2 + 4y^2 = 16$$
$$y^2 = 1$$
$$y = \pm 1$$

If $x = -2$,
$$3(-2)^2 + 4y^2 = 16$$
$$y = \pm 1$$

The solution set is
$\{(2, 1), (2, -1), (-2, 1), (-2, -1)\}$.

25.
$$x^2 + y^2 = 25$$
$$(x - 8)^2 + y^2 = 41$$

Expand the second equation and eliminate x^2 and y^2–terms by multiplying the first equation by -1 and adding the resulting equations.

$$x^2 - 16x + 64 + y^2 = 41$$
$$\underline{-x^2 - y^2 = -25}$$
$$-16x + 64 = 16$$
$$-16x = -48$$
$$x = 3$$

If $x = 3$,
$$(3)^2 + y^2 = 25$$
$$y^2 = 16$$
$$y = \pm 4$$

The solution set is $\{(3, 4), (3, -4)\}$.

27.
$$y^2 - x = 4$$
$$x^2 + y^2 = 4$$

Eliminate the y^2–terms by multiplying the first equation by -1 and adding the resulting equations.

$$x - y^2 = -4$$
$$\underline{x^2 + y^2 = 4}$$
$$x^2 + x = 0$$
$$x(x + 1) = 0$$
$$x = 0 \quad \text{or} \quad x + 1 = 0$$
$$x = -1$$

If $x = 0$,
$$y^2 = 4$$
$$y = \pm 2$$

If $x = -1$,
$$y^2 - (-1) = 4$$
$$y^2 = 3$$
$$y = \pm\sqrt{3}$$

The solution set is
$\left\{(0, 2), (0, -2), \left(-1, \sqrt{3}\right), \left(-1, -\sqrt{3}\right)\right\}$.

29. The addition method is used here to solve the system.

$$3x^2 + 4y^2 = 16$$
$$2x^2 - 3y^2 = 5$$

Eliminate the y^2–terms by multiplying the first equation by 3 and the second equation by 4. Add the resulting equations.

$$9x^2 + 12y^2 = 48$$
$$\underline{8x^2 - 12y^2 = 20}$$
$$17x^2 = 68$$
$$x^2 = 4$$
$$x = \pm 2$$

If $x = 2$,
$$3(2)^2 + 4y^2 = 16$$
$$y^2 = 1$$
$$y = \pm 1$$

If $x = -2$,
$$3(-2)^2 + 4y^2 = 16$$
$$y = \pm 1$$

The solution set is
$\{(2, 1), (2, -1), (-2, 1), (-2, -1)\}$.

31. The substitution method is used here to solve the system.

$$2x^2 + y^2 = 18$$
$$xy = 4$$

Solve the second equation for y.

$$y = \frac{4}{x}$$

Substitute the expression $\frac{4}{x}$ for y in the first equation and solve for x.

$$2x^2 + \left(\frac{4}{x}\right)^2 = 18$$
$$2x^2 + \frac{16}{x^2} = 18$$
$$2x^4 + 16 = 18x^2$$
$$x^4 - 9x^2 + 8 = 0$$
$$\left(x^2 - 8\right)\left(x^2 - 1\right) = 0$$
$$x^2 - 8 = 0 \quad \text{or} \quad x^2 - 1 = 0$$
$$x^2 = 8 \quad \text{or} \quad x^2 = 1$$
$$x = \pm 2\sqrt{2} \quad \text{or} \quad x = \pm 1$$

If $x = 2\sqrt{2}$, $y = \dfrac{4}{2\sqrt{2}} = \sqrt{2}$.

If $x = -2\sqrt{2}$, $y = \dfrac{4}{-2\sqrt{2}} = -\sqrt{2}$.

If $x = 1$, $y = \dfrac{4}{1} = 4$.

If $x = -1$, $y = \dfrac{4}{-1} = -4$.

The solution set is

$$\left\{\left(2\sqrt{2}, \sqrt{2}\right), \left(-2\sqrt{2}, -\sqrt{2}\right), (1, 4), (-1, -4)\right\}.$$

33. The substitution method is used here to solve the system.

$$x^2 + 4y^2 = 20$$
$$x + 2y = 6$$

Solve the second equation for x.

$$x = 6 - 2y$$

Substitute the expression $6 - 2y$ for x in the first equation and solve for y.

$$(6 - 2y)^2 + 4y^2 = 20$$
$$36 - 24y + 4y^2 + 4y^2 - 20 = 0$$
$$8y^2 - 24y + 16 = 0$$
$$y^2 - 3y + 2 = 0$$
$$(y - 2)(y - 1) = 0$$

$$y - 2 = 0 \quad \text{or} \quad y - 1 = 0$$
$$y = 2 \quad \text{or} \quad y = 1$$

If $y = 2$, $x = 6 - 2(2) = 2$.

If $y = 1$, $x = 6 - 2(1) = 4$.

The solution set is $\left\{(2, 2), (4, 1)\right\}$.

35. Eliminate y by adding the equations.

$$x^3 + y = 0$$
$$\underline{x^2 - y = 0}$$
$$x^3 + x^2 = 0$$
$$x^2(x + 1) = 0$$
$$x^2 = 0 \quad \text{or} \quad x + 1 = 0$$
$$x = 0 \quad \text{or} \quad x = -1$$

If $x = 0$,
$$(0)^3 + y = 0$$
$$y = 0$$

If $x = -1$,
$$(-1)^3 + y = 0$$
$$y = 1$$

The solution set is $\left\{(0, 0), (-1, 1)\right\}$.

37. The substitution method is used here to solve the system.

$$x^2 + (y - 2)^2 = 4$$
$$x^2 - 2y = 0$$

Solve the second equation for x^2.

$$x^2 = 2y$$

Substitute the expression $2y$ for x^2 in the first equation and solve for y.

$$2y + (y - 2)^2 = 4$$
$$2y + y^2 - 4y + 4 = 4$$
$$y^2 - 2y = 0$$
$$y(y - 2) = 0$$
$$y = 0 \quad \text{or} \quad y - 2 = 0$$
$$y = 2$$

If $y = 0$,
$$x^2 = 2(0)$$
$$x^2 = 0$$
$$x = 0$$

If $y = 2$,
$$x^2 = 2(2)$$
$$x^2 = 4$$
$$x = \pm 2$$

The solution set is $\{(0, 0), (-2, 2), (2, 2)\}$.

39. The substitution method is used here to solve the system.

$$y = (x+3)^2$$
$$x + 2y = -2$$

Solve the first equation for x.

$$x = -2y - 2$$

Substitute the expression $-2y-2$ for x in the first equation and solve for y.

$$y = (-2y - 2 + 3)^2 = (-2y + 1)^2$$
$$y = 4y^2 - 4y + 1$$
$$4y^2 - 5y + 1 = 0$$
$$(4y - 1)(y - 1) = 0$$
$$4y - 1 = 0 \quad \text{or} \quad y - 1 = 0$$
$$y = \frac{1}{4} \quad \text{or} \quad y = 1$$

If $y = \frac{1}{4}$, $x = -2\left(\frac{1}{4}\right) - 2 = -\frac{5}{2}$.

If $y = 1$, $x = -2(1) - 2 = -4$.

The solution set is $\left\{(-4, 1), \left(-\frac{5}{2}, \frac{1}{4}\right)\right\}$.

41. The substitution method is used here to solve the system.

$$x^2 + y^2 + 3y = 22$$
$$2x + y = -1$$

Solve the second equation for y.

$$y = -2x - 1$$

Substitute the expression $-2x-1$ for y in the first equation and solve for x.

$$x^2 + (-2x - 1)^2 + 3(-2x - 1) - 22 = 0$$
$$x^2 + 4x^2 + 4x + 1 - 6x - 3 - 22 = 0$$
$$5x^2 - 2x - 24 = 0$$
$$(5x - 12)(x + 2) = 0$$
$$5x - 12 = 0 \quad \text{or} \quad x + 2 = 0$$
$$x = \frac{12}{5} \quad \text{or} \quad x = -2$$

If $x = \frac{12}{5}$, $y = -2\left(\frac{12}{5}\right) - 1 = -\frac{29}{5}$.

If $x = -2$, $y = -2(-2) - 1 = 3$.

The solution set is $\left\{\left(\frac{12}{5}, -\frac{29}{5}\right), (-2, 3)\right\}$.

43. The substitution method is used here to solve the system.

$$x + y = 10$$
$$xy = 24$$

Solve the first equation for y.

$$y = 10 - x$$

Substitute the expression $10 - x$ for y in the second equation and solve for x.

$$x(10 - x) = 24$$
$$10x - x^2 = 24$$
$$x^2 - 10x + 24 = 0$$
$$(x - 4)(x - 6) = 0$$
$$x - 4 = 0 \quad \text{or} \quad x - 6 = 0$$
$$x = 4 \quad \text{or} \quad x = 6$$

If $x = 4$, $y = 10 - 4 = 6$.

If $x = 6$, $y = 10 - 6 = 4$.

The numbers are 4 and 6.

45. Eliminate the y^2-terms by adding the equations.

$$x^2 - y^2 = 3$$
$$\underline{2x^2 + y^2 = 9}$$
$$3x^2 = 12$$
$$x^2 = 4$$
$$x = \pm 2$$

If $x = 2$,
$$2(2)^2 + y^2 = 9$$
$$y^2 = 1$$
$$y = \pm 1$$

If $x = -2$,
$$2(-2)^2 + y^2 = 9$$
$$y^2 = 1$$
$$y = \pm 1$$

The numbers are 2 and 1, 2 and -1, -2 and 1, or -2 and -1.

47.
$$2x^2 + xy = 6$$
$$x^2 + 2xy = 0$$

Multiply the first equation by -2 and add the two equations.

$$-4x^2 - 2xy = -12$$
$$\underline{x^2 + 2xy = 0}$$
$$-3x^2 = -12$$
$$x^2 = 4$$
$$x = \pm 2$$

Back-substitute these values for x in the second equation and solve for y.

For $x = -2$: $(-2)^2 + 2(-2)y = 0$

$$4 - 4y = 0$$
$$-4y = -4$$
$$y = 1$$

For $x = 2$: $(2)^2 + 2(2)y = 0$

$$4 + 4y = 0$$
$$4y = -4$$
$$y = -1$$

The solution set is $\{(-2, 1), (2, -1)\}$.

49. $-4x + y = 12$

$y = x^3 + 3x^2$

Substitute $x^3 + 3x^2$ for y in the first equation and solve for x.

$$-4x + (x^3 + 3x^2) = 12$$
$$x^3 + 3x^2 - 4x - 12 = 0$$
$$x^2(x + 3) - 4(x + 3) = 0$$
$$(x + 3)(x^2 - 4) = 0$$
$$(x + 3)(x - 2)(x + 2) = 0$$
$$x = -3, \ x = 2, \text{ or } x = -2$$

Substitute these values for x in the second equation and solve for y.

For $x = -3$: $y = (-3)^3 + 3(-3)^2$

$$= -27 + 27$$
$$= 0$$

For $x = 2$: $y = (2)^3 + 3(2)^2$

$$= 8 + 12$$
$$= 20$$

For $x = -2$: $y = (-2)^3 + 3(-2)^2$

$$= -8 + 12$$
$$= 4$$

The solution set is $\{(-3, 0), (2, 20), (-2, 4)\}$.

51. $\dfrac{3}{x^2} + \dfrac{1}{y^2} = 7$

$\dfrac{5}{x^2} - \dfrac{2}{y^2} = -3$

Multiply the first equation by 2 and add the equations.

$$\frac{6}{x^2} + \frac{2}{y^2} = 14$$
$$\underline{\frac{5}{x^2} - \frac{2}{y^2} = -3}$$
$$\frac{11}{x^2} = 11$$
$$x^2 = 1$$
$$x = \pm 1$$

Back-substitute these values for x in the first equation and solve for y.

For $x = -1$:

$$\frac{3}{(-1)^2} + \frac{1}{y^2} = 7$$
$$3 + \frac{1}{y^2} = 7$$
$$\frac{1}{y^2} = 4$$
$$y^2 = \frac{1}{4}$$
$$y = \pm\frac{1}{2}$$

For $x = 1$:

$$\frac{3}{(1)^2} + \frac{1}{y^2} = 7$$
$$3 + \frac{1}{y^2} = 7$$
$$\frac{1}{y^2} = 4$$
$$y^2 = \frac{1}{4}$$
$$y = \pm\frac{1}{2}$$

The solution set is

$$\left\{ \left(-1, -\frac{1}{2}\right), \left(-1, \frac{1}{2}\right), \left(1, -\frac{1}{2}\right), \left(1, \frac{1}{2}\right) \right\}.$$

53.

$y = x^2 - 4$
$y = x$

55. $16x^2 + 4y^2 = 64$

$$y = x^2 - 4$$

Substitute the expression $x^2 - 4$ for y in the first equation and solve for x.

$$16x^2 + 4(x^2 - 4)^2 = 64$$
$$16x^2 + 4(x^4 - 8x^2 + 16) = 64$$
$$16x^2 + 4x^4 - 32x^2 + 64 = 64$$
$$4x^4 - 16x^2 = 0$$
$$x^4 - 4x^2 = 0$$
$$x^2(x^2 - 4) = 0$$

$x^2 = 0$ or $x^2 - 4 = 0$

$x = 0$ or $x^2 = 4$

$x = \pm 2$

If $x = 0$, $y = (0)^2 - 4 = -4$.

If $x = 2$, $y = (2)^2 - 4 = 0$.

If $x = -2$, $y = (-2)^2 - 4 = 0$.

It is possible for the comet to intersect the orbiting body at $(0, -4)$, $(-2, 0)$, $(2, 0)$.

57. $2L + 2W = 36$

$LW = 77$

Divide each term in the first equation by 2 and solve L.

$L + W = 18$

$L = 18 - W$

Substitute the expression $18 - W$ for L in the second equation and solve for W.

$(18 - W)W = 77$

$18W - W^2 = 77$

$W^2 - 18W + 77 = 0$

$(W - 11)(W - 7) = 0$

$W - 11 = 0$ or $W - 7 = 0$

$W = 11$ or $W = 7$

If $W = 11$, $L = 18 - 11 = 7$.

If $W = 7$, $L = 18 - 7 = 11$.

The dimensions are 11 feet by 7 feet.

59. $L^2 + W^2 = 10^2 = 100$

$LW = 48$

Solve the second equation for L. $L = \dfrac{48}{W}$

Substitute the expression $\dfrac{48}{W}$ for L in the first equation and solve for W.

$\left(\dfrac{48}{W}\right)^2 + W^2 = 100$

$\dfrac{2304}{W^2} + W^2 - 100 = 0$

$2304 + W^4 - 100W^2 = 0$

$W^4 - 100W^2 + 2304 = 0$

$(W^2 - 36)(W^2 - 64) = 0$

$W^2 - 36 = 0$ or $W^2 - 64 = 0$

$W^2 = 36$ or $W^2 = 64$

$W = \pm 6$ or $W = \pm 8$

The width cannot be -6 or -8 inches.

If $W = 6$,

$L = \dfrac{48}{6} = 8$

If $W = 8$,

$L = \dfrac{48}{8} = 6$

The dimensions are 8 inches by 6 inches.

61. $x^2 - y^2 = 21$

$4x + 2y = 24$

Divide each term in the second equation by 2 and solve for y.

$2x + y = 12$

$y = 12 - 2x$

Substitute the expression $12 - 2x$ for y in the first equation and solve for x.

$x^2 - (12 - 2x)^2 = 21$

$x^2 - (144 - 48x + 4x^2) = 21$

$3x^2 - 48x + 165 = 0$

$x^2 - 16x + 55 = 0$

$(x - 5)(x - 11) = 0$

$x - 5 = 0$ or $x - 11 = 0$

$x = 5$ or $x = 11$

If $x = 11$, $y = 12 - 2(11) = -10$.

If $x = 5$, $y = 12 - 2(5) = 2$.

The dimensions of the floor are 5 meters by 5 meters and the dimensions of the square that will accommodate the pool are 2 meters by 2 meters.

63. Substitute $-0.5x^2 + 5.8x + 185.8$ for y in the other equation.

$5.4x - \overbrace{(-0.5x^2 + 5.8x + 185.8)}^{y} + 146.5 = 0$

$5.4x + 0.5x^2 - 5.8x - 185.8 + 146.5 = 0$

$0.5x^2 - 0.4x - 39.3 = 0$

The quadratic formula gives $x = -8.47$ or $x = 9.27$.   The negative value for x is rejected because the functions domain is after 1990. Back-substitute $x = 9.27$ into either equation to find y.

$y = -0.5x^2 + 5.8x + 185.8$

$y = -0.5(9.27)^2 + 5.8(9.27) + 185.8$

$y \approx 196.58$

This means that the function predicts that about 9 years after 1990, or 1999, men and women received the same number of science and engineering degrees. The graph shows that the actual time that this occurred was during 1999.

71. First determine the solution to the following system of equations.

$$xy = 20$$
$$x^2 + y^2 = 41$$

Solve the first equation for x.

$$x = \frac{20}{y}$$

Substitute the expression $\frac{20}{y}$ for x in the second

equation and solve for in the second equation and solve for y.

$$\left(\frac{20}{y}\right)^2 + y^2 = 41$$

$$\frac{400}{y^2} + y^2 - 41 = 0$$

$$y^4 - 41y^2 + 400 = 0$$

$$\left(y^2 - 25\right)\left(y^2 - 16\right) = 0$$

$$y^2 - 25 = 0 \quad \text{or} \quad y^2 - 16 = 0$$
$$y^2 = 25 \quad \text{or} \quad\quad y^2 = 16$$
$$y = \pm 5 \quad \text{or} \quad\quad y = \pm 4$$

If $y = 5$, $x = \dfrac{20}{5} = 4$.

If $y = -5$, $x = \dfrac{20}{-5} = -4$.

If $y = 4$, $x = \dfrac{20}{4} = 5$.

If $y = -4$, $x = \dfrac{20}{-4} = -5$.

The rectangle formed by joining the points of intersection has sides a and b. The length of a is

$\sqrt{(5-4)^2 + (4-5)^2} = \sqrt{2}$. The length of b is

$\sqrt{(4-(-5))^2 + (5-(-4))^2} = 9\sqrt{2}$.

The area of the rectangle is

$a \cdot b = \left(\sqrt{2}\right)\left(9\sqrt{2}\right) = 18$ square units.

73. $\log_y x = 3$

$\log_y (4x) = 5$

$x = y^3$

$4x = y^5$

Substitute y^3 for x in the equation $4x = y^5$ and solve for y.

$$4(y^3) = y^5$$
$$4 = y^2$$
$$y = \pm 2$$

Keep the positive base.

$x = 2^3 = 8$

The solution set is $\{(8, 2)\}$.

Mid-Chapter 7 Check Point

1.
$$x = 3y - 7$$
$$4x + 3y = 2$$

Since the first equation is solved for x already, we will use substitution.
Let $x = 3y - 7$ in the second equation and solve for y.

$$4(3y - 7) + 3y = 2$$
$$12y - 28 + 3y = 2$$
$$15y = 30$$
$$y = 2$$

Substitute this value for y in the first equation.
$$x = 3(2) - 7 = 6 - 7 = -1$$

The solution is $(-1, 2)$.

2. $\quad 3x + 4y = -5$
$$2x - 3y = 8$$

Multiply the first equation by 3 and the second equation by 4, then add the equations.

$$9x + 12y = -15$$
$$\underline{8x - 12y = 32}$$
$$17x = 17$$
$$x = 1$$

Back-substitute to solve for y.
$$3x + 4y = -5$$
$$3(1) + 4y = -5$$
$$3 + 4y = -5$$
$$4y = -8$$
$$y = -2$$

The solution is $(1, -2)$.

3. $\quad \dfrac{2x}{3} + \dfrac{y}{5} = 6$

$$\dfrac{x}{6} - \dfrac{y}{2} = -4$$

Multiply the first equation by 15 and the second equation by 6 to eliminate the fractions.

$$15\left(\dfrac{2x}{3} + \dfrac{y}{5}\right) = 15(6)$$
$$10x + 3y = 90$$

$$6\left(\dfrac{x}{6} - \dfrac{y}{2}\right) = 6(-4)$$
$$x - 3y = -24$$

We now need to solve the equivalent system
$$10x + 3y = 90$$
$$x - 3y = -24$$

Add the two equations to eliminate y.
$$10x + 3y = 90$$
$$\underline{x - 3y = -24}$$
$$11x = 66$$
$$x = 6$$

Back-substitute to solve for y.
$$x - 3y = -24$$
$$6 - 3y = -24$$
$$-3y = -30$$
$$y = 10$$

The solution is $(6, 10)$.

4. $\quad y = 4x - 5$
$$8x - 2y = 10$$

Since the first equation is already solved for y, we will use substitution.
Let $y = 4x - 5$ in the second equation and solve for x.

$$8x - 2(4x - 5) = 10$$
$$8x - 8x + 10 = 10$$
$$10 = 10$$

This statement is an identity. The system is dependent so there are an infinite number of solutions. The solution set is $\{(x, y) \mid y = 4x - 5\}$.

5. $2x + 5y = 3$

$3x - 2y = 1$

Multiply the first equation by 3 and the second equation by -2, then add the equations.

$6x + 15y = 9$

$\underline{-6x + 4y = -2}$

$19y = 7$

$y = \dfrac{7}{19}$

Back-substitute to solve for x.

$2x + 5y = 3$

$2x + 5\left(\dfrac{7}{19}\right) = 3$

$2x + \dfrac{35}{19} = 3$

$2x = \dfrac{22}{19}$

$x = \dfrac{11}{19}$

The solution is $\left(\dfrac{11}{19}, \dfrac{7}{19}\right)$.

6. $\dfrac{x}{12} - y = \dfrac{1}{4}$

$4x - 48y = 16$

Solve the first equation for y.

$\dfrac{x}{12} - y = \dfrac{1}{4}$

$-y = -\dfrac{x}{12} + \dfrac{1}{4}$

$y = \dfrac{x}{12} - \dfrac{1}{4}$

Let $y = \dfrac{x}{12} - \dfrac{1}{4}$ in the second equation and solve for x.

$4x - 48\left(\dfrac{x}{12} - \dfrac{1}{4}\right) = 16$

$4x - 4x + 12 = 16$

$12 = 16$

This statement is a contradiction. The system is inconsistent so there is no solution. The solution is $\{\ \}$ or $\varnothing$.

7. $2x - y + 2z = -8$

$x + 2y - 3z = 9$

$3x - y - 4z = 3$

Multiply the first equation by 2 and add to the second equation.

$4x - 2y + 4z = -16$

$\underline{x + 2y - 3z = 9}$

$5x + z = -7$

Multiply the first equation by -1 and add to the third equation.

$-2x + y - 2z = 8$

$\underline{3x - y - 4z = 3}$

$x - 6z = 11$

Use the two reduced equations to get the following system:

$5x + z = -7$

$x - 6z = 11$

Multiply the first equation by 6 and add to the second equation.

$30x + 6z = -42$

$\underline{x - 6z = 11}$

$31x = -31$

$x = -1$

Back-substitute to solve for z.

$5x + z = -7$

$5(-1) + z = -7$

$-5 + z = -7$

$z = -2$

Back-substitute to solve for y.

$2x - y + 2z = -8$

$2(-1) - y + 2(-2) = -8$

$-2 - y - 4 = -8$

$-y = -2$

$y = 2$

The solution is $(-1, 2, -2)$.

8.
$$x \quad\ -3z = -5$$
$$2x - y + 2z = 16$$
$$7x - 3y - 5z = 19$$

Multiply the second equation by -3 and add to the third equation.
$$-6x + 3y - 6z = -48$$
$$\underline{7x - 3y - 5z = 19}$$
$$x - 11z = -29$$

Use this reduced equation and the original first equation to obtain the following system:
$$x - 3z = -5$$
$$x - 11z = -29$$

Multiply the second equation by -1 and add to the first equation.
$$x - 3z = -5$$
$$\underline{-x + 11z = 29}$$
$$8z = 24$$
$$z = 3$$

Back-substitute to solve for x.
$$x - 3z = -5$$
$$x - 3(3) = -5$$
$$x - 9 = -5$$
$$x = 4$$

Back-substitute to solve for y.
$$2x - y + 2z = 16$$
$$2(4) - y + 2(3) = 16$$
$$8 - y + 6 = 16$$
$$-y = 2$$
$$y = -2$$

The solution is $(4, -2, 3)$.

9. Solve $x + 2y - 3 = 0$ for x and substitute into the other equation.
$$(\overbrace{-2y + 3}^{x})^2 + y^2 = 9$$
$$4y^2 - 12y + 9 + y^2 = 9$$
$$5y^2 - 12y = 0$$
$$y(5y - 12) = 0$$
$$y = 0 \text{ or } y = \frac{12}{5}$$

Back-substitute these values to find x.
When $y = 0$, $x = -2(0) + 3 = 3$.

When $y = \frac{12}{5}$, $x = -2\left(\frac{12}{5}\right) + 3 = -\frac{9}{5}$.

The solution set is $\left\{(3, 0), \left(-\frac{9}{5}, \frac{12}{5}\right)\right\}$.

10.
$$3x^2 + 2y^2 = 14$$
$$2x^2 - y^2 = 7$$

Multiply the second equation by 2 and add.
$$3x^2 + 2y^2 = 14$$
$$\underline{4x^2 - 2y^2 = 14}$$
$$7x^2 = 28$$
$$x^2 = 4$$
$$x = \pm 2$$

Back-substitute these values to find y.
$$3(2)^2 + 2y^2 = 14$$
$$12 + 2y^2 = 14$$
$$2y^2 = 2$$
$$y^2 = 1$$
$$y = \pm 1$$
$$3(-2)^2 + 2y^2 = 14$$
$$12 + 2y^2 = 14$$
$$2y^2 = 2$$
$$y^2 = 1$$
$$y = \pm 1$$

The solution set is
$$\{(2, 1), (2, -1), (-2, 1), (-2, -1)\}.$$

11. Use the first equation to substitute for y in the second equation.

$$x^2 + \overbrace{(x^2 - 6)^2}^{y} = 8$$

$$x^2 + (x^2 - 6)^2 = 8$$

$$x^2 + x^4 - 12x^2 + 36 = 8$$

$$x^4 - 11x^2 + 28 = 0$$

$$(x^2 - 4)(x^2 - 7) = 0$$

$$x = \pm 2 \text{ or } x = \pm\sqrt{7}$$

Back-substitute these values to find x.

$$y = (2)^2 - 6 \qquad y = (-2)^2 - 6$$

$$y = -2 \qquad\qquad y = -2$$

$$y = (\sqrt{7})^2 - 6 \qquad y = (-\sqrt{7})^2 - 6$$

$$y = 1 \qquad\qquad\quad y = 1$$

The solution set is

$$\left\{ (2, -2), (-2, -2), \left(\sqrt{7}, 1\right), \left(-\sqrt{7}, 1\right) \right\}.$$

12. Use the first equation to substitute for x in the second equation.

$$2y^2 + \overbrace{(2y + 4)}^{x}y = 8$$

$$2y^2 + (2y + 4)y = 8$$

$$2y^2 + 2y^2 + 4y = 8$$

$$4y^2 + 4y - 8 = 0$$

$$y^2 + y - 2 = 0$$

$$(y + 2)(y - 1) = 0$$

$$y = -2 \text{ or } y = 1$$

Back-substitute these values to find x.

$$x = 2(-2) + 4 \quad x = 2(1) + 4$$

$$x = 0 \qquad\qquad y = 6$$

The solution set is $\left\{ (0, -2), (6, 1) \right\}.$

13. $\dfrac{x^2 - 6x + 3}{(x - 2)^3} = \dfrac{A}{x - 2} + \dfrac{B}{(x - 2)^2} + \dfrac{C}{(x - 2)^3}$

Multiply both sides of the equation by the common denominator $(x - 2)^3$.

$$(x - 2)^3 \frac{x^2 - 6x + 3}{(x - 2)^3} = (x - 2)^3 \left(\frac{A}{x - 2} + \frac{B}{(x - 2)^2} + \frac{C}{(x - 2)^3} \right)$$

$$x^2 - 6x + 3 = A(x - 2)^2 + B(x - 2) + C$$

$$x^2 - 6x + 3 = A(x^2 - 4x + 4) + Bx - 2B + C$$

$$x^2 - 6x + 3 = Ax^2 - 4Ax + 4A + Bx - 2B + C$$

$$x^2 - 6x + 3 = (A)x^2 + (-4A + B)x + (4A - 2B + C)$$

Equate coefficients of like powers of x and equate constant terms.

$$A = 1$$

$$-4A + B = -6$$

$$4A - 2B + C = 3$$

Since $A = 1$, we find that $B = -2$ and $C = -5$ by substitution.

$$\frac{2x^2 - 6x + 3}{(x - 2)^3} = \frac{1}{x - 2} + \frac{-2}{(x - 2)^2} + \frac{-5}{(x - 2)^3}$$

14. $\dfrac{10x^2 + 9x - 7}{(x + 2)(x^2 - 1)} = \dfrac{10x^2 + 9x - 7}{(x + 2)(x + 1)(x - 1)} = \dfrac{A}{x + 2} + \dfrac{B}{x + 1} + \dfrac{C}{x - 1}$

Multiply both sides of the equation by the least common denominator.

$$(x + 2)(x + 1)(x - 1) \frac{10x^2 + 9x - 7}{(x + 2)(x + 1)(x - 1)} = (x + 2)(x + 1)(x - 1) \left(\frac{A}{x + 2} + \frac{B}{x + 1} + \frac{C}{x - 1} \right)$$

$$10x^2 + 9x - 7 = (x + 1)(x - 1)A + (x + 2)(x - 1)B + (x + 2)(x + 1)C$$

$$10x^2 + 9x - 7 = (x^2 - 1)A + (x^2 + x - 2)B + (x^2 + 3x + 2)C$$

$$10x^2 + 9x - 7 = x^2A - A + x^2B + xB - 2B + x^2C + 3xC + 2C$$

$$10x^2 + 9x - 7 = (A + B + C)x^2 + (B + 3C)x + (-A - 2B + 2C)$$

Equate coefficients of like powers of x, and equate constant terms.

$$A + B + C = 10$$
$$B + 3C = 9$$
$$-A - 2B + 2C = -7$$

Solving the above system for A, B, and C, we find $A = 5$, $B = 3$, and $C = 2$.

$$\frac{10x^2 + 9x - 7}{(x+2)(x^2-1)} = \frac{5}{x+2} + \frac{3}{x+1} + \frac{2}{x-1}$$

15. $\dfrac{x^2 + 4x - 23}{(x+3)(x^2+4)} = \dfrac{A}{x+3} + \dfrac{Bx+C}{x^2+4}$

Multiply both sides of the equation by the least common denominator.

$$(x+3)(x^2+4)\frac{x^2+4x-23}{(x+3)(x^2+4)} = (x+3)(x^2+4)\left(\frac{A}{x+3} + \frac{Bx+C}{x^2+4}\right)$$

$$x^2 + 4x - 23 = (x^2+4)A + (x+3)(Bx+C)$$

$$x^2 + 4x - 23 = x^2A + 4A + x^2B + 3xB + xC + 3C$$

$$x^2 + 4x - 23 = (A+B)x^2 + (3B+C)x + (4A+3C)$$

Equate coefficients of like powers of x, and equate constant terms.

$$A + B = 1$$
$$3B + C = 4$$
$$4A + 3C = -23$$

Solving the above system for A, B, and C, we find $A = -2$, $B = 3$, and $C = -5$.

$$\frac{x^2 + 4x - 23}{(x+3)(x^2+4)} = \frac{-2}{x+3} + \frac{3x-5}{x^2+4}$$

16. $\dfrac{x^3}{\left(x^2+4\right)^2} = \dfrac{Ax+B}{x^2+4} + \dfrac{Cx+D}{\left(x^2+4\right)^2}$

Multiply both sides of the equation by the least common denominator.

$$\left(x^2+4\right)^2\frac{x^3}{\left(x^2+4\right)^2} = \left(x^2+4\right)^2\left(\frac{Ax+B}{x^2+4} + \frac{Cx+D}{\left(x^2+4\right)^2}\right)$$

$$x^3 = \left(x^2+4\right)(Ax+B) + (Cx+D)$$

$$x^3 = x^3A + x^2B + 4xA + 4B + Cx + D$$

$$x^3 = (A)x^3 + (B)x^2 + (4A+C)x + (4B+D)$$

Equate coefficients of like powers of x, and equate constant terms.

$$A = 1$$
$$B = 0$$
$$4A + C = 0$$
$$4B + D = 0$$

Since $A = 1$ and $B = 0$, we find that $C = -4$ and $D = 0$ by substitution.

$$\frac{x^3}{\left(x^2+4\right)^2} = \frac{1x+0}{x^2+4} + \frac{-4x+0}{\left(x^2+4\right)^2} = \frac{x}{x^2+4} + \frac{-4x}{\left(x^2+4\right)^2}$$

17. **a.** $C(x) = 400,000 + 20x$

     b. $R(x) = 100x$

     c. $P(x) = R(x) - C(x)$

$$= 100x - (400,000 + 20x)$$
$$= 80x - 400,000$$

     d.   The break even point is the point where cost and revenue are the same. We need to solve the system

$$y = 400,000 + 20x$$
$$y = 100x$$

Let $y = 400,000 + 20x$ in the second equation and solve for x.

$$400,000 + 20x = 100x$$
$$400,000 = 80x$$
$$5000 = x$$

Back-substitute to solve for y.

$$y = 100x$$
$$= 100(5000)$$
$$= 500,000$$

Thus, the break-even point is $(5000, \ 500,000)$. The company will break even when it produces and sells 5000 PDAs. At this level, the cost and revenue will both be \$500,000.

18. Let x = the number of roses.
Let y = the number of carnations.

$$x + y = 20$$
$$3x + 1.5y = 39$$

Solve the first equation for x.

$$x + y = 20$$
$$x = 20 - y$$

Substitute this expression for x in the second equation and solve for y.

$$3(20 - y) + 1.5y = 39$$
$$60 - 3y + 1.5y = 39$$
$$-1.5y = -21$$
$$y = 14$$

Back-substitute to solve for x.

$$x = 20 - y = 20 - 14 = 6$$

There are 6 roses and 14 carnations in the bouquet.

19. Let x = number of students at the north campus.
Let y = number of students at the south campus.

$$x + y = 1200$$
$$0.10x + 0.50y = 0.40(1200)$$

or

$$x + y = 1200$$
$$0.1x + 0.5y = 480$$

Solve the first equation for x.

$$x + y = 1200$$
$$x = 1200 - y$$

Substitute this expression for x in the second equation.

$$0.1(1200 - y) + 0.5y = 480$$
$$120 - 0.1y + 0.5y = 480$$
$$120 + 0.4y = 480$$
$$0.4y = 360$$
$$\frac{0.4y}{0.4} = \frac{360}{0.4}$$
$$y = 900$$

Back-substitute and solve for x.

$$x = 1200 - y$$
$$= 1200 - 900$$
$$= 300$$

There were 300 students at the north campus and 900 students at the south campus.

20. x = velocity of the boat
y = velocity of the current

Velocity	Time	Distance
$x + y$	2	$2(x + y)$
$x - y$	6	$6(x - y)$

$$2(x + y) = 9 \quad \rightarrow \quad x + y = 4.5$$
$$6(x - y) = 9 \quad \rightarrow \quad x - y = 1.5$$
$$\overline{\qquad\qquad\qquad\quad 2x \ \ = 6}$$
$$x = 3$$

$$x + y = 4.5$$
$$3 + y = 4.5$$
$$y = 1.5$$

The rowing velocity in still water is 3 mph and the current is 1.5 mph.

21. Because the sum of the measures of the angles of any triangle is $180°$, or

$$x + y + 90 = 180$$
$$x + y = 90.$$

Because the angle with measures x and $(3y + 20)$ are supplementary,

$$x + (3y + 20) = 180.$$

Simplify this equation.

$$x + 3y + 20 = 180$$
$$x + 3y = 160$$

We now have the system

$$x + y = 90$$
$$x + 3y = 160.$$

To solve this system by the addition method, multiply the first equation by -1 and add to the second equation.

$$\begin{array}{r} -x - y = -90 \\ x + 3y = 160 \\ \hline 2y = 70 \\ y = 35 \end{array}$$

Back-substitute.

$$x + y = 90$$
$$x + 35 = 90$$
$$x = 55$$

Thus, $x = 55°$, $y = 35°$, and $(3y + 20) = 125°$.

22. Using the points $(-1, 0)$, $(1, 4)$, and $(2, 3)$ in the equation $y = ax^2 + bx + c$, we get the following system of equations:

$$a - b + c = 0$$
$$a + b + c = 4$$
$$4a + 2b + c = 3$$

Add the first two equations.

$$\begin{array}{r} a - b + c = 0 \\ a + b + c = 4 \\ \hline 2a + 2c = 4 \end{array}$$

Multiply the first equation by 2 and add to the third equation.

$$\begin{array}{r} 2a - 2b + 2c = 0 \\ 4a + 2b + c = 3 \\ \hline 6a + 3c = 3 \end{array}$$

Using the two reduced equations, we get the following system of equations:

$$2a + 2c = 4$$
$$6a + 3c = 3$$

Multiply the first equation by -3 and add to the

second equation.

$$\begin{array}{r} -6a - 6c = -12 \\ 6a + 3c = 3 \\ \hline -3c = -9 \\ c = 3 \end{array}$$

Back-substitute to solve for a.

$$2a + 2c = 4$$
$$2a + 2(3) = 4$$
$$2a + 6 = 4$$
$$2a = -2$$
$$a = -1$$

Back-substitute to solve for b.

$$a + b + c = 4$$
$$-1 + b + 3 = 4$$
$$b = 2$$

The equation is $y = -x^2 + 2x + 3$.

23. $$2l + 2w = 21$$
$$lw = 20$$

Solving $lw = 20$ for l gives $l = \dfrac{20}{w}$.

Substitute into the other equation:

$$2\overbrace{\left(\frac{20}{w}\right)}^{l} + 2w = 21$$

$$\frac{40}{w} + 2w = 21$$

$$w\left(\frac{40}{w} + 2w\right) = w(21)$$

$$40 + 2w^2 = 21w$$
$$2w^2 - 21w + 40 = 0$$
$$(2w - 5)(w - 8) = 0$$

$$w = \frac{5}{2} \text{ or } w = 8.$$

Back-substitute to find l.

When $w = \dfrac{5}{2}$, $l = \dfrac{20}{\frac{5}{2}} = 8$.

When $w = 8$, $l = \dfrac{20}{8} = \dfrac{5}{2}$.

The dimensions of the rectangle are 2.5 m by 8 m.

Section 7.5

Check Point Exercises

1. $4x - 2y \geq 8$

Graph the equation $4x - 2y = 8$ as a solid line.

Choose a test point that is not on the line.

     Test $(0, 0)$

$$4x - 2y \geq 8$$
$$4(0) - 2(0) \geq 8$$
$$0 \geq 8, \quad \text{false}$$

Since the statement is false, shade the other half-plane.

2. $y > -\dfrac{3}{4}x$

Graph the equation $y = -\dfrac{3}{4}x$ as a dashed line.

Choose a test point that is not on the line.

     Test $(1, 1)$

$$y > -\frac{3}{4}x$$
$$1 > -\frac{3}{4}(1)$$
$$1 > -\frac{3}{4}, \quad \text{true}$$

Since the statement is true, shade the half-plane containing the point.

3.   a. $y > 1$

Graph the equation $y = 1$ as a dashed line.

Choose a test point that is not on the line.

     Test $(0, 0)$

$$y > 1$$
$$0 > 1, \quad \text{false}$$

Since the statement is false, shade the other half-plane.

  b.   Graph the equation $x = -2$ as a solid line. Choose a test point that is not on the line.

     Test $(0, 0)$

$$x \leq -2$$
$$0 \leq -2, \quad \text{false}$$

Since the statement is false, shade the other half-plane.

4.   Graph $x^2 + y^2 = 16$ as a solid circle with radius 4 and center $(0, 0)$.

     Test $(0, 0)$

$$x^2 + y^2 \geq 16$$
$$(0)^2 + (0)^2 \geq 16$$
$$0 \geq 16, \quad \text{false}$$

Shade the region not containing $(0, 0)$.

$$x^2 + y^2 \geq 16$$

5.   Graph the equation $x - 3y = 6$ as a dashed line.

$$\underline{\text{Test } (0,0)}$$

$$x - 3y < 6$$

$$(0) - 3(0) < 6$$

$$0 < 6, \text{ true}$$

Since the statement is true, shade the half-plane containing the point.
Graph the equation $2x + 3y = -6$ as a solid line.

$$\underline{\text{Test } (0,0)}$$

$$2x + 3y \geq -6$$

$$2(0) + 3(0) \geq -6$$

$$0 \geq -6, \text{ true}$$

Since the statement is true, shade the half-plane containing the point.
For the solution graph, place an open circle at the point of intersection and shade the region that satisfies both inequalities.

$x - 3y < 6$
$2x + 3y \geq -6$

6.   Begin by graphing $y = x^2 - 4$ as a solid parabola with vertex $(0, -4)$ and x-intercepts $(-2, 0)$ and $(2, 0)$. Since $(0, 0)$ makes the inequality $y \geq x^2 - 4$ true, shade the region containing $(0, 0)$. Graph $x + y = 2$ as a solid line by using its x-intercept, $(2, 0)$, and its y-intercept $(0, 2)$. Since $(0, 0)$ makes the inequality $x + y \leq 2$ true, shade the region containing $(0, 0)$.

$y \geq x^2 - 4$
$x + y \leq 2$

7.   Graph the lines $x + y = 2$, $x = 1$, and $y = -3$ with dashed lines.
Graph the line $x = -2$ with a solid line.
Test points indicate that the solution contains the region to the right of -2, to the left of 1, above -3, and below the line $x + y = 2$. The corner points are represented as open circles because none satisfy all three inequalities.

$x + y < 2$
$-2 \leq x < 1$
$y > -3$

8.   Test $T = 60$ and $P = 20$ in each inequality.

$$T \geq 35$$

$$60 \geq 35 \quad \text{True}$$

$$5T - 7P \geq 70$$

$$5(60) - 7(20) \geq 70$$

$$160 \geq 70 \quad \text{True}$$

$$3T - 35P \leq -140$$

$$3(60) - 35(20) \leq -140$$

$$-520 \leq -140 \quad \text{True}$$

The point $(60, 20)$ checks in all three equations.

Exercise Set 7.5

1.   Graph $x + 2y = 8$ as a solid line using its x-intercept, $(8, 0)$, and its y-intercept, $(0, 4)$.
Test $(0, 0)$:
$0 + 2(0) \leq 8$?
$0 \leq 8$ true
Shade the half-plane containing $(0, 0)$.

$x + 2y \leq 8$

3.　Graph $x - 2y = 10$ as a dashed line using its x-intercept, $(10, 0)$, and its y-intercept, $(0, -5)$.
Test $(0, 0)$:
$0 - 2(0) > 10$?
　　　$0 > 10$ false
Shade the half-plane not containing $(0, 0)$.

$$x - 2y > 10$$

5.　Graph $y = \dfrac{1}{3}x$ as a solid line using its slope, $\dfrac{1}{3}$, and its y-intercept $(0, 0)$.
Test $(1, 1)$:
$$1 \le \frac{1}{3}(1)?$$
$$1 \le \frac{1}{3} \text{ false}$$
Shade the half-plane not containing $(1, 1)$.

$$y \le \frac{1}{3}x$$

7.　Graph $y = 2x - 1$ as a dashed line using its
x-intercept, $\left(\dfrac{1}{2}, 0\right)$ and its y-intercept, $(0, -1)$.
Test $(0, 0)$:
$0 > 2(0) - 1$?
$0 > -1$ true
Shade the half-plane containing $(0, 0)$.

$$y > 2x - 1$$

9.　Graph $x = 1$ as a solid vertical line.
Test $(0, 0)$:
$0 \le 1$ true
Shade the half-plane containing $(0, 0)$.

$$x \le 1$$

11.　Graph $y = 1$ as a dashed horizontal line.
Test $(0, 0)$:
$0 > 1$ false
Shade the half-plane not containing $(0, 0)$.

$$y > 1$$

13.　Graph $x^2 + y^2 = 1$ as a solid circle with radius 1 and center $(0, 0)$.
Test $(0, 0)$:
$(0)^2 + (0)^2 \le 1$?
　　　$0 \le 1$ true
Shade the region containing $(0, 0)$.

$$x^2 + y^2 \le 1$$

15. Graph $x^2 + y^2 = 25$ as a dashed circle with radius 5 and center (0, 0).
Test (0, 0):
$(0)^2 + (0)^2 > 25?$

$0 > 25$ false

Shade the region not containing (0, 0).

$x^2 + y^2 > 25$

17. Graph $(x-2)^2 + (y+1)^2 = 9$ as a dashed circle.

Test (0,0)

$(x-2)^2 + (y+1)^2 < 9$

$(0-2)^2 + (0+1)^2 < 9$

$5 < 9, \quad \text{true}$

Shade the region containing (0, 0).

$(x-2)^2 + (y+1)^2 < 9$

19. Graph $y = x^2 - 1$ as a dashed parabola with vertex (0, −1) and x-intercepts (1, 0) and (−1, 0).
Test (0, 0):
$0 < (0)^2 - 1?$

$0 < -1$ false

Shade the region not containing (0, 0).

$y < x^2 - 1$

21. Graph $y = x^2 - 9$ as a solid parabola with vertex (0, −9) and x-intercepts (3, 0) and (−3, 0).
Test (0, 0):
$0 \geq (0)^2 - 9?$

$0 \geq -9$ true

Shade the region containing (0, 0).

$y \geq x^2 - 9$

23. Graph $y = 2^x$ as a dashed exponential function with base 2 that passes through the point (0, 1).
Test (0, 0):
$0 > 2^0?$

$0 > 1$ false

Shade the region not containing (0, 0).

$y > 2^x$

25. Graph $y = \log_2(x+1)$ as a solid logarithmic function.
Test (0, 0):
$y \geq \log_2(x+1)$

$0 \geq \log_2(0+1)$

$0 \geq 0, \quad \text{true}$

Shade the region containing (0, 0).

$y \geq \log_2(x+1)$

27. Begin by graphing $3x + 6y = 6$ as a solid line using its x-intercept, $(2, 0)$, and its y-intercept, $(0, 1)$. Since $(0, 0)$ makes the inequality $3x + 6y \le 6$ true, shade the half-plane containing $(0, 0)$. Graph $2x + y = 8$ as a solid line using its x-intercept, $(4, 0)$, and its y-intercept, $(0, 8)$. Since $(0, 0)$ makes the inequality $2x + y \le 8$ true, shade the half-plane containing $(0, 0)$. The solution set of the system is the intersection of the above shaded half-planes, and is shown as the shaded region in the following graph.

$3x + 6y \le 6$
$2x + y \le 8$

29. Begin by graphing $2x - 5y = 10$ as a solid line using its x-intercept, $(5, 0)$, and its y-intercept, $(0, -2)$. Since $(0, 0)$ makes the inequality $2x - 5y \le 10$ true, shade the half-plane containing $(0, 0)$. Graph $3x - 2y = 6$ as a dashed line using its x-intercept, $(2, 0)$, and its y-intercept, $(0, -3)$. Since $(0, 0)$ makes the inequality $3x - 2y > 6$ false, shade the half-plane containing $(0, 0)$. The solution set of the system is the intersection of the above shaded half-planes, and is shown as the shaded region in the following graph.

$2x - 5y \le 10$
$3x - 2y > 6$

31. Begin by graphing $y = 2x - 3$ as a dashed line using its slope, 2, and its y-intercept, $(0, -3)$. Since $(0, 0)$ makes the inequality $y > 2x - 3$ true, shade the half-plane containing $(0, 0)$. Graph $y = -x + 6$ as a dashed line using its slope, -1, and its y-intercept, $(0, 6)$. Since $(0, 0)$ makes the inequality $y < -x + 6$ true, shade the half-plane containing $(0, 0)$. The solution set of the system

is the intersection of the above shaded half-planes, and is shown as the shaded region in the following graph.

$y > 2x - 3$
$y < -x + 6$

33. Begin by graphing $x + 2y = 4$ as a solid line using its x-intercept, $(4, 0)$, and its y-intercept, $(0, 2)$. Since $(0, 0)$ makes the inequality $x + 2y \le 4$ true, shade the half-plane containing $(0, 0)$. Graph $y = x - 3$ as a solid line using its slope, 1, and its y-intercept, $(0, -3)$. Since $(0, 0)$ makes the inequality $y \ge x - 3$ true, shade the half-plane containing $(0, 0)$. The solution set of the system is the intersection of the above shaded half-planes, and is shown as the shaded region in the following graph.

$x + 2y \le 4$
$y \ge x - 3$

35. Begin by graphing $x = 2$ as a solid vertical line. Since $(0, 0)$ makes the inequality $x \le 2$ true, shade the half-plane containing $(0, 0)$. Graph $y = 1$ as a solid horizontal line. Since $(0, 0)$ makes the inequality $y \ge -1$ true, shade the half-plane containing $(0, 0)$. The solution set of the system is the intersection of the above shaded half-planes, and is shown as the shaded region in the following graph.

$x \le 2$
$y \ge -1$

37. Graph $x = -2$ as a solid vertical line and $x = 5$ as a dashed vertical line. Since $(0, 0)$ makes the inequality $-2 \leq x < 5$ true, shade the region between the two lines.

$-2 \leq x < 5$

39. Begin by graphing $x - y = 1$ as a solid line using its x-intercept, $(1, 0)$, and its y-intercept $(0, -1)$. Since $(0, 0)$ makes the inequality $x - y \leq 1$ true, shade the half-plane containing $(0, 0)$. Graph $x = 2$ as a solid horizontal line. Since $(0, 0)$ makes the inequality $x \geq 2$ false, shade the half-plane not containing $(0, 0)$. The solution set of the system is the intersection of the above shaded half-planes, and is shown as the shaded region in the following graph.

$-y \leq 1$
$x \geq 2$

41. $x + y > 4$
    $x + y < -1$

Begin by graphing $x + y = 4$ as a dashed line using its x-intercept, $(4, 0)$, and its y-intercept $(0, 4)$. Since $(0, 0)$ makes the inequality $x + y > 4$ false, shade the half-plane not containing $(0, 0)$. Graph $x + y = -1$ as a dashed line using its x-intercept, $(-1, 0)$, and its y-intercept, $(0, -1)$. Since $(0, 0)$ makes the inequality $x + y < -1$ false, shade the half-plane not containing $(0, 0)$. Since these half-planes do not intersect the system has no solution.

43. Begin by graphing $x + y = 4$ as a dashed line using its x-intercept, $(4, 0)$, and its y-intercept, $(0, 4)$. Since $(0, 0)$ makes the inequality $x + y > 4$ false, shade the half-plane not containing $(0, 0)$. Graph $x + y = -1$ as a dashed line using its x-intercept, $(-1, 0)$, and its y-intercept, $(0, -1)$. Since $(0, 0)$ makes the inequality $x + y > -1$ true, shade the half-plane containing $(0, 0)$. The solution set of the system is the intersection of the above half-planes, and is shown as the shaded region in the following graph.

$x + y > 4$
$x + y > -1$

45. Begin by graphing $y = x^2 - 1$ as a solid parabola with vertex $(0, -1)$ and x-intercepts, $(-1, 0)$, and $(1, 0)$. Since $(0, 0)$ makes the inequality $y \geq x^2 - 1$ true, shade the half-plane containing $(0, 0)$. Graph $x - y = -1$ as a solid line using its x-intercept, $(-1, 0)$, and its y-intercept, $(0, 1)$. Since $(0, 0)$ makes the inequality $x - y \geq -1$ true, shade the half-plane containing $(0, 0)$. The solution set of the system is the intersection of the above half-planes, and is shown as the shaded region in the following graph.

$y \geq x^2 - 1$
$x - y \geq -1$

47. Begin by graphing $x^2 + y^2 = 16$ as a solid circle with radius 4 and center, (0, 0). Since (0, 0) makes the inequality $x^2 + y^2 \leq 16$ true, shade the half-plane containing (0, 0). Graph $x + y = 2$ as a dashed line using its x-intercept, (2, 0), and its y-intercept, (0, 2). Since (0, 0) makes the inequality $x + y > 2$ false, shade the half-plane not containing (0, 0). The solution set of the system is the intersection of the above half-planes, and is shown as the shaded region in the following graph.

$$x^2 + y^2 \leq 16$$
$$x + y > 2$$

49. Begin by graphing $x^2 + y^2 = 1$ as a dashed circle with radius 1 and center, (0, 0). Since (0, 0) makes the inequality $x^2 + y^2 > 1$ false, shade the half-plane not containing (0, 0). Graph $x^2 + y^2 = 4$ as a dashed circle with radius 2 and center (0, 0). Since (0, 0) makes the inequality $x^2 + y^2 < 4$ true, shade the half-plane containing (0, 0). The solution set of the system is the intersection of the above half-planes, and is shown as the shaded region in the following graph.

$$x^2 + y^2 > 1$$
$$x^2 + y^2 < 4$$

51.

$$(x - 1)^2 + (y + 1)^2 < 25$$
$$(x - 1) + (y + 1)^2 \geq 16$$

53.

$$x^2 + y^2 \leq 1$$
$$y - x^2 > 0$$

55.

$$x^2 + y^2 < 16$$
$$y \geq 2^x$$

57. Begin by graphing $x - y = 2$ as a solid line using its x-intercept, (2, 0), and its y-intercept, (0, –2). Since (0, 0) makes the inequality $x - y \leq 2$ true, shade the half-plane containing (0, 0). Graph $x = -2$ as a solid vertical line. Since (0, 0) makes the inequality $x \geq -2$ true, shade the half-plane containing (0, 0). Graph $y = 3$ as a solid horizontal line. Since (0, 0) makes the inequality $y \leq 3$ true, shade the half-plane containing (0, 0). The solution set of the system is the intersection of the above half-planes, and is shown as the shaded region in the following graph.

$$x - y \leq 2$$
$$x > -2$$
$$y \leq 3$$

59. Since $x \geq 0$ and $y \geq 0$ the solution to the system lies in the first quadrant. Graph $2x + 5y = 10$ as a solid line using its x-intercept, $(5, 0)$, and its y-intercept, $(0, 2)$. Since $(0, 0)$ makes the inequality $2x + 5y \leq 10$ true, shade the half-plane containing $(0, 0)$. Graph $3x + 4y = 12$ as a solid line by using its x-intercept, $(4, 0)$, and its y-intercept, $(0, 3)$. Since $(0, 0)$ makes the inequality $3x + 4y \leq 12$ true, shade the half-plane containing $(0, 0)$. The solution set of the system is the intersection of the above half-planes which lies in the first quadrant, and is shown as the shaded region in the following graph.

$$x \geq 0$$
$$y \geq 0$$
$$2x + 5y < 10$$
$$3x + 4y \leq 12$$

61. Begin by graphing $3x + y = 6$ as a solid line using its x-intercept, $(2, 0)$, and its y-intercept, $(0, 6)$. Since $(0, 0)$ makes the inequality $3x + y \leq 6$ true, shade the half-plane containing $(0, 0)$. Graph $2x - y = -1$ as a solid line using its x-intercept, $\left(-\frac{1}{2}, 0\right)$, and its y-intercept, $(0, 1)$. Since $(0, 0)$ makes the inequality $2x - y \leq -1$ false, shade the half-plane not containing $(0, 0)$. Graph $x = -2$ as a solid vertical line. Since $(0, 0)$ makes the inequality $x \geq -2$ true, shade the half-plane containing $(0, 0)$. Graph $y = 4$ as a solid horizontal line. Since $(0, 0)$ makes the inequality $y \leq 4$ true, shade the half-plane containing $(0, 0)$. The solution set of the system is the intersection of the above half-planes, and is shown as the shaded region in the following graph.

$$3x + y \leq 6$$
$$2x - y \leq -1$$
$$x > -2$$
$$y < 4$$

63. $y \geq -2x + 4$

65. $x + y \leq 4$
$3x + y \leq 6$

67.

$$x + y \leq 2$$
$$y \geq x^2 - 4$$

69. $-2 \leq x \leq 2$
$-3 \leq y \leq 3$

71. Find the union of solutions of
$$y > \frac{3}{2}x - 2 \text{ and } y < 4.$$

![graph for 71]

73. The system $\begin{array}{l} 3x+3y<9 \\ 3x+3y>9 \end{array}$ has no solution.

The number $3x+3y$ cannot both be less than 9 and greater than 9 at the same time.

75. The system has an infinite number of solutions. The solution is the set of points that make up the circle $(x+4)^2+(y-3)^2=9$

77. a. The coordinates of point A are $(20,150)$.

This means that a 20 year-old person with a pulse rate of 150 beats per minute falls within the target zone.

b. $10 \le a \le 70$
$10 \le 20 \le 70$
True
$150 \ge 0.7(220-20)$
True
$150 \le 0.8(220-20)$
True

Since point A makes all three inequalities true, it is a solution of the system.

79. $10 \le a \le 70$
$H \ge 0.6(220-a)$
$H \le 0.7(220-a)$

81. a. $50x+150y>2000$

b. Graph $50x+150y$ as a dashed line using its x-intercept, $(40, 0)$, and its y-intercept, $\left(0,\dfrac{40}{3}\right)$.
Test $(0, 0)$:
$50(0)+150(0)>2000$?
$\qquad 0>2000$ false
Shade the half-plane not containing $(0, 0)$.

$50x + 150y > 2000$

c. Ordered pairs may vary.

83. a. $\begin{array}{c} y \ge 0 \\ x+y \ge 5 \\ x \ge 1 \\ 200x+100y \le 700 \end{array}$

b. $\begin{array}{l} \mathbf{y \ge 0} \\ \mathbf{x + y \ge 5} \\ \mathbf{x \ge 1} \\ \mathbf{200x + 100y \le 700} \end{array}$

c. 2 nights

85. a. $\text{BMI} = \dfrac{703W}{H^2} = \dfrac{703(200)}{72^2} \approx 27.1$

b. A 20 year old man with a BMI of 27.1 is classified as overweight.

97.

99. $y \ge x^2-4$

101. $2x+y \le 6$

107. $y > x-3$
$y \le x$

109. $x+2y \le 6$ or $2x+y \le 6$

111. $y \geq nx + b$ $(n < 0,\ b > 0)$

   $y \leq mx + b$ $(m > 0,\ b > 0)$

   $y \geq nx + b$ $y = mx + b$
   $y \leq mx + b$
       $(0, b)$

   $y = nx + b$

Section 7.6

Check Point Exercises

1. The total profit is 25 times the number of bookshelves, x, plus 55 times the number of desks, y. The objective function is $z = 25x + 55y$

2. Not more than a total of 80 bookshelves and desks can be manufactured per day. This is represented by the inequality $x + y \leq 80$.

3. Objective function: $z = 25x + 55y$
    Constraints: $x + y \leq 80$
    $$30 \leq x \leq 80$$
    $$10 \leq y \leq 30$$

4. Graph the constraints and find the corners, or vertices, of the region of intersection.

Find the value of the objective function at each corner of the graphed region.

Corner (x, y)	Objective Function $z = 25x + 55y$ z
$(30, 10)$	$z = 25(30) + 55(10)$ $= 750 + 550 = 1300$
$(30, 30)$	$z = 25(30) + 55(30)$ $= 750 + 1650 = 2400$
$(50, 30)$	$z = 25(50) + 55(30)$ $= 1250 + 1650 = 2900 \leftarrow$ Maximum
$(70, 10)$	$z = 25(70) + 55(10)$ $= 1750 + 550 = 2300$

The maximum value of z is 2900 and it occurs at the point (50, 30).
In order to maximize profit, 50 bookshelves and 30 desks must be produced each day for a profit of $2900.

5. objective function: $z = 3x + 5y$
    constraints: $x \geq 0$, $y \geq 0$
    $$x + y \geq 1$$
    $$x + y \leq 6$$

Evaluate the objective function at the four vertices of the region shown:

$(1, 0): 3(1) + 5(0) = 3$

$(0, 1): 3(0) + 5(1) = 5$

$(0, 6): 3(0) + 5(6) = 30$

$(6, 0): 3(6) + 5(0) = 18$

The maximum value of z is 30 and this occurs when $x = 0$ and $y = 6$.

Exercise Set 7.6

1. $z = 5x + 6y$

     $(1, 2)$: $5(1) + 6(2) = 5 + 12 = 17$

     $(2, 10)$: $5(2) + 6(10) = 10 + 60 = 70$

     $(7, 5)$: $5(7) + 6(5) = 35 + 30 = 65$

     $(8, 3)$: $5(8) + 6(3) = 40 + 18 = 58$

     The maximum value is $z = 70$; the minimum value is $z = 17$.

3. $z = 40x + 50y$

     $(0, 0)$: $40(0) + 50(0) = 0 + 0 = 0$

     $(0, 8)$: $40(0) + 50(8) = 0 + 400 = 400$

     $(4, 9)$: $40(4) + 50(9) = 160 + 450 = 610$

     $(8, 0)$: $40(8) + 50(0) = 320 + 0 = 320$

     The maximum value is $z = 610$; the minimum value is $z = 0$.

5. $z = 3x + 2y$

     $x \geq 0, y \geq 0$

     $2x + y \leq 8$

     $x + y \geq 4$

   a.

   b. $(0,8): z = 3(0) + 2(8) = 16$

        $(0,4): z = 3(0) + 2(4) = 8$

        $(4,0): z = 3(4) + 2(0) = 12$

   c.   The maximum value is 16 at $x = 0$ and $y = 8$.

7. $z = 4x + y$

     $x \geq 0, y \geq 0$

     $2x + 3y \leq 12$

     $x + y \geq 3$

   a.

   b. $(0, 4)$: $z = 4(0) + 4 = 4$

        $(0, 3)$: $z = 4(0) + 3 = 3$

        $(3, 0)$: $z = 4(3) + 0 = 12$

        $(6, 0)$: $z = 4(6) + 0 = 24$

   c.   The maximum value is 24 at $x = 6$ and $y = 0$.

9. $z = 3x - 2y$

     $1 \leq x \leq 5$

     $y \geq 2$

     $x - y \geq -3$

   a.

   b. $(1, 2)$: $z = 3(1) - 2(2) = -1$

        $(1, 4)$: $z = 3(1) - 2(4) = -5$

        $(5, 8)$: $z = 3(5) - 2(8) = -1$

        $(5, 2)$: $z = 3(5) - 2(2) = 11$

   c.   Maximum value is 11 at $x = 5$ and $y = 2$.

11. $z = 4x + 2y$
$$x \geq 0, y \geq 0$$
$$2x + 3y \leq 12$$
$$3x + 2y \leq 12$$
$$x + y \geq 2$$

a.

b. $(0, 4): z = 4(0) + 2(4) = 8$
$(0, 2): z = 4(0) + 2(2) = 4$
$(2, 0): z = 4(2) + 2(0) = 8$
$(4, 0): z = 4(4) + 2(0) = 16$
$$\left(\frac{12}{5}, \frac{12}{5}\right): z = 4\left(\frac{12}{5}\right) + 2\left(\frac{12}{5}\right)$$
$$= \frac{48}{5} + \frac{24}{5} = \frac{72}{5}$$

c. The maximum value is 16 at $x = 4$ and $y = 0$.

13. $z = 10x + 12y$
$$x \geq 0, y \geq 0$$
$$x + y \leq 7$$
$$2x + y \leq 10$$
$$2x + 3y \leq 18$$

a.

b. $(0, 6): z = 10(0) + 12(6) = 72$
$(0, 0): z = 10(0) + 12(0) = 0$
$(5, 0): z = 10(5) + 12(0) = 50$
$(3, 4): z = 10(3) + 12(4)$
$$= 30 + 48 = 78$$

c. The maximum value is 78 at $x = 3$ and $y = 4$.

15. a. $z = 125x + 200y$

b. $x \leq 450$
$y \leq 200$
$600x + 900y \leq 360,000$

c. Simplify the third inequality by dividing by 300 to get $2x + 3y \leq 1200$.

d. $(0, 0): 125(0) + 200(0) = 0 + 0 = 0$
$(0, 200): 125(0) + 200(200)$
$$= 0 + 40,000 = 40,000$$
$(300, 200): 125(300) + 200(200)$
$$= 37,500 + 40,000 = 77,500$$
$(450, 100): 125(450) + 200(100)$
$$= 56,250 + 20,000 = 76,250$$
$(450, 0): 125(450) + 200(0)$
$$= 56,250 + 0 = 56,250$$

e. The television manufacturer will make the greatest profit by manufacturing <u>300</u> console televisions each month and <u>200</u> wide-screen televisions each month. The maximum monthly profit is <u>$77,500</u>.

17. Let x = number of model A bicycles and y = number of model B bicycles.
The constraints are
$$5x + 4y \leq 200$$
$$2x + 3y \leq 108$$
Graph these inequalities in the first quadrant, since x and y cannot be negative.

The quantity to be maximized is the profit, which is $25x + 15y$.
$(0, 0): 25(0) + 15(0) = 0 + 0 = 0$
$(0, 36): 25(0) + 15(36) = 0 + 540 = 540$
$(24, 20): 25(24) + 15(20) = 600 + 300 = 900$
$(40, 0): 25(40) + 15(0) = 1000 + 0 = 1000$
40 model A bicycles and no model B bicycles should be produced.

19. Let x = the number of cartons of food and
y = the number of cartons of clothing.
The constraints are:
$20x + 10y \leq 8,000$ or $2x + y \leq 8000$
$50x + 20y \leq 19,000$ or $5x + 2y \leq 1900$
Graph these inequalities in the first quadrant,
since x and y cannot be negative.

The quantity to be maximized is the number of
people helped, which is $12x + 5y$.
$(0, 0)$: $12(0) + 5(0) = 0 + 0 = 0$
$(0, 800)$: $12(0) + 5(800) = 0 + 4000 = 4000$
$(300, 200)$: $12(300) + 5(200) = 4600$
$(380, 0)$: $12(380) + 5(0) = 4500$
300 cartons of food and 200 cartons of clothing
should be shipped. This will help 4600 people.

21. Let x = number of students attending and
y = number of parents attending.
The constraints are
$x + y \leq 150$
$\quad 2x \geq y$
or
$\quad x + y \leq 150$
$2x - y \geq 0$
Graph these inequalities in the first quadrant,
since x and y cannot be negative.

The quantity to be maximized is the amount of
money raised, which is $x + 2y$.
$(0, 0)$: $0 + 2(0) = 0 + 0 = 0$
$(50, 100)$: $50 + 2(100) = 50 + 200 = 250$
$(150, 0)$: $150 + 2(0) = 150 + 0 = 150$
50 students and 100 parents should attend.

23. Let x = number of Boeing 727s, y = number of
Falcon 20s.
Maximize $z = x + y$ with the following
constraints:
$1400x + 500y \leq 35,000$ or $14x + 5y \leq 350$
$42,000x + 6000y \geq 672,000$ or $7x + y \geq 112$
$x \leq 20$
$x \geq 0, y \geq 0$

$(16, 0) : z = 16$

$(20, 0) : z = 20$

$(20, 14) : z = 34$

$(10, 42) : z = 52$

Federal Express should have purchased 10
Boeing 727s and 42 Falcon 20s.

29. Let x = amount invested in stocks and
y = amount invested in bonds.
The constraints are:
$x + y \leq 10,000$
$\quad\quad y \geq 3000$
$\quad\quad x \geq 2000$
$\quad\quad y \geq x$
Graph these inequalities in the first quadrant,
since x and y cannot be negative.

The quantity to be maximized is the return on the investment, which is $0.12x + 0.08y$.

(2000, 3000):
$0.12(2000) + 0.08(3000) = 240 + 240 = 480$

(2000, 8000):
$0.12(2000) + 0.08(8000) = 240 + 640 = 880$

(5000, 5000):
$0.12(5000) + 0.08(5000) = 600 + 400 = 1000$

(3000, 3000):
$0.12(3000) + 0.08(3000) = 360 + 240 = 600$

The greatest return occurs when \$5000 is invested in stocks and \$5000 is invested in bonds.

Chapter 7 Review Exercises

1.
$$y = 4x + 1$$
$$3x + 2y = 13$$
Substitute $4x + 1$ for y in the second equation:
$$3x + 2(4x + 1) = 13$$
$$3x + 8x + 2 = 13$$
$$11x = 11$$
$$x = 1$$
$$y = 4(1) + 1 = 5$$
The solution set is $\{(1, 5)\}$.

2.
$$x + 4y = 14$$
$$2x - y = 1$$
Multiply the second equation by 4 and add to the first equation.
$$x + 4y = 14$$
$$\underline{8x - 4y = 4}$$
$$9x = 18$$
$$x = 2$$
$$2(2) - y = 1$$
$$-y = -3$$
$$y = 3$$
The solution set is $\{(2, 3)\}$.

3.
$$5x + 3y = 1$$
$$3x + 4y = -6$$
Multiply the first equation by 4 and the second equation by −3. Then add.
$$20x + 12y = 4$$
$$\underline{-9x - 12y = 18}$$
$$11x = 22$$
$$x = 2$$
$$5(2) + 3y = 1$$
$$3y = -9$$
$$y = -3$$
The solution set is $\{(2, -3)\}$.

4.
$$2y - 6x = 7$$
$$3x - y = 9$$
The second equation can be written as $y = 3x - 9$.
Substitute:
$$2(3x - 9) - 6x = 7$$
$$6x - 18 - 6x = 7$$
$$-18 = 7$$
Since this is false, the system has no solution. The solution set is the empty set, $\varnothing$.

5.
$$4x - 8y = 16$$
$$3x - 6y = 12$$
Divide the first equation by 4 and the second equation by 3.
$$x - 2y = 4$$
$$x - 2y = 4$$
Since these equations are identical, the system has an infinite number of solutions.
The solution set is $\{(x, y) \mid 3x - 6y = 12\}$.

6. a. $C(x) = 60,000 + 200x$

b. $R(x) = 450x$

c.
$$450x = 60000 + 200x$$
$$250x = 60000$$
$$x = 240$$
$$450(240) = 108,000$$
The company must make 240 desks at a cost of \$108,000 to break even.

7. Let x = the number of years of healthy life expectancy of people in Japan.
Let y = the number of years of healthy life expectancy of people in Switzerland.

The system to solve is
$x + y = 146.4$

$x - y = 0.8$

Add the two equations:
$x + y = 146.4$

$\underline{x - y = 0.8}$

$\quad 2x = 147.2$

$\quad x = 73.6$

Back substitute to find y:
$x + y = 146.4$

$73.6 + y = 146.4$

$\quad y = 72.8$

The number of years of healthy life expectancy in Japan is 73.6 years and in Switzerland is 72.8 years.

8. Let x = the cost of the hotel
y = the cost of the car
$3x + 2y = 360$
$4x + 3y = 500$
Solve the system.
$12x + 8y = 1440$

$-12x - 9y = -1500$

$\quad -y = -60$

$\quad y = 60$

$3x + 2(60) = 360$

$\quad 3x = 240$

$\quad x = 80$

The room costs $80 a day and the car rents for $60 a day.

9. x = ml of 34% solution
y = ml of 4% solution
$$x + y = 100$$
$$0.34x + 0.04y = 0.07(100)$$

$$y = 100 - x$$

$$0.34x + 0.04(100 - x) = 7$$
$$0.34x + 4 - 0.04x = 7$$
$$0.3x = 3$$
$$x = 10$$

$$y = 100 - 10 = 90$$

Mix 10 ml of 34% solution and 90 ml of 4% solution.

10. x = average velocity of the plane
y = average velocity of the wind

Velocity	Time	Distance
$x + y$	3	$3(x + y)$
$x - y$	4	$4(x - y)$

$3(x + y) = 2160$

$4(x - y) = 2160$

$x + y = 720$

$x - y = 540$

$2x = 1260$

$x = 630$

$x + y = 720$

$630 + y = 720$

$y = 90$

The average velocity of the plane is 630 mph and the wind is 90 mph.

11. $2x - y + z = 1 (1)$
$3x - 3y + 4z = 5 (2)$
$4x - 2y + 3z = 4 (3)$
Eliminate y from (1) and (2) by multiplying (1) by –3 and adding the result to (2).
$-6x + 3y - 3z = -3$
$\underline{3x - 3y + 4z = 5}$
$-3x + z = 2 \quad (4)$

Eliminate y from (1) and (3) by multiplying (1) by –2 and adding the result to (3).
$-4x + 2y - 2z = -2$
$\underline{4x - 2y + 3z = 4}$
$z = 2$

Substituting $z = 2$ into (4), we get:
$-3x + 2 = 2$
$-3x = 0$
$x = 0$
Substituting $x = 0$ and $z = 2$ into (1), we have:
$2(0) - y + 2 = 1$
$-y = -1$
$y = 1$
The solution set is $\{(0, 1, 2)\}$.

12. $x + 2y - z = 5 \quad (1)$
$2x - y + 3z = 0 \quad (2)$
$2y + z = 1 \quad (3)$
Eliminate x from (1) and (2) by multiplying (1) by –2 and adding the result to (2).
$-2x - 4y + 2z = -10$
$\underline{2x - y + 3z = 0}$
$-5y + 5z = -10$
$y - z = 2 \quad (4)$
Adding (3) and (4), we get:
$2y + z = 1$
$\underline{y - z = 2}$
$3y = 3$
$y = 1$
Substituting $y = 1$ into (3), we have:
$2(1) + z = 1$
$z = -1$
Substituting $y = 1$ and $z = -1$ into (1), we obtain:
$x + 2(1) - (-1) = 5$
$x + 3 = 5$
$x = 2$
The solution set is $\{(2, 1, -1)\}$.

13. $y = ax^2 + bx + c$
$(1, 4) : 4 = a + b + c \qquad (1)$
$(3, 20) : 20 = 9a + 3b + c \qquad (2)$
$(-2, 25) : 25 = 4a - 2b + c \qquad (3)$
Multiply (1) by –1 and add to (2).
$20 = 9a + 3b + c$
$\underline{-4 = -a - b - c}$
$16 = 8a + 2b$
$8 = 4a + b$
$8 = 4a + b \qquad (4)$
Multiply (1) by –1 and add to (3).
$25 = 4a - 2b + c$
$\underline{-4 = -a - b - c}$
$21 = 3a - 3b$
$7 = a - b \qquad (5)$
Add (4) and (5).
$8 = 4a + b$
$\underline{7 = a - b}$
$15 = 5a$
$a = 3$
$8 = 4(3) + b$
$b = -4$
$3 - 4 + c = 4$
$c = 5$
Hence, the quadratic function is
$y = 3x^2 - 4x + 5$.

14. a. $(0, 3.5) \ (15, 5.0) \ (33, 3.8)$

b. Substitute point values into the equation
$y = ax^2 + bx + c$.
$3.5 = a(0)^2 + b(0) + c$
$3.5 = c$

$5.0 = a(15)^2 + b(15) + c$
$5.0 = 225a + 15b + c$

$3.8 = a(33)^2 + b(33) + c$
$3.8 = 1089a + 33b + c$

15. Model the given information as a system of equations.

$$x - (y + z) = 48$$

or $x - y - z = 48$ Equation 1

$x - 3z = 9$ Equation 2

$x + y + z = 246$ Equation 3

Add equation 1 and 3 and solve for x.

$$x - y - z = 48$$
$$\underline{x + y + z = 246}$$
$$2x = 294$$
$$x = 147$$

Back-substitute into equation 2 to find z.

$$x - 3z = 9$$
$$147 - 3z = 9$$
$$-3z = -138$$
$$z = 46$$

Back-substitute into equation 3 to find y.

$$147 + y + 46 = 246$$
$$y = 53$$

The registrations for Labs was 147 thousand, for Golden retrievers 53 thousand, and for German shepherds 46 thousand.

16. $\dfrac{x}{(x-3)(x+2)} = \dfrac{A}{x-3} + \dfrac{B}{x+2}$

$x = A(x + 2) + B(x - 3)$

$\quad = (A + B)x + (2A - 3B)$

$A + B = 1$

$2A - 3B = 0$

Multiply first equation by 3, then add to second equation.

$$3A + 3B = 3$$
$$\underline{2A - 3B = 0}$$
$$5A = 3$$

$A = \dfrac{3}{5}, B = \dfrac{2}{5}$

$\dfrac{x}{(x-3)(x+2)} = \dfrac{3}{5(x-3)} + \dfrac{2}{5(x+2)}$

17. $\dfrac{11x - 2}{x^2 - x - 12} = \dfrac{11x - 2}{(x-4)(x+3)} = \dfrac{A}{x-4} + \dfrac{B}{x+3}$

$11x - 2 = A(x + 3) + B(x - 4)$

$\quad = Ax + 3A + Bx - 4B$

$\quad = (A + B)x + (3A - 4B)$

$A + B = 11$

$3A - 4B = -2$

Multiply first equation by 4, then add to second

equation.

$$3A - 4B = -2$$
$$\underline{4A + 4B = 44}$$
$$7A = 42$$

$A = 6, B = 5$

$\dfrac{11x - 2}{x^2 - x - 12} = \dfrac{6}{x-4} + \dfrac{5}{x+3}$

18. $\dfrac{4x^2 - 3x - 4}{x^3 + x^2 - 2x} = \dfrac{4x^2 - 3x - 4}{x(x+2)(x-1)}$

$\quad = \dfrac{A}{x} + \dfrac{B}{x+2} + \dfrac{C}{x-1}$

$4x^2 - 3x - 4 = A(x+2)(x-1) + Bx(x-1) + Cx(x+2)$

$\quad = A(x^2 + x - 2) + Bx^2 - Bx + Cx^2 + 2Cx$

$\quad = Ax^2 + Ax - 2A + Bx^2 - Bx + Cx^2 + 2Cx$

$\quad = (A + B + C)x^2 + (A - B + 2C)x - 2A$

$\quad A + B + C = 4$

$\quad A - B + 2C = -3$

$\quad -2A = -4$

$\quad A = 2$

$\quad B + C = 2$

$\quad \underline{-B + 2C = -5}$

$\quad 3C = -3$

$\quad C = -1$

$\quad B - 1 = 2$

$\quad B = 3$

$\dfrac{4x^2 - 3x - 4}{x^3 + x^2 - 2x} = \dfrac{2}{x} + \dfrac{3}{x+2} - \dfrac{1}{x-1}$

19. $\dfrac{2x + 1}{(x-2)^2} = \dfrac{A}{x-2} + \dfrac{B}{(x-2)^2}$

$2x + 1 = A(x - 2) + B = Ax - 2A + B$

$\quad A = 2$

$\quad -2A + B = 1$

$\quad -2(2) + B = 1$

$\quad B = 5$

$\dfrac{2x + 1}{(x-2)^2} = \dfrac{2}{x-2} + \dfrac{5}{(x-2)^2}$

20. $\dfrac{2x-6}{(x-1)(x-2)^2} = \dfrac{A}{x-1} + \dfrac{B}{x-2} + \dfrac{C}{(x-2)^2}$

$2x - 6 = A(x-2)^2 + B(x-1)(x-2) + C(x-1)$

$\qquad = A(x^2 - 4x + 4) + B(x^2 - 3x + 2) + C(x-1)$

$\qquad = Ax^2 - 4Ax + 4A + Bx^2 - 3Bx + 2B + Cx - C$

$\qquad = (A+B)x^2 + (-4A - 3B + C)x + (4A + 2B - C)$

$\qquad A + B = 0$

$-4A - 3B + C = 2$

$\underline{\quad 4A + 2B - C = -6 \quad}$

$\qquad\qquad -B = -4$

$\qquad\qquad B = 4$

$\qquad\qquad\qquad A = -4$

$4(-4) + 2(4) - C = -6$

$\qquad -16 + 8 - C = -6$

$\qquad\qquad -C - 8 = -6$

$\qquad\qquad\qquad -C = 2$

$\qquad\qquad\qquad C = -2$

$\dfrac{2x-6}{(x-1)(x-2)^2} = -\dfrac{4}{x-1} + \dfrac{4}{x-2} - \dfrac{2}{(x-2)^2}$

21. $\dfrac{3x}{(x-2)(x^2+1)} = \dfrac{A}{x-2} + \dfrac{Bx+C}{x^2+1}$

$3x = A(x^2 + 1) + (Bx + C)(x-2)$

$\quad = Ax^2 + A + Bx^2 - 2Bx + Cx - 2C$

$\quad = (A+B)x^2 + (-2B + C)x - (2C - A)$

$\quad A + B = 0$

$-2B + C = 3$

$2C - A = 0$

$\qquad A = 2C$

$B + 2C = 0$

$\underline{4B - 2C = -6}$

$\qquad 5B = -6$

$\qquad B = -\dfrac{6}{5}$

$\qquad A = \dfrac{6}{5}$

$\qquad C = \dfrac{6}{10} = \dfrac{3}{5}$

$\dfrac{3x}{(x-2)(x^2+1)} = \dfrac{6}{5(x-2)} + \dfrac{-6x+3}{5(x^2+1)}$

22. $\dfrac{7x^2 - 7x + 23}{(x-3)(x^2+4)} = \dfrac{A}{x-3} + \dfrac{Bx+C}{x^2+4}$

$7x^2 - 7x + 23 = A(x^2 + 4) + (Bx + C)(x-3)$

$\qquad = Ax^2 + 4A + Bx^2 - 3Bx + Cx - 3C$

$\qquad = (A+B)x^2 + (-3B + C)x + (4A - 3C)$

$\qquad A + B = 7$

$-3B + C = -7$

$4A - 3C = 23$

$3A + 3B = 21$

$\underline{-3B + C = -7}$

$\quad 3A + C = 14$

$\quad 9A + 3C = 42$

$\underline{4A - 3C = 23}$

$\quad 13A = 65$

$\qquad A = 5$

$\qquad 5 + B = 7$

$\qquad\qquad B = 7 - 5 = 2$

$-3(2) + C = -7$

$\qquad C = -7 + 6 = -1$

$\dfrac{7x^2 - 7x + 23}{(x-3)(x^2+4)} = \dfrac{5}{x-3} + \dfrac{2x-1}{x^2+4}$

23. $\dfrac{x^3}{(x^2+4)^2} = \dfrac{Ax+B}{x^2+4} + \dfrac{Cx+D}{(x^2+4)^2}$

$x^3 = (Ax + B)(x^2 + 4) + Cx + D$

$\quad = Ax^3 + 4Ax + Bx^2 + 4B + Cx + D$

$\quad = Ax^3 + Bx^2 + (4A + C)x + (4B + D)$

$\qquad A = 1$

$\qquad B = 0$

$4A + C = 0$

$4B + D = 0$

$\qquad C = -4$

$0 + D = 0, D = 0$

$\dfrac{x^2}{(x^2+4)^2} = \dfrac{x}{x^2+4} - \dfrac{4x}{(x^2+4)^2}$

24. $\dfrac{4x^3 + 5x^2 + 7x - 1}{(x^2 + x + 1)^2} = \dfrac{Ax + B}{x^2 + x + 1} + \dfrac{Cx + D}{(x^2 + x + 1)^2}$

$4x^3 + 5x^2 + 7x - 1$

$= (Ax + B)(x^2 + x + 1) + Cx + D$

$= Ax^3 + Ax^2 + Ax + Bx^2 + Bx + B + Cx + D$

$= Ax^3 + (A + B)x^2 (A + B + C)x + (B + D)$

$\qquad\qquad A = 4$

$\qquad\quad A + B = 5$

$\qquad A + B + C = 7$

$\qquad\qquad B + D = -1$

$\qquad 4 + B = 5, B = 1$

$\qquad 4 + 1 + C = 7, C = 2$

$\qquad\quad 1 + D = -1, D = -2$

$\dfrac{4x^3 + 5x^2 + 7x - 1}{(x^2 + x + 1)^2} = \dfrac{4x + 1}{x^2 + x + 1} + \dfrac{2x - 2}{(x^2 + x + 1)^2}$

25. $\qquad\qquad 5y = x^2 - 1$

$\qquad\qquad x - y = 1$

$\qquad\qquad\quad y = x - 1$

$\qquad\quad 5(x - 1) = x^2 - 1$

$\qquad\quad 5x - 5 = x^2 - 1$

$\quad x^2 - 5x + 4 = 0$

$\quad (x - 4)(x - 1) = 0$

$\qquad\qquad\quad x = 4, 1$

If $x = 4, y = 4 - 1 = 3$.

If $x = 1, y = 1 - 1 = 0$.

The solution set is $\{(4, 3), (1, 0)\}$.

26. $\quad y = x^2 + 2x + 1$

$\qquad x + y = 1$

$\qquad\quad y = 1 - x$

$\quad 1 - x = x^2 + 2x + 1$

$\quad x^2 + 3x = 0$

$\quad x(x + 3) = 0$

$\qquad\quad x = 0, -3$

If $x = 0, y = 1 - 0 = 1$.

If $x = -3, y = 1 - (-3) = 4$.

The solution set is $\{(0, 1), (-3, 4)\}$.

27. $\qquad x^2 + y^2 = 2$

$\qquad\quad x + y = 0$

$\qquad\qquad x = -y$

$\quad (-y)^2 + y^2 = 2$

$\qquad\qquad 2y^2 = 2$

$\qquad\qquad\quad y^2 = 1$

$\qquad\qquad\quad y = 1, -1$

If $y = 1, x = -1$.

If $y = -1, x = 1$.

The solution set is $\{(1, -1), (-1, 1)\}$.

28. $\quad 2x^2 + y^2 = 24$

$\qquad x^2 + y^2 = 15$

$\qquad 2x^2 + y^2 = 24$

$\qquad \underline{-x^2 - y^2 = -15}$

$\qquad\qquad\quad x^2 = 9$

$\qquad\qquad\quad x = 3, -3$

If $x = 3, 3^2 + y^2 = 15, y^2 = 6$ and $y = \pm\sqrt{6}$.

If $x = -3, y = \pm\sqrt{6}$.

The solution set is

$\left\{ \left(3, \sqrt{6}\right), \left(3, -\sqrt{6}\right), \left(-3, \sqrt{6}\right), \left(-3, -\sqrt{6}\right) \right\}$.

29. $\quad xy - 4 = 0$

$\qquad y - x = 0$

$\qquad\quad y = x$

$\qquad\quad xy = 4$

$\qquad\quad x^2 = 4$

$\qquad\qquad x = 2, -2$

If $x = 2, y = 2$.

If $x = -2, y = -2$.

The solution set is $\{(2, 2), (-2, -2)\}$.

30.
$$y^2 = 4x$$
$$x - 2y + 3 = 0$$
$$x = \frac{y^2}{4}$$
$$\frac{y^2}{4} - 2y + 3 = 0$$
$$y^2 - 8y + 12 = 0$$
$$(y-6)(y-2) = 0$$
$$y = 6, 2$$
If $y = 6, x = \dfrac{36}{4} = 9$.

If $y = 2, x = \dfrac{4}{4} = 1$.

The solution set is $\{(9,6),(1,2)\}$.

31.
$$x^2 + y^2 = 10$$
$$y = x + 2$$
$$x^2 + (x+2)^2 = 10$$
$$x^2 + x^2 + 4x + 4 - 10 = 0$$
$$2x^2 + 4x - 6 = 0$$
$$x^2 + 2x - 3 = 0$$
$$(x+3)(x-1) = 0$$
$$x = -3, 1$$
If $x = -3, y = -3 + 2 = -1$.
If $x = 1, y = 1 + 2 = 3$.
The solution set is $\{(-3,-1),(1,3)\}$.

32.
$$xy = 1$$
$$y = 2x + 1$$
$$x(2x+1) = 1$$
$$2x^2 + x - 1 = 0$$
$$(2x-1)(x+1) = 0$$
$$x = \frac{1}{2}, -1$$
If $x = \dfrac{1}{2}, y = 2\left(\dfrac{1}{2}\right) + 1 = 2$.

If $x = -1, y = 2(-1) + 1 = -1$.

The solution set is $\left\{\left(\dfrac{1}{2}, 2\right), (-1,-1)\right\}$.

33.
$$x + y + 1 = 0$$
$$x^2 + y^2 + 6y - x = -5$$
$$x = -y - 1$$
$$(-y-1)^2 + y^2 + 6y - (-y-1) + 5 = 0$$
$$y^2 + 2y + 1 + y^2 + 6y + y + 1 + 5 = 0$$
$$2y^2 + 9y + 7 = 0$$
$$(2y+7)(y+1) = 0$$
$$y = -\frac{7}{2}, -1$$
If $y = -\dfrac{7}{2}, x = \dfrac{7}{2} - 1 = \dfrac{5}{2}$.

If $y = -1, x = 1 - 1 = 0$.

The solution set is $\left\{\left(\dfrac{5}{2}, -\dfrac{7}{2}\right), (0,-1)\right\}$.

34.
$$x^2 + y^2 = 13$$
$$x^2 - y = 7$$
$$x^2 + y^2 = 13$$
$$\underline{-x^2 + y = -7}$$
$$y^2 + y = 6$$
$$y^2 + y - 6 = 0$$
$$(y+3)(y-2) = 0$$
$$y = -3, 2$$
If $y = -3, x^2 + 3 = 7$
$$x^2 = 4, x = 2, -2$$
If $y = 2, x^2 - 2 = 7, x^2 = 9, x = 3, -3$.
The solution set is
$\{(2,-3),(-2,-3),(3,2),(-3,2)\}$.

35.
$$2x^2 + 3y^2 = 21$$
$$3x^2 - 4y^2 = 23$$
$$8x^2 + 12y^2 = 84$$
$$\underline{9x^2 - 12y^2 = 69}$$
$$17x^2 = 153$$
$$x^2 = \frac{153}{17} = 9$$
$$x = 3, -3$$
If $x = 3, 2(3)^2 + 3y^2 = 21$.
$$3y^2 = 21 - 18 = 3$$
$$y^2 = 1, y = 1, -1$$
If $x = -3, y = 1, -1$.
The solution set is
$\{(3,1),(3,-1),(-3,1),(-3,-1)\}$.

36. $2L + 2W = 26$

$LW = 40$

$L = \dfrac{40}{W}$

$2\left(\dfrac{40}{W}\right) + 2W = 26$

$\dfrac{80}{W} + 2W = 26$

$80 + 2W^2 = 26W$

$2W^2 - 26W + 80 = 0$

$W^2 - 13W + 40 = 0$

$(W - 8)(W - 5) = 0$

$W = 8, 5$

If $W = 5, L = \dfrac{40}{5} = 8$

The dimensions are 8 m by 5 m.

37. $xy = 6$

$y = \dfrac{6}{x}$

$2x + y = 8$

$2x + \dfrac{6}{x} = 8$

$2x^2 + 6 = 8x$

$2x^2 - 8x + 6 = 0$

$x^2 - 4x + 3 = 0$

$(x - 1)(x - 3) = 0$

$x = 1, 3$

If $x = 1, y = 6$.

If $x = 3, y = 2$.

The solution set is $\{(1, 6), (3, 2)\}$.

38. $x^2 + y^2 = 2900$

$4x + 2y = 240$

$2x + y = 120$

$y = 120 - 2x$

$x^2 + (120 - 2x)^2 = 2900$

$x^2 + 14,400 - 480x + 4x^2 - 2900 = 0$

$5x^2 - 480x + 11,500 = 0$

$x^2 - 96x + 2300 = 0$

$(x - 46)(x - 50) = 0$

$x = 46, 50$

If $x = 46, y = 120 - 2(46) = 28$.

If $x = 50, y = 120 - 2(50) = 20$.

$x = 46$ ft and $y = 28$ ft or

$x = 50$ ft and $y = 20$ ft

39.

$3x - 4y > 12$

40.

$y \le -\dfrac{1}{2}x + 2$

41.

$x < -2$

42.

$y \ge 3$

43.

$x^2 + y^2 > 4$

44.

$$y \le x^2 - 1$$

45.

$$y \le 2^x$$

46.

$$3x + 2y \ge 6$$
$$2x + y \ge 6$$

4⁷.

$$2x - y \ge 4$$
$$x + 2y < 2$$

48.

$$y < x$$
$$y \le 2$$

49.

$$x + y \le 6$$
$$y \ge 2x - 3$$

50.

$$0 \le x \le 3$$
$$y > 2$$

51. no solution

52.

$$x^2 + y^2 \le 16$$
$$x + y < 2$$

53.

$$x^2 + y^2 \le 9$$
$$y < -3x + 1$$

54.

$$y > x^2$$
$$x + y < 6$$
$$y < x + 6$$

55.

$$y \geq 0$$
$$3x + 2y \geq 4$$
$$x - y \leq 3$$

56. $z = 2x + 3y$

$(2,2): z = 2(2) + 3(2) = 10$

$(4,0): z = 2(4) + 3(0) = 8$

$\left(\dfrac{1}{2}, \dfrac{1}{2}\right): z = 2\left(\dfrac{1}{2}\right) + 3\left(\dfrac{1}{2}\right) = \dfrac{5}{2}$

$(1,0): z = 2(1) + 3(0) = 2$

The maximum value is 10 and the minimum value is 2.

57. $z = 2x + 3y$

$$x \geq 0, \ y \geq 0$$
$$x + y \leq 8$$
$$3x + 2y \geq 6$$

$(0,8): z = 2(0) + 3(8) = 24$

$(8,0): z = 2(8) + 3(0) = 16$

$(0,3): z = 2(0) + 3(3) = 9$

$(2,0): z = 2(2) + 3(0) = 6$

Maximum value is 24 at $(0, 8)$.

58. $z = x + 4y$

$$0 \leq x \leq 5$$
$$0 \leq y \leq 7$$
$$x + y \geq 3$$

$(0,3): z = 0 + 4(3) = 12$

$(3,0): z = 3 + 4(0) = 3$

$(0,7): z = 0 + 4(7) = 28$

$(5,0): z = 5 + 4(0) = 5$

$(5,7): z = 5 + 4(7) = 33$

Maximum value is 33 at $(5,7)$.

59. $z = 5x + 6y$

$$x \geq 0, \ y \geq 0$$
$$y \leq x$$
$$2x + y \leq 12$$
$$2x + 3y \geq 6$$

$(3,0): z = 5(3) + 6(0) = 15$

$(6,0): z = 5(6) + 6(0) = 30$

$\left(\dfrac{6}{5}, \dfrac{6}{5}\right): z = 5\left(\dfrac{6}{5}\right) + 6\left(\dfrac{6}{5}\right) = \dfrac{66}{5} = 13.2$

$(4,4): 5(4) + 6(4) = 44$

The maximum value is 44.

60. a. $z = 500x + 350y$

b. $x + y \leq 200$
$x \geq 10$
$y \geq 80$

c.

$$x + y \le 200$$
$$x \ge 10, y \ge 80$$

d.   Vertex   Objective Function

$$z = 500x + 350y$$

(10, 80) $z = 500(10) + 350(80)$
                   $= 33,000$

(10, 190) $z = 500(10) + 350(190)$
                   $= 71,500$

(120, 80) $z = 500(120) + 350(80)$
                   $= 88,000$

e.   The company will make the greatest profit by producing 120 units of writing paper and 80 units of newsprint each day. The maximum daily profit is $88,000.

61. Let x = number of model A tents produced and y = number of model B tents produced. The constraints are:
$$0.9x + 1.8y \le 864$$
$$0.8x + 1.2y \le 672$$
$$x \ge 0$$
$$y \ge 0$$

The vertices of the region are (0, 0), (0, 480), (480, 240), and (840, 0).
The objective is to maximize $25x + 40y$.
(0, 0): $25(0) + 40(0) = 0 + 0 = 0$
(0, 480): $25(0) + 40(480) = 0 + 19,200 = 19,200$
(480,240): $25(480) + 40(240) = 12,000 + 9600$
             $= 21,600$
(840, 0): $25(840) + 40(0) = 21,000 + 0 = 21,000$
The manufacturer should make 480 of model A and 240 of model B.

Chapter 7 Test

1. $x = y + 4$
      $3x + 7y = -18$
      Substitute $y + 4$ for x into second equation.
      $3(y + 4) + 7y = -18$
      $3y + 12 + 7y = -18$
      $10y = -30$
      $y = -3$
      $x = -3 + 4 = 1$
      The solution set to the system is $\{(1, -3)\}$.

2. $2x + 5y = -2$
      $3x - 4y = 20$
      Multiply the first equation by 3 and the second equation by -2 and add the result.
      $6 + 15y = -6$
      $\underline{-6x + 8y = -40}$
      $23y = -46$
      $y = -2$
      Substitute $y = -2$ into the first equation:
      $2x + 5(-2) = -2$
      $2x - 10 = -2$
      $2x = 8$
      $x = 4$
      The solution to the system is $\{(4, -2)\}$.

3. $x + y + z = 6 (1)$
      $3x + 4y - 7z = 1 (2)$
      $2x - y + 3z = 5 (3)$
      Eliminate x by multiplying (1) by -3 and adding the result to (2) and by multiplying (1) by -2 and adding the result to (3).
      $-3x - 3y - 3z = -18$
      $\underline{3x + 4y - 7z = 1}$
      $y - 10z = -17 (4)$
      $-2x - 2y - 2z = -12$
      $\underline{2x - y + 3z = 5}$
      $-3y + z = -7 (5)$

      Multiply (4) by 3 and add the result to (5) to eliminate y.
      $3y - 30z = -51$
      $\underline{-3y + z = -7}$
      $-29z = -58$
      $z = 2$
      Substitute $z = 2$ into (5).
      $-3y + 2 = -7$
      $-3y = -9$
      $y = 3$

Substitute $z = 2$ and $y = 3$ into (1).
$$x + 3 + 2 = 6$$
$$x = 1$$
The solution to the system is $\{(1, 3, 2)\}$.

4. $x^2 + y^2 = 25$

$x + y = 1$

$y = 1 - x$

Substitute $1 - x$ for y in the first equation.
$$x^2 + (1 - x)^2 = 25$$
$$x^2 + 1 - 2x + x^2 = 25$$
$$2x^2 - 2x - 24 = 0$$
$$x^2 - x - 12 = 0$$
$$(x - 4)(x + 3) = 0$$
$$x = 4, -3$$

If $x = 4, y = 1 - 4 = -3$.

If $x = -3, y = 1 - (-3) = 4$.

The solution set is $\{(4, -3), (-3, 4)\}$.

5. $2x^2 - 5y^2 = -2$

$3x^2 + 2y^2 = 35$

Multiply first equation by 2 and the second equation by 5. Then add.
$$4x^2 - 10y^2 = -4$$
$$\underline{15x^2 + 10y^2 = 175}$$
$$19x^2 = 171$$
$$x^2 = 9$$
$$x = 3, -3$$

If $x = 3, 2(3)^2 - 5y^2 = -2$.
$$18 - 5y^2 = -2$$
$$-5y^2 = -20$$
$$y^2 = 4$$
$$y = 2, -2$$

If $x = -3, y = -2$.

The solution to the system is
$$\{(3, 2), (3, -2), (-3, 2), (-3, -2)\}.$$

6. $\dfrac{x}{(x+1)(x^2+9)} = \dfrac{A}{x+1} + \dfrac{Bx+C}{x^2+9}$

$x = A(x^2 + 9) + (Bx + C)(x + 1)$

$= Ax^2 + 9A + Bx^2 + Bx + Cx + C$

$= (A + B)x^2 + (B + C)x + (9A + C)$

$A + B = 0 \rightarrow A = -B$

$$B + C = 1$$
$$9A + C = 0$$
$$-9B + C = 0$$
$$9B - C = 0$$
$$\underline{B + C = 1}$$
$$10B = 1$$
$$B = \frac{1}{10}$$

$$A = -\frac{1}{10}$$

$$\frac{1}{10} + C = 1, \ C = \frac{9}{10}$$

$$\frac{x}{(x+1)(x^2+9)} = \frac{-1}{10(x+1)} + \frac{x+9}{10(x^2+9)}$$

7.

$x - 2y < 8$

8.

$x \geq 0, \ y \geq 0$

$3x + y \leq 9$

$2x + 3y \geq 6$

9.

$x^2 + y^2 > 1$

$x^2 + y^2 < 4$

10.

$$y \le 1 - x^2$$
$$x^2 + y^2 \le 9$$

11. $z = 3x + 5y$
$x \ge 0, y \ge 0$
$x + y \le 6$
$x \ge 2$

$(2,0): z = 3(2) + 5(0) = 6$
$(6,0): z = 3(6) + 5(0) = 18$
$(2,4): z = 3(2) + 5(4) = 26$
Maximum value is 26.

12. x = mg of cholesterol in one ounce of shrimp
y = mg of cholesterol in one ounce of scallops
$3x + 2y = 156$
$5x + 3y = 255$
Multiply the first equation by –3 and multiply the second equation by 2.
Add the resulting equations together.
$-9x - 6y = -468$
$\underline{10x + 6y = \ 510}$
$\quad\quad x = \ 42$

$3(42) + 2y = 156$
$126 + 2y = 156$
$2y = 30$
$y = 15$
$3(42) + 2y = 156$
$126 + 2y = 156$
$2y = 30$
$y = 15$
Shrimp: 42 mg of cholesterol per ounce
Scallops: 15 mg of cholesterol per ounce

13. a. $C(x) = 360,000 + 850x$

b. $R(x) = 1150x$

c. $1150x = 360000 + 850x$
$300x = 360000$
$x = 1200$
$1150(1200) = 1,380,000$
1200 computers need to be sold to make $1,380,00 for the company to break even.

14. x = ounces of 20% solution
y = ounces of 50% solution
$x + y = 60$
$0.2x + 0.5y = 0.3(60)$

$y = 60 - x$

$0.2x + 0.5(60 - x) = 18$
$0.2x + 30 - 0.5x = 18$
$-0.3x = -12$
$x = 40$

$y = 60 - 40 = 20$
Mix 40 ounces of 20% solution and 20 ml of 50% solution.

15. x = average velocity of the plane
y = average velocity of the wind

Velocity	Time	Distance
$x + y$	2	$2(x + y)$
$x - y$	3	$3(x - y)$

$2(x + y) = 1600$
$3(x - y) = 1950$

$x + y = 800$
$x - y = 650$

$2x = 1450$
$x = 725$

$x + y = 800$
$725 + y = 75$
$y = 90$
The average velocity of the plane is 725 mph and the wind is 75 mph.

16. $y = ax^2 + bx + c$

$(-1, -2): -2 = a - b + c$

$(2, 1): 1 = 4a + 2b + c$

$(-2, 1): 1 = 4a - 2b + c$

$\begin{array}{r} 4a + 2b + c = 1 \\ -4a + 2b - c = -1 \\ \hline 4b = 0 \\ b = 0 \end{array}$

$a + c = -2$

$\begin{array}{r} 4a + c = 1 \\ -a - c = 2 \\ \hline 3a = 3 \\ a = 1 \end{array}$

$a + c = -2$

$c = -3$

The quadratic function is $y = x^2 - 3$.

17. $2x + y = 39$

$xy = 180$

$y = 39 - 2x$

$x(39 - 2x) = 180$

$39x - 2x^2 = 180$

$2x^2 - 39x + 180 = 0$

$(2x - 15)(x - 12) = 0$

$x = \dfrac{15}{2}, 12$

If $x = \dfrac{15}{2}, \dfrac{15}{2} y = 180$ and $y = 24$.

If $x = 12, 12y = 180$ and $y = 15$.

The dimensions are 7.5 ft by 24 ft or 12 ft by 15 ft

18. Let x = regular, y = deluxe.

objective function: $z = 200x + 250y$

constraints: $x \geq 50, y \geq 75$

$x + y \leq 150$

$(50, 75): z = 200(50) + 250(75) = 28,750$

$(50, 100): z = 200(50) + 250(100) = 35,000$

$(75, 75): z = 200(75) + 250(75) = 33,750$

For a maximum profit of $35,000 a week, the company should manufacture 50 regular and 100 deluxe jet skis.

Cumulative Review Exercises (Chapters P–7)

1. Domain: $(-\infty, \infty)$ Range: $[-\infty, 3)$

2. -1 and 1 are both zeros with a minimum multiplicity of 1.

3. The relative maximum is $y = 3$ and it occurs at $x = 0$.

4. $f(x)$ is decreasing on the interval $(0, 2)$.

5. At $x = -0.7$, the curve is above the x-axis and thus $f(x)$ is positive.

6. $(f \circ f)(-1) = f\big(f(-1)\big) = f(0) = 3$

7. $f(x) \to -\infty$ as $x \to -2^+$ or as $x \to 2^-$.

8. $f(-x) = f(x)$ thus the function is even.

9. The graph of $g(x) = f(x + 2) - 1$ can be obtained by shifting $f(x)$ 2 units left and 1 unit down.

$g(x) = f(x + 2) - 1$

10. The graph of $h(x) = \frac{1}{2} f\left(\frac{1}{2} x\right)$ can be obtained by shrinking the graph of $f(x)$ horizontally by a factor of $\frac{1}{2}$ and vertically by a factor of $\frac{1}{2}$.

$$h(x) = \frac{1}{2} f\left(\frac{1}{2} x\right)$$

11.
$$\sqrt{x^2 - 3x} = 2x - 6$$
$$x^2 - 3x = 4x^2 - 24x + 36$$
$$3x^2 - 21x + 36 = 0$$
$$x^2 - 7x + 12 = 0$$
$$(x-3)(x-4) = 0$$
$$x = 3, 4$$
The solution set is $\{3, 4\}$.

12.
$$4x^2 = 8x - 7$$
$$4x^2 - 8x + 7 = 0$$
$$x = \frac{8 \pm \sqrt{64 - 112}}{8} = \frac{8 \pm \sqrt{-48}}{8}$$
$$= \frac{8 \pm 4\sqrt{3}i}{8} = \frac{2 \pm \sqrt{3}i}{2}$$
The solution set is $\left\{ \frac{2 + i\sqrt{3}}{2}, \frac{2 - i\sqrt{3}}{2} \right\}$.

13. $\left| \frac{x}{3} + 2 \right| < 4$

$$-4 < \frac{x}{3} + 2 < 4$$
$$-6 < \frac{x}{3} < 2$$
$$-18 < x < 6$$
The solution is $\{x \mid -18 < x < 6\}$ or $(-18, 6)$.

14.
$$\frac{x+5}{x-1} > 2$$
$$\frac{x+5}{x-1} - 2 > 0$$
$$\frac{x + 5 - 2(x-1)}{x-1} > 0$$
$$\frac{x + 5 - 2x + 2}{x-1} > 0$$
$$\frac{-x + 7}{x-1} > 0$$

$\dfrac{-x+7}{x-1} = 0$ when $x = 7$ and is undefined when $x = 1$.

Test $x = 0$:
$$\frac{0+5}{0-1} > 2 ?$$
$$\frac{5}{-1} > 2 ?$$
$$-5 \not> 2$$

Test $x = 2$:
$$\frac{2+5}{2-1} > 2 ?$$
$$\frac{7}{1} > 2 ?$$
$$7 > 2$$

Test $x = 8$:
$$\frac{8+5}{8-1} > 2 ?$$
$$\frac{13}{7} > 2 ?$$
$$\frac{13}{7} \geq \frac{14}{7}$$

The solution is $\{x \mid 1 < x < 7\}$ or $(1, 7)$.

15. $2x^3 + x^2 - 13x + 6 = 0$

$f(x) = 2x^3 + x^2 - 13x + 6$ has 2 sign changes: 2 or 0 positive real roots.

$f(-x) = -2x^3 + x^2 + 13x + 6$ has 1 sign change: 1 negative real root.

$p: \pm 1, \pm 2, \pm 3, \pm 6$

$q: \pm 1, \pm 2$

$\dfrac{p}{q}: \pm 1, \pm \dfrac{1}{2}, \pm 2, \pm 3, \pm \dfrac{3}{2}, \pm 6$

$$
\begin{array}{r|rrrr}
-3 & 2 & 1 & -13 & 6 \\
   &   & -6 & 15 & -6 \\
\hline
   & 2 & -5 & 2 & 0
\end{array}
$$

$2x^3 + x^2 - 13x + 6 = (x+3)(2x^2 - 5x + 2)$
$\qquad\qquad\qquad\quad = (x+3)(2x-1)(x-2)$

$x = -3, \; x = \dfrac{1}{2}, \; x = 2$

The solution set is $\left\{-3, \frac{1}{2}, 2\right\}$.

16. $6x - 3(5x + 2) = 4(1 - x)$

$6x - 15x - 6 = 4 - 4x$

$-9x - 6 = 4 - 4x$

$-5x = 10$

$x = -2$

The solution set is $\{-2\}$.

17. $\log(x + 3) + \log x = 1$

$\log x(x + 3) = 1$

$x(x + 3) = 10$

$x^2 + 3x - 10 = 0$

$(x + 5)(x - 2) = 0$

$\qquad\qquad x = -5 \text{ or } x = 2$

$x = -5$ is extraneous.

$\qquad\qquad x = 2$

The solution set is $\{2\}$.

18. $3^{x+2} = 11$

$\log_3 3^{x+2} = \log_3 11$

$x + 2 = \log_3 11$

$x = -2 + \log_3 11$

$x = -2 + \dfrac{\log 11}{\log 3} \approx 0.18$

The solution set is $\left\{-2 + \log_3 11\right\}$.

19. $x^{\frac{1}{2}} - 2x^{\frac{1}{4}} - 15 = 0$

$\sqrt[4]{x^2} - 2\sqrt[4]{x} - 15 = 0$

$\left(\sqrt[4]{x} + 3\right)\left(\sqrt[4]{x} - 5\right) = 0$

$\begin{array}{lll} \sqrt[4]{x} + 3 = 0 & & \sqrt[4]{x} - 5 = 0 \\ \sqrt[4]{x} = -3 & \text{or} & \sqrt[4]{x} = 5 \\ x = (-3)^4 & & x = 5^4 \\ x = 81 & & x = 625 \end{array}$

81 does not check. The solution set is $\{625\}$.

20. $3x - y = -2$

$2x^2 - y = 0$

Solve the first equation for y.

$3x - y = -2$

$\qquad y = 3x + 2$

Use this equation to substitute into the other equation.

$2x^2 - (\overbrace{3x + 2}^{y}) = 0$

$2x^2 - 3x - 2 = 0$

$(2x + 1)(x - 2) = 0$

$x = -\dfrac{1}{2} \text{ or } x = 2.$

Back-substitute to find y.

$\begin{array}{lll} y = 3x + 2 & \text{or} & y = 3x + 2 \\ y = 3(2) + 2 & & y = 3\left(-\dfrac{1}{2}\right) + 2 \\ y = 8 & & y = \dfrac{1}{2} \end{array}$

$y = 3x + 2$

The solution set is $\left\{(2, 8), \left(-\dfrac{1}{2}, \dfrac{1}{2}\right)\right\}$.

21. $x + 2y + 3z = -2$

$3x + 3y + 10z = -2$

$\qquad\quad 2y - 5z = 6$

Multiply equation 1 by -3 and add to equation 2.

$-3x - 6y - 9z = 6$

$\underline{3x + 3y + 10z = -2}$

$\qquad -3y + z = 4 \quad$ Equation 4

Multiply equation 4 by 5 and add to equation 3 and solve for y.

$$-15y + 5z = 20$$
$$\underline{2y - 5z = 6}$$
$$-13y = 26$$
$$y = -2$$

Back-substitute to find z.
$$-3y + z = 4$$
$$-3(-2) + z = 4$$
$$z = -2$$

Back-substitute to find x.
$$x + 2y + 3z = -2$$
$$x + 2(-2) + 3(-2) = -2$$
$$x = 8$$

The solution set is $\{8, -2, -2\}$.

22. vertex: $(-2, -4)$
    y-intercept:
    $$f(0) = (0 + 2)^2 - 4 = 0$$
    x-intercepts:
    $$(x + 2)^2 - 4 = 0$$
    $$x^2 + 4x + 4 - 4 = 0$$
    $$x^2 + 4x = 0$$
    $$x(x + 4) = 0$$
    $$x = 0, x - 4$$

$$f(x) = (x + 2)^2 - 4$$

23.

$$2x - 3y \leq 6$$

24.

$$y = 3^{x-2}$$

25. vertical asymptote: $x = -1$
    horizontal asymptote: $m > n$, none
    x-intercepts:
    $$x^2 - x - 6 = 0$$
    $$(x - 3)(x + 2) = 0$$
    $$x = 3, x = -2$$
    y-intercept:
    $$f(0) = \frac{0^2 - 0 - 6}{0 + 1} = -6$$

$$f(x) = \frac{x^2 - x - 6}{x + 1}$$

26.

$$f(x) = 2x - 4$$
$$f^{-1}(x) = \frac{x + 4}{2}$$

27.

$$(x - 2)^2 + (y - 4)^2 > 9$$

28.

$$f(x) = |x|$$
$$g(x) = -|x - 2|$$

29. $(f \circ g)(x) = f(g(x))$

$$= 2(1-x)^2 - (1-x) - 1$$
$$= 2x^2 - 3x$$

$(g \circ f) = g(f(x))$

$$= 1 - (2x^2 - x - 1)$$
$$= 1 - 2x^2 + x + 1$$
$$= -2x^2 + x + 2$$

30. $\dfrac{f(x+h) - f(x)}{h}$

$$= \frac{\left[2(x+h)^2 - (x+h) - 1\right] - \left[2x^2 - x - 1\right]}{h}$$

$$= \frac{2x^2 + 4hx + 2h^2 - x - h - 1 - 2x^2 + x + 1}{h}$$

$$= \frac{4hx + 2h^2 - h}{h}$$

$$= 4x + 2h - 1$$

31. Find slope: $m = \dfrac{4 - (-2)}{2 - 4} = \dfrac{6}{-2} = -3$

Use point slope form to find an equation.

$$y - y_1 = m(x - x_1)$$
$$y - 4 = -3(x - 2)$$

Put in slope-intercept form.

$$y - 4 = -3(x - 2)$$
$$y - 4 = -3x + 6$$
$$y = -3x + 10$$

32. Find the slope of the perpendicular line by putting in slope-intercept form.

$$x + 3y - 6 = 0$$
$$3y = -x + 6$$
$$y = -\frac{1}{3}x + 2$$

The slope of the perpendicular line is $-\dfrac{1}{3}$ so the slope of the desired line is the negative reciprocal, or 3.

Use point slope form to find an equation.

$$y - y_1 = m(x - x_1)$$
$$y - 0 = 3(x + 1)$$

Put in slope-intercept form.

$$y - 0 = 3(x + 1)$$
$$y = 3x + 3$$

33. Let x = the amount invested at 12%
Let $4000 - x$ = the amount invested at 14%

$$0.12x + 0.14(4000 - x) = 508$$
$$0.12x + 560 - 0.14x = 508$$
$$-0.02x = -52$$
$$x = \frac{-52}{-0.02}$$
$$x = 2600$$

$4000 - x = 4000 - 2600 = 1400$
Thus, \$2600 was invested at 12% and \$1400 was invested at 14%.

34.
$$L = 2W + 1$$
$$LW = 36$$
$$W(2W + 1) = 36$$
$$2W^2 + W - 36 = 0$$
$$(2W + 9)(W - 4) = 0$$
$$W = -\frac{9}{2} \text{ or } 4$$

Length cannot be negative. If $W = 4$, $4L = 36$, $L = 9$. The dimensions are 4 m by 9 m.

35. $A = Pe^{rt}$
$$18,000 = 6000e^{10r}$$
$$3 = e^{10r}$$
$$\ln 3 = \ln e^{10r}$$
$$\ln 3 = 10r$$
$$r = \frac{\ln 3}{10} \approx 0.1099$$

10.99%

36. $\sec\theta - \cos\theta = \dfrac{1}{\cos\theta} - \cos\theta$

$\qquad\qquad = \dfrac{1-\cos^2\theta}{\cos\theta}$

$\qquad\qquad = \dfrac{\sin^2\theta}{\cos\theta}$

$\qquad\qquad = \dfrac{\sin\theta}{\cos\theta}\cdot\sin\theta$

$\qquad\qquad = \tan\theta\cdot\sin\theta$

37. $\tan x + \tan y = \dfrac{\sin x}{\cos x} + \dfrac{\sin y}{\cos y}$

$\qquad\qquad = \dfrac{\sin x\cdot\cos y+\sin y\cdot\cos x}{\cos x\cdot\cos y}$

$\qquad\qquad = \dfrac{\sin(x+y)}{\cos x\cdot\cos y}$

38.
$$\sin\theta = \tan\theta$$
$$\sin\theta = \frac{\sin\theta}{\cos\theta}$$
$$\sin\theta - \frac{\sin\theta}{\cos\theta} = 0$$
$$\sin\theta\left(1-\frac{1}{\cos\theta}\right) = 0$$

$\sin\theta = 0 \qquad$ or $\qquad 1-\dfrac{1}{\cos\theta}=0$

$\theta = 0,\ \pi \quad$ or $\qquad\qquad 1 = \dfrac{1}{\cos\theta}$

$$\cos\theta = 1$$
$$\theta = 0$$

The solutions in the interval $[0,\,2\pi)$ are 0 and π.

39.
$$2+\cos 2\theta = 3\cos\theta$$
$$2+(2\cos^2\theta-1) = 3\cos\theta$$
$$2\cos^2\theta+1 = 3\cos\theta$$
$$2\cos^2\theta-3\cos\theta+1 = 0$$
$$(2\cos\theta-1)(\cos\theta-1) = 0$$

$2\cos\theta-1=0 \quad$ or $\quad \cos\theta-1=0$

$2\cos\theta=1 \qquad\qquad \cos\theta=1$

$\cos\theta = \dfrac{1}{2}$

$\theta = \dfrac{\pi}{3},\ \dfrac{5\pi}{3} \quad$ or $\qquad \theta = 0$

The solutions in the interval $[0,\,2\pi)$ are

$0,\ \dfrac{\pi}{3},$ and $\dfrac{5\pi}{3}$.

40. $\qquad \dfrac{b}{\sin B} = \dfrac{a}{\sin A}$

$\qquad\quad \dfrac{b}{\sin 75°} = \dfrac{20}{\sin 12°}$

$\qquad\qquad b = \dfrac{20\sin 75°}{\sin 12°} \approx 92.9$

Chapter 8

Section 8.1

Check Point Exercises

1.
$$\begin{bmatrix} 1 & -1 & 1 & | & 8 \\ 0 & 1 & -12 & | & -15 \\ 0 & 0 & 1 & | & 1 \end{bmatrix} \rightarrow \begin{array}{l} 1x - 1y + 1z = 8 \\ 0x + 1y - 12z = -15 \\ 0x + 0y + 1z = 1 \end{array}$$

$x - y + z = 8$

$\quad y - 12z = -15$

$\qquad z = 1$

Solve for y by back-substitution.

$y - 12(1) = -15$

$\quad y - 12 = -15$

$\qquad y = -3$

Use back substitution for x.

$x - (-3) + 1 = 8$

$\qquad x + 4 = 8$

$\qquad\quad x = 4$

The solution set for the system is $\{(4, -3, 1)\}$.

2. **a.** The notation $R_1 \leftrightarrow R_2$ means to interchange the elements in row 1 and row 2. This results in the row-equivalent matrix

$$\begin{bmatrix} 1 & 6 & -3 & | & 7 \\ 4 & 12 & -20 & | & 8 \\ -3 & -2 & 1 & | & -9 \end{bmatrix}.$$

b. The notation $\frac{1}{4}R_1$ means to multiply each element in row 1 by $\frac{1}{4}$. This results in the row-equivalent

matrix

$$\begin{bmatrix} \frac{1}{4}(4) & \frac{1}{4}(12) & \frac{1}{4}(-20) & | & \frac{1}{4}(8) \\ 1 & 6 & -3 & | & 7 \\ -3 & -2 & 1 & | & -9 \end{bmatrix} = \begin{bmatrix} 1 & 3 & -5 & | & 2 \\ 1 & 6 & -3 & | & 7 \\ -3 & -2 & 1 & | & -9 \end{bmatrix}$$

c. The notation $3R_2 + R_3$ means to add 3 times the elements in row 2 to the corresponding elements in row 3. Replace the elements in row 3 by these sums. First, we find 3 times the elements in row 2: $3(1) = 3$, $3(6) = 18$, $3(-3) = -9$, $3(7) = 21$. Now we add these products to the corresponding elements in row 3. This results in the row equivalent matrix

$$\begin{bmatrix} 4 & 12 & -20 & | & 8 \\ 1 & 6 & -3 & | & 7 \\ -3+3=0 & -2+18=16 & 1-9=-8 & | & -9+21=12 \end{bmatrix} = \begin{bmatrix} 4 & 12 & -20 & | & 8 \\ 1 & 6 & -3 & | & 7 \\ 0 & 16 & -8 & | & 12 \end{bmatrix}.$$

3. $\begin{aligned} 2x+y+2z &=18 \\ x-y+2z &=9 \\ x+2y-z &=6 \end{aligned} \rightarrow \begin{bmatrix} 2 & 1 & 2 & | & 18 \\ 1 & -1 & 2 & | & 9 \\ 1 & 2 & -1 & | & 6 \end{bmatrix}$

Interchange row 1 with row 2 to get 1 in the top position of the first column.

$$\begin{bmatrix} 1 & -1 & 2 & | & 9 \\ 2 & 1 & 2 & | & 18 \\ 1 & 2 & -1 & | & 6 \end{bmatrix}$$

Multiply the first row by –2 and add these products to row 2.

$$\begin{bmatrix} 1 & -1 & 2 & | & 9 \\ 2+-2=0 & 1+2=3 & 2+-4=-2 & | & -18+18=0 \\ 1 & 2 & -1 & | & 6 \end{bmatrix} = \begin{bmatrix} 1 & -1 & 2 & | & 9 \\ 0 & 3 & -2 & | & 0 \\ 1 & 2 & -1 & | & 6 \end{bmatrix}$$

Next, multiply the top row by –1 and add these products to row 3.

$$\begin{bmatrix} 1 & -1 & 2 & | & 9 \\ 0 & 3 & -2 & | & 0 \\ 1+-1=0 & 2+1=3 & -1-2=-3 & | & 6-9=-3 \end{bmatrix} = \begin{bmatrix} 1 & -1 & 2 & | & 9 \\ 0 & 3 & -2 & | & 0 \\ 0 & 3 & -3 & | & -3 \end{bmatrix}$$

Next, to obtain a 1 in the second row, second column, multiply 3 by its reciprocal, $\frac{1}{3}$. Therefore, we multiply

all the numbers in the second row by $\frac{1}{3}$ to get

$$\begin{bmatrix} 1 & -1 & 2 & | & 9 \\ 0 & 1 & -\frac{2}{3} & | & 0 \\ 0 & 3 & -3 & | & -3 \end{bmatrix}.$$

Next, to obtain a 0 in the third row, second column, multiply the second row by –3 and add the products to row three. The resulting matrix is

$$\begin{bmatrix} 1 & -1 & 2 & | & 9 \\ 0 & 1 & -\frac{2}{3} & | & 0 \\ 0 & 0 & -1 & | & -3 \end{bmatrix}.$$

To get 1 in the third row, third column, multiply –1 by its reciprocal, –1. Multiply all numbers in the third row by –1 to obtain the resulting matrix

$$\begin{bmatrix} 1 & -1 & 2 & | & 9 \\ 0 & 1 & -\frac{2}{3} & | & 0 \\ 0 & 0 & 1 & | & 3 \end{bmatrix}.$$

The system represented by this matrix is:
$$x-y+2z=9$$
$$y-\frac{2}{3}z=0$$
$$z=3$$

Use back substitution to find y and x.

$$y-\frac{2}{3}(3)=0 \qquad x-2+6=9$$
$$y-2=0 \qquad\qquad x+4=9$$
$$y=2 \qquad\qquad\quad x=5$$

The solution set for the original system is $\{(5, 2, 3)\}$.

4. $w - 3x - 2y + z = -3$
          $2w - 7x - y + 2z = 1$
          $3w - 7x - 3y + 3z = -5$
          $5w + x + 4y - 2z = 18$

The augmented matrix is

$$\begin{bmatrix} 1 & -3 & -2 & 1 & | & -3 \\ 2 & -7 & -1 & 2 & | & 1 \\ 3 & -7 & -3 & 3 & | & -5 \\ 5 & 1 & 4 & -2 & | & 18 \end{bmatrix}.$$

Multiply the top row by –2 and add the products to the second row. Multiply the top row by –3 and add the products to the third row. Multiply the top row by –5 and add the products to the fourth row. The resulting matrix is

$$\begin{bmatrix} 1 & -3 & -2 & 1 & | & -3 \\ 0 & -1 & 3 & 0 & | & 7 \\ 0 & 2 & 3 & 0 & | & 4 \\ 0 & 16 & 14 & -7 & | & 33 \end{bmatrix}.$$

Next, multiply the second row by –1 to obtain a 1 in the second row, second column.

$$\begin{bmatrix} 1 & -3 & -2 & 1 & | & -3 \\ 0 & 1 & -3 & 0 & | & -7 \\ 0 & 2 & 3 & 0 & | & 4 \\ 0 & 16 & 14 & -7 & | & 33 \end{bmatrix}$$

Next, multiply the second row by –2 and add the products to the third row. Multiply the second row by –16 and add the products to the fourth row. The resulting matrix is

$$\begin{bmatrix} 1 & -3 & -2 & 1 & | & -3 \\ 0 & 1 & -3 & 0 & | & -7 \\ 0 & 0 & 9 & 0 & | & 18 \\ 0 & 0 & 62 & -7 & | & 145 \end{bmatrix}.$$

Next, multiply the third row by $\frac{1}{9}$ to obtain a 1 in the third row, third column. The resulting matrix is

$$\begin{bmatrix} 1 & -3 & -2 & 1 & | & -3 \\ 0 & 1 & -3 & 0 & | & -7 \\ 0 & 0 & 1 & 0 & | & 2 \\ 0 & 0 & 62 & -7 & | & 145 \end{bmatrix}.$$

Multiply the third row by –62 and add the products to the fourth row to obtain the resulting matrix

$$\begin{bmatrix} 1 & -3 & -2 & 1 & | & -3 \\ 0 & 1 & -3 & 0 & | & -7 \\ 0 & 0 & 1 & 0 & | & 2 \\ 0 & 0 & 0 & -7 & | & 21 \end{bmatrix}.$$

Multiply the fourth row by $-\frac{1}{7}$, the reciprocal of –7. The resulting matrix is

$$\begin{bmatrix} 1 & -3 & -2 & 1 & | & -3 \\ 0 & 1 & -3 & 0 & | & -7 \\ 0 & 0 & 1 & 0 & | & 2 \\ 0 & 0 & 0 & 1 & | & -3 \end{bmatrix}.$$

The system of linear equations corresponding to the resulting matrix is

$$w - 3x - 2y + z = -3$$
$$x - 3y = -7$$
$$y = 2$$
$$z = -3$$

Using back-substitution solve for x and w.

$$x - 3(2) = -7$$
$$x = -1$$

$$w - 3(-1) - 2(2) - 3 = -3$$
$$w - 4 = -3$$
$$w = 1$$

The solution set is $\{(1, -1, 2, -3)\}$.

5. The matrix obtained in 3 will be the starting point.

$$\begin{bmatrix} 1 & -1 & 2 & | & 9 \\ 0 & 1 & -\frac{2}{3} & | & 0 \\ 0 & 0 & 1 & | & 3 \end{bmatrix}$$

Next, multiply the third row by $\dfrac{2}{3}$ and add the products to the second row. Multiply the third row by 2 and add the products to the first row. The resulting matrix is

$$\begin{bmatrix} 1 & -1 & 0 & 3 \\ 0 & 1 & 0 & 2 \\ 0 & 0 & 1 & 3 \end{bmatrix}.$$

Add the second row to the first row and replace the first row.

$$\begin{bmatrix} 1 & 0 & 0 & 5 \\ 0 & 1 & 0 & 2 \\ 0 & 0 & 1 & 3 \end{bmatrix}$$

This matrix corresponds to $x = 5$, $y = 2$ and $z = 3$. The solution set is $\{(5, 2, 3)\}$.

Exercise Set 8.1

1. $\begin{bmatrix} 2 & 1 & 2 & | & 2 \\ 3 & -5 & -1 & | & 4 \\ 1 & -2 & -3 & | & -6 \end{bmatrix}$

3. $\begin{bmatrix} 1 & -1 & 1 & | & 8 \\ 0 & 1 & -12 & | & -15 \\ 0 & 0 & 1 & | & 1 \end{bmatrix}$

5. $\begin{bmatrix} 5 & -2 & -3 & | & 0 \\ 1 & 1 & 0 & | & 5 \\ 2 & 0 & -3 & | & 4 \end{bmatrix}$

7. $\begin{bmatrix} 2 & 5 & -3 & 1 & | & 2 \\ 0 & 3 & 1 & 0 & | & 4 \\ 1 & -1 & 5 & 0 & | & 9 \\ 5 & -5 & -2 & 0 & | & 1 \end{bmatrix}$

9. $5x + 3z = -11$
    $y - 4z = 12$
    $7x + 2y = 3$

11. $w + x + 4y + z = 3$
      $-w + x - y = 7$
      $12w + 5z = 11$
      $12y + 4z = 5$

13.
$$x - 4z = 5$$
$$y - 12z = 13$$
$$z = -\frac{1}{2}$$
$$y - 12\left(-\frac{1}{2}\right) = 13$$
$$y + 6 = 13$$
$$y = 7$$
$$x - 4\left(-\frac{1}{2}\right) = 5$$
$$x + 2 = 5$$
$$x = 3$$

The solution set is $\left\{\left(3, \ 7, \ -\frac{1}{2}\right)\right\}$.

15.
$$\begin{bmatrix} 1 & \frac{1}{2} & 1 & | & \frac{11}{2} \\ 0 & 1 & \frac{3}{2} & | & 7 \\ 0 & 0 & 1 & | & 4 \end{bmatrix}$$
$$x + \frac{1}{2}y + z = \frac{11}{2}$$
$$y + \frac{3}{2}z = 7$$
$$z = 4$$
$$y + \frac{3}{2}(4) = 7$$
$$y + 6 = 7$$
$$y = 1$$
$$x + \frac{1}{2}(1) + 4 = \frac{11}{2}$$
$$x + \frac{9}{2} = \frac{11}{2}$$
$$x = \frac{11}{2} - \frac{9}{2}$$
$$x = 1$$

The solution set is $\{(1, \ 1, \ 4)\}$.

17.
$$\begin{bmatrix} 1 & -1 & 1 & 1 & | & 3 \\ 0 & 1 & -2 & -1 & | & 0 \\ 0 & 0 & 1 & 6 & | & 17 \\ 0 & 0 & 0 & 1 & | & 3 \end{bmatrix}$$
$$w - x + y + z = 3$$
$$x - 2y - z = 0$$
$$y + 6z = 17$$
$$z = 3$$

$$y + 6(3) = 17$$
$$y + 18 = 17$$
$$y = -1$$

$$x - 2(-1) - 3 = 0$$
$$x - 1 = 0$$
$$x = 1$$

$$w - 1 + (-1) + 3 = 3$$
$$w + 1 = 3$$
$$w = 2$$
The solution set is $\{(2, \ 1, \ -1, \ 3)\}$.

19.
$$\begin{bmatrix} 2\left(\frac{1}{2}\right) & -6\left(\frac{1}{2}\right) & 4\left(\frac{1}{2}\right) & | & 10\left(\frac{1}{2}\right) \\ 1 & 5 & -5 & | & 0 \\ 3 & 0 & 4 & | & 7 \end{bmatrix} \frac{1}{2}R_1$$
$$\begin{bmatrix} 1 & -3 & 2 & | & 5 \\ 1 & 5 & -5 & | & 0 \\ 3 & 0 & 4 & | & 7 \end{bmatrix}$$

21.
$$\begin{bmatrix} 1 & -3 & 2 & | & 0 \\ -3(1)+3 & -3(-3)+1 & -3(2)+-1 & | & -3(0)+7 \\ 2 & -2 & 1 & | & 3 \end{bmatrix} -3R_1 + R_2$$

$$\begin{bmatrix} 1 & -3 & 2 & | & 0 \\ 0 & 10 & -7 & | & 7 \\ 2 & -2 & 1 & | & 3 \end{bmatrix}$$

23.
$$\begin{bmatrix} 1 & -1 & 1 & 1 & | & 3 \\ 0 & 1 & -2 & -1 & | & 0 \\ 2 & 0 & 3 & 4 & | & 11 \\ 5 & 1 & 2 & 4 & | & 6 \end{bmatrix} \begin{matrix} \\ \\ -2R_1 + R_3 \\ -5R_1 + R_4 \end{matrix}$$

$$\begin{bmatrix} 1 & -1 & 1 & 1 & | & 3 \\ 0 & 1 & -2 & -1 & | & 0 \\ -2(1)+2 & -2(-1)+0 & -2(1)+3 & -2(1)+4 & | & -2(3)+11 \\ -5(1)+5 & -5(-1)+1 & -5(1)+2 & -5(1)+4 & | & -5(3)+6 \end{bmatrix} = \begin{bmatrix} 1 & -1 & 1 & 1 & | & 3 \\ 0 & 1 & -2 & -1 & | & 0 \\ 0 & 2 & 1 & 2 & | & 5 \\ 0 & 6 & -3 & -1 & | & -9 \end{bmatrix}$$

25.
$$\begin{bmatrix} 1 & -1 & 1 & | & 8 \\ 2 & 3 & -1 & | & -2 \\ 3 & -2 & -9 & | & 9 \end{bmatrix}$$

$$\begin{bmatrix} 1 & -1 & 1 & | & 8 \\ -2(1)+2 & -2(-1)+3 & -2(1)-1 & | & -2(8)-2 \\ -3(1)+3 & -3(-1)-2 & -3(1)-9 & | & -3(8)+9 \end{bmatrix}$$

$$\begin{bmatrix} 1 & -1 & 1 & | & 8 \\ 0 & 5 & \boxed{-3} & | & \boxed{-18} \\ 0 & 1 & \boxed{-12} & | & \boxed{-15} \end{bmatrix}$$

$$\begin{bmatrix} 1 & -1 & 1 & | & 8 \\ 0\left(\frac{1}{5}\right) & 1\left(\frac{1}{5}\right) & -3\left(\frac{1}{5}\right) & | & -18\left(\frac{1}{5}\right) \\ 0 & 1 & -12 & | & -15 \end{bmatrix}$$

$$\begin{bmatrix} 1 & -1 & 1 & | & 8 \\ 0 & 1 & \boxed{-\frac{3}{5}} & | & \boxed{-\frac{18}{5}} \\ 0 & 1 & \boxed{-12} & | & \boxed{-15} \end{bmatrix}$$

27.
$$x + y - z = -2$$
$$2x - y + z = 5$$
$$-x + 2y + 2z = 1$$

$$\begin{bmatrix} 1 & 1 & -1 & | & -2 \\ 2 & -1 & 1 & | & 5 \\ -1 & 2 & 2 & | & 1 \end{bmatrix} -2R_1 + R_2$$

$$\begin{bmatrix} 1 & 1 & -1 & | & -2 \\ 0 & -3 & 3 & | & 9 \\ -1 & 2 & 2 & | & 1 \end{bmatrix} 1R_1 + R_3$$

$$\begin{bmatrix} 1 & 1 & -1 & | & -2 \\ 0 & -3 & 3 & | & 9 \\ 0 & 3 & 1 & | & -1 \end{bmatrix} -\frac{1}{3}R_2$$

$$\begin{bmatrix} 1 & 1 & -1 & | & -2 \\ 0 & 1 & -1 & | & -3 \\ 0 & 3 & 1 & | & -1 \end{bmatrix} -3R_2 + R_3$$

$$= \begin{bmatrix} 1 & 1 & -1 & | & -2 \\ 0 & 1 & -1 & | & -3 \\ 0 & 0 & 4 & | & 8 \end{bmatrix}$$

$$4z = 8$$
$$z = 2$$
$$y - z = -3$$
$$y - 2 = -3$$
$$y = -1$$
$$x + y - z = -2$$
$$x - 1 - 2 = -2$$
$$x - 3 = -2$$
$$x = 1$$

The solution set is $\{(1, -1, 2)\}$.

29.
$$x + 3y = 0$$
$$x + y + z = 1$$
$$3x - y - z = 11$$

$$\begin{bmatrix} 1 & 3 & 0 & | & 0 \\ 1 & 1 & 1 & | & 1 \\ 3 & -1 & -1 & | & 11 \end{bmatrix} -1R_1 + R_2$$

$$\begin{bmatrix} 1 & 3 & 0 & | & 0 \\ 0 & -2 & 1 & | & 1 \\ 3 & -1 & -1 & | & 11 \end{bmatrix} -3R_1 + R_3$$

$$\begin{bmatrix} 1 & 3 & 0 & | & 0 \\ 0 & -2 & 1 & | & 1 \\ 0 & -10 & -1 & | & 11 \end{bmatrix} -\frac{1}{2}R_2$$

$$\begin{bmatrix} 1 & 3 & 0 & | & 0 \\ 0 & 1 & -\frac{1}{2} & | & -\frac{1}{2} \\ 0 & -10 & -1 & | & 11 \end{bmatrix} 10R_2 + R_3$$

$$\begin{bmatrix} 1 & 3 & 0 & | & 0 \\ 0 & 1 & -\frac{1}{2} & | & -\frac{1}{2} \\ 0 & 0 & -6 & | & 6 \end{bmatrix} -\frac{1}{6}R_3$$

$$\begin{bmatrix} 1 & 3 & 0 & | & 0 \\ 0 & 1 & -\frac{1}{2} & | & -\frac{1}{2} \\ 0 & 0 & 1 & | & -1 \end{bmatrix}$$

$$z = -1$$
$$y - \frac{1}{2}z = -\frac{1}{2}$$
$$y - \frac{1}{2}(-1) = -\frac{1}{2}$$
$$y + \frac{1}{2} = -\frac{1}{2}$$
$$y = -1$$

Interchange row one and row two.

$$x + 3y = 0$$
$$x + 3(-1) = 0$$
$$x = 3$$

The solution set is $\{(3, -1, -1)\}$.

31.
$$2x - y - z = 4$$
$$x + y - 5z = -4$$
$$x - 2y = 4$$

$$\begin{bmatrix} 2 & -1 & -1 & 4 \\ 1 & 1 & -5 & -4 \\ 1 & -2 & 0 & 4 \end{bmatrix}$$

Interchange rows one and two.

$$\begin{bmatrix} 1 & 1 & -5 & -4 \\ 2 & -1 & -1 & 4 \\ 1 & -2 & 0 & 4 \end{bmatrix}$$

Replace row two with $-2R_1 + R_2$.
Replace row three with $-R_1 + R_3$.

$$\begin{bmatrix} 1 & 1 & -5 & -4 \\ 0 & -3 & 9 & 12 \\ 0 & -3 & 5 & 8 \end{bmatrix}$$

Replace row two with $-\dfrac{1}{3} R_2$.

$$\begin{bmatrix} 1 & 1 & -5 & -4 \\ 0 & 1 & -3 & -4 \\ 0 & -3 & 5 & 8 \end{bmatrix}$$

Replace row three with $3R_2 + R_3$.

$$\begin{bmatrix} 1 & 1 & -5 & -4 \\ 0 & 1 & -3 & -4 \\ 0 & 0 & -4 & -4 \end{bmatrix}$$

Replace row three with $-\dfrac{1}{4} R_3$.

$$\begin{bmatrix} 1 & 1 & -5 & -4 \\ 0 & 1 & -3 & -4 \\ 0 & 0 & 1 & 1 \end{bmatrix}$$

$$z = 1$$
$$y - 3z = -4$$
$$y - 3(1) = -4$$
$$y = -1$$
$$x + y - 5z = -4$$
$$x - 1 - 5(1) = -4$$
$$x - 6 = -4$$
$$x = 2$$

The solution set is $\{(2, -1, 1)\}$.

33.
$$x + y + z = 4$$
$$x - y - z = 0$$
$$x - y + z = 2$$

$$\begin{bmatrix} 1 & 1 & 1 & 4 \\ 1 & -1 & -1 & 0 \\ 1 & -1 & 1 & 2 \end{bmatrix}$$

Replace row two with $-R_1 + R_2$.
Replace row three with $-R_1 + R_3$.

$$\begin{bmatrix} 1 & 1 & 1 & 4 \\ 0 & -2 & -2 & -4 \\ 0 & -2 & 0 & -2 \end{bmatrix}$$

Replace row two with $-\dfrac{1}{2} R_2$.

$$\begin{bmatrix} 1 & 1 & 1 & 4 \\ 0 & 1 & 1 & 2 \\ 0 & -2 & 0 & -2 \end{bmatrix}$$

Replace row 3 with $2R_2 + R_3$.

$$\begin{bmatrix} 1 & 1 & 1 & 4 \\ 0 & 1 & 1 & 2 \\ 0 & 0 & 2 & 2 \end{bmatrix}$$

Replace row 3 with $\dfrac{1}{2} R_3$.

$$\begin{bmatrix} 1 & 1 & 1 & 4 \\ 0 & 1 & 1 & 2 \\ 0 & 0 & 1 & 1 \end{bmatrix}$$

$$z = 1$$
$$y + 1 = 2$$
$$y = 1$$
$$x + 1 + 1 = 4$$
$$x = 2$$

The solution set is $\{(2, 1, 1)\}$.

35. Write the equations in standard form.

$$x + 2y - z = -1$$
$$x - y + z = 4$$
$$x + y - 3z = -2$$

$$\begin{bmatrix} 1 & 2 & -1 & -1 \\ 1 & -1 & 1 & 4 \\ 1 & 1 & -3 & -2 \end{bmatrix}$$

Replace row two with $-R_1 + R_2$.
Replace row three with $-R_1 + R_3$.

$$\begin{bmatrix} 1 & 2 & -1 & -1 \\ 0 & -3 & 2 & 5 \\ 0 & -1 & -2 & -1 \end{bmatrix}$$

Replace row two with $-R_3$.
Replace row three with R_2.

$$\begin{bmatrix} 1 & 2 & -1 & -1 \\ 0 & 1 & 2 & 1 \\ 0 & -3 & 2 & 5 \end{bmatrix}$$

Replace row 3 with $3R_2 + R_3$.

$$\begin{bmatrix} 1 & 2 & -1 & -1 \\ 0 & 1 & 2 & 1 \\ 0 & 0 & 8 & 8 \end{bmatrix}$$

Replace row 3 with $\frac{1}{8}R_3$.

$$\begin{bmatrix} 1 & 2 & -1 & -1 \\ 0 & 1 & 2 & 1 \\ 0 & 0 & 1 & 1 \end{bmatrix}$$

$z = 1$
$y + 2(1) = 1$
$y = -1$
$x + 2(-1) - 1 = -1$
$x = 2$

The solution set is $\{(2, -1, 1)\}$.

37.
$$3a - b - 4c = 3$$
$$2a - b + 2c = -8$$
$$a + 2b - 3c = 9$$

Interchange equations 1 and 3.

$$\begin{bmatrix} 1 & 2 & -3 & 9 \\ 2 & -1 & 2 & -8 \\ 3 & -1 & -4 & 3 \end{bmatrix}$$

Replace row two with $-2R_1 + R_2$.
Replace row three with $-3R_1 + R_3$.

$$\begin{bmatrix} 1 & 2 & -3 & 9 \\ 0 & -5 & 8 & -26 \\ 0 & -7 & 5 & -24 \end{bmatrix}$$

Replace row two with $-\frac{1}{5}R_2$

$$\begin{bmatrix} 1 & 2 & -3 & 9 \\ 0 & 1 & -\frac{8}{5} & \frac{26}{5} \\ 0 & -7 & 5 & -24 \end{bmatrix}$$

Replace row three with $7R_2 + R_3$.

$$\begin{bmatrix} 1 & 2 & -3 & 9 \\ 0 & 1 & -\frac{8}{5} & \frac{26}{5} \\ 0 & 0 & -\frac{31}{5} & \frac{62}{5} \end{bmatrix}$$

Replace row 3 with $-\frac{5}{31}R_3$.

$$\begin{bmatrix} 1 & 2 & -3 & 9 \\ 0 & 1 & -\frac{8}{5} & \frac{26}{5} \\ 0 & 0 & 1 & -2 \end{bmatrix}$$

$z = -2$

$$y - \frac{8}{5}(-2) = \frac{26}{5}$$
$$y + \frac{16}{5} = \frac{26}{5}$$
$$y = 2$$
$$x + 2(2) - 3(-2) = 9$$
$$x + 4 + 6 = 9$$
$$x = -1$$

The solution set is $\{(-1, 2, -2)\}$.

39. $2x + 2y + 7z = -1$

$2x + y + 2z = 2$

$4x + 6y + z = 15$

$$\begin{bmatrix} 2 & 2 & 7 & | & -1 \\ 2 & 1 & 2 & | & 2 \\ 4 & 6 & 1 & | & 15 \end{bmatrix} \frac{1}{2}R_1$$

$$\begin{bmatrix} 1 & 1 & \frac{7}{2} & | & -\frac{1}{2} \\ 2 & 1 & 2 & | & 2 \\ 4 & 6 & 1 & | & 15 \end{bmatrix} -2R_1 + R_2$$

$$\begin{bmatrix} 1 & 1 & \frac{7}{2} & | & -\frac{1}{2} \\ 0 & -1 & -5 & | & 3 \\ 4 & 6 & 1 & | & 15 \end{bmatrix} -4R_1 + R_3$$

$$\begin{bmatrix} 1 & 1 & \frac{7}{2} & | & -\frac{1}{2} \\ 0 & -1 & -5 & | & 3 \\ 0 & 2 & -13 & | & 17 \end{bmatrix} -1R_2$$

$$\begin{bmatrix} 1 & 1 & \frac{7}{2} & | & -\frac{1}{2} \\ 0 & 1 & 5 & | & -3 \\ 0 & 2 & -13 & | & 17 \end{bmatrix} -2R_2 + R_3$$

$$\begin{bmatrix} 1 & 1 & \frac{7}{2} & | & -\frac{1}{2} \\ 0 & 1 & 5 & | & -3 \\ 0 & 0 & -23 & | & 23 \end{bmatrix} -\frac{1}{23}R_3$$

$$\begin{bmatrix} 1 & 1 & \frac{7}{2} & | & -\frac{1}{2} \\ 0 & 1 & 5 & | & -3 \\ 0 & 0 & 1 & | & -1 \end{bmatrix}$$

$z = -1$

$y + 5z = -3$

$y + 5(-1) = -3$

$y - 5 = -3$

$y = 2$

$x + y + \dfrac{7}{2}z = -\dfrac{1}{2}$

$x + 2 + \dfrac{7}{2}(-1) = -\dfrac{1}{2}$

$x - \dfrac{3}{2} = -\dfrac{1}{2}$

$x = 1$

The solution set is $\{(1, 2, -1)\}$.

41. $w + x + y + z = 4$

$2w + x - 2y - z = 0$

$w - 2x - y - 2z = -2$

$3w + 2x + y + 3z = 4$

$$\begin{bmatrix} 1 & 1 & 1 & 1 & | & 4 \\ 2 & 1 & -2 & -1 & | & 0 \\ 1 & -2 & -1 & -2 & | & -2 \\ 3 & 2 & 1 & 3 & | & 4 \end{bmatrix} -2R_1 + R_2$$

$$\begin{bmatrix} 1 & 1 & 1 & 1 & | & 4 \\ 0 & -1 & -4 & -3 & | & -8 \\ 1 & -2 & -1 & -2 & | & -2 \\ 3 & 2 & 1 & 3 & | & 4 \end{bmatrix} -1R_1 + R_3$$

$$\begin{bmatrix} 1 & 1 & 1 & 1 & | & 4 \\ 0 & -1 & -4 & -3 & | & -8 \\ 0 & -3 & -2 & -3 & | & -6 \\ 3 & 2 & 1 & 3 & | & 4 \end{bmatrix} -3R_1 + R_4$$

$$\begin{bmatrix} 1 & 1 & 1 & 1 & | & 4 \\ 0 & -1 & -4 & -3 & | & -8 \\ 0 & -3 & -2 & -3 & | & -6 \\ 0 & -1 & -2 & 0 & | & -8 \end{bmatrix} -1R_2$$

$$\begin{bmatrix} 1 & 1 & 1 & 1 & | & 4 \\ 0 & 1 & 4 & 3 & | & 8 \\ 0 & -3 & -2 & -3 & | & -6 \\ 0 & -1 & -2 & 0 & | & -8 \end{bmatrix} 3R_2 + R_3$$

$$\begin{bmatrix} 1 & 1 & 1 & 1 & | & 4 \\ 0 & 1 & 4 & 3 & | & 8 \\ 0 & 0 & 10 & 6 & | & 18 \\ 0 & -1 & -2 & 0 & | & -8 \end{bmatrix} 1R_2 + R_4$$

$$\begin{bmatrix} 1 & 1 & 1 & 1 & | & 4 \\ 0 & 1 & 4 & 3 & | & 8 \\ 0 & 0 & 10 & 6 & | & 18 \\ 0 & 0 & 2 & 3 & | & 0 \end{bmatrix} \frac{1}{10}R_3$$

$$\begin{bmatrix} 1 & 1 & 1 & 1 & | & 4 \\ 0 & 1 & 4 & 3 & | & 8 \\ 0 & 0 & 1 & \frac{3}{5} & | & \frac{9}{5} \\ 0 & 0 & 2 & 3 & | & 0 \end{bmatrix} -2R_3 + R_4$$

$$\begin{bmatrix} 1 & 1 & 1 & 1 & | & 4 \\ 0 & 1 & 4 & 3 & | & 8 \\ 0 & 0 & 1 & \frac{3}{5} & | & \frac{9}{5} \\ 0 & 0 & 0 & \frac{9}{5} & | & -\frac{18}{5} \end{bmatrix} \frac{5}{9}R_4$$

$$\begin{bmatrix} 1 & 1 & 1 & 1 & | & 4 \\ 0 & 1 & 4 & 3 & | & 8 \\ 0 & 0 & 1 & \frac{3}{5} & | & \frac{9}{5} \\ 0 & 0 & 0 & 1 & | & -2 \end{bmatrix}$$

$z = -2$

$$y + \frac{3}{5}z = \frac{9}{5}$$

$$y + \frac{3}{5}(-2) = \frac{9}{5}$$

$$y - \frac{6}{5} = \frac{9}{5}$$

$$y = 3$$

$$x + 4y + 3z = 8$$

$$x + 4(3) + 3(-2) = 8$$

$$x + 6 = 8$$

$$x = 2$$

$$w + x + y + z = 4$$

$$w + 2 + 3 - 2 = 4$$

$$w + 3 = 4$$

$$w = 1$$

The solution set is $\{(1, 2, 3, -2)\}$.

43.

$$3w - 4x + y + z = 9$$
$$w + x - y - z = 0$$
$$2w + x + 4y - 2z = 3$$
$$-w + 2x + y - 3z = 3$$

$$\begin{bmatrix} 3 & -4 & 1 & 1 & | & 9 \\ 1 & 1 & -1 & -1 & | & 0 \\ 2 & 1 & 4 & -2 & | & 3 \\ -1 & 2 & 1 & -3 & | & 3 \end{bmatrix} R_1 \leftrightarrow R_2$$

$$\begin{bmatrix} 1 & 1 & -1 & -1 & | & 0 \\ 3 & -4 & 1 & 1 & | & 9 \\ 2 & 1 & 4 & -2 & | & 3 \\ -1 & 2 & 1 & -3 & | & 3 \end{bmatrix} -3R_1 + R_2$$

$$\begin{bmatrix} 1 & 1 & -1 & -1 & | & 0 \\ 0 & -7 & 4 & 4 & | & 9 \\ 2 & 1 & 4 & -2 & | & 3 \\ -1 & 2 & 1 & -3 & | & 3 \end{bmatrix} -2R_1 + R_3$$

$$\begin{bmatrix} 1 & 1 & -1 & -1 & | & 0 \\ 0 & -7 & 4 & 4 & | & 9 \\ 0 & -1 & 6 & 0 & | & 3 \\ -1 & 2 & 1 & -3 & | & 3 \end{bmatrix} 1R_1 + R_4$$

$$\begin{bmatrix} 1 & 1 & -1 & -1 & | & 0 \\ 0 & -7 & 4 & 4 & | & 9 \\ 0 & -1 & 6 & 0 & | & 3 \\ 0 & 3 & 0 & -4 & | & 3 \end{bmatrix} R_2 \leftrightarrow R_3$$

$$\begin{bmatrix} 1 & 1 & -1 & -1 & | & 0 \\ 0 & -1 & 6 & 0 & | & 3 \\ 0 & -7 & 4 & 4 & | & 9 \\ 0 & 3 & 0 & -4 & | & 3 \end{bmatrix} -R_2$$

$$\begin{bmatrix} 1 & 1 & -1 & -1 & | & 0 \\ 0 & 1 & -6 & 0 & | & -3 \\ 0 & -7 & 4 & 4 & | & 9 \\ 0 & 3 & 0 & -4 & | & 3 \end{bmatrix} 7R_2 + R_3$$

$$\begin{bmatrix} 1 & 1 & -1 & -1 & | & 0 \\ 0 & 1 & -6 & 0 & | & -3 \\ 0 & 0 & -38 & 4 & | & -12 \\ 0 & 3 & 0 & -4 & | & 3 \end{bmatrix} -3R_2 + R_4$$

$$\begin{bmatrix} 1 & 1 & -1 & -1 & | & 0 \\ 0 & 1 & -6 & 0 & | & -3 \\ 0 & 0 & -38 & 4 & | & -12 \\ 0 & 0 & 18 & -4 & | & 12 \end{bmatrix} -\frac{1}{38}R_3$$

$$\begin{bmatrix} 1 & 1 & -1 & -1 & | & 0 \\ 0 & 1 & -6 & 0 & | & -3 \\ 0 & 0 & 1 & -\frac{2}{19} & | & \frac{6}{19} \\ 0 & 0 & 18 & -4 & | & 12 \end{bmatrix} -18R_3 + R_4$$

$$\begin{bmatrix} 1 & 1 & -1 & -1 & | & 0 \\ 0 & 1 & -6 & 0 & | & -3 \\ 0 & 0 & 1 & -\frac{2}{19} & | & \frac{6}{19} \\ 0 & 0 & 0 & -\frac{40}{19} & | & \frac{120}{19} \end{bmatrix} -\frac{19}{40}R_4$$

$$\begin{bmatrix} 1 & 1 & -1 & -1 & | & 0 \\ 0 & 1 & -6 & 0 & | & -3 \\ 0 & 0 & 1 & -\frac{2}{19} & | & \frac{6}{19} \\ 0 & 0 & 0 & 1 & | & -3 \end{bmatrix}$$

$z = -3$

$$y - \frac{2}{19}z = \frac{6}{19}$$

$$y - \frac{2}{19}(-3) = \frac{6}{19}$$

$$y + \frac{6}{19} = \frac{6}{19}$$

$$y = 0$$

$$x - 6y = -3$$

$$x - 6(0) = -3$$

$$x = -3$$

$$w + x - y - z = 0$$

$$w - 3 + 0 + 3 = 0$$

$$w = 0$$

The solution set is $\{(0, -3, 0, -3)\}$.

45. $f(x) = ax^2 + bx + c$

Use the given function values to find three equations in terms of a, b, and c.

$$f(-2) = a(-2)^2 + b(-2) + c = -4$$
$$4a - 2b + c = -4$$

$$f(1) = a(1)^2 + b(1) + c = 2$$
$$a + b + c = 2$$

$$f(2) = a(2)^2 + b(2) + c = 0$$
$$4a + 2b + c = 0$$

System of equations:
$$4a - 2b + c = -4$$
$$a + b + c = 2$$
$$4a + 2b + c = 0$$

Matrix:
$$\begin{bmatrix} 4 & -2 & 1 & | & -4 \\ 1 & 1 & 1 & | & 2 \\ 4 & 2 & 1 & | & 0 \end{bmatrix}$$

This gives $a = -1$, $b = 1$, and $c = 2$.

Thus, $f(x) = -x^2 + x + 2$.

47. $f(x) = ax^3 + bx^2 + cx + d$

Use the given function values to find four equations in terms of a, b, c, and d.

$$f(-1) = a(-1)^3 + b(-1)^2 + c(-1) + d = 0$$
$$-a + b - c + d = 0$$

$$f(1) = a(1)^3 + b(1)^2 + c(1) + d = 2$$
$$a + b + c + d = 2$$

$$f(2) = a(2)^3 + b(2)^2 + c(2) + d = 3$$
$$8a + 4b + 2c + d = 3$$

$$f(3) = a(3)^3 + b(3)^2 + c(3) + d = 12$$
$$27a + 9b + 3c + d = 12$$

System of equations:
$$-a + b - c + d = 0$$
$$a + b + c + d = 2$$
$$8a + 4b + 2c + d = 3$$
$$27a + 9b + 3c + d = 12$$

Matrix:
$$\begin{bmatrix} -1 & 1 & -1 & 1 & | & 0 \\ 1 & 1 & 1 & 1 & | & 2 \\ 8 & 4 & 2 & 1 & | & 3 \\ 27 & 9 & 3 & 1 & | & 12 \end{bmatrix}$$

This gives $a = 1$, $b = -2$, $c = 0$, and $d = 3$.

Thus, $f(x) = x^3 - 2x^2 + 3$.

49. Let $A = \ln w$, $B = \ln x$, $C = \ln y$, and $D = \ln z$.

System of equations:

$2A + B + 3C - 2D = -6$

$4A + 3B + C - D = -2$

$A + B + C + D = -5$

$A + B - C - D = 5$

Matrix:

$$\begin{bmatrix} 2 & 1 & 3 & -2 & | & -6 \\ 4 & 3 & 1 & -1 & | & -2 \\ 1 & 1 & 1 & 1 & | & -5 \\ 1 & 1 & -1 & -1 & | & 5 \end{bmatrix}$$

This gives $A = -1$, $B = 1$, $C = -3$, and $D = -2$.

Substitute back to find w, x, y, and z.

$A = -1$ $B = 1$

$\ln w = -1$ $\ln x = 1$

$w = e^{-1}$ $x = e^{1}$

$w \approx 0.37$ $x \approx 2.72$

$C = -3$ $D = -2$

$\ln y = -3$ $\ln z = -2$

$y = e^{-3}$ $z = e^{-2}$

$y \approx 0.05$ $z \approx 0.14$

51. **a.** $s(t) = \dfrac{1}{2} a t^2 + v_0 t + s_0$

Use the given function values to find three equations in terms of a, v_0, and s_0.

$s(1) = \dfrac{1}{2} a(1)^2 + v_0(1) + s_0 = 40$

$\dfrac{1}{2} a + v_0 + s_0 = 40$

$s(2) = \dfrac{1}{2} a(2)^2 + v_0(2) + s_0 = 48$

$2a + 2v_0 + s_0 = 48$

$s(3) = \dfrac{1}{2} a(3)^2 + v_0(3) + s_0 = 24$

$\dfrac{9}{2} a + 3v_0 + s_0 = 24$

System of equations:

$\dfrac{1}{2} a + v_0 + s_0 = 40$

$2a + 2v_0 + s_0 = 48$

$\dfrac{9}{2} a + 3v_0 + s_0 = 24$

Matrix:

$$\begin{bmatrix} \dfrac{1}{2} & 1 & 1 & | & 40 \\ 2 & 2 & 1 & | & 48 \\ \dfrac{9}{2} & 3 & 1 & | & 24 \end{bmatrix}$$

This gives $a = -32$, $v_0 = 56$, and $s_0 = 0$.

Thus, $s(t) = \dfrac{1}{2}(-32)t^2 + (56)t + (0)$

$s(t) = -16t^2 + 56t$

b. $s(t) = -16t^2 + 56t$

$s(3.5) = -16(3.5)^2 + 56(3.5) = 0$

This is the point $(3.5, 0)$.

The ball's height is 0 feet after 3.5 seconds. This is the point $(3.5, 0)$.

c.   The maximum occurs when $x = -\dfrac{b}{2a}$.

$x = -\dfrac{b}{2a} = -\dfrac{v_0}{2a} = -\dfrac{56}{2(-16)} = 1.75$

$s(1.75) = -16(1.75)^2 + 56(1.75) = 49$

At 1.75 seconds the ball will reach its maximum height of 49 feet.

53. Let $x =$ those who said yes

Let $y =$ those who said no

Let $z =$ those who are not sure

$x + y + z = 100$

$y = x + z + 22$

$2x = y + 7$

Write the equations in standard form.

$x + y + z = 100$

$-x + y - z = 22$

$2x - y = 7$

$$\begin{bmatrix} 1 & 1 & 1 & | & 100 \\ -1 & 1 & -1 & | & 22 \\ 2 & -1 & 0 & | & 7 \end{bmatrix}$$

Replace row two with $R_1 + R_2$.

Replace row three with $-2R_1 + R_3$.

$$\begin{bmatrix} 1 & 1 & 1 & | & 100 \\ 0 & 2 & 0 & | & 122 \\ 0 & -3 & -2 & | & -193 \end{bmatrix}$$

Replace row two with $\dfrac{1}{2} R_2$.

$$\begin{bmatrix} 1 & 1 & 1 & 100 \\ 0 & 1 & 0 & 61 \\ 0 & -3 & -2 & -193 \end{bmatrix}$$

Replace row three with $3R_2 + R_3$.

$$\begin{bmatrix} 1 & 1 & 1 & 100 \\ 0 & 1 & 0 & 61 \\ 0 & 0 & -2 & -10 \end{bmatrix}$$

Replace row three with $-\dfrac{1}{2}R_3$.

$$\begin{bmatrix} 1 & 1 & 1 & 100 \\ 0 & 1 & 0 & 61 \\ 0 & 0 & 1 & 5 \end{bmatrix}$$

$z = 5$

$y = 61$

$x + y + z = 100$

$x + 61 + 5 = 100$

$x = 34$

34% of single women said yes, 61% said no, 5% did not know.

55. Let x = Food A

Let y = Food B

Let z = Food C

$40x + 200y + 400z = 660$

$5x + 2y + 4z = 25$

$30x + 10y + 300z = 425$

$2x + 10y + 20z = 33$

$5x + 2y + 4z = 25$

$6x + 2y + 60z = 85$

$$\begin{bmatrix} 2 & 10 & 20 & 33 \\ 5 & 2 & 4 & 25 \\ 6 & 2 & 60 & 85 \end{bmatrix} \tfrac{1}{2}R_1$$

$$\begin{bmatrix} 1 & 5 & 10 & \frac{33}{2} \\ 5 & 2 & 4 & 25 \\ 6 & 2 & 60 & 85 \end{bmatrix} -5R_1 + R_2$$

$$\begin{bmatrix} 1 & 5 & 10 & \frac{33}{2} \\ 0 & -23 & -46 & -\frac{115}{2} \\ 6 & 2 & 60 & 85 \end{bmatrix} -6R_1 + R_3$$

$$\begin{bmatrix} 1 & 5 & 10 & \frac{33}{2} \\ 0 & -23 & -46 & -\frac{115}{2} \\ 0 & -28 & 0 & -14 \end{bmatrix} -\tfrac{1}{23}R_2$$

$$\begin{bmatrix} 1 & 5 & 10 & \frac{33}{2} \\ 0 & 1 & 2 & \frac{5}{2} \\ 0 & -28 & 0 & -14 \end{bmatrix} 28R_2 + R_3$$

$$\begin{bmatrix} 1 & 5 & 10 & \frac{33}{2} \\ 0 & 1 & 2 & \frac{5}{2} \\ 0 & 0 & 56 & 56 \end{bmatrix} \tfrac{1}{56}R_3$$

$$\begin{bmatrix} 1 & 5 & 10 & \frac{33}{2} \\ 0 & 1 & 2 & \frac{5}{2} \\ 0 & 0 & 1 & 1 \end{bmatrix}$$

$z = 1$

$y + 2z = \dfrac{5}{2}$

$y + 2 = \dfrac{5}{2}$

$2y + 4 = 5$

$2y = 1$

$y = \dfrac{1}{2}$

$x + 5y + 10z = \dfrac{33}{2}$

$x + \dfrac{5}{2} + 10 = \dfrac{33}{2}$

$2x + 5 + 20 = 33$

$2x + 25 = 33$

$2x = 8$

$x = 4$

4 ounces of Food A

$\dfrac{1}{2}$ ounce of Food B

1 ounce of Food C

65. Statement **d.** is true.

Statement **a.** is false. Multiplying a row by a negative fraction is permitted.

Statement **b.** is false because there are three variables in the system. The augmented matrix should be:

$$\begin{bmatrix} 1 & -3 & 0 & 5 \\ 0 & 1 & -2 & 7 \\ 2 & 0 & 1 & 4 \end{bmatrix}$$

Statement **c.** is false. When solving a system of three equations in three variables, we use row operations to obtain ones along the diagonal and zeros below the ones.

Section 8.2

Check Point Exercises

1. $\begin{aligned} x-2y-z &= 5 \\ 2x-3y-z &= 0 \\ 3x-4y-z &= 1 \end{aligned} \rightarrow \left[\begin{array}{ccc|c} 1 & -2 & -1 & -5 \\ 2 & -3 & -1 & 0 \\ 3 & -4 & -1 & 1 \end{array}\right]$

$\left[\begin{array}{ccc|c} 1 & -2 & -1 & -5 \\ 2 & -3 & -1 & 0 \\ 3 & -4 & -1 & 1 \end{array}\right] \begin{array}{l} -2R_1 + R_2 \\ -3R_1 + R_3 \end{array}$

$\left[\begin{array}{ccc|c} 1 & -2 & -1 & -5 \\ 0 & 1 & 1 & 10 \\ 0 & 2 & 2 & 16 \end{array}\right] -2R_2 + R_3$

$\left[\begin{array}{ccc|c} 1 & -2 & -1 & -5 \\ 0 & 1 & -1 & -10 \\ 0 & 0 & 0 & -4 \end{array}\right]$

$0x + 0y + 0z = -4$ This equation can never be a true statement. Consequently, the system has no solution. The solution set is $\varnothing$, the empty set.

2. $\begin{aligned} x-2y-z &= 5 \\ 2x-5y+3z &= 16 \\ x-3y+4z &= 1 \end{aligned} \rightarrow \left[\begin{array}{ccc|c} 1 & -2 & -1 & 5 \\ 2 & -5 & 3 & 6 \\ 1 & -3 & 4 & 1 \end{array}\right]$

$\left[\begin{array}{ccc|c} 1 & -2 & -1 & 5 \\ 2 & -5 & 3 & 6 \\ 1 & -3 & 4 & 1 \end{array}\right] \begin{array}{l} -2R_1 + R_2 \\ -1R_1 + R_3 \end{array}$

$\left[\begin{array}{ccc|c} 1 & -2 & -1 & 5 \\ 0 & -1 & 5 & -4 \\ 0 & -1 & 5 & -4 \end{array}\right] -1R_2$

$\left[\begin{array}{ccc|c} 1 & -2 & -1 & 5 \\ 0 & 1 & -5 & 4 \\ 0 & -1 & 5 & -4 \end{array}\right] 1R_2 + R_3$

$\left[\begin{array}{ccc|c} 1 & -2 & -1 & 5 \\ 0 & 1 & -5 & 4 \\ 0 & 0 & 0 & 0 \end{array}\right]$

$0x + 0y + 0z = 0$ or $0 = 0$

This equation, $0x + 0y + 0z = 0$ is *dependent* on the other two equations. Thus, it can be dropped from the system which can now be expressed in the form

$\left[\begin{array}{ccc|c} 1 & -2 & -1 & 5 \\ 0 & 1 & -5 & 4 \end{array}\right]$

The original system is equivalent to the system

$\begin{aligned} x-2y-z &= 5 \\ y-5z &= 4 \end{aligned}$

Solve for x and y in terms of z.

$y = 5z + 4$

Use back-substitution for y in the previous equation.

$x - 2(5z + 4) - z = 5$

$x - 10z - 8 - z = 5$

$x = 11z + 13$

Finally, letting $z = t$ (or any letter of your choice), the solutions to the system are all of the form $x = 11t + 13$, $y = 5t + 4$, $z = t$, where t is a real number. The solution set of the system with dependent equations can be written as $\{(11t + 13,\ 5t + 4,\ t)\}$.

3. $\begin{aligned} x+2y+3z &= 70 \\ x+y+z &= 60 \end{aligned} \rightarrow \left[\begin{array}{ccc|c} 1 & 2 & 3 & 70 \\ 1 & 1 & 1 & 60 \end{array}\right]$

$\left[\begin{array}{ccc|c} 1 & 2 & 3 & 70 \\ 1 & 1 & 1 & 60 \end{array}\right] -1R_1 + R_2$

$\left[\begin{array}{ccc|c} 1 & 2 & 3 & 70 \\ 0 & -1 & -2 & -10 \end{array}\right] -1R_2$

$\left[\begin{array}{ccc|c} 1 & 2 & 3 & 70 \\ 0 & 1 & 2 & 10 \end{array}\right] \rightarrow \begin{aligned} x+2y+3z &= 70 \\ y+2z &= 10 \end{aligned}$

Express x and y in terms of z using back-substitution.

$y = -2z + 10$

$x + 2(-2z + 10) + 3z = 70$

$x - 4z + 20 + 3z = 70$

$x = z + 50$

With $z = t$, the ordered solution (x, y, z) enables us to express the system's solution set as $\{(t + 50,\ -2t + 10,\ t)\}$.

4. a. I^1: $10 + 5 = 15$ cars enter I^1, and $w + z$ cars leave I_1, then $w + z = 15$.

I^2: $20 + 10 = 30$ cars enter I^2 and $w + x$ cars leave I^2, then $w + x = 30$.

I^3: $15 + 30 = 45$ cars enter I_3 and $x + y$ cars leave I^3, then $x + y = 45$.

I^4: $10 + 20 = 30$ cars enter I_4 and $y + z$ cars leave I^4, then $y + z = 30$.

The system of equations that describes this situation is given by

$\begin{aligned} w + z &= 15 \\ w + x &= 30 \\ x + y &= 45 \\ y + z &= 30 \end{aligned}$

b.
$$\left[\begin{array}{cccc|c} 1 & 0 & 0 & 1 & 15 \\ 1 & 1 & 0 & 0 & 30 \\ 0 & 1 & 1 & 0 & 45 \\ 0 & 0 & 1 & 1 & 30 \end{array}\right] \begin{array}{l} \\ -1R_1 + R_2 \\ \\ \\ \end{array}$$

$$\left[\begin{array}{cccc|c} 1 & 0 & 0 & 1 & 15 \\ 0 & 1 & 0 & -1 & 15 \\ 0 & 1 & 1 & 0 & 45 \\ 0 & 0 & 1 & 1 & 30 \end{array}\right] \begin{array}{l} \\ \\ -1R_2 + R_3 \\ \\ \end{array}$$

$$\left[\begin{array}{cccc|c} 1 & 0 & 0 & 1 & 15 \\ 0 & 1 & 0 & -1 & 15 \\ 0 & 0 & 1 & 1 & 30 \\ 0 & 0 & 1 & 1 & 30 \end{array}\right] \begin{array}{l} \\ \\ \\ -1R_3 + R_4 \\ \end{array}$$

$$\left[\begin{array}{cccc|c} 1 & 0 & 0 & 1 & 15 \\ 0 & 1 & 0 & -1 & 15 \\ 0 & 0 & 1 & 1 & 30 \\ 0 & 0 & 0 & 0 & 0 \end{array}\right]$$

$x + w = 15$

$y - w = 15$

$z + w = 30$

The last row of the matrix shows that the system has dependent equations and infinitely many solutions.
Let z be any real number.
Express w, x and y in terms of z:

$w = 15 - z$

$x = 15 + z$

$y = 30 - z$

With $w = t$, the ordered solution (w, x, y, z) enables us to express the system's solution set as $\{(-t+15, t+15, -t+30, t)\}$

Exercise Set 8.2

1.
$$\left[\begin{array}{ccc|c} 5 & 12 & 1 & 10 \\ 2 & 5 & 2 & -1 \\ 1 & 2 & -3 & 5 \end{array}\right] R_1 \leftrightarrow R_3$$

$$\left[\begin{array}{ccc|c} 1 & 2 & -3 & 5 \\ 2 & 5 & 2 & -1 \\ 5 & 12 & 1 & 10 \end{array}\right] \begin{array}{l} \\ -2R_1 + R_2 \\ -5R_1 + R_3 \end{array}$$

$$\left[\begin{array}{ccc|c} 1 & 2 & -3 & 5 \\ 0 & 1 & 8 & -11 \\ 0 & 2 & 16 & -15 \end{array}\right] -2R_2 + R_3$$

$$\left[\begin{array}{ccc|c} 1 & 2 & 3 & 5 \\ 0 & 1 & 8 & -11 \\ 0 & 0 & 0 & 7 \end{array}\right]$$

From the last row, we see that the system has no solution. The solution set is $\varnothing$, the empty set.

3.
$$\left[\begin{array}{ccc|c} 5 & 8 & -6 & 14 \\ 3 & 4 & -2 & 8 \\ 1 & 2 & -2 & 3 \end{array}\right] R_1 \leftrightarrow R_3$$

$$\left[\begin{array}{ccc|c} 1 & 2 & -2 & 3 \\ 3 & 4 & -2 & 8 \\ 5 & 8 & -6 & 14 \end{array}\right] \begin{array}{l} \\ -3R_1 + R_2 \\ -5R_1 + R_3 \end{array}$$

$$\left[\begin{array}{ccc|c} 1 & 2 & -2 & 3 \\ 0 & -2 & 4 & -1 \\ 0 & -2 & 4 & -1 \end{array}\right] -1R_2 + R_3$$

$$\left[\begin{array}{ccc|c} 1 & 2 & -2 & 3 \\ 0 & -2 & 4 & -1 \\ 0 & 0 & 0 & 0 \end{array}\right] -\frac{1}{2}R_2$$

$$\left[\begin{array}{ccc|c} 1 & 2 & -2 & 3 \\ 0 & 1 & -2 & \frac{1}{2} \\ 0 & 0 & 0 & 0 \end{array}\right]$$

The system $\begin{array}{l} x + 2y - 2z = 3 \\ y - 2z = \frac{1}{2} \end{array}$ has no unique

solution. Express x and y in terms of z:

$y = 2z + \frac{1}{2}$

$x + 2\left(2z + \frac{1}{2}\right) - 2z = 3$

$x + 4z + 1 - 2z = 3$

$x + 2z + 1 = 3$

$x = -2z + 2$

With $z = t$, the complete solution to the system is $\left\{\left(-2t+2, \ 2t+\frac{1}{2}, \ t\right)\right\}$.

5. $\begin{bmatrix} 3 & 4 & 2 & | & 3 \\ 4 & -2 & -8 & | & -4 \\ 1 & 1 & -1 & | & 3 \end{bmatrix} R_1 \leftrightarrow R_3$

$\begin{bmatrix} 1 & 1 & -1 & | & 3 \\ 4 & -2 & -8 & | & -4 \\ 3 & 4 & 2 & | & 3 \end{bmatrix} \begin{matrix} -4R_1 + R_2 \\ -3R_1 + R_3 \end{matrix}$

$\begin{bmatrix} 1 & 1 & -1 & | & 3 \\ 0 & -6 & -4 & | & -16 \\ 0 & 1 & 5 & | & -6 \end{bmatrix} R_2 \leftrightarrow R_3$

$\begin{bmatrix} 1 & 1 & -1 & | & 3 \\ 0 & 1 & 5 & | & -6 \\ 0 & -6 & -4 & | & -16 \end{bmatrix} 6R_2 + R_3$

$\begin{bmatrix} 1 & 1 & 1 & | & 3 \\ 0 & 1 & 5 & | & -6 \\ 0 & 0 & 26 & | & -52 \end{bmatrix} \dfrac{1}{26}R_3$

$\begin{bmatrix} 1 & 1 & -1 & | & 3 \\ 0 & 1 & 5 & | & -6 \\ 0 & 0 & 1 & | & -2 \end{bmatrix}$

This corresponds to the system
$x + y - z = 3$
$y + 5z = -6$
$z = -2$
Use back-substitution to find the values of x and y:
$y + 5(-2) = -6$
$y - 10 = -6$
$y = 4$
$x + 4 + 2 = 3$
$x + 6 = 3$
$x = -3$
The solution to the system is $\{(-3, 4, -2)\}$.

7. $\begin{bmatrix} 8 & 5 & 11 & | & 30 \\ -1 & -4 & 2 & | & 3 \\ 2 & -1 & 5 & | & 12 \end{bmatrix} R_1 \leftrightarrow R_2$

$\begin{bmatrix} -1 & -4 & 2 & | & 3 \\ 8 & 5 & 11 & | & 30 \\ 2 & -1 & 5 & | & 12 \end{bmatrix} -1R_1$

$\begin{bmatrix} 1 & 4 & -2 & | & -3 \\ 8 & 5 & 11 & | & 30 \\ 2 & -1 & 5 & | & 12 \end{bmatrix} \begin{matrix} -8R_1 + R_2 \\ -2R_1 + R_3 \end{matrix}$

$\begin{bmatrix} 1 & 4 & -2 & | & -3 \\ 0 & -27 & 27 & | & 54 \\ 0 & -9 & 9 & | & 18 \end{bmatrix} -\dfrac{1}{27}R_2$

$\begin{bmatrix} 1 & 4 & -2 & | & -3 \\ 0 & 1 & -1 & | & -2 \\ 0 & -9 & 9 & | & 18 \end{bmatrix} 9R_2 + R_3$

$\begin{bmatrix} 1 & 4 & -2 & | & -3 \\ 0 & 1 & -1 & | & -2 \\ 0 & 0 & 0 & | & 0 \end{bmatrix}$

The system $\begin{matrix} x + 4y - 2z = -3 \\ y - z = -2 \end{matrix}$ has no unique

solution. Express x and y in terms of z:
$y = -2 + z$
$x + 4(-2 + z) - 2z = -3$
$x - 8 + 4z - 2z = -3$
$x - 8 + 2z = -3$
$x = 5 - 2z$
With $z = t$, the complete solution to the system is
$\{(5 - 2t, -2 + t, t)\}$.

9. $\begin{bmatrix} 1 & -2 & -1 & -3 & | & -9 \\ 1 & 1 & -1 & 0 & | & 0 \\ 3 & 4 & 0 & 1 & | & 6 \\ 0 & 2 & -2 & 1 & | & 3 \end{bmatrix} \begin{matrix} -1R_1 + R_2 \\ -3R_1 + R_3 \end{matrix}$

$\begin{bmatrix} 1 & -2 & -1 & -3 & | & -9 \\ 0 & 3 & 0 & 3 & | & 9 \\ 0 & 10 & 3 & 10 & | & 33 \\ 0 & 2 & -2 & 1 & | & 3 \end{bmatrix} \dfrac{1}{3}R_2$

$\begin{bmatrix} 1 & -2 & -1 & -3 & | & -9 \\ 0 & 1 & 0 & 1 & | & 3 \\ 0 & 10 & 3 & 10 & | & 33 \\ 0 & 2 & -2 & 1 & | & 3 \end{bmatrix} \begin{matrix} -10R_2 + R_3 \\ -2R_2 + R_4 \end{matrix}$

$\begin{bmatrix} 1 & -2 & -1 & -3 & | & -9 \\ 0 & 1 & 0 & 1 & | & 3 \\ 0 & 0 & 3 & 0 & | & 3 \\ 0 & 0 & -2 & -1 & | & -3 \end{bmatrix} \dfrac{1}{3}R_3$

$\begin{bmatrix} 1 & -2 & -1 & -3 & | & -9 \\ 0 & 1 & 0 & 1 & | & 3 \\ 0 & 0 & 1 & 0 & | & 1 \\ 0 & 0 & -2 & -1 & | & -3 \end{bmatrix} 2R_3 + R_4$

$$\begin{bmatrix} 1 & -2 & -1 & -3 & | & -9 \\ 0 & 1 & 0 & 1 & | & 3 \\ 0 & 0 & 1 & 0 & | & 1 \\ 0 & 0 & 0 & -1 & | & -1 \end{bmatrix} -1R_4$$

$$\begin{bmatrix} 1 & -2 & -1 & -3 & | & -9 \\ 0 & 1 & 0 & 1 & | & 3 \\ 0 & 0 & 1 & 0 & | & 1 \\ 0 & 0 & 0 & 1 & | & 1 \end{bmatrix}$$

This corresponds to the system
$$w - 2x - y - 3z = -9$$
$$x + z = 3$$
$$y = 1$$
$$z = 1$$

Use back-substitution to find the values of w and x:
$$x + 1 = 3$$
$$x = 2$$
$$w - 2(2) - 1 - 3(1) = -9$$
$$w - 4 - 1 - 3 = -9$$
$$w - 8 = -9$$
$$w = -1$$

The solution to the system is $\{(-1, 2, 1, 1)\}$.

11. $$\begin{bmatrix} 2 & 1 & -1 & 0 & | & 3 \\ 1 & -3 & 2 & 0 & | & -4 \\ 3 & 1 & -3 & 1 & | & 1 \\ 1 & 2 & -4 & -1 & | & -2 \end{bmatrix} R_1 \leftrightarrow R_2$$

$$\begin{bmatrix} 1 & -3 & 2 & 0 & | & -4 \\ 2 & 1 & -1 & 0 & | & 3 \\ 3 & 1 & -3 & 1 & | & 1 \\ 1 & 2 & -4 & -1 & | & -2 \end{bmatrix} \begin{matrix} -2R_1 + R_2 \\ -3R_1 + R_3 \\ -1R_1 + R_4 \end{matrix}$$

$$\begin{bmatrix} 1 & -3 & 2 & 0 & | & -4 \\ 0 & 7 & -5 & 0 & | & 11 \\ 0 & 10 & -9 & 1 & | & 13 \\ 0 & 5 & -6 & -1 & | & 2 \end{bmatrix} \frac{1}{7}R_2$$

$$\begin{bmatrix} 1 & -3 & 2 & 0 & | & -4 \\ 0 & 1 & -\frac{5}{7} & 0 & | & \frac{11}{7} \\ 0 & 10 & -9 & 1 & | & 13 \\ 0 & 5 & -6 & -1 & | & 2 \end{bmatrix} \begin{matrix} -10R_2 + R_3 \\ -5R_2 + R_4 \end{matrix}$$

$$\begin{bmatrix} 1 & -3 & 2 & 0 & | & -4 \\ 0 & 1 & -\frac{5}{7} & 0 & | & \frac{11}{7} \\ 0 & 0 & -\frac{13}{7} & 1 & | & -\frac{19}{7} \\ 0 & 0 & -\frac{17}{7} & -1 & | & -\frac{41}{7} \end{bmatrix} -\frac{7}{13}R_3$$

$$\begin{bmatrix} 1 & -3 & 2 & 0 & | & -4 \\ 0 & 1 & -\frac{5}{7} & 0 & | & \frac{11}{7} \\ 0 & 0 & 1 & -\frac{7}{13} & | & \frac{19}{13} \\ 0 & 0 & -\frac{17}{7} & -1 & | & -\frac{41}{7} \end{bmatrix} \frac{17}{7}R_3 + R_4$$

$$\begin{bmatrix} 1 & -3 & 2 & 0 & | & -4 \\ 0 & 1 & -\frac{5}{7} & 0 & | & \frac{11}{7} \\ 0 & 0 & 1 & -\frac{7}{13} & | & \frac{19}{13} \\ 0 & 0 & 0 & -\frac{30}{13} & | & -\frac{30}{13} \end{bmatrix} -\frac{13}{30}R_4$$

$$\begin{bmatrix} 1 & -3 & 2 & 0 & | & -4 \\ 0 & 1 & -\frac{5}{7} & 0 & | & \frac{11}{7} \\ 0 & 0 & 1 & -\frac{7}{13} & | & \frac{19}{13} \\ 0 & 0 & 0 & 1 & | & 1 \end{bmatrix}$$

This corresponds to the system
$$w - 3x + 2y = -4$$
$$x - \frac{5}{7}y = \frac{11}{7}$$
$$y - \frac{7}{13}z = \frac{19}{13}$$
$$z = 1$$

Use back-substitution to find the values of w, x, and y:
$$y - \frac{7}{13}z = \frac{19}{13}$$
$$y - \frac{7}{13}(1) = \frac{19}{13}$$
$$y = 2$$
$$x - \frac{5}{7}(2) = \frac{11}{7}$$
$$x - \frac{10}{7} = \frac{11}{7}$$
$$x = 3$$
$$w - 3(3) + 2(2) = -4$$
$$w - 9 + 4 = -4$$
$$w - 5 = -4$$
$$w = 1$$

The solution to the system is $\{(1, 3, 2, 1)\}$.

13. $$\begin{bmatrix} 1 & -3 & 1 & -4 & | & 4 \\ -2 & 1 & 2 & 0 & | & -2 \\ 3 & -2 & 1 & -6 & | & 2 \\ -1 & 3 & 2 & -1 & | & -6 \end{bmatrix} \begin{matrix} 2R_1 + R_2 \\ -3R_1 + R_3 \\ R_1 + R_4 \end{matrix}$$

$$\begin{bmatrix} 1 & -3 & 1 & -4 & | & 4 \\ 0 & -5 & 4 & -8 & | & 6 \\ 0 & 7 & -2 & 6 & | & -10 \\ 0 & 0 & 3 & -5 & | & -2 \end{bmatrix} -\frac{1}{5}R_2$$

$$\begin{bmatrix} 1 & -3 & 1 & -4 & | & 4 \\ 0 & 1 & -\frac{4}{5} & \frac{8}{5} & | & -\frac{6}{5} \\ 0 & 7 & -2 & 6 & | & -10 \\ 0 & 0 & 3 & -5 & | & -2 \end{bmatrix} -7R_2 + R_3$$

$$\begin{bmatrix} 1 & -3 & 1 & -4 & | & 4 \\ 0 & 1 & -\frac{4}{5} & \frac{8}{5} & | & -\frac{6}{5} \\ 0 & 0 & \frac{18}{5} & -\frac{26}{5} & | & -\frac{8}{5} \\ 0 & 0 & 3 & -5 & | & -2 \end{bmatrix} \frac{5}{18}R_3$$

$$\begin{bmatrix} 1 & -3 & 1 & -4 & | & 4 \\ 0 & 1 & -\frac{4}{5} & \frac{8}{5} & | & -\frac{6}{5} \\ 0 & 0 & 1 & -\frac{13}{9} & | & -\frac{4}{9} \\ 0 & 0 & 3 & -5 & | & -2 \end{bmatrix} -3R_3 + R_4$$

$$\begin{bmatrix} 1 & -3 & 1 & -4 & | & 4 \\ 0 & 1 & -\frac{4}{5} & \frac{8}{5} & | & -\frac{6}{5} \\ 0 & 0 & 1 & -\frac{13}{9} & | & -\frac{4}{9} \\ 0 & 0 & 0 & -\frac{2}{3} & | & -\frac{2}{3} \end{bmatrix} -\frac{3}{2}R_4$$

$$\begin{bmatrix} 1 & -3 & 1 & -4 & | & 4 \\ 0 & 1 & -\frac{4}{5} & \frac{8}{5} & | & -\frac{6}{5} \\ 0 & 0 & 1 & -\frac{13}{9} & | & -\frac{4}{9} \\ 0 & 0 & 0 & 1 & | & 1 \end{bmatrix}$$

This corresponds to the system
$$w - 3x + y - 4z = 4$$
$$x - \frac{4}{5}y + \frac{8}{5}z = -\frac{6}{5}$$
$$y - \frac{13}{9}z = -\frac{4}{9}$$
$$z = 1$$

Use back-substitution to find the values of w, z, and y:
$$y - \frac{13}{9}(1) = -\frac{4}{9}$$
$$y = 1$$
$$x - \frac{4}{5}(1) + \frac{8}{5}(1) = -\frac{6}{5}$$
$$x + \frac{4}{5} = -\frac{6}{5}$$
$$x = -2$$
$$w - 3(-2) + 1 - 4 = 4$$
$$w + 6 - 3 = 4$$
$$w = 1$$
The solution to the system is $\{(1, -2, 1, 1)\}$.

15. $\begin{bmatrix} 2 & 1 & -1 & | & 2 \\ 3 & 3 & -2 & | & 3 \end{bmatrix} \frac{1}{2}R_1$ $\begin{bmatrix} 1 & \frac{1}{2} & -\frac{1}{2} & | & 1 \\ 3 & 3 & -2 & | & 3 \end{bmatrix} -3R_1 + R_2$

$\begin{bmatrix} 1 & \frac{1}{2} & -\frac{1}{2} & | & 1 \\ 0 & \frac{3}{2} & -\frac{1}{2} & | & 0 \end{bmatrix} \frac{2}{3}R_2$

$\begin{bmatrix} 1 & \frac{1}{2} & -\frac{1}{2} & | & 1 \\ 0 & 1 & -\frac{1}{3} & | & 0 \end{bmatrix}$

The system $x + \frac{1}{2}y - \frac{1}{2}z = 1$ has no unique
$$y - \frac{1}{3}z = 0$$
solution. Express x and y in terms of z:
$$y = \frac{1}{3}z$$
$$x + \frac{1}{2}\left(\frac{1}{3}z\right) - \frac{1}{2}z = 1$$
$$x + \frac{1}{6}z - \frac{1}{2}z = 1$$
$$x - \frac{1}{3}z = 1$$
$$x = 1 + \frac{1}{3}z$$

With $z = t$, the complete solution to the system is
$$\left\{\left(1 + \frac{1}{3}t, \frac{1}{3}t, t\right)\right\}.$$

17. The system $\begin{array}{l} x + 2y + 3z = 5 \\ y - 5z = 0 \end{array}$ has no unique

solution. Express x and y in terms of z:
$$y = 5z$$
$$x + 2(5z) + 3z = 5$$
$$x + 10z + 3z = 5$$
$$x = -13z + 5$$
With $z = t$, the complete solution to the system is
$\{(-13t + 5, 5t, t)\}$.

19. $\begin{bmatrix} 1 & 1 & -2 & | & 2 \\ 3 & -1 & -6 & | & -7 \end{bmatrix} -3R_1 + R_2$

$\begin{bmatrix} 1 & 1 & -2 & | & 2 \\ 0 & -4 & 0 & | & -13 \end{bmatrix} -\frac{1}{4}R_2$

$\begin{bmatrix} 1 & 1 & -2 & | & 2 \\ 0 & 1 & 0 & | & \frac{13}{4} \end{bmatrix}$

$$x + y - 2z = 2$$
The system $\quad y = \dfrac{13}{4}$ has no unique

solution. Express x in terms of z:

$$x + \frac{13}{4} - 2z = 2$$

$$x = 2z - \frac{5}{4}$$

With $z = t$, the complete solution to the system is

$$\left\{ \left(2t - \frac{5}{4}, \frac{13}{4}, t \right) \right\}.$$

21. $\begin{bmatrix} 1 & 1 & -1 & 1 & | & -2 \\ 2 & -1 & 2 & -1 & | & 7 \\ -1 & 2 & 1 & 2 & | & -1 \end{bmatrix} \begin{matrix} \\ -2R_1 + R_2 \\ 1R_1 + R_3 \end{matrix}$

$\begin{bmatrix} 1 & 1 & -1 & 1 & | & -2 \\ 0 & -3 & 4 & -3 & | & 11 \\ 0 & 3 & 0 & 3 & | & -3 \end{bmatrix} R_2 \leftrightarrow R_3$

$\begin{bmatrix} 1 & 1 & -1 & 1 & | & -2 \\ 0 & 3 & 0 & 3 & | & -3 \\ 0 & -3 & 4 & -3 & | & 11 \end{bmatrix} \tfrac{1}{3}R_2$

$\begin{bmatrix} 1 & 1 & -1 & 1 & | & -2 \\ 0 & 1 & 0 & 1 & | & -1 \\ 0 & -3 & 4 & -3 & | & 11 \end{bmatrix} 3R_2 + R_3$

$\begin{bmatrix} 1 & 1 & -1 & 1 & | & -2 \\ 0 & 1 & 0 & 1 & | & -1 \\ 0 & 0 & 4 & 0 & | & 8 \end{bmatrix} \tfrac{1}{4}R_3$

$\begin{bmatrix} 1 & 1 & -1 & 1 & | & -2 \\ 0 & 1 & 0 & 1 & | & -1 \\ 0 & 0 & 1 & 0 & | & 2 \end{bmatrix}$

$$x + y - z + w = -2$$

The system $\quad x + z = -1\quad$ has no unique

$$y = 2$$

solution. Let $z = t$ and use back substitution to find remaining variables. The complete solution to the system is $\{(1, -t - 1, 2, t)\}$.

23. $\begin{bmatrix} 1 & 2 & 3 & -1 & | & 7 \\ 0 & 2 & -3 & 1 & | & 4 \\ 1 & -4 & 1 & 0 & | & 3 \end{bmatrix} -1R_1 + R_3$

$\begin{bmatrix} 1 & 2 & 3 & -1 & | & 7 \\ 0 & 2 & -3 & 1 & | & 4 \\ 0 & -6 & -2 & 1 & | & -4 \end{bmatrix} \tfrac{1}{2}R_2$

$\begin{bmatrix} 1 & 2 & 3 & -1 & | & 7 \\ 0 & 1 & -\frac{3}{2} & \frac{1}{2} & | & 2 \\ 0 & -6 & -2 & 1 & | & -4 \end{bmatrix} 6R_2 + R_3$

$\begin{bmatrix} 1 & 2 & 3 & -1 & | & 7 \\ 0 & 1 & -\frac{3}{2} & \frac{1}{2} & | & 2 \\ 0 & 0 & -11 & 4 & | & 8 \end{bmatrix} -\tfrac{1}{11}R_3$

$\begin{bmatrix} 1 & 2 & 3 & -1 & | & 7 \\ 0 & 1 & -\frac{3}{2} & \frac{1}{2} & | & 2 \\ 0 & 0 & 1 & -\frac{4}{11} & | & -\frac{8}{11} \end{bmatrix}$

The system has no unique solution. Let $z = t$ and use back substitution to find remaining variables. The complete solution to the system

is $\left\{ \left(-\frac{2}{11}t + \frac{81}{11}, \frac{1}{22}t + \frac{10}{11}, \frac{4}{11}t - \frac{8}{11}, t \right) \right\}$.

25. a.   System of equations:

$$4w - 2x + 2y - 3z = 0$$

$$7w - x - y - 3z = 0$$

$$w + x - y - z = 0$$

b.   Reduced system:

$$w - 0.5z = 0$$

$$x = 0$$

$$y - 0.5z = 0$$

Find w and y in terms of z.

$$w - 0.5z = 0$$

$$w = 0.5z$$

$$y - 0.5z = 0$$

$$y = 0.5z$$

The complete solution to the system is

$$\{(0.5z, 0, 0.5z, z)\}.$$

27. a.   System of equations:

$$w + 2x + 5y + 5z = 3$$

$$w + x + 3y + 4z = -1$$

$$w - x - y + 2z = 3$$

b.   Reduced system:

$$w + y + 3z = 1$$

$$x + 2y + z = -2$$

Find w and x in terms of y and z.

$$w + y + 3z = 1$$

$$w = 1 - y - 3z$$

$$x + 2y + z = -2$$

$$x = -2 - 2y - z$$

The complete solution to the system is

$$\{(1 - y - 3z, \, -2 - 2y - z, \, y, \, z)\}.$$

29. $z + 12 = x + 6$

31. $x - y = 4$

$x - z = 6$

$y - z = 2$

$$\begin{bmatrix} 1 & -1 & 0 & | & 4 \\ 1 & 0 & -1 & | & 6 \\ 0 & 1 & -1 & | & 2 \end{bmatrix} -1R_1 + R_2$$

$$\begin{bmatrix} 1 & -1 & 0 & 4 \\ 0 & -1 & 1 & -2 \\ 0 & 1 & -1 & 2 \end{bmatrix} -1R_2$$

$$\begin{bmatrix} 1 & -1 & 0 & 4 \\ 0 & 1 & -1 & 2 \\ 0 & 1 & -1 & 2 \end{bmatrix} \begin{matrix} -1R_2 + R_3 \\ 1R_2 + R_1 \end{matrix}$$

$$\begin{bmatrix} 1 & 0 & -1 & 6 \\ 0 & 1 & -1 & 2 \\ 0 & 0 & 0 & 0 \end{bmatrix}$$

The system has no unique solution. Express x and y in terms of z:

$x - z = 6$

$y - z = 2$

$x = z + 6$

$y = z + 2$

With $z = t$, the complete solution to the system is $\{(t + 6, t + 2, t)\}$.

33. a. From left to right along Palm Drive, then along Sunset Drive, we get the equations

$w + z = 200 + 180 = 380$;

$w + x = 400 + 200 = 600$;

$z + 70 = y + 20$ or $y - z = 50$;

$y + 200 = x + 30$ or $x - y = 170$.

The system is

$w + z = 380$

$w + x = 600$

$y - z = 50$

$x - y = 170$

b.

$$\begin{bmatrix} 1 & 0 & 0 & 1 & | & 380 \\ 0 & 1 & 0 & -1 & | & 220 \\ 0 & 0 & 1 & -1 & | & 50 \\ 0 & 1 & -1 & 0 & | & 170 \end{bmatrix} -1R_2 + R_4$$

$$\begin{bmatrix} 1 & 0 & 0 & 1 & | & 380 \\ 0 & 1 & 0 & -1 & | & 220 \\ 0 & 0 & 1 & -1 & | & 50 \\ 0 & 0 & -1 & 1 & | & -50 \end{bmatrix} 1R_3 + R_4$$

$$\begin{bmatrix} 1 & 0 & 0 & 1 & | & 380 \\ 0 & 1 & 0 & -1 & | & 220 \\ 0 & 0 & 1 & -1 & | & 50 \\ 0 & 0 & 0 & 0 & | & 0 \end{bmatrix}$$

The system has no unique solution.

Express x and y and z in terms of z:

$w = 380 - z$

$x = 220 + z$

$y = 50 + z$

With $z = t$, the complete solution to the system is $\{(380 - t, 220 + t, 50 + t, t)\}$.

c. Letting $z = 50$, the solution is

$w = 380 - 50 = 330$

$x = 220 + 50 = 270$

$y = 50 + 50 = 100$

35. Let $x =$ the amount of Food 1,

$y =$ the amount of Food 2, and

$z =$ the amount of Food 3, in ounces.

The amount of vitamin A is $20x + 30y + 10z$; the amount of iron is $20x + 10y + 10z$; the amount of calcium is $10x + 10y + 30z$.

a. Not having Food 1 means that all x terms are left out. The vitamin A requirement can then be represented by $30y + 10z = 220$; the iron requirement is $10y + 10z = 180$; the calcium requirement is $10y + 30z = 340$. The corresponding system is

$30y + 10z = 220$

$10y + 10z = 180$

$10y + 30z = 340$.

Dividing all of the numbers by 10, the matrix for this system is

$$\begin{bmatrix} 3 & 1 & | & 22 \\ 1 & 1 & | & 18 \\ 1 & 3 & | & 34 \end{bmatrix} R_1 \leftrightarrow R_2$$

$$\begin{bmatrix} 1 & 1 & | & 18 \\ 3 & 1 & | & 22 \\ 1 & 3 & | & 34 \end{bmatrix} \begin{matrix} \\ -3R_1 + R_2 \\ -1R_1 + R_3 \end{matrix}$$

$$\begin{bmatrix} 1 & 1 & | & 18 \\ 0 & -2 & | & -32 \\ 0 & 2 & | & 16 \end{bmatrix} 1R_2 + R_3$$

$$\begin{bmatrix} 1 & 1 & | & 18 \\ 0 & -2 & | & -32 \\ 0 & 0 & | & -16 \end{bmatrix}.$$

From the last row, we see that the system has no solution, so there is no way to satisfy these dietary requirements with no Food 1 available.

b. With Food 1 available, and dropping the vitamin A requirement, the system is
$20x + 10y + 10z = 180$
$10x + 10y + 30z = 340$.
Dividing all of the numbers by 10, the matrix for this system is

$$\begin{bmatrix} 2 & 1 & 1 & | & 18 \\ 1 & 1 & 3 & | & 34 \end{bmatrix} R_1 \leftrightarrow R_2$$

$$\begin{bmatrix} 1 & 1 & 3 & | & 34 \\ 2 & 1 & 1 & | & 18 \end{bmatrix} -2R_1 + R_2$$

$$\begin{bmatrix} 1 & 1 & 3 & | & 34 \\ 0 & -1 & -5 & | & -50 \end{bmatrix} -1R_2$$

$$\begin{bmatrix} 1 & 1 & 3 & | & 34 \\ 0 & 1 & 5 & | & 50 \end{bmatrix}.$$

The system $\begin{matrix} x + y + 3z = 34 \\ y + 5z = 50 \end{matrix}$ has no unique

solution. Express x and y in terms of z:
$y = -5z + 50$
$x + (-5z + 50) + 3z = 34$
$x - 2z + 50 = 34$
$x = 2z - 16$
Now we can choose a value for z, i.e., an amount of Food 3, and find the corresponding values of x and y. Note that negative amounts of food are not realistic, so $z \geq 0$, $y = -5z + 50 \geq 0$, and $x = 2z - 16 \geq 0$. These conditions are equivalent to $8 \leq z \leq 10$.
Using $z = 8$ and $z = 10$, two possibilities are 0 ounces of Food 1, 10 ounces of Food 2, and 8 ounces of Food 3 or 4 ounces of Food 1, 0 ounces of Food 2, and 10 ounces of Food 3. (Other answers are possible.)

41. $$\begin{bmatrix} 1 & 3 & 1 & | & a^2 \\ 2 & 5 & 2a & | & 0 \\ 1 & 1 & a^2 & | & -9 \end{bmatrix} \begin{matrix} \\ -2R_1 + R_2 \\ -1R_1 + R_3 \end{matrix}$$

$$\begin{bmatrix} 1 & 3 & 1 & | & a^2 \\ 0 & -1 & 2a-2 & | & -2a^2 \\ 0 & -2 & a^2-1 & | & -9-a^2 \end{bmatrix} -1R_2$$

$$\begin{bmatrix} 1 & 3 & 1 & | & a^2 \\ 0 & 1 & 2-2a & | & 2a^2 \\ 0 & -2 & a^2-1 & | & -9-a^2 \end{bmatrix} 2R_2 + R_3$$

$$\begin{bmatrix} 1 & 3 & 1 & | & a^2 \\ 0 & 1 & 2-2a & | & 2a^2 \\ 0 & 0 & a^2-4a+3 & | & -9+3a^2 \end{bmatrix}$$

The system will be inconsistent when
$a^2 - 4a + 3 = 0$ but $-9 + 3a^2 \neq 0$.
$a^2 - 4a + 3 = (a-1)(a-3) = 0$ when $a = 1$ or
$a = 3$. $-9 + 3a^2 = 0$ when $a = \pm\sqrt{3}$.
Thus, the system is inconsistent when $a = 1$ or
$a = 3$.

Section 8.3

Check Point Exercises

1. a. The matrix $A = \begin{bmatrix} 5 & -2 \\ -3 & \pi \\ 1 & 6 \end{bmatrix}$ has 3 rows and

2 columns, so it is of order 3×2.

b. The element a_{12} is in the first row and second column. Thus, $a_{12} = -2$. The element a_{31} is in the third row and first column. Thus, $a_{31} = 1$.

2. a.
$$\begin{bmatrix} -4 & 3 \\ 7 & -6 \end{bmatrix} + \begin{bmatrix} 6 & -3 \\ 2 & -4 \end{bmatrix}$$
$$= \begin{bmatrix} -4+6 & 3+(-3) \\ 7+2 & -6+(-4) \end{bmatrix} = \begin{bmatrix} 2 & 0 \\ 9 & -10 \end{bmatrix}$$

b.
$$\begin{bmatrix} 5 & 4 \\ -3 & 7 \\ 0 & 1 \end{bmatrix} - \begin{bmatrix} -4 & 8 \\ 6 & 0 \\ -5 & 3 \end{bmatrix}$$
$$= \begin{bmatrix} 5-(-4) & 4-8 \\ -3-6 & 7-0 \\ 0-(-5) & 1-3 \end{bmatrix}$$
$$= \begin{bmatrix} 9 & -4 \\ -9 & 7 \\ 5 & -2 \end{bmatrix}$$

3. a.
$$-6B = -6\begin{bmatrix} -1 & -2 \\ 8 & 5 \end{bmatrix}$$
$$= \begin{bmatrix} -6(-1) & -6(-2) \\ -6(8) & -6(5) \end{bmatrix}$$
$$= \begin{bmatrix} -6 & 12 \\ -48 & -30 \end{bmatrix}$$

b.
$$3A + 2B = \begin{bmatrix} -4 & 1 \\ 3 & 0 \end{bmatrix} + 2\begin{bmatrix} -1 & -2 \\ 8 & 5 \end{bmatrix}$$
$$= \begin{bmatrix} 3(-4) & 3(1) \\ 3(3) & 3(0) \end{bmatrix} + \begin{bmatrix} 2(-1) & 2(-2) \\ 2(8) & 2(5) \end{bmatrix}$$
$$= \begin{bmatrix} -12 & 3 \\ 9 & 0 \end{bmatrix} + \begin{bmatrix} -2 & -4 \\ 16 & 10 \end{bmatrix}$$
$$= \begin{bmatrix} -12+(-2) & 3+(-4) \\ 9+16 & 0+10 \end{bmatrix}$$
$$= \begin{bmatrix} -14 & -1 \\ 25 & 10 \end{bmatrix}$$

4. $3X + A = B$
$3X = B - A$
$$X = \frac{1}{3}(B - A)$$
$$X = \frac{1}{3}\left(\begin{bmatrix} -10 & 1 \\ -9 & 17 \end{bmatrix} - \begin{bmatrix} 2 & -8 \\ 0 & 4 \end{bmatrix}\right)$$
$$X = \frac{1}{3}\begin{bmatrix} -12 & 9 \\ -9 & 13 \end{bmatrix}$$
$$X = \begin{bmatrix} -4 & 3 \\ -3 & \frac{13}{3} \end{bmatrix}$$

5. Given $A = \begin{bmatrix} 1 & 3 \\ 2 & 5 \end{bmatrix}$ and $B = \begin{bmatrix} 4 & 6 \\ 1 & 0 \end{bmatrix}$,
$$AB = \begin{bmatrix} 1 & 3 \\ 2 & 5 \end{bmatrix} \cdot \begin{bmatrix} 4 & 6 \\ 1 & 0 \end{bmatrix} = \begin{bmatrix} 1(4)+3(1) & 1(6)+3(0) \\ 2(4)+5(1) & 2(6)+5(0) \end{bmatrix}$$
$$= \begin{bmatrix} 7 & 6 \\ 13 & 12 \end{bmatrix}$$

6. If $A = \begin{bmatrix} 2 & 0 & 4 \end{bmatrix}$ and $B = \begin{bmatrix} 1 \\ 3 \\ 7 \end{bmatrix}$, then

$$AB = \begin{bmatrix} 2 & 0 & 4 \end{bmatrix} \begin{bmatrix} 1 \\ 3 \\ 7 \end{bmatrix}$$

$$= \begin{bmatrix} 2(1) + 0(3) + 4(7) \end{bmatrix}$$

$$= \begin{bmatrix} 2 + 0 + 28 \end{bmatrix}$$

$$= \begin{bmatrix} 30 \end{bmatrix}$$

and $BA = \begin{bmatrix} 1 \\ 3 \\ 7 \end{bmatrix} \begin{bmatrix} 2 & 0 & 4 \end{bmatrix} = \begin{bmatrix} 1(2) & 1(0) & 1(4) \\ 3(2) & 3(0) & 3(4) \\ 7(2) & 7(0) & 7(4) \end{bmatrix} = \begin{bmatrix} 2 & 0 & 4 \\ 6 & 0 & 12 \\ 14 & 0 & 28 \end{bmatrix}$.

7. a. $\begin{bmatrix} 1 & 3 \\ 0 & 2 \end{bmatrix} \cdot \begin{bmatrix} 2 & 3 & -1 & 6 \\ 0 & 5 & 4 & 1 \end{bmatrix}$

$$= \begin{bmatrix} 1(2) + 3(0) & 1(3) + 3(5) & 1(-1) + 3(4) & 1(6) + 3(1) \\ 0(2) + 2(0) & 0(3) + 2(5) & 0(-1) + 2(4) & 0(6) + 2(1) \end{bmatrix}$$

$$= \begin{bmatrix} 2 & 18 & 11 & 9 \\ 0 & 10 & 8 & 2 \end{bmatrix}$$

b. $\begin{bmatrix} 2 & 3 & -1 & 6 \\ 0 & 5 & 4 & 1 \end{bmatrix} \begin{bmatrix} 1 & 3 \\ 0 & 2 \end{bmatrix}$

The number of columns in the first matrix does not equal the number of rows in the second matrix. Thus, the product of these two matrices is undefined.

8. Because the L is dark gray and the background is light gray, the digital photograph can be represented by the matrix

$$\begin{bmatrix} 2 & 1 & 1 \\ 2 & 1 & 1 \\ 2 & 2 & 1 \end{bmatrix}$$

We can make the L light gray by decreasing each 2 in the above matrix to 1. We can make the background black by increasing each 1 in the matrix to 3. This is accomplished using the following matrix addition.

$$\begin{bmatrix} 2 & 1 & 1 \\ 2 & 1 & 1 \\ 2 & 2 & 1 \end{bmatrix} + \begin{bmatrix} -1 & 2 & 2 \\ -1 & 2 & 2 \\ -1 & -1 & 2 \end{bmatrix} = \begin{bmatrix} 1 & 3 & 3 \\ 1 & 3 & 3 \\ 1 & 1 & 3 \end{bmatrix}$$

9. a. $\begin{bmatrix} 0 & 3 & 4 \\ 0 & 5 & 2 \end{bmatrix} + \begin{bmatrix} -3 & -3 & -3 \\ -1 & -1 & -1 \end{bmatrix} = \begin{bmatrix} -3 & 0 & 1 \\ -1 & 4 & 1 \end{bmatrix}$

b. $2\begin{bmatrix} 0 & 3 & 4 \\ 0 & 5 & 2 \end{bmatrix} = \begin{bmatrix} 0 & 6 & 8 \\ 0 & 10 & 4 \end{bmatrix}$

c. $\begin{bmatrix} 1 & 0 \\ 0 & -1 \end{bmatrix}\begin{bmatrix} 0 & 3 & 4 \\ 0 & 5 & 2 \end{bmatrix} = \begin{bmatrix} (-1)(0)+0(0) & (-1)(3)+0(5) & (-1)(4)+0(2) \\ 0(0)+1(0) & 0(3)+1(5) & 0(4)+1(2) \end{bmatrix}$

$$= \begin{bmatrix} 0 & -3 & -4 \\ 0 & 5 & 2 \end{bmatrix}$$

Multiplication with $\begin{bmatrix} 1 & 0 \\ 0 & -1 \end{bmatrix}$ reflects the triangle over the *x*-axis.

Exercise Set 8.3

1. **a.** 2×3

    b. a_{32} does not exist (A only has 2 rows).

        $a_{23} = -1$

3. **a.** 3×4

    b. $a_{32} = \dfrac{1}{2}$; $a_{23} = -6$

5. $\begin{bmatrix} x \\ 4 \end{bmatrix} = \begin{bmatrix} 6 \\ y \end{bmatrix}$

        $x = 6$

        $y = 4$

7. $\begin{bmatrix} x & 2y \\ z & 9 \end{bmatrix} = \begin{bmatrix} 4 & 12 \\ 3 & 9 \end{bmatrix}$

    $x = 4$

    $2y = 12$

      $y = 6$

      $z = 3$

9. **a.** $A+B = \begin{bmatrix} 4+5 & 1+9 \\ 3+0 & 2+7 \end{bmatrix} = \begin{bmatrix} 9 & 10 \\ 3 & 9 \end{bmatrix}$

    b. $A-B = \begin{bmatrix} 4-5 & 1-9 \\ 3-0 & 2-7 \end{bmatrix} = \begin{bmatrix} -1 & -8 \\ 3 & -5 \end{bmatrix}$

    c. $-4A = \begin{bmatrix} -16 & -4 \\ -12 & -8 \end{bmatrix}$

    d. $3A+2B = \begin{bmatrix} 12+10 & 3+18 \\ 9+0 & 6+14 \end{bmatrix} = \begin{bmatrix} 22 & 21 \\ 9 & 20 \end{bmatrix}$

11. **a.** $A+B = \begin{bmatrix} 1+2 & 3+(-1) \\ 3+3 & 4+(-2) \\ 5+0 & 6+1 \end{bmatrix} = \begin{bmatrix} 3 & 2 \\ 6 & 2 \\ 5 & 7 \end{bmatrix}$

    b. $A-B = \begin{bmatrix} 1-2 & 3-(-1) \\ 3-3 & 4-(-2) \\ 5-0 & 6-1 \end{bmatrix} = \begin{bmatrix} -1 & 4 \\ 0 & 6 \\ 5 & 5 \end{bmatrix}$

    c. $-4A = \begin{bmatrix} -4 & -12 \\ -12 & -16 \\ -20 & -24 \end{bmatrix}$

    d. $3A+2B = \begin{bmatrix} 3+4 & 9-2 \\ 9+6 & 12-4 \\ 15+0 & 18+2 \end{bmatrix} = \begin{bmatrix} 7 & 7 \\ 15 & 8 \\ 15 & 20 \end{bmatrix}$

13. **a.** $A+B = \begin{bmatrix} 2+(-5) \\ -4+3 \\ 1+(-1) \end{bmatrix} = \begin{bmatrix} -3 \\ -1 \\ 0 \end{bmatrix}$

    b. $A-B = \begin{bmatrix} 2-(-5) \\ -4-3 \\ 1-(-1) \end{bmatrix} = \begin{bmatrix} 7 \\ -7 \\ 2 \end{bmatrix}$

    c. $-4A = \begin{bmatrix} -8 \\ 16 \\ -4 \end{bmatrix}$

    d. $3A+2B = \begin{bmatrix} 6-10 \\ -12+6 \\ 3-2 \end{bmatrix} = \begin{bmatrix} -4 \\ -6 \\ 1 \end{bmatrix}$

15. **a.** $A + B = \begin{bmatrix} 2+6 & -10+10 & -2+(-2) \\ 14+0 & 12+(-12) & 10+(-4) \\ 4+(-5) & -2+2 & 2+(-2) \end{bmatrix}$

$= \begin{bmatrix} 8 & 0 & -4 \\ 14 & 0 & 6 \\ -1 & 0 & 0 \end{bmatrix}$

b. $A - B = \begin{bmatrix} 2-6 & -10-10 & -2-(-2) \\ 14-0 & 12-(-12) & 10-(-4) \\ 4-(-5) & -2-2 & 2-(-2) \end{bmatrix}$

$= \begin{bmatrix} -4 & -20 & 0 \\ 14 & 24 & 14 \\ 9 & -4 & 4 \end{bmatrix}$

c. $-4A = \begin{bmatrix} -8 & 40 & 8 \\ -56 & -48 & -40 \\ -16 & 8 & -8 \end{bmatrix}$

d. $3A + 2B = \begin{bmatrix} 6+12 & -30+20 & -6-4 \\ 42+0 & 36-24 & 30-8 \\ 12-10 & -6+4 & 6-4 \end{bmatrix}$

$= \begin{bmatrix} 18 & -10 & -10 \\ 42 & 12 & 22 \\ 2 & -2 & 2 \end{bmatrix}$

17. $X - A = B$

$\quad X = A + B$

$\quad X = \begin{bmatrix} -3 & -7 \\ 2 & -9 \\ 5 & 0 \end{bmatrix} + \begin{bmatrix} -5 & -1 \\ 0 & 0 \\ 3 & -4 \end{bmatrix} = \begin{bmatrix} -8 & -8 \\ 2 & -9 \\ 8 & -4 \end{bmatrix}$

19. $2X + A = B$

$\quad 2X = B - A$

$\quad X = \frac{1}{2}(B - A)$

$X = \frac{1}{2}\left(\begin{bmatrix} -5 & -1 \\ 0 & 0 \\ 3 & -4 \end{bmatrix} - \begin{bmatrix} -3 & -7 \\ 2 & -9 \\ 5 & 0 \end{bmatrix} \right) = \frac{1}{2}\begin{bmatrix} -2 & 6 \\ -2 & 9 \\ -2 & -4 \end{bmatrix} = \begin{bmatrix} -1 & 3 \\ -1 & \frac{9}{2} \\ -1 & -2 \end{bmatrix}$

21. $3X + 2A = B$

$\qquad 3X = B - 2A$

$\qquad X = \dfrac{1}{3}(B - 2A)$

$$X = \frac{1}{3}\left(\begin{bmatrix} -5 & -1 \\ 0 & 0 \\ 3 & -4 \end{bmatrix} - 2\begin{bmatrix} -3 & -7 \\ 2 & -9 \\ 5 & 0 \end{bmatrix}\right) = \frac{1}{3}\begin{bmatrix} 1 & 13 \\ -4 & 18 \\ -7 & -4 \end{bmatrix} = \begin{bmatrix} \dfrac{1}{3} & \dfrac{13}{3} \\ -\dfrac{4}{3} & 6 \\ -\dfrac{7}{3} & -\dfrac{4}{3} \end{bmatrix}$$

23. $\quad B - X = 4A$

$\quad B - 4A = X$

$$X = \begin{bmatrix} -5 & -1 \\ 0 & 0 \\ 3 & -4 \end{bmatrix} - 4\begin{bmatrix} -3 & -7 \\ 2 & -9 \\ 5 & 0 \end{bmatrix} = \begin{bmatrix} -5 & -1 \\ 0 & 0 \\ 3 & -4 \end{bmatrix} + \begin{bmatrix} 12 & 28 \\ -8 & 36 \\ -20 & 0 \end{bmatrix} = \begin{bmatrix} 7 & 27 \\ -8 & 36 \\ -17 & -4 \end{bmatrix}$$

25. $\qquad 4A + 3B = -2X$

$\quad -\dfrac{1}{2}(4A + 3B) = X$

$$X = -\frac{1}{2}\left(4\begin{bmatrix} -3 & -7 \\ 2 & -9 \\ 5 & 0 \end{bmatrix} + 3\begin{bmatrix} -5 & -1 \\ 0 & 0 \\ 3 & -4 \end{bmatrix}\right) = -\frac{1}{2}\left(\begin{bmatrix} -12 & -28 \\ 8 & -36 \\ 20 & 0 \end{bmatrix} + \begin{bmatrix} -15 & -3 \\ 0 & 0 \\ 9 & -12 \end{bmatrix}\right) = -\frac{1}{2}\begin{bmatrix} -27 & -31 \\ 8 & -36 \\ 29 & -12 \end{bmatrix} = \begin{bmatrix} \dfrac{27}{2} & \dfrac{31}{2} \\ -4 & 18 \\ -\dfrac{29}{2} & 6 \end{bmatrix}$$

27. a. $AB = \begin{bmatrix} 1 & 3 \\ 5 & 3 \end{bmatrix}\begin{bmatrix} 3 & -2 \\ -1 & 6 \end{bmatrix} = \begin{bmatrix} (1)(3) + (3)(-1) & (1)(-2) + (3)(6) \\ (5)(3) + (3)(-1) & (5)(-2) + (3)(6) \end{bmatrix} = \begin{bmatrix} 3-3 & -2+18 \\ 15-3 & -10+18 \end{bmatrix} = \begin{bmatrix} 0 & 16 \\ 12 & 8 \end{bmatrix}$

b. $BA = \begin{bmatrix} 3 & -2 \\ -1 & 6 \end{bmatrix}\begin{bmatrix} 1 & 3 \\ 5 & 3 \end{bmatrix} = \begin{bmatrix} (3)(1) + (-2)(5) & (3)(3) + (-2)(3) \\ (-1)(1) + (6)(5) & (-1)(3) + (6)(3) \end{bmatrix} = \begin{bmatrix} 3-10 & 9-6 \\ -1+30 & -3+18 \end{bmatrix} = \begin{bmatrix} -7 & 3 \\ 29 & 15 \end{bmatrix}$

29. a. $AB = \begin{bmatrix} 1 & 2 & 3 & 4 \end{bmatrix}\begin{bmatrix} 1 \\ 2 \\ 3 \\ 4 \end{bmatrix} = [(1)(1) + (2)(2) + (3)(3) + (4)(4)] = [1 + 4 + 9 + 16] = [30]$

b. $BA = \begin{bmatrix} 1 \\ 2 \\ 3 \\ 4 \end{bmatrix}\begin{bmatrix} 1 & 2 & 3 & 4 \end{bmatrix} = \begin{bmatrix} (1)(1) & (1)(2) & (1)(3) & (1)(4) \\ (2)(1) & (2)(2) & (2)(3) & (2)(4) \\ (3)(1) & (3)(2) & (3)(3) & (3)(4) \\ (4)(1) & (4)(2) & (4)(3) & (4)(4) \end{bmatrix} = \begin{bmatrix} 1 & 2 & 3 & 4 \\ 2 & 4 & 6 & 8 \\ 3 & 6 & 9 & 12 \\ 4 & 8 & 12 & 16 \end{bmatrix}$

31. a. $AB = \begin{bmatrix} 1 & -1 & 4 \\ 4 & -1 & 3 \\ 2 & 0 & -2 \end{bmatrix} \begin{bmatrix} 1 & 1 & 0 \\ 1 & 2 & 4 \\ 1 & -1 & 3 \end{bmatrix}$

$= \begin{bmatrix} (1)(1)+(-1)(1)+(4)(1) & (1)(1)+(-1)(2)+(4)(-1) & (1)(0)+(-1)(4)+(4)(3) \\ (4)(1)+(-1)(1)+(3)(1) & (4)(1)+(-1)(2)+(3)(-1) & (4)(0)+(-1)(4)+(3)(3) \\ (2)(1)+(0)(1)+(-2)(1) & (2)(1)+(0)(2)+(-2)(-1) & (2)(0)+(0)(4)+(-2)(3) \end{bmatrix}$

$= \begin{bmatrix} 1-1+4 & 1-2-4 & 0-4+12 \\ 4-1+3 & 4-2-3 & 0-4+9 \\ 2+0-2 & 2+0+2 & 0+0-6 \end{bmatrix} = \begin{bmatrix} 4 & -5 & 8 \\ 6 & -1 & 5 \\ 0 & 4 & -6 \end{bmatrix}$

b. $BA = \begin{bmatrix} 1 & 1 & 0 \\ 1 & 2 & 4 \\ 1 & -1 & 3 \end{bmatrix} \begin{bmatrix} 1 & -1 & 4 \\ 4 & -1 & 3 \\ 2 & 0 & -2 \end{bmatrix}$

$= \begin{bmatrix} (1)(1)+(1)(4)+(0)(2) & (1)(-1)+(1)(-1)+(0)(0) & (1)(4)+(1)(3)+(0)(-2) \\ (1)(1)+(2)(4)+(4)(2) & (1)(-1)+(2)(-1)+(4)(0) & (1)(4)+(2)(3)+(4)(-2) \\ (1)(1)+(-1)(4)+(3)(2) & (1)(-1)+(-1)(-1)+(3)(0) & (1)(4)+(-1)(3)+(3)(-2) \end{bmatrix}$

$= \begin{bmatrix} 1+4+0 & -1-1+0 & 4+3+0 \\ 1+8+8 & -1-2+0 & 4+6-8 \\ 1-4+6 & -1+1+0 & 4-3-6 \end{bmatrix} = \begin{bmatrix} 5 & -2 & 7 \\ 17 & -3 & 2 \\ 3 & 0 & -5 \end{bmatrix}$

33. a. $AB = \begin{bmatrix} 4 & 2 \\ 6 & 1 \\ 3 & 5 \end{bmatrix} \begin{bmatrix} 2 & 3 & 4 \\ -1 & -2 & 0 \end{bmatrix} = \begin{bmatrix} (4)(2)+(2)(-1) & (4)(3)+(2)(-2) & (4)(4)+(2)(0) \\ (6)(2)+(1)(-1) & (6)(3)+(1)(-2) & (6)(4)+(1)(0) \\ (3)(2)+(5)(-1) & (3)(3)+(5)(-2) & (3)(4)+(5)(0) \end{bmatrix}$

$= \begin{bmatrix} 8-2 & 12-4 & 16+0 \\ 12-1 & 18-2 & 24+0 \\ 6-5 & 9-10 & 12+0 \end{bmatrix} = \begin{bmatrix} 6 & 8 & 16 \\ 11 & 16 & 24 \\ 1 & -1 & 12 \end{bmatrix}$

b. $BA = \begin{bmatrix} 2 & 3 & 4 \\ -1 & -2 & 0 \end{bmatrix} \begin{bmatrix} 4 & 2 \\ 6 & 1 \\ 3 & 5 \end{bmatrix} = \begin{bmatrix} (2)(4)+(3)(6)+(4)(3) & (2)(2)+(3)(1)+(4)(5) \\ (-1)(4)+(-2)(6)+(0)(3) & (-1)(2)+(-2)(1)+(0)(5) \end{bmatrix}$

$= \begin{bmatrix} 8+18+12 & 4+3+20 \\ -4-12+0 & -2-2+0 \end{bmatrix} = \begin{bmatrix} 38 & 27 \\ -16 & -4 \end{bmatrix}$

35. a. $AB = \begin{bmatrix} 2 & -3 & 1 & -1 \\ 1 & 1 & -2 & 1 \end{bmatrix} \begin{bmatrix} 1 & 2 \\ -1 & 1 \\ 5 & 4 \\ 10 & 5 \end{bmatrix} = \begin{bmatrix} (2)(1)+(-3)(-1)+(1)(5)+(-1)(10) & (2)(2)+(-3)(1)+(1)(4)+(-1)(5) \\ (1)(1)+(1)(-1)+(-2)(5)+(1)(10) & (1)(2)+(1)(1)+(-2)(4)+(1)(5) \end{bmatrix}$

$= \begin{bmatrix} 2+3+5-10 & 4-3+4-5 \\ 1-1-10+10 & 2+1-8+5 \end{bmatrix} = \begin{bmatrix} 0 & 0 \\ 0 & 0 \end{bmatrix}$

b. $BA = \begin{bmatrix} 1 & 2 \\ -1 & 1 \\ 5 & 4 \\ 10 & 5 \end{bmatrix} \begin{bmatrix} 2 & -3 & 1 & -1 \\ 1 & 1 & -2 & 1 \end{bmatrix}$

$= \begin{bmatrix} (1)(2)+(2)(1) & (1)(-3)+(2)(1) & (1)(1)+(2)(-2) & (1)(-1)+(2)(1) \\ (-1)(2)+(1)(1) & (-1)(-3)+(1)(1) & (-1)(1)+(1)(-2) & (-1)(-1)+(1)(1) \\ (5)(2)+(4)(1) & (5)(-3)+(4)(1) & (5)(1)+(4)(-2) & (5)(-1)+(4)(1) \\ (10)(2)+(5)(1) & (10)(-3)+(5)(1) & (10)(1)+(5)(-2) & (10)(-1)+(5)(1) \end{bmatrix}$

$= \begin{bmatrix} 2+2 & -3+2 & 1-4 & -1+2 \\ -2+1 & 3+1 & -1-2 & 1+1 \\ 10+4 & -15+4 & 5-8 & -5+4 \\ 20+5 & -30+5 & 10-10 & -10+5 \end{bmatrix} = \begin{bmatrix} 4 & -1 & -3 & 1 \\ -1 & 4 & -3 & 2 \\ 14 & -11 & -3 & -1 \\ 25 & -25 & 0 & -5 \end{bmatrix}$

37. $4B - 3C = \begin{bmatrix} 20 & 4 \\ -8 & -8 \end{bmatrix} - \begin{bmatrix} 3 & -3 \\ -3 & 3 \end{bmatrix} = \begin{bmatrix} 20-3 & 4-(-3) \\ -8-(-3) & -8-3 \end{bmatrix} = \begin{bmatrix} 17 & 7 \\ -5 & -11 \end{bmatrix}$

39. $BC + CB = \begin{bmatrix} 5-1 & -5+1 \\ -2+2 & 2-2 \end{bmatrix} + \begin{bmatrix} 5+2 & 1+2 \\ -5-2 & -1-2 \end{bmatrix} = \begin{bmatrix} 4 & -4 \\ 0 & 0 \end{bmatrix} + \begin{bmatrix} 7 & 3 \\ -7 & -3 \end{bmatrix} = \begin{bmatrix} 11 & -1 \\ -7 & -3 \end{bmatrix}$

41. $A - C$ is not defined because A is 3 x 2 and C is 2 x 2.

43. $A(BC) = \begin{bmatrix} 4 & 0 \\ -3 & 5 \\ 0 & 1 \end{bmatrix} \begin{bmatrix} 5-1 & -5+1 \\ -2+2 & 2-2 \end{bmatrix} = \begin{bmatrix} 4 & 0 \\ -3 & 5 \\ 0 & 1 \end{bmatrix} \begin{bmatrix} 4 & -4 \\ 0 & 0 \end{bmatrix} = \begin{bmatrix} 16+0 & -16+0 \\ -12+0 & 12+0 \\ 0+0 & 0+0 \end{bmatrix} = \begin{bmatrix} 16 & -16 \\ -12 & 12 \\ 0 & 0 \end{bmatrix}$

45. $(A+B)(C-D) = \left(\begin{bmatrix} 1 & 0 \\ 0 & 1 \end{bmatrix} + \begin{bmatrix} 1 & 0 \\ 0 & -1 \end{bmatrix} \right) \left(\begin{bmatrix} -1 & 0 \\ 0 & 1 \end{bmatrix} - \begin{bmatrix} -1 & 0 \\ 0 & -1 \end{bmatrix} \right) = \left(\begin{bmatrix} 2 & 0 \\ 0 & 0 \end{bmatrix} \right) \left(\begin{bmatrix} 0 & 0 \\ 0 & 2 \end{bmatrix} \right) = \begin{bmatrix} 0 & 0 \\ 0 & 0 \end{bmatrix}$

49. $BZ = \begin{bmatrix} 1 & 0 \\ 0 & -1 \end{bmatrix} \begin{bmatrix} x \\ y \end{bmatrix} = \begin{bmatrix} x \\ -y \end{bmatrix}$ This reflects the graphic about the x-axis because all y-coordinates are negated.

51. a. $\begin{bmatrix} 1 & 3 & 1 \\ 3 & 3 & 3 \\ 1 & 3 & 1 \end{bmatrix}$ **b.** $\begin{bmatrix} 1 & 3 & 1 \\ 3 & 3 & 3 \\ 1 & 3 & 1 \end{bmatrix} + \begin{bmatrix} -1 & -1 & -1 \\ -1 & -1 & -1 \\ -1 & -1 & -1 \end{bmatrix} = \begin{bmatrix} 0 & 2 & 0 \\ 2 & 2 & 2 \\ 0 & 2 & 0 \end{bmatrix}$ **c.** $\begin{bmatrix} 1 & 3 & 1 \\ 3 & 3 & 3 \\ 1 & 3 & 1 \end{bmatrix} + \begin{bmatrix} 1 & -2 & 1 \\ -2 & -2 & -2 \\ 1 & -2 & 1 \end{bmatrix} = \begin{bmatrix} 2 & 1 & 2 \\ 1 & 1 & 1 \\ 2 & 1 & 2 \end{bmatrix}$

53. $\begin{bmatrix} 0 & 3 & 3 & 1 & 1 & 0 \\ 0 & 0 & 1 & 1 & 5 & 5 \end{bmatrix} + \begin{bmatrix} -2 & -2 & -2 & -2 & -2 & -2 \\ -3 & -3 & -3 & -3 & -3 & -3 \end{bmatrix} = \begin{bmatrix} -2 & 1 & 1 & -1 & -1 & -2 \\ -3 & -3 & -2 & -2 & 2 & 2 \end{bmatrix}$

55. $0.5\begin{bmatrix} 0 & 3 & 3 & 1 & 1 & 0 \\ 0 & 0 & 1 & 1 & 5 & 5 \end{bmatrix} + \begin{bmatrix} 0 & 0 & 0 & 0 & 0 & 0 \\ 1 & 1 & 1 & 1 & 1 & 1 \end{bmatrix} = \begin{bmatrix} 0 & 1.5 & 1.5 & 0.5 & 0.5 & 0 \\ 0 & 0 & 0.5 & 0.5 & 2.5 & 2.5 \end{bmatrix} + \begin{bmatrix} 0 & 0 & 0 & 0 & 0 & 0 \\ 1 & 1 & 1 & 1 & 1 & 1 \end{bmatrix}$

$= \begin{bmatrix} 0 & 1.5 & 1.5 & 0.5 & 0.5 & 0 \\ 1 & 1 & 1.5 & 1.5 & 3.5 & 3.5 \end{bmatrix}$

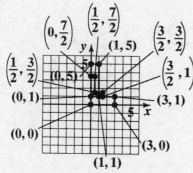

57. **a.** $AB = \begin{bmatrix} 1 & 0 \\ 0 & -1 \end{bmatrix} \cdot \begin{bmatrix} 0 & 3 & 3 & 1 & 1 & 0 \\ 0 & 0 & 1 & 1 & 5 & 5 \end{bmatrix} = \begin{bmatrix} 0 & 3 & 3 & 1 & 1 & 0 \\ 0 & 0 & -1 & -1 & -5 & -5 \end{bmatrix}$

b.

Rotated L about the *x*-axis.

59. **a.** $AB = \begin{bmatrix} 0 & -1 \\ 1 & 0 \end{bmatrix} \cdot \begin{bmatrix} 0 & 3 & 3 & 1 & 1 & 0 \\ 0 & 0 & 1 & 1 & 5 & 5 \end{bmatrix} = \begin{bmatrix} 0 & 0 & -1 & -1 & -5 & -5 \\ 0 & 3 & 3 & 1 & 1 & 0 \end{bmatrix}$

b.

Rotated L 90° counterclockwise about the origin.

61. **a.** $A = \begin{bmatrix} 61 & 24 \\ 33 & 47 \\ 6 & 29 \end{bmatrix}$

b. $B = \begin{bmatrix} 67 & 23 \\ 28 & 44 \\ 5 & 33 \end{bmatrix}$

c. $B - A = \begin{bmatrix} 67 & 23 \\ 28 & 44 \\ 5 & 33 \end{bmatrix} - \begin{bmatrix} 61 & 24 \\ 33 & 47 \\ 6 & 29 \end{bmatrix} = \begin{bmatrix} 6 & -1 \\ -5 & -3 \\ -1 & 4 \end{bmatrix}$

$B - A$ represents the percent change from 2000 to 2004.

63. a. System 1: The midterm and final both count for 50% of the course grade.
System 2: The midterm counts for 30% of the course grade and the final counts for 70%

b. $AB = \begin{bmatrix} 84 & 87.2 \\ 79 & 81 \\ 90 & 88.4 \\ 73 & 68.6 \\ 69 & 73.4 \end{bmatrix}$

System 1 grades are listed first (if different).
Student 1: B; Student 2: C or B; Student 3: A or B; Student 4: C or D; Student 5: D or C

79. $AB = \begin{bmatrix} 0 & -1 \\ 1 & 0 \end{bmatrix} \begin{bmatrix} 1 & 0 \\ 0 & -1 \end{bmatrix} = \begin{bmatrix} 0 & 1 \\ 1 & 0 \end{bmatrix}$

$-BA = \begin{bmatrix} 1 & 0 \\ 0 & -1 \end{bmatrix} \begin{bmatrix} 0 & -1 \\ 1 & 0 \end{bmatrix} = -\begin{bmatrix} 0 & -1 \\ -1 & 0 \end{bmatrix} = \begin{bmatrix} 0 & 1 \\ 1 & 0 \end{bmatrix}$

$AB = -BA$ so they are anticommutative.

Mid-Chapter 8 Check Point

1. $\begin{bmatrix} 1 & 2 & -3 & | & -7 \\ 3 & -1 & 2 & | & 8 \\ 2 & -1 & 1 & | & 5 \end{bmatrix} \begin{matrix} \\ -3R_1 + R_2 \\ -2R_1 + R_3 \end{matrix}$

$\begin{bmatrix} 1 & 2 & -3 & | & -7 \\ 0 & -7 & 11 & | & 29 \\ 0 & -5 & 7 & | & 19 \end{bmatrix} \begin{matrix} \\ -\frac{1}{7}R_2 \\ -\frac{1}{5}R_3 \end{matrix}$

$\begin{bmatrix} 1 & 2 & -3 & | & -7 \\ 0 & 1 & -\frac{11}{7} & | & -\frac{29}{7} \\ 0 & 1 & -\frac{7}{5} & | & -\frac{19}{5} \end{bmatrix} \begin{matrix} \\ \\ -R_2 + R_3 \end{matrix}$

$\begin{bmatrix} 1 & 2 & -3 & | & -7 \\ 0 & 1 & -\frac{11}{7} & | & -\frac{29}{7} \\ 0 & 0 & \frac{6}{35} & | & \frac{12}{35} \end{bmatrix} \frac{35}{6}R_3$

$\begin{bmatrix} 1 & 2 & -3 & | & -7 \\ 0 & 1 & -\frac{11}{7} & | & -\frac{29}{7} \\ 0 & 0 & 1 & | & 2 \end{bmatrix}$

Back-substitute to find y.

$y - \frac{11}{7}z = -\frac{29}{7}$

$y - \frac{11}{7}(2) = -\frac{29}{7}$

$y - \frac{22}{7} = -\frac{29}{7}$

$y = -\frac{7}{7}$

$y = -1$

Back-substitute to find x.

$x + 2y - 3z = -7$

$x + 2(-1) - 3(2) = -7$

$x - 2 - 6 = -7$

$x - 8 = -7$

$x = 1$

The solution is $\{(1, -1, 2)\}$.

2. $\begin{bmatrix} 2 & 4 & 5 & | & 2 \\ 1 & 1 & 2 & | & 1 \\ 3 & 5 & 7 & | & 4 \end{bmatrix} R_1 \leftrightarrow R_3$

$\begin{bmatrix} 1 & 1 & 2 & | & 1 \\ 2 & 4 & 5 & | & 2 \\ 3 & 5 & 7 & | & 4 \end{bmatrix} \begin{matrix} \\ -2R_1 + R_2 \\ -3R_1 + R_3 \end{matrix}$

$\begin{bmatrix} 1 & 1 & 2 & | & 1 \\ 0 & 2 & 1 & | & 0 \\ 0 & 2 & 1 & | & 1 \end{bmatrix} \begin{matrix} \\ \\ -R_2 + R_3 \end{matrix}$

$\begin{bmatrix} 1 & 1 & 2 & | & 1 \\ 0 & 2 & 1 & | & 0 \\ 0 & 0 & 0 & | & 1 \end{bmatrix}$

The third row of the matrix is equivalent to
$0x + 0y + 0z = 1$ which is false.

The solution is $\varnothing$.

3. $\begin{bmatrix} 1 & -2 & 2 & | & -2 \\ 2 & 3 & -1 & | & 1 \end{bmatrix} -2R_1 + R_2$

$\begin{bmatrix} 1 & -2 & 2 & | & -2 \\ 0 & 7 & -5 & | & 5 \end{bmatrix} \frac{1}{7}R_2$

$\begin{bmatrix} 1 & -2 & 2 & | & -2 \\ 0 & 1 & -\frac{5}{7} & | & \frac{5}{7} \end{bmatrix}$

Back-substitute to find y in terms of z.
$y - \frac{5}{7}z = \frac{5}{7}$
$\qquad y = \frac{5}{7}z + \frac{5}{7}$

Back-substitute to find x in terms of z.
$\qquad x - 2y + 2z = -2$
$x - 2\left(\frac{5}{7}z + \frac{5}{7}\right) + 2z = -2$
$\quad x - \frac{10}{7}z - \frac{10}{7} + 2z = -2$
$\qquad\quad x + \frac{4}{7}z - \frac{10}{7} = -2$
$\qquad\qquad\quad x = -\frac{4}{7}z - \frac{4}{7}$

The solution is $\left\{ \left(-\frac{4}{7}z - \frac{4}{7}, \frac{5}{7}z + \frac{5}{7}, z \right) \right\}$.

4. $\begin{bmatrix} 1 & 1 & 1 & 1 & | & 6 \\ 1 & -1 & 3 & 1 & | & -14 \\ 1 & 2 & 0 & -3 & | & 12 \\ 2 & 3 & 6 & 1 & | & 1 \end{bmatrix} \begin{matrix} \\ -R_1 + R_2 \\ -R_1 + R_3 \\ -2R_1 + R_4 \end{matrix}$

$\begin{bmatrix} 1 & 1 & 1 & 1 & | & 6 \\ 0 & -2 & 2 & 0 & | & -20 \\ 0 & 1 & -1 & -4 & | & 6 \\ 0 & 1 & 4 & -1 & | & -11 \end{bmatrix} R_2 \leftrightarrow R_3$

$\begin{bmatrix} 1 & 1 & 1 & 1 & | & 6 \\ 0 & 1 & -1 & -4 & | & 6 \\ 0 & -2 & 2 & 0 & | & -20 \\ 0 & 1 & 4 & -1 & | & -11 \end{bmatrix} \begin{matrix} \\ \\ 2R_2 + R_3 \\ -R_2 + R_4 \end{matrix}$

$\begin{bmatrix} 1 & 1 & 1 & 1 & | & 6 \\ 0 & 1 & -1 & -4 & | & 6 \\ 0 & 0 & 0 & -8 & | & -8 \\ 0 & 0 & 5 & 3 & | & -17 \end{bmatrix} R_3 \leftrightarrow R_4$

$\begin{bmatrix} 1 & 1 & 1 & 1 & | & 6 \\ 0 & 1 & -1 & -4 & | & 6 \\ 0 & 0 & 5 & 3 & | & -17 \\ 0 & 0 & 0 & -8 & | & -8 \end{bmatrix} \begin{matrix} \\ \\ \frac{1}{5}R_3 \\ -\frac{1}{8}R_4 \end{matrix}$

$\begin{bmatrix} 1 & 1 & 1 & 1 & | & 6 \\ 0 & 1 & -1 & -4 & | & 6 \\ 0 & 0 & 1 & \frac{3}{5} & | & -\frac{17}{5} \\ 0 & 0 & 0 & 1 & | & 1 \end{bmatrix}$

Back-substitute to find y in terms of z.
$y + \frac{3}{5}z = -\frac{17}{5}$
$y + \frac{3}{5}(1) = -\frac{17}{5}$
$\quad y + \frac{3}{5} = -\frac{17}{5}$
$\qquad\quad y = -\frac{20}{5}$
$\qquad\quad y = -4$

Back-substitute to find x in terms of z.
$\qquad x - y - 4z = 6$
$x - (-4) - 4(1) = 6$
$\quad x + 4 - 4 = 6$
$\qquad\qquad x = 6$

Back-substitute to find w in terms of z.
$\qquad w + x + y + z = 6$
$w + (6) + (-4) + (1) = 6$
$\qquad\qquad w + 3 = 6$
$\qquad\qquad\quad w = 3$

The solution is $\left\{ (3, 6, -4, 1) \right\}$.

5.
$$\begin{bmatrix} 2 & -2 & 2 & | & 5 \\ 1 & -1 & 1 & | & 2 \\ 2 & 1 & -1 & | & 1 \end{bmatrix} \begin{matrix} -R_2 + R_1 \\ \\ -R_1 + R_3 \end{matrix}$$

$$\begin{bmatrix} 1 & -1 & 1 & | & 3 \\ 1 & -1 & 1 & | & 2 \\ 0 & 3 & -3 & | & -4 \end{bmatrix} -R_1 + R_2$$

$$\begin{bmatrix} 1 & -1 & 1 & | & 3 \\ 0 & 0 & 0 & | & -1 \\ 0 & 3 & -3 & | & -4 \end{bmatrix}$$

The second row of the matrix is equivalent to $0x + 0y + 0z = -1$ which is false.

The solution is $\varnothing$.

6. $2C - \dfrac{1}{2}B$

$$= 2\begin{bmatrix} -1 & 0 \\ 0 & 1 \end{bmatrix} - \frac{1}{2}\begin{bmatrix} 4 & 1 \\ -6 & -2 \end{bmatrix}$$

$$= \begin{bmatrix} -2 & 0 \\ 0 & 2 \end{bmatrix} - \begin{bmatrix} 2 & \frac{1}{2} \\ -3 & -1 \end{bmatrix}$$

$$= \begin{bmatrix} -4 & -\frac{1}{2} \\ 3 & 3 \end{bmatrix}$$

7. $A(B+C)$

$$= \begin{bmatrix} 0 & 2 \\ -1 & 3 \\ 1 & 0 \end{bmatrix}\left(\begin{bmatrix} 4 & 1 \\ -6 & -2 \end{bmatrix} + \begin{bmatrix} -1 & 0 \\ 0 & 1 \end{bmatrix}\right)$$

$$= \begin{bmatrix} 0 & 2 \\ -1 & 3 \\ 1 & 0 \end{bmatrix}\left(\begin{bmatrix} 3 & 1 \\ -6 & -1 \end{bmatrix}\right)$$

$$= \begin{bmatrix} -12 & -2 \\ -21 & -4 \\ 3 & 1 \end{bmatrix}$$

8. $A(BC)$

$$= \begin{bmatrix} 0 & 2 \\ -1 & 3 \\ 1 & 0 \end{bmatrix}\left(\begin{bmatrix} 4 & 1 \\ -6 & -2 \end{bmatrix} \cdot \begin{bmatrix} -1 & 0 \\ 0 & 1 \end{bmatrix}\right)$$

$$= \begin{bmatrix} 0 & 2 \\ -1 & 3 \\ 1 & 0 \end{bmatrix}\left(\begin{bmatrix} -4 & 1 \\ 6 & -2 \end{bmatrix}\right)$$

$$= \begin{bmatrix} 12 & -4 \\ 22 & -7 \\ -4 & 1 \end{bmatrix}$$

9. The operation is not defined. Matrices must have the same dimensions in order to be added.

10. $2X - 3C = B$
$$2X = B + 3C$$
$$X = \tfrac{1}{2}(B + 3C)$$

$$= \frac{1}{2}\left(\begin{bmatrix} 4 & 1 \\ -6 & -2 \end{bmatrix} + 3\begin{bmatrix} -1 & 0 \\ 0 & 1 \end{bmatrix}\right)$$

$$= \frac{1}{2}\left(\begin{bmatrix} 4 & 1 \\ -6 & -2 \end{bmatrix} + \begin{bmatrix} -3 & 0 \\ 0 & 3 \end{bmatrix}\right)$$

$$= \frac{1}{2}\left(\begin{bmatrix} 1 & 1 \\ -6 & 1 \end{bmatrix}\right)$$

$$= \begin{bmatrix} \frac{1}{2} & \frac{1}{2} \\ -3 & \frac{1}{2} \end{bmatrix}$$

Section 8.4

Check Point Exercises

1. We must show that: $AB = I_2 = \begin{bmatrix} 1 & 0 \\ 0 & 1 \end{bmatrix}$, and

$$BA = I_2 = \begin{bmatrix} 1 & 0 \\ 0 & 1 \end{bmatrix}.$$

$$AB = \begin{bmatrix} 2 & 1 \\ 1 & 1 \end{bmatrix}\begin{bmatrix} 1 & -1 \\ -1 & 2 \end{bmatrix}$$

$$= \begin{bmatrix} 2(1) + 1(-1) & 2(-1) + 1(2) \\ 1(1) + 1(-1) & 1(-1) + 1(2) \end{bmatrix}$$

$$= \begin{bmatrix} 1 & 0 \\ 0 & 1 \end{bmatrix}$$

$$BA = \begin{bmatrix} 1 & -1 \\ -1 & 2 \end{bmatrix}\begin{bmatrix} 2 & 1 \\ 1 & 1 \end{bmatrix}$$

$$= \begin{bmatrix} 1(2) + -1(1) & 1(1) + -1(1) \\ -1(2) + 2(1) & -1(1) + 2(1) \end{bmatrix}$$

$$= \begin{bmatrix} 1 & 0 \\ 0 & 1 \end{bmatrix}$$

Both products (AB and BA) give the multiplicative identity matrix, I_2. Thus, B is the multiplicative inverse of A.

2. Let us denote the multiplicative inverse of A by $A^{-1} = \begin{bmatrix} w & x \\ y & z \end{bmatrix}$. Because A is a 2×2 matrix, we use the equation $AA^{-1} = I_2$ to find values for w, x, y and z.

$$\begin{bmatrix} 5 & 7 \\ 2 & 3 \end{bmatrix} \begin{bmatrix} w & x \\ y & z \end{bmatrix} = \begin{bmatrix} 1 & 0 \\ 0 & 1 \end{bmatrix}$$

$$\begin{bmatrix} 5w+7y & 5x+7z \\ 2w+3y & 2x+3z \end{bmatrix} = \begin{bmatrix} 1 & 0 \\ 0 & 1 \end{bmatrix}$$

$5w + 7y = 1 \qquad 5x + 7z = 0$

$2w + 3y = 0 \qquad 2x + 3z = 1$

Each of these systems can be solved using the addition method.

Multiply by –2: $5w + 7y = 1 \rightarrow -10w - 14y = -2$

Multiply by 5: $2w + 3y = 0 \rightarrow 10w + 15y = 0$

Use back substitution: $w = 3$, $y = -2$

Multiply by –2: $5x + 7z = 0 \rightarrow -10x - 14z = 0$

Multiply by 5: $2x + 3z = 1 \rightarrow 10x + 15z = 5$

Use back substitution: $x = -7$, $z = 5$

Using these values, we have

$$A^{-1} = \begin{bmatrix} 3 & -7 \\ -2 & 5 \end{bmatrix}.$$

3.
$$A^{-1} = \frac{1}{ad-bc} \begin{bmatrix} d & -b \\ -c & a \end{bmatrix}$$

$$= \frac{1}{3(1)-(-2)(-1)} \begin{bmatrix} 1 & -(-2) \\ -(-1) & 3 \end{bmatrix}$$

$$= \frac{1}{3-2} \begin{bmatrix} 1 & 2 \\ 1 & 3 \end{bmatrix}$$

$$= \frac{1}{1} \begin{bmatrix} 1 & 2 \\ 1 & 3 \end{bmatrix}$$

$$= \begin{bmatrix} 1 & 2 \\ 1 & 3 \end{bmatrix}$$

4. The augmented matrix $[A \mid I_3]$ is

$$\begin{bmatrix} 1 & 0 & 2 & | & 1 & 0 & 0 \\ -1 & 2 & 3 & | & 0 & 1 & 0 \\ 1 & -1 & 0 & | & 0 & 0 & 1 \end{bmatrix}.$$

Perform row transformations on $[A \mid I_3]$ to obtain a matrix of the form $[I_3 \mid B]$.

$$\begin{bmatrix} 1 & 0 & 2 & | & 1 & 0 & 0 \\ -1 & 2 & 3 & | & 0 & 1 & 0 \\ 1 & -1 & 0 & | & 0 & 0 & 1 \end{bmatrix} 1R_1 / R_2$$

$$= \begin{bmatrix} 1 & 0 & 2 & | & 1 & 0 & 0 \\ 0 & 2 & 5 & | & 1 & 1 & 0 \\ 1 & -1 & 0 & | & 0 & 0 & 1 \end{bmatrix} -1R_3$$

$$= \begin{bmatrix} 1 & 0 & 2 & | & 1 & 0 & 0 \\ 0 & 2 & 5 & | & 1 & 1 & 0 \\ -1 & 1 & 0 & | & 0 & 0 & -1 \end{bmatrix} R_1 + R_3$$

$$= \begin{bmatrix} 1 & 0 & 2 & | & 1 & 0 & 0 \\ 0 & 2 & 5 & | & 1 & 1 & 0 \\ 0 & 1 & 2 & | & 1 & 0 & -1 \end{bmatrix} \tfrac{1}{2}R_2$$

$$= \begin{bmatrix} 1 & 0 & 2 & | & 1 & 0 & 0 \\ 0 & 1 & \tfrac{5}{2} & | & \tfrac{1}{2} & \tfrac{1}{2} & 0 \\ 0 & 1 & 2 & | & 1 & 0 & -1 \end{bmatrix} -1R_2 + R_3$$

$$= \begin{bmatrix} 1 & 0 & 2 & | & 1 & 0 & 0 \\ 0 & 1 & \tfrac{5}{2} & | & \tfrac{1}{2} & \tfrac{1}{2} & 0 \\ 0 & 0 & -\tfrac{1}{2} & | & \tfrac{1}{2} & -\tfrac{1}{2} & -1 \end{bmatrix} -2R_3$$

$$= \begin{bmatrix} 1 & 0 & 2 & | & 1 & 0 & 0 \\ 0 & 1 & \tfrac{5}{2} & | & \tfrac{1}{2} & \tfrac{1}{2} & 0 \\ 0 & 0 & 1 & | & -1 & 1 & 2 \end{bmatrix} \begin{matrix} -2R_3 + R_1 \\ -\tfrac{5}{2}R_3 + R_2 \end{matrix}$$

$$= \begin{bmatrix} 1 & 0 & 0 & | & 3 & -2 & -4 \\ 0 & 1 & 0 & | & 3 & -2 & -5 \\ 0 & 0 & 1 & | & 1 & 1 & 2 \end{bmatrix}$$

Thus, the multiplicative inverse of A is

$$A^{-1} = \begin{bmatrix} 3 & -2 & -4 \\ 3 & -2 & -5 \\ -1 & 1 & 2 \end{bmatrix}.$$

5. The linear system can be written as $AX = B$.

$$\begin{bmatrix} 1 & 0 & 2 \\ -1 & 2 & 3 \\ 1 & -1 & 0 \end{bmatrix} \begin{bmatrix} x \\ y \\ z \end{bmatrix} = \begin{bmatrix} 6 \\ -5 \\ 6 \end{bmatrix}.$$

$$X = A^{-1}B = \begin{bmatrix} 3 & -2 & -4 \\ 3 & -2 & -5 \\ -1 & 1 & 2 \end{bmatrix} \begin{bmatrix} 6 \\ -5 \\ 6 \end{bmatrix}$$

$$= \begin{bmatrix} 3(6) + -2(-5) + -4(6) \\ 3(6) + -2(-5) + -5(6) \\ -1(6) + 1(-5) + 2(6) \end{bmatrix}$$

$$= \begin{bmatrix} 18 + 10 - 24 \\ 18 + 10 - 30 \\ -6 - 5 + 12 \end{bmatrix} = \begin{bmatrix} 4 \\ -2 \\ 1 \end{bmatrix}$$

Thus, $x = 4$, $y = -2$, and $z = 1$. The solution set is $\{(4, -2, 1)\}$.

6. The numerical representation of the word BASE is 2, 1, 19, 5. The 2×2 matrix formed is $\begin{bmatrix} 2 & 19 \\ 1 & 5 \end{bmatrix}$.

$$\begin{bmatrix} -2 & -3 \\ 3 & 4 \end{bmatrix} \begin{bmatrix} 2 & 19 \\ 1 & 5 \end{bmatrix}$$

$$= \begin{bmatrix} -2(2) + -3(1) & -2(19) + -3(5) \\ 3(2) + 4(1) & 3(19) + 4(5) \end{bmatrix}$$

$$= \begin{bmatrix} -4 - 3 & -38 - 15 \\ 6 + 4 & 57 + 20 \end{bmatrix} = \begin{bmatrix} -7 & -53 \\ 10 & 77 \end{bmatrix}$$

The encoded message is $-7, 10, -53, 77$.

7. Use the multiplicative inverse of the coding matrix. It is $\begin{bmatrix} 4 & 3 \\ -3 & -2 \end{bmatrix}$.

$$\begin{bmatrix} 4 & 3 \\ -3 & -2 \end{bmatrix} \begin{bmatrix} -7 & -53 \\ 10 & 77 \end{bmatrix}$$

$$= \begin{bmatrix} 4(-7) + 3(10) & 4(-53) + 3(77) \\ -3(-7) + -2(10) & -3(-53) + -2(77) \end{bmatrix}$$

$$= \begin{bmatrix} -28 + 30 & -212 + 231 \\ 21 - 20 & 159 - 154 \end{bmatrix} = \begin{bmatrix} 2 & 19 \\ 1 & 5 \end{bmatrix}$$

The numbers are 2, 1, 19, and 5. Using letters, the decoded message is BASE.

Exercise Set 8.4

1. $A = \begin{bmatrix} 4 & -3 \\ -5 & 4 \end{bmatrix}$ $B = \begin{bmatrix} 4 & 3 \\ 5 & 4 \end{bmatrix}$

$$AB = \begin{bmatrix} 16 - 15 & 12 - 12 \\ -20 + 20 & -15 + 16 \end{bmatrix} = \begin{bmatrix} 1 & 0 \\ 0 & 1 \end{bmatrix}$$

$$BA = \begin{bmatrix} 16 - 15 & -12 + 12 \\ 20 - 20 & -15 + 16 \end{bmatrix} = \begin{bmatrix} 1 & 0 \\ 0 & 1 \end{bmatrix}$$

Since $AB = I_2$ $BA = I_2$, $B = A^{-1}$.

3. $AB = \begin{bmatrix} 8 + 0 & -16 + 0 \\ -2 + 0 & 4 + 3 \end{bmatrix} = \begin{bmatrix} 8 & -16 \\ -2 & 7 \end{bmatrix}$

$$BA = \begin{bmatrix} 8 + 4 & 0 + 12 \\ 0 + 1 & 0 + 3 \end{bmatrix} = \begin{bmatrix} 12 & 12 \\ 1 & 3 \end{bmatrix}$$

If B is the multiplicative inverse of A, both products (AB and BA) will be the multiplicative identity matrix, I_2. Therefore, B is not the multiplicative inverse of A. That is, $B \neq A^{-1}$.

5. $AB = \begin{bmatrix} -2 + 3 & -4 + 4 \\ \frac{3}{2} - \frac{3}{2} & 3 - 2 \end{bmatrix} = \begin{bmatrix} 1 & 0 \\ 0 & 1 \end{bmatrix}$

$$BA = \begin{bmatrix} -2 + 3 & 1 - 1 \\ -6 + 6 & 3 - 2 \end{bmatrix} = \begin{bmatrix} 1 & 0 \\ 0 & 1 \end{bmatrix}$$

Since $AB = I_2$ and $BA = I_2$, $B = A^{-1}$.

7. $A = \begin{bmatrix} 0 & 1 & 0 \\ 0 & 0 & 1 \\ 1 & 0 & 0 \end{bmatrix}$ $B = \begin{bmatrix} 0 & 0 & 1 \\ 1 & 0 & 0 \\ 0 & 1 & 0 \end{bmatrix}$

$$AB = \begin{bmatrix} 0 + 1 + 0 & 0 + 0 + 0 & 0 + 0 + 0 \\ 0 + 0 + 0 & 0 + 0 + 1 & 0 + 0 + 0 \\ 0 + 0 + 0 & 0 + 0 + 0 & 1 + 0 + 0 \end{bmatrix} = \begin{bmatrix} 1 & 0 & 0 \\ 0 & 1 & 0 \\ 0 & 0 & 1 \end{bmatrix}$$

$$BA = \begin{bmatrix} 0 + 0 + 1 & 0 + 0 + 0 & 0 + 0 + 0 \\ 0 + 0 + 0 & 1 + 0 + 0 & 0 + 0 + 0 \\ 0 + 0 + 0 & 0 + 0 + 0 & 0 + 1 + 0 \end{bmatrix} = \begin{bmatrix} 1 & 0 & 0 \\ 0 & 1 & 0 \\ 0 & 0 & 1 \end{bmatrix}$$

Since $AB = I_3$ and $BA = I_3$, $B = A^{-1}$.

9. $AB = \begin{bmatrix} \frac{7}{2}-1-\frac{3}{2} & -3+0+3 & \frac{1}{2}+1-\frac{3}{2} \\ \frac{7}{2}-\frac{3}{2}-2 & -3+0+4 & \frac{1}{2}+\frac{3}{2}-2 \\ \frac{7}{2}-2-\frac{3}{2} & -3+0+3 & \frac{1}{2}+2-\frac{3}{2} \end{bmatrix} = \begin{bmatrix} 1 & 0 & 0 \\ 0 & 1 & 0 \\ 0 & 0 & 1 \end{bmatrix}$

$BA = \begin{bmatrix} \frac{7}{2}-3+\frac{1}{2} & 7-9+2 & \frac{21}{2}-12+\frac{3}{2} \\ -\frac{1}{2}+0+\frac{1}{2} & -1+0+2 & -\frac{3}{2}+0+\frac{3}{2} \\ -\frac{1}{2}+1-\frac{1}{2} & -1+3-2 & -\frac{3}{2}+4-\frac{3}{2} \end{bmatrix} = \begin{bmatrix} 1 & 0 & 0 \\ 0 & 1 & 0 \\ 0 & 0 & 1 \end{bmatrix}$

Since $AB = I_3$ and $BA = I_3$, $B = A^{-1}$.

11. $AB = \begin{bmatrix} 0+0+0+1 & 0+0-2+2 & 0+0+0+0 & 0+0-2+2 \\ -1+0+0+1 & -2+0+1+2 & 0+0+0+0 & -3+0+1+2 \\ 0+0+0+0 & 0+1-1+0 & 0+1+0+0 & 0+1-1+0 \\ 1+0+0-1 & 2+0+0-2 & 0+0+0+0 & 3+0+0-2 \end{bmatrix} = \begin{bmatrix} 1 & 0 & 0 & 0 \\ 0 & 1 & 0 & 0 \\ 0 & 0 & 1 & 0 \\ 0 & 0 & 0 & 1 \end{bmatrix}$

$BA = \begin{bmatrix} 0-2+0+3 & 0+0+0+0 & -2+2+0+0 & 1+2+0-3 \\ 0-1+0+1 & 0+0+1+0 & 0+1-1+0 & 0+1+0-1 \\ 0-1+0+1 & 0+0+0+0 & 0+1+0+0 & 0+1+0-1 \\ 0-2+0+2 & 0+0+0+0 & -2+2+0+0 & 1+2+0-2 \end{bmatrix} = \begin{bmatrix} 1 & 0 & 0 & 0 \\ 0 & 1 & 0 & 0 \\ 0 & 0 & 1 & 0 \\ 0 & 0 & 0 & 1 \end{bmatrix}$

Since $AB = I_4$ and $BA = I_4$, $B = A^{-1}$.

13. $ad - bc = (2)(2) - (3)(-1) = 4 + 3 = 7$

$A^{-1} = \frac{1}{7}\begin{bmatrix} 2 & -3 \\ 1 & 2 \end{bmatrix} = \begin{bmatrix} \frac{2}{7} & -\frac{3}{7} \\ \frac{1}{7} & \frac{2}{7} \end{bmatrix}$

$AA^{-1} = \begin{bmatrix} \frac{4}{7}+\frac{3}{7} & -\frac{6}{7}+\frac{6}{7} \\ -\frac{2}{7}+\frac{2}{7} & \frac{3}{7}+\frac{4}{7} \end{bmatrix} = \begin{bmatrix} 1 & 0 \\ 0 & 1 \end{bmatrix}$ and $A^{-1}A = \begin{bmatrix} \frac{4}{7}+\frac{3}{7} & \frac{6}{7}-\frac{6}{7} \\ \frac{2}{7}-\frac{2}{7} & \frac{3}{7}+\frac{4}{7} \end{bmatrix} = \begin{bmatrix} 1 & 0 \\ 0 & 1 \end{bmatrix}$

15. $ad - bc = (3)(2) - (-1)(-4) = 6 - 4 = 2$

$A^{-1} = \frac{1}{2}\begin{bmatrix} 2 & 1 \\ 4 & 3 \end{bmatrix} = \begin{bmatrix} 1 & \frac{1}{2} \\ 2 & \frac{3}{2} \end{bmatrix}$

$AA^{-1} = \begin{bmatrix} 3-2 & \frac{3}{2}-\frac{3}{2} \\ -4+4 & -\frac{4}{2}+\frac{6}{2} \end{bmatrix} = \begin{bmatrix} 1 & 0 \\ 0 & 1 \end{bmatrix}$ and $A^{-1}A = \begin{bmatrix} 3-\frac{4}{2} & -1+\frac{2}{2} \\ 6-\frac{12}{2} & -2+\frac{6}{2} \end{bmatrix} = \begin{bmatrix} 1 & 0 \\ 0 & 1 \end{bmatrix}$

17. $ad - bc = (10)(1) - (-2)(-5) = 10 - 10 = 0$
Since division by zero is undefined, A does not have an inverse.
For Problems 19–24, verification that $AA^{-1} = I$ and $A^{-1}A = I$ is left to the student.

For Problems 19–23, verification that $AA^{-1} = I$ and $A^{-1}A = I$ is left to the student.

19. $\begin{bmatrix} 2 & 0 & 0 & 1 & 0 & 0 \\ 0 & 4 & 0 & 0 & 1 & 0 \\ 0 & 0 & 6 & 0 & 0 & 1 \end{bmatrix}$

Divide row 1 by 2, divide row 2 by 4 and divide row 4 by 6.

$\begin{bmatrix} 1 & 0 & 0 & \frac{1}{2} & 0 & 0 \\ 0 & 1 & 0 & 0 & \frac{1}{4} & 0 \\ 0 & 0 & 1 & 0 & 0 & \frac{1}{6} \end{bmatrix}$

$A^{-1} = \begin{bmatrix} \frac{1}{2} & 0 & 0 \\ 0 & \frac{1}{4} & 0 \\ 0 & 0 & \frac{1}{6} \end{bmatrix}$

21. $\begin{bmatrix} 1 & 2 & -1 & 1 & 0 & 0 \\ -2 & 0 & 1 & 0 & 1 & 0 \\ 1 & -1 & 0 & 0 & 0 & 1 \end{bmatrix}$

Replace row 2 with $2R_1 + R_2$.
Replace row 3 with $R_1 - R_3$.

$\begin{bmatrix} 1 & 2 & -1 & 1 & 0 & 0 \\ 0 & 4 & -1 & 2 & 1 & 0 \\ 0 & 3 & -1 & 1 & 0 & -1 \end{bmatrix}$

Replace row 1 with $R_2 - 2R_1$.
Replace row 3 with $-3R_2 + 4R_3$.

$\begin{bmatrix} -2 & 0 & 1 & 0 & 1 & 0 \\ 0 & 4 & -1 & 2 & 1 & 0 \\ 0 & 0 & -1 & -2 & -3 & -4 \end{bmatrix}$

Replace row 1 with $R_3 + R_1$.
Replace row 2 with $R_2 - R_3$.
Replace row 3 with $-R_3$.

$\begin{bmatrix} -2 & 0 & 0 & -2 & -2 & -4 \\ 0 & 4 & 0 & 4 & 4 & 4 \\ 0 & 0 & 1 & 2 & 3 & 4 \end{bmatrix}$

Divide row 1 by –2 and divide row 2 by 4.

$\begin{bmatrix} 1 & 0 & 0 & 1 & 1 & 2 \\ 0 & 1 & 0 & 1 & 1 & 1 \\ 0 & 0 & 1 & 2 & 3 & 4 \end{bmatrix}$

$A^{-1} = \begin{bmatrix} 1 & 1 & 2 \\ 1 & 1 & 1 \\ 2 & 3 & 4 \end{bmatrix}$

23. $\begin{bmatrix} 2 & 2 & -1 & 1 & 0 & 0 \\ 0 & 3 & -1 & 0 & 1 & 0 \\ -1 & -2 & 1 & 0 & 0 & 1 \end{bmatrix} R_1 \leftrightarrow R_3$

$\begin{bmatrix} -1 & -2 & 1 & 0 & 0 & 1 \\ 0 & 3 & -1 & 0 & 1 & 0 \\ 2 & 2 & -1 & 1 & 0 & 0 \end{bmatrix} -1R_1$

$\begin{bmatrix} 1 & 2 & -1 & 0 & 0 & -1 \\ 0 & 3 & -1 & 0 & 1 & 0 \\ 2 & 2 & -1 & 1 & 0 & 0 \end{bmatrix} -2R_1 + R_3$

$\begin{bmatrix} 1 & 2 & -1 & 0 & 0 & -1 \\ 0 & 3 & -1 & 0 & 1 & 0 \\ 0 & -2 & 1 & 1 & 0 & 2 \end{bmatrix} \frac{1}{3}R_2$

$\begin{bmatrix} 1 & 2 & -1 & 0 & 0 & -1 \\ 0 & 1 & -\frac{1}{3} & 0 & \frac{1}{3} & 0 \\ 0 & -2 & 1 & 1 & 0 & 2 \end{bmatrix} \begin{array}{l} -2R_2 + R_1 \\ 2R_2 + R_3 \end{array}$

$\begin{bmatrix} 1 & 0 & -\frac{1}{3} & 0 & -\frac{2}{3} & -1 \\ 0 & 1 & -\frac{1}{3} & 0 & \frac{1}{3} & 0 \\ 0 & 0 & \frac{1}{3} & 1 & \frac{2}{3} & 2 \end{bmatrix} \begin{array}{l} 1R_3 + R_1 \\ 1R_2 + R_1 \end{array}$

$\begin{bmatrix} 1 & 0 & 0 & 1 & 0 & 1 \\ 0 & 1 & 0 & 1 & 1 & 2 \\ 0 & 0 & \frac{1}{3} & 1 & \frac{2}{3} & 2 \end{bmatrix} 3R_3$

$\begin{bmatrix} 1 & 0 & 0 & 1 & 0 & 1 \\ 0 & 1 & 0 & 1 & 1 & 2 \\ 0 & 0 & 1 & 3 & 2 & 6 \end{bmatrix}$

$A^{-1} = \begin{bmatrix} 1 & 0 & 1 \\ 1 & 1 & 2 \\ 3 & 2 & 6 \end{bmatrix}$

25.
$$\left[\begin{array}{rrr|rrr} 5 & 0 & 2 & 1 & 0 & 0 \\ 2 & 2 & 1 & 0 & 1 & 0 \\ -3 & 1 & -1 & 0 & 0 & 1 \end{array}\right] \frac{1}{5}R_1$$

$$\left[\begin{array}{rrr|rrr} 1 & 0 & \frac{2}{5} & \frac{1}{5} & 0 & 0 \\ 2 & 2 & 1 & 0 & 1 & 0 \\ -3 & 1 & -1 & 0 & 0 & 1 \end{array}\right] \begin{array}{l} -2R_1 + R_2 \\ 3R_1 + R_3 \end{array}$$

$$\left[\begin{array}{rrr|rrr} 1 & 0 & \frac{2}{5} & \frac{1}{5} & 0 & 0 \\ 0 & 2 & \frac{1}{5} & -\frac{2}{5} & 1 & 0 \\ 0 & 1 & \frac{1}{5} & \frac{3}{5} & 0 & 1 \end{array}\right] R_2 \leftrightarrow R_3$$

$$\left[\begin{array}{rrr|rrr} 1 & 0 & \frac{2}{5} & \frac{1}{5} & 0 & 0 \\ 0 & 1 & \frac{1}{5} & \frac{3}{5} & 0 & 1 \\ 0 & 2 & \frac{1}{5} & -\frac{2}{5} & 1 & 0 \end{array}\right] -2R_2 + R_3$$

$$\left[\begin{array}{rrr|rrr} 1 & 0 & \frac{2}{5} & \frac{1}{5} & 0 & 0 \\ 0 & 1 & \frac{1}{5} & \frac{3}{5} & 0 & 1 \\ 0 & 0 & -\frac{1}{5} & -\frac{8}{5} & 1 & -2 \end{array}\right] \begin{array}{l} 2R_3 + R_1 \\ 1R_3 + R_2 \end{array}$$

$$\left[\begin{array}{rrr|rrr} 1 & 0 & 0 & -3 & 2 & -4 \\ 0 & 1 & 0 & -1 & 1 & -1 \\ 0 & 0 & -\frac{1}{5} & -\frac{8}{5} & 1 & -2 \end{array}\right] -5R_3$$

$$\left[\begin{array}{rrr|rrr} 1 & 0 & 0 & -3 & 2 & -4 \\ 0 & 1 & 0 & -1 & 1 & -1 \\ 0 & 0 & 1 & 8 & -5 & 10 \end{array}\right]$$

$$A^{-1} = \left[\begin{array}{rrr} -3 & 2 & -4 \\ -1 & 1 & -1 \\ 8 & -5 & 10 \end{array}\right]$$

27.
$$\left[\begin{array}{rrrr|rrrr} 1 & 0 & 0 & 0 & 1 & 0 & 0 & 0 \\ 0 & -1 & 0 & 0 & 0 & 1 & 0 & 0 \\ 0 & 0 & 3 & 0 & 0 & 0 & 1 & 0 \\ 1 & 0 & 0 & 1 & 0 & 0 & 0 & 1 \end{array}\right] -1R_1 + R_4$$

$$\left[\begin{array}{rrrr|rrrr} 1 & 0 & 0 & 0 & 1 & 0 & 0 & 0 \\ 0 & -1 & 0 & 0 & 0 & 1 & 0 & 0 \\ 0 & 0 & 3 & 0 & 0 & 0 & 1 & 0 \\ 0 & 0 & 0 & 1 & -1 & 0 & 0 & 1 \end{array}\right] -1R_2$$

$$\left[\begin{array}{rrrr|rrrr} 1 & 0 & 0 & 0 & 1 & 0 & 0 & 0 \\ 0 & 1 & 0 & 0 & 0 & -1 & 0 & 0 \\ 0 & 0 & 3 & 0 & 0 & 0 & 1 & 0 \\ 0 & 0 & 0 & 1 & -1 & 0 & 0 & 1 \end{array}\right] \frac{1}{3}R_3$$

$$\left[\begin{array}{rrrr|rrrr} 1 & 0 & 0 & 0 & 1 & 0 & 0 & 0 \\ 0 & 1 & 0 & 0 & 0 & -1 & 0 & 0 \\ 0 & 0 & 1 & 0 & 0 & 0 & \frac{1}{3} & 0 \\ 0 & 0 & 0 & 1 & -1 & 0 & 0 & 1 \end{array}\right]$$

$$A^{-1} = \left[\begin{array}{rrrr} 1 & 0 & 0 & 0 \\ 0 & -1 & 0 & 0 \\ 0 & 0 & \frac{1}{3} & 0 \\ -1 & 0 & 0 & 1 \end{array}\right]$$

29. $\begin{bmatrix} 6 & 5 \\ 5 & 4 \end{bmatrix} \begin{bmatrix} x \\ y \end{bmatrix} = \begin{bmatrix} 13 \\ 10 \end{bmatrix}$

31. $\begin{bmatrix} 1 & 3 & 4 \\ 1 & 2 & 3 \\ 1 & 4 & 3 \end{bmatrix} \begin{bmatrix} x \\ y \\ z \end{bmatrix} = \begin{bmatrix} -3 \\ -2 \\ -6 \end{bmatrix}$

33. $4x - 7y = -3$
$2x - 3y = 1$

35. $2x - z = 6$
$3y = 9$
$x + y = 5$

37. a. $\begin{bmatrix} 2 & 6 & 6 \\ 2 & 7 & 6 \\ 2 & 7 & 7 \end{bmatrix} \begin{bmatrix} x \\ y \\ z \end{bmatrix} = \begin{bmatrix} 8 \\ 10 \\ 9 \end{bmatrix}$

$\begin{bmatrix} \frac{7}{2} & 0 & -3 \\ -1 & 1 & 0 \\ 0 & -1 & 1 \end{bmatrix} \begin{bmatrix} 8 \\ 10 \\ 9 \end{bmatrix} = \begin{bmatrix} 28 + 0 - 27 \\ -8 + 10 + 0 \\ 0 - 10 + 9 \end{bmatrix} = \begin{bmatrix} 1 \\ 2 \\ -1 \end{bmatrix}$

The solution to the system is $\{(1, 2, -1)\}$.

39. a. $\begin{bmatrix} 1 & -1 & 1 \\ 0 & 2 & -1 \\ 2 & 3 & 0 \end{bmatrix} \begin{bmatrix} x \\ y \\ z \end{bmatrix} = \begin{bmatrix} 8 \\ -7 \\ 1 \end{bmatrix}$

b. $\begin{bmatrix} 3 & 3 & -1 \\ -2 & -2 & 1 \\ -4 & -5 & 2 \end{bmatrix} \begin{bmatrix} 8 \\ -7 \\ 1 \end{bmatrix}$

$= \begin{bmatrix} 24 - 21 - 1 \\ -16 + 14 + 1 \\ -32 + 35 + 2 \end{bmatrix} = \begin{bmatrix} 2 \\ -1 \\ 5 \end{bmatrix}$

The solution to the system is $\{(2, -1, 5)\}$.

41. a. $\begin{bmatrix} 1 & -1 & 2 & 0 \\ 0 & 1 & -1 & 1 \\ -1 & 1 & -1 & 2 \\ 0 & -1 & 1 & -2 \end{bmatrix} \begin{bmatrix} w \\ x \\ y \\ z \end{bmatrix} = \begin{bmatrix} -3 \\ 4 \\ 2 \\ -4 \end{bmatrix}$

b. $\begin{bmatrix} 0 & 0 & -1 & -1 \\ 1 & 4 & 1 & 3 \\ 1 & 2 & 1 & 2 \\ 0 & -1 & 0 & -1 \end{bmatrix} \begin{bmatrix} -3 \\ 4 \\ 2 \\ -4 \end{bmatrix}$

$= \begin{bmatrix} 0+0-2+4 \\ -3+16+2-12 \\ -3+8+2-8 \\ 0-4+0+4 \end{bmatrix} = \begin{bmatrix} 2 \\ 3 \\ -1 \\ 0 \end{bmatrix}$

The solution to the system is
$\{(2, 3, -1, 0)\}$.

43. $A = \begin{bmatrix} e^x & e^{3x} \\ -e^{3x} & e^{5x} \end{bmatrix}$

$A^{-1} = \dfrac{1}{ad-bc} \begin{bmatrix} d & -b \\ -c & a \end{bmatrix}$

$A^{-1} = \dfrac{1}{(e^x)(e^{5x}) - (e^{3x})(-e^{3x})} \begin{bmatrix} e^{5x} & -e^{3x} \\ -(-e^{3x}) & e^x \end{bmatrix}$

$A^{-1} = \dfrac{1}{e^{6x} + e^{6x}} \begin{bmatrix} e^{5x} & -e^{3x} \\ e^{3x} & e^x \end{bmatrix}$

$A^{-1} = \dfrac{1}{2e^{6x}} \begin{bmatrix} e^{5x} & -e^{3x} \\ e^{3x} & e^x \end{bmatrix}$

$A^{-1} = \begin{bmatrix} \frac{e^{5x}}{2e^{6x}} & \frac{-e^{3x}}{2e^{6x}} \\ \frac{e^{3x}}{2e^{6x}} & \frac{e^x}{2e^{6x}} \end{bmatrix}$

$A^{-1} = \begin{bmatrix} \frac{1}{2e^x} & -\frac{1}{2e^{3x}} \\ \frac{1}{2e^{3x}} & \frac{1}{2e^{5x}} \end{bmatrix}$ or $\begin{bmatrix} \frac{e^{-x}}{2} & -\frac{e^{-3x}}{2} \\ \frac{e^{-3x}}{2} & \frac{e^{-5x}}{2} \end{bmatrix}$

Check:

$\begin{bmatrix} e^x & e^{3x} \\ -e^{3x} & e^{5x} \end{bmatrix} \cdot \begin{bmatrix} \frac{1}{2e^x} & -\frac{1}{2e^{3x}} \\ \frac{1}{2e^{3x}} & \frac{1}{2e^{5x}} \end{bmatrix} = \begin{bmatrix} 1 & 0 \\ 0 & 1 \end{bmatrix}$

45. $A = \begin{bmatrix} 8 & -5 \\ -3 & 2 \end{bmatrix}$

$I - A = \begin{bmatrix} 1 & 0 \\ 0 & 1 \end{bmatrix} - \begin{bmatrix} 8 & -5 \\ -3 & 2 \end{bmatrix} = \begin{bmatrix} -7 & 5 \\ 3 & -1 \end{bmatrix}$

$(I-A)^{-1} = \dfrac{1}{(-7)(-1)-(5)(3)} \begin{bmatrix} -1 & -(5) \\ -(3) & -7 \end{bmatrix}$

$(I-A)^{-1} = \dfrac{1}{7-15} \begin{bmatrix} -1 & -5 \\ -3 & -7 \end{bmatrix}$

$(I-A)^{-1} = \dfrac{1}{-8} \begin{bmatrix} -1 & -5 \\ -3 & -7 \end{bmatrix}$

$(I-A)^{-1} = \begin{bmatrix} \frac{-1}{-8} & \frac{-5}{-8} \\ \frac{-3}{-8} & \frac{-7}{-8} \end{bmatrix}$

$(I-A)^{-1} = \begin{bmatrix} \frac{1}{8} & \frac{5}{8} \\ \frac{3}{8} & \frac{7}{8} \end{bmatrix}$

47. $A = \begin{bmatrix} 2 & 1 \\ 3 & 1 \end{bmatrix}$ $B = \begin{bmatrix} 4 & 7 \\ 1 & 2 \end{bmatrix}$

$A^{-1} = \begin{bmatrix} -1 & 1 \\ 3 & -2 \end{bmatrix}$ $B^{-1} = \begin{bmatrix} 2 & -7 \\ -1 & 4 \end{bmatrix}$

$AB = \begin{bmatrix} 2 & 1 \\ 3 & 1 \end{bmatrix} \begin{bmatrix} 4 & 7 \\ 1 & 2 \end{bmatrix} = \begin{bmatrix} 9 & 16 \\ 13 & 23 \end{bmatrix}$

$(AB)^{-1} = \left(\begin{bmatrix} 9 & 16 \\ 13 & 23 \end{bmatrix} \right)^{-1} = \begin{bmatrix} -23 & 16 \\ 13 & -9 \end{bmatrix}$

$A^{-1}B^{-1} = \begin{bmatrix} -1 & 1 \\ 3 & -2 \end{bmatrix} \begin{bmatrix} 2 & -7 \\ -1 & 4 \end{bmatrix} = \begin{bmatrix} -3 & 11 \\ 8 & -29 \end{bmatrix}$

$B^{-1}A^{-1} = \begin{bmatrix} 2 & -7 \\ -1 & 4 \end{bmatrix} \begin{bmatrix} -1 & 1 \\ 3 & -2 \end{bmatrix} = \begin{bmatrix} -23 & 16 \\ 13 & -9 \end{bmatrix}$

Observe that $(AB)^{-1} = B^{-1}A^{-1}$.

49. $\begin{bmatrix} a & 0 & 0 \\ 0 & b & 0 \\ 0 & 0 & c \end{bmatrix}\begin{bmatrix} \frac{1}{a} & 0 & 0 \\ 0 & \frac{1}{b} & 0 \\ 0 & 0 & \frac{1}{c} \end{bmatrix}$

$= \begin{bmatrix} (a)(\frac{1}{a})+(0)(0)+(0)(0) & (a)(0)+(0)(\frac{1}{b})+(0)(0) & (a)(0)+(0)(0)+(0)(\frac{1}{c}) \\ (0)(\frac{1}{a})+(b)(0)+(0)(0) & (0)(0)+(b)(\frac{1}{b})+(0)(0) & (0)(0)+(b)(0)+(0)(\frac{1}{c}) \\ (0)(\frac{1}{a})+(0)(0)+(c)(0) & (0)(0)+(0)(\frac{1}{b})+(c)(0) & (0)(0)+(0)(0)+(c)(\frac{1}{c}) \end{bmatrix}$

$= \begin{bmatrix} \frac{a}{a}+0+0 & 0+0+0 & 0+0+0 \\ 0+0+0 & 0+\frac{b}{b}+0 & 0+0+0 \\ 0+0+0 & 0+0+0 & 0+0+\frac{c}{c} \end{bmatrix} = \begin{bmatrix} 1 & 0 & 0 \\ 0 & 1 & 0 \\ 0 & 0 & 1 \end{bmatrix}$

51. The numerical equivalent of HELP is
8, 5, 12, 16.
$\begin{bmatrix} 4 & -1 \\ -3 & 1 \end{bmatrix}\begin{bmatrix} 8 \\ 5 \end{bmatrix} = \begin{bmatrix} 27 \\ -19 \end{bmatrix}$,
$\begin{bmatrix} 4 & -1 \\ -3 & 1 \end{bmatrix}\begin{bmatrix} 12 \\ 16 \end{bmatrix} = \begin{bmatrix} 32 \\ -20 \end{bmatrix}$
The encoded message is 27, –19, 32, –20.
$\begin{bmatrix} 1 & 1 \\ 3 & 4 \end{bmatrix}\begin{bmatrix} 27 \\ -19 \end{bmatrix} = \begin{bmatrix} 8 \\ 5 \end{bmatrix}$, $\begin{bmatrix} 1 & 1 \\ 3 & 4 \end{bmatrix}\begin{bmatrix} 32 \\ -20 \end{bmatrix} = \begin{bmatrix} 12 \\ 16 \end{bmatrix}$
The decoded message is 8, 5, 12, 16 or HELP.

53. $\begin{bmatrix} 1 & -1 & 0 \\ 3 & 0 & 2 \\ -1 & 0 & -1 \end{bmatrix}\begin{bmatrix} 19 & 4 & 1 \\ 5 & 0 & 19 \\ 14 & 3 & 8 \end{bmatrix}$

$= \begin{bmatrix} 19-5+0 & 4+0+0 & 1-19+0 \\ 57+0+28 & 12+0+6 & 3+0+16 \\ -19+0-14 & -4+0-3 & -1+0-8 \end{bmatrix}$

$= \begin{bmatrix} 14 & 4 & -18 \\ 85 & 18 & 19 \\ -33 & -7 & -9 \end{bmatrix}$

The encoded message is 14, 85, –33, 4, 18, –7, –18, 19, –9.

$\begin{bmatrix} 0 & 1 & 2 \\ -1 & 1 & 2 \\ 0 & -1 & -3 \end{bmatrix}\begin{bmatrix} 14 & 4 & -18 \\ 85 & 18 & 19 \\ -33 & -7 & -9 \end{bmatrix}$

$= \begin{bmatrix} 0+85-66 & 0+18-14 & 0+19-18 \\ -14+85-66 & -4+18-14 & 18+19-18 \\ 0-85+99 & 0-18+21 & 0-19+27 \end{bmatrix}$

$= \begin{bmatrix} 19 & 4 & 1 \\ 5 & 0 & 19 \\ 14 & 3 & 8 \end{bmatrix}$

The decoded message is 19, 5, 14, 4, 0, 3, 1, 19, 8 or SEND_CASH.

65. Enter the matrix $\begin{bmatrix} 3 & -1 \\ -2 & 1 \end{bmatrix}$ as $[A]$, then use $[A]^{-1}$.

$[A]^{-1} = \begin{bmatrix} 1 & 1 \\ 2 & 3 \end{bmatrix}$

Verify this result by showing that $[A][A]^{-1} = I_2$ and $[A]^{-1}[A] = I_2$.

67. Enter the matrix $\begin{bmatrix} -2 & 1 & -1 \\ -5 & 2 & -1 \\ 3 & -1 & 1 \end{bmatrix}$ as $[A]$, then use $[A]^{-1}$.

$$[A]^{-1} = \begin{bmatrix} 1 & 0 & 1 \\ 2 & 1 & 3 \\ -1 & 1 & 1 \end{bmatrix}$$

Verify this result by showing that $[A][A]^{-1} = I_3$ and $[A]^{-1}[A] = I_3$.

69. Enter the matrix $\begin{bmatrix} 7 & -3 & 0 & 2 \\ -2 & 1 & 0 & -1 \\ 4 & 0 & 1 & -2 \\ -1 & 1 & 0 & -1 \end{bmatrix}$ as $[A]$, then use $[A]^{-1}$. $[A]^{-1} = \begin{bmatrix} 0 & -1 & 0 & 1 \\ -1 & -5 & 0 & 3 \\ -2 & -4 & 1 & -2 \\ -1 & -4 & 0 & 1 \end{bmatrix}$

Verify this result by showing that $[A][A]^{-1} = I_4$ and $[A]^{-1}[A] = I_4$.

71. The system is $AX = B$ where

$A = \begin{bmatrix} 1 & -1 & 1 \\ 4 & 2 & 1 \\ 4 & -2 & 1 \end{bmatrix}$, $X = \begin{bmatrix} x \\ y \\ z \end{bmatrix}$, and $B = \begin{bmatrix} -6 \\ 9 \\ -3 \end{bmatrix}$. $X = \begin{bmatrix} 2 \\ 3 \\ -5 \end{bmatrix}$, so the solution to the system is $\{(2, 3, -5)\}$.

73. The system is $AX = B$ where $A = \begin{bmatrix} 3 & -2 & 1 \\ 4 & -5 & 3 \\ 2 & -1 & 5 \end{bmatrix}$, $X = \begin{bmatrix} x \\ y \\ z \end{bmatrix}$, and $B = \begin{bmatrix} -2 \\ -9 \\ -5 \end{bmatrix}$.

$X = \begin{bmatrix} 1 \\ 2 \\ -1 \end{bmatrix}$ so the solution to the system is $\{(1, 2, -1)\}$.

75. The system is $AX = B$ where $A = \begin{bmatrix} 1 & 0 & -3 & 0 & 1 \\ 0 & 1 & 0 & 1 & 0 \\ 0 & 0 & 1 & 0 & 1 \\ 1 & 1 & -1 & 4 & 0 \\ 1 & 1 & 1 & 1 & 1 \end{bmatrix}$, $X = \begin{bmatrix} v \\ w \\ x \\ y \\ z \end{bmatrix}$ and $B = \begin{bmatrix} -3 \\ -1 \\ 7 \\ -8 \\ 8 \end{bmatrix}$. $X = \begin{bmatrix} 2 \\ 1 \\ 3 \\ -2 \\ 4 \end{bmatrix}$, so the solution to

the system is $\{(2, 1, 3, -2, 4)\}$.

79. a. False; only square matrices have inverses.

b. False; $\begin{bmatrix} 3 & 6 \\ 2 & 4 \end{bmatrix}$ does not have an inverse since $(3)(4) - (6)(2) = 12 - 12 = 0$ and division by zero is undefined.

c. True; $\begin{bmatrix} 1 & 2 \\ 2 & 3 \end{bmatrix} + \begin{bmatrix} 2 & 4 \\ 0 & 1 \end{bmatrix} = \begin{bmatrix} 3 & 6 \\ 2 & 4 \end{bmatrix}$ and $\begin{bmatrix} 1 & 2 \\ 2 & 3 \end{bmatrix}^{-1} = \begin{bmatrix} -3 & 2 \\ 2 & -1 \end{bmatrix}$,

$\begin{bmatrix} 2 & 4 \\ 0 & 1 \end{bmatrix}^{-1} = \begin{bmatrix} \frac{1}{2} & -2 \\ 0 & 1 \end{bmatrix}$ while $\begin{bmatrix} 3 & 6 \\ 2 & 4 \end{bmatrix}$ does not have an inverse. [See part (b).]

d. False; to solve the matrix equation for X, multiply the inverse of A and B $(A^{-1}B)$ provided the inverse of A exists.

(c) is true.

83. Using the statement before problems 9–14, we want to find values for a such that
$(1)(4) - (a + 1)(a - 2) = 0$.

$(1)(4) - (a+1)(a-2) = 4 - (a^2 - a - 2)$

$= -a^2 + a + 6$

$0 = -a^2 + a + 6$

$0 = a^2 - a - 6$

$0 = (a-3)(a+2)$

$a = 3, -2$

Section 8.5

Check Point Exercises

1. **a.** $\begin{vmatrix} 10 & 9 \\ 6 & 5 \end{vmatrix} = 10 \cdot 5 - 6 \cdot 9 = 50 - 54 = -4$

 b. $\begin{vmatrix} 4 & 3 \\ -5 & -8 \end{vmatrix} = 4 \cdot (-8) - (-5) \cdot (3) = -32 + 15 = -17$

2. $5x + 4y = 12$

$3x - 6y = 24$

$D = \begin{vmatrix} 5 & 4 \\ 3 & -6 \end{vmatrix} = 5 \cdot (-6) - 3 \cdot 4 = -30 - 12 = -42$

$D_x = \begin{vmatrix} 12 & 4 \\ 24 & -6 \end{vmatrix} = 12(-6) - 24(4) = -72 - 96 = -168$

$D_y = \begin{vmatrix} 5 & 12 \\ 3 & 24 \end{vmatrix} = 5(24) - 3(12) = 120 - 36 = 84$

Thus, $x = \dfrac{D_x}{D} = \dfrac{-168}{-42} = 4$

$y = \dfrac{D_y}{D} = \dfrac{84}{-42} = -2$

The solution set is $\{(4, -2)\}$.

3. $\begin{bmatrix} 2 & 1 & 7 \\ -5 & 6 & 0 \\ -4 & 3 & 1 \end{bmatrix}$

The minor for 2 is $\begin{vmatrix} 6 & 0 \\ 3 & 1 \end{vmatrix}$.

The minor for -5 is $\begin{vmatrix} 1 & 7 \\ 3 & 1 \end{vmatrix}$.

The minor for -4 is $\begin{vmatrix} 1 & 7 \\ 6 & 0 \end{vmatrix}$.

$\begin{bmatrix} 2 & 1 & 7 \\ -5 & 6 & 0 \\ -4 & 3 & 1 \end{bmatrix} = 2\begin{vmatrix} 6 & 0 \\ 3 & 1 \end{vmatrix} - (-5)\begin{vmatrix} 1 & 7 \\ 3 & 1 \end{vmatrix} - 4\begin{vmatrix} 1 & 7 \\ 6 & 0 \end{vmatrix} = 2(6\cdot 1 - 3\cdot 0) + 5(1\cdot 1 - 3\cdot 7) - 4(1\cdot 0 - 6\cdot 7)$

$\qquad = 2(6-0) + 5(1-21) - 4(0-42) = 12 - 100 + 168 = 80$

4. $\begin{vmatrix} 6 & 4 & 0 \\ -3 & -5 & 3 \\ 1 & 2 & 0 \end{vmatrix} = 0\begin{vmatrix} -3 & -5 \\ 1 & 2 \end{vmatrix} - 3\begin{vmatrix} 6 & 4 \\ 1 & 2 \end{vmatrix} + 0\begin{vmatrix} 6 & 4 \\ -3 & -5 \end{vmatrix} = 0 - 3(6\cdot 2 - 1\cdot 4) + 0 = -3(12-4) = -3(8) = -24$

5. $3x - 2y + z = 16$
$2x + 3y - z = -9$
$x + 4y + 3z = 2$

$D = \begin{vmatrix} 3 & -2 & 1 \\ 2 & 3 & -1 \\ 1 & 4 & 3 \end{vmatrix}; \quad D_x = \begin{vmatrix} 16 & -2 & 1 \\ -9 & 3 & -1 \\ 2 & 4 & 3 \end{vmatrix}; \quad D_y = \begin{vmatrix} 3 & 16 & 1 \\ 2 & -9 & -1 \\ 1 & 2 & 3 \end{vmatrix}; \quad D_z = \begin{vmatrix} 3 & -2 & 16 \\ 2 & 3 & -9 \\ 1 & 4 & 2 \end{vmatrix}$

$D = \begin{vmatrix} 3 & -2 & 1 \\ 2 & 3 & -1 \\ 1 & 4 & 3 \end{vmatrix} = 3\begin{vmatrix} 3 & -1 \\ 4 & 3 \end{vmatrix} - 2\begin{vmatrix} -2 & 1 \\ 4 & 3 \end{vmatrix} + 1\begin{vmatrix} -2 & 1 \\ 3 & -1 \end{vmatrix} = 3[(3)\cdot 3 - 4\cdot(-1)] - 2[(-2)\cdot 3 - 4\cdot 1] + 1[(-2)\cdot(-1) - (3)\cdot 1]$

$\qquad = 3(9+4) - 2(-6-4) + 1(2-3) = 39 + 20 - 1 = 58$

$D_x = \begin{vmatrix} 16 & -2 & 1 \\ -9 & 3 & -1 \\ 2 & 4 & 3 \end{vmatrix} = 1\begin{vmatrix} -9 & 3 \\ 2 & 4 \end{vmatrix} - (-1)\begin{vmatrix} 16 & -2 \\ 2 & 4 \end{vmatrix} + 3\begin{vmatrix} 16 & -2 \\ -9 & 3 \end{vmatrix} = 1[(-9)\cdot 4 - 2\cdot (3)] + 1[16\cdot 4 - 2(-2)] + 3[16\cdot(3) - (-9)\cdot(-2)]$

$\qquad = 1(-36-6) + 1(64+4) + 3(48-18) = -42 + 68 + 90 = 116$

$D_y = \begin{vmatrix} 3 & 16 & 1 \\ 2 & -9 & -1 \\ 1 & 2 & 3 \end{vmatrix} = 3\begin{vmatrix} -9 & -1 \\ 2 & 3 \end{vmatrix} - 2\begin{vmatrix} 16 & 1 \\ 2 & 3 \end{vmatrix} + 1\begin{vmatrix} 16 & 1 \\ -9 & -1 \end{vmatrix} = 3[(-9)\cdot 3 - 2\cdot(-1)] - 2[16\cdot 3 - 2\cdot 1] + 1[16(-1) - (-9)\cdot 1]$

$\qquad = 3(-27+2) - 2(48-2) + 1(-16+9) = -75 - 92 - 7 = -174$

$D_z = \begin{vmatrix} 3 & -2 & 16 \\ 2 & 3 & -9 \\ 1 & 4 & 2 \end{vmatrix} = 3\begin{vmatrix} 3 & -9 \\ 4 & 2 \end{vmatrix} - 2\begin{vmatrix} -2 & 16 \\ 4 & 2 \end{vmatrix} + 1\begin{vmatrix} -2 & 16 \\ 3 & -9 \end{vmatrix} = 3[(3)2 - 4(-9)] - 2[(-2)2 - 4\cdot 16] + 1[(-2)(-9) - (3)\cdot 16]$

$\qquad = 3(6+36) - 2(-4-64) + 1(18-48) = 126 + 136 - 30 = 232$

$$x = \frac{D_x}{D} = \frac{116}{58} = 2$$

$$y = \frac{D_y}{D} = \frac{-174}{58} = -3$$

$$z = \frac{D_z}{D} = \frac{232}{58} = 4$$

The solution to the system is $\{(2, -3, 4)\}$.

6. $|A| = \begin{vmatrix} 0 & 4 & 0 & -3 \\ -1 & 1 & 5 & 2 \\ 1 & -2 & 0 & 6 \\ 3 & 0 & 0 & 1 \end{vmatrix} = (-1)^{2+3} 5 \begin{vmatrix} 0 & 4 & -3 \\ 1 & -2 & 6 \\ 3 & 0 & 1 \end{vmatrix} = -5 \begin{vmatrix} 0 & 4 & -3 \\ 1 & -2 & 6 \\ 3 & 0 & 1 \end{vmatrix}$

Evaluate the third-order determinant to get $|A| = -5(50) = -250$.

Exercise Set 8.5

1. $\begin{vmatrix} 5 & 7 \\ 2 & 3 \end{vmatrix} = 5 \cdot 3 - 2 \cdot 7 = 15 - 14 = 1$

3. $\begin{vmatrix} -4 & 1 \\ 5 & 6 \end{vmatrix} = (-4)6 - 5 \cdot 1 = -24 - 5 = -29$

5. $\begin{vmatrix} -7 & 14 \\ 2 & -4 \end{vmatrix} = (-7)(-4) - 2(14) = 28 - 28 = 0$

7. $\begin{vmatrix} -5 & -1 \\ -2 & -7 \end{vmatrix} = (-5)(-7) - (-2)(-1) = 35 - 2 = 33$

9. $\begin{vmatrix} \frac{1}{2} & \frac{1}{2} \\ \frac{1}{8} & -\frac{3}{4} \end{vmatrix} = \frac{1}{2}\left(-\frac{3}{4}\right) - \frac{1}{8} \cdot \frac{1}{2} = -\frac{3}{8} - \frac{1}{16} = -\frac{7}{16}$

11. $D = \begin{vmatrix} 1 & 1 \\ 1 & -1 \end{vmatrix} = -1 - 1 = -2$

$D_x = \begin{vmatrix} 7 & 1 \\ 3 & -1 \end{vmatrix} = -7 - 3 = -10$

$D_y = \begin{vmatrix} 1 & 7 \\ 1 & 3 \end{vmatrix} = 3 - 7 = -4$

$x = \frac{D_x}{D} = \frac{-10}{-2} = 5$

$y = \frac{D_y}{D} = \frac{-4}{-2} = 2$

The solution set is $\{(5, 2)\}$.

13. $D = \begin{vmatrix} 12 & 3 \\ 2 & -3 \end{vmatrix} = -36 - 6 = -42$

$D_x = \begin{vmatrix} 15 & 3 \\ 13 & -3 \end{vmatrix} = -45 - 39 = -84$

$D_y = \begin{vmatrix} 12 & 15 \\ 2 & 13 \end{vmatrix} = 156 - 30 = 126$

$x = \dfrac{D_x}{D} = \dfrac{-84}{-42} = 2$

$y = \dfrac{D_y}{D} = \dfrac{126}{-42} = -3$

The solution set is $\{(2, -3)\}$.

15. $D = \begin{vmatrix} 4 & -5 \\ 2 & 3 \end{vmatrix} = 12 - (-10) = 22$

$D_x = \begin{vmatrix} 17 & -5 \\ 3 & 3 \end{vmatrix} = 51 - (-15) = 66$

$D_y = \begin{vmatrix} 4 & 17 \\ 2 & 3 \end{vmatrix} = 12 - 34 = -22$

$x = \dfrac{D_x}{D} = \dfrac{66}{22} = 3$

$y = \dfrac{D_y}{D} = \dfrac{-22}{22} = -1$

The solution set is $\{(3, -1)\}$.

17. $D = \begin{vmatrix} 1 & 2 \\ 5 & 10 \end{vmatrix} = 10 - 10 = 0$

$D_x = \begin{vmatrix} 3 & 2 \\ 15 & 10 \end{vmatrix} = 30 - 30 = 0$

$D_y = \begin{vmatrix} 1 & 3 \\ 5 & 15 \end{vmatrix} = 15 - 15 = 0$

Because all 3 determinants equal zero, the system is dependent.

19. $D = \begin{vmatrix} 3 & -4 \\ 2 & 2 \end{vmatrix} = 6 - (-8) = 14$

$D_x = \begin{vmatrix} 4 & -4 \\ 12 & 2 \end{vmatrix} = 8 - (-48) = 56$

$D_y = \begin{vmatrix} 3 & 4 \\ 2 & 12 \end{vmatrix} = 36 - 8 = 28$

$x = \dfrac{D_x}{D} = \dfrac{56}{14} = 4$

$y = \dfrac{D_y}{D} = \dfrac{28}{14} = 2$

The solution set is $\{(4, 2)\}$.

21. $D = \begin{vmatrix} 2 & -3 \\ 5 & 4 \end{vmatrix} = 8 - (-15) = 23$

$D_x = \begin{vmatrix} 2 & -3 \\ 51 & 4 \end{vmatrix} = 8 - (-153) = 161$

$D_y = \begin{vmatrix} 2 & 2 \\ 5 & 51 \end{vmatrix} = 102 - 10 = 92$

$x = \dfrac{D_x}{D} = \dfrac{161}{23} = 7$

$y = \dfrac{D_y}{D} = \dfrac{92}{23} = 4$

The solution set is $\{(7, 4)\}$.

23. $D = \begin{vmatrix} 3 & 3 \\ 2 & 2 \end{vmatrix} = 6 - 6 = 0$

$D_x = \begin{vmatrix} 2 & 3 \\ 3 & 2 \end{vmatrix} = 4 - 9 = -5$

$D_y = \begin{vmatrix} 3 & 2 \\ 2 & 3 \end{vmatrix} = 9 - 4 = 5$

Because $D = 0$ but D_x or $D_y \neq 0$, the system is inconsistent.

25. Write the equations in standard form.

$3x + 4y = 16$

$6x + 8y = 32$

$$D = \begin{bmatrix} 3 & 4 \\ 6 & 8 \end{bmatrix} = 24 - 24 = 0$$

$$D_x = \begin{bmatrix} 16 & 4 \\ 32 & 8 \end{bmatrix} = 128 - 128 = 0$$

$$D_y = \begin{bmatrix} 3 & 16 \\ 6 & 32 \end{bmatrix} = 96 - 69 = 0$$

Since all determinants are zero, the system is dependent.

27. $\begin{vmatrix} 3 & 0 & 0 \\ 2 & 1 & -5 \\ -2 & 5 & -1 \end{vmatrix} = 3\begin{vmatrix} 1 & -5 \\ 5 & -1 \end{vmatrix} - 0\begin{vmatrix} 2 & -5 \\ -2 & -1 \end{vmatrix} + 0\begin{vmatrix} 2 & 1 \\ -2 & 5 \end{vmatrix}$

$= 3[(1)(-1) - (5)(-5)]$

$= 3(-1 + 25) = 3(24)$

$= 72$

29. $\begin{vmatrix} 3 & 1 & 0 \\ -3 & 4 & 0 \\ -1 & 3 & -5 \end{vmatrix} = 0\begin{vmatrix} -3 & 4 \\ -1 & 3 \end{vmatrix} - 0\begin{vmatrix} 3 & 1 \\ -1 & 3 \end{vmatrix} + (-5)\begin{vmatrix} 3 & 1 \\ -3 & 4 \end{vmatrix}$

$= -5[3 \cdot 4 - (-3)(1)]$

$= -5(12 + 3) = -5(15)$

$= -75$

31. $\begin{vmatrix} 1 & 1 & 1 \\ 2 & 2 & 2 \\ -3 & 4 & -5 \end{vmatrix} -2R_1 + R_2$

$\begin{vmatrix} 1 & 1 & 1 \\ 0 & 0 & 0 \\ -3 & 4 & -5 \end{vmatrix} = 0$

33. $D = \begin{vmatrix} 1 & 1 & 1 \\ 2 & -1 & 1 \\ -1 & 3 & -1 \end{vmatrix}$

$= \begin{vmatrix} -1 & 1 \\ 3 & -1 \end{vmatrix} - \begin{vmatrix} 2 & 1 \\ -1 & -1 \end{vmatrix} + \begin{vmatrix} 2 & -1 \\ -1 & 3 \end{vmatrix}$

$= (1 - 3) - [-2 - (-1)] + (6 - 1)$

$= -2 - (-1) + 5 = -2 + 1 + 5 = 4$

$D_x = \begin{vmatrix} 0 & 1 & 1 \\ -1 & -1 & 1 \\ -8 & 3 & -1 \end{vmatrix} = (-1)\begin{vmatrix} -1 & 1 \\ -8 & -1 \end{vmatrix} + \begin{vmatrix} -1 & -1 \\ -8 & 3 \end{vmatrix}$

$= (-1)[1 - (-8)] + (-3 - 8) = (-1)(9) - 11$

$= -20$

$D_y = \begin{vmatrix} 1 & 0 & 1 \\ 2 & -1 & 1 \\ -1 & -8 & -1 \end{vmatrix} = \begin{vmatrix} -1 & 1 \\ -8 & -1 \end{vmatrix} + \begin{vmatrix} 2 & -1 \\ -1 & -8 \end{vmatrix}$

$= 1 - (-8) + (-16 - 1) = 1 + 8 - 17 = -8$

$D_z = \begin{vmatrix} 1 & 1 & 0 \\ 2 & -1 & -1 \\ -1 & 3 & -8 \end{vmatrix} = 1\begin{vmatrix} -1 & -1 \\ 3 & -8 \end{vmatrix} - 1\begin{vmatrix} 2 & -1 \\ -1 & -8 \end{vmatrix}$

$= 8 - (-3) - 1(-16 - 1) = 11 + 17 = 28$

$x = \dfrac{D_x}{D} = \dfrac{-20}{4} = -5$

$y = \dfrac{D_y}{D} = \dfrac{-8}{4} = -2$

$z = \dfrac{D_z}{D} = \dfrac{28}{4} = 7$

The solution to the system is $\{(-5, -2, 7)\}$.

35. $D = \begin{vmatrix} 4 & -5 & -6 \\ 1 & -2 & -5 \\ 2 & -1 & 0 \end{vmatrix} = 2\begin{vmatrix} -5 & -6 \\ -2 & -5 \end{vmatrix} - (-1)\begin{vmatrix} 4 & -6 \\ 1 & -5 \end{vmatrix}$

$= 2(25 - 12) + [-20 - (-6)] = 2(13) + (-14)$

$= 26 - 14 = 12$

$D_x = \begin{vmatrix} -1 & -5 & -6 \\ -12 & -2 & -5 \\ 7 & -1 & 0 \end{vmatrix}$

$= 7\begin{vmatrix} -5 & -6 \\ -2 & -5 \end{vmatrix} - (-1)\begin{vmatrix} -1 & -6 \\ -12 & -5 \end{vmatrix}$

$= 7(25 - 12) + (5 - 72) = 7(13) - 67$

$= 91 - 67 = 24$

$D_y = \begin{vmatrix} 4 & -1 & -6 \\ 1 & -12 & -5 \\ 2 & 7 & 0 \end{vmatrix} = 2\begin{vmatrix} -1 & -6 \\ -12 & -5 \end{vmatrix} - 7\begin{vmatrix} 4 & -6 \\ 1 & -5 \end{vmatrix}$

$= 2(5 - 72) - 7[-20 - (-6)]$

$= 2(-67) - 7(-14) = -134 + 98 = -36$

$D_z = \begin{vmatrix} 4 & -5 & -1 \\ 1 & -2 & -12 \\ 2 & -1 & 7 \end{vmatrix}$

$= 4\begin{vmatrix} -2 & -12 \\ -1 & 7 \end{vmatrix} - (-5)\begin{vmatrix} 1 & -12 \\ 2 & 7 \end{vmatrix} + (-1)\begin{vmatrix} 1 & -2 \\ 2 & -1 \end{vmatrix}$

$= 4(-14 - 12) + 5[7 - (-24)] - [-1 - (-4)]$

$= 4(-26) + 5(31) - (3) = -104 + 155 - 3 = 48$

$x = \dfrac{D_x}{D} = \dfrac{24}{12} = 2, \; y = \dfrac{D_y}{D} = \dfrac{-36}{12} = -3,$

$z = \dfrac{D_z}{D} = \dfrac{48}{12} = 4$

The solution set is $\{(2, -3, 4)\}$.

37. $D = \begin{vmatrix} 1 & 1 & 1 \\ 1 & -2 & 1 \\ 1 & 3 & 2 \end{vmatrix} = 1\begin{vmatrix} -2 & 1 \\ 3 & 2 \end{vmatrix} - 1\begin{vmatrix} 1 & 1 \\ 1 & 2 \end{vmatrix} + 1\begin{vmatrix} 1 & -2 \\ 1 & 3 \end{vmatrix}$

$= -4 - 3 - (2 - 1) + [3 - (-2)]$
$= -7 - 1 + 5 = -3$

$D_x = \begin{vmatrix} 4 & 1 & 1 \\ 7 & -2 & 1 \\ 4 & 3 & 2 \end{vmatrix} = 4\begin{vmatrix} -2 & 1 \\ 3 & 2 \end{vmatrix} - 1\begin{vmatrix} 7 & 1 \\ 4 & 2 \end{vmatrix} + 1\begin{vmatrix} 7 & -2 \\ 4 & 3 \end{vmatrix}$

$= 4(-4 - 3) - (14 - 4) + [21 - (-8)]$
$= 4(-7) - 10 + 29 = -28 + 19 = -9$

$D_y = \begin{vmatrix} 1 & 4 & 1 \\ 1 & 7 & 1 \\ 1 & 4 & 2 \end{vmatrix} = 1\begin{vmatrix} 7 & 1 \\ 4 & 2 \end{vmatrix} - 1\begin{vmatrix} 4 & 1 \\ 4 & 2 \end{vmatrix} + 1\begin{vmatrix} 4 & 1 \\ 7 & 1 \end{vmatrix}$

$= 14 - 4 - (8 - 4) + (4 - 7) = 10 - 4 - 3 = 3$

$D_z = \begin{vmatrix} 1 & 1 & 4 \\ 1 & -2 & 7 \\ 1 & 3 & 4 \end{vmatrix} = 1\begin{vmatrix} -2 & 7 \\ 3 & 4 \end{vmatrix} - 1\begin{vmatrix} 1 & 4 \\ 3 & 4 \end{vmatrix} + 1\begin{vmatrix} 1 & 4 \\ -2 & 7 \end{vmatrix}$

$= -8 - 21 - (4 - 12) + [7 - (-8)]$
$= -29 + 8 + 15 = -6$

$x = \dfrac{D_x}{D} = \dfrac{-9}{-3} = 3, \quad y = \dfrac{D_y}{D} = \dfrac{3}{-3} = -1,$

$z = \dfrac{D_z}{D} = \dfrac{-6}{-3} = 2$

The solution set is $\{3, -1, 2\}$.

39. $D = \begin{vmatrix} 1 & 0 & 2 \\ 0 & 2 & -1 \\ 2 & 3 & 0 \end{vmatrix} = \begin{vmatrix} 2 & -1 \\ 3 & 0 \end{vmatrix} + 2\begin{vmatrix} 0 & 2 \\ 2 & 3 \end{vmatrix}$

$= 0 - (-3) + 2(0 - 4) = 3 - 8 = -5$

$D_x = \begin{vmatrix} 4 & 0 & 2 \\ 5 & 2 & -1 \\ 13 & 3 & 0 \end{vmatrix} = 4\begin{vmatrix} 2 & -1 \\ 3 & 0 \end{vmatrix} + 2\begin{vmatrix} 5 & 2 \\ 13 & 3 \end{vmatrix}$

$= 4[0 - (-3)] + 2(15 - 26)$
$= 4(3) + 2(-11) = 12 - 22 = -10$

$D_y = \begin{vmatrix} 1 & 4 & 2 \\ 0 & 5 & -1 \\ 2 & 13 & 0 \end{vmatrix} = \begin{vmatrix} 5 & -1 \\ 13 & 0 \end{vmatrix} + 2\begin{vmatrix} 4 & 2 \\ 5 & -1 \end{vmatrix}$

$= 0 - (-13) + 2(-4 - 10)$
$= 13 + 2(-14) = 13 - 28 = -15$

$D_z = \begin{vmatrix} 1 & 0 & 4 \\ 0 & 2 & 5 \\ 2 & 3 & 13 \end{vmatrix} = \begin{vmatrix} 2 & 5 \\ 3 & 13 \end{vmatrix} + 4\begin{vmatrix} 0 & 2 \\ 2 & 3 \end{vmatrix}$

$= 26 - 15 + 4(0 - 4) = 11 + 4(-4)$
$= 11 - 16 = -5$

$x = \dfrac{D_x}{D} = \dfrac{-10}{-5} = 2, \quad y = \dfrac{D_y}{D} = \dfrac{-15}{-5} = 3,$

$z = \dfrac{D_z}{D} = \dfrac{-5}{-5} = 1$

The solution set is $\{(2, 3, 1)\}$.

41. $\begin{vmatrix} 4 & 2 & 8 & -7 \\ -2 & 0 & 4 & 1 \\ 5 & 0 & 0 & 5 \\ 4 & 0 & 0 & -1 \end{vmatrix} = -2\begin{vmatrix} -2 & 4 & 1 \\ 5 & 0 & 5 \\ 4 & 0 & -1 \end{vmatrix} + 0\begin{vmatrix} 4 & 8 & -7 \\ 5 & 0 & 5 \\ 4 & 0 & -1 \end{vmatrix} - 0\begin{vmatrix} 4 & 8 & -7 \\ -2 & 4 & 1 \\ 4 & 0 & -1 \end{vmatrix} + 0\begin{vmatrix} 4 & 8 & -7 \\ -2 & 4 & 1 \\ 5 & 0 & 5 \end{vmatrix}$

$= (-2)\left[(-4)\begin{vmatrix} 5 & 5 \\ 4 & -1 \end{vmatrix} + 0\begin{vmatrix} -2 & 1 \\ 4 & -1 \end{vmatrix} - 0\begin{vmatrix} -2 & 1 \\ 5 & 5 \end{vmatrix} \right] = (-2)(-4)[5(-1) - 4 \cdot 5] = 8(-5 - 20) = 8(-25) = -200$

43. $\begin{vmatrix} -2 & -3 & 3 & 5 \\ 1 & -4 & 0 & 0 \\ 1 & 2 & 2 & -3 \\ 2 & 0 & 1 & 1 \end{vmatrix} = -1\begin{vmatrix} -3 & 3 & 5 \\ 2 & 2 & -3 \\ 0 & 1 & 1 \end{vmatrix} + (-4)\begin{vmatrix} -2 & 3 & 5 \\ 1 & 2 & -3 \\ 2 & 1 & 1 \end{vmatrix} - 0\begin{vmatrix} -2 & -3 & 5 \\ 1 & 2 & -3 \\ 2 & 0 & 1 \end{vmatrix} + 0\begin{vmatrix} -2 & -3 & 3 \\ 1 & 2 & 2 \\ 2 & 0 & 1 \end{vmatrix}$

$= (-1)\left[0\begin{vmatrix} 3 & 5 \\ 2 & -3 \end{vmatrix} - 1\begin{vmatrix} -3 & 5 \\ 2 & -3 \end{vmatrix} + 1\begin{vmatrix} -3 & 3 \\ 2 & 2 \end{vmatrix} \right] - 4\left[2\begin{vmatrix} 3 & 5 \\ 2 & -3 \end{vmatrix} - 1\begin{vmatrix} -2 & 5 \\ 1 & -3 \end{vmatrix} + 1\begin{vmatrix} -2 & 3 \\ 1 & 2 \end{vmatrix} \right]$

$= (-1)\{(-1)[(-3)(-3) - 2 \cdot 5] + [(-3)(2) - 2 \cdot 3]\} - 4\{2[3(-3) - 2 \cdot 5] - [(-2)(-3) - 1 \cdot 5] + [(-2)(2) - 1 \cdot 3]\} = 195$

45.

$$\begin{Vmatrix} \begin{vmatrix} 3 & 1 \\ -2 & 3 \end{vmatrix} & \begin{vmatrix} 7 & 0 \\ 1 & 5 \end{vmatrix} \\ \begin{vmatrix} 3 & 0 \\ 0 & 7 \end{vmatrix} & \begin{vmatrix} 9 & -6 \\ 3 & 5 \end{vmatrix} \end{Vmatrix} = \begin{vmatrix} 3(3)-(-2)(1) & 7(5)-1(0) \\ 3(7)-0(0) & 9(5)-3(-6) \end{vmatrix} = \begin{vmatrix} 9+2 & 35-0 \\ 21-0 & 45+18 \end{vmatrix} = \begin{vmatrix} 11 & 35 \\ 21 & 63 \end{vmatrix}$$

$$= 11(63) - 21(35) = 693 - 735 = -42$$

47.

From $D = \begin{vmatrix} 2 & -4 \\ 3 & 5 \end{vmatrix}$ we obtain the coefficients of the variables in our equations:

$$2x - 4y = c_1$$
$$3x + 5y = c_2$$

From $D_x = \begin{vmatrix} 8 & -4 \\ -10 & 5 \end{vmatrix}$ we obtain the constant coefficients: 8 and -10

$$2x - 4y = 8$$
$$3x + 5y = -10$$

49.

$$\begin{vmatrix} -2 & x \\ 4 & 6 \end{vmatrix} = 32$$
$$-2(6) - 4(x) = 32$$
$$-12 - 4x = 32$$
$$-4x = 44$$
$$x = -11$$

The solution is -11.

51.

$$\begin{vmatrix} 1 & x & -2 \\ 3 & 1 & 1 \\ 0 & -2 & 2 \end{vmatrix} = -8$$

$$0\begin{vmatrix} x & -2 \\ 1 & 1 \end{vmatrix} - (-2)\begin{vmatrix} 1 & -2 \\ 3 & 1 \end{vmatrix} + 2\begin{vmatrix} 1 & x \\ 3 & 1 \end{vmatrix} = -8$$

$$2\left[1(1) - 3(-2)\right] + 2\left[1(1) - 3(x)\right] = -8$$
$$2(1+6) + 2(1-3x) = -8$$
$$2(7) + 2(1-3x) = -8$$
$$14 + 2 - 6x = -8$$
$$-6x = -24$$
$$x = 4$$

The solution is 4.

53.   Area $= \pm\dfrac{1}{2}\begin{vmatrix} 3 & -5 & 1 \\ 2 & 6 & 1 \\ -3 & 5 & 1 \end{vmatrix} = \pm\dfrac{1}{2}\begin{vmatrix} 3 & -5 & 1 \\ -1 & 11 & 0 \\ -6 & 10 & 0 \end{vmatrix} = \pm\dfrac{1}{2}\begin{vmatrix} -1 & 11 \\ -6 & 10 \end{vmatrix} = \pm\dfrac{1}{2}[-10-(-66)] = \pm\dfrac{1}{2}(56) = 28$

The area is 28 square units.

The slope of the line through $(3, -5)$ and $(-3, 5)$ is $m = \dfrac{5-(-5)}{-3-3} = \dfrac{10}{-6} = -\dfrac{5}{3}$.

The equation of the line is $y-(-5) = -\dfrac{5}{3}(x-3)$ or $y = -\dfrac{5}{3}x$.

The line perpendicular to $y = -\dfrac{5}{3}x$ through $(2, 6)$ has equation $y-6 = \dfrac{3}{5}(x-2)$ or $y = \dfrac{3}{5}x + \dfrac{24}{5}$.

These lines intersect where $-\dfrac{5}{3}x = \dfrac{3}{5}x + \dfrac{24}{5}$.

$-\dfrac{36}{17} = x$ and $-\dfrac{24}{5} = \dfrac{34}{15}x$ $y = -\dfrac{5}{3}\left(-\dfrac{36}{17}\right) = \dfrac{60}{17}$

Using the side connecting $(3, -5)$ and $(-3, 5)$ as the base, the height is the distance from $(2, 6)$ to $\left(-\dfrac{36}{17}, \dfrac{60}{17}\right)$.

$b = \sqrt{[3-(-3)]^2 + (-5-5)^2}$
$= \sqrt{36+100} = \sqrt{136} = 2\sqrt{34}$

$h = \sqrt{\left[2-\left(-\dfrac{36}{17}\right)\right]^2 + \left(6-\dfrac{60}{17}\right)^2}$

$= \sqrt{\dfrac{4900}{289} + \dfrac{1764}{289}} = \dfrac{14\sqrt{34}}{17}$

$\dfrac{1}{2}bh = \dfrac{1}{2}\left(2\sqrt{34}\right)\left(\dfrac{14\sqrt{34}}{17}\right) = \dfrac{14(34)}{17}$

$= 14(2) = 28$ square units

55. $\begin{vmatrix} 3 & -1 & 1 \\ 0 & -3 & 1 \\ 12 & 5 & 1 \end{vmatrix} = \begin{vmatrix} 3 & -1 & 1 \\ -3 & -2 & 0 \\ 9 & 6 & 0 \end{vmatrix} = \begin{vmatrix} -3 & -2 \\ 9 & 6 \end{vmatrix}$

$= -18-(-18) = 0$
Yes, the points are collinear.

57. $\begin{vmatrix} x & y & 1 \\ 3 & -5 & 1 \\ -2 & 6 & 1 \end{vmatrix} = x\begin{vmatrix} -5 & 1 \\ 6 & 1 \end{vmatrix} - y\begin{vmatrix} 3 & 1 \\ -2 & 1 \end{vmatrix} + \begin{vmatrix} 3 & -5 \\ -2 & 6 \end{vmatrix} = x(-5-6) - y[3-(-2)] + (18-10)$

$= -11x - 5y + 8$

The equation of the line is $-11x - 5y + 8 = 0$. The equation of the line in slope-intercept form is $y = -\dfrac{11}{5}x + \dfrac{8}{5}$.

69. Input the matrix as $[A]$, then use det$[A]$ to find the determinant.

$$\begin{vmatrix} 8 & 2 & 6 & -1 & 0 \\ 2 & 0 & -3 & 4 & 7 \\ 2 & 1 & -3 & 6 & -5 \\ -1 & 2 & 1 & 5 & -1 \\ 4 & 5 & -2 & 3 & -8 \end{vmatrix} = 13,200$$

In exercise 71, expansions are all done about the first column of the matrix and the resulting products of 0 and a determinant are not shown.

71. a. $\begin{vmatrix} a & a \\ 0 & a \end{vmatrix} = a^2 - 0 = a^2$

b. $\begin{vmatrix} a & a & a \\ 0 & a & a \\ 0 & 0 & a \end{vmatrix} = a\begin{vmatrix} a & a \\ 0 & a \end{vmatrix} - 0 + 0$

$= a\left(a^2\right) = a^3$

c. $\begin{vmatrix} a & a & a & a \\ 0 & a & a & a \\ 0 & 0 & a & a \\ 0 & 0 & 0 & a \end{vmatrix} = a\begin{vmatrix} a & a & a \\ 0 & a & a \\ 0 & 0 & a \end{vmatrix} - 0 + 0 - 0$

$= a\left(a^3\right) = a^4$

d. Each determinant has zeros below the main diagonal and a's everywhere else.

e. Each determinant equals a raised to the power equal to the order of the determinant.

73. The sign of the value is changed when 2 columns are interchanged in a 2nd order determinant.

75. Evaluate the determinate and write the equation in slope intercept form.

$$\begin{vmatrix} x & y & 1 \\ x_1 & y_1 & 1 \\ x_2 & y_2 & 1 \end{vmatrix} = 0$$

$$x\begin{vmatrix} y_1 & 1 \\ y_2 & 1 \end{vmatrix} - y\begin{vmatrix} x_1 & 1 \\ x_2 & 1 \end{vmatrix} + 1\begin{vmatrix} x_1 & y_1 \\ x_2 & y_2 \end{vmatrix} = 0$$

$$x(y_1 - y_2) - y(x_1 - x_2) + x_1 y_2 - x_2 y_1 = 0$$

$$-y(x_1 - x_2) = -x(y_1 - y_2) + x_2 y_1 - x_1 y_2$$

$$y(x_2 - x_1) = x(y_2 - y_1) + x_2 y_1 - x_1 y_2$$

$$y = \frac{y_2 - y_1}{x_2 - x_1}x + \frac{x_2 y_1 - x_1 y_2}{x_2 - x_1}$$

$$m = \frac{y_2 - y_1}{x_2 - x_1} \qquad b = \frac{x_2 y_1 - x_1 y_2}{x_2 - x_1}$$

Write the slope-point equation of the line the in point slope form.

$$y - y_1 = \frac{y_2 - y_1}{x_2 - x_1}(x - x_1)$$

$$y - y_1 = \frac{y_2 - y_1}{x_2 - x_1}x + \frac{-x_1 y_2 + x_1 y_1}{x_2 - x_1}$$

$$y = \frac{y_2 - y_1}{x_2 - x_1}x + \frac{-x_1 y_2 + x_1 y_1}{x_2 - x_1} + y_1$$

$$y = \frac{y_2 - y_1}{x_2 - x_1}x + \frac{-x_1 y_2 + x_1 y_1}{x_2 - x_1} + \frac{x_2 y_1 - x_1 y_1}{x_2 - x_1}$$

$$y = \frac{y_2 - y_1}{x_2 - x_1}x + \frac{x_2 y_1 - x_1 y_2}{x_2 - x_1}$$

$$m = \frac{y_2 - y_1}{x_2 - x_1} \qquad b = \frac{x_2 y_1 - x_1 y_2}{x_2 - x_1}$$

Since both forms give the same slope and y-intercept, the determinant does give the equation of the line.

Chapter 8 Review Exercises

1.
$$x + y + 3z = 12$$
$$y - 2z = -4$$
$$z = 3$$

$$y - 2(3) = -4$$
$$y - 6 = -4$$
$$y = 2$$

$$x + 2 + 3(3) = 12$$
$$x + 11 = 12$$
$$x = 1$$

The solution to the system is $\{(1, 2, 3)\}$.

2.
$$w - 2y + 2z = 1$$
$$x + y - z = 0$$
$$y - \frac{7}{3}x = -\frac{1}{3}$$
$$z = 1$$
$$y - \frac{7}{3}(1) = -\frac{1}{3}$$
$$y - \frac{7}{3} = -\frac{1}{3}$$
$$y = \frac{6}{3}$$
$$y = 2$$

$$x + 2 - 1 = 0$$
$$x + 1 = 0$$
$$x = -1$$

$$w - 2(2) + 2(1) = 1$$
$$w - 2 = 1$$
$$w = 3$$

The solution to the system is $\{(3, -1, 2, 1)\}$.

3.
$$\begin{bmatrix} 1 & 2 & 2 & | & 2 \\ 0 & 1 & -1 & | & 2 \\ 0 & 5 & 4 & | & 1 \end{bmatrix} -5R_2 + R_3$$

$$\begin{bmatrix} 1 & 2 & 2 & | & 2 \\ 0 & 1 & -1 & | & 2 \\ 0 & 0 & 9 & | & -9 \end{bmatrix}$$

4.
$$\begin{bmatrix} 2 & -2 & 1 & | & -1 \\ 1 & 2 & -1 & | & 2 \\ 6 & 4 & 3 & | & 5 \end{bmatrix} \frac{1}{2}R_1$$

$$\begin{bmatrix} 1 & -1 & \frac{1}{2} & | & -\frac{1}{2} \\ 1 & 2 & -1 & | & 2 \\ 6 & 4 & 3 & | & 5 \end{bmatrix}$$

5.
$$\begin{bmatrix} 1 & 2 & 3 & | & -5 \\ 2 & 1 & 1 & | & 1 \\ 1 & 1 & -1 & | & 8 \end{bmatrix} \begin{matrix} -2R_1 + R_2 \\ -1R_1 + R_3 \end{matrix}$$

$$\begin{bmatrix} 1 & 2 & 3 & | & -5 \\ 0 & -3 & -5 & | & 11 \\ 0 & -1 & -4 & | & 13 \end{bmatrix} R_2 \leftrightarrow R_3$$

$$\begin{bmatrix} 1 & 2 & 3 & | & -5 \\ 0 & -1 & -4 & | & 13 \\ 0 & -3 & -5 & | & 11 \end{bmatrix} -1R_2$$

$$\begin{bmatrix} 1 & 2 & 3 & | & -5 \\ 0 & 1 & 4 & | & -13 \\ 0 & -3 & -5 & | & 11 \end{bmatrix} 3R_2 + R_3$$

$$\begin{bmatrix} 1 & 2 & 3 & | & -5 \\ 0 & 1 & 4 & | & -13 \\ 0 & 0 & 7 & | & -28 \end{bmatrix} \frac{1}{7}R_3$$

$$\begin{bmatrix} 1 & 2 & 3 & | & -5 \\ 0 & 1 & 4 & | & -13 \\ 0 & 0 & 1 & | & -4 \end{bmatrix} -2R_2 + R_1$$

$$\begin{bmatrix} 1 & 0 & -5 & | & 21 \\ 0 & 1 & 4 & | & -13 \\ 0 & 0 & 1 & | & -4 \end{bmatrix} \begin{matrix} 5R_3 + R_1 \\ -4R_3 + R_2 \end{matrix}$$

$$\begin{bmatrix} 1 & 0 & 0 & | & 1 \\ 0 & 1 & 0 & | & 3 \\ 0 & 0 & 1 & | & -4 \end{bmatrix}$$

The solution set is $\{(1, 3, -4)\}$.

6. $\begin{bmatrix} 1 & -2 & 1 & | & 0 \\ 0 & 1 & -3 & | & -1 \\ 0 & 2 & 5 & | & -2 \end{bmatrix} -2R_2 + R_3$

$\begin{bmatrix} 1 & -2 & 1 & | & 0 \\ 0 & 1 & -3 & | & -1 \\ 0 & 0 & 11 & | & 0 \end{bmatrix} \frac{1}{11} R_3$

$\begin{bmatrix} 1 & -2 & 1 & | & 0 \\ 0 & 1 & -3 & | & -1 \\ 0 & 0 & 1 & | & 0 \end{bmatrix} 2R_2 + R_1$

$\begin{bmatrix} 1 & 0 & -5 & | & -2 \\ 0 & 1 & -3 & | & -1 \\ 0 & 0 & 1 & | & 0 \end{bmatrix} \begin{matrix} 3R_3 + R_2 \\ 5R_3 + R_1 \end{matrix}$

$\begin{bmatrix} 1 & 0 & 0 & | & -2 \\ 0 & 1 & 0 & | & -1 \\ 0 & 0 & 1 & | & 0 \end{bmatrix}$

$x = -2; y = -1; z = 0$

The solution set is $\{(-2, -1, 0)\}$.

7. $\begin{bmatrix} 3 & 5 & -8 & 5 & | & -8 \\ 1 & 2 & -3 & 1 & | & -7 \\ 2 & 3 & -7 & 3 & | & -11 \\ 4 & 8 & -10 & 7 & | & -10 \end{bmatrix} R_1 \leftrightarrow R_2$

$\begin{bmatrix} 1 & 2 & -3 & 1 & | & -7 \\ 3 & 5 & -8 & 5 & | & -8 \\ 2 & 3 & -7 & 3 & | & -11 \\ 4 & 8 & -10 & 7 & | & -10 \end{bmatrix} \begin{matrix} -3R_1 + R_2 \\ -2R_1 + R_3 \\ -4R_1 + R_4 \end{matrix}$

$\begin{bmatrix} 1 & 2 & -3 & 1 & | & -7 \\ 0 & -1 & 1 & 2 & | & 13 \\ 0 & -1 & -1 & 1 & | & 3 \\ 0 & 0 & 2 & 3 & | & 18 \end{bmatrix} -1R_2$

$\begin{bmatrix} 1 & 2 & -3 & 1 & | & -7 \\ 0 & 1 & -1 & -2 & | & -13 \\ 0 & -1 & -1 & 1 & | & 3 \\ 0 & 0 & 2 & 3 & | & 18 \end{bmatrix} \begin{matrix} -2R_2 + R_1 \\ 1R_2 + R_3 \end{matrix}$

$\begin{bmatrix} 1 & 0 & -1 & 5 & | & 19 \\ 0 & 1 & -1 & -2 & | & -13 \\ 0 & 0 & -2 & -1 & | & -10 \\ 0 & 0 & 2 & 3 & | & 18 \end{bmatrix} -\frac{1}{2} R_3$

$\begin{bmatrix} 1 & 0 & -1 & 5 & | & 19 \\ 0 & 1 & -1 & -2 & | & -13 \\ 0 & 0 & 1 & \frac{1}{2} & | & 5 \\ 0 & 0 & 2 & 3 & | & 18 \end{bmatrix} \begin{matrix} 1R_3 + R_1 \\ 1R_3 + R_2 \\ -2R_3 + R_4 \end{matrix}$

$\begin{bmatrix} 1 & 0 & 0 & \frac{11}{2} & | & 24 \\ 0 & 1 & 0 & -\frac{3}{2} & | & -8 \\ 0 & 0 & 1 & \frac{1}{2} & | & 5 \\ 0 & 0 & 0 & 2 & | & 8 \end{bmatrix} \frac{1}{2} R_4$

$\begin{bmatrix} 1 & 0 & 0 & \frac{11}{2} & | & 24 \\ 0 & 1 & 0 & -\frac{3}{2} & | & -8 \\ 0 & 0 & 1 & \frac{1}{2} & | & 5 \\ 0 & 0 & 0 & 1 & | & 4 \end{bmatrix} \begin{matrix} -\frac{11}{2} R_4 + R_1 \\ \frac{3}{2} R_4 + R_2 \\ -\frac{1}{2} R_4 + R_3 \end{matrix}$

$\begin{bmatrix} 1 & 0 & 0 & 0 & | & 2 \\ 0 & 1 & 0 & 0 & | & -2 \\ 0 & 0 & 1 & 0 & | & 3 \\ 0 & 0 & 0 & 1 & | & 4 \end{bmatrix}$

The solution set is $\{(2, -2, 3, 4)\}$.

8. a.   The function must satisfy:
$98 = 4a = 2b + c$
$138 = 16a + 4b + c$
$162 = 100a + 10b + c.$

$\begin{bmatrix} 4 & 2 & 1 & | & 98 \\ 16 & 4 & 1 & | & 138 \\ 100 & 10 & 1 & | & 162 \end{bmatrix} \frac{1}{4} R_1$

$\begin{bmatrix} 1 & \frac{1}{2} & \frac{1}{4} & | & \frac{49}{2} \\ 16 & 4 & 1 & | & 138 \\ 100 & 10 & 1 & | & 162 \end{bmatrix} \begin{matrix} -16R_1 + R_2 \\ -100R_1 + R_3 \end{matrix}$

$\begin{bmatrix} 1 & \frac{1}{2} & \frac{1}{4} & | & \frac{49}{2} \\ 0 & -4 & -3 & | & -254 \\ 0 & -40 & -24 & | & -2288 \end{bmatrix} -\frac{1}{4} R_2$

$\begin{bmatrix} 1 & \frac{1}{2} & \frac{1}{4} & | & \frac{49}{2} \\ 0 & 1 & \frac{3}{4} & | & \frac{127}{2} \\ 0 & -40 & -24 & | & -2288 \end{bmatrix} 40R_2 + R_3$

$\begin{bmatrix} 1 & \frac{1}{2} & \frac{1}{4} & | & \frac{49}{2} \\ 0 & 1 & \frac{3}{4} & | & \frac{127}{2} \\ 0 & 0 & 6 & | & 252 \end{bmatrix} \frac{1}{6} R_3$

$\begin{bmatrix} 1 & \frac{1}{2} & \frac{1}{4} & | & \frac{49}{2} \\ 0 & 1 & \frac{3}{4} & | & \frac{127}{2} \\ 0 & 0 & 1 & | & 42 \end{bmatrix} \begin{matrix} -\frac{1}{4} R_3 + R_1 \\ -\frac{3}{4} R_3 + R_2 \end{matrix}$

$\begin{bmatrix} 1 & \frac{1}{2} & 0 & | & 14 \\ 0 & 1 & 0 & | & 32 \\ 0 & 0 & 1 & | & 42 \end{bmatrix} -\frac{1}{2} R_3 + R_1$

$\begin{bmatrix} 1 & 0 & 0 & | & -2 \\ 0 & 1 & 0 & | & 32 \\ 0 & 0 & 1 & | & 42 \end{bmatrix}$

The function is $y = -2x^2 + 32x + 42$ and
$a = -2$, $b = 32$ and $c = 42$.

b. $y = -2x^2 + 32x + 42$ is a parabola.

The maximum occurs when

$$x = \frac{-32}{2(-2)} = \frac{-32}{-4} = 8.$$

The air pollution level is a maximum 8 hours after 6 A.M., which is 2 P.M.

When $x = 8$, $y = -2(64) + 32(8) + 42$
$$= -128 + 256 + 42.$$
$$= 170.$$

The maximum level is 170 parts per million at 2 P.M.

9.
$$\begin{bmatrix} 2 & -3 & 1 & | & 1 \\ 1 & -2 & 3 & | & 2 \\ 3 & -4 & -1 & | & 1 \end{bmatrix} R_1 \leftrightarrow R_2$$

$$\begin{bmatrix} 1 & -2 & 3 & | & 2 \\ 2 & -3 & 1 & | & 1 \\ 3 & -4 & -1 & | & 1 \end{bmatrix} \begin{matrix} -2R_1 + R_2 \\ -3R_1 + R_3 \end{matrix}$$

$$\begin{bmatrix} 1 & -2 & 3 & | & 2 \\ 0 & 1 & -5 & | & -3 \\ 0 & 2 & -10 & | & -5 \end{bmatrix} -2R_2 + R_3$$

$$\begin{bmatrix} 1 & -2 & 3 & | & 2 \\ 0 & 1 & -5 & | & -3 \\ 0 & 0 & 0 & | & 1 \end{bmatrix}$$

From the last line, we see that the system has no solution. Thus, the solution set is $\varnothing$.

10.
$$\begin{bmatrix} 1 & -3 & 1 & | & 1 \\ -2 & 1 & 3 & | & -7 \\ 1 & -4 & 2 & | & 0 \end{bmatrix} \begin{matrix} 2R_1 + R_2 \\ -1R_1 + R_3 \end{matrix}$$

$$\begin{bmatrix} 1 & -3 & 1 & | & 1 \\ 0 & -5 & 5 & | & -5 \\ 0 & -1 & 1 & | & -1 \end{bmatrix} -\frac{1}{5}R_2$$

$$\begin{bmatrix} 1 & -3 & 1 & | & 1 \\ 0 & 1 & -1 & | & 1 \\ 0 & -1 & 1 & | & -1 \end{bmatrix} 1R_2 + R_3$$

$$\begin{bmatrix} 1 & -3 & 1 & | & 1 \\ 0 & 1 & -1 & | & 1 \\ 0 & 0 & 0 & | & 0 \end{bmatrix}$$

The system $\begin{aligned} x - 3y + z &= 1 \\ y - z &= 1 \end{aligned}$ has no unique solution.

Express x and y in terms of z:

$y = z + 1$

$x - 3(z + 1) + z = 1$

$x - 3z - 3 + z = 1$

$x = 2z + 4$

With $z = t$, the complete solution to the system is $\{(2t + 4, t + 1, t)\}$.

11.
$$\begin{bmatrix} 1 & 4 & 3 & -6 & | & 5 \\ 1 & 3 & 1 & -4 & | & 3 \\ 2 & 8 & 7 & -5 & | & 11 \\ 2 & 5 & 0 & -6 & | & 4 \end{bmatrix} \begin{matrix} -1R_1 + R_2 \\ -2R_1 + R_3 \\ -2R_1 + R_4 \end{matrix}$$

$$\begin{bmatrix} 1 & 4 & 3 & -6 & | & 5 \\ 0 & -1 & -2 & 2 & | & -2 \\ 0 & 0 & 1 & 7 & | & 1 \\ 0 & -3 & -6 & 6 & | & -6 \end{bmatrix} -1R_2$$

$$\begin{bmatrix} 1 & 4 & 3 & -6 & | & 5 \\ 0 & 1 & 2 & -2 & | & 2 \\ 0 & 0 & 1 & 7 & | & 1 \\ 0 & -3 & -6 & 6 & | & -6 \end{bmatrix} 3R_2 + R_4$$

$$\begin{bmatrix} 1 & 4 & 3 & -6 & | & 5 \\ 0 & 1 & 2 & -2 & | & 2 \\ 0 & 0 & 1 & 7 & | & 1 \\ 0 & 0 & 0 & 0 & | & 0 \end{bmatrix}$$

The system $\begin{aligned} x_1 + 4x_2 + 3x_3 - 6x_4 &= 5 \\ x_2 + 2x_3 - 2x_4 &= 2 \\ x_3 + 7x_4 &= 1 \end{aligned}$

does not have a unique solution.

Express x_1, x_2, and x_3 in terms of x_4:

$x_3 = -7x_4 + 1$

$x_2 + 2(-7x_4 + 1) - 2x_4 = 2$

$x_2 - 14x_4 + 2 - 2x_4 = 2$

$x_2 = 16x_4$

$x_1 + 4(16x_4) + 3(-7x_4 + 1) - 6x_4 = 5$

$x_1 + 64x_4 - 21x_4 + 3 - 6x_4 = 5$

$x_1 = -37x_4 + 2$

With $x_4 = t$, the complete solution to the system is $\{(-37t + 2, 16t, -7t + 1, t)\}$.

12. $\begin{bmatrix} 2 & 3 & -5 & | & 15 \\ 1 & 2 & -1 & | & 4 \end{bmatrix} R_1 \leftrightarrow R_2$

$\begin{bmatrix} 1 & 2 & -1 & | & 4 \\ 2 & 3 & -5 & | & 15 \end{bmatrix} -2R_1 + R_2$

$\begin{bmatrix} 1 & 2 & -1 & | & 4 \\ 0 & -1 & -3 & | & 7 \end{bmatrix} -1R_2$

$\begin{bmatrix} 1 & 2 & -1 & | & 4 \\ 0 & 1 & 3 & | & -7 \end{bmatrix}$

The system $\begin{array}{c} x + 2y - z = 4 \\ y + 3z = -7 \end{array}$ has no unique

solution. Express x and y in terms of z:
$y = -3z - 7$
$x + 2(-3z - 7) - z = 4$
$\quad x - 6z - 14 - z = 4$
$\qquad\qquad\qquad x = 7z + 18$
With $z = t$, the complete solution to the system is
$\{(7t + 18, -3t - 7, t)\}$.

13. a. $350 + 400 = x + z$
$450 + z = y + 700$
$x + y = 300 + 200$
or
$x + z = 750$
$y - z = -250$
$x + y = 500$

b. $\begin{bmatrix} 1 & 0 & 1 & | & 750 \\ 0 & 1 & -1 & | & -250 \\ 1 & 1 & 0 & | & 500 \end{bmatrix} -1R_1 + R_3$

$\begin{bmatrix} 1 & 0 & 1 & | & 750 \\ 0 & 1 & -1 & | & -250 \\ 0 & 1 & -1 & | & -250 \end{bmatrix} -1R_2 + R_3$

$\begin{bmatrix} 1 & 0 & 1 & | & 750 \\ 0 & 1 & -1 & | & -250 \\ 0 & 0 & 0 & | & 0 \end{bmatrix}$

The system $\begin{array}{c} x + z = 750 \\ y - z = -250 \end{array}$ has no unique

solution.
Express x and y in terms of z:
$y = z - 250$
$x = -z + 750$
With $z = t$, the complete solution to the
system is $\{(-t + 750, t - 250, t)\}$.

c. $x = -400 + 750 = 350$
$\quad y = 400 - 250 = 150$

14. $2x = -10$
$\quad\quad x = -5$
$\quad y + 7 = 13$
$\quad\quad\quad y = 6$
$\quad\quad\quad z = 6$
$x = -5;\ y = 6;\ z = 6$

15. $A + D = \begin{bmatrix} 2-2 & -1+3 & 2+1 \\ 5+3 & 3-2 & -1+4 \end{bmatrix} = \begin{bmatrix} 0 & 2 & 3 \\ 8 & 1 & 3 \end{bmatrix}$

16. $2B = \begin{bmatrix} 2(0) & 2(-2) \\ 2(3) & 2(2) \\ 2(1) & 2(-5) \end{bmatrix} = \begin{bmatrix} 0 & -4 \\ 6 & 4 \\ 2 & -10 \end{bmatrix}$

17. $D - A = \begin{bmatrix} -2-2 & 3+1 & 1-2 \\ 3-5 & -2-3 & 4+1 \end{bmatrix}$

$= \begin{bmatrix} -4 & 4 & -1 \\ -2 & -5 & 5 \end{bmatrix}$

18. Not possible since B is 3×2 and C is 3×3.

19. $3A + 2D = \begin{bmatrix} 6 & -3 & 6 \\ 15 & 9 & -3 \end{bmatrix} + \begin{bmatrix} -4 & 6 & 2 \\ 6 & -4 & 8 \end{bmatrix}$

$= \begin{bmatrix} 2 & 3 & 8 \\ 21 & 5 & 5 \end{bmatrix}$

20. $-2A + 4D = \begin{bmatrix} -4 & 2 & -4 \\ -10 & -6 & 2 \end{bmatrix} + \begin{bmatrix} -8 & 12 & 4 \\ 12 & -8 & 16 \end{bmatrix}$

$= \begin{bmatrix} -12 & 14 & 0 \\ 2 & -14 & 18 \end{bmatrix}$

21. $-5(A + D) = -5\left(\begin{bmatrix} 0 & 2 & 3 \\ 8 & 1 & 3 \end{bmatrix} \right)$

$= \begin{bmatrix} 0 & -10 & -15 \\ -40 & -5 & -15 \end{bmatrix}$

22. $AB = \begin{bmatrix} 0-3+2 & -4-2-10 \\ 0+9-1 & -10+6+5 \end{bmatrix} = \begin{bmatrix} -1 & -16 \\ 8 & 1 \end{bmatrix}$

23. $BA = \begin{bmatrix} 0-10 & 0-6 & 0+2 \\ 6+10 & -3+6 & 6-2 \\ 2-25 & -1-15 & 2+5 \end{bmatrix} = \begin{bmatrix} -10 & -6 & 2 \\ 16 & 3 & 4 \\ -23 & -16 & 7 \end{bmatrix}$

24. $BD = \begin{bmatrix} 0-6 & 0+4 & 0-8 \\ -6+6 & 9-4 & 3+8 \\ -2-15 & 3+10 & 1-20 \end{bmatrix} = \begin{bmatrix} -6 & 4 & -8 \\ 0 & 5 & 11 \\ -17 & 13 & -19 \end{bmatrix}$

25. $DB = \begin{bmatrix} 0+9+1 & 4+6-5 \\ 0-6+4 & -6-4-20 \end{bmatrix} = \begin{bmatrix} 10 & 5 \\ -2 & -30 \end{bmatrix}$

26. Not possible since AB is 2 x 2 and BA is 3 x 3.

27. $(A-D)C = \begin{bmatrix} 4 & -4 & 1 \\ 2 & 5 & -5 \end{bmatrix}\begin{bmatrix} 1 & 2 & 3 \\ -1 & 1 & 2 \\ -1 & 2 & 1 \end{bmatrix} = \begin{bmatrix} 4+4-1 & 8-4+2 & 12-8+1 \\ 2-5+5 & 4+5-10 & 6+10-5 \end{bmatrix} = \begin{bmatrix} 7 & 6 & 5 \\ 2 & -1 & 11 \end{bmatrix}$

28. $B(AC) = \begin{bmatrix} 0 & -2 \\ 3 & 2 \\ 1 & -5 \end{bmatrix}\begin{bmatrix} 2+1-2 & 4-1+4 & 6-2+2 \\ 5-3+1 & 10+3-2 & 15+6-1 \end{bmatrix}$

$= \begin{bmatrix} 0 & -2 \\ 3 & 2 \\ 1 & -5 \end{bmatrix}\begin{bmatrix} 1 & 7 & 6 \\ 3 & 11 & 20 \end{bmatrix}$

$= \begin{bmatrix} 0-6 & 0-22 & 0-40 \\ 3+6 & 21+22 & 18+40 \\ 1-15 & 7-55 & 6-100 \end{bmatrix}$

$= \begin{bmatrix} -6 & -22 & -40 \\ 9 & 43 & 58 \\ -14 & -48 & -94 \end{bmatrix}$

29. $3X + A = B$

$3X = B - A$

$X = \frac{1}{3}(B-A)$

$X = \frac{1}{3}\left(\begin{bmatrix} -2 & -12 \\ 4 & 1 \end{bmatrix} - \begin{bmatrix} 4 & 6 \\ -5 & 0 \end{bmatrix}\right)$

$X = \frac{1}{3}\begin{bmatrix} -6 & -18 \\ 9 & 1 \end{bmatrix}$

$X = \begin{bmatrix} -2 & -6 \\ 3 & \frac{1}{3} \end{bmatrix}$

30. $\begin{bmatrix} 2 & 2 & 2 \\ 1 & 2 & 1 \\ 1 & 2 & 1 \end{bmatrix}$

31. $\begin{bmatrix} 2 & 2 & 2 \\ 1 & 2 & 1 \\ 1 & 2 & 1 \end{bmatrix} + \begin{bmatrix} 1 & 1 & 1 \\ -1 & 1 & -1 \\ -1 & 1 & -1 \end{bmatrix} = \begin{bmatrix} 3 & 3 & 3 \\ 0 & 3 & 0 \\ 0 & 3 & 0 \end{bmatrix}$

$B = \begin{bmatrix} 3 & 3 & 3 \\ 0 & 3 & 0 \\ 0 & 3 & 0 \end{bmatrix}$

32. $\begin{bmatrix} 0 & 2 & 2 \\ 0 & 0 & -4 \end{bmatrix} + \begin{bmatrix} -2 & -2 & -2 \\ 1 & 1 & 1 \end{bmatrix} = \begin{bmatrix} -2 & 0 & 0 \\ 1 & 1 & -3 \end{bmatrix}$

33. $\frac{1}{2}\begin{bmatrix} 0 & 2 & 2 \\ 0 & 0 & -4 \end{bmatrix} + \begin{bmatrix} 0 & 0 & 0 \\ -2 & -2 & -2 \end{bmatrix} = \begin{bmatrix} -2 & -1 & -1 \\ -2 & -2 & -4 \end{bmatrix}$

34. $\begin{bmatrix} 1 & 0 \\ 0 & -1 \end{bmatrix}\begin{bmatrix} 0 & 2 & 2 \\ 0 & 0 & -4 \end{bmatrix} = \begin{bmatrix} 0 & 2 & 2 \\ 0 & 0 & 4 \end{bmatrix}$

The triangle is reflected about the *x*-axis.

35. $\begin{bmatrix} -1 & 0 \\ 0 & 1 \end{bmatrix}\begin{bmatrix} 0 & 2 & 2 \\ 0 & 0 & -4 \end{bmatrix} = \begin{bmatrix} 0 & -2 & -2 \\ 0 & 0 & -4 \end{bmatrix}$

The triangle is reflected about the *y*-axis.

36. $\begin{bmatrix} 0 & -1 \\ 1 & 0 \end{bmatrix}\begin{bmatrix} 0 & 2 & 2 \\ 0 & 0 & -4 \end{bmatrix} = \begin{bmatrix} 0 & 0 & 4 \\ 0 & 2 & 2 \end{bmatrix}$

The triangle is rotated 90° counterclockwise about the origin.

37. $\begin{bmatrix} 2 & 0 \\ 0 & 1 \end{bmatrix}\begin{bmatrix} 0 & 2 & 2 \\ 0 & 0 & -4 \end{bmatrix} = \begin{bmatrix} 0 & 4 & 4 \\ 0 & 0 & -4 \end{bmatrix}$

The triangle is stretched by a factor of 2 horizontally.

38. $AB = \begin{bmatrix} 8-7 & -14+21 \\ 4-4 & -7+12 \end{bmatrix} = \begin{bmatrix} 1 & 7 \\ 0 & 5 \end{bmatrix}$

$BA = \begin{bmatrix} 8-7 & 28-28 \\ -2+3 & -7+12 \end{bmatrix} = \begin{bmatrix} 1 & 0 \\ 1 & 5 \end{bmatrix}$

If *B* is the multiplicative inverse of *A*, both products (*AB* and *BA*) will be the multiplicative identity matrix, I_2. Therefore, *B* is not the multiplicative inverse of *A*.

39. $AB = \begin{bmatrix} 1 & 0 & 0 \\ 0 & 2 & -7 \\ 0 & -1 & 4 \end{bmatrix}\begin{bmatrix} 1 & 0 & 0 \\ 0 & 4 & 7 \\ 0 & 1 & 2 \end{bmatrix} = \begin{bmatrix} 1 & 0 & 0 \\ 0 & 1 & 0 \\ 0 & 0 & 1 \end{bmatrix}$

$BA = \begin{bmatrix} 1 & 0 & 0 \\ 0 & 4 & 7 \\ 0 & 1 & 2 \end{bmatrix}\begin{bmatrix} 1 & 0 & 0 \\ 0 & 2 & -7 \\ 0 & -1 & 4 \end{bmatrix} = \begin{bmatrix} 1 & 0 & 0 \\ 0 & 1 & 0 \\ 0 & 0 & 1 \end{bmatrix}$

If B is the multiplicative inverse of A, both products (AB and BA) will be the multiplicative identity matrix, I_3. Therefore, B is the multiplicative inverse of A.

40. $A^{-1} = \frac{1}{3-2}\begin{bmatrix} 3 & 1 \\ 2 & 1 \end{bmatrix} = \begin{bmatrix} 3 & 1 \\ 2 & 1 \end{bmatrix}$

$AA^{-1} = \begin{bmatrix} 1 & -1 \\ -2 & 3 \end{bmatrix}\begin{bmatrix} 3 & 1 \\ 2 & 1 \end{bmatrix}$

$= \begin{bmatrix} 3-2 & 1-1 \\ -6+6 & -2+3 \end{bmatrix}$

$= \begin{bmatrix} 1 & 0 \\ 0 & 1 \end{bmatrix}$

$A^{-1}A = \begin{bmatrix} 3 & 1 \\ 2 & 1 \end{bmatrix}\begin{bmatrix} 1 & -1 \\ -2 & 3 \end{bmatrix}$

$= \begin{bmatrix} 3-2 & 3+3 \\ 2-2 & -2+3 \end{bmatrix}$

$= \begin{bmatrix} 1 & 0 \\ 0 & 1 \end{bmatrix}$

41. $A^{-1} = \frac{1}{0-5}\begin{bmatrix} 3 & -1 \\ -5 & 0 \end{bmatrix}$

$= \frac{-1}{5}\begin{bmatrix} 3 & -1 \\ -5 & 0 \end{bmatrix}$

$= \begin{bmatrix} -\frac{3}{5} & \frac{1}{5} \\ 1 & 0 \end{bmatrix}$

$AA^{-1} = \begin{bmatrix} 0 & 1 \\ 5 & 3 \end{bmatrix}\begin{bmatrix} -\frac{3}{5} & \frac{1}{5} \\ 1 & 0 \end{bmatrix}$

$= \begin{bmatrix} 0+1 & 0+0 \\ -3+3 & 1+0 \end{bmatrix}$

$= \begin{bmatrix} 1 & 0 \\ 0 & 1 \end{bmatrix}$

$A^{-1}A = \begin{bmatrix} -\frac{3}{5} & \frac{1}{5} \\ 1 & 0 \end{bmatrix}\begin{bmatrix} 0 & 1 \\ 5 & 3 \end{bmatrix}$

$= \begin{bmatrix} 0+1 & -\frac{3}{5}+\frac{3}{5} \\ 0+0 & 1+0 \end{bmatrix}$

$= \begin{bmatrix} 1 & 0 \\ 0 & 1 \end{bmatrix}$

42. $\left[\begin{array}{ccc|ccc} 1 & 0 & -2 & 1 & 0 & 0 \\ 2 & 1 & 0 & 0 & 1 & 0 \\ 1 & 0 & -3 & 0 & 0 & 1 \end{array}\right] \begin{matrix} \\ -2R_1+R_2 \\ -1R_1+R_3 \end{matrix}$

$\left[\begin{array}{ccc|ccc} 1 & 0 & -2 & 1 & 0 & 0 \\ 0 & 1 & 4 & -2 & 1 & 0 \\ 0 & 0 & -1 & -1 & 0 & 1 \end{array}\right] \begin{matrix} \\ \\ -1R_3 \end{matrix}$

$\left[\begin{array}{ccc|ccc} 1 & 0 & -2 & 1 & 0 & 0 \\ 0 & 1 & 4 & -2 & 1 & 0 \\ 0 & 0 & 1 & 1 & 0 & -1 \end{array}\right] \begin{matrix} 2R_3+R_1 \\ \\ -4R_3+R_2 \end{matrix}$

$\left[\begin{array}{ccc|ccc} 1 & 0 & 0 & 3 & 0 & -2 \\ 0 & 1 & 0 & -6 & 1 & 4 \\ 0 & 0 & 1 & 1 & 0 & -1 \end{array}\right]$

$A^{-1} = \begin{bmatrix} 3 & 0 & -2 \\ -6 & 1 & 4 \\ 1 & 0 & -1 \end{bmatrix}$

$AA^{-1} = \begin{bmatrix} 1 & 0 & -2 \\ 2 & 1 & 0 \\ 1 & 0 & -3 \end{bmatrix}\begin{bmatrix} 3 & 0 & -2 \\ -6 & 1 & 4 \\ 1 & 0 & -1 \end{bmatrix}$

$= \begin{bmatrix} 3+0-2 & 0+0+0 & -2+0+2 \\ 6-6+0 & 0+1+0 & -4+4+0 \\ 3+0-3 & 0+0+0 & -2+0+3 \end{bmatrix}$

$= \begin{bmatrix} 1 & 0 & 0 \\ 0 & 1 & 0 \\ 0 & 0 & 1 \end{bmatrix}$

$A^{-1}A = \begin{bmatrix} 3 & 0 & -2 \\ -6 & 1 & 4 \\ 1 & 0 & -1 \end{bmatrix}\begin{bmatrix} 1 & 0 & -2 \\ 2 & 1 & 0 \\ 1 & 0 & -3 \end{bmatrix}$

$= \begin{bmatrix} 3+0-2 & 0+0+0 & -6+0+6 \\ -6+2+4 & 0+1+0 & 12+0-12 \\ 1+0-1 & 0+0+0 & -2+0+3 \end{bmatrix}$

$= \begin{bmatrix} 1 & 0 & 0 \\ 0 & 1 & 0 \\ 0 & 0 & 1 \end{bmatrix}$

43.
$$\left[\begin{array}{ccc|ccc} 1 & 3 & -2 & 1 & 0 & 0 \\ 4 & 13 & -7 & 0 & 1 & 0 \\ 5 & 16 & -8 & 0 & 0 & 1 \end{array}\right] \begin{array}{l} -4R_1 + R_2 \\ \\ -5R_1 + R_3 \end{array}$$

$$\left[\begin{array}{ccc|ccc} 1 & 3 & -2 & 1 & 0 & 0 \\ 0 & 1 & 1 & -4 & 1 & 0 \\ 0 & 1 & 2 & -5 & 0 & 1 \end{array}\right] \begin{array}{l} -1R_2 + R_3 \\ \\ -3R_2 + R_1 \end{array}$$

$$\left[\begin{array}{ccc|ccc} 1 & 0 & -5 & 13 & -3 & 0 \\ 0 & 1 & 1 & -4 & 1 & 0 \\ 0 & 0 & 1 & -1 & -1 & 1 \end{array}\right] \begin{array}{l} -1R_3 + R_2 \\ \\ 5R_3 + R_1 \end{array}$$

$$\left[\begin{array}{ccc|ccc} 1 & 0 & 0 & 8 & -8 & 5 \\ 0 & 1 & 0 & -3 & 2 & -1 \\ 0 & 0 & 1 & -1 & -1 & 1 \end{array}\right]$$

$$A^{-1} = \left[\begin{array}{ccc} 8 & -8 & 5 \\ -3 & 2 & -1 \\ -1 & -1 & 1 \end{array}\right]$$

$$AA^{-1} = \left[\begin{array}{ccc} 1 & 3 & -2 \\ 4 & 13 & -7 \\ 5 & 16 & -8 \end{array}\right]\left[\begin{array}{ccc} 8 & -8 & 5 \\ -3 & 2 & -1 \\ -1 & -1 & 1 \end{array}\right] = \left[\begin{array}{ccc} 8-9+2 & -8+6+2 & 5-3-2 \\ 32-39+7 & -32+26+7 & 20-13-7 \\ 40-48+8 & -40+32+8 & 25-16-8 \end{array}\right] = \left[\begin{array}{ccc} 1 & 0 & 0 \\ 0 & 1 & 0 \\ 0 & 0 & 1 \end{array}\right]$$

$$A^{-1}A = \left[\begin{array}{ccc} 8 & -8 & 5 \\ -3 & 2 & -1 \\ -1 & -1 & -1 \end{array}\right]\left[\begin{array}{ccc} 1 & 3 & -2 \\ 4 & 13 & -7 \\ 5 & 16 & -8 \end{array}\right] = \left[\begin{array}{ccc} 8-32+25 & 24-104+80 & -16+56-40 \\ -3+8-5 & -9+26-16 & 6-14+8 \\ -1-4+5 & -3-13+16 & 2+7-8 \end{array}\right] = \left[\begin{array}{ccc} 1 & 0 & 0 \\ 0 & 1 & 0 \\ 0 & 0 & 1 \end{array}\right]$$

44. a.
$$\left[\begin{array}{ccc} 1 & 1 & 2 \\ 0 & 1 & 3 \\ 3 & 0 & -2 \end{array}\right]\left[\begin{array}{c} x \\ y \\ z \end{array}\right] = \left[\begin{array}{c} 7 \\ -2 \\ 0 \end{array}\right].$$

b.
$$A^{-1}B = \left[\begin{array}{ccc} -2 & 2 & 1 \\ 9 & -8 & -3 \\ -3 & 3 & 1 \end{array}\right]\left[\begin{array}{c} 7 \\ -2 \\ 0 \end{array}\right] = \left[\begin{array}{c} -14-4+0 \\ 63+16+0 \\ -21-6+0 \end{array}\right] = \left[\begin{array}{c} -18 \\ 79 \\ -27 \end{array}\right]$$

The solution to the system is $\{(-18, 79, -27)\}$.

45. a.
$$\left[\begin{array}{ccc} 1 & -1 & 2 \\ 0 & 1 & -1 \\ 1 & 0 & 2 \end{array}\right]\left[\begin{array}{c} x \\ y \\ z \end{array}\right] = \left[\begin{array}{c} 12 \\ -5 \\ 10 \end{array}\right]$$

b.
$$A^{-1}B = \left[\begin{array}{ccc} 2 & 2 & -1 \\ -1 & 0 & 1 \\ -1 & -1 & 1 \end{array}\right]\left[\begin{array}{c} 12 \\ -5 \\ 10 \end{array}\right] = \left[\begin{array}{c} 24-10-10 \\ -12+10 \\ -12+5+10 \end{array}\right] = \left[\begin{array}{c} 4 \\ -2 \\ 3 \end{array}\right]$$

The solution to the system is $\{(4, -2, 3)\}$.

46. R U L E has a numerical equivalent of 18, 21, 12, 5.

$$\begin{bmatrix} 3 & 2 \\ 4 & 3 \end{bmatrix}\begin{bmatrix} 18 & 12 \\ 21 & 5 \end{bmatrix} = \begin{bmatrix} 54+42 & 36+10 \\ 72+63 & 48+15 \end{bmatrix} = \begin{bmatrix} 96 & 46 \\ 135 & 63 \end{bmatrix}$$

The encoded message is 96, 135, 46, 63.

$$\begin{bmatrix} 3 & -2 \\ -4 & 3 \end{bmatrix}\begin{bmatrix} 96 & 46 \\ 135 & 63 \end{bmatrix} = \begin{bmatrix} 288-270 & 138-126 \\ -384+405 & -184+189 \end{bmatrix} = \begin{bmatrix} 18 & 12 \\ 21 & 5 \end{bmatrix}$$

The decoded message is 18, 21, 12, 5 or RULE.

47. $\begin{vmatrix} 3 & 2 \\ -1 & 5 \end{vmatrix} = 15 - (-2) = 17$

48. $\begin{vmatrix} -2 & -3 \\ -4 & -8 \end{vmatrix} = 16 - 12 = 4$

49. $\begin{vmatrix} 2 & 4 & -3 \\ 1 & -1 & 5 \\ -2 & 4 & 0 \end{vmatrix} = -2\begin{vmatrix} 4 & -3 \\ -1 & 5 \end{vmatrix} - 4\begin{vmatrix} 2 & -3 \\ 1 & 5 \end{vmatrix} + 0\begin{vmatrix} 2 & 4 \\ 1 & -1 \end{vmatrix}$

$$= -2(20-3) - 4[10-(-3)] + 0$$
$$= -2(17) - 4(13)$$
$$= -34 - 52$$
$$= -86$$

50. $\begin{vmatrix} 4 & 7 & 0 \\ -5 & 6 & 0 \\ 3 & 2 & -4 \end{vmatrix} = 4\begin{vmatrix} 6 & 0 \\ 2 & -4 \end{vmatrix} + 5\begin{vmatrix} 7 & 0 \\ 2 & -4 \end{vmatrix} + 3\begin{vmatrix} 7 & 0 \\ 6 & 0 \end{vmatrix}$

$$= 4(-24-0) + 5(-28-0) + 3(0-0)$$
$$= 4(-24) + 5(-28) + 0$$
$$= -236$$

51. $\begin{vmatrix} 1 & 1 & 0 & 2 \\ 0 & 3 & 2 & 1 \\ 0 & -2 & 4 & 0 \\ 0 & 3 & 0 & 1 \end{vmatrix} = \begin{vmatrix} 3 & 2 & 1 \\ -2 & 4 & 0 \\ 3 & 0 & 1 \end{vmatrix}$

$$= 3\begin{vmatrix} 2 & 1 \\ 4 & 0 \end{vmatrix} + \begin{vmatrix} 3 & 2 \\ -2 & 4 \end{vmatrix}$$
$$= 3(0-4) + [12-(-4)]$$
$$= 3(-4) + 16$$
$$= -12 + 16$$
$$= 4$$

52.
$$\begin{vmatrix} 2 & 2 & 2 & 2 \\ 0 & 2 & 2 & 2 \\ 0 & 0 & 2 & 2 \\ 0 & 0 & 0 & 2 \end{vmatrix} = 2\begin{vmatrix} 2 & 2 & 2 \\ 0 & 2 & 2 \\ 0 & 0 & 2 \end{vmatrix}$$

$$= 2(2)\begin{vmatrix} 2 & 2 \\ 0 & 2 \end{vmatrix}$$

$$= 2(2)(4)$$

$$= 16$$

53. $D = \begin{vmatrix} 1 & -2 \\ 3 & 2 \end{vmatrix} = 2 - (-6) = 2 + 6 = 8$

$D_x = \begin{vmatrix} 8 & -2 \\ -1 & 2 \end{vmatrix} = 16 - 2 = 14$

$D_y = \begin{vmatrix} 1 & 8 \\ 3 & -1 \end{vmatrix} = -1 - 24 = -25$

$x = \dfrac{D_x}{D} = \dfrac{14}{8} = \dfrac{7}{4}, \; y = \dfrac{D_y}{D} = \dfrac{-25}{8} = -\dfrac{25}{8}$

The solution to the system is $\left\{\left(\dfrac{7}{4}, -\dfrac{25}{8}\right)\right\}$.

54. $D = \begin{vmatrix} 7 & 2 \\ 2 & 1 \end{vmatrix} = 7 - 4 = 3$

$D = \begin{vmatrix} 7 & 2 \\ 2 & 1 \end{vmatrix} = 7 - 4 = 3$

$D_x = \begin{vmatrix} 0 & 2 \\ -3 & 1 \end{vmatrix} = 0 - (-6) = 6$

$D_y = \begin{vmatrix} 7 & 0 \\ 2 & -3 \end{vmatrix} = -21 - 0 = -21$

$x = \dfrac{D_x}{D} = \dfrac{6}{3} = 2$

$y = \dfrac{D_y}{D} = \dfrac{-21}{3} = -7$

The solution to the system is $\{(2, -7)\}$.

55. $D = \begin{vmatrix} 1 & 2 & 2 \\ 2 & 4 & 7 \\ -2 & -5 & -2 \end{vmatrix}$

$$= \begin{vmatrix} 1 & 2 & 2 \\ 0 & 0 & 3 \\ 0 & -1 & 2 \end{vmatrix}$$

$$= \begin{vmatrix} 0 & 3 \\ -1 & 2 \end{vmatrix}$$

$$= 0 - (-3)$$

$$= 3$$

$D_x = \begin{vmatrix} 5 & 2 & 2 \\ 19 & 4 & 7 \\ 8 & -5 & -2 \end{vmatrix}$

$$= 5\begin{vmatrix} 4 & 7 \\ -5 & -2 \end{vmatrix} - 2\begin{vmatrix} 19 & 7 \\ 8 & -2 \end{vmatrix} + 2\begin{vmatrix} 19 & 4 \\ 8 & -5 \end{vmatrix}$$

$$= 5[-8 - (-35)] - 2(-38 - 56) + 2(-95 - 32)$$

$$= 5(27) - 2(-94) - 2(127)$$

$$= 135 + 188 - 254$$

$$= 69$$

$D_y = \begin{vmatrix} 1 & 5 & 2 \\ 2 & 19 & 7 \\ -2 & 8 & -2 \end{vmatrix}$

$$= \begin{vmatrix} 1 & 5 & 2 \\ 0 & 9 & 3 \\ 0 & 18 & 2 \end{vmatrix}$$

$$= \begin{vmatrix} 9 & 3 \\ 18 & 2 \end{vmatrix}$$

$$= 18 - 54$$

$$= -36$$

$D_z = \begin{vmatrix} 1 & 2 & 5 \\ 2 & 4 & 19 \\ -2 & -5 & 8 \end{vmatrix}$

$$= \begin{vmatrix} 1 & 2 & 5 \\ 0 & 0 & 9 \\ 0 & -1 & 18 \end{vmatrix}$$

$$= \begin{vmatrix} 0 & 9 \\ -1 & 18 \end{vmatrix}$$

$$= 0 - (-9)$$

$$= 9$$

$x = \dfrac{D_x}{D} = \dfrac{69}{3} = 23, \; y = \dfrac{D_y}{D} = \dfrac{-36}{3} = -12,$

$z = \dfrac{D_z}{D} = \dfrac{9}{3} = 3$

The solution to the system is $\{(23, -12, 3)\}$.

56.

$$D = \begin{vmatrix} 2 & 1 & 0 \\ 0 & 1 & -2 \\ 3 & 0 & -2 \end{vmatrix}$$

$$= 2\begin{vmatrix} 1 & -2 \\ 0 & -2 \end{vmatrix} + 3\begin{vmatrix} 1 & 0 \\ 1 & -2 \end{vmatrix}$$

$$= 2(-2-0) + 3(-2-0)$$

$$= 2(-2) + 3(-2)$$

$$= -4 - 6$$

$$= -10$$

$$D_x = \begin{vmatrix} -4 & 1 & 0 \\ 0 & 1 & -2 \\ -11 & 0 & -2 \end{vmatrix}$$

$$= -1\begin{vmatrix} 0 & -2 \\ -11 & -2 \end{vmatrix} + 1\begin{vmatrix} -4 & 0 \\ -11 & -2 \end{vmatrix}$$

$$= -1(0-22) + 1(8-0)$$

$$= 22 + 8$$

$$= 30$$

$$D_y = \begin{vmatrix} 2 & -4 & 0 \\ 0 & 0 & -2 \\ 3 & -11 & -2 \end{vmatrix}$$

$$= 2\begin{vmatrix} 0 & -2 \\ -11 & -2 \end{vmatrix} + 3\begin{vmatrix} -4 & 0 \\ 0 & -2 \end{vmatrix}$$

$$= 2(0-22) + 3(8-0)$$

$$= 2(-22) + 3(8)$$

$$= -44 + 24$$

$$= -20$$

$$D_z = \begin{vmatrix} 2 & 1 & -4 \\ 0 & 1 & 0 \\ 3 & 0 & -11 \end{vmatrix}$$

$$= 2\begin{vmatrix} 1 & 0 \\ 0 & -11 \end{vmatrix} + 3\begin{vmatrix} 1 & -4 \\ 1 & 0 \end{vmatrix}$$

$$= 2(-11-0) + 3(0+4)$$

$$= 2(-11) + 3(+4) = -22 + 12$$

$$= -10$$

$$x = \frac{D_x}{D} = \frac{30}{-10} = -3$$

$$y = \frac{D_y}{D} = \frac{-20}{-10} = 2$$

$$z = \frac{D_z}{D} = \frac{-10}{-10} = 1$$

The solution to the system is $\{(-3, 2, 1)\}$.

57. The quadratic function must satisfy

$$f(20) = 400 = 400a + 20b + c$$
$$f(40) = 150 = 1600a + 40b + c$$
$$f(60) = 400 = 3600a + 60b + c$$

$$D = \begin{vmatrix} 400 & 20 & 1 \\ 1600 & 40 & 1 \\ 3600 & 60 & 1 \end{vmatrix}$$

$$= (400)(20)\begin{vmatrix} 1 & 1 & 1 \\ 4 & 2 & 1 \\ 9 & 3 & 1 \end{vmatrix}$$

$$= 8000\begin{vmatrix} 1 & 1 & 1 \\ 3 & 1 & 0 \\ 8 & 2 & 0 \end{vmatrix} = 8000\begin{vmatrix} 3 & 1 \\ 8 & 2 \end{vmatrix}$$

$$= 8000(6-8)$$

$$= 8000(-2)$$

$$= -16,000$$

$$D_a = \begin{vmatrix} 400 & 20 & 1 \\ 150 & 40 & 1 \\ 400 & 60 & 1 \end{vmatrix}$$

$$= (50)(20)\begin{vmatrix} 8 & 1 & 1 \\ 3 & 2 & 1 \\ 8 & 3 & 1 \end{vmatrix}$$

$$= 1000\begin{vmatrix} 8 & 1 & 1 \\ -5 & 1 & 0 \\ 0 & 2 & 0 \end{vmatrix}$$

$$= 1000\begin{vmatrix} -5 & 1 \\ 0 & 2 \end{vmatrix}$$

$$= 1000(-10-0)$$

$$= -10,000$$

$$D_b = \begin{vmatrix} 400 & 400 & 1 \\ 1600 & 150 & 1 \\ 3600 & 400 & 1 \end{vmatrix}$$

$$= (400)(50)\begin{vmatrix} 1 & 8 & 1 \\ 4 & 3 & 1 \\ 9 & 8 & 1 \end{vmatrix}$$

$$= 20,000\begin{vmatrix} 1 & 8 & 1 \\ 3 & -5 & 0 \\ 8 & 0 & 0 \end{vmatrix}$$

$$= 20,000\begin{vmatrix} 3 & -5 \\ 8 & 0 \end{vmatrix}$$

$$= 20,000[0 - (-40)]$$
$$= 20,000(40)$$
$$= 800,000$$

$$D_c = \begin{vmatrix} 400 & 20 & 400 \\ 1600 & 40 & 150 \\ 3600 & 60 & 400 \end{vmatrix}$$

$$= (400)(20)(50)\begin{vmatrix} 1 & 1 & 8 \\ 4 & 2 & 3 \\ 9 & 3 & 8 \end{vmatrix}$$

$$= 400,000\begin{vmatrix} 1 & 0 & 0 \\ 4 & -2 & -29 \\ 2 & -6 & -64 \end{vmatrix}$$

$$= 400,000\begin{vmatrix} -2 & -29 \\ -6 & -64 \end{vmatrix}$$

$$= 400,000(128 - 174)$$
$$= 400,000(-46)$$
$$= -18,400,000$$

$$a = \frac{D_a}{D} = \frac{-10,000}{-16,000} = \frac{5}{8},$$

$$b = \frac{D_b}{D} = \frac{800,000}{-16,000} = -50,$$

$$c = \frac{D_c}{D} = \frac{-18,400,000}{-16,000} = 1150$$

The model is $f(x) = \frac{5}{8}x^2 - 50x + 1150$.

$$f(30) = \frac{5}{8}(900) - 50(30) + 1150$$
$$= 562.5 - 1500 + 1150$$
$$= 212.5$$

$$f(50) = \frac{5}{8}(2500) - 50(50) + 1150$$
$$= 1562.8 - 2500 + 1150$$
$$= 212.5$$

30- and 50-year-olds are involved in an average of 212.5 automobile accidents per day.

Chapter 8 Test

1. $\begin{bmatrix} 1 & 2 & -1 & | & -3 \\ 2 & -4 & 1 & | & -7 \\ -2 & 2 & -3 & | & 4 \end{bmatrix} \begin{matrix} -2R_1 + R_2 \\ \\ 2R_1 + R_3 \end{matrix}$

$\begin{bmatrix} 1 & 2 & -1 & | & -3 \\ 0 & -8 & 3 & | & -1 \\ 0 & 6 & -5 & | & -2 \end{bmatrix} -\frac{1}{8}R_2$

$\begin{bmatrix} 1 & 2 & -1 & | & -3 \\ 0 & 1 & -\frac{3}{8} & | & \frac{1}{8} \\ 0 & 6 & -5 & | & -2 \end{bmatrix} -6R_2 + R_3$

$\begin{bmatrix} 1 & 2 & -1 & | & -3 \\ 0 & 1 & -\frac{3}{8} & | & \frac{1}{8} \\ 0 & 0 & -\frac{11}{4} & | & -\frac{11}{4} \end{bmatrix} -\frac{4}{11}R_3$

$\begin{bmatrix} 1 & 2 & -1 & | & -3 \\ 0 & 1 & -\frac{3}{8} & | & \frac{1}{8} \\ 0 & 0 & 1 & | & 1 \end{bmatrix}$

$$x + 2y - z = -3$$
$$y - \frac{3}{8}z = \frac{1}{8}$$
$$z = 1$$

Using back substitution,

$$y - \frac{3}{8}(1) = \frac{1}{8} \quad \text{and} \quad x + 2\left(\frac{1}{2}\right) - 1 = -3.$$
$$y = \frac{1}{2} \qquad\qquad x + 1 - 1 = -3$$
$$\qquad\qquad\qquad x = -3$$

The solution to the system is $\left\{\left(-3, \frac{1}{2}, 1\right)\right\}$.

2. $\begin{bmatrix} 1 & -2 & 1 & | & 2 \\ 2 & -1 & -1 & | & 1 \end{bmatrix} -2R_1 + R_2$

$\begin{bmatrix} 1 & -2 & 1 & | & 2 \\ 0 & 3 & -3 & | & -3 \end{bmatrix} \frac{1}{3}R_2$

$\begin{bmatrix} 1 & -2 & 1 & | & 2 \\ 0 & 1 & -1 & | & -1 \end{bmatrix}$

The system $\begin{matrix} x - 2y + z = 2 \\ y - z = -1 \end{matrix}$ has no unique

solution. Express x and y in terms of z:
$$y = z - 1$$
$$x - 2(z - 1) + z = 2$$
$$x - 2z + 2 + z = 2$$
$$x = z$$

With $z = t$, the complete solution to the system is $\{(t, t - 1, t)\}$.

3. $2B + 3C = \begin{bmatrix} 2 & -2 \\ 4 & 2 \end{bmatrix} + \begin{bmatrix} 3 & 6 \\ -3 & 9 \end{bmatrix} = \begin{bmatrix} 5 & 4 \\ 1 & 11 \end{bmatrix}$

4. $AB = \begin{bmatrix} 3+2 & -3+1 \\ 1+0 & -1+0 \\ 2+2 & -2+1 \end{bmatrix} = \begin{bmatrix} 5 & -2 \\ 1 & -1 \\ 4 & -1 \end{bmatrix}$

5. $C^{-1} = \dfrac{1}{(1)(3)-(2)(-1)} \begin{bmatrix} 3 & -2 \\ 1 & 1 \end{bmatrix}$

$= \dfrac{1}{3+2} \begin{bmatrix} 3 & -2 \\ 1 & 1 \end{bmatrix} = \begin{bmatrix} \frac{3}{5} & -\frac{2}{5} \\ \frac{1}{5} & \frac{1}{5} \end{bmatrix}$

6. $BC = \begin{bmatrix} 1+1 & 2-3 \\ 2-1 & 4+3 \end{bmatrix} = \begin{bmatrix} 2 & -1 \\ 1 & 7 \end{bmatrix}$

$BC - 3B = \begin{bmatrix} 2 & -1 \\ 1 & 7 \end{bmatrix} - \begin{bmatrix} 3 & -3 \\ 6 & 3 \end{bmatrix} = \begin{bmatrix} -1 & 2 \\ -5 & 4 \end{bmatrix}$

7. $AB = \begin{bmatrix} -3+14-10 & 2-8+6 & 0+2-2 \\ -6+21-15 & 4-12+9 & 0+3-3 \\ -3-7+10 & 2+4-6 & 0-1+2 \end{bmatrix}$

$= \begin{bmatrix} 1 & 0 & 0 \\ 0 & 1 & 0 \\ 0 & 0 & 1 \end{bmatrix} = I_3$

$BA = \begin{bmatrix} -3+4+0 & -6+6+0 & -6+6+0 \\ 7-8+1 & 14-12-1 & 14-12-2 \\ -5+6-1 & -10+9+1 & -10+9+2 \end{bmatrix}$

$= \begin{bmatrix} 1 & 0 & 0 \\ 0 & 1 & 0 \\ 0 & 0 & 1 \end{bmatrix} = I_3$

8. a. $\begin{bmatrix} 3 & 5 \\ 2 & -3 \end{bmatrix} \begin{bmatrix} x \\ y \end{bmatrix} = \begin{bmatrix} 9 \\ -13 \end{bmatrix}$

b. $A^{-1} = \dfrac{1}{(3)(-3)-(5)(2)} \begin{bmatrix} -3 & -5 \\ -2 & 3 \end{bmatrix}$

$= \dfrac{1}{-19} \begin{bmatrix} -3 & -5 \\ -2 & 3 \end{bmatrix} = \begin{bmatrix} \frac{3}{19} & \frac{5}{19} \\ \frac{2}{19} & -\frac{3}{19} \end{bmatrix}$

c. $A^{-1}B = \begin{bmatrix} \frac{3}{19} & \frac{5}{19} \\ \frac{2}{19} & -\frac{3}{19} \end{bmatrix} \begin{bmatrix} 9 \\ -13 \end{bmatrix} = \begin{bmatrix} \frac{27}{19} - \frac{65}{19} \\ \frac{18}{19} + \frac{39}{19} \end{bmatrix} = \begin{bmatrix} -2 \\ 3 \end{bmatrix}$

The solution to the system is $\{(-2, 3)\}$.

9. $\begin{vmatrix} 4 & -1 & 3 \\ 0 & 5 & -1 \\ 5 & 2 & 4 \end{vmatrix} = 4 \begin{vmatrix} 5 & -1 \\ 2 & 4 \end{vmatrix} + 5 \begin{vmatrix} -1 & 3 \\ 5 & -1 \end{vmatrix}$

$= 4[20 - (-2)] + 5(1 - 15)$

$= 4(22) + 5(-14)$

$= 88 - 70$

$= 18$

10. $D = \begin{vmatrix} 3 & 1 & -2 \\ 2 & 7 & 3 \\ 4 & -3 & -1 \end{vmatrix} = 3 \begin{vmatrix} 7 & 3 \\ -3 & -1 \end{vmatrix} - 1 \begin{vmatrix} 2 & 3 \\ 4 & -1 \end{vmatrix} - 2 \begin{vmatrix} 2 & 7 \\ 4 & -3 \end{vmatrix}$

$= 3[-7 - (-9)] - 1(-2 - 12) - 2(-6 - 28)$

$= 3(2) - 1(-14) - 2(-34)$

$= 6 + 14 + 68$

$= 88$

$D_x = \begin{vmatrix} -3 & 1 & -2 \\ 9 & 7 & 3 \\ 7 & -3 & -1 \end{vmatrix} - 3 \begin{vmatrix} 7 & 3 \\ -3 & -1 \end{vmatrix} - 1 \begin{vmatrix} 9 & 3 \\ 7 & -1 \end{vmatrix} - 2 \begin{vmatrix} 9 & 7 \\ 7 & -3 \end{vmatrix}$

$= -3[-7 - (-9)] - 1(-9 - 21) - 2(-27 - 49)$

$= -3(2) - 1(-30) - 2(-76)$

$= -6 + 30 + 152$

$= 176$

$x = \dfrac{D_x}{D} = \dfrac{176}{88} = 2$

Cumulative Review Exercises (Chapters P–8)

1. $2x^2 = 4 - x$

$2x^2 + x - 4 = 0$

$x = \dfrac{-1 \pm \sqrt{1^2 - 4(2)(-4)}}{2(2)}$

$x = \dfrac{-1 \pm \sqrt{1 - 32}}{4}$

$x = \dfrac{-1 \pm \sqrt{33}}{4}$

The solution set is $\left\{ \dfrac{-1+\sqrt{33}}{4}, \dfrac{-1-\sqrt{33}}{4} \right\}$.

2. $5x + 8 \le 7(1 + x)$

$5x + 8 \le 7 + 7x$

$-2x \le -1$

$x \ge \dfrac{1}{2}$

The solution set is $\left\{ x \mid x \ge \dfrac{1}{2} \right\}$ or $\left[\dfrac{1}{2}, \infty \right)$.

3. $x^3 + x^2 - 4x - 4 \ge 0$

First, solve the related equation to find boundary points.

$x^3 + x^2 - 4x - 4 = 0$

$x^2(x+1) - 4(x+1) = 0$

$(x+1)(x^2 - 4) = 0$

$(x+1)(x+2)(x-2) = 0$

Boundary points: $-2, -1, 2$

Next, substitute test points from each interval to determine which intervals satisfy the inequality. The solution is $[-2, -1] \cup [2, \infty)$.

4. $3x^3 + 8x^2 - 15x + 4 = 0$

$p = 61, 62, 64$

$q = 61, 63$

$\dfrac{p}{q} = 61, 6\dfrac{1}{3}, 62, 6\dfrac{2}{3},\ 64, 6\dfrac{4}{3}$

$$
\begin{array}{r|rrrr}
-4 & 3 & 8 & -15 & 4 \\
   &   & -12 & 16 & -4 \\
\hline
   & 3 & -4 & 1 & 0 \\
\end{array}
$$

$(x+4)(3x^2 - 4x + 1) = 0$

$(x+4)(3x-1)(x-1) = 0$

$x = -4,\ x = \dfrac{1}{3},\ x = 1$

The solution set is $\left\{ -4, \dfrac{1}{3}, 1 \right\}$.

5. $e^{2x} - 14e^x + 45 = 0\ \ le + t = e^x$

$t^2 - 14t + 45 = 0$

$(t-5)(t-9) = 0$

$t = 5\ \ t = 9$

$e^x = 5\ \ e^x = 9$

$\ln e^x = \ln 5\ \ \ln e^x = \ln 9$

$x = e^x = \ln 5\ \ x = \ln 9$

The solution set is $\{\ln 5, \ln 9\}$.

6. $\log_3 x + \log_3 (x+2) = 1$

$\log_3 x^2 + 2x = 1$

$3^1 = x^2 + 2x$

$x^2 + 2x - 3 = 0$

$(x-1)(x+3) = 0$

$x = 1,\ x = -3$

$x = -3$ does not check. The solution set is $\{1\}$.

7. $\begin{bmatrix} 1 & -1 & 1 & | & 17 \\ 2 & 3 & 1 & | & 8 \\ -4 & 1 & 5 & | & -2 \end{bmatrix} \begin{matrix} \\ -2R_1 + R_2 \\ 4R_1 + R_3 \end{matrix}$

$\begin{bmatrix} 1 & -1 & 1 & | & 17 \\ 0 & 5 & -1 & | & -26 \\ 0 & -3 & 9 & | & 66 \end{bmatrix} \begin{matrix} \\ \\ -\frac{1}{3}R_3 \end{matrix}$

$\begin{bmatrix} 1 & -1 & 1 & | & 17 \\ 0 & 1 & -3 & | & -22 \\ 0 & 5 & -1 & | & -26 \end{bmatrix} \begin{matrix} \\ -5R_2 + R_3 \\ 1R_2 + R_1 \end{matrix}$

$$\begin{bmatrix} 1 & 0 & -2 & | & -5 \\ 0 & 1 & -3 & | & -22 \\ 0 & 0 & 14 & | & 84 \end{bmatrix} \frac{1}{14}R_3$$

$$\begin{bmatrix} 1 & 0 & -2 & | & -5 \\ 0 & 1 & -3 & | & -22 \\ 0 & 0 & 1 & | & 6 \end{bmatrix} \begin{matrix} \\ 3R_3 + R_2 \\ 2R_3 + R_1 \end{matrix}$$

$$\begin{bmatrix} 1 & 0 & 0 & | & 7 \\ 0 & 1 & 0 & | & -4 \\ 0 & 0 & 1 & | & 6 \end{bmatrix}$$

$x = 7 \quad y = -4 \quad z = 6$

The solution set is $\{(7, -4, 6)\}$.

8. $D = \begin{vmatrix} 1 & -2 & 1 \\ 2 & 1 & -1 \\ 3 & 2 & -2 \end{vmatrix}$

$= 1\begin{vmatrix} 1 & -1 \\ 2 & -2 \end{vmatrix} - 2\begin{vmatrix} -2 & 1 \\ 2 & -2 \end{vmatrix} + 3\begin{vmatrix} -2 & 1 \\ 1 & 1 \end{vmatrix}$

$= 1(-2+2) - 2(4-2) + 3(2-1)$

$= 0 - 4 + 3$

$= -1$

$D_y = \begin{vmatrix} 1 & 7 & 1 \\ 2 & 0 & -1 \\ 3 & -2 & -2 \end{vmatrix} = 7\begin{vmatrix} 2 & -1 \\ 3 & -2 \end{vmatrix} - 2\begin{vmatrix} 1 & 1 \\ 2 & -1 \end{vmatrix}$

$= 7(-4+3) - 2(-1-2)$

$= -7 + 6 = 1$

$y = \dfrac{D_y}{D} = \dfrac{1}{-1} = -1$

$y = -1$

9. $y = \sqrt{4x-7}$

$x = \sqrt{4y-7}$

$x^2 = 4y - 7$

$x^2 + 7 - 4y$

$\dfrac{x^2 + 7}{4} = y$

$f^{-1}(x) = \dfrac{x^2 + 7}{4} \ (x \ge 0)$

10. $f(x) = \dfrac{x}{x^2 - 16}$

$f(0) = \dfrac{0}{-16} = 0$

y-intercept at 0

$0 = \dfrac{x}{x^2 - 16}$

$0 = x$

x-intercept at 0

$f(x) = \dfrac{x}{(x+4)(x-4)}$

vertical asymptotes at 4, –4
horizontal asymptote at 0

$x = -4 \quad\quad x = 4$

$$f(x) = \dfrac{x}{x^2 - 16}$$

11. $f(x) = 4x^4 - 4x^3 - 25x^2 + x + 6$

-2	4	-4	-25	1	6
		-8	24	2	-6
3	4	-12	-1	3	0
		12	0	-3	
	4	0	-1	0	

$f(x) = (x+2)(x-3)(4x^2 - 1)$
$f(x) = (x+2)(x-3)(2x+1)(2x-1)$

12. $y = \log_2 x$

        $2^y = x$

x	y
1	0
2	1
$\frac{1}{2}$	−1

   $y = \log_2(x + 1)$

Shift the graph of $y = \log_2{}^x$ left one unit.

13.   **a.** $A = A_0 e^{kt}$

          $450 = 900 e^{k(40)}$

          $\dfrac{1}{2} = e^{40k}$

          $\ln\left(\dfrac{1}{2}\right) = \ln\left(e^{40k}\right)$

          $\ln\left(\dfrac{1}{2}\right) = 40k$

          $k = \dfrac{\ln\left(\dfrac{1}{2}\right)}{40} \approx -0.017$

          $A = 900 e^{-0.017t}$

   b. $A = 900 e^{-0.017(10)}$

          $A = 900 e^{-0.17}$

          $A \approx 759.30$ grams

14. $\begin{bmatrix} 1 & -1 & 0 \\ 2 & 1 & 3 \end{bmatrix} \begin{bmatrix} 4 & -1 \\ 2 & 0 \\ 1 & 1 \end{bmatrix} = \begin{bmatrix} 4-2+0 & -1+0+0 \\ 8+2+3 & -2+0+3 \end{bmatrix}$

                                   $= \begin{bmatrix} 2 & -1 \\ 13 & 1 \end{bmatrix}$

15. $\dfrac{3x^2 + 17x - 38}{(x-3)(x-2)(x+2)} = \dfrac{A}{x-3} + \dfrac{B}{x-2} + \dfrac{C}{x+2}$

   $3x^2 + 17x - 38$

      $= A(x^2 - 4) + B(x^2 - x - 6) + C(x^2 - 5x + 6)$

   $3x^2 + 17x - 38$

      $= Ax^2 - 4A + Bx^2 - Bx - 6B + Cx^2 - 5Cx + 6c$

   $3x^2 + 17x - 38$

      $= (A + B + C)x^2 + (-B - 5C)x - (4A + 6B - 6C)$

      $A + B + C = 3$

        $-B - 5C = 17$

   $4A + 6B - 6C = 38$

$\begin{bmatrix} 1 & 1 & 1 & | & 3 \\ 0 & -1 & -5 & | & 17 \\ 4 & 6 & -6 & | & 38 \end{bmatrix} \begin{matrix} \\ \\ -4R_1 + R_3 \end{matrix}$

$\begin{bmatrix} 1 & 1 & 1 & | & 3 \\ 0 & -1 & -5 & | & 17 \\ 0 & 2 & -10 & | & 26 \end{bmatrix} \begin{matrix} \\ -1R_2 \\ \end{matrix}$

$\begin{bmatrix} 1 & 1 & 1 & | & 3 \\ 0 & 1 & 5 & | & -17 \\ 0 & 2 & -10 & | & 26 \end{bmatrix} \begin{matrix} \\ -2R_2 + R_3 \\ -1R_2 + R_1 \end{matrix}$

$\begin{bmatrix} 1 & 0 & -4 & | & 20 \\ 0 & 1 & 5 & | & -17 \\ 0 & 0 & -20 & | & 60 \end{bmatrix} \begin{matrix} \\ \\ -\frac{1}{20}R_3 \end{matrix}$

$\begin{bmatrix} 1 & 0 & -4 & | & 20 \\ 0 & 1 & 5 & | & -17 \\ 0 & 0 & 1 & | & -3 \end{bmatrix} \begin{matrix} \\ -5R_3 + R_2 \\ 4R_3 + R_1 \end{matrix}$

$\begin{bmatrix} 1 & 0 & 0 & | & 8 \\ 0 & 1 & 0 & | & -2 \\ 0 & 0 & 1 & | & -3 \end{bmatrix}$

$A = 8, \quad B = -2, \quad C = -3$

   $\dfrac{3x^2 + 17x - 38}{(x-3)(x-2)(x+2)} = \dfrac{8}{x-3} + \dfrac{-2}{x-2} + \dfrac{-3}{x+2}$

16. $y = -\dfrac{2}{3}x - 1$

x	y
0	−1
3	−3
−3	1

$$y = -\frac{2}{3}x - 1$$

17. $3x - 5y < 15$

$-5y < -3x + 15$

$y > \dfrac{3}{5}x - 3$

$$3x - 5y < 15$$

18. $f(x) = x^2 - 2x - 3$

$f(x) = (x^2 - 2x + 1) - 3 - 1$

$f(x) = (x - 1)^2 - 4$

$$f(x) = x^2 - 2x - 3$$

19. $(x - 1)^2 + (y + 1)^2 = 9$

center $(1, -1)$

radius $= 3$

$$(x - 1)^2 + (y + 1)^2 = 9$$

20.

```
 2 |  1    0   -6    4
   |       2    4   -4
   ────────────────────
      1    2   -2    0
```

$$\frac{x^3 - 6x + 4}{x - 2} = x^2 + 2x - 2$$

21. $y = 2\sin 2\pi x, \; 0 \le x \le 2$

Amplitude: $|A| = |2| = 2$

Period: $\dfrac{2\pi}{B} = \dfrac{2\pi}{2\pi} = 1$

x-intercepts:

$(0, 0), \left(\dfrac{1}{2}, 0\right), (1, 0), \left(\dfrac{3}{2}, 0\right), (2, 0)$

22. $\cos\left[\tan^{-1}\left(-\dfrac{4}{3}\right)\right]$

If $\tan\theta = -\dfrac{4}{3}$, θ lies in quadrant IV.

$\tan\theta = -\dfrac{4}{3} = \dfrac{y}{x} = \dfrac{-4}{3}$

$r = \sqrt{(3)^2 + (-4)^2} = \sqrt{9 + 16} = \sqrt{25} = 5$

$\cos\left[\tan^{-1}\left(-\dfrac{4}{3}\right)\right] = \dfrac{x}{r} = \dfrac{3}{5}$

23. $\dfrac{\cos 2x}{\cos x - \sin x} = \dfrac{\cos^2 x - \sin^2 x}{\cos x - \sin x}$

$\qquad\qquad = \dfrac{(\cos x - \sin x)(\cos x + \sin x)}{\cos x - \sin x}$

$\qquad\qquad = \cos x + \sin x$

24. $\cos^2 x + \sin x + 1 = 0$

$(1 - \sin^2 x) + \sin x + 1 = 0$

$-\sin^2 x + \sin x + 2 = 0$

$\sin^2 x - \sin x - 2 = 0$

$(\sin x - 2)(\sin x + 1) = 0$

$\sin x - 2 = 0$ or $\sin x + 1 = 0$

$\sin x = 2$ $\sin x = -1$

no solution   or $x = \dfrac{3\pi}{2}$

The solution in the interval $[0, 2\pi)$ is $\dfrac{3\pi}{2}$.

25. $4\mathbf{w} - 5\mathbf{v} = 4(-7\mathbf{i} + 3\mathbf{j}) - 5(-6\mathbf{i} + 5\mathbf{j})$

$= -28\mathbf{i} + 12\mathbf{j} + 30\mathbf{i} - 25\mathbf{j}$

$= 2\mathbf{i} - 13\mathbf{j}$

Chapter 9

Section 9.1

Check Point Exercises

1. $a^2 = 36,\ a = 6$

$b^2 = 9,\ b = 3$

$c^2 = a^2 - b^2 = 36 - 9 = 27$

$c = \sqrt{27} = 3\sqrt{3}$

The foci are located at $(-3\sqrt{3},\ 0)$ and $(3\sqrt{3},\ 0)$.

$$\frac{x^2}{36} + \frac{y^2}{9} = 1$$

2. $\dfrac{16x^2}{144} + \dfrac{9y^2}{144} = \dfrac{144}{144}$

$\dfrac{x^2}{9} + \dfrac{y^2}{16} = 1$

$a^2 = 16,\ a = 4$

$b^2 = 9,\ b = 3$

$c^2 = a^2 - b^2 = 16 - 9 = 7$

$c = \sqrt{7}$

The foci are located at $(0,\ -\sqrt{7})$ and $(0,\ \sqrt{7})$.

$$16x^2 + 9y^2 = 144$$

3. $c^2 = 4,\ a^2 = 9$

$b^2 = a^2 - c^2 = 9 - 4 = 5$

$\dfrac{x^2}{9} + \dfrac{y^2}{5} = 1$

4. $a^2 = 9,\ a = 3$

$b^2 = 4,\ b = 2$

center at $(-1, 2)$

$c^2 = a^2 - b^2$

$c^2 = 9 - 4$

$c^2 = 5$

$c = \sqrt{5}$

The foci are located at

$(-1 - \sqrt{5},\ 2)$ and $(-1 + \sqrt{5},\ 2)$.

$$\frac{(x+1)^2}{9} + \frac{(y-2)^2}{4} = 1$$

5. $\dfrac{x^2}{20^2} + \dfrac{y^2}{10^2} = 1$

$\dfrac{x^2}{400} + \dfrac{y^2}{100} = 1$

Since the truck is 12 feet wide, substitute $x = 6$ into the equation to find y.

$$\frac{6^2}{400} + \frac{y^2}{100} = 1$$

$$400\left(\frac{36}{400} + \frac{y^2}{100}\right) = 400(1)$$

$$36 + 4y^2 = 400$$

$$4y^2 = 364$$

$$y^2 = 91$$

$$y = \sqrt{91}$$

$$y \approx 9.54$$

6 feet from the center, the height of the archway is 9.54 feet. Since the truck's height is 9 feet, it will fit under the archway.

Exercise Set 9.1

1. $\dfrac{x^2}{16} + \dfrac{y^2}{4} = 1$

$a^2 = 16,\ a = 4$

$b^2 = 4,\ b = 2$

$c^2 = a^2 - b^2 = 16 - 4 = 12$

$\quad c = \sqrt{12} = 2\sqrt{3}$

The foci are located at $(-2\sqrt{3},\ 0)$ and $(2\sqrt{3},\ 0)$.

$$\dfrac{x^2}{16} + \dfrac{y^2}{4} = 1$$

3. $a^2 = 36,\ a = 6$

$b^2 = 9,\ b = 3$

$c^2 = a^2 - b^2 = 36 - 9 = 27$

$\quad c = \sqrt{27} = 3\sqrt{3}$

The foci are located at $(0,\ -3\sqrt{3})$ and $(0,\ 3\sqrt{3})$.

$$\dfrac{x^2}{9} + \dfrac{y^2}{36} = 1$$

5. $a^2 = 64,\ a = 8$

$b^2 = 25,\ b = 5$

$c^2 = a^2 - b^2 = 64 - 25 = 39$

$\quad c = \sqrt{39}$

The foci are located at $(0,\ -\sqrt{39})$ and $(0,\ \sqrt{39})$.

$$\dfrac{x^2}{25} + \dfrac{y^2}{64} = 1$$

7. $a^2 = 81,\ a = 9$

$b^2 = 49,\ b = 7$

$c^2 = a^2 - b^2 = 81 - 49 = 32$

$\quad c = \sqrt{32} = 4\sqrt{2}$

The foci are located at $(0,\ -4\sqrt{2})$ and $(0,\ 4\sqrt{2})$.

$$\dfrac{x^2}{49} + \dfrac{y^2}{81} = 1$$

9.
$$\frac{x^2}{\frac{9}{4}} + \frac{y^2}{\frac{25}{4}} = 1$$

$$c^2 = \frac{25}{4} - \frac{9}{4}$$

$$c^2 = \frac{16}{4}$$

$$c^2 = 4$$

$$c = 2$$

The foci are located at (0, 2) and (0, –2).

11.
$$x^2 = 1 - 4y^2$$

$$x^2 + 4y^2 = 1$$

$$x^2 + \frac{y^2}{\frac{1}{4}} = 1$$

$$c^2 = 1 - \frac{1}{4}$$

$$c^2 = \frac{3}{4}$$

$$c = \pm\frac{\sqrt{3}}{2}$$

$$c \approx \pm 0.9$$

The foci are located at $\left(\frac{\sqrt{3}}{2}, 0\right)$ and $\left(-\frac{\sqrt{3}}{2}, 0\right)$.

13.
$$25x^2 + 4y^2 = 100$$

$$\frac{25x^2}{100} + \frac{4y^2}{100} = \frac{100}{100}$$

$$\frac{x^2}{4} + \frac{y^2}{25} = 1$$

$$a^2 = 25, \ a = 5$$

$$b^2 = 4, \ b = 2$$

$$c^2 = a^2 = b^2 = 25 - 4 = 21$$

The foci are located at $(0, -\sqrt{21})$ and $(0, \sqrt{21})$.

15.
$$4x^2 + 16y^2 = 64$$

$$\frac{x^2}{16} + \frac{y^2}{4} = 1$$

$$a^2 = 16, a = 4$$

$$b^2 = 4, b = 2$$

$$c^2 = 16 - 4$$

$$c^2 = 12$$

$$c = \pm\sqrt{12}$$

$$c = \pm 2\sqrt{3}$$

$$c \approx \pm 3.5$$

The foci are located at $(2\sqrt{3}, 0)$ and $(-2\sqrt{3}, 0)$.

17.
$$7x^2 = 35 - 5y^2$$
$$7x^2 + 5y^2 = 35$$
$$\frac{x^2}{5} + \frac{y^2}{7} = 1$$
$$a^2 = 7, a = \sqrt{7}$$
$$b^2 = 5, b = \sqrt{5}$$
$$c^2 = 7 - 5$$
$$c^2 = 2$$
$$c = \pm\sqrt{2}$$
$$c \approx \pm 1.4$$
The foci are located at $(0, \sqrt{2})$ and $(0, -\sqrt{2})$.

19. $a^2 = 4$, $b^2 = 1$, center at $(0, 0)$
$$\frac{x^2}{4} + \frac{y^2}{1} = 1$$
$$c^2 = a^2 - b^2 = 4 - 1 = 3$$
$$c = \sqrt{3}$$
The foci are at $(-\sqrt{3}, 0)$ and $(\sqrt{3}, 0)$.

21. $a^2 = 4$, $b^2 = 1$,
center: $(0, 0)$
$$\frac{x^2}{1} + \frac{y^2}{4} = 1$$
$$c^2 = a^2 - b^2 = 4 - 1 = 3$$
$$c = \sqrt{3}$$
The foci are at $(0, \sqrt{3})$ and $(0, -\sqrt{3})$.

23. $\dfrac{(x+1)^2}{4} + \dfrac{(y-1)^2}{1} = 1$
$$a^2 = 4, \quad b^2 = 1$$
$$c^2 = 4 - 1$$
$$c^2 = 3$$
$$c = \pm\sqrt{3}$$
The foci are located at
$(-1+\sqrt{3}, 1)$ and $(-1-\sqrt{3}, 1)$.

25. $c^2 = 25$, $a^2 = 64$
$$b^2 = a^2 - c^2 = 64 - 25 = 39$$
$$\frac{x^2}{64} + \frac{y^2}{39} = 1$$

27. $c^2 = 16$, $a^2 = 49$
$$b^2 = a^2 - c^2 = 49 - 16 = 33$$
$$\frac{x^2}{33} + \frac{y^2}{49} = 1$$

29. $c^2 = 4$, $b^2 = 9$
$$a^2 = b^2 + c^2 = 9 + 4 = 13$$
$$\frac{x^2}{13} + \frac{y^2}{9} = 1$$

31. $2a = 8$, $a = 4$, $a^2 = 16$
$$2b = 4, \ b = 2, \ b^2 = 4$$
$$\frac{x^2}{16} + \frac{y^2}{4} = 1$$

33. $2a = 10$, $a = 5$, $a^2 = 25$
$$2b = 4, \ b = 2, \ b^2 = 4$$
$$\frac{(x+2)^2}{4} + \frac{(y-3)^2}{25} = 1$$

35. length of the major axis $= 9 - 3 = 6$
$2a = 6$, $a = 3$ major axis is vertical
length of the minor axis $= 9 - 5 = 4$
$2b = 4$, $b = 2$
Center is at $(7, 6)$.
$$\frac{(x-7)^2}{4} + \frac{(y-6)^2}{9} = 1$$

37. $a^2 = 9$, $a = 3$
$$b^2 = 4, \ b = 2$$
center: $(2, 1)$
$$c^2 = a^2 - b^2 = 9 - 4 = 5$$
$$c = \sqrt{5}$$

The foci are at $(2-\sqrt{5}, 1)$ and $(2+\sqrt{5}, 1)$.

$$\frac{(x-2)^2}{9} + \frac{(y-1)^2}{4} = 1$$

39. $\dfrac{(x+3)^2}{16} + \dfrac{4(y-2)^2}{16} = \dfrac{16}{16}$

$\dfrac{(x+3)^2}{16} + \dfrac{(y-2)^2}{4} = 1$

$a^2 = 16, a = 4$

$b^2 = 4, b = 2$

center: $(-3, 2)$

$c^2 = a^2 - b^2 = 16 - 4 = 12$

$c = \sqrt{12} = 2\sqrt{3}$

The foci are at $(-3 - 2\sqrt{3}, 2)$ and

$(-3 + 2\sqrt{3}, 2)$.

$$(x+3)^2 + 4(y-2)^2 = 16$$

41. $a^2 = 25, a = 5$

$b^2 = 9, b = 3$

center: $(4, -2)$

$c^2 = a^2 - b^2 = 25 - 9 = 16$

$c = 4$

The foci are at $(4, 2)$ and $(4, -6)$.

$$\frac{(x-4)^2}{9} + \frac{(y+2)^2}{25} = 1$$

43. $a^2 = 36, a = 6$

$b^2 = 25, b = 5$

center: $(0, 2)$

$c^2 = a^2 - b^2 = 36 - 25 = 11$

$c = \sqrt{11}$

The foci are at $(0, 2+\sqrt{11})$ and $(0, 2-\sqrt{11})$.

$$\frac{x^2}{25} + \frac{(y-2)^2}{36} = 1$$

45. $a^2 = 9, a = 3$

$b^2 = 1, b = 1$

center: $(-3, 2)$

$c^2 = a^2 - b^2 = 9 - 1 = 8$

$c = \sqrt{8} = 2\sqrt{2}$

The foci are at $(-3 - 2\sqrt{2}, 2)$ and

$(-3 + 2\sqrt{2}, 2)$.

$$\frac{(x+3)^2}{9} + (y-2)^2 = 1$$

47. $c^2 = 5 - 2$

$c^2 = 3$

$c = \pm\sqrt{3}$

$c \approx \pm 1.7$

The foci are located at $(1, -3 + \sqrt{3})$ and $(1, -3 - \sqrt{3})$.

$$\frac{(x-1)^2}{2} + \frac{(y+3)^2}{5} = 1$$

49. $\dfrac{9(x-1)^2}{36} + \dfrac{4(y+3)^2}{36} = \dfrac{36}{36}$

$\dfrac{(x-1)^2}{4} + \dfrac{(y+3)^2}{9} = 1$

$a^2 = 9, a = 3$

$b^2 = 4, b = 2$

center: $(1, -3)$

$c^2 = a^2 - b^2 = 9 - 4 = 5$

$c = \sqrt{5}$

The foci are at $(1, -3 + \sqrt{5})$ and $(1, -3 - \sqrt{5})$.

$$9(x-1)^2 + 4(y+3)^2 = 36$$

51. $(9x^2 - 36x) + (25y^2 + 50y) = 164$

$9(x^2 - 4x) + 25(y^2 + 2y) = 164$

$9(x^2 - 4x + 4) + 25(y^2 + 2y + 1)$

$= 164 + 36 + 25$

$9(x-2)^2 + 25(y+1)^2 = 225$

$\dfrac{9(x-2)^2}{225} + \dfrac{25(y+1)^2}{225} = \dfrac{225}{225}$

$\dfrac{(x-2)^2}{25} + \dfrac{(y+1)^2}{9} = 1$

center: $(2, -1)$

$a^2 = 25, a = 5$

$b^2 = 9, b = 3$

$c^2 = a^2 - b^2 = 25 - 9 = 16$

$c = 4$

The foci are at $(-2, -1)$ and $(6, -1)$.

$$9x^2 + 25y^2 - 36x + 50y - 164 = 0$$

53. $(9x^2 - 18x) + (16y^2 + 64y) = 71$

$9(x^2 - 2x) + 16(y^2 + 4y) = 71$

$9(x^2 - 2x + 1) + 16(y^2 + 4y + 4)$

$= 71 + 9 + 64$

$9(x-1)^2 + 16(y+2)^2 = 144$

$\dfrac{9(x-1)^2}{144} + \dfrac{16(y+2)^2}{144} = \dfrac{144}{144}$

$\dfrac{(x-1)^2}{16} + \dfrac{(y+2)^2}{9} = 1$

center: $(1, -2)$

$a^2 = 16, a = 4$

$b^2 = 9, b = 3$

$c^2 = a^2 - b^2 = 16 - 9 = 7$

$c = \sqrt{7}$

The foci are at $(1 - \sqrt{7}, -2)$ and $(1 + \sqrt{7}, -2)$.

$$9x^2 + 16y^2 - 18x + 64y - 71 = 0$$

55.
$$(4x^2+16x)+(y^2-6y)=39$$
$$4(x^2+4x)+(y^2-6y)=39$$
$$4(x^2+4x+4)+(y^2-6y+9)=39+16+9$$
$$4(x+2)^2+(y-3)^2=64$$
$$\frac{4(x+2)^2}{64}+\frac{(y-3)^2}{64}=\frac{64}{64}$$
$$\frac{(x+2)^2}{16}+\frac{(y-3)^2}{64}=1$$

center: $(-2, 3)$

$a^2=64,\ a=8$

$b^2=16,\ b=4$

$c^2=a^2-b^2=64-16=48$

$c=\sqrt{48}=4\sqrt{3}$

The foci are at $(-2, 3+4\sqrt{3})$ and $(-2, 3-4\sqrt{3})$.

$$4x^2+y^2+16x-6y-39=0$$

57. $x^2+y^2=1 \qquad x^2+9y^2=9$
$$\frac{x^2}{9}+\frac{9y^2}{9}=\frac{9}{9}$$
$$\frac{x^2}{9}+\frac{y^2}{1}=1$$

The first equation is that of a circle with center at the origin and $r=1$. The second equation is that of an ellipse with center at the origin, horizontal major axis of length 6 units $(a=3)$, and vertical minor axis of length 2 units $(b=1)$.

Check each intersection point.

The solution set is $\{(0,-1),(0,1)\}$.

59. $\dfrac{x^2}{25}+\dfrac{y^2}{9}=1 \qquad y=3$

The first equation is for an ellipse centered at the origin with horizontal major axis of length 10 units and vertical minor axis of length 6 units. The second equation is for a horizontal line with a y-intercept of 3.

Check the intersection point.

The solution set is $\{(0,3)\}$.

61. $4x^2+y^2=4 \qquad 2x-y=2$
$$\frac{4x^2}{4}+\frac{y^2}{4}=\frac{4}{4} \qquad -y=-2x+2$$
$$\frac{x^2}{1}+\frac{y^2}{4}=1 \qquad\quad y=2x-2$$

The first equation is for an ellipse centered at the origin with vertical major axis of length 4 units $(b=2)$ and horizontal minor axis of length 2 units $(a=1)$. The second equation is for a line with slope 2 and y-intercept -2.

Check the intersection points.

The solution set is $\{(0,-2),(1,0)\}$.

753

63.
$$y^2 = \left(-\sqrt{16-4x^2}\right)^2$$
$$y^2 = 16-4x^2$$
$$4x^2 + y^2 = 16$$
$$\frac{x^2}{4} + \frac{y^2}{16} = 1$$

We want to graph the bottom half of an ellipse centered at the origin with a vertical major axis of length 8 units ($b = 4$) and horizontal minor axis of length 4 units $(a = 2)$.

$$y = -\sqrt{16-4x^2}$$

65. $a = 15$, $b = 10$
$$\frac{x^2}{225} + \frac{y^2}{100} = 1$$
Let $x = 4$
$$\frac{4^2}{225} + \frac{y^2}{100} = 1$$
$$900\left(\frac{16}{225} + \frac{y^2}{100}\right) = 900(1)$$
$$64 + 9y^2 = 900$$
$$9y^2 = 836$$
$$y = \sqrt{\frac{836}{9}} \approx 9.64$$

Yes, the truck only needs 7 feet so it will clear.

67. a. $a = 48$, $a^2 = 2304$
$b = 23$, $b^2 = 529$
$$\frac{x^2}{2304} + \frac{y^2}{529} = 1$$

b. $c^2 = a^2 - b^2 = 2304 - 529 = 1775$
$c = \sqrt{1775} \approx 42.13$
He situated his desk about 42 feet from the center of the ellipse, along the major axis.

79. $a = 6$, $a^2 = 36$
$$\frac{x^2}{b^2} + \frac{y^2}{36} = 1$$
When $x = 2$ and $y = -4$,
$$\frac{2^2}{b^2} + \frac{(-4)^2}{36} = 1$$
$$\frac{4}{b^2} + \frac{16}{36} = 1$$
$$\frac{4}{b^2} = \frac{5}{9}$$
$$36 = 5b^2$$
$$b^2 = \frac{36}{5}$$
$$\frac{x^2}{\frac{36}{5}} + \frac{y^2}{36} = 1$$

81. The large circle has radius 5 with center $(0, 0)$. Its equation is $x^2 + y^2 = 25$. The small circle has radius 3 with center $(0, 0)$. Its equation is $x^2 + y^2 = 9$.

Section 9.2

Check Point Exercises

1. a. $a^2 = 25$, $a = 5$
vertices: $(5, 0)$ and $(-5, 0)$
$b^2 = 16$
$c^2 = a^2 + b^2 = 25 + 16 = 41$
$c = \sqrt{41}$
The foci are at $(\sqrt{41}, 0)$ and $(-\sqrt{41}, 0)$.

b. $a^2 = 25$, $a = 5$
vertices: $(0, 5)$ and $(0, -5)$
$b^2 = 16$
$c^2 = a^2 + b^2 = 25 + 16 = 41$
$c = \sqrt{41}$
The foci are at $(0, \sqrt{41})$ and $(0, -\sqrt{41})$.

2. $a = 3$, $c = 5$
$b^2 = c^2 - a^2 = 25 - 9 = 16$
$$\frac{y^2}{9} - \frac{x^2}{16} = 1$$

3. $a^2 = 36$, $a = 6$

The vertices are (6, 0) and (-6, 0).

$b^2 = 9$, $b = 3$

asymptotes: $y = \pm \dfrac{b}{a} x = \pm \dfrac{3}{6} x = \pm \dfrac{1}{2} x$

$c^2 = a^2 + b^2 = 36 + 9 = 45$

$c = \sqrt{45} = 3\sqrt{5}$

The foci are at $(-3\sqrt{5},\, 0)$ and $(3\sqrt{5},\, 0)$.

$$\frac{x^2}{36} - \frac{y^2}{9} = 1$$

4. $\dfrac{y^2}{4} - \dfrac{4x^2}{4} = \dfrac{4}{4}$

$\dfrac{y^2}{4} - x^2 = 1$

$a^2 = 4$, $a = 2$

The vertices are (0, 2) and (0, –2).

$b^2 = 1$, $b = 1$

asymptotes: $y = \pm \dfrac{a}{b} x = \pm 2x$

$c^2 = a^2 + b^2 = 4 + 1 = 5$

$c = \sqrt{5}$

The foci are at $(0,\, \sqrt{5})$ and $(0,\, -\sqrt{5})$.

$$y^2 - 4x^2 = 4$$

5.   center at (3, 1)

$a^2 = 4$, $a = 2$

$b^2 = 1$, $b = 1$

The vertices are (1, 1) and (5, 1).

asymptotes: $y - 1 = \pm \dfrac{1}{2}(x - 3)$

$c^2 = a^2 + b^2 = 4 + 1 = 5$

$c = \sqrt{5}$

The foci are at $(3 - \sqrt{5},\, 1)$ and $(3 + \sqrt{5},\, 1)$.

$$\frac{(x - 3)^2}{4} - \frac{(y - 1)^2}{1} = 1$$

6. $4\left(x^2 - 6x \quad\right) - 9\left(y^2 + 10y \quad\right) = 153$

$4\left(x^2 - 6x + 9\right) - 9\left(y^2 + 10y + 25\right) = 153 + 36 + (-225)$

$4(x-3)^2 - 9(y+5)^2 = -36$

$\dfrac{4(x-3)^2}{-36} - \dfrac{9(y+5)^2}{-36} = \dfrac{-36}{-36}$

$-\dfrac{(x-3)^2}{9} + \dfrac{(y+5)^2}{4} = 1$

$\dfrac{(y+5)^2}{4} - \dfrac{(x-3)^2}{9} = 1$

center at $(3, -5)$

$a^2 = 4,\ a = 2$

$b^2 = 9,\ b = 3$

The vertices are $(3, -3)$ and $(3, -7)$.

asymptotes: $y + 5 = \pm\dfrac{2}{3}(x-3)$

$c^2 = a^2 + b^2 = 4 + 9 = 13$

$c = \sqrt{13}$

The foci are at $(3, -5 - \sqrt{13})$ and $(3, -5 + \sqrt{13})$.

$4x^2 - 24x - 9y^2 - 90y - 153 = 0$

7. $c = 5280$

$2a = 3300,\ a = 1650$

$b^2 = c^2 - a^2 = 5280^2 - 1650^2 = 25,155,900$

The explosion occurred somewhere at the right branch of the hyperbola given by

$\dfrac{x^2}{2,722,500} - \dfrac{y^2}{25,155,900} = 1.$

Exercise Set 9.2

1. $a^2 = 4,\ a = 2$

The vertices are $(2, 0)$ and $(-2, 0)$.

$b^2 = 1$

$c^2 = a^2 + b^2 = 4 + 1 = 5$

$c = \sqrt{5}$

The foci are located at $(\sqrt{5}, 0)$ and $(-\sqrt{5}, 0)$.

graph (b)

3. $a^2 = 4,\ a = 2$

The vertices are $(0, 2)$ and $(0, -2)$.

$b^2 = 1$

$c^2 = a^2 + b^2 = 4 + 1 = 5$

$c = \sqrt{5}$

The foci are located at
$(0, \sqrt{5})$ and $(0, -\sqrt{5})$.

graph (a)

5. $a = 1,\ c = 3$

$b^2 = c^2 - a^2 = 9 - 1 = 8$

$y^2 - \dfrac{x^2}{8} = 1$

7. $a = 3,\ c = 4$

$b^2 = c^2 - a^2 = 16 - 9 = 7$

$\dfrac{x^2}{9} - \dfrac{y^2}{7} = 1$

9. $2a = 6 - (-6)$

$2a = 12$

$a = 6$

$\dfrac{a}{b} = 2$

$\dfrac{6}{b} = 2$

$6 = 2b$

$3 = b$

Transverse axis is vertical.

$\dfrac{y^2}{36} - \dfrac{x^2}{9} = 1$

11. $a = 2,\ c = 7 - 4 = 3$

$$2^2 + b^2 = 3^2$$
$$4 + b^2 = 9$$
$$b^2 = 5$$

Transverse axis is horizontal.

$$\frac{(x-4)^2}{4} - \frac{(y+2)^2}{5} = 1$$

13. $a^2 = 9,\ a = 3$

$b^2 = 25,\ b = 5$

vertices: $(3, 0)$ and $(-3, 0)$

asymptotes: $y = \pm\dfrac{b}{a}x = \pm\dfrac{5}{3}x$

$c^2 = a^2 + b^2 = 9 + 25 = 34$

$c = \sqrt{34}$ on x-axis

The foci are at $(\sqrt{34}, 0)$ and $(-\sqrt{34}, 0)$.

$$\frac{x^2}{9} - \frac{y^2}{25} = 1$$

15. $a^2 = 100,\ a = 10$

$b^2 = 64,\ b = 8$

vertices: $(10, 0)$ and $(-10, 0)$

asymptotes: $y = \pm\dfrac{b}{a}x = \pm\dfrac{8}{10}x$

or $y = \pm\dfrac{4}{5}x$

$c^2 = a^2 + b^2 = 100 + 64 = 164$

$c = \sqrt{164} = 2\sqrt{41}$ on x-axis

The foci are at $(2\sqrt{41}, 0)$ and $(-2\sqrt{41}, 0)$.

$$\frac{x^2}{100} - \frac{y^2}{64} = 1$$

17. $a^2 = 16,\ a = 4$

$b^2 = 36,\ b = 6$

vertices: $(0, 4)$ and $(0, -4)$

asymptotes: $y = \pm\dfrac{a}{b}x = \pm\dfrac{4}{6}x = \pm\dfrac{2}{3}x$

or $y = \pm\dfrac{2}{3}x$

$c^2 = a^2 + b^2 = 16 + 36 = 52$

$c = \sqrt{52} = 2\sqrt{13}$ on y-axis

The foci are at $(0, 2\sqrt{13})$ and $(0, -2\sqrt{13})$.

$$\frac{y^2}{16} - \frac{x^2}{36} = 1$$

19. $\dfrac{y^2}{\frac{1}{4}} - x^2 = 1$

$a^2 = \dfrac{1}{4},\ a = \dfrac{1}{2}$

$b^2 = 1,\ b = 1$

$c^2 = a^2 + b^2$

$c^2 = \dfrac{1}{4} + 1$

$c^2 = \dfrac{5}{4}$

$c = \pm\dfrac{\sqrt{5}}{2}$

$c \approx \pm1.1$

The foci are located at $\left(0, \dfrac{\sqrt{5}}{2}\right)$ and $\left(0, -\dfrac{\sqrt{5}}{2}\right)$.

asymptotes: $y = \pm\dfrac{\frac{1}{2}}{1}x$

$y = \pm\dfrac{1}{2}x$

$$4y^2 - x^2 = 1$$

21. $\dfrac{9x^2}{36} - \dfrac{4y^2}{36} = \dfrac{36}{36}$

$\dfrac{x^2}{4} - \dfrac{y^2}{9} = 1$

$a^2 = 4,\ a = 2$
$b^2 = 9,\ b = 3$
vertices: $(2, 0)$ and $(-2, 0)$

asymptotes: $y = \pm\dfrac{b}{a}x = \pm\dfrac{3}{2}x$

$c^2 = a^2 + b^2 = 4 + 9 = 13$

$c = \sqrt{13}$ on x-axis

The foci are at $(\sqrt{13}, 0)$ and $(-\sqrt{13}, 0)$.

$9x^2 - 4y^2 = 36$

23. $\dfrac{9y^2}{225} - \dfrac{25x^2}{225} = \dfrac{225}{225}$

$\dfrac{y^2}{25} - \dfrac{x^2}{9} = 1$

$a^2 = 25,\ a = 5$
$b^2 = 9,\ b = 3$
vertices: $(0, 5)$ and $(0, -5)$

asymptotes: $y = \pm\dfrac{a}{b}x = \pm\dfrac{5}{3}x$

$c^2 = a^2 + b^2 = 25 + 9 = 34$

$c = \sqrt{34}$ on y-axis

The foci are at $(0, \sqrt{34})$ and $(0, -\sqrt{34})$.

$9y^2 - 25x^2 = 225$

25. $y^2 = x^2 - 2$

$2 = x^2 - y^2$

$1 = \dfrac{x^2}{2} - \dfrac{y^2}{2}$

$a^2 = 2,\ a = \sqrt{2}$
$b^2 = 2,\ b = \sqrt{2}$
$c^2 = 2 + 2$
$c^2 = 4$
$c = 2$

The foci are located at $(2,0)$ and $(-2, 0)$.

asymptotes: $y = \pm\dfrac{\sqrt{2}}{\sqrt{2}}x$

$y = \pm x$

$y = \pm\sqrt{x^2 - 2}$

27. $a = 3,\ b = 5$

$\dfrac{x^2}{9} - \dfrac{y^2}{25} = 1$

29. $a = 2,\ b = 3$

$\dfrac{y^2}{4} - \dfrac{x^2}{9} = 1$

31. Center $(2, -3)$, $a = 2$, $b = 3$

$\dfrac{(x-2)^2}{4} - \dfrac{(y+3)^2}{9} = 1$

33. center: $(-4, -3)$
$a^2 = 9,\ a = 3$
$b^2 = 16,\ b = 4$
vertices: $(-7, -3)$ and $(-1, -3)$

asymptotes: $y + 3 = \pm\dfrac{4}{3}(x + 4)$

$c^2 = a^2 + b^2 = 9 + 16 = 25$

$c = \pm 5$ parallel to x-axis

The foci are at $(-9, -3)$ and $(1, -3)$.

$\dfrac{(x+4)^2}{9} - \dfrac{(y+3)^2}{16} = 1$

35. center: $(-3, 0)$

$a^2 = 25$, $a = 5$

$b^2 = 16$, $b = 4$

vertices: $(2, 0)$ and $(-8, 0)$

asymptotes: $y = \pm\frac{4}{5}(x+3)$

$c^2 = a^2 + b^2 = 25 + 16 = 41$

$c = \sqrt{41}$

The foci are at $(-3+\sqrt{41}, 0)$ and $(-3-\sqrt{41}, 0)$.

$$\frac{(x+3)^2}{25} - \frac{y^2}{16} = 1$$

37. center: $(1, -2)$

$a^2 = 4$, $a = 2$

$b^2 = 16$, $b = 4$

vertices: $(1, 0)$ and $(1, -4)$

asymptotes: $y + 2 = \pm\frac{1}{2}(x-1)$

$c^2 = a^2 + b^2 = 4 + 16 = 20$

$c = \sqrt{20} = 2\sqrt{5}$ parallel to y-axis

The foci are at $(1, -2+2\sqrt{5})$ and $(1, -2-2\sqrt{5})$.

$$\frac{(y+2)^2}{4} - \frac{(x-1)^2}{16} = 1$$

39. $\frac{(x-3)^2}{4} - \frac{4(y+3)^2}{4} = \frac{4}{4}$

$\frac{(x-3)^2}{4} - (y+3)^2 = 1$

center: $(3, -3)$

$a^2 = 4$, $a = 2$

$b^2 = 1$, $b = 1$

vertices: $(1, -3)$ and $(5, -3)$

asymptotes: $y + 3 = \pm\frac{1}{2}(x-3)$

$c^2 = a^2 + b^2 = 4 + 1 = 5$

$c = \sqrt{5}$

The foci are at $(3+\sqrt{5}, -3)$ and $(3-\sqrt{5}, -3)$.

$$(x-3)^2 - 4(y+3)^2 = 4$$

41. $\frac{(x-1)^2}{3} - \frac{(y-2)^2}{3} = 1$

center: $(1, 2)$

$a^2 = 3$, $a = \sqrt{3}$

$b^2 = $, $b = \sqrt{3}$

vertices: $(-1, 2)$ and $(3, 2)$

asymptotes: $y - 2 = \pm(x - 1)$

$c^2 = a^2 + b^2 = 3 + 3 = 6$

$c = \sqrt{6}$ parallel to y-axis

The foci are at $(1+\sqrt{6}, 2)$ and $(1-\sqrt{6}, 2)$.

$$(x-1)^2 - (y-2)^2 = 3$$

43.
$$(x^2 - 2x) - (y^2 + 4y) = 4$$
$$(x^2 - 2x + 1) - (y^2 + 4y + 4) = 4 + 1 - 4$$
$$(x - 1)^2 - (y + 2)^2 = 1$$
center: $(1, -2)$
$a^2 = 1,\ a = 1$
$b^2 = 1,\ b = 1$
$c^2 = a^2 + b^2 = 1 + 1 = 2$
$c = \sqrt{2}$

asymptotes: $y + 2 = \pm(x - 1)$

The foci are at $(1 + \sqrt{2}, -2)$ and $(1 - \sqrt{2}, -2)$.

$$x^2 - y^2 - 2x - 4y - 4 = 0$$

45.
$$(16x^2 + 64x) - (y^2 + 2y) = -67$$
$$16(x^2 + 4x + 4) - (y^2 + 2y + 1)$$
$$= -67 + 64 - 1$$
$$16(x + 2)^2 - (y + 1)^2 = -4$$
$$\frac{16(x + 2)^2}{-4} - \frac{(y + 1)^2}{-4} = \frac{-4}{-4}$$
$$\frac{(y + 1)^2}{4} - \frac{(x + 2)^2}{\frac{1}{4}} = 1$$

center: $(-2, -1)$
$a^2 = 4,\ a = 2$
$b^2 = \dfrac{1}{4},\ b = \dfrac{1}{2}$
$c^2 = a^2 + b^2 = 4 + \dfrac{1}{4} = \dfrac{17}{4}$
$c = \sqrt{\dfrac{17}{4}} = \sqrt{4.25}$

asymptotes:
$$(y + 1) = \pm \frac{2}{\frac{1}{2}}(x + 2)$$
$$y + 1 = \pm 4(x + 2)$$

The foci are at $\left(-2, -1 + \sqrt{4.25}\right)$ and
$\left(-2, -1 - \sqrt{4.25}\right)$.

$$16x^2 - y^2 + 64x - 2y + 67 = 0$$

47.
$$(4x^2 - 16x) - (9y^2 - 54y) = 101$$
$$4(x^2 - 4x + 4) - 9(y^2 - 6y + 9)$$
$$= 101 + 16 - 81$$
$$4(x - 2)^2 - 9(y - 3)^2 = 36$$
$$\frac{(x - 2)^2}{9} - \frac{(y - 3)^2}{4} = 1$$
center: $(2, 3)$
$a^2 = 9,\ a = 3$
$b^2 = 4,\ b = 2$
$c^2 = a^2 + b^2 = 9 + 4 = 13$
$c = \sqrt{13}$

asymptotes: $y - 3 = \pm \dfrac{2}{3}(x - 2)$

The foci are at $(2 + \sqrt{13}, 3)$ and $(2 - \sqrt{13}, 3)$.

$$4x^2 - 9y^2 - 16x + 5y - 101 = 0$$

49.
$$(4x^2 - 32x) - 25y^2 = -164$$
$$4(x^2 - 8x + 16) - 25y^2 = -164 + 64$$
$$4(x - 4)^2 - 25y^2 = -100$$
$$\frac{4(x - 4)^2}{-100} - \frac{25y^2}{-100} = \frac{-100}{-100}$$
$$\frac{y^2}{4} - \frac{(x - 4)^2}{25} = 1$$

center: $(4, 0)$
$a^2 = 4,\ a = 2$
$b^2 = 25,\ b = 5$
$c^2 = a^2 + b^2 = 4 + 25 = 29$
$c = \sqrt{29}$

asymptotes: $y = \pm \dfrac{2}{5}(x - 4)$

The foci are at $(4, \sqrt{29})$ and $(4, -\sqrt{29})$.

$$4x^2 - 25y^2 - 32x + 164 = 0$$

51. $\dfrac{x^2}{9} - \dfrac{y^2}{16} = 1$

The equation is for a hyperbola in standard form with the transverse axis on the x-axis. We have $a^2 = 9$ and $b^2 = 16$, so $a = 3$ and $b = 4$. Therefore, the vertices are at $(\pm a, 0)$ or $(\pm 3, 0)$.

Using a dashed line, we construct a rectangle using the ± 3 on the x-axis and ± 4 on the y-axis. Then use dashed lines to draw extended diagonals for the rectangle. These represent the asymptotes of the graph.

$$\dfrac{x^2}{9} - \dfrac{y^2}{16} = 1$$

From the graph we determine the following:
Domain: $\{x \mid x \le -3 \text{ or } x \ge 3\}$ or $(-\infty, -3] \cup [3, \infty)$
Range: $\{y \mid y \text{ is a real number}\}$ or $(-\infty, \infty)$

53. $\dfrac{x^2}{9} + \dfrac{y^2}{16} = 1$

The equation is for an ellipse in standard form with major axis along the y-axis. We have $a^2 = 16$ and $b^2 = 9$, so $a = 4$ and $b = 3$. Therefore, the vertices are $(0, \pm a)$ or $(0, \pm 4)$. The endpoints of the minor axis are $(\pm b, 0)$ or $(\pm 3, 0)$.

$$\dfrac{x^2}{9} + \dfrac{y^2}{16} = 1$$

From the graph we determine the following:
Domain: $\{x \mid -3 \le x \le 3\}$ or $[-3, 3]$
Range: $\{y \mid -4 \le y \le 4\}$ or $[-4, 4]$.

55. $\dfrac{y^2}{16} - \dfrac{x^2}{9} = 1$

The equation is in standard form with the transverse axis on the y-axis. We have $a^2 = 16$ and $b^2 = 9$, so $a = 4$ and $b = 3$. Therefore, the vertices are at $(0, \pm a)$ or $(0, \pm 4)$. Using a dashed line, we construct a rectangle using the ± 4 on the y-axis and ± 3 on the x-axis. Then use dashed lines to draw extended diagonals for the rectangle. These represent the asymptotes of the graph.

$$\dfrac{y^2}{16} - \dfrac{x^2}{9} = 1$$

From the graph we determine the following:
Domain: $\{x \mid x \text{ is a real number}\}$ or $(-\infty, \infty)$
Range: $\{y \mid y \le -4 \text{ or } y \ge 4\}$ or $(-\infty, -4] \cup [4, \infty)$

57. $x^2 - y^2 = 4$

$x^2 + y^2 = 4$

Check $(-2, 0)$:

$(-2)^2 - 0^2 = 4$	$(-2)^2 + 0^2 = 4$
$4 - 0 = 4$	$4 + 0 = 4$
$4 = 4$ true	$4 = 4$ true

Check $(2, 0)$:

$(2)^2 - 0^2 = 4$	$(2)^2 + 0^2 = 4$
$4 - 0 = 4$	$4 + 0 = 4$
$4 = 4$ true	$4 = 4$ true

The solution set is $\{(-2, 0), (2, 0)\}$.

59.
$$9x^2 + y^2 = 9 \quad \text{or} \quad \frac{x^2}{1} + \frac{y^2}{9} = 1$$
$$y^2 - 9x^2 = 9 \qquad\qquad \frac{y^2}{9} - \frac{x^2}{1} = 1$$

Check $(0,-3)$:

$9(0)^2 + (-3)^2 = 9$	$(-3)^2 - 9(0)^2 = 9$
$0 + 9 = 9$	$9 - 0 = 9$
$9 = 9$	$9 = 9$
true	true

Check $(0,3)$:

$9(0)^2 + (3)^2 = 9$	$(3)^2 - 9(0)^2 = 9$
$0 + 9 = 9$	$9 - 0 = 9$
$9 = 9$	$9 = 9$
true	true

The solution set is $\{(0,-3),(0,3)\}$.

61. $|d_2 - d_1| = 2a = (2 \text{ s})(1100 \text{ ft / s}) = 2200 \text{ ft}$
$a = 1100 \text{ ft}$
$2c = 5280 \text{ ft}, c = 2640 \text{ ft}$
$b^2 = c^2 - a^2 = (2640)^2 - (1100)^2$
$\qquad = 5,759,600$

$$\frac{x^2}{(1100)^2} - \frac{y^2}{5,759,600} = 1$$

$$\frac{x^2}{1,210,000} - \frac{y^2}{5,759,600} = 1$$

If M_1 is located 2640 feet to the right of the origin on the x-axis, the explosion is located on the right branch of the hyperbola given by the equation above.

63.
$$625y^2 - 400x^2 = 250,000$$
$$\frac{625y^2}{250,000} - \frac{400x^2}{250,000} = \frac{250,000}{250,000}$$
$$\frac{y^2}{400} - \frac{x^2}{625} = 1$$
$a^2 = 400, a = \sqrt{400} = 20$
$2a = 40$
The houses are 40 yards apart at their closest point.

75.
$$\frac{x^2}{4} - \frac{y^2}{9} = 0$$
$$y^2 = \frac{9}{4}x^2$$
$$y = \pm\frac{3}{2}x$$

No; in general, the graph is two intersecting lines.

77. $4x^2 - 6xy + 2y^2 - 3x + 10y - 6 = 0$
$2y^2 + (10 - 6x)y + (4x^2 - 3x - 6) = 0$

$$y = \frac{6x - 10 \pm \sqrt{(10 - 6x)^2 - 8(4x^2 - 3x - 6)}}{4}$$

$$y = \frac{6x - 10 \pm \sqrt{4(x^2 - 24x + 37)}}{4}$$

$$y = \frac{3x - 5 \pm \sqrt{x^2 - 24x + 37}}{2}$$

The xy-term rotates the hyperbola. Separation of terms into ones containing only x or only y would not be possible.

79. **a.** False; one branch of the hyperbola

$\dfrac{x^2}{a^2} - \dfrac{y^2}{b^2} = 1$ will not pass the vertical line test,

so will not define y as a function of x.

b. False; none of the points on the asymptotes satisfy the hyperbola's equation, since the hyperbola never touches its asymptotes.

c. True; $y = -\dfrac{2}{3}x$ is one of the asymptotes of

the hyperbola and they will not intersect.

d. False; for example, $\dfrac{x^2}{4} - \dfrac{y^2}{4} = 1$ and

$\dfrac{y^2}{4} - \dfrac{x^2}{4} = 1$ each have asymptotes

$y = \pm x$, but are different hyperbolas.

(c) is true.

81. The center is at the midpoint of the line segment joining the vertices, so it is located at $(5, 0)$. The standard form is:

$\dfrac{(y-k)^2}{a^2} - \dfrac{(x-h)^2}{b^2} = 1$

$(h, k) = (5, 0)$, and $a = 6$, so $a^2 = 36$.

$\dfrac{y^2}{36} - \dfrac{(x-5)^2}{b^2} = 1$.

Substitute $x = 0$ and $y = 9$:

$\dfrac{9^2}{36} - \dfrac{(0-5)^2}{b^2} = 1$

$-\dfrac{25}{b^2} = -\dfrac{5}{4}$

$-100 = -5b^2$

$b^2 = 20$

Standard form: $\dfrac{y^2}{36} - \dfrac{(x-5)^2}{20} = 1$

Section 9.3

Check Point Exercises

1. $4p = 8,\ p = 2$
focus: $(2, 0)$
directrix: $x = -2$

$y^2 = 8x$

2. $x^2 = -12y$
$4p = -12,\ p = 3$
focus: $(0, -3)$
directrix: $y = 3$

3. $p = 8$
$y^2 = 4 \cdot 8x$
$y^2 = 32x$

4. $4p = 4,\ p = 1$
vertex: $(2, -1)$
focus: $(2, 0)$
directrix: $y = -2$

$(x - 2)^2 = 4(y + 1)$

5.
$$y^2 + 2y = -4x + 7$$
$$y^2 + 2y + 1 = -4x + 7 + 1$$
$$(y+1)^2 = -4(x-2)$$
$$4p = -4, \ p = -1$$
vertex: $(2, -1)$
focus: $(1, -1)$
directrix: $x = 3$

$y^2 + 2y + 4x - 7 = 0$

6. $x^2 = 4py$
Let $x = 3$ and $y = 4$.
$$3^2 = 4p \cdot 4$$
$$9 = 16p$$
$$p = \frac{9}{16}$$
$$x^2 = \frac{9}{4}y$$

The light should be placed at $\left(0, \dfrac{9}{16}\right)$ or $\dfrac{9}{16}$

inch above the vertex.

Exercise Set 9.3

1. $y^2 = 4x$
$4p = 4, \ p = 1$
vertex: $(0, 0)$
focus: $(1, 0)$
directrix: $x = -1$
graph (c)

3. $x^2 = -4y$
$4p = -4, \ p = -1$
vertex: $(0, 0)$
focus: $(0, -1)$
directrix: $y = 1$
graph (b)

5. $4p = 16, \ p = 4$
vertex: $(0, 0)$
focus: $(4, 0)$
directrix: $x = -4$

$y^2 = 16x$

7. $4p = -8, \ p = -2$
vertex: $(0, 0)$
focus: $(-2, 0)$
directrix: $x = 2$

$y^2 = -8x$

9. $4p = 12, \ p = 3$
vertex: $(0, 0)$
focus: $(0, 3)$
directrix: $y = -3$

$x^2 = 12y$

11. $4p = -16, \ p = -4$
vertex: $(0, 0)$
focus: $(0, -4)$
directrix: $y = 4$

$x^2 = -16y$

13. $y^2 = 6x$

$4p = 6,\ p = \dfrac{6}{4} = \dfrac{3}{2}$

vertex: $(0,\ 0)$

focus: $\left(\dfrac{3}{2},\ 0\right)$

directrix: $x = -\dfrac{3}{2}$

$y^2 - 6x = 0$

15. $8x^2 = -4y$

$x^2 = -\dfrac{1}{2}y$

$4p = -\dfrac{1}{2}$

$p = -\dfrac{1}{8}$

focus: $\left(0,\ -\dfrac{1}{8}\right)$

directrix: $y = \dfrac{1}{8}$

$8x^2 + 4y = 0$

17. $p = 7,\ 4p = 28$
$y^2 = 28x$

19. $p = -5,\ 4p = -20$
$y^2 = -20x$

21. $p = 15,\ 4p = 60$
$x^2 = 60y$

23. $p = -25,\ 4p = -100$
$x^2 = -100y$

25. $p = -5 - (-3) = -2$ Vertex, $(2,\ -3)$
$(x - 2)^2 = -8(y + 3)$

27.   vertex: $(1,\ 2)$ $p = 2$
$(y - 2)^2 = 8(x - 1)$

29.   vertex: $(-3,\ 3),\ p = 1$
$(x + 3)^2 = 4(y - 3)$

31. $(y - 1)^2 = 4(x - 1)$
$4p = 4,\ p = 1$
vertex: $(1,\ 1)$
focus: $(2,\ 1)$
directrix: $x = 0$
graph (c)

33. $(x + 1)^2 = -4(y + 1)$
$4p = -4,\ p = -1$
vertex: $(-1,\ -1)$
focus: $(-1,\ -2)$
directrix: $y = 0$
graph (d)

35. $4p = 8,\ p = 2$
vertex: $(2,\ 1)$
focus: $(2,\ 3)$
directrix: $y = -1$

$(x - 2)^2 = 8(y - 1)$

37. $4p = -8,\ p = -2$
vertex: $(-1,\ -1)$
focus: $(-1,\ -3)$
directrix: $y = 1$

$(x + 1)^2 = -8(y + 1)$

39. $4p = 12, p = 3$
vertex: $(-1, -3)$
focus: $(2, -3)$
directrix: $x = -4$

$(y + 3)^2 = 12(x + 1)$

41. $(y + 1)^2 = -8(x - 0)$
$4p = -8, p = -2$
vertex: $(0, -1)$
focus: $(-2, -1)$
directrix: $x = 2$

$(y + 1)^2 = -8x$

43. $x^2 - 2x + 1 = 4y - 9 + 1$
         $(x - 1)^2 = 4y - 8$
         $(x - 1)^2 = 4(y - 2)$
$4p = 4, p = 1$
vertex: $(1, 2)$
focus: $(1, 3)$
directrix: $y = 1$

$x^2 - 2x - 4y + 9 = 0$

45. $y^2 - 2y + 1 = -12x + 35 + 1$
         $(y - 1)^2 = -12x + 36$
         $(y - 1)^2 = -12(x - 3)$
$4p = -12, p = -3$
vertex: $(3, 1)$
focus: $(0, 1)$
directrix: $x = 6$

$y^2 - 2y + 12x - 35 = 0$

47. $x^2 + 6x = 4y - 1$
      $x^2 + 6x + 9 = 4y - 1 + 9$
         $(x + 3)^2 = 4(y + 2)$
$4p = 4, p = 1$
vertex: $(-3, -2)$
focus: $(-3, -1)$
directrix: $y = -3$

$x^2 + 6x - 4y + 1 = 0$

49. The y-coordinate of the vertex is
$$y = -\frac{b}{2a} = -\frac{6}{2(1)} = -3$$
The x-coordinate of the vertex is
$$x = (-3)^2 + 6(-3) + 5$$
$$= 9 - 18 + 5$$
$$= -4$$
The vertex is $(-4, -3)$.

Since the squared term is y and $a > 0$, the graph opens to the right.

Domain: $\{x \mid x \geq -4\}$ or $[-4, \infty)$

Range: $\{y \mid y \text{ is a real number}\}$ or $(-\infty, \infty)$

The relation is not a function.

51. The x-coordinate of the vertex is

$$x = -\frac{b}{2a} = -\frac{(4)}{2(-1)} = 2$$

The y-coordinate of the vertex is

$$y = -(2)^2 + 4(2) - 3$$
$$= -4 + 8 - 3$$
$$= 1$$

The vertex is $(2,1)$.

Since the squared term is x and $a < 0$, the graph opens down.

Domain: $\{x \mid x$ is a real number$\}$ or $(-\infty, \infty)$

Range: $\{y \mid y \le 1\}$ or $(-\infty, 1]$

The relation is a function.

53. The equation is in the form $x = a(y-k)^2 + h$

From the equation, we can see that the vertex is $(3,1)$.

Since the squared term is y and $a < 0$, the graph opens to the left.

Domain: $\{x \mid x \le 3\}$ or $(-\infty, 3]$

Range: $\{y \mid y$ is a real number$\}$ or $(-\infty, \infty)$

The relation is not a function.

55.

Check $(-4, 2)$:

$$-4 = (2-2)^2 - 4 \qquad 2 = -\frac{1}{2}(-4)$$
$$-4 = 0 - 4 \qquad\qquad 2 = 2$$
$$-4 = -4 \qquad\qquad\quad \text{true}$$
$$\text{true}$$

Check $(0, 0)$:

$$0 = (0-2)^2 - 4 \qquad 0 = -\frac{1}{2}(0)$$
$$0 = 4 - 4 \qquad\qquad 0 = 0$$
$$0 = 0 \qquad\qquad\quad \text{true}$$
$$\text{true}$$

The solution set is $\{(-4, 2), (0, 0)\}$.

57.

Check $(-2, 1)$:

$$-2 = (1)^2 - 3 \qquad -2 = (1)^2 - 3(1)$$
$$-2 = 1 - 3 \qquad\quad -2 = 1 - 3$$
$$-2 = -2 \ \text{true} \qquad -2 = -2 \ \text{true}$$

The solution set is $\{(-2, 1)\}$.

59.

The two graphs do not cross. Therefore, the solution set is the empty set, $\{ \ \}$ or $\varnothing$.

61. $x^2 = 4py$
$$2^2 = 4p(1)$$
$$4 = 4$$
$$p = 1$$

The light bulb should be placed 1 inch above the vertex.

63. $x^2 = 4py$
$$6^2 = 4p(2)$$
$$36 = 8p$$
$$p = \frac{36}{8} = \frac{9}{2} = 4.5$$

The receiver should be located 4.5 feet from the base of the dish.

65.
$$x^2 = 4py$$
$$(640)^2 = 4p(160)$$
$$p = \frac{(640)^2}{640} = 640$$
$$x = 640 - 200 = 440$$
$$(440)^2 = 4(640)y$$
$$y = \frac{(440)^2}{4(640)} = 75.625$$

The height is 76 meters.

67.
$$x^2 = 4py$$
$$\left(\frac{200}{2}\right)^2 = 4p(-50)$$
$$\frac{10,000}{-50} = 4p$$
$$4p = -200$$
$$x^2 = -200y$$
$$(30)^2 = -200y$$
$$y = \frac{900}{-200} = -4.5$$

(height of bridge) $= 50 - 4.5 = 45.5$ feet.
Yes, the boat will clear the arch.

77.
$$y^2 + 2y - 6x + 13 = 0$$
$$y^2 + 2y + (-6x + 13) = 0$$
$$y = \frac{-2 \pm \sqrt{2^2 - 4(-6x + 13)}}{2}$$
$$y = \frac{-2 \pm \sqrt{24x - 48}}{2}$$
$$y = -1 \pm \sqrt{6x - 12}$$

79.
$$16x^2 - 24xy + 9y^2 - 60x - 80y + 100 = 0$$
$$9y^2 - (24x + 80)y + (16x^2 - 60x + 100) = 0$$
$$y = \frac{24x + 80 \pm \sqrt{(24x + 80)^2 - 36(16x^2 - 60x + 100)}}{18}$$
$$y = \frac{24x + 80 \pm \sqrt{6000x + 2800}}{18}$$
$$y = \frac{24x + 80 \pm 20\sqrt{15x + 7}}{18}$$
$$y = \frac{12x + 40 \pm 10\sqrt{15x + 7}}{9}$$

81. a. False; it opens to the left.

    b. True; it opens to the right and has a domain $[3, \infty)$.

    c. False; any parabola that opens to the right will not be a function of x because at least one x-value will be paired with more than 1 y-value.

    d. False; the graph is a line.

    (b) is true.

83. $y = 4$ is the directrix and $(-1, 0)$ is the focus. The vertex must be located halfway between them at the point $(-1, 2)$. $p = -2$ and the parabola opens down.
$$(x + 1)^2 = 4(-2)(y - 2)$$
$$(x + 1)^2 = -8(y - 2)$$

Mid-Chapter 9 Check Point

1. Center: $(0,0)$

Because the denominator of the x^2 – term is greater than the denominator of the y^2 – term, the major axis is horizontal. Since $a^2 = 25$, $a = 5$ and the vertices are $(-5,0)$ and $(5,0)$. Since $b^2 = 4$, $b = 2$ and endpoints of the minor axis are $(0,-2)$ and $(0,2)$.

Foci: $\left(\pm\sqrt{21},0\right)$

$$\frac{x^2}{25} + \frac{y^2}{4} = 1$$

2. Divide both sides by 36 to get the standard form:
$$\frac{x^2}{4} + \frac{y^2}{9} = 1$$

Center: $(0,0)$

Because the denominator of the y^2 – term is greater than the denominator of the x^2 – term, the major axis is vertical. Since $a^2 = 9$, $a = 3$ and the vertices are $(0,-3)$ and $(0,3)$. Since $b^2 = 4$, $b = 2$ and endpoints of the minor axis are $(-2,0)$ and $(2,0)$.

Foci: $\left(0,\pm\sqrt{5}\right)$

$$9x^2 + 4y^2 = 36$$

3. Center: $(2,-1)$

Because the denominator of the y^2 – term is greater than the denominator of the x^2 – term, the major axis is vertical. We have $a^2 = 25$ and $b^2 = 16$, so $a = 5$ and $b = 4$. The vertices lie 5 units above and below the center. The endpoints of the minor axis lie 4 units to the left and right of the center.

Vertices: $(2,4)$ and $(2,-6)$

Minor endpoints: $(-2,-1)$ and $(6,-1)$

Foci: $(2,2)$, $(2,-4)$

$$\frac{(x - 2)^2}{16} + \frac{(y + 1)^2}{25} = 1$$

4. Center: $(-2,1)$

Because the denominator of the x^2 – term is greater than the denominator of the y^2 – term, the major axis is horizontal. We have $a^2 = 25$ and $b^2 = 16$, so $a = 5$ and $b = 4$. The vertices lie 5 units to the left and right of the center. The endpoints of the minor axis lie 4 units above and below the center.

Vertices: $(-7,1)$ and $(3,1)$

Minor endpoints: $(-2,5)$ and $(-2,-3)$

Foci: $(-5,1)$, $(1,1)$

$$\frac{(x+2)^2}{25} + \frac{(y-1)^2}{16} = 1$$

5.
$$x^2 - 4x + 9y^2 + 54y = -49$$
$$\left(x^2 - 4x \quad\right) + 9\left(y^2 + 6y \quad\right) = -49$$
$$\left(x^2 - 4x + 4\right) + 9\left(y^2 + 6y + 9\right) = -49 + 4 + 81$$
$$(x-2)^2 + 9(y+3)^2 = 36$$
$$\frac{(x-2)^2}{36} + \frac{9(y+3)^2}{36} = \frac{36}{36}$$
$$\frac{(x-2)^2}{36} + \frac{(y+3)^2}{4} = 1$$

Center: $(2,-3)$

Foci: $\left(2 \pm 4\sqrt{2}, -3\right)$

$$x^2 + 9y^2 - 4x + 54y + 49 = 0$$

6. The equation is for a hyperbola in standard form with the transverse axis on the x-axis. We have $a^2 = 9$ and $b^2 = 1$, so $a = 3$ and $b = 1$. Therefore, the vertices are at $(\pm a, 0)$ or $(\pm 3, 0)$.

Using a dashed line, we construct a rectangle using the ± 3 on the x-axis and ± 1 on the y-axis. Then use dashed lines to draw extended diagonals for the rectangle. These represent the asymptotes of the graph.

Foci: $\left(\pm\sqrt{10}, 0\right)$

$$\frac{x^2}{9} - y^2 = 1$$

7. The equation is in the form $\dfrac{y^2}{a^2} - \dfrac{x^2}{b^2} = 1$ with $a^2 = 9$, and $b^2 = 1$. We know the transverse axis lies on the y-axis and the vertices are $(0,-3)$ and $(0,3)$. Because $a^2 = 9$ and $b^2 = 1$, $a = 3$ and $b = 1$. Construct a rectangle using -1 and 1 on the x–axis, and -3 and 3 on the y–axis. Draw extended diagonals to obtain the asymptotes.

Foci: $\left(0, \pm\sqrt{10}\right)$

$$\frac{y^2}{9} - x^2 = 1$$

8. $\dfrac{y^2}{16} - \dfrac{x^2}{4} = 1$

The equation is in the form $\dfrac{y^2}{a^2} - \dfrac{x^2}{b^2} = 1$ with

$a^2 = 16$, and $b^2 = 4$. We know the transverse axis lies on the y-axis and the vertices are $(0,-4)$ and $(0,4)$. Because

$a^2 = 16$ and $b^2 = 4$, $a = 4$ and $b = 2$. Construct a rectangle using -2 and 2 on the x–axis, and -4 and 4 on the y–axis. Draw extended diagonals to obtain the asymptotes.

Foci: $\left(0, \pm 2\sqrt{5}\right)$

$$y^2 - 4x^2 = 16$$

9. $\dfrac{x^2}{49} - \dfrac{y^2}{4} = 1$

The equation is for a hyperbola in standard form with the transverse axis on the x-axis. We have $a^2 = 49$ and $b^2 = 4$, so $a = 7$ and $b = 2$.

Therefore, the vertices are at $(\pm a, 0)$ or $(\pm 7, 0)$.

Using a dashed line, we construct a rectangle using the ± 7 on the x-axis and ± 2 on the y-axis. Then use dashed lines to draw extended diagonals for the rectangle. These represent the asymptotes of the graph.

Foci: $\left(\pm\sqrt{53}, 0\right)$

$$4x^2 - 49y^2 = 196$$

10.   The equation is for a hyperbola in standard form with center $(2, -2)$. We have $a^2 = 9$ and $b^2 = 16$, so $a = 3$ and $b = 4$.

Asymptotes: $y + 2 = \pm\dfrac{4}{3}(x - 2)$

Foci: $(-3, -2)$, $(7, -2)$

$$\dfrac{(x-2)^2}{9} - \dfrac{(y+2)^2}{16} = 1$$

11.   Write the equation for the hyperbola in standard form:

$$4x^2 - y^2 + 8x + 6y + 11 = 0$$
$$4x^2 + 8x \;\;\; -y^2 + 6y \;\;\; = -11$$
$$4\left(x^2 + 2x \;\;\;\right) - \left(y^2 - 6y \;\;\;\right) = -11$$
$$4\left(x^2 + 2x + 1\right) - \left(y^2 - 6y + 9\right) = -11 + 4 - 9$$
$$4\left(x + 1\right)^2 - \left(y - 3\right)^2 = -16$$
$$\dfrac{4\left(x+1\right)^2}{-16} - \dfrac{\left(y-3\right)^2}{-16} = \dfrac{-16}{-16}$$
$$\dfrac{\left(y-3\right)^2}{16} - \dfrac{\left(x+1\right)^2}{4} = 1$$

Center $(-1, 3)$.

Asymptotes: $y - 3 = \pm 2(x + 1)$

Foci: $\left(-1, 3 \pm 2\sqrt{5}\right)$, $(7, -2)$

$$4x^2 - y^2 + 8x + 6y + 11 = 0$$

12. $(x-2)^2 = -12(y+1)$

$h = 2$

$k = -1$

$4p = -12$

$p = -3$

Vertex: (h, k)

$\qquad (2, -1)$

Focus: $(h, k+p)$

$\qquad (2, -1-3)$

$\qquad (2, -4)$

Directrix: $y = k - p$

$\qquad y = -1 - (-3)$

$\qquad y = 2$

$(x-2)^2 = -12(y+1)$

13. $y^2 - 2x - 2y - 5 = 0$

$y^2 - 2y \qquad = 2x + 5$

$y^2 - 2y + 1 = 2x + 5 + 1$

$(y-1)^2 = 2x + 6$

$(y-1)^2 = 2(x+3)$

$h = -3$

$k = 1$

$4p = 2$

$p = \dfrac{1}{2}$

Vertex: (h, k)

$\qquad (-3, 1)$

Focus: $(h+p, k)$

$\qquad \left(-3 + \dfrac{1}{2}, 1\right)$

$\qquad \left(-\dfrac{5}{2}, 1\right)$

Directrix: $y = h - p$

$\qquad y = -3 - \left(\dfrac{1}{2}\right)$

$\qquad y = -\dfrac{7}{2}$

14. This is the equation of a circle centered at the origin with radius $r = \sqrt{4} = 2$.
We can plot points that are 2 units to the left, right, above, and below the origin and then graph the circle. The points are $(-2, 0)$, $(2, 0)$, $(0, 2)$, and $(0, -2)$.

$x^2 + y^2 = 4$

15. $x + y = 4$

$\qquad y = -x + 4$

This is the equation of a line with slope $m = -1$ and a y-intercept of 4. We can plot the point $(0, 4)$, use the slope to get an additional point, connect the points with a straight line and then extend the line to represent the graph of the equation.

$x + y = 4$

16. $x^2 - y^2 = 4$

$$\frac{x^2}{4} - \frac{y^2}{4} = 1$$

The equation is for a hyperbola in standard form with the transverse axis on the *x*-axis. We have $a^2 = 4$ and $b^2 = 4$, so $a = 2$ and $b = 2$.

Therefore, the vertices are at $(\pm a, 0)$ or $(\pm 2, 0)$.

Using a dashed line, we construct a rectangle using the ± 2 on the *x*-axis and ± 2 on the *y*-axis. Then use dashed lines to draw extended diagonals for the rectangle. These represent the asymptotes of the graph.

Graph the hyperbola.

$$x^2 - y^2 = 4$$

17. $x^2 + 4y^2 = 4$

$$\frac{x^2}{4} + \frac{y^2}{1} = 1$$

Center: $(0, 0)$

Because the denominator of the x^2 – term is greater than the denominator of the y^2 – term, the major axis is horizontal. We have $a^2 = 4$ and $b^2 = 1$, so $a = 2$ and $b = 1$. The vertices lie 2 units to the left and right of the center. The endpoints of the minor axis lie 1 unit above and below the center.

Vertices: $(-2, 0)$ and $(2, 0)$

Minor endpoints: $(0, -1)$ and $(0, 1)$

$$x^2 + 4y^2 = 4$$

18. Center: $(-1, 1)$

Radius: $r = \sqrt{4} = 2$

We plot the points that are 2 units to the left, right, above and below the center.

These points are $(-3, 1)$, $(1, 1)$, $(-1, 3)$, and $(-1. -1)$.

$$(x + 1)^2 + (y - 1)^2 = 4$$

19. $x^2 + 4(y - 1)^2 = 4$

$$\frac{x^2}{4} + \frac{(y-1)^2}{1} = 1$$

$$x^2 + 4(y - 1)^2 = 4$$

20. $(x-1)^2 - (y-1)^2 = 4$

$$\frac{(x-1)^2}{4} - \frac{(y-1)^2}{4} = 1$$

The equation is for a hyperbola in standard form centered at (1, 1). We have $a^2 = 4$ and $b^2 = 4$, so $a = 2$ and $b = 2$.

$$(x-1)^2 - (y-1)^2 = 4$$

21. $(y+1)^2 = 4(x-1)$

$h = 1$

$k = -1$

$4p = 4$

$p = 1$

Vertex: (h, k)

$\qquad (1, -1)$

Focus: $(h+p, k)$

$\qquad (1+1, -1)$

$\qquad (2, -1)$

Directrix: $y = h - p$

$\qquad y = 1 - 1$

$\qquad y = 0$

22. The foci and vertices show that c is 4 and a is 5.

$c^2 = a^2 - b^2$

$4^2 = 5^2 - b^2$

$b^2 = 25 - 16$

$b^2 = 9$

$\dfrac{x^2}{25} + \dfrac{y^2}{9} = 1$

23. The endpoints show that the center is $(1, 2)$.

Since $2a = 18$, $a = 9$ and $a^2 = 81$.

Since $2c = 10$, $c = 5$ and $c^2 = 25$.

$c^2 = a^2 - b^2$

$25 = 81 - b^2$

$b^2 = 81 - 25$

$b^2 = 56$

$\dfrac{(x-1)^2}{81} + \dfrac{(y-2)^2}{56} = 1$

24. The foci and vertices show that c is 3 and a is 2.

$b^2 = c^2 - a^2$

$b^2 = 3^2 - 2^2$

$b^2 = 9 - 4$

$b^2 = 5$

$\dfrac{x^2}{4} - \dfrac{y^2}{5} = 1$

25. The endpoints show that the center is $(-1, 5)$.

Since $2a = 4$, $a = 2$ and $a^2 = 4$.

Since $2c = 6$, $c = 3$ and $c^2 = 9$.

$b^2 = c^2 - a^2$

$b^2 = 9 - 4$

$b^2 = 5$

$\dfrac{(x+1)^2}{4} + \dfrac{(y-5)^2}{5} = 1$

26. Focus: $(h, \overset{4}{\overbrace{}}, \overset{5}{\overbrace{k+p}})$

Directrix: $y = \overset{-1}{\overbrace{k-p}}$

$(k+p) + (k-p) = (5) + (-1)$

$\qquad\qquad 2k = 4$

$\qquad\qquad\; k = 2$

$k + p = 5$

$\qquad p = 5 - k$

$\qquad p = 5 - 2$

$\qquad p = 3$

$(x-h)^2 = 4p(y-k)$

$(x-4)^2 = 4(3)(y-2)$

$(x-4)^2 = 12(y-2)$

27. Focus: $(\overbrace{h+p}^{-2}, \overbrace{k}^{6})$

Directrix: $x = \overbrace{h-p}^{8}$

$(h+p)+(h-p) = (-2)+(8)$

$2h = 6$

$h = 3$

$h+p = -2$

$p = -2-h$

$p = -2-3$

$p = -5$

$(y-k)^2 = 4p(x-h)$

$(y-6)^2 = 4(-5)(x-3)$

$(y-6)^2 = -20(x-3)$

28. $a = 15, b = 10$

$\dfrac{x^2}{15^2} + \dfrac{y^2}{10^2} = 1$

$\dfrac{x^2}{225} + \dfrac{y^2}{100} = 1$

Since the truck is 10 feet wide, substitute $x = 5$ into the equation to find y.

$\dfrac{5^2}{225} + \dfrac{y^2}{100} = 1$

$\dfrac{25}{225} + \dfrac{y^2}{100} = 1$

$\dfrac{1}{9} + \dfrac{y^2}{100} = 1$

$900\left(\dfrac{1}{9} + \dfrac{y^2}{100}\right) = 900(1)$

$100 + 9y^2 = 900$

$9y^2 = 800$

$y^2 = 88.8889$

$y = \sqrt{88.8889}$

$y \approx 9.43$

5 feet from the center, the height of the archway is 9.43 feet. Since the truck's height is 9.5 feet, it will not fit under the archway.

29. Find the distance between the foci.

Since $2a = 40$, $a = 20$ and $a^2 = 400$.

Since $2b = 20$, $b = 10$ and $b^2 = 100$.

$c^2 = a^2 - b^2$

$c^2 = 400 - 100$

$c^2 = 300$

$c = \sqrt{300}$

$= 10\sqrt{3}$

$2c = 20\sqrt{3}$

$2c \approx 34.64$

The kidney stone should be 34.64 cm from the electrode that sends the ultrasound waves.

30. a. Since $2c = 6$, $c = 3$ and $c^2 = 9$.

The ranger at the primary station heard the explosion 6 seconds before the other ranger. This means that the explosion occurred $6 \times 0.35 = 2.1$ miles closer to the primary station.

Since $2a = 2.1$, $a = 1.05$ and $a^2 = 1.1025$.

$b^2 = c^2 - a^2$

$b^2 = 9 - 1.1025$

$b^2 = 7.8975$

$\dfrac{x^2}{1.1025} - \dfrac{y^2}{7.8975} = 1$

b.

31. Consider the peak of the dome as the point $(0, 10)$. Since the width is 15 meters, the points $(\pm 7.5, 0)$ are on the parabola.

Use standard form to find p.

$(x-h)^2 = 4p(y-k)$

$(7.5-0)^2 = 4p(0-10)$

$7.5^2 = -40p$

$\dfrac{56.25}{-40} = p$

$p \approx -1.4$

The light should be about 1.4 meters below the peak of the ceiling.

Section 9.4

Check Point Exercises

1. **a.** $A = 3$ and $C = 2$.
    $AC = 3(2) = 6$. Since $A \neq C$ and $AC > 0$, the graph is an ellipse.

    b. $A = 1$ and $C = 1$. Since $A = C$, the graph is a circle.

    c. $A = 0$ and $C = 1$. Since $AC = 0$, the graph is a parabola.

    d. $A = 9$ and $C = -16$. Since $AC < 0$, the graph is a hyperbola.

2.
$$x = x'\cos 45° - y'\sin 45° = x'\left(\frac{\sqrt{2}}{2}\right) - y'\left(\frac{\sqrt{2}}{2}\right) = \frac{\sqrt{2}}{2}(x' - y')$$

$$y = x'\sin 45° + y'\cos 45° = x'\left(\frac{\sqrt{2}}{2}\right) + y'\left(\frac{\sqrt{2}}{2}\right) = \frac{\sqrt{2}}{2}(x' + y')$$

Substitute into the equation: $xy = 2$

$$\left[\frac{\sqrt{2}}{2}(x' - y')\right]\left[\frac{\sqrt{2}}{2}(x' + y')\right] = 2$$

$$\frac{1}{2}\left(x'^2 - y'^2\right) = 2$$

$$\frac{x'^2}{4} - \frac{y'^2}{4} = 1$$

3. $2x^2 + \sqrt{3}xy + y^2 - 2 = 0$
    Step 1
    $A = 2, B = \sqrt{3}$, and $C = 1$.

    $$\cot 2\theta = \frac{A - C}{B} = \frac{2 - 1}{\sqrt{3}} = \frac{1}{\sqrt{3}} = \frac{\sqrt{3}}{3}$$

    Step 2
    Since $\cot 2\theta = \frac{\sqrt{3}}{3}$, $2\theta = 60°$. Thus, $\theta = 30°$.

    Step 3
    $$x = x'\cos 30° - y'\sin 30° = x'\left(\frac{\sqrt{3}}{2}\right) - y'\left(\frac{1}{2}\right) = \frac{\sqrt{3}x' - y'}{2}$$

    $$y = x'\sin 30° + y'\cos 30° = x'\left(\frac{1}{2}\right) + y'\left(\frac{\sqrt{3}}{2}\right) = \frac{x' + \sqrt{3}y'}{2}$$

Step 4

Substitute into the equation:

$$2x^2 + \sqrt{3}xy + y^2 - 2 = 0$$

$$2\left(\frac{\sqrt{3}x' - y'}{2}\right)^2 + \sqrt{3}\left(\frac{\sqrt{3}x' - y'}{2}\right)\left(\frac{x' + \sqrt{3}y'}{2}\right) + \left(\frac{x' + \sqrt{3}y'}{2}\right)^2 - 2 = 0$$

$$2\left(\frac{3x'^2 - 2\sqrt{3}x'y' + y'^2}{4}\right) + \sqrt{3}\left(\frac{\sqrt{3}x'^2 + 2x'y' - \sqrt{3}y'^2}{4}\right) + \frac{x'^2 + 2\sqrt{3}x'y' + 3y'^2}{4} = 2$$

$$6x'^2 - 4\sqrt{3}x'y' + 2y'^2 + 3x'^2 + 2\sqrt{3}x'y' - 3y'^2 + x'^2 + 2\sqrt{3}x'y' + 3y'^2 = 8$$

$$10x'^2 + 2y'^2 = 8$$

$$\frac{10x'^2}{8} + \frac{2y'^2}{8} = \frac{8}{8}$$

$$\frac{x'^2}{\frac{4}{5}} + \frac{y^2}{4} = 1$$

4. $4x^2 - 4xy + y^2 - 8\sqrt{5}x - 16\sqrt{5}y = 0$

Step 1:

$A = 4, B = -4,$ and $C = 1.$

$$\cot 2\theta = \frac{A - C}{B} = \frac{4 - 1}{-4} = \frac{-3}{4}$$

Step 2: Since θ is always acute, and $\cot 2\theta$ is negative, 2θ is in quadrant II.

The third side of the right tiangle is found using the Pythagorean theorem:

$$(-3)^2 + 4^2 = r^2$$

$$25 = r^2$$

$$r = 5$$

So, $\cos 2\theta = \dfrac{\text{adjacent}}{\text{hypotenuse}} = \dfrac{-3}{5}.$

$$\sin\theta = \sqrt{\frac{1 - \cos 2\theta}{2}} = \sqrt{\frac{1 - \left(-\frac{3}{5}\right)}{2}} = \sqrt{\frac{8}{10}} = \sqrt{\frac{4}{5}} = \frac{2\sqrt{5}}{5} \text{ and}$$

$$\cos\theta = \sqrt{\frac{1 + \cos 2\theta}{2}} = \sqrt{\frac{1 + \left(-\frac{3}{5}\right)}{2}} = \sqrt{\frac{1}{5}} = \frac{\sqrt{5}}{5}$$

Step 3:

$$x = x'\cos\theta - y'\sin\theta = x'\left(\frac{\sqrt{5}}{5}\right) - y'\left(\frac{2\sqrt{5}}{5}\right) = \sqrt{5}\left(\frac{x'-2y'}{5}\right)$$

$$y = x'\sin\theta + y'\cos\theta = x'\left(\frac{2\sqrt{5}}{5}\right) + y'\left(\frac{\sqrt{5}}{5}\right) = \sqrt{5}\left(\frac{2x'+y'}{5}\right)$$

Step 4: Substitute into the equation: $4x^2 - 4xy + y^2 - 8\sqrt{5}x - 16\sqrt{5}y = 0$

$$4\left[\sqrt{5}\left(\frac{x'-2y'}{5}\right)\right]^2 - 4\left[\sqrt{5}\left(\frac{x'-2y'}{5}\right)\right]\left[\sqrt{5}\left(\frac{2x'+y'}{5}\right)\right] + \left[\sqrt{5}\left(\frac{2x'+y'}{5}\right)\right]^2 - 8\sqrt{5}\left[\sqrt{5}\left(\frac{x'-2y'}{5}\right)\right]$$

$$-16\sqrt{5}\left[\sqrt{5}\left(\frac{2x'+y'}{5}\right)\right] = 0$$

$$20\left(\frac{x'^2-4x'y'+4y'^2}{25}\right) - 20\left(\frac{2x'^2-3x'y'-2y'^2}{25}\right) + 5\left(\frac{4x'^2+4x'y'+y'^2}{25}\right) - 40\left(\frac{x'-2y'}{5}\right)$$

$$-80\left(\frac{2x'+y'}{5}\right) = 0$$

Multiply both sides by 25:

$$20x'^2 - 80x'y' + 80y'^2 - 40x'^2 + 60x'y' + 40y'^2 + 20x'^2 + 20x'y' + 5y'^2 - 200x' + 400y'$$

$$-800x' - 400y' = 0$$

$$125y'^2 - 1000x' = 0$$

$$y'^2 - 8x' = 0$$

Step 5: This is a parabola, since it has only the y' squared.

$$y'^2 - 8x' = 0$$

$$y'^2 = 8x'$$

The vertex of the parabola, relative to the $x'y'$ system, is (0, 0). Using a calculator to solve

$\sin\theta = \frac{2\sqrt{5}}{5}$, we find $\theta = \sin^{-1}\left(\frac{2\sqrt{5}}{5}\right) \approx 63°$. Rotate the axes through approximately 63°.

5. $3x^2 - 2\sqrt{3}xy + y^2 + 2x + 2\sqrt{3}y = 0$

$A = 3, B = -2\sqrt{3},$ and $C = 1.$

$B^2 - 4AC = \left(-2\sqrt{3}\right)^2 - 4(3)(1) = 12 - 12 = 0$

Because $B^2 - 4AC = 0,$ the graph of the equation is a parabola.

Exercise Set 9.4

1. $A = 0$ and $C = 1$. Since $AC = 0$, the graph is a parabola.

3. $A = 4$ and $C = -9$. Since $AC = -36 < 0$, the graph is a hyperbola.

5. $A = 4$ and $C = 4$. Since $A = C$, the graph is a circle.

7. $A = 100$ and $C = -7$. Since $AC = -700 < 0$, the graph is a hyperbola.

9. $x = x'\cos 45° - y'\sin 45° = x'\left(\dfrac{\sqrt{2}}{2}\right) - y'\left(\dfrac{\sqrt{2}}{2}\right) = \dfrac{\sqrt{2}}{2}(x' - y')$

$y = x'\sin 45° + y'\cos 45° = x'\left(\dfrac{\sqrt{2}}{2}\right) + y'\left(\dfrac{\sqrt{2}}{2}\right) = \dfrac{\sqrt{2}}{2}(x' + y')$

Substitute into the equation: $xy = -1$

$$\left[\dfrac{\sqrt{2}}{2}(x' - y')\right]\left[\dfrac{\sqrt{2}}{2}(x' + y')\right] = -1$$

$$\dfrac{1}{2}\left(x'^2 - y'^2\right) = -1$$

$$\dfrac{y'^2}{2} - \dfrac{x'^2}{2} = 1$$

11. $x = x'\cos 45° - y'\sin 45° = x'\left(\dfrac{\sqrt{2}}{2}\right) - y'\left(\dfrac{\sqrt{2}}{2}\right) = \dfrac{\sqrt{2}}{2}(x' - y')$

$y = x'\sin 45° + y'\cos 45° = x'\left(\dfrac{\sqrt{2}}{2}\right) + y'\left(\dfrac{\sqrt{2}}{2}\right) = \dfrac{\sqrt{2}}{2}(x' + y')$

Substitute into the equation: $x^2 - 4xy + y^2 - 3 = 0$

$$\left[\dfrac{\sqrt{2}}{2}(x' - y')\right]^2 - 4\left[\dfrac{\sqrt{2}}{2}(x' - y')\right]\left[\dfrac{\sqrt{2}}{2}(x' + y')\right] + \left[\dfrac{\sqrt{2}}{2}(x' + y')\right]^2 - 3 = 0$$

$$\dfrac{1}{2}(x' - y')^2 - 4\left[\dfrac{1}{2}\left(x'^2 - y'^2\right)\right] + \dfrac{1}{2}(x' + y')^2 = 3$$

$$\dfrac{1}{2}\left(x'^2 - 2x'y' + y'^2\right) - 2x'^2 + 2y'^2 + \dfrac{1}{2}\left(x'^2 + 2x'y' + y'^2\right) = 3$$

$$\dfrac{1}{2}x'^2 - x'y' + \dfrac{1}{2}y'^2 - 2x'^2 + 2y'^2 + \dfrac{1}{2}x'^2 + x'y' + \dfrac{1}{2}y'^2 = 3$$

$$-x'^2 + 3y'^2 = 3$$

$$\dfrac{-x'^2}{3} + \dfrac{3y'^2}{3} = \dfrac{3}{3}$$

$$\dfrac{y'^2}{1} - \dfrac{x'^2}{3} = 1$$

13. $x = x'\cos 30° - y'\sin 30° = x'\left(\dfrac{\sqrt{3}}{2}\right) - y'\left(\dfrac{1}{2}\right) = \dfrac{\sqrt{3}x' - y'}{2}$

$y = x'\sin 30° + y'\cos 30° = x'\left(\dfrac{1}{2}\right) + y'\left(\dfrac{\sqrt{3}}{2}\right) = \dfrac{x' + \sqrt{3}y'}{2}$

Substitute into the equation: $23x^2 + 26\sqrt{3}xy - 3y^2 - 144 = 0$

$$23\left(\dfrac{\sqrt{3}x' - y'}{2}\right)^2 + 26\sqrt{3}\left(\dfrac{\sqrt{3}x' - y'}{2}\right)\left(\dfrac{x' + \sqrt{3}y'}{2}\right) - 3\left(\dfrac{x' + \sqrt{3}y'}{2}\right)^2 = 144$$

$$23\left(\dfrac{3x'^2 - 2\sqrt{3}x'y' + y'^2}{4}\right) + 26\sqrt{3}\left(\dfrac{\sqrt{3}x'^2 + 2x'y' - \sqrt{3}y'^2}{4}\right) - 3\left(\dfrac{x'^2 + 2\sqrt{3}x'y' + 3y'^2}{4}\right) = 144$$

$$69x'^2 - 46\sqrt{3}x'y' + 23y'^2 + 78x'^2 + 52\sqrt{3}x'y' - 78y'^2 - 3x'^2 - 6\sqrt{3}x'y' - 9y'^2 = 576$$

$$144x'^2 - 64y'^2 = 576$$

$$\dfrac{144x'^2}{576} - \dfrac{64y'^2}{576} = \dfrac{576}{576}$$

$$\dfrac{x'^2}{4} - \dfrac{y'^2}{9} = 1$$

15. $x^2 + xy + y^2 - 10 = 0$

$A = 1, B = 1,$ and $C = 1.$

$\cot 2\theta = \dfrac{A - C}{B} = \dfrac{1 - 1}{1} = 0$

$2\theta = 90°$

$\theta = 45°$

$x = x'\cos 45° - y'\sin 45° = x'\left(\dfrac{\sqrt{2}}{2}\right) - y'\left(\dfrac{\sqrt{2}}{2}\right) = \dfrac{\sqrt{2}}{2}(x' - y')$

$y = x'\sin 45° + y'\cos 45° = x'\left(\dfrac{\sqrt{2}}{2}\right) + y'\left(\dfrac{\sqrt{2}}{2}\right) = \dfrac{\sqrt{2}}{2}(x' + y')$

17. $3x^2 - 10xy + 3y^2 - 32 = 0$

$A = 3, B = -10,$ and $C = 3.$

$\cot 2\theta = \dfrac{A - C}{B} = \dfrac{3 - 3}{-10} = 0$

$2\theta = 90°$

$\theta = 45°$

$x = x'\cos 45° - y'\sin 45° = x'\left(\dfrac{\sqrt{2}}{2}\right) - y'\left(\dfrac{\sqrt{2}}{2}\right) = \dfrac{\sqrt{2}}{2}(x' - y')$

$y = x'\sin 45° + y'\cos 45° = x'\left(\dfrac{\sqrt{2}}{2}\right) + y'\left(\dfrac{\sqrt{2}}{2}\right) = \dfrac{\sqrt{2}}{2}(x' + y')$

19. $11x^2 + 10\sqrt{3}xy + y^2 - 4 = 0$

$A = 11, B = 10\sqrt{3}$, and $C = 1$.

$$x = x'\cos 30° - y'\sin 30°$$

$$x = x'\left(\frac{\sqrt{3}}{2}\right) - y'\left(\frac{1}{2}\right)$$

$$\cot 2\theta = \frac{A-C}{B} = \frac{11-1}{10\sqrt{3}} = \frac{10}{10\sqrt{3}} = \frac{1}{\sqrt{3}} = \frac{\sqrt{3}}{3} \qquad x = \frac{\sqrt{3}x' - y'}{2}$$

$$2\theta = 60° \qquad\qquad\qquad y = x'\sin 30° + y'\cos 30°$$

$$\theta = 30° \qquad\qquad\qquad y = x'\left(\frac{1}{2}\right) + y'\left(\frac{\sqrt{3}}{2}\right)$$

$$y = \frac{x' + \sqrt{3}y'}{2}$$

21. $10x^2 + 24xy + 17y^2 - 9 = 0$

$A = 10, B = 24$, and $C = 17$.

$$\cot 2\theta = \frac{A-C}{B} = \frac{10-17}{24} = \frac{-7}{24}$$

Since θ is always acute, and $\cot 2\theta$ is negative, 2θ is in quadrant II.
The third side of the right triangle is found by using the Pythagorean theorem:

$$(-7)^2 + 24^2 = r^2$$

$$625 = r^2$$

$$r = 25$$

So, $\cos 2\theta = \frac{-7}{25}$.

$$\sin\theta = \sqrt{\frac{1-\cos 2\theta}{2}} = \sqrt{\frac{1-\left(\frac{-7}{25}\right)}{2}} = \frac{4}{5} \text{ and}$$

$$\cos\theta = \sqrt{\frac{1+\cos 2\theta}{2}} = \sqrt{\frac{1+\left(\frac{-7}{25}\right)}{2}} = \frac{3}{5}$$

$$x = x'\cos\theta - y'\sin\theta$$

$$x = x'\left(\frac{3}{5}\right) - y'\left(\frac{4}{5}\right)$$

$$x = \frac{3x' - 4y'}{5}$$

$$y = x'\sin\theta + y'\cos\theta$$

$$y = x'\left(\frac{4}{5}\right) + y'\left(\frac{3}{5}\right)$$

$$y = \frac{4x' + 3y'}{5}$$

23. $x^2 + 4xy - 2y^2 - 1 = 0$

$A = 1, B = 4,$ and $C = -2.$

$\cot 2\theta = \dfrac{A-C}{B} = \dfrac{1-(-2)}{4} = \dfrac{3}{4}$

Since θ is always acute, and $\cot 2\theta$ is positive, 2θ is in quadrant I.

The third side of the right triangle is found using the Pythagorean theorem:

$3^2 + 4^2 = r^2$

$\qquad 25 = r^2$

$\qquad r = 5$

So, $\cos 2\theta = \dfrac{3}{5}.$

$\sin\theta = \sqrt{\dfrac{1-\cos 2\theta}{2}} = \sqrt{\dfrac{1-\frac{3}{5}}{2}} = \dfrac{\sqrt{5}}{5}$ and

$\cos\theta = \sqrt{\dfrac{1+\cos 2\theta}{2}} = \sqrt{\dfrac{1+\frac{3}{5}}{2}} = \dfrac{2\sqrt{5}}{5}$

$x = x'\cos\theta - y'\sin\theta$

$x = x'\left(\dfrac{2\sqrt{5}}{5}\right) - y'\left(\dfrac{\sqrt{5}}{5}\right)$

$x = \sqrt{5}\left(\dfrac{2x'-y'}{5}\right)$

$y = x'\sin\theta + y'\cos\theta$

$y = x'\left(\dfrac{\sqrt{5}}{5}\right) + y'\left(\dfrac{2\sqrt{5}}{5}\right)$

$y = \sqrt{5}\left(\dfrac{x'+2y'}{5}\right)$

25. $34x^2 - 24xy + 41y^2 - 25 = 0$

$A = 34, B = -24,$ and $C = 41.$

$\cot 2\theta = \dfrac{A-C}{B} = \dfrac{34-41}{-24} = \dfrac{-7}{-24} = \dfrac{7}{24}$

Since θ is always acute, and $\cot 2\theta$ is positive, 2θ is in quadrant I.

The third side of the right triangle is found using the Pythagorean theorem:

$7^2 + 24^2 = r^2$

$\qquad 625 = r^2$

$\qquad r = 25$

So, $\cos 2\theta = \dfrac{7}{25}.$

$\sin\theta = \sqrt{\dfrac{1-\cos 2\theta}{2}} = \sqrt{\dfrac{1-\frac{7}{25}}{2}} = \dfrac{3}{5}$ and $\cos\theta = \sqrt{\dfrac{1+\cos 2\theta}{2}} = \sqrt{\dfrac{1+\frac{7}{25}}{2}} = \dfrac{4}{5}$

$x = x'\cos\theta - y'\sin\theta = x'\left(\dfrac{4}{5}\right) - y'\left(\dfrac{3}{5}\right) = \dfrac{4x'-3y'}{5}$

$y = x'\sin\theta + y'\cos\theta = x'\left(\dfrac{3}{5}\right) + y'\left(\dfrac{4}{5}\right) = \dfrac{3x'+4y'}{5}$

27. a. From Exercise 15,

$$x = \frac{\sqrt{2}}{2}\left(x' - y'\right) \text{ and } y = \frac{\sqrt{2}}{2}\left(x' + y'\right).$$

Substitute into the equation: $x^2 + xy + y^2 - 10 = 0$

$$\left[\frac{\sqrt{2}}{2}\left(x' - y'\right)\right]^2 + \left[\frac{\sqrt{2}}{2}\left(x' - y'\right)\right]\left[\frac{\sqrt{2}}{2}\left(x' + y'\right)\right] + \left[\frac{\sqrt{2}}{2}\left(x' + y'\right)\right]^2 - 10 = 0$$

$$\frac{1}{2}\left(x'^2 - 2x'y' + y'^2\right) + \frac{1}{2}\left(x'^2 - y'^2\right) + \frac{1}{2}\left(x'^2 + 2x'y' + y'^2\right) = 10$$

Multiply both sides by 2.

$$x'^2 - 2x'y' + y'^2 + x'^2 - y'^2 + x'^2 + 2x'y' + y'^2 = 20$$

$$3x'^2 + y'^2 = 20$$

b. $\dfrac{x'^2}{\frac{20}{3}} + \dfrac{y'^2}{20} = 1$

c.

29. a. From Exercise 17, $x = \dfrac{\sqrt{2}}{2}\left(x' - y'\right)$ and $y = \dfrac{\sqrt{2}}{2}\left(x' + y'\right).$

Substitute into the equation: $3x^2 - 10xy + 3y^2 - 32 = 0$

$$3\left[\frac{\sqrt{2}}{2}\left(x' - y'\right)\right]^2 - 10\left[\frac{\sqrt{2}}{2}\left(x' - y'\right)\right]\left[\frac{\sqrt{2}}{2}\left(x' + y'\right)\right] + 3\left[\frac{\sqrt{2}}{2}\left(x' + y'\right)\right]^2 - 32 = 0$$

$$3\left[\frac{1}{2}\left(x'^2 - 2x'y' + y'^2\right)\right] - 10\left[\frac{1}{2}\left(x'^2 - y'^2\right)\right] + 3\left[\frac{1}{2}\left(x'^2 + 2x'y' + y'^2\right)\right] = 32$$

Multiply both sides by 2.

$$3x'^2 - 6x'y' + 3y'^2 - 10x'^2 + 10y'^2 + 3x'^2 + 6x'y' + 3y'^2 = 64$$

$$-4x'^2 + 16y'^2 = 64$$

b. $\dfrac{y'^2}{4} - \dfrac{x'^2}{16} = 1$

c.

783

31. a. From Exercise 19,

$$x = \frac{\sqrt{3}x' - y'}{2} \text{ and } y = \frac{x' + \sqrt{3}y'}{2}.$$

Substitute into the equation: $11x^2 + 10\sqrt{3}xy + y^2 - 4 = 0$

$$11\left(\frac{\sqrt{3}x' - y'}{2}\right)^2 + 10\sqrt{3}\left(\frac{\sqrt{3}x' - y'}{2}\right)\left(\frac{x' + \sqrt{3}y'}{2}\right) + \left(\frac{x' + \sqrt{3}y'}{2}\right)^2 - 4 = 0$$

$$11\left(\frac{3x'^2 - 2\sqrt{3}x'y' + y'^2}{4}\right) + 10\sqrt{3}\left(\frac{\sqrt{3}x'^2 + 2x'y' - \sqrt{3}y'^2}{4}\right) + \frac{x'^2 + 2\sqrt{3}x'y' + 3y'^2}{4} = 4$$

Multiply both sides by 4:

$$33x'^2 - 22\sqrt{3}x'y' + 11y'^2 + 30x'^2 + 20\sqrt{3}x'y' - 30y'^2 + x'^2 + 2\sqrt{3}x'y' + 3y'^2 = 16$$

$$64x'^2 - 16y'^2 = 16$$

b. $\dfrac{x'^2}{\frac{1}{4}} - \dfrac{y'^2}{1} = 1$

c.

33. a. From Exercise 21, $x = \dfrac{3x' - 4y'}{5}$ and $y = \dfrac{4x' + 3y'}{5}$.

Substitute into the equation: $10x^2 + 24xy + 17y^2 - 9 = 0$

$$10\left(\frac{3x' - 4y'}{5}\right)^2 + 24\left(\frac{3x' - 4y'}{5}\right)\left(\frac{4x' + 3y'}{5}\right) + 17\left(\frac{4x' + 3y'}{5}\right)^2 - 9 = 0$$

$$10\left(\frac{9x'^2 - 24x'y' + 16y'^2}{25}\right) + 24\left(\frac{12x'^2 - 7x'y' - 12y'^2}{25}\right) + 17\left(\frac{16x'^2 + 24x'y' + 9y'^2}{25}\right) = 9$$

Multiply both sides by 25:

$$90x'^2 - 240x'y' + 160y'^2 + 288x'^2 - 168x'y' - 288y'^2 + 272x'^2 + 408x'y' + 153y'^2 = 225$$

$$650x'^2 + 25y'^2 = 225$$

b. $\dfrac{x'^2}{\frac{9}{26}} + \dfrac{y'^2}{9} = 1$

c.

The axes are rotated by $\theta = \sin^{-1}\left(\dfrac{4}{5}\right) \approx 53°$.

35. a. From Exercise 23,

$$x = \sqrt{5}\left(\frac{2x'-y'}{5}\right) \text{ and } y = \sqrt{5}\left(\frac{x'+2y'}{5}\right).$$

Substitute into the equation: $x^2 + 4xy - 2y^2 - 1 = 0$

$$\left[\sqrt{5}\left(\frac{2x'-y'}{5}\right)\right]^2 + 4\left[\sqrt{5}\left(\frac{2x'-y'}{5}\right)\right]\left[\sqrt{5}\left(\frac{x'+2y'}{5}\right)\right] - 2\left[\sqrt{5}\left(\frac{x'+2y'}{5}\right)\right]^2 = 1$$

$$5\left(\frac{4x'^2 - 4x'y' + y'^2}{25}\right) + 20\left(\frac{2x'^2 + 3x'y' - 2y'^2}{25}\right) - 10\left(\frac{x'^2 + 4x'y' + 4y'^2}{25}\right) = 1$$

Multiply both sides by 25:

$$20x'^2 - 20x'y' + 5y'^2 + 40x'^2 + 60x'y' - 40y'^2 - 10x'^2 - 40x'y' - 40y'^2 = 25$$

$$50x'^2 - 75y'^2 = 25$$

b. $\dfrac{x'^2}{\frac{1}{2}} - \dfrac{y'^2}{\frac{1}{3}} = 1$

c.

The axes are rotated by $\theta = \sin^{-1}\left(\dfrac{\sqrt{5}}{5}\right) \approx 27°$.

37. a. From Exercise 25,

$$x = \frac{4x'-3y'}{5} \text{ and } y = \frac{3x'+4y'}{5}.$$

Substitute into the equation: $34x^2 - 24xy + 41y^2 - 25 = 0$

$$34\left(\frac{4x'-3y'}{5}\right)^2 - 24\left(\frac{4x'-3y'}{5}\right)\left(\frac{3x'+4y'}{5}\right) + 41\left(\frac{3x'+4y'}{5}\right)^2 = 25$$

$$34\left(\frac{16x'^2 - 24x'y' + 9y'^2}{25}\right) - 24\left(\frac{12x'^2 + 7x'y' - 12y'^2}{25}\right) + 41\left(\frac{9x'^2 + 24x'y' + 16y'^2}{25}\right) = 25$$

Multiply both sides by 25:

$$544x'^2 - 816x'y' + 306y'^2 - 288x'^2 - 168x'y' + 288y'^2 + 369x'^2 + 984x'y' + 656y'^2 = 625$$

$$625x'^2 + 1250y'^2 = 625$$

b. $$\frac{625x'^2 + 1250y'^2}{625} = \frac{625}{625}$$

$$\frac{x'^2}{1} + \frac{y'^2}{\frac{1}{2}} = 1$$

c.

The axes are rotated by $\theta = \sin^{-1}\left(\dfrac{3}{5}\right) \approx 37°$.

39. $5x^2 - 2xy + 5y^2 - 12 = 0$

$A = 5, B = -2,$ and $C = 5$.

$B^2 - 4AC = (-2)^2 - 4(5)(5) = -96$.

Since $B^2 - 4AC < 0$, the graph is an ellipse or a circle.

41. $24x^2 + 16\sqrt{3}xy + 8y^2 - x + \sqrt{3}y - 8 = 0$

$A = 24, B = 16\sqrt{3},$ and $C = 8$.

$B^2 - 4AC = \left(16\sqrt{3}\right)^2 - 4(24)(8) = 768 - 768 = 0$

Since $B^2 - 4AC = 0$, the graph is a parabola.

43. $23x^2 + 26\sqrt{3}xy - 3y^2 - 144 = 0$

$A = 23, B = 26\sqrt{3},$ and $C = -3$.

$B^2 - 4AC = \left(26\sqrt{3}\right)^2 - 4(23)(-3) = 2028 + 276 = 2304$

Since $B^2 - 4AC > 0$, the graph is a hyperbola.

45. Find θ:

$\cot 2\theta = \dfrac{A - C}{B} = \dfrac{5 - 5}{-6} = 0$

$2\theta = 90°$

$\theta = 45°$

Substitute θ into rotation formulas:

$x = x'\cos\theta - y'\sin\theta = x'\cos 45° - y'\sin 45° = x'\dfrac{\sqrt{2}}{2} - y'\dfrac{\sqrt{2}}{2} = \dfrac{x'\sqrt{2} - y'\sqrt{2}}{2}$

$y = x'\sin\theta + y'\cos\theta = x'\sin 45° + y'\cos 45° = x'\dfrac{\sqrt{2}}{2} + y'\dfrac{\sqrt{2}}{2} = \dfrac{x'\sqrt{2} + y'\sqrt{2}}{2}$

Substitute into equation:

$$5x^2 - 6xy + 5y^2 - 8 = 0$$

$$5\left(\dfrac{x'\sqrt{2} - y'\sqrt{2}}{2}\right)^2 - 6\left(\dfrac{x'\sqrt{2} - y'\sqrt{2}}{2}\right)\left(\dfrac{x'\sqrt{2} + y'\sqrt{2}}{2}\right) + 5\left(\dfrac{x'\sqrt{2} + y'\sqrt{2}}{2}\right)^2 - 8 = 0$$

$$\dfrac{x'^2}{4} + \dfrac{y'^2}{1} = 1$$

$\dfrac{x'^2}{4} + \dfrac{y'^2}{1} = 1$ is an ellipse with minor axis vertices of $(0, -1)$ and $(0, 1)$.

47. Find $\sin\theta$ and $\cos\theta$:

$$\cot 2\theta = \frac{A-C}{B} = \frac{1-4}{-4} = \frac{3}{4}$$

$$\cot 2\theta = \frac{x}{y} = \frac{3}{4}$$

$$r = \sqrt{x^2 + y^2} = \sqrt{3^2 + 4^2} = 5$$

$$\sin\theta = \sqrt{\frac{1-\cos 2\theta}{2}} = \sqrt{\frac{1-\left(\dfrac{3}{5}\right)}{2}} = \frac{\sqrt{5}}{5} \quad \text{and} \quad \cos\theta = \sqrt{\frac{1+\cos 2\theta}{2}} = \sqrt{\frac{1+\left(\dfrac{3}{5}\right)}{2}} = \frac{2\sqrt{5}}{5}$$

Substitute into rotation formulas:

$$x = x'\cos\theta - y'\sin\theta = x'\frac{2\sqrt{5}}{5} - y'\frac{\sqrt{5}}{5} = \frac{x'2\sqrt{5} - y'\sqrt{5}}{5}$$

$$y = x'\sin\theta + y'\cos\theta = x'\frac{\sqrt{5}}{5} + y'\frac{2\sqrt{5}}{5} = \frac{x'\sqrt{5} - y'2\sqrt{5}}{5}$$

Substitute into equation:

$$x^2 - 4xy + 4y^2 + 5\sqrt{5}y - 10 = 0$$

$$\left(\frac{x'2\sqrt{5} - y'\sqrt{5}}{5}\right)^2 - 4\left(\frac{x'2\sqrt{5} - y'\sqrt{5}}{5}\right)\left(\frac{x'\sqrt{5} + y'2\sqrt{5}}{5}\right) + 4\left(\frac{x'\sqrt{5} + y'2\sqrt{5}}{5}\right)^2 + 5\sqrt{5}\left(\frac{x'\sqrt{5} + y'2\sqrt{5}}{5}\right) - 10 = 0$$

$$x' + y'^2 + 2y' - 2 = 0$$

$$x' = -y'^2 - 2y' + 2$$

$$x' = -\left(y'^2 + 2y'\right) + 2$$

$$x' = -\left(y'^2 + 2y' + 1\right) + 2 + 1$$

$$x' = -\left(y' + 1\right)^2 + 3$$

$x' = -\left(y' + 1\right)^2 + 3$ is a parabola with vertex $(3, -1.)$

In Exercises 55–59, use the following equations:

$$y_1 = \frac{-\left(Bx + E\right) + \sqrt{\left(Bx + E\right)^2 - 4C\left(Ax^2 + Dx + F\right)}}{2C} \quad \text{and} \quad y_2 = \frac{-\left(Bx + E\right) - \sqrt{\left(Bx + E\right)^2 - 4C\left(Ax^2 + Dx + F\right)}}{2C}$$

for equations of the form $Ax^2 + Bxy + Cy^2 + Dx + Ey + F = 0$.

55. $A = 7$, $B = 8$, $C = 1$, $D = 0$, $E = 0$, and $F = -1$.

Graph $y_1 = \dfrac{-8x + \sqrt{64x^2 - 4\left(7x^2 - 1\right)}}{2}$ and $y_2 = \dfrac{-8x - \sqrt{64x^2 - 4\left(7x^2 - 1\right)}}{2}$.

57. $A = 3, B = -6, C = 3, D = 10, E = -8,$ and $F = -2.$

Graph $y_1 = \dfrac{-(-6x-8)+\sqrt{(-6x-8)^2 - 12\left(3x^2 + 10x - 2\right)}}{6}$ and

$y_2 = \dfrac{-(-6x-8)-\sqrt{(-6x-8)^2 - 12\left(3x^2 + 10x - 2\right)}}{6}$.

59. $A = 1, B = 4, C = 4, D = 10\sqrt{5}, E = 0,$ and $F = -9.$

Graph $y_1 = \dfrac{-4x + \sqrt{16x^2 - 16\left(x^2 + 10\sqrt{5}x - 9\right)}}{8}$ and $y_2 = \dfrac{-4x - \sqrt{16x^2 - 16\left(x^2 + 10\sqrt{5}x - 9\right)}}{8}$.

61. $A = 3, B = 2,$ and $C = 3.$

$\cot 2\theta = \dfrac{A - C}{B} = \dfrac{3 - 3}{2} = 0$

$2\theta = 90°$

$\theta = 45°$

$x = x'\cos 45° - y'\sin 45° = x'\left(\dfrac{\sqrt{2}}{2}\right) - y'\left(\dfrac{\sqrt{2}}{2}\right) = \dfrac{\sqrt{2}}{2}(x' - y')$

$y = x'\sin 45° + y'\cos 45° = x'\left(\dfrac{\sqrt{2}}{2}\right) + y'\left(\dfrac{\sqrt{2}}{2}\right) = \dfrac{\sqrt{2}}{2}(x' + y')$

Substitute into the equation: $3x^2 - 2xy + 3y^2 + 2 = 0$

$3\left[\dfrac{\sqrt{2}}{2}(x' - y')\right]^2 - 2\left[\dfrac{\sqrt{2}}{2}(x' - y')\right]\left[\dfrac{\sqrt{2}}{2}(x' + y')\right] + 3\left[\dfrac{\sqrt{2}}{2}(x' + y')\right]^2 + 2 = 0$

$\dfrac{3}{2}\left(x'^2 - 2x'y' + y'^2\right) - \left(x'^2 - y'^2\right) + \dfrac{3}{2}\left(x'^2 + 2x'y' + y'^2\right) = -2$

Multiply both sides by 2:

$3x'^2 - 6x'y' + 3y'^2 - 2x'^2 + 2y'^2 + 3x'^2 + 6x'y' + 3y'^2 = -4$

$4x'^2 + 8y'^2 = -4$

$\dfrac{4x'^2 + 8y'^2}{-4} = \dfrac{-4}{-4}$

$-x'^2 - 2y'^2 = 1$

There are no solutions to this equation since the left side of the equation is negative or 0 for all values of x' and y'. Thus, there are no points on the graph of this equation, just as one hand clapping makes no sound.

63.
$$A' = A\cos^2\theta + B\sin\theta\cos\theta + C\sin^2\theta$$
$$C' = A\sin^2\theta - B\sin\theta\cos\theta + C\cos^2\theta$$
$$A' + C' = A\cos^2\theta + B\sin\theta\cos\theta + C\sin^2\theta + A\sin^2\theta - B\sin\theta\cos\theta + C\cos^2\theta$$
$$= A\left(\cos^2\theta + \sin^2\theta\right) + B\left(\sin\theta\cos\theta - \sin\theta\cos\theta\right) + C\left(\sin^2\theta + \cos^2\theta\right)$$
$$= A(1) + B(0) + C(1)$$
$$= A + C$$

Section 9.5

Check Point Exercises

1.

t	$x = t^2 + 1$	$y = 3t$	(x, y)
-2	$(-2)^2 + 1 = 5$	$3(-2) = -6$	$(5, -6)$
-1	$(-1)^2 + 1 = 2$	$3(-1) = -3$	$(2, -3)$
0	$0^2 + 1 = 1$	$3(0) = 0$	$(1, 0)$
1	$1^2 + 1 = 2$	$3(1) = 3$	$(2, 3)$
2	$2^2 + 1 = 5$	$3(2) = 6$	$(5, 6)$

2. $x = \sqrt{t} \implies t = x^2$

Using $t = x^2$ and $y = 2t - 1$, $y = 2x^2 - 1$.

Since $t \geq 0$, x is nonnegative.

3. $x = 6\cos t$ and $y = 4\sin t$, $\pi \le t \le 2\pi$

$\dfrac{x}{6} = \cos t \qquad \dfrac{y}{4} = \sin t$

Square and add the equations:

$$\dfrac{x^2}{36} = \cos^2 t$$

$$+ \qquad \dfrac{y^2}{16} = \sin^2 t$$

$$\overline{\qquad\qquad\qquad\qquad\qquad}$$

$$\dfrac{x^2}{36} + \dfrac{y^2}{16} = \cos^2 t + \sin^2 t$$

$$\dfrac{x^2}{36} + \dfrac{y^2}{16} = 1$$

Since t is in the interval $\left[\pi, 2\pi\right]$, we use

$t = \pi$, $t = \dfrac{3\pi}{2}$, and $t = 2\pi$:

$t = \pi$: $x = 6\cos\pi = -6$

$\qquad\qquad y = 4\sin\pi = 0$

$t = \dfrac{3\pi}{2}$: $x = 6\cos\dfrac{3\pi}{2} = 0$

$\qquad\qquad y = 4\sin\dfrac{3\pi}{2} = -4$

$t = 2\pi$: $x = 6\cos 2\pi = 6$

$\qquad\qquad y = 4\cos 2\pi = 0$

4. $y = x^2 - 25$

Let $x = t$. Then $y = t^2 - 25$.

The parametric equations are $x = t$ and

$y = t^2 - 25$.

Exercise Set 9.5

1. $x = 3 - 5(1) = -2$

$y = 4 + 2(1) = 6$;

$\quad (-2, 6)$

3. $x = 2^2 + 1 = 5$

$y = 5 - 2^3 = 5 - 8 = -3$;

$\quad (5, -3)$

5. $x = 4 + 2\cos\dfrac{\pi}{2} = 4 + 2(0) = 4$

$y = 3 + 5\sin\dfrac{\pi}{2} = 3 + 5(1) = 8$;

$\quad (4, 8)$

7. $x = (60\cos 30°)(2) = \left(60 \cdot \dfrac{\sqrt{3}}{2}\right)(2) = 60\sqrt{3}$

$y = 5 + (60\sin 30°)(2) - 16(2)^2$

$\quad = 5 + \left(60 \cdot \dfrac{1}{2}\right)(2) - 16 \cdot 4$

$\quad = 5 + 60 - 64 = 1$;

$\quad \left(60\sqrt{3}, 1\right)$

9.

t	$x = t + 2$	$y = t^2$	(x, y)
-2	$-2 + 2 = 0$	$(-2)^2 = 4$	$(0, 4)$
-1	$-1 + 2 = 1$	$(-1)^2 = 1$	$(1, 1)$
0	$0 + 2 = 2$	$0^2 = 0$	$(2, 0)$
1	$1 + 2 = 3$	$1^2 = 1$	$(3, 1)$
2	$2 + 2 = 4$	$2^2 = 4$	$(4, 4)$

11.

t	$x = t - 2$	$y = 2t + 1$	(x, y)
-2	$-2 - 2 = -4$	$2(-2) + 1 = -3$	$(-4, -3)$
-1	$-1 - 2 = -3$	$2(-1) + 1 = -1$	$(-3, -1)$
0	$0 - 2 = -2$	$2(0) + 1 = 1$	$(-2, 1)$
1	$1 - 2 = -1$	$2(1) + 1 = 3$	$(-1, 3)$
2	$2 - 2 = 0$	$2(2) + 1 = 5$	$(0, 5)$
3	$3 - 2 = 1$	$2(3) + 1 = 7$	$(1, 7)$

13.

t	$x = t + 1$	$y = \sqrt{t}$	(x, y)
0	$0 + 1 = 1$	$\sqrt{0} = 0$	$(1, 0)$
1	$1 + 1 = 2$	$\sqrt{1} = 1$	$(2, 1)$
4	$4 + 1 = 5$	$\sqrt{4} = 2$	$(5, 2)$
9	$9 + 1 = 10$	$\sqrt{9} = 3$	$(10, 3)$

15.

t	$x = \cos t$	$y = \sin t$	(x, y)
0	$\cos 0 = 1$	$\sin 0 = 0$	$(1, 0)$
$\dfrac{\pi}{2}$	$\cos \dfrac{\pi}{2} = 0$	$\sin \dfrac{\pi}{2} = 1$	$(0, 1)$
π	$\cos \pi = -1$	$\sin \pi = 0$	$(-1, 0)$
$\dfrac{3\pi}{2}$	$\cos \dfrac{3\pi}{2} = 0$	$\sin \dfrac{3\pi}{2} = -1$	$(0, -1)$
2π	$\cos 2\pi = 1$	$\sin 2\pi = 0$	$(1, 0)$

17.

t	$x = t^2$	$y = t^3$	(x, y)
-2	$(-2)^2 = 4$	$(-2)^3 = -8$	$(4, -8)$
-1	$(-1)^2 = 1$	$(-1)^3 = -1$	$(1, -1)$
0	$0^2 = 0$	$0^3 = 0$	$(0, 0)$
1	$1^2 = 1$	$1^3 = 1$	$(1, 1)$
2	$2^2 = 4$	$2^3 = 8$	$(4, 8)$

19.

t	$x = 2t$	$y = |t - 1|$	(x, y)
-2	$2(-2) = -4$	$|-2 - 1| = 3$	$(-4, 3)$
-1	$2(-1) = -2$	$|-1 - 1| = 2$	$(-2, 2)$
0	$2(0) = 0$	$|0 - 1| = 1$	$(0, 1)$
1	$2(1) = 2$	$|1 - 1| = 0$	$(2, 0)$
2	$2(2) = 4$	$|2 - 1| = 1$	$(4, 1)$

21. $x = t \Rightarrow y = 2x$

23. $x = 2t - 4$

$\dfrac{x+4}{2} = t$

Substitute into y:

$y = 4\left(\dfrac{x+4}{2}\right)^2 = (x+4)^2$

$y = (x+4)^2$

25. $x = \sqrt{t}$

$x^2 = t$

Substitute into y:

$y = x^2 - 1$

Since $t \geq 0$ in $x = \sqrt{t}$, $x \geq 0$.

27. $x = 2\sin t$ and $y = 2\cos t$

$\dfrac{x}{2} = \sin t \qquad \dfrac{y}{2} = \cos t$

Square and add the equations:

$\dfrac{x^2}{4} = \sin^2 t$

$+ \quad \dfrac{y^2}{4} = \cos^2 t$

$\rule{4cm}{0.4pt}$

$\dfrac{x^2}{4} + \dfrac{y^2}{4} = \sin^2 t + \cos^2 t$

$\dfrac{x^2}{4} + \dfrac{y^2}{4} = 1$

$x^2 + y^2 = 4$

The circle centered at $(0, 0)$ with radius 2.

29. $x = 1 + 3\cos t$ and $y = 2 + 3\sin t$

$\dfrac{x-1}{3} = \cos t$ $\qquad$ $\dfrac{y-2}{3} = \sin t$

Square and add the equations:

$$\dfrac{(x-1)^2}{9} = \cos^2 t$$

$$+ \quad \dfrac{(y-2)^2}{9} = \sin^2 t$$

$$\dfrac{(x-1)^2}{9} + \dfrac{(y-2)^2}{9} = \cos^2 t + \sin^2 t$$

$$\dfrac{(x-1)^2}{9} + \dfrac{(y-2)^2}{9} = 1$$

$$(x-1)^2 + (y-2)^2 = 9$$

This is a circle centered at (1, 2) with radius 3.

31. $x = 2\cos t$ and $y = 3\sin t$

$\dfrac{x}{2} = \cos t$ $\qquad$ $\dfrac{y}{3} = \sin t$

Square and add the equations:

$$\dfrac{x^2}{4} = \cos^2 t$$

$$+ \quad \dfrac{y^2}{9} = \sin^2 t$$

$$\dfrac{x^2}{4} + \dfrac{y^2}{9} = \cos^2 t + \sin^2 t$$

$$\dfrac{x^2}{4} + \dfrac{y^2}{9} = 1$$

This is an ellipse centered at (0, 0).

33. $x = 1 + 3\cos t$ and $y = -1 + 2\sin t$

$\dfrac{x-1}{3} = \cos t$ $\qquad$ $\dfrac{y+1}{2} = \sin t$

Square and add the equations:

$$\dfrac{(x-1)^2}{9} = \cos^2 t$$

$$+ \quad \dfrac{(y+1)^2}{4} = \sin^2 t$$

$$\dfrac{(x-1)^2}{9} + \dfrac{(y+1)^2}{4} = \cos^2 t + \sin^2 t$$

$$\dfrac{(x-1)^2}{9} + \dfrac{(y+1)^2}{4} = 1$$

Since $0 \le t \le \pi$, $-1 \le \cos t \le 1$ and $0 \le \sin t \le 1$.

Thus, $-1 \le \dfrac{x-1}{3} \le 1$ and $0 \le \dfrac{y+1}{2} \le 1$. Hence,

$-2 \le x \le 4$ and $-1 \le y \le 1$. This is the upper half of an ellipse centered at (−1, 1).

35. $x = \sec t$ and $y = \tan t$

Square and subtract the equations:

$$x^2 = \sec^2 t$$

$$- \quad (y^2 = \tan^2 t)$$

$$x^2 - y^2 = \sec^2 t - \tan^2 t$$

$$x^2 - y^2 = 1$$

This is a hyperbola centered at (0, 0).

37. $x = t^2 + 2$ and $y = t^2 - 2$

$x - 2 = t^2$

Substitute $x - 2$ into $y = t^2 - 2$ for t^2:

$y = (x - 2) - 2$

$y = x - 4$

Since $t^2 \geq 0$ for all t, $x \geq 2$ and $y \geq -2$.

39. $x = 2^t$ and $y = 2^{-t}$

$$y = \left(2^t\right)^{-1}$$

Substitute x in $y = \left(2^t\right)^{-1}$ for 2^t:

$y = (x)^{-1}$

$y = \dfrac{1}{x}$

Since $t \geq 0$, $x \geq 1$ and $y \geq 0$.

41. $x = h + r\cos t$ and $y = k + r\sin t$

$\dfrac{x - h}{r} = \cos t$ $\dfrac{y - k}{r} = \sin t$

Square and add the equations:

$$\frac{(x-h)^2}{r^2} = \cos^2 t$$

$$+ \quad \frac{(y-k)^2}{r^2} = \sin^2 t$$

$$\frac{(x-h)^2}{r^2} + \frac{(y-k)^2}{r^2} = \cos^2 t + \sin^2 t$$

$$\frac{(x-h)^2}{r^2} + \frac{(y-k)^2}{r^2} = 1$$

$$(x-h)^2 + (y-k)^2 = r^2$$

43. $x = h + a\sec t$ and $y = k + b\tan t$

$\dfrac{x - h}{a} = \sec t$ $\dfrac{y - k}{b} = \tan t$

Square and subtract the equations:

$$\frac{(x-h)^2}{a^2} = \sec^2 t$$

$$- \quad \left(\frac{(y-k)^2}{b^2} = \tan^2 t\right)$$

$$\frac{(x-h)^2}{a^2} - \frac{(y-k)^2}{b^2} = \sec^2 t - \tan^2 t$$

$$\frac{(x-h)^2}{a^2} - \frac{(y-k)^2}{b^2} = 1$$

45. $h = 3$, $k = 5$, and $r = 6$

$x = h + r\cos t$ and $y = k + r\sin t$

$x = 3 + 6\cos t$ $y = 5 + 6\sin t$

47. $h = -2$, $k = 3$, $a = 5$, $b = 2$

$x = h + a\cos t$ and $y = k + b\sin t$

$x = -2 + 5\cos t$ $y = 3 + 2\sin t$

49. $h = 0$, $k = 0$, $a = 4$, $c = 6$

$c^2 = a^2 + b^2$

$6^2 = 4^2 + b^2$

$36 - 16 = b^2$

$b = \sqrt{20} = 2\sqrt{5}$

$x = h + a\sec t$ and $y = k + b\tan t$

$x = 0 + 4\sec t$ $y = 0 + 2\sqrt{5}\tan t$

$x = 4\sec t$ $y = 2\sqrt{5}\tan t$

51. $x_1 = -2$, $y_1 = 4$, $x_2 = 1$, $y_2 = 7$

53. Answers may vary.
Sample answer:
$x = t$ and $y = 4t - 3$; $x = t + 1$ and $y = 4t + 1$

55. Answers may vary.
Sample answer:
$x = t$ and $y = t^2 + 4$; $x = t + 1$ and $y = t^2 + 2t + 5$

57. a.

b.

c.

d.

Explanations of how the curves differ from each other may vary.

59.

Domain: [−2, 6];
Range: [−5, 3]

61.

Domain: $\left[\dfrac{3}{4}, \infty\right)$;

Range: $[-\infty, \infty]$

63.

a. increasing: $[-\infty, \infty]$

b. no maximum or minimum

65.

a. decreasing: $[-\infty, 1]$; increasing: $(1, \infty)$

b. minimum of −5 at $x = 1$

67.

a. increasing: $(1, 2\pi)$; decreasing: $(2\pi, 4\pi)$

b. maximum of 4 at $x = 2\pi$,
minimum of 0 at $x = 0$ and $x = 4\pi$

69. a. $x = (180\cos 40°)t$

$y = 3 + (180\sin 40°)t - 16t^2$

b. After 1 second:
$x = (180\cos 40°) \cdot 1$
≈ 137.9 feet in distance

$y = 3 + (180\sin 40°)1 - 16 \cdot 1^2$
≈ 102.7 feet in height

After 2 seconds:
$x = (180\cos 40°) \cdot 2$
≈ 275.8 feet in distance

$y = 3 + (180\sin 40°) \cdot 2 - 16 \cdot 2^2$
≈ 170.4 feet in height

After 3 seconds:
$x = (180\cos 40°) \cdot 3$
≈ 413.7 feet in distance

$y = 3 + (180\sin 40°) \cdot 3 - 16 \cdot 3^2$
≈ 206.1 feet in height

The points on the curve are (137.9, 102.7), (275.8, 170.4), (413.7, 206.1).

c. The ball is no longer in flight when its height above ground is zero:

$0 = 3 + (180\sin 40°)t - 16t^2$

$0 = -16t^2 + (180\sin 40°)t + 3$

$t = \dfrac{-(180\sin 40°) \pm \sqrt{(180\sin 40°)^2 - 4 \cdot (-16)(3)}}{2(-16)}$

$t \approx -.03$　or　$t \approx 7.3$

Since we cannot use the negative time, the ball hits the ground at $t \approx 7.3$ seconds. The total horizontal distance is:

$x = (180\cos 40°) \cdot (7.3) \approx 1006.6$ feet

d. Answers may vary.

79.

81.

In Exercises 83-85, use the equations:

$x = (v_0\cos\theta)t$　and　$y = h + (v_0\sin\theta)t - 16t^2$　where v_0 is the initial velocity, θ is the angle from horizontal, h is the height above the ground, and t is the time, in seconds.

83.　$x = (200\cos 55°)t$　and　$y = (200\sin 55°)t - 16t^2$

Window: $[-100, 1500] \times [-100, 500]$

The maximum height is 419.4 feet at a time of 5.1 seconds. The range of the projective is 1174.6 feet horizontally. It hits the ground at 10.2 seconds.

85. a.　$x = (140\cos 22°)t$　and
　　　$y = 5 + (140\sin 22°)t - 16t^2$

b.

Window:　$[-100, 500] \times [-10, 60]$

c. The maximum height is 48.0 feet. It occurs at 1.6 seconds.

d. The ball is in the air for 3.4 seconds.

e. The ball travels 437.5 feet.

87.　$x = 3\sin t$　and　$y = 3\cos t$

Section 9.6

Check Point Exercises

1. Graph $r = \dfrac{4}{2 - \cos \theta}$.

    Step 1: Divide numerator and denominator by 2 to write the equation in standard form:

    $$r = \frac{2}{1 - \frac{1}{2}\cos \theta}$$

    Step 2: $e = \dfrac{1}{2}$ and $ep = \dfrac{1}{2}p = 2$, so $p = 4$.

    Since $e < 1$, the graph is an ellipse.

    Step 3: The graph has symmetry with respect to the polar axis. One focus is at the pole and the directrix is $x = -4$.

    Find the vertices by selecting $\theta = 0$ and $\theta = \pi$:

    $(4, 0)$ and $\left(\dfrac{4}{3}, \pi\right)$.

    Sketch the upper half by plotting some points, then use the symmetry of the graph to sketch the lower half.

2. Graph $r = \dfrac{8}{4 + 4\sin \theta}$.

    Step 1: Divide numerator and denominator by 4 to write the equation in standard form:

    $$r = \frac{2}{1 + \sin \theta}$$

    Step 2: $e = 1$ and $ep = 1$ $p = 2$, so $p = 2$.

    Since $e = 1$, the graph is parabola.

    Step 3: The graph has symmetry with respect to

    $\theta = \dfrac{\pi}{2}$. The focus is at the pole and the directrix

    is $y = 2$. Since the vertex is on the line $\theta = \dfrac{\pi}{2}$

    (y-axis) the vertex is at $\left(1, \dfrac{\pi}{2}\right)$. To find the

    intercepts on the polar axis, select $\theta = 0$ and

$\theta = \pi$: $(2, 0)$ and $(2, \pi)$.

Sketch the right half by plotting some points, then use symmetry to sketch the left half.

3. Graph $r = \dfrac{9}{3 - 9\cos \theta}$.

    Step 1: Divide numerator and denominator by 3 to write the equation in standard form:

    $$r = \frac{3}{1 - 3\cos \theta}$$

    Step 2: $e = 3$ and $ep = 3p = 3$, so $p = 1$. Since $e > 1$, the graph is a hyperbola.

    Step 3: The graph is symmetric with respect to the polar axis. One focus is at the pole and the directrix is at $x = -1$. The transverse axis is horizontal and the vertices lie on the polar axis. Find them by selecting $\theta = 0$ and $0 = \pi$:

    $\left(-\dfrac{3}{2}, 0\right)$ and $\left(\dfrac{3}{4}, \pi\right)$.

    Sketch the upper half of the hyperbola by plotting some points, then use symmetry to sketch the lower half.

Exercise Set 9.6

1. $r = \dfrac{3}{1 + \sin\theta}$

   $e = 1$ and $ep = 3$, so $p = 3$.

   a.   The graph is a parabola.

   b.   The directrix is 3 units above the pole, at $y = 3$.

3. $r = \dfrac{6}{3 - 2\cos\theta}$

   Divide numerator and denominator

   by 3: $r = \dfrac{2}{1 - \frac{2}{3}\cos\theta}$.

   $e = \dfrac{2}{3}$ and $ep = 2$, so $p = 3$.

   a.   The graph is an ellipse.

   b.   The directrix is 3 units to the left of the pole, at $x = -3$.

5. $r = \dfrac{8}{2 + 2\sin\theta}$

   Divide numerator and denominator

   by 2: $r = \dfrac{4}{1 + \sin\theta}$.

   $e = 1$ and $ep = 4$, so $p = 4$.

   a.   The graph is a parabola.

   b.   The directrix is 4 units above the pole, at $y = 4$.

7. $r = \dfrac{12}{2 - 4\cos\theta}$

   Divide numerator and denominator

   by 2: $r = \dfrac{6}{1 - 2\cos\theta}$.

   $e = 2$ and $ep = 6$, so $p = 3$.

   a.   The graph is a hyperbola.

   b.   The directrix is 3 units to the left of the pole, at $x = -3$.

9. $r = \dfrac{1}{1 + \sin\theta}$

   $e = 1$ and $ep = 1$, so $p = 1$.

   Since $e = 1$, the graph is a parabola. It is

symmetric with respect to the y-axis and has a

directrix at $y = 1$. The vertex is at $\left(\dfrac{1}{2}, \dfrac{\pi}{2}\right)$.

11. $r = \dfrac{2}{1 - \cos\theta}$

    $e = 1$ and $ep = 2$, so $p = 2$.

    Since $e = 1$, the graph is a parabola. It is
    symmetric with respect to the polar axis and has
    a directrix at $x = -2$. The vertex is at $(1, \pi)$.

13. $r = \dfrac{12}{5 + 3\cos\theta}$

    Write in standard form:

    $r = \dfrac{\frac{12}{5}}{1 + \frac{3}{5}\cos\theta}$

    $e = \dfrac{3}{5}$ and $ep = \dfrac{12}{5}$, so $p = 4$. Since $e < 1$, the

    graph is an ellipse. It is symmetric with respect
    to the polar axis and has a directrix at $x = 4$.

15. $r = \dfrac{6}{2 - 2\sin\theta}$

Write in standard form: $r = \dfrac{3}{1 - \sin\theta}$

$e = 1$ and $ep = 3$, so $p = 3$. Since $e = 1$, the graph is a parabola. It is symmetric with respect to the y-axis and has a directrix at $y = -3$. The vertex is at $\left(\dfrac{3}{2}, \dfrac{3\pi}{2}\right)$.

17. $r = \dfrac{8}{2 - 4\cos\theta}$

Write in standard form:

$r = \dfrac{4}{1 - 2\cos\theta}$

$e = 2$ and $ep = 4$, so $p = 2$. Since $e > 1$, the graph is a hyperbola. It is symmetric with respect to the polar axis and it has a directrix at $x = -2$. The transverse axis is horizontal and the vertices lie on the polar axis

19. $r = \dfrac{12}{3 - 6\cos\theta}$

Write in standard form:

$r = \dfrac{4}{1 - 2\cos\theta}$

$e = 2$ and $ep = 4$, so $p = 2$. Since $e > 2$, the graph is a hyperbola. It is symmetric with respect to the polar axis and has a directrix at $x = -2$. The transverse axis is horizontal and the

vertices lie on the polar axis

21. $[-3, 15, 1]$ by $[-7, 7, 1]$

23. $[-4, 2, 1]$ by $[-10, 10, 1]$

25. $[-2, 5, 1]$ by $[-10, 10, 1]$

27. $[-4, 4, 1]$ by $[-10, 0.4, 1]$

29. The shortest distance from the sun occurs on the positive y-axis, at $\theta = \dfrac{\pi}{2}$.

When $\theta = \dfrac{\pi}{2}$, $r = \dfrac{1.069}{1 + 0.967\sin\frac{\pi}{2}} = \dfrac{1.069}{1.967}$

≈ 0.54 astronomical units or about 51 million miles.

31. His greatest distance from Earth's center occurred when $\theta = 0$:

$r = \dfrac{4090.76}{1 - 0.0076\cos 0} = \dfrac{4090.76}{0.9924}$

≈ 4122 miles from the center of the earth. Assuming the earth to be perfectly spherical, he was $4122 - 3960 = 162$ miles from the surface of the earth.

41. Write the equation in standard form:

$r = \dfrac{3}{1 + \frac{5}{4}\sin\theta}$

Since $e = \dfrac{5}{4} > 1$, the graph is a hyperbola.

43.

The graph appears to be rotated counter-clockwise through an angle of $\frac{\pi}{4}$ radians.

45. Mercury: $r = \dfrac{\left(1 - 0.2056^2\right)\left(36.0 \times 10^6\right)}{1 - 0.2056 \cos\theta}$

Earth: $r = \dfrac{\left(1 - 0.0167^2\right)\left(92.96 \times 10^6\right)}{1 - 0.0167 \cos\theta}$

$r : -150{,}000{,}000 - 150{,}000{,}000$

$y : -100{,}000{,}000, -100{,}000{,}000$

Answers may vary.

47. Since the equation is an ellipse with a vertex at (4, 0), the polar axis is the major axis. Since

$\dfrac{PF}{PD} = e,$ then at the point (4, 0),

$\dfrac{4}{x} = \dfrac{1}{2}$, where x is the distance between the

point (4, 0) and the directrix. Thus, $x = 8$ and the distance between the point (4, 0) and the directrix is 8. The directrix is either $x = -4$ or $x = 12$. There are two polar equations that meet the given conditions. If the directrix is

$x = -4,\quad r = \dfrac{\frac{1}{2}(4)}{1 - \frac{1}{2}\cos\theta} = \dfrac{2}{1 - \frac{1}{2}\cos\theta}.$

If the directrix is $x = 12$,

$r = \dfrac{\frac{1}{2}(12)}{1 + \frac{1}{2}\cos\theta} = \dfrac{6}{1 + \frac{1}{2}\cos\theta}.$

49. $r = \dfrac{1}{2 - 2\cos\theta}$

Write the equation in standard form:

$r = \dfrac{\frac{1}{2}}{1 - \cos\theta}$

Since $e = 1$, the graph is a parabola.
Write in rectangular coordinates:

$r = \dfrac{\frac{1}{2}}{1 - \cos\theta}$

$r(1 - \cos\theta) = \dfrac{1}{2}$

$r - r\cos\theta = \dfrac{1}{2}$

                Distributive property

$r = r\cos\theta + \dfrac{1}{2}$

$r = x + \dfrac{1}{2}$

Substitution: $x = r\cos\theta$

$r^2 = \left(x + \dfrac{1}{2}\right)^2$

Square both sides

$x^2 + y^2 = \left(x + \dfrac{1}{2}\right)^2$

Substitution: $r^2 = x^2 + y^2$

$x^2 + y^2 = x^2 + x + \dfrac{1}{4}$

$y^2 = x + \dfrac{1}{4}$

Chapter 9 Review Exercises

1. $a^2 = 36, a = 6$
$b^2 = 25, b = 5$
$c^2 = a^2 - b^2 = 36 - 25 = 11$
$c = \sqrt{11}$

The foci are at $(\sqrt{11}, 0)$ and $(-\sqrt{11}, 0)$

$$\frac{x^2}{36} + \frac{y^2}{25} = 1$$

2. $a^2 = 25, a = 5$
$b^2 = 16, b = 4$
$c^2 = a^2 - b^2$
$c^2 = 25 - 16$
$c^2 = 9$
$c = 3$

The foci are $(0, 3)$ and $(0, -3)$.

$$\frac{y^2}{25} + \frac{x^2}{16} = 1$$

3. $\dfrac{4x^2}{16} + \dfrac{y^2}{16} = \dfrac{16}{16}$

$\dfrac{x^2}{4} + \dfrac{y^2}{16} = 1$

$b^2 = 4, b = 2$
$a^2 = 16, a = 4$
$c^2 = a^2 - b^2 = 16 - 4 = 12$
$c = \sqrt{12} = 2\sqrt{3}$

The foci are at $(0, 2\sqrt{3})$ and $(0, -2\sqrt{3})$.

$$4x^2 + y^2 = 16$$

4. $\dfrac{4x^2}{36} + \dfrac{9y^2}{36} = \dfrac{36}{36}$

$\dfrac{x^2}{9} + \dfrac{y^2}{4} = 1$

$a^2 = 9, a = 3$
$b^2 = 4, b = 2$
$c^2 = a^2 - b^2 = 9 - 4 = 5, c = \sqrt{5}$

The foci are at $(\sqrt{5}, 0)$ and $(-\sqrt{5}, 0)$.

$$4x^2 + 9y^2 = 36$$

5. $a^2 = 16 \ a = 4$
$b^2 = 9 \ b = 3$
$c^2 = 16 - 9 = 7, c = \sqrt{7}$
center: $(1, -2)$

The foci are at $(1 + \sqrt{7}, -2)$ and $(1 - \sqrt{7}, -2)$.

$$\frac{(x - 1)^2}{16} + \frac{(y + 2)^2}{9} = 1$$

6. $a^2 = 16,\ a = 4$

$b^2 = 9,\ b = 3$

$c^2 = a^2 - b^2 = 16 - 9 = 7,\ c = \sqrt{7}$

center: $(-1, 2)$

The foci are at $(-1, 2 + \sqrt{7})$ and $(-1, 2 - \sqrt{7})$.

$$\frac{(x+1)^2}{9} + \frac{(y-2)^2}{16} = 1$$

7. $4x^2 + 24x + 9y^2 - 36y = -36$

$4(x^2 + 6x + 9) + 9(y^2 - 4y + 4)$

$= -36 + 36 + 36$

$= 4(x+3)^2 + 9(y-2)^2 = 36$

$$\frac{(x+3)^2}{9} + \frac{(y-2)^2}{4} = 1$$

$c^2 = a^2 - b^2 = 5,\ c = \sqrt{5}$

center: $(-3, 2)$

The foci are at $(-3 + \sqrt{5}, 2)$ and $(-3 - \sqrt{5}, 2)$.

$4x^2 + 9y^2 + 24x - 36y + 36 = 0$

8. $9x^2 - 18x + 4y^2 + 8y = 23$

$9(x^2 - 2x + 1) + 4(y^2 + 2y + 1) = 23 + 9 + 4$

$9(x-1)^2 + 4(y+1)^2 = 36$

$$\frac{(x-1)^2}{4} + \frac{(y+1)^2}{9} = 1$$

$c^2 = a^2 - b^2 = 9 - 4 = 5,\ c = \sqrt{5}$

center: $(1, -1)$

The foci are at $(1, -1 + \sqrt{5})$ and $(1, -1 - \sqrt{5})$.

$9x^2 + 4y^2 - 18x + 8y - 23 = 0$

9. $c = 4,\ c^2 = 16$

$a = 5,\ a^2 = 25$

$b^2 = a^2 - c^2 = 25 - 16 = 9$

$$\frac{x^2}{25} + \frac{y^2}{9} = 1$$

10. $c = 3,\ c^2 = 9$

$a = 6,\ a^2 = 36$

$b^2 = a^2 - c^2 = 36 - 9 = 27$

$$\frac{x^2}{27} + \frac{y^2}{36} = 1$$

11. $2a = 12,\ a = 6,\ a^2 = 36$

$2b = 4,\ b = 2,\ b^2 = 4$

$$\frac{(x+3)^2}{36} + \frac{(y-5)^2}{4} = 1$$

12. $2a = 20,\ a = 10,\ a^2 = 100$

$b = 6,\ b^2 = 36$

$$\frac{x^2}{100} + \frac{y^2}{36} = 1$$

13. $2a = 50,\ a = 25$

$b = 15$

$$\frac{x^2}{625} + \frac{y^2}{225} = 1$$

Let $x = 14$.

$$\frac{(14)^2}{625} + \frac{y^2}{225} = 1$$

$$y^2 = 225\left(1 - \frac{196}{625}\right)$$

$y \approx 15(0.8285) \approx 12.4 > 12$

Yes, the truck can drive under the archway.

14. The hit ball will collide with the other ball.

15. $c^2 = a^2 + b^2 = 16 + 1 = 17, c = \sqrt{17}$

The foci are at $(\sqrt{17}, 0)$ and $(-\sqrt{17}, 0)$.

Asymptotes: $y = \pm\dfrac{1}{4}x$

$$\frac{x^2}{16} - y^2 = 1$$

16. $c^2 = a^2 + b^2 = 16 + 1 = 17$

$c = \sqrt{17}$

The foci are at $(0, \sqrt{17})$ and $(0, -\sqrt{17})$.

Asymptotes: $y = \pm 4x$

$$\frac{y^2}{16} - x^2 = 1$$

17. $\dfrac{x^2}{16} - \dfrac{y^2}{9} = 1$

$c^2 = a^2 + b^2 = 16 + 9 = 25, c = 5$

The foci are at $(5, 0)$ and $(-5, 0)$.

Asymptotes: $y = \pm\dfrac{3}{4}x$

$$9x^2 - 16y^2 = 144$$

18. $\dfrac{y^2}{4} - \dfrac{x^2}{16} = 1$

$c^2 = a^2 + b^2 = 4 + 16 = 20$

$c = \sqrt{20} = 2\sqrt{5}$

The foci are at $(0, 2\sqrt{5})$ and $(0, -2\sqrt{5})$.

Asymptotes: $y = \pm\dfrac{1}{2}x$

$$4y^2 - x^2 = 16$$

19. $c^2 = a^2 + b^2 = 25 + 16 = 41, c = \sqrt{41}$

center: $(2, -3)$

The foci are at

$(2 + \sqrt{41}, -3)$ and $(2 - \sqrt{41}, -3)$.

Asymptotes: $y + 3 = \pm\dfrac{4}{5}(x - 2)$

$$\frac{(x-2)^2}{25} - \frac{(y+3)^2}{16} = 1$$

20. $c^2 = a^2 + b^2 = 25 + 16 = 41, c = \sqrt{41}$

center: $(3, -2)$

The foci are at

$(3, -2 + \sqrt{41})$ and $(3, -2 - \sqrt{41})$.

Asymptotes: $y + 2 = \pm\dfrac{5}{4}(x - 3)$

$$\frac{(y+2)^2}{25} - \frac{(x-3)^2}{16} = 1$$

21.
$$y^2 - 4y - 4x^2 + 8x - 4 = 0$$
$$(y^2 - 4y + 4) - 4(x^2 - 2x + 1) = 4 + 4 - 4$$
$$(y - 2)^2 - 4(x - 1)^2 = 4$$

$$\frac{(y-2)^2}{4} - (x-1)^2 = 1$$

$c^2 = a^2 + b^2 = 4 + 1 = 5,\ c = \sqrt{5}$

center: $(1, 2)$

The foci are at $(1, 2 + \sqrt{5})$ and $(1, 2 - \sqrt{5})$.

Asymptotes: $y - 2 = \pm 2(x - 1)$

$$y^2 - 4y - 4x^2 + 8x - 4 = 0$$

22. $x^2 - 2x - y^2 - 2y = 1$

$(x^2 - 2x + 1) - (y^2 + 2y + 1) = 1 + 1 - 1$

$(x - 1)^2 - (y + 1)^2 = 1$

$c^2 = a^2 + b^2 = 1 + 1 = 2,\ c = \sqrt{2}$

center: $(1, -1)$

The foci are at $(1 + \sqrt{2}, -1)$ and $(1 - \sqrt{2}, -1)$.

asymptotes: $y + 1 = \pm(x - 1)$

$$x^2 - y^2 - 2x - 2y - 1 = 0$$

23. $c = 4,\ c^2 = 16$

$a = 2,\ a^2 = 4$

$b^2 = c^2 - a^2 = 16 - 4 = 12$

$$\frac{y^2}{4} - \frac{x^2}{12} = 1$$

24. $c = 8,\ c^2 = 64$

$a = 3,\ a^2 = 9$

$b^2 = c^2 - a^2 = 64 - 9 = 55$

$$\frac{x^2}{9} - \frac{y^2}{55} = 1$$

25. If the foci are at $(0, -2)$ and $(0, 2)$, then $c = 2$. If the vertices are at $(0, -3)$ and $(0, 3)$ then $a = 3$. This is not possible since c must be greater than a.

26. foci: $(\pm 100, 0),\ c = 100$

$$|d_1 - d_2| = \left(0.186\,\frac{\text{mi}}{\mu\text{s}}\right)(500\,\mu\text{s}) = 93\ \text{mi} = 2a$$

$$a = \frac{93}{2}$$

$$b^2 = c^2 - a^2 = (100)^2 - \left(\frac{93}{2}\right)^2 = 7837.75$$

$$\frac{x^2}{\left(\frac{93}{2}\right)^2} - \frac{y^2}{7837.75} = 1$$

$$\frac{x^2}{2162.25} - \frac{y^2}{7837.75} = 1$$

27. $4p = 8,\ p = 2$

vertex: $(0, 0)$

focus: $(2, 0)$

directrix: $x = -2$

$$y^2 = 8x$$

28. $x^2 + 16y = 0$

$$x^2 = -16y$$

$4p = -16$

$p = -4$

vertex: $(0, 0)$

focus: $(0, -4)$

directrix: $y = 4$

$$x^2 + 16y = 0$$

29. $4p = -16$
$p = -4$
vertex: $(0, 2)$
focus: $(-4, 2)$
directrix: $x = 4$

$(y - 2)^2 = -16x$

30. $4p = 4, p = 1$
vertex: $(4, -1)$
focus: $(4, 0)$
directrix: $y = -2$

$(x - 4)^2 = 4(y + 1)$

31. $x^2 = -4y + 4$
$x^2 = -4 (y - 1)$
$4p = -4, p = -1$
vertex: $(0, 1)$
focus: $(0, 0)$
directrix: $y = 2$

$x^2 + 4y = 4$

32. $y^2 - 10y = 4x - 21$
$y^2 - 10y + 25 = 4x - 21 + 25$
$(y - 5)^2 = 4(x + 1)$
$4p = 4, p = 1$
vertex: $(-1, 5)$
focus: $(0, 5)$
directrix: $x = -2$

$y^2 - 4x - 10y + 21 = 0$

33. $x^2 - 4x - 2y = 0$
$x^2 - 4x = 2y$
$(x^2 - 4x + 4) = 2y + 4$
$(x - 2)^2 = 2(y + 2)$
$4p = 2, p = \dfrac{1}{2}$
vertex: $(2, -2)$
focus: $\left(2, -\dfrac{3}{2}\right)$

directrix: $y = -\dfrac{5}{2}$

$x^2 - 4x - 2y = 0$

34. $p = 12$
$y^2 = 48x$

35. $p = -11$
$x^2 = -44y$

36. $x^2 = 4py$
$(6)^2 = 4p(3)$
$p = 3$
$x^2 = 12y$

Place the light 3 inches from the vertex at $(0, 3)$.

37. $x^2 = 4py$

$(1750)^2 = 4p(316)$

$4p \approx 9691$

$x^2 = 9691y$

Let $x = 1750 - 1000 = 750$.

$y = \dfrac{x^2}{9691} = \dfrac{(750)^2}{9691} \approx 58$

The height is approximately 58 feet.

38. $x^2 = 4py$

$(150)^2 = 4p(44)$

$22{,}500 = 176p$

$p \approx 128$

The receiver should be placed approximately 128 feet from the base of the dish.

39. $A = 0, C = 1$.

$AC = 0$, so the graph is a parabola.

40. $A = 1, C = 16$.

$AC = 16 > 0$ and $A \neq C$, so the graph is an ellipse.

41. $A = 16, C = 9$.

$AC = 16 \cdot 9 = 144 > 0$ and $A \neq C$, so the graph is an ellipse.

42. $A = 4, C = -9$.

$AC = 4(-9) = 36 < 0$, so the graph is a hyperbola.

43. $A = 5, B = 2\sqrt{3}, C = 3$.

$B^2 - 4AC = \left(2\sqrt{3}\right)^2 - 4(5)(3) = 12 - 60 = -48$ Since $B^2 - 4AC < 0$, the graph is an ellipse or a circle.

44. $A = 5, B = -8, C = 7$.

$B^2 - 4AC = (-8)^2 - 4(5)(7) = 64 - 140 = -76$. Since $B^2 - 4AC < 0$, the graph is an ellipse or a circle.

45. $A = 1, B = 6, C = 9$.

$B^2 - 4AC = 6^2 - 4(1)(9) = 36 - 36 = 0$. Since $B^2 - 4AC = 0$, the graph is a parabola.

46. $A = 1, B = -2, C = 3$.

$B^2 - 4AC = (-2)^2 - 4(1)(3) = 4 - 12 = -8$ Since $B^2 - 4AC < 0$, the graph is an ellipse or a circle.

47. $xy - 4 = 0$

    a. $A = 0, B = 1, C = 0$.

$$\cot 2\theta = \frac{A-C}{B} = \frac{0-0}{1} = 0$$

$$2\theta = 90°$$

$$\theta = 45°$$

$$x = x'\cos 45° - y'\sin 45° = x'\left(\frac{\sqrt{2}}{2}\right) - y'\left(\frac{\sqrt{2}}{2}\right) = \frac{\sqrt{2}}{2}(x' - y')$$

$$y = x'\sin 45° + y'\cos 45° = x'\left(\frac{\sqrt{2}}{2}\right) + y'\left(\frac{\sqrt{2}}{2}\right) = \frac{\sqrt{2}}{2}(x' + y')$$

Substitute into the equation: $xy - 4 = 0$

$$\left[\frac{\sqrt{2}}{2}(x' - y')\right]\left[\frac{\sqrt{2}}{2}(x' - y')\right] - 4 = 0$$

$$\frac{1}{2}\left(x'^2 - y'^2\right) - 4 = 0$$

$$x'^2 - y'^2 = 8$$

b. $\dfrac{x'^2}{8} - \dfrac{y'^2}{8} = 1$

c.

48. $x^2 + xy + y^2 - 1 = 0$

a. $A = 1$, $B = 1$, $C = 1$.

$$\cot 2\theta = \frac{A-C}{B} = \frac{1-1}{1} = \frac{0}{1} = 0$$

$$2\theta = 90°$$

$$\theta = 45°$$

$$x = x'\cos 45° - y'\sin 45° = \frac{\sqrt{2}}{2}(x' - y')$$

$$y = x'\sin 45° + y'\cos 45° = \frac{\sqrt{2}}{2}(x' + y')$$

Substitute into the equation: $x^2 + xy + y^2 - 1 = 0$

$$\left[\frac{\sqrt{2}}{2}(x' - y')\right]^2 + \left[\frac{\sqrt{2}}{2}(x' - y')\right]\left[\frac{\sqrt{2}}{2}(x' + y')\right] + \left[\frac{\sqrt{2}}{2}(x' + y')\right]^2 - 1 = 0$$

$$\frac{1}{2}\left(x'^2 - 2x'y' + y'^2\right) + \frac{1}{2}\left(x'^2 - y'^2\right) + \frac{1}{2}\left(x'^2 + 2x'y' + y'^2\right) = 1$$

Multiply both sides by 2 and simplify: $3x'^2 + y'^2 = 2$

b. $\dfrac{x'^2}{\frac{2}{3}} + \dfrac{y'^2}{2} = 1$

c.

49. $4x^2 + 10xy + 4y^2 - 9 = 0$

a. $A = 4, B = 10, C = 4.$

$$\cot 2\theta = \frac{A-C}{B} = \frac{4-4}{10} = \frac{0}{10} = 0$$

$$2\theta = 90°$$

$$\theta = 45°$$

$$x = x'\cos 45° - y'\sin 45° = \frac{\sqrt{2}}{2}(x' - y')$$

$$y = x'\sin 45° + y'\cos 45° = \frac{\sqrt{2}}{2}(x' + y')$$

Substitute into the equation: $4x^2 + 10xy + 4y^2 - 9 = 0$

$$4\left[\frac{\sqrt{2}}{2}(x' - y')\right]^2 + 10\left[\frac{\sqrt{2}}{2}(x' - y')\right]\left[\frac{\sqrt{2}}{2}(x' + y')\right] + 4\left[\frac{\sqrt{2}}{2}(x' + y')\right]^2 - 9 = 0$$

$$4 \cdot \frac{1}{2}\left(x'^2 - 2x'y' + y'^2\right) + 10 \cdot \frac{1}{2}\left(x'^2 - y'^2\right) + 4 \cdot \frac{1}{2}\left(x'^2 + 2x'y' + y'^2\right) = 9$$

Multiply both sides by 2 and simplify: $18x'^2 - 2y'^2 = 18$

b. $\dfrac{x'^2}{1} - \dfrac{y'^2}{9} = 1$

c.

$\theta = 45°$

50. $6x^2 - 6xy + 14y^2 - 45 = 0$

a. $A = 6, B = -6\ C = 14$

$$\cot 2\theta = \frac{A-C}{B} = \frac{6-14}{-6} = \frac{-8}{-6} = \frac{4}{3}$$

Since θ is always acute, and $\cot 2\theta$ is positive, 2θ lies in quadrant I. The third side of the right triangle is found using the Pythagorean Theorem.

$$4^2 + 3^2 = r^2$$

$$r = 5$$

So, $\cos 2\theta = \dfrac{4}{5}.$

$$\sin\theta = \sqrt{\frac{1 - \cos 2\theta}{2}} = \sqrt{\frac{1 - \frac{4}{5}}{2}} = \frac{\sqrt{10}}{10} \text{ and } \cos\theta = \sqrt{\frac{1 + \cos 2\theta}{2}} = \sqrt{\frac{1 + \frac{4}{5}}{2}} = \frac{3\sqrt{10}}{10}.$$

So, $x = x'\cos\theta - y'\sin\theta = x'\left(\dfrac{3\sqrt{10}}{10}\right) - y'\left(\dfrac{\sqrt{10}}{10}\right) = \dfrac{\sqrt{10}}{10}(3x' - y')$

and $y = x' \sin\theta - y' \cos\theta = x'\left(\dfrac{\sqrt{10}}{10}\right) + y'\left(\dfrac{3\sqrt{10}}{10}\right) = \dfrac{\sqrt{10}}{10}(x' + 3y')$.

Substitute into the equation: $6x^2 - 6xy + 14y^2 - 45 = 0$

$$6\left[\dfrac{\sqrt{10}}{10}(3x' - y')\right]^2 - 6\left[\dfrac{\sqrt{10}}{10}(3x' - y')\right]\left[\dfrac{\sqrt{10}}{10}(x' + 3y')\right] + 14\left[\dfrac{\sqrt{10}}{10}(x' + 3y')\right]^2 - 45 = 0$$

$$6\left[\dfrac{1}{10}\left(9x'^2 - 6x'y' + y'^2\right)\right] - 6\left[\dfrac{1}{10}\left(3x'^2 + 8x'y' - 3y'^2\right)\right] + 14\left[\dfrac{1}{10}\left(x'^2 + 6x'y' + 9y'^2\right)\right] = 45$$

Multiply both sides by 10 and simplify: $50x'^2 + 150y'^2 = 450$

b. $\dfrac{x'^2}{9} + \dfrac{y'^2}{3} = 1$

c.

The axes are rotated by $\theta = \sin^{-1}\left(\dfrac{\sqrt{10}}{10}\right) \approx 18°$.

51. $x^2 + 2\sqrt{3}\,xy + 3y^2 - 12\sqrt{3}\,x + 12y = 0$

$A = 1,\ B = 2\sqrt{3},\ C = 3$

$\cot 2\theta = \dfrac{A - C}{B} = \dfrac{1 - 3}{2\sqrt{3}} = \dfrac{-2}{2\sqrt{3}} = \dfrac{-\sqrt{3}}{3}$

$\quad 2\theta = 120°$

$\quad \theta = 60°$

$x = x' \cos 60° - y' \sin 60° = x'\left(\dfrac{1}{2}\right) - y'\left(\dfrac{\sqrt{3}}{2}\right) = \dfrac{1}{2}\left(x' - \sqrt{3}\,y'\right)$

and $y = x' \sin 60° + y' \cos 60° = x'\left(\dfrac{\sqrt{3}}{2}\right) + y'\left(\dfrac{1}{2}\right) = \dfrac{1}{2}\left(\sqrt{3}\,x' + y'\right)$

Substitute into the equation: $x^2 + 2\sqrt{3}xy + 3y^2 - 12\sqrt{3}x + 12y = 0$

$$\left[\frac{1}{2}\left(x' - \sqrt{3}y'\right)\right]^2 + 2\sqrt{3}\left[\frac{1}{2}\left(x' - \sqrt{3}y'\right)\right]\left[\frac{1}{2}\left(\sqrt{3}x' + y'\right)\right] + 3\left[\frac{1}{2}\left(\sqrt{3}x' + y'\right)\right]^2 - 12\sqrt{3}\left[\frac{1}{2}\left(x' - \sqrt{3}y'\right)\right]$$

$$+ 12\left[\frac{1}{2}\left(\sqrt{3}x' + y'\right)\right] = 0$$

$$\frac{1}{4}\left(x'^2 - 2\sqrt{3}x'y' + 3y'^2\right) + 2\sqrt{3} \cdot \frac{1}{4}\left(\sqrt{3}x'^2 - 2x'y' - \sqrt{3}y'^2\right) + 3 \cdot \frac{1}{4}\left(3x'^2 + 2\sqrt{3}x'y' + y'^2\right) - 6\sqrt{3}x' + 18y'$$

$$+ 6\sqrt{3}x' + 6y' = 0$$

Multiply both sides by 4 and simplify: $16x'^2 + 96y' = 0$

b. $16x'^2 = -96y'$

$\qquad x'^2 = -6y'$

c.

52. $x = 2t - 1$ and $y = 1 - t$; $-\infty < t < \infty$

$\dfrac{x+1}{2} = t$

Substitute into y: $y = 1 - \left(\dfrac{x+1}{2}\right)$

$y = -\dfrac{1}{2}x + \dfrac{1}{2}$

53. $x = t^2$ and $y = t - 1$; $-1 \le t \le 3$

$\qquad y + 1 = t$

Substitute into x:

$x = (y+1)^2$

$(y+1)^2 = x$

$0 \le x \le 9, \; -2 \le y \le 2$

54. $x = 4t^2$ and $y = t + 1$; $-\infty < t < \infty$

$y - 1 = t$

Substitute into x:

$x = 4(y-1)^2$

$\frac{1}{4}x = (y-1)^2$

$(y-1)^2 = \frac{1}{4}x$

55. $x = 4\sin t$, $y = 3\cos t$; $0 \le t < \pi$

$\frac{x}{4} = \sin t$ $\quad$ $\frac{y}{3} = \cos t$

Square and add the equations:

$\frac{x^2}{16} = \sin^2 t$

$+ \quad \frac{y^2}{9} = \cos^2 t$

$\overline{\frac{x^2}{16} + \frac{y^2}{9} = \sin^2 t + \cos^2 t}$

$\frac{x^2}{16} + \frac{y^2}{9} = \sin^2 t + \cos^2 t$

$\frac{x^2}{16} + \frac{y^2}{9} = 1$

$0 \le x \le 4, \ -3 \le y \le 3$

56. $x = 3 + 2\cos t$, $y = 1 + 2\sin t$; $0 \le t < 2\pi$

$\frac{x-3}{2} = \cos t$ $\quad$ $\frac{y-1}{2} = \sin t$

Square and add the equations:

$\frac{(x-3)^2}{4} = \cos^2 t$

$+ \quad \frac{(y-1)^2}{4} = \sin^2 t$

$\overline{\frac{(x-3)^2}{4} + \frac{(y-1)^2}{4} = \cos^2 t + \sin^2 t}$

$\frac{(x-3)^2}{4} + \frac{(y-1)^2}{4} = 1$

or $(x-3)^2 + (y-1)^2 = 4$

57. $x = 3\sec t$, $y = 3\tan t$; $0 \le t \le \frac{\pi}{4}$

$\frac{x}{3} = \sec t$ $\quad$ $\frac{y}{3} = \tan t$

Square and subtract the equations:

$\frac{x^2}{9} = \sec^2 t$

$- \left(\frac{y^2}{9} = \tan^2 t \right)$

$\overline{\frac{x^2}{9} - \frac{y^2}{9} = \sec^2 t - \tan^2 t}$

$\frac{x^2}{9} - \frac{y^2}{9} = 1$

$3 \le x \le 3\sqrt{2}, \ 0 \le y \le 3$

58. Answers may vary. Sample answer:

$x = t$ and $y = t^2 + 6$; $x = t + 1$ and

$y = t^2 + 2t + 7$

59. a. $x = (100\cos 40°)t$

$y = 6 + (100\sin 40°)t - 16t^2$

b.   After 1 second:
$x = (100\cos 40°) \cdot 1$
≈ 76.6 feet in distance
$y = 6 + (100\sin 40°) \cdot 1 - 16(1)^2$
≈ 54.3 feet in height
After 2 seconds:
$x = (100\cos 40°) \cdot 2$
≈ 153.2 feet in distance
$y = 6 + (100\sin 40°) \cdot 2 - 16(2)^2$
≈ 70.6 feet in height
After 3 seconds:
$x = (100\cos 40°) \cdot 3$
≈ 229.8 feet in distance
$y = 6 + (100\sin 40°) \cdot 3 - 16(3)^2$
≈ 54.8 feet in height

c. $0 = 6t(100\sin 40°)t - 16t^2$
Using the quadratic formula with
$a = -16$, $b = 100\sin 40°$, and $c = 6$,

$$t = \frac{-100\sin 40° \pm \sqrt{(100\sin 40°)^2 - 4(-16)(6)}}{2(-16)}$$

$t \approx -0.1$ or $t \approx 4.1$
Since t cannot be negative, we discard
$t \approx -0.1$.
At $t \approx 4.1$, $x = (100\cos 40°)(4.1) \approx 314.1$
The ball is in flight for 4.1 seconds. It travels a total horizontal distance of 314.1 feet.

d.

The ball is at its maximum height at 2.0 seconds. The maximum height is 70.6 feet.

60. a. $r = \dfrac{4}{1 - \sin\theta}$

b. $e = 1$ and $ep = 4$, so $p = 4$. Since $e = 1$, the graph is a parabola.

c.

61. a. $r = \dfrac{6}{1 + \cos\theta}$

b. $e = 1$ and $ep = 6$, so $p = 6$. Since $e = 1$, the graph is a parabola.

c.

62. a.   Divide numerator and denominator by 2:
$$r = \frac{3}{1 + \frac{1}{2}\sin\theta}$$

b. $e = \dfrac{1}{2}$ and $ep = 3$, so $p = 6$. Since $e < 1$, the graph is an ellipse.

c.

63.   a.   Divide the numerator and denominator by 3:

$$r = \frac{\frac{2}{3}}{1 - \frac{2}{3}\cos\theta}$$

b. $e = \frac{2}{3}$ and $ep = \frac{2}{3}$, so $p = 1$. Since $e < 1$, the graph is an ellipse.

c.

64.   a.   Divide the numerator and denominator by 3:

$$r = \frac{2}{1 + 2\sin\theta}$$

b. $e = 2$ and $ep = 2$, so $p = 1$. Since $e > 1$, the graph is a hyperbola.

c.

65.   a.   Divide the numerator and denominator by 4:

$$r = \frac{2}{1 + 4\cos\theta}$$

b. $e = 4$ and $ep = 2$, so $p = \frac{1}{2}$. Since $e > 1$, the graph is a hyperbola.

c.

Chapter 9 Test

1. $\dfrac{x^2}{4} - \dfrac{y^2}{9} = 1$

$c^2 = a^2 + b^2 = 4 + 9 = 13$, $c = \sqrt{13}$

hyperbola

The foci are at $\left(\sqrt{13}, 0\right)$ and $\left(-\sqrt{13}, 0\right)$.

Asymptotes: $y = \pm\dfrac{3}{2}x$

$9x^2 - 4y^2 = 36$

2. $4p = -8$, $p = -2$
parabola
vertex: $(0, 0)$
focus: $(0, -2)$
directrix: $y = 2$

$x^2 = -8y$

3.   The center is at $(-2, 5)$.

$c^2 = a^2 - b^2 = 25 - 9 = 16$, $c = 4$

ellipse

The foci are at $(-6, 5)$ and $(2, 5)$.

$$\frac{(x + 2)^2}{25} + \frac{(y - 5)^2}{9} = 1$$

4.
$$4x^2 - y^2 + 8x + 2y + 7 = 0$$

$$\left(4x^2 + 8x\right) - \left(y^2 - 2y\right) = -7$$

$$4\left(x^2 + 2x + 1\right) - \left(y^2 - 2y + 1\right) = -7 + 4 - 1$$

$$4\left(x + 1\right)^2 - \left(y - 1\right)^2 = -4$$

$$\left(y - 1\right)^2 - 4\left(x + 1\right)^2 = 4$$

$$\frac{\left(y - 1\right)^2}{4} - \left(x + 1\right)^2 = 1$$

$c^2 = a^2 + b^2 = 4 + 1 = 5$, $c = \sqrt{5}$

The center is at $(-1, 1)$.

Asymptotes: $y - 1 = \pm 2(x + 1)$

hyperbola

The foci are at $\left(-1, 1 + \sqrt{5}\right)$ and $\left(-1, 1 - \sqrt{5}\right)$.

$4x^2 - y^2 + 8x + 2y + 7 = 0$

5. $4p = 8$, $p = 2$

parabola

vertex: $(-5, 1)$

focus: $(-5, 3)$

directrix: $y = -1$

$(x + 5)^2 = 8(y - 1)$

6. $c = 7$, $c^2 = 49$

$a = 10$, $a^2 = 100$

$b^2 = a^2 - c^2 = 100 - 49 = 51$

$$\frac{x^2}{100} + \frac{y^2}{51} = 1$$

7. $c = 10$, $c^2 = 100$

$a = 7$, $a^2 = 49$

$b^2 = c^2 - a^2 = 100 - 49 = 51$

$$\frac{y^2}{49} - \frac{x^2}{51} = 1$$

8. $p = 50$

$y^2 = 4px$

$y^2 = 200x$

9. $b = 24$, $b^2 = 576$

$2a = 80$, $a = 40$, $a^2 = 1600$

$c^2 = a^2 - b^2 = 1600 - 576 = 1024$

$c = \sqrt{1024} = 32$

The two people should each stand 32 feet from the center of the room, along the major axis.

10. a. $x^2 = 4py$

when $x = \pm 3, y = 3$

$9 = 4p(3)$

$3 = 4p$

$\dfrac{3}{4} = p$

$x^2 = 3y$

b. focus: $\left(0, \dfrac{3}{4}\right)$

The light is placed $\dfrac{3}{4}$ inch above the vertex.

11. $A = 1, C = 9$

$AC = 1 \cdot 9 = 9 > 0$, so the graph is an ellipse.

12. $A = 1, B = 1, C = 1$

$B^2 - 4AC = 1^2 - 4(1)(1) = -3$.

Since $B^2 - 4AC < 0$, the graph is an ellipse or circle.

13. $7x^2 - 6\sqrt{3}xy + 13y^2 - 16 = 0$

$A = 7, B = -6\sqrt{3}, C = 13$

$\cot 2\theta = \dfrac{A - C}{B} = \dfrac{7 - 13}{-6\sqrt{3}}$

$= \dfrac{-6}{-6\sqrt{3}} = \dfrac{1}{\sqrt{3}} = \dfrac{\sqrt{3}}{3}$

$2\theta = 60°$

$\theta = 30°$

14. $x = t^2, \quad y = t - 1; \ -\infty < t < \infty$

$y + 1 = t$

Substitute into x:

$x = (y + 1)^2$

$(y + 1)^2 = x$

15. $x = 1 + 3\sin t, \quad y = 2\cos t; 0 \le t < 2\pi$

$\dfrac{x - 1}{3} = \sin t \qquad \dfrac{y}{2} = \cos t$

Square and add the equations:

$\dfrac{(x-1)^2}{9} = \sin^2 t$

$+ \qquad \dfrac{y^2}{4} = \cos^2 t$

$\dfrac{(x-1)^2}{9} + \dfrac{y^2}{4} = \sin^2 t + \cos^2 t$

$\dfrac{(x-1)^2}{9} + \dfrac{y^2}{4} = 1$

16. $r = \dfrac{2}{1 - \cos\theta}$

$e = 1$ and $ep = 2$, so $p = 2$.

Since $e = 1$, the graph is a parabola.

17. $r = \dfrac{4}{2 + \sin\theta}$

Divide the numerator and denominator by 2:

$$r = \dfrac{2}{1 + \dfrac{1}{2}\sin\theta}$$

$e = \dfrac{1}{2}$ and $ep = 2$, so $p = 4$. Since $e < 1$, the graph is an ellipse.

Cumulative Review Exercises (Chapters P–9)

1. $2(x - 3) + 5x = 8(x - 1)$

$2x - 6 + 5x = 8x - 8$

$7x - 6 = 8x - 8$

$-x = -2$

$x = 2$

The solution set is $\{2\}$.

2. $-3(2x - 4) > 2(6x - 12)$

$-6x + 12 > 12x - 24$

$-18x > -36$

$x < 2$

The solution set is $\{x \mid x < 2\}$.

3. $x - 5 = \sqrt{x + 7}$

$(x - 5)^2 = x + 7$

$x^2 - 10x + 25 = x + 7$

$x^2 - 11x + 18 = 0$

$(x - 2)(x - 9) = 0$

$x = 2$ or $x = 9$

The solution $x = 2$ is extraneous, so the only solution is $x = 9$.

The solution set is $\{9\}$.

4. $(x - 2)^2 = 20$

$x - 2 = \pm\sqrt{20}$

$x - 2 = \pm 2\sqrt{5}$

$x = 2 \pm 2\sqrt{5}$

The solution set is $\left\{2 + 2\sqrt{5},\ 2 - 2\sqrt{5}\right\}$.

5. $|2x - 1| \geq 7$

$2x - 1 \geq 7$ or $2x - 1 \leq -7$

$2x \geq 8$ \qquad\qquad $2x \leq -6$

$x \geq 4$ or \qquad $x \leq -3$

The solution set is $\{x \mid x \leq -3 \text{ or } x \geq 4\}$

6. $3x^3 + 4x^2 - 7x + 2 = 0$

$p : \pm 1, \pm 2$

$q : \pm 1, \pm 3$

$\dfrac{p}{q} : \pm 1,\ \pm 2,\ \pm\dfrac{1}{3},\ \pm\dfrac{2}{3}$

Let $f(x) = 3x^3 + 4x^2 - 7x + 2$.

Evaluate f at the possible rational zeros to find $f\left(\dfrac{2}{3}\right) = 0$.

$\dfrac{2}{3}$	3	4	−7	2
		2	4	−2
	3	6	−3	0

$\left(x - \dfrac{2}{3}\right)(3x^2 + 6x - 3) = 0$

$(3x - 2)(x^2 + 2x - 1) = 0$

$x = \dfrac{2}{3}$ or $x = \dfrac{-2 \pm \sqrt{(2)^2 - 4(1)(-1)}}{2}$

$x = \dfrac{-2 \pm \sqrt{8}}{2}$

$x = -1 \pm \sqrt{2}$

The solution set is $\left\{\dfrac{2}{3},\ -1 + \sqrt{2},\ -1 - \sqrt{2}\right\}$.

7. $\log_2(x+1)+\log_2(x-1)=3$

$$\log_2(x^2-1)=3$$
$$x^2-1=2^3$$
$$x^2=9$$
$$x=\pm3$$

$x=-3$ is not a solution of the original equation.
The solution set is $\{3\}$.

8. $3x+4y=2$
$2x+5y=-1$

$$6x+8y=4$$
$$\underline{-6x-15y=3}$$
$$-7y=7$$
$$y=-1$$
$$3x+4(-1)=2$$
$$3x=6$$
$$x=2$$

The solution set is $\{(2,-1)\}$.

9. $2x^2-y^2=-8$
$x-y=6$

$$x-y=6$$
$$x=y+6$$
$$x^2=(y+6)^2=y^2+12y+36$$

Substitute into first equation.
$$2(y^2+12y+36)-y^2=-8$$
$$2y^2+24y+72-y^2=-8$$
$$y^2+24y+80=0$$
$$(y+4)(y+20)=0$$
$$y=-4 \text{ or } y=-20$$
$$x=2 \qquad x=-14$$

The solution set is $\{(2,-4),(-14,-20)\}$.

10.   Set up the augmented matrix and use Gauss-Jordan reduction.

$$\begin{bmatrix} 1 & -1 & 1 & | & 17 \\ -4 & 1 & 5 & | & -2 \\ 2 & 3 & 1 & | & 8 \end{bmatrix}$$

$$\begin{bmatrix} 1 & -1 & 1 & | & 17 \\ 0 & -3 & 9 & | & 66 \\ 0 & 5 & -1 & | & -26 \end{bmatrix} \begin{matrix} \\ 4R_1+R_2 \\ -2R_1+R_3 \end{matrix}$$

$$\begin{bmatrix} 1 & -1 & 1 & | & 17 \\ 0 & 1 & -3 & | & -22 \\ 0 & 5 & -1 & | & -26 \end{bmatrix} -\frac{1}{3}R_2$$

$$\begin{bmatrix} 1 & 0 & -2 & | & -5 \\ 0 & 1 & -3 & | & -22 \\ 0 & 0 & 14 & | & 84 \end{bmatrix} \begin{matrix} R_2+R_1 \\ \\ -5R_2+R_3 \end{matrix}$$

$$\begin{bmatrix} 1 & 0 & -2 & | & -5 \\ 0 & 1 & -3 & | & -22 \\ 0 & 0 & 1 & | & 6 \end{bmatrix} \frac{1}{14}R_3$$

$$\begin{bmatrix} 1 & 0 & 0 & | & 7 \\ 0 & 1 & 0 & | & -4 \\ 0 & 0 & 1 & | & 6 \end{bmatrix} \begin{matrix} 2R_3+R_1 \\ 3R_3+R_2 \end{matrix}$$

$x=7, y=-4, z=6$
The solution set is $\{(7,-4,6)\}$.

11.   Parabola with vertex at $(1,-4)$.

$$f(x)=(x-1)^2-4$$

12.   Ellipse with center at $(0,0)$ and vertices at $(3,0)$ and $(-3,0)$.

$$\frac{x^2}{9}+\frac{y^2}{4}=1$$

13. $5x + y \le 10$ $y \ge \dfrac{1}{4}x + 2$

$y \le -5x + 10$

Graph with solid line $y = -5x + 10$ and

$y = \dfrac{1}{4}x + 2$. Shade the region that is below the

line $y = -5x + 10$ and above the line

$y = \dfrac{1}{4}x + 2$. Then dash the solid lines that do

not contain the solution set.

14. a. $p : \pm 1, \pm 3$

$q : \pm 1, \pm 2, \pm 4, \pm 8, \pm 16, \pm 32$

$\dfrac{p}{q} : \pm 1, \ \pm 3, \ \pm \dfrac{1}{2}, \ \pm \dfrac{3}{2}, \ \pm \dfrac{1}{4}, \ \pm \dfrac{3}{4}, \ \pm \dfrac{1}{8},$

$\pm \dfrac{3}{8}, \ \pm \dfrac{1}{16}, \ \pm \dfrac{3}{16}, \ \pm \dfrac{1}{32}, \ \pm \dfrac{3}{32}$

b. $x = 1$ appears to be a root.

```
 1 |  32   -52    17     3
   |        32   -20    -3
   |_____
        32   -20    -3     0
```

$32x^3 - 52x^2 + 17x + 3 = 0$

$(x - 1)(32x^2 - 20x - 3) = 0$

$(x - 1)(4x - 3)(8x + 1) = 0$

$x = 1 \text{ or } x = \dfrac{3}{4} \text{ or } x = -\dfrac{1}{8}$

The solution set is $\left\{ -\dfrac{1}{8}, \dfrac{3}{4}, 1 \right\}$.

15. a.   domain: $(-2, 2)$

range: $[-3, \infty)$

b.   the relative minimum of -3 occurs

at $x = 0$.

c.   increasing: $(0, 2)$

d. $f(-1) - f(0) = 0 - (-3) = 3$

e. $(f \circ f)(1) = f(f(1)) = f(0) = -3$

f. $f(x) \to \infty$ as $x \to -2^+$ or as $x \to 2^-$

g.

$g(x) = f(x - 2) + 1$

h.

$h(x) = -f(2x)$

16. $f(x) = x^2 - 4, \ g(x) = x + 2$

$(g \circ f)(x) = g\left(x^2 - 4\right) = \left(x^2 - 4\right) + 2 = x^2 - 2$

17. $\log_5 \dfrac{x^3 \sqrt{y}}{125} = \log_5 x^3 \sqrt{y} - \log_5 125$

$= \log_5 x^3 + \log_5 \sqrt{y} - 3$

$= 3 \log_5 x + \dfrac{1}{2} \log_5 y - 3$

18. $m = \dfrac{y_2 - y_1}{x_2 - x_1} = \dfrac{8 - (-4)}{-5 - 1} = \dfrac{12}{-6} = -2$

$y - y_1 = m(x - x_1)$

$y + 4 = -2(x - 1)$

$y = -2x - 2$

19.   Let $R =$ the cost of a rental at Rent-a-Truck and let $A =$ the cost of a rental at Ace Truck Rentals.

$R = 39 + 0.16m$

$A = 25 + 0.24m$

where m is the number of miles.

$39 + 0.16m = 25 + 0.24m$

$\qquad\quad 14 = 0.08m$

$\qquad\qquad m = 175$

$R = 39 + 0.16(175) = 67$

The cost will be the same when the number of miles driven is 175 miles. The cost will be \$67.

20. Let x = cost of basic cable,
Let y = cost of movie channel.
$$x + y = 35$$
$$x + 2y = 45$$
Multiply the first equation by -1 and then add the two equations.
$$-x - y = -35$$
$$\underline{x + 2y = 45}$$
$$y = 10$$
Use back-substitution to find x.
$$x + 10 = 35$$
$$x = 25$$
Basic cable costs \$25 and one movie channel costs \$10.

21.
$$\frac{\csc\theta - \sin\theta}{\sin\theta} = \frac{\frac{1}{\sin\theta} - \sin\theta}{\sin\theta} \cdot \frac{\sin\theta}{\sin\theta}$$
$$= \frac{1 - \sin^2\theta}{\sin^2\theta}$$
$$= \frac{\cos^2\theta}{\sin^2\theta}$$
$$= \left(\frac{\cos\theta}{\sin\theta}\right)^2$$
$$= \cot^2\theta$$

22. $y = 2\cos(2x + \pi)$
$A = 2$, $B = 2$, $C = -\pi$
Amplitude: $|A| = |2| = 2$
Period: $\dfrac{2\pi}{B} = \dfrac{2\pi}{2} = \pi$
Phase Shift: $\dfrac{C}{B} = \dfrac{-\pi}{2} = -\dfrac{\pi}{2}$
$(0, -2)$, $\left(\dfrac{\pi}{4}, 0\right)$, $\left(\dfrac{\pi}{2}, 2\right)$, $\left(\dfrac{3\pi}{4}, 0\right)$, $(\pi, -2)$

23.
$$(\mathbf{v}\cdot\mathbf{w})\mathbf{w} = \left[(3\mathbf{i} - 6\mathbf{j})\cdot(\mathbf{i} + \mathbf{j})\right](\mathbf{i} + \mathbf{j})$$
$$= \left[3(1) - 6(1)\right](\mathbf{i} + \mathbf{j})$$
$$= (3 - 6)(\mathbf{i} + \mathbf{j})$$
$$= -3(\mathbf{i} + \mathbf{j})$$
$$= -3\mathbf{i} - 3\mathbf{j}$$

24.
$$\sin 2\theta = \sin\theta, \ 0 \le \theta < 2\pi$$
$$2\sin\theta\cos\theta = \sin\theta$$
$$2\sin\theta\cos\theta - \sin\theta = 0$$
$$\sin\theta(2\cos\theta - 1) = 0$$
$$\sin\theta = 0 \quad \text{or} \quad 2\cos\theta - 1 = 0$$
$$\theta = 0, \ \pi \qquad\qquad 2\cos\theta = 1$$
$$\cos\theta = \frac{1}{2}$$
$$\theta = \frac{\pi}{3}, \frac{5\pi}{3}$$
The solutions in the interval $[0, 2\pi)$ are 0, π, $\dfrac{\pi}{3}$, and $\dfrac{5\pi}{3}$.

25.
$$A + B + C = 180°$$
$$64° + 72° + C = 180°$$
$$136° + C = 180°$$
$$C = 44°$$
$$\frac{b}{\sin B} = \frac{a}{\sin A}$$
$$\frac{b}{\sin 72°} = \frac{13.6}{\sin 64°}$$
$$b = \frac{13.6\sin 72°}{\sin 64°} \approx 14.4$$
$$\frac{c}{\sin C} = \frac{a}{\sin A}$$
$$\frac{c}{\sin 44°} = \frac{13.6}{\sin 64°}$$
$$c = \frac{13.6\sin 44°}{\sin 64°} \approx 10.5$$
The solution is $C = 44°$, $b \approx 14.4$, and $c \approx 10.5$.

Chapter 10

Check Point Exercises

1. **a.** $a_n = 2n + 5$

$a_1 = 2(1) + 5 = 7$

$a_2 = 2(2) + 5 = 9$

$a_3 = 2(3) + 5 = 11$

$a_4 = 2(4) + 5 = 13$

The first four terms are 7, 9, 11, and 13.

b. $a_n = \dfrac{(-1)^n}{2^n + 1}$

$a_1 = \dfrac{(-1)^1}{2^1 + 1} = = \dfrac{-1}{3} - \dfrac{1}{3}$

$a_2 = \dfrac{(-1)^2}{2^2 + 1} = \dfrac{1}{5}$

$a_3 = \dfrac{(-1)^3}{2^3 + 1} = \dfrac{-1}{9} = -\dfrac{1}{9}$

$a_4 = \dfrac{(-1)^4}{2^4 + 1} = \dfrac{1}{17}$

The first four terms are $-\dfrac{1}{3}, \dfrac{1}{5}, -\dfrac{1}{9},$

and $\dfrac{1}{17}$.

2. $a_1 = 3$ and $a_n = 2a_{n-1} + 5$ for $n \geq 2$

$a_2 = 2a_1 + 5$

$\quad = 2(3) + 5 = 11$

$a_3 = 2a_2 + 5$

$\quad = 2(11) + 5 = 27$

$a_4 = 2a_3 + 5$

$\quad = 2(27) + 5 = 59$

The first four terms are 3, 11, 27, and 59.

3. $a_n = \dfrac{20}{(n+1)!}$

$a_1 = \dfrac{20}{(1+1)!} = \dfrac{20}{2!} = 10$

$a_2 = \dfrac{20}{(2+1)!} = \dfrac{20}{3!} = \dfrac{20}{6} = \dfrac{10}{3}$

$a_3 = \dfrac{20}{(3+1)!} = \dfrac{20}{4!} = \dfrac{20}{24} = \dfrac{5}{6}$

$a_4 = \dfrac{20}{(4+1)!} = \dfrac{20}{5!} = \dfrac{20}{120} = \dfrac{1}{6}$

The first four terms are $10, \frac{10}{3}, \frac{5}{6},$ and $\frac{1}{6}$.

4. **a.** $\dfrac{14!}{2! \, 12!} = \dfrac{14 \cdot 13 \cdot 12!}{2! \, 12!} = \dfrac{14 \cdot 13}{2 \cdot 1} = 91$

b. $\dfrac{n!}{(n-1)!} = \dfrac{n \cdot (n-1)!}{(n-1)!} = n$

5. **a.** $\displaystyle\sum_{i=1}^{6} 2i^2$

$= 2(1)^2 + 2(2)^2 + 2(3)^2$

$\quad + 2(4)^2 + 2(5)^2 + 2(6)^2$

$= 2 + 8 + 18 + 32 + 50 + 72$

$= 182$

b. $\displaystyle\sum_{k=3}^{5} \left(2^k - 3\right)$

$= \left(2^3 - 3\right) + \left(2^4 - 3\right) + \left(2^5 - 3\right)$

$= (8 - 3) + (16 - 3) + (32 - 3)$

$= 5 + 13 + 29$

$= 47$

c. $\displaystyle\sum_{i=1}^{5} 4 = 4 + 4 + 4 + 4 + 4 = 20$

6. **a.** The sum has nine terms, each of the form i^2, starting at $i = 1$ and ending at $i = 9$.

$1^2 + 2^2 + 3^2 + \cdots + 9^2 = \displaystyle\sum_{i=1}^{9} i^2$

b. The sum has n terms, each of the form $\frac{1}{2^{i-1}}$, starting at $i = 1$ and ending at $i = n$.

$1 + \dfrac{1}{2} + \dfrac{1}{4} + \dfrac{1}{8} + \cdots + \dfrac{1}{2^{n-1}} = \displaystyle\sum_{i=1}^{n} \dfrac{1}{2^{i-1}}$

Exercise Set 10.1

1. $a_n = 3n + 2$

$a_1 = 3(1) + 2 = 5$

$a_2 = 3(2) + 2 = 8$

$a_3 = 3(3) + 2 = 11$

$a_4 = 3(4) + 2 = 14$

The first four terms are 5, 8, 11, and 14.

3. $a_n = 3^n$

$a_1 = 3^1 = 3$

$a_2 = 3^2 = 9$

$a_3 = 3^3 = 27$

$a_4 = 3^4 = 81$

The first four terms are 3, 9, 27, and 81.

5. $a_n = (-3)^n$

$a_1 = (-3)^1 = -3$

$a_2 = (-3)^2 = 9$

$a_3 = (-3)^3 = -27$

$a_4 = (-3)^4 = 81$

The first four terms are –3, 9, –27, and 81.

7. $a_n = (-1)^n (n + 3)$

$a_1 = (-1)^1 (1 + 3) = -4$

$a_2 = (-1)^2 (2 + 3) = 5$

$a_3 = (-1)^3 (3 + 3) = -6$

$a_4 = (-1)^4 (4 + 3) = 7$

The first four terms are –4, 5, –6, and 7.

9. $a_n = \dfrac{2n}{n + 4}$

$a_1 = \dfrac{2(1)}{1 + 4} = \dfrac{2}{5}$

$a_2 = \dfrac{2(2)}{2 + 4} = \dfrac{4}{6} = \dfrac{2}{3}$

$a_3 = \dfrac{2(3)}{3 + 4} = \dfrac{6}{7}$

$a_4 = \dfrac{2(4)}{4 + 4} = \dfrac{8}{8} = 1$

The first four terms are $\frac{2}{5}, \frac{2}{3}, \frac{6}{7}$, and 1.

11. $a_n = \dfrac{(-1)^{n+1}}{2^n - 1}$

$a_1 = \dfrac{(-1)^{1+1}}{2^1 - 1} = \dfrac{1}{1}$ $n = 1$

$a_2 = \dfrac{(-1)^{2+1}}{2^2 - 1} = -\dfrac{1}{3}$

$a_3 = \dfrac{(-1)^{3+1}}{2^3 - 1} = \dfrac{1}{7}$

$a_4 = \dfrac{(-1)^{4+1}}{2^4 - 1} = -\dfrac{1}{15}$

The first four terms are $1, -\frac{1}{3}, \frac{1}{7},$ and $-\frac{1}{15}$.

13. $a_1 = 7$ and $a_n = a_{n-1} + 5$ for $n \geq 2$

$a_2 = a_1 + 5 = 7 + 5 = 12$

$a_3 = a_2 + 5 = 12 + 5 = 17$

$a_4 = a_3 + 5 = 17 + 5 = 22$

The first four terms are 7, 12, 17, and 22.

15. $a_1 = 3$ and $a_n = 4a_{n-1}$ for $n \geq 2$

$a_2 = 4a_1 = 4(3) = 12$

$a_3 = 4a_2 = 4(12) = 48$

$a_4 = 4a_3 = 4(48) = 192$

The first four terms are 3, 12, 48, and 192.

17. $a_1 = 4$ and $a_n = 2a_{n-1} + 3$

$a_2 = 2(4) + 3 = 11$

$a_3 = 2(11) + 3 = 25$

$a_4 = 2(25) + 3 = 53$

The first four terms are 4, 11, 25, and 53.

19. $a_n = \dfrac{n^2}{n!}$

$a_1 = \dfrac{1^2}{1!} = 1$

$a_2 = \dfrac{2^2}{2!} = 2$

$a_3 = \dfrac{3^2}{3!} = \dfrac{9}{6} = \dfrac{3}{2}$

$a_4 = \dfrac{4^2}{4!} = \dfrac{16}{24} = \dfrac{2}{3}$

The first four terms are $1, \; 2, \; \frac{3}{2},$ and $\frac{2}{3}$.

21. $a_n = 2(n+1)!$

$a_1 = 2(1+1)! = 2(2) = 4$

$a_2 = 2(2+1)! = 2(6) = 12$

$a_3 = 2(3+1)! = 2(24) = 48$

$a_4 = 2(4+1)! = 2(120) = 240$

The first four terms are 4, 12, 48, and 240.

23. $\dfrac{17!}{15!} = \dfrac{17 \cdot 16 \cdot 15!}{15!} = 17 \cdot 16 = 272$

25. $\dfrac{16!}{2! \cdot 14!} = \dfrac{16 \cdot 15 \cdot 14!}{2! 14!} = \dfrac{16 \cdot 15}{2 \cdot 1} = \dfrac{8 \cdot 15}{1} = 120$

27. $\dfrac{(n+2)!}{n!} = \dfrac{(n+2)(n+1)n!}{n!} = (n+2)(n+1)$

29. $\displaystyle\sum_{i=1}^{6} 5i = 5 \cdot 1 + 5 \cdot 2 + 5 \cdot 3 + 5 \cdot 4 + 5 \cdot 5 + 5 \cdot 6$

$= 5 + 10 + 15 + 20 + 25 + 30$

$= 105$

31. $\displaystyle\sum_{i=1}^{4} 2i^2 = 2 \cdot 1^2 + 2 \cdot 2^2 + 2 \cdot 3^2 + 2 \cdot 4^2$

$= 2 + 8 + 18 + 32$

$= 60$

33. $\displaystyle\sum_{k=1}^{5} k(k+4) = 1(5) + 2(6) + 3(7) + 4(8) + 5(9)$

$= 5 + 12 + 21 + 32 + 45$

$= 115$

35. $\displaystyle\sum_{i=1}^{4} \left(\dfrac{-1}{2} \right)^i$

$= \left(-\dfrac{1}{2} \right)^1 + \left(-\dfrac{1}{2} \right)^2 + \left(-\dfrac{1}{2} \right)^3 + \left(-\dfrac{1}{2} \right)^4$

$= -\dfrac{1}{2} + \dfrac{1}{4} + -\dfrac{1}{8} + \dfrac{1}{16}$

$= -\dfrac{5}{16}$

37. $\displaystyle\sum_{i=5}^{9} 11 = 11 + 11 + 11 + 11 + 11 = 55$

39. $\displaystyle\sum_{i=0}^{4} \dfrac{(-1)^i}{i!}$

$= \dfrac{(-1)^0}{0!} + \dfrac{(-1)^1}{1!} + \dfrac{(-1)^2}{2!} + \dfrac{(-1)^3}{3!} + \dfrac{(-1)^4}{4!}$

$= 1 - 1 + \dfrac{1}{2} - \dfrac{1}{6} + \dfrac{1}{24}$

$= \dfrac{9}{24} = \dfrac{3}{8}$

41. $\displaystyle\sum_{i=1}^{5} \dfrac{i!}{(i-1)!} = \dfrac{1!}{0!} + \dfrac{2!}{1!} + \dfrac{3!}{2!} + \dfrac{4!}{3!} + \dfrac{5!}{4!}$

$= 1 + 2 + 3 + 4 + 5 = 15$

43. $1^2 + 2^2 + 3^2 + \cdots + 15^2 = \displaystyle\sum_{i=1}^{15} i^2$

45. $2 + 2^2 + 2^3 + 2^4 + \cdots + 2^{11} = \displaystyle\sum_{i=1}^{11} 2^i$

47. $1 + 2 + 3 + \cdots + 30 = \displaystyle\sum_{i=1}^{30} i$

49. $\dfrac{1}{2} + \dfrac{2}{3} + \dfrac{3}{4} + \cdots + \dfrac{14}{14+1} = \displaystyle\sum_{i=1}^{14} \dfrac{i}{i+1}$

51. $4 + \dfrac{4^2}{2} + \dfrac{4^3}{3} + \cdots + \dfrac{4^n}{n} = \displaystyle\sum_{i=1}^{n} \dfrac{4^i}{i}$

53. $1 + 3 + 5 + \cdots + (2n-1) = \displaystyle\sum_{i=1}^{n} (2i-1)$

55. $5 + 7 + 9 + \cdots + 31$

Possible answer: $\displaystyle\sum_{k=1}^{14} (2k+3)$

57. $a + ar + ar^2 + \cdots + ar^{12}$

Possible answer: $\displaystyle\sum_{k=0}^{12} ar^k$

59. $a + (a+d) + (a+2d) + \cdots + (a+nd)$

Possible answer: $\displaystyle\sum_{k=0}^{n} (a+kd)$

61.
$$\sum_{i=1}^{5}(a_i^2+1)=\left((-4)^2+1\right)+\left((-2)^2+1\right)+\left((0)^2+1\right)+\left((2)^2+1\right)+\left((4)^2+1\right)$$
$$=17+5+1+5+17$$
$$=45$$

63.
$$\sum_{i=1}^{5}(2a_i+b_i)=\left(2(-4)+4\right)+\left(2(-2)+2\right)+\left(2(0)+0\right)+\left(2(2)+(-2)\right)+\left(2(4)+(-4)\right)$$
$$=-4+(-2)+0+2+4=0$$

65.
$$\sum_{i=4}^{5}\left(\frac{a_i}{b_i}\right)^2=\left(\frac{2}{-2}\right)^2+\left(\frac{4}{-4}\right)^2=(-1)^2+(-1)^2=1+1=2$$

67.
$$\sum_{i=1}^{5}a_i^2+\sum_{i=1}^{5}b_i^2=\left((-4)^2+(-2)^2+0^2+2^2+4^2\right)+\left(4^2+2^2+0^2+(-2)^2+(-4)^2\right)$$
$$=(16+4+0+4+16)+(16+4+0+4+16)=80$$

69. a.
$$\sum_{i=1}^{8}a_i=36.4+36.5+35.6+34.5+32.3+31.6+32.9+34.6=274.4$$

b.
$$\frac{\sum_{i=1}^{8}a_i}{8}=\frac{274.4}{8}=34.3$$

From 1995 through 2002, the average number of people living below poverty level each year was approximately 34.3 million.

71. a.
$$\frac{1}{10}\sum_{i=1}^{10}a_i=\frac{1}{10}(14.2+13.7+12.6+10.9+8.7+7.6+5.9+5.4+5.1+5.0)=\frac{1}{10}(89.1)=8.91$$

From 1994 through 2003, there was an average of 8.91 million Welfare recipients in the US.

b.
$$\frac{1}{10}\sum_{n=1}^{10}(-1.18n+15.41)$$

$$=\frac{1}{10}\big[(-1.18\cdot1+15.41)+(-1.18\cdot2+15.41)+(-1.18\cdot3+15.41)+(-1.18\cdot4+15.41)+(-1.18\cdot5+15.41)$$

$$+(-1.18\cdot6+15.41)+(-1.18\cdot7+15.41)+(-1.18\cdot8+15.41)+(-1.18\cdot9+15.41)+(-1.18\cdot10+15.41)\big]$$

$$=\frac{1}{10}(89.2)$$

$$=8.92$$

The model is very close to the actual average.

73. $a_n = 6000\left(1 + \dfrac{0.06}{4}\right)^n, n = 1, 2, 3, \cdots$

$$a_{20} = 6000\left(1 + \dfrac{0.06}{4}\right)^{20} \approx 8081.13$$

After five years, the balance is \$8081.13.

83. Most calculators give error message if the expression is entered directly.

However,

$$\dfrac{200!}{198!} = \dfrac{200 \cdot 199 \cdot 198!}{198!} = 200 \cdot 199 = 39,800$$

85. $\dfrac{20!}{300} = 8,109,673,360,588,800$

However, most calculators give a rounded answer in scientific notation.

87. $\dfrac{54!}{(54-3)3!} = 24,804$

91. $a_n = \dfrac{n}{n+1}$

As *n* gets larger, a_n approaches 1.

93. $a_n = \dfrac{2n^2 + 5n - 7}{n^3}$

As *n* gets larger, a_n approaches 0.

95. **a.**   False; $\dfrac{n!}{(n-1)!} = \dfrac{n \cdot (n-1)!}{(n-1)!} = n$

     b.   True

     c.   False; $\displaystyle\sum_{i=1}^{2} (-1)^i 2^i = -2 + 4 = 2$

     d.   False; $a_1 b_1 + a_2 b_2 \neq \left(a_1 + a_2\right) + \left(b_1 + b_2\right)$

     (b) is true.

Section 10.2

Check Point Exercises

1. $a_1 = 51.5$

$a_2 = a_1 + 2.18 = 51.5 + 2.18 = 53.68$

$a_3 = a_2 + 2.18 = 53.68 + 2.18 = 55.86$

$a_4 = a_3 + 2.18 = 55.86 + 2.18 = 58.04$

$a_5 = a_4 + 2.18 = 58.04 + 2.18 = 60.22$

The first five terms are 51.5, 53.68, 55.86, 58.04, and 60.22.

2. $a_1 = 6, d = -5$

To find the ninth term, a_9, replace *n* in the formula with 9, a_1 with 6, and *d* with –5.

$a_n = a_1 + (n-1)d$

$a_9 = 6 + (9-1)(-5)$

    $= 6 + 8(-5)$

    $= 6 + (-40)$

    $= -34$

3. **a.** $a_n = a_1 + (n-1)d = 159,000 + (n-1)9700$

        $a_n = 9700n + 149,300$

    b. a_1 represents 1995 so a_{16} represents 2010.

        $a_n = 9700n + 149,300$

        $a_{16} = 9700(16) + 149,300$

          $= 304,500$

        In 2010, a new one-family house will cost \$304,500.

4.   3, 6, 9, 12, ...

To find the sum of the first 15 terms, S_{15}, replace *n* in the formula with 15.

$$S_n = \dfrac{n}{2}(a_1 + a_n)$$

$$S_{15} = \dfrac{15}{2}(a_1 + a_{15})$$

Use the formula for the general term of a sequence to find a_{15}. The common difference, *d*, is 3, and the first term, a_1, is 3.

$a_n = a_1 + (n-1)d$

$a_{15} = 3 + (15-1)(3)$

    $= 3 + 14(3)$

    $= 3 + 42$

    $= 45$

Thus, $S_{15} = \dfrac{15}{2}(3 + 45) = \dfrac{15}{2}(48) = 360$.

5. $\sum_{i=1}^{30}(6i-11) = (6 \cdot 1 - 11) + (6 \cdot 2 - 11) +$

$+ (6 \cdot 3 - 11) + \ldots + (6 \cdot 30 - 11)$

$= -5 + 1 + 7 + \ldots + 169$

So the first term, a_1, is -5; the common difference, d, is $1 - (-5) = 6$; the last term, a_{30}, is 169. Substitute $n = 30$, $a_1 = -5$, and

$a_{30} = 169$ in the formula $S_n = \frac{n}{2}(a_1 + a_n)$.

$S_{30} = \frac{30}{2}(-5 + 169) = 15(164) = 2460$

Thus, $\sum_{i=1}^{30}(6i-11) = 2460$

6. $a_n = 1800n + 58,730$

$a_1 = 1800(1) + 58,730 = 60,530$

$a_{10} = 1800(10) + 58,730 = 76,730$

$S_n = \frac{n}{2}(a_1 + a_n)$

$S_{10} = \frac{10}{2}(a_1 + a_{10})$

$= 5(60,530 + 76,730)$

$= 5(137,260)$

$= \$686,300$

It would cost \$686,300 for the ten-year period beginning in 2006.

Exercise Set 10.2

1. $a_1 = 200$, $d = 20$
The first six terms are 200, 220, 240, 260, 280, and 300.

3. $a_1 = -7$, $d = 4$
The first six terms are -7, -3, 1, 5, 9, and 13.

5. $a_1 = 300$, $d = -90$
The first six terms are 300, 210, 120, 30, -60, and -150.

7. $a_1 = \frac{5}{2}$, $d = -\frac{1}{2}$

The first six terms are $\frac{5}{2}, 2, \frac{3}{2}, 1, \frac{1}{2}$, and 0.

9. $a_n = a_{n-1} + 6$, $a_1 = -9$
The first six terms are -9, -3, 3, 9, 15, and 21.

11. $a_n = a_{n-1} - 10$, $a_1 = 30$
The first six terms are 30, 20, 10, 0, -10, and -20.

13. $a_n = a_{n-1} - 0.4$, $a_1 = 1.6$
The first six terms are 1.6, 1.2, 0.8, 0.4, 0, and -0.4.

15. $a_1 = 13$, $d = -4$

$a_n = 13 + (n-1)4$

$a_6 = 13 + 5(4) = 13 + 20 = 33$

17. $a_1 = 7$, $d = 5$

$a_n = 7 + (n-1)2$

$a_{50} = 7 + 49(5) = 252$

19. $a_1 = -40$, $d = 5$

$a_n = -40 + (n-1)5$

$a_{200} = -40 + (199)5 = 955$

21. $a_1 = 35$, $d = -3$

$a_n = 35 - 3(n-1)$

$a_{60} = 35 - 3(59) = -142$

23. 1, 5, 9, 13, ...

$d = 5 - 1, = 4$

$a_n = 1 + (n-1)4 = 1 + 4n - 4$

$a_n = 4n - 3$

$a_{20} = 4(20) - 3 = 77$

25. 7, 3, -1, -5, ...

$d = 3 - 7 = -4$

$a_n = 7 + (n-1)(-4) = 7 - 4n + 4$

$a_n = 11 - 4n$

$a_{20} = 11 - 4(20) = -69$

27. $a_1 = 9$, $d = 2$

$a_n = 9 + (n-1)(2)$

$a_n = 7 + 2n$

$a_{20} = 7 + 2(20) = 47$

29. $a_1 = -20$, $d = -4$

$a_n = -20 + (n-1)(-4)$

$a_n = -20 - 4n + 4$

$a_n = -16 - 4n$

$a_{20} = -16 - 4(20) = -96$

31. $a_n = a_{n-1} + 3, \ a_1 = 4$

$d = 3$

$a_n = 4 + (n-1)(3)$

$a_n = 1 + 3n$

$a_{20} = 1 + 3(20) = 61$

33. $a_n = a_{n-1} - 10, \ a_1 = 30, \ d = -10$

$a_n = 30 - 10(n-1) = 30 - 10n + 10$

$a_n = 40 - 10n$

$a_{20} = 40 - 10(20) = -160$

35. $4, 10, 16, 22, \ldots$

$d = 10 - 4 = 6$

$a_n = 4 + (n-1)(6)$

$a_{20} = 4 + (19)(6) = 118$

$S_{20} = \dfrac{20}{2}(4 + 118) = 1220$

37. $-10, -6, -2, 2, \ldots$

$d = -6 - (-10) = -6 + 10 = 4$

$a_n = -10 + (n-1)4$

$a_{50} = -10 + (49)4 = 186$

$S_{50} = \dfrac{50}{2}(-10 + 186) = 4400$

39. $1 + 2 + 3 + 4 + \cdots + 100$

$S_{100} = \dfrac{100}{2}(1 + 100) = 5050$

41. $2 + 4 + 6 + \cdots + 120$

$S_{60} = \dfrac{60}{2}(2 + 120) = 3660$

43. even integers between 21 and 45;

$22 + 24 + 26 + \cdots + 44$

$S_{12} = \dfrac{12}{2}(22 + 44) = 396$

45. $\displaystyle\sum_{i=1}^{17}(5i + 3) = (5 + 3) + (10 + 3) + (15 + 3) + \cdots + (85 + 3) = 8 + 13 + 18 + \cdots + 88$

$S_{17} = \dfrac{17}{2}(8 + 88) = 816$

47. $\displaystyle\sum_{i=1}^{30}(-3i + 5) = (-3 + 5) + (-6 + 5) + (-9 + 5) + \cdots + (-90 + 5) = 2 - 1 - 4 - \cdots - 85$

$S_{30} = \dfrac{30}{2}(2 - 85) = -1245$

49. $\displaystyle\sum_{i=1}^{100} 4i = 4 + 8 + 12 + \cdots + 400$

$S_{100} = \dfrac{100}{2}(4 + 400) = 20,200$

51. First find a_{14} and b_{12}:

$a_{14} = a_1 + (n-1)d$

$\quad = 1 + (14-1)(-3-1) = -51$

$b_{12} = b_1 + (n-1)d$

$\quad = 3 + (12-1)(8-3) = 58$

So, $a_{14} + b_{12} = -51 + 58 = 7$.

53. $a_n = a_1 + (n-1)d$

$-83 = 1 + (n-1)(-3-1)$

$-83 = 1 + -4(n-1)$

$-84 = -4n + 4$

$-88 = -4n$

$n = 22$

There are 22 terms.

55. $S_n = \frac{n}{2}(a_1 + a_n)$

For $\{a_n\}$: $S_{14} = \frac{14}{2}(a_1 + a_{14}) = 7(1 + (-51)) = -350$

For $\{b_n\}$: $S_{14} = \frac{14}{2}(b_1 + b_{14}) = 7(3 + 68) = 497$

So $\sum_{n=1}^{14} b_n - \sum_{n=1}^{14} a_n = 497 - (-350) = 847$

57. Two points on the graph are $(1, 1)$ and $(2, -3)$.
Finding the slope of the line;

$m = \frac{y_2 - y_1}{x_2 - x_2} = \frac{-3 - 1}{2 - 1} = \frac{-4}{1} = -4$

Using the point-slope form of an equation of a line;

$y - y_2 = m(x - x_2)$

$y - 1 = -4(x - 1)$

$y - 1 = -4x + 4$

$y = -4x + 5$

Thus, $f(x) = -4x + 5$.

59. Using $a_n = a_1 + (n-1)d$ and $a_2 = 4$:

$a_2 = a_1 + (2-1)d$

$4 = a_1 + d$

And since $a_6 = 16$:

$a_6 = a_1 + (6-1)d$

$16 = a_1 + 5d$

The system of equations is

$4 = a_1 + d$

$16 = a_1 + 5d$

Solving the first equation for a_1:

$a_1 = 4 - d$

Substituting the value into the second equation and solving for d:

$16 = (4 - d) + 5d$

$16 = 4 + 4d$

$12 = 4d$

$3 = d$

Back-substitute:

$a_1 = 4 - d$

$a_1 = 4 - 3)$

$a_1 = 1$

Then $a_n = a_1 + (n-1)d$

$a_n = 1 + (n-1)3$

$a_n = 1 + 3n - 3$

$a_n = 3n - 2$

61. a. $a_n = 23.08 + 0.12n$

b. $a_{40} = 23.08 + 0.12(40) = 27.88$ years old

63. Median age of first marriage for women:
$a_n = 20.66 + 0.14n$

$a_{40} = 20.66 + 0.14(40) = 26.26$ years old

Young adults living with parents:
$a_n = 47.21 + 0.09n$

$a_{40} = 47.21 + 0.09(40) = 50.81\%$

Number completing four or more years of college:
$a_n = 10.84 + 1.16n$

$a_{40} = 10.84 + 1.16(40) = 57.24$ million

65. a. Total cost: $\$7107 + \$7310 + \$7586 + \$8046$
$\qquad = \$30,049$

b. $a_1 = 309(1) + 6739 = 7048$

$a_2 = 309(2) + 6739 = 7357$

$a_3 = 309(3) + 6739 = 7666$

$a_4 = 309(4) + 6739 = 7975$

Total cost:

$7048 + 7357 + 7666 + 7975 = \$30,046$

The model describes the actual sum very well.

67. $a_n = 33,000 + (n-1)(2500)$

$a_{10} = 33,000 + 9(2500) = 55,500$

$S_n = \frac{10}{2}(33,000 + 55,500) = 442,500$

The total ten year salary is $\$442,500$.

69. $a_n = 30 + (n-1)2$

$a_{26} = 30 + (25)2 = 80$

$S_{26} = \frac{26}{2}(30 + 80) = 1430$

The theater has 1430 seats.

79. Degree days: 23, 25, 27, …
$a_1 = 23, d = 2$

$a_{10} = 23 + 9(2) = 41$

$S_{10} = \frac{10}{2}(a_1 + a_{10})$

$S_{10} = \frac{10}{2}(23 + 41) = 320$

There are 320 degree-days.

Section 10.3

Check Point Exercises

1. $a_1 = 12, \ r = \dfrac{1}{2}$

$a_2 = 12\left(\dfrac{1}{2}\right)^1 = 6$

$a_3 = 12\left(\dfrac{1}{2}\right)^2 = \dfrac{12}{4} = 3$

$a_4 = 12\left(\dfrac{1}{2}\right)^3 = \dfrac{12}{8} = \dfrac{3}{2}$

$a_5 = 12\left(\dfrac{1}{2}\right)^4 = \dfrac{12}{16} = \dfrac{3}{4}$

$a_6 = 12\left(\dfrac{1}{2}\right)^5 = \dfrac{12}{32} = \dfrac{3}{8}$

The first six terms are $12, \ 6, \ 3, \ \dfrac{3}{2}, \ \dfrac{3}{4}, \text{and} \ \dfrac{3}{8}$.

2. $a_1 = 5, \ r = -3$

$a_n = 5r^{n-1}$

$a_7 = 5(-3)^{7-1} = 5(-3)^6 = 5(729) = 3645$

The seventh term is 3645.

3. $3, \ 6, \ 12, \ 24, \ 48, \ ...$

$r = \dfrac{6}{3} = 2, \ a_1 = 3$

$a_n = 3(2)^{n-1}$

$a_8 = 3(2)^{8-1} = 3(2)^7 = 3(128) = 384$

The eighth term is 384.

4. $a_1 = 2, \ r = \dfrac{-6}{2} = -3$

$S_n = \dfrac{a_1(1-r^r)}{1-r}$

$S_9 = \dfrac{2\left(1-(-3)^9\right)}{1-(-3)} = \dfrac{2(19,684)}{4} = 9842$

The sum of the first nine terms is 9842.

5. $\displaystyle\sum_{i=1}^{8} 2 \cdot 3^i$

$a_1 = 2 \cdot (3)^1 = 6, \ r = 3$

$S_n = \dfrac{a_1(1-r^n)}{1-r}$

$S_8 = \dfrac{6\left(1-3^8\right)}{1-3} = \dfrac{6(-6560)}{-2} = 19,680$

Thus, $\displaystyle\sum_{i=1}^{8} 2 \cdot 3^i = 19,680$.

6. $a_1 = 30,000, \ r = 1.06$

$S_n = \dfrac{a_1(1-r^n)}{1-r}$

$S_{30} = \dfrac{30,000\left(1-(1.06)^{30}\right)}{1-1.06} \approx 2,371,746$

The total lifetime salary is \$2,371,746.

7. $A = P\dfrac{\left(1+\frac{r}{n}\right)^{nt} - 1}{\frac{r}{n}}$

$P = 3000, \ r = 0.10, \ n = 1, \ t = 40$

$A = 3000\dfrac{(1+0.10)^{40} - 1}{0.10} \approx 1,327,778$

The value of the IRA will be \$1,327,778.

8. $3 + 2 + \dfrac{4}{3} + \dfrac{8}{9} + \cdots$

$a_1 = 3, \ r = \dfrac{2}{3}$

$S = \dfrac{a_1}{1-r}$

$S = \dfrac{3}{1-\frac{2}{3}} = \dfrac{3}{\frac{1}{3}} = 9$

The sum of this infinite geometric series is 9.

9. $0.\overline{9} = 0.9999\cdots = \dfrac{9}{10} + \dfrac{9}{100} + \dfrac{9}{1000} + \cdots$

$a_1 = \dfrac{9}{10}, r = \dfrac{1}{10}$

$S = \dfrac{\frac{9}{10}}{1-\frac{1}{10}} = \dfrac{\frac{9}{10}}{\frac{9}{10}} = 1$

An equivalent fraction for $0.\overline{9}$ is 1.

10. $a_1 = 1000(0.8) = 800$, $r = 0.8$

$S = \dfrac{800}{1 - 0.8} = 4000$

The total amount spent is $4000.

Exercise Set 10.3

1. $a_1 = 5$, $r = 3$
First five terms: 5, 15, 45, 135, 405.

3. $a_1 = 20$, $r = \dfrac{1}{2}$
First five terms: 20, 10, 5, $\frac{5}{2}$, $\frac{5}{4}$ $\frac{5}{4}$.

5. $a_n = -4a_{n-1}$, $a_1 = 10$
First five terms: 10, –40, 160, –640, 2560.

7. $a_n = -5a_{n-1}$, $a_1 = -6$
First five terms: –6, 30, –150, 750, –3750.

9. $a_1 = 6$, $r = 2$
$a_n = 6 \cdot 2^{n-1}$
$a_8 = 6 \cdot 2^7 = 768$

11. $a_1 = 5$, $r = -2$
$a_n = 5 \cdot (-2)^{n-1}$
$a_{12} = 5 \cdot (-2)^{11} = -10{,}240$

13.
$a_1 = 1000$, $r = -\dfrac{1}{2}$

$a_n = 1000\left(-\dfrac{1}{2}\right)^{n-1}$

$a_{40} = 1000\left(-\dfrac{1}{2}\right)^{39}$
≈ 0.000000002

15. $a_1 = 1{,}000{,}000$, $r = 0.1$
$a_n = 1{,}000{,}000(0.1)^{n-1}$
$a_8 = 1{,}000{,}000(0.1)^7 = 0.1$

17. 3, 12, 48, 192, …
$r = \dfrac{12}{3} = 4$
$a_n = 3(4)^{n-1}$
$a_7 = 3(4)^6 = 12{,}288$

19. $19, 6, 2, \dfrac{2}{3}, \cdots$ $r = \dfrac{6}{18} = \dfrac{1}{3}$

$a_n = 18\left(\dfrac{1}{3}\right)^{n-1}$

$a_7 = 18\left(\dfrac{1}{3}\right)^6 = \dfrac{2}{81}$

21. 1.5, –3, 6, –12, …
$r = \dfrac{6}{-3} = -2$
$a_n = 1.5(-2)^{n-1}$
$a_7 = 1.5(-2)^6 = 96$

23. 0.0004, –0.004, 0.04, –0.4, …
$r = \dfrac{-0.004}{0.0004} = -10$
$a_n = 0.0004(-10)^{n-1}$
$a_7 = 0.0004(-10)^6 = 400$

25. 2, 6, 18, 54, …
$r = \dfrac{6}{2} = 3$

$S_{12} = \dfrac{2\left(1 - 3^{12}\right)}{1 - 3} = \dfrac{2(-531{,}440)}{-2} = 531{,}440$

27. 3, –6, 12, –24, …
$r = \dfrac{-6}{3} = -2$

$S_{11} = \dfrac{3\left[1 - (-2)^{11}\right]}{1 - (-2)} = \dfrac{3(2049)}{3} = 2049$

29. $-\dfrac{3}{2}, 3, -6, 12, \cdots$

$r = \dfrac{3}{-\dfrac{3}{2}} = -2$

$S_{14} = \dfrac{-\dfrac{3}{2}\left[1 - (-2)^{14}\right]}{1 - (-2)} = \dfrac{-\dfrac{3}{2}(-16{,}383)}{3} = \dfrac{16{,}383}{2}$

31. $\displaystyle\sum_{i=1}^{8} 3^i$
$r = 3$, $a_1 = 3$
$S_8 = \dfrac{3\left(1 - 3^8\right)}{1 - 3} = \dfrac{3(-6560)}{-2} = 9840$

33. $\displaystyle\sum_{i=1}^{10} 5 \cdot 2^i$

$r = 2, \quad a_1 = 10$

$S_{10} = \dfrac{10\left(1 - 2^{10}\right)}{1 - 2} = \dfrac{10(-1023)}{-1} = 10{,}230$

35. $\displaystyle\sum_{i=1}^{6} \left(\dfrac{1}{2}\right)^{i+1}$

$r = \dfrac{1}{2}, \quad a_1 = \dfrac{1}{4}$

$S_6 = \dfrac{\dfrac{1}{4}\left(1 - \left(\dfrac{1}{2}\right)^6\right)}{1 - \dfrac{1}{2}} = \dfrac{\dfrac{1}{4}\left(\dfrac{63}{64}\right)}{\dfrac{1}{2}} = \dfrac{63}{128}$

37. $r = \dfrac{1}{3}$

$S_\infty = \dfrac{1}{1 - \dfrac{1}{3}} = \dfrac{1}{\dfrac{2}{3}} = \dfrac{3}{2}$

39. $r = \dfrac{1}{4}$

$S_\infty = \dfrac{3}{1 - \dfrac{1}{4}} = \dfrac{3}{\dfrac{3}{4}} = 4$

41. $r = -\dfrac{1}{2}$

$S_\infty = \dfrac{1}{1 - \left(-\dfrac{1}{2}\right)} = \dfrac{1}{\dfrac{3}{2}} = \dfrac{2}{3}$

43. $r = -0.3$

$S_\infty = \dfrac{8}{1 - (-0.3)} = \dfrac{8}{1.3} \approx 6.15385$

45. $r = \dfrac{1}{10}$

$S_\infty = \dfrac{\dfrac{5}{10}}{1 - \dfrac{1}{10}} = \dfrac{\dfrac{5}{10}}{\dfrac{9}{10}} = \dfrac{5}{9}$

47. $r = \dfrac{1}{100}$

$S_\infty = \dfrac{\dfrac{47}{100}}{1 - \dfrac{1}{100}} = \dfrac{\dfrac{47}{100}}{\dfrac{99}{100}} = \dfrac{47}{99}$

49. $0.\overline{257} = \dfrac{257}{1000} + \dfrac{257}{10^6} + \dfrac{257}{10^9} + \cdots$

$r = \dfrac{1}{1000}$

$S_\infty = \dfrac{\dfrac{257}{1000}}{1 - \dfrac{1}{1000}} = \dfrac{\dfrac{257}{1000}}{\dfrac{999}{1000}} = \dfrac{257}{999}$

51. $a_n = n + 5$

arithmetic, $d = 1$

53. $a_n = 2^n$

geometric, $r = 2$

55. $a_n = n^2 + 5$

neither

57. First find a_{10} and b_{10}:

$a_{10} = a_1 r^{n-1}$

$\quad = (-5)\left(\dfrac{10}{-5}\right)^{10-1} = (-5)(-2)^9$

$\quad = 2560$

$b_{10} = b_1 + (n-1)d$

$\quad = 10 + (10-1)(-5-10)$

$\quad = 10 + (9)(-15) = -125$

So, $a_{10} + b_{10} = 2560 + (-125) = 2435$.

59. From Exercise 65, $a_{10} = 2560$ and $b_{10} = -125$.

For $\{a_n\}$, $r = \dfrac{10}{-5} = -2$ and :

$S_{10} = \dfrac{a_1\left(1 - r^n\right)}{1 - r} = \dfrac{(-5)\left(1 - (-2)^{10}\right)}{1 - (-2)}$

$\quad = \dfrac{(-5)(-1023)}{3} = 1705$

For $\{b_n\}$, $S_n = \dfrac{n}{2}\left(b_1 + b_n\right) = \dfrac{10}{2}(10 + (-125))$

$\quad = 5(-115) = -575$

So, $\displaystyle\sum_{n=1}^{10} a_n - \sum_{n=1}^{10} b_n = 1705 - (-575) = 2280$

61. For $\{a_n\}$,

$$S_6 = \frac{a_1(1-r^n)}{1-r} = \frac{(-5)\left(1-(-2)^6\right)}{1-(-2)}$$

$$= \frac{(-5)(-63)}{3} = 105$$

For $\{c_n\}$,

$$S = \frac{a_1}{1-r} = \frac{-2}{1-\frac{1}{-2}} = \frac{-2}{\frac{3}{2}} = -\frac{4}{3}$$

So, $S_6 \cdot S = 105\left(-\frac{4}{3}\right) = -140$

63. It is given that $a_4 = 27$. Using the formula $a_n = a_1 r^{n-1}$ when $n = 4$ we have:

$$27 = 8r^{4-1}$$

$$\frac{27}{8} = r^3$$

$$r = \sqrt[3]{\frac{27}{8}} = \frac{3}{2}$$

Then

$$a_n = a_1 r^{n-1}$$

$$a_2 = 8\left(\frac{3}{2}\right)^{2-1} = 8\left(\frac{3}{2}\right) = 12$$

$$a_3 = 8\left(\frac{3}{2}\right)^{3-1} = 8\left(\frac{3}{2}\right)^2 = 8\left(\frac{9}{4}\right) = 18$$

65. $1, 2, 4, 8, \ldots$

$r = 2$

$a_n = 2^{n-1}$

$a_{15} = 2^{14} = \$16,384$

67. $a_1 = 3,000,000$

$r = 1.04$

$a_n = 3,000,000(1.04)^{n-1}$

$a_7 = 3,000,000(1.04)^6 = \$3,795,957$

69. a. $\dfrac{30.15}{29.76} \approx 1.013$

$\dfrac{30.54}{30.15} \approx 1.013$

$\dfrac{30.94}{30.54} \approx 1.013$

The population is increasing geometrically with $r \approx 1.013$.

b. $a_n = 29.76 \cdot 1.013^{n-1}$

c. $2000 - 1989 = 11$

$a_{11} = 29.76 \cdot 1.013^{11-1} = 33.86$

In 2000, the model predicts California population will be 33.86. This is very close to the actual population.

71. $1, 2, 4, 8, \ldots$

$r = 2$

$$S_{15} = \frac{1(1-2^{15})}{1-2} = 32,767$$

The total savings is \$32,767.

73. $a_1 = 24,000, \ r = 1.05$

$$S_{20} = \frac{24,000\left[1-(1.05)^{20}\right]}{1-1.05} = 793,582.90$$

The total salary is \$793,583.

75. $r = 0.9$

$$S_{10} = \frac{20(1-0.9^{10})}{1-0.9} \approx 130.26$$

The total length is 130.26 inches.

77. $A = 2500\dfrac{(1+0.09)^{40}-1}{0.09} \approx 844,706.11$

In 40 years, the value is \$844,706.

79. $A = 600\dfrac{\left(1+\dfrac{0.08}{4}\right)^{72}-1}{\dfrac{0.08}{4}} \approx 94,834.21$

After 18 years, the value is \$94,834.

81. $r = 0.6$

$$S_\infty = \frac{6(0.6)}{1-0.6} = 9$$

The total economic impact is \$9 million.

83. $r = \dfrac{1}{4}$

$$S_\infty = \frac{\frac{1}{4}}{1-\frac{1}{4}} = \frac{1}{4}\cdot\frac{4}{3} = \frac{1}{3}$$

95.

$$f(x) = \frac{2\left[1-\left(\frac{1}{3}\right)^x\right]}{1-\frac{1}{3}}$$

$$S = \frac{2}{1-\frac{1}{3}} = \frac{2}{\frac{2}{3}} = 2 \div \frac{2}{3} = 2 \cdot \frac{3}{2} = 3$$

The sum of the series is 3 and the asymptote of the function is $y = 3$.

97. a. False; there is no common ratio.

b. False; the sum can be calculated exactly, since the series is geometric $\left(r = \frac{1}{2}\right)$.

c. False; $10 - 5 + \frac{5}{2} - \frac{5}{4} \cdots = \frac{10}{1+\frac{1}{2}}$

d. True; $r = 0.5 = \frac{1}{2}$

(d) is true.

99. $1,000,000 = P \dfrac{\left(1+\frac{0.1}{12}\right)^{360} - 1}{\frac{0.1}{12}}$

$1,000,000 \approx 2260.49P$

$P \approx 442.38$

You must deposit $442 monthly.

Mid-Chapter 10 Check Point

1.

$$a_n = (-1)^{n+1} \frac{n}{(n-1)!}$$

$$a_1 = (-1)^{1+1} \frac{1}{(1-1)!} = (-1)^2 \frac{1}{0!} = 1 \cdot 1 = 1$$

$$a_2 = (-1)^{2+1} \frac{2}{(2-1)!} = (-1)^3 \frac{2}{1!} = (-1)(2) = -2$$

$$a_3 = (-1)^{3+1} \frac{3}{(3-1)!} = (-1)^4 \frac{3}{2!} = 1 \cdot \frac{3}{2} = \frac{3}{2}$$

$$a_4 = (-1)^{4+1} \frac{4}{(4-1)!} = (-1)^5 \frac{4}{3!} = (-1)\frac{4}{6} = -\frac{2}{3}$$

$$a_5 = (-1)^{5+1} \frac{5}{(5-1)!} = (-1)^6 \frac{5}{4!} = 1 \cdot \frac{5}{24} = \frac{5}{24}$$

2. Using $a_n = a_1 + (n-1)d$;

$a_1 = 5$

$a_2 = 5 + (2-1)(-3) = 5 + 1(-3) = 5 - 3 = 2$

$a_3 = 5 + (3-1)(-3) = 5 + 2(-3) = 5 - 6 = -1$

$a_4 = 5 + (4-1)(-3) = 5 + 3(-3) = 5 - 9 = -4$

$a_5 = 5 + (5-1)(-3) = 5 + 4(-3) = 5 - 12 = -7$

3.   Using $a_n = a_1 r^{n-1}$;

$a_1 = 5$

$a_2 = 5(-3)^{2-1} = 5(-3)^1 = 5(-3) = -15$

$a_3 = 5(-3)^{3-1} = 5(-3)^2 = 5(9) = 45$

$a_4 = 5(-3)^{4-1} = 5(-3)^3 = 5(-27) = -135$

$a_5 = 5(-3)^{5-1} = 5(-3)^4 = 5(81) = 405$

4. $a_n = -a_{n-1} + 4$

$a_1 = 3$

$a_2 = -a_1 + 4 = -3 + 4 = 1$

$a_3 = -a_2 + 4 = -1 + 4 = 3$

$a_4 = -a_3 + 4 = -3 + 4 = 1$

$a_5 = -a_4 + 4 = -1 + 4 = 3$

5. $d = a_2 - a_1 = 6 - 2 = 4$

$a_n = a_1 + (n-1)d$

$\quad = 2 + (n-1)4$

$\quad = 2 + 4n - 4$

$\quad = 4n - 2$

$a_{20} = 4(20) - 2 = 78$

6. $r = \dfrac{a_2}{a_1} = \dfrac{6}{3} = 2$

$a_n = a_1 r^{n-1}$

$\quad = 3(2)^{n-1}$

$a_{10} = 3(2)^{10-1}$

$\quad = 3(2)^9$

$\quad = 1536$

7. $d = a_2 - a_1 = 1 - \dfrac{3}{2} = -\dfrac{1}{2}$

$a_n = a_1 + (n-1)d$

$\quad = \dfrac{3}{2} + (n-1)\left(-\dfrac{1}{2}\right)$

$\quad = \dfrac{3}{2} - \dfrac{1}{2}n + \dfrac{1}{2}$

$\quad = -\dfrac{1}{2}n + 2$

$a_{30} = -\dfrac{1}{2}(30) + 2$

$\quad = -15 + 2$

$\quad = -13$

8. $S_n = \dfrac{a_1(1 - r^n)}{1 - r}; r = \dfrac{a_2}{a_1} = \dfrac{10}{5} = 2$

$S_{10} = \dfrac{5(1 - 2^{10})}{1 - 2} = \dfrac{5(-1023)}{-1} = 5115$

9.   First find a_{10} ;

$d = a_2 - a_1 = 0 - (-2) = 2$

$a_{50} = a_1 + (n-1)d = -2 + (50-1)(2) = -2 + 49(2) = 96$

$S_{50} = \dfrac{n}{2}(a_1 + a_n) = \dfrac{50}{2}(-2 + 96) = 25(94) = 2350$

10.   First find a_{10} ;

$r = \dfrac{a_2}{a_1} = \dfrac{40}{-20} = -2$

$a_{10} = a_1 r^{n-1} = -20(2)^{10-1} = -20(2)^9 = -20(512) = -10240$

$S_{10} = \dfrac{a_1(1 - r^n)}{1 - r} = \dfrac{-20(-1 - (-2)^{10})}{1 - (-2)} = \dfrac{-20(-1023)}{3} = \dfrac{20460}{3} = 6820$

11. First find a_{100};

    $d = a_2 - a_1 = -2 - 4 = -6$

    $a_{100} = a_1 + (n-1)d = 4 + (100-1)(-6) = 4 + 99(-6) = -590$

    $S_{100} = \frac{n}{2}(a_1 + a_n) = \frac{100}{2}(4 - 590) = 50(-586) = -29,300$

12.
$$\sum_{i=1}^{4}(i+4)(i-1) = (1+4)(1-1) + (2+4)(2-1) + (3+4)(3-1) + (4+4)(4-1)$$
$$= 5(0) + 6(1) + 7(2) + 8(3) = 0 + 6 + 14 + 24 = 44$$

13.
$$\sum_{i=1}^{50}(3i-2) = (3 \cdot 1 - 2) + (3 \cdot 2 - 2) + (3 \cdot 3 - 3) + \ldots + (3 \cdot 50 - 2)$$
$$= (3-2) + (6-2) + (9-3) + \ldots + (150-2)$$
$$= 1 + 4 + 6 + \ldots + 148$$

The sum of this arithmetic sequence is given by $S_n = \frac{n}{2}(a_1 + a_n)$;

$$S_{50} = \frac{50}{2}(1 + 148) = 25(149) = 3725$$

14.
$$\sum_{i=1}^{6}\left(\frac{3}{2}\right)^i = \left(\frac{3}{2}\right)^1 + \left(\frac{3}{2}\right)^2 + \left(\frac{3}{2}\right)^3 + \left(\frac{3}{2}\right)^4 + \left(\frac{3}{2}\right)^5 + \left(\frac{3}{2}\right)^6$$
$$= \frac{3}{2} + \frac{9}{4} + \frac{27}{8} + \frac{81}{16} + \frac{243}{32} + \frac{729}{64} = \frac{1995}{64}$$

15.
$$\sum_{i=1}^{\infty}\left(-\frac{2}{5}\right)^{i-1} = \left(-\frac{2}{5}\right)^{1-1} + \left(-\frac{2}{5}\right)^{2-1} + \left(-\frac{2}{5}\right)^{3-1} + \ldots$$
$$= \left(-\frac{2}{5}\right)^0 + \left(-\frac{2}{5}\right)^1 + \left(-\frac{2}{5}\right)^2 + \ldots$$
$$= 1 + \left(-\frac{2}{5}\right) + \frac{4}{25} + \ldots$$

This is an infinite geometric sequence with $r = \frac{a_2}{a_1} = \frac{-\frac{2}{5}}{1} = -\frac{2}{5}$.

Using $S = \frac{a_1}{1-r} = \frac{1}{1-\left(-\frac{2}{5}\right)} = \frac{1}{\frac{7}{5}} = \frac{5}{7}$

16.
$$0.\overline{45} = \frac{a_1}{1-r} = \frac{\frac{45}{100}}{1-\frac{1}{100}} = \frac{\frac{45}{100}}{\frac{99}{100}}$$
$$= \frac{45}{100} \div \frac{99}{100} = \frac{45}{100} \cdot \frac{100}{99} = \frac{45}{99} = \frac{5}{11}$$

17. Answers may vary. An example is $\sum_{i=1}^{18}\frac{i}{i+2}$.

18. The arithmetic sequence is 16, 48, 80, 112, ...
    First find a_{15} where $d = a_2 - a_1 = 48 - 16 = 32$.

    $a_{15} = a_1 + (n-1)d = 16 + (15-1)(32) = 16 + 14(32) = 16 + 448 = 464$.

    The distance the skydiver falls during the 15th second is 464 feet.

    $$S_{15} = \frac{n}{2}(a_1 + a_n) = \frac{15}{2}(16 + 464) = 7.5(480) = 3600$$

    The total distance the skydiver falls in 15 seconds is 3600 feet.

19. $r = 0.10$

    $A = P(1+r)^t$

    $\quad = 120000(1 + 0.10)^{10}$

    $\quad \approx 311249$

    The value of the house after 10 years is \$311,249.

Section 10.4

Check Point Exercises

1. **a.** $S_1 : 2 = 1(1+1)$

    $S_k : 2 + 4 + 6 + \cdots 2k = k(k+1)$

    $S_{k+1} : 2 + 4 + 6 + \cdots + 2(k+1) = (k+1)(k+2)$

    b. $S_1 : 1^3 = \dfrac{1^2(1+1)^2}{4}$

    $S_k = 1^3 + 2^3 + 3^3 + \cdots + k^3 = \dfrac{k^2(k+1)^2}{4}$

    $S_{k+1} = 1^3 + 2^3 + 3^3 + \cdots + (k+1)^3 = \dfrac{(k+1)^2(k+2)^2}{4}$

2. $S_1 : 2 = 1(1+1)$

    $2 = 2$ is true.

    $S_k : 2 + 4 + 6 + \cdots + 2k = k(k+1)$

    $S_{k+1} : 2 + 4 + 6 + \cdots + 2k + 2(k+1) = (k+1)(k+2)$

    Add $2(k+1)$ to both sides of S_k :

    $2 + 4 + 6 + \cdots + 2k + 2(k+1) = k(k+1) + 2(k+1)$

    Simplify the right-hand side:

    $k(k+1) + 2(k+1) = (k+1)(k+2)$

    If S_k is true, then S_{k+1} is true. The statement is true for all n.

3. $S_1 : 1^3 = \dfrac{1^2(1+1)^2}{4}$

$1 = \dfrac{4}{4}$

$1 = 1$ is true.

$S_k : 1^3 + 2^3 + 3^3 + \cdots + k^3 = \dfrac{k^2(k+1)^2}{4}$

$S_{k+1} : 1^3 + 2^3 + 3^3 + \cdots + k^3 + (k+1)^3 = \dfrac{(k+1)^2(k+2)^2}{4}$

Add $(k+1)^3$ to both sides of S_k :

$1^3 + 2^3 + 3^3 + \cdots + k^3 + (k+1)^3 = \dfrac{k^2(k+1)^2}{4} + (k+1)^3$

Simplify the right hand side:

$\dfrac{k^2(k+1)^2}{4} + (k+1)^3 = \dfrac{k^2(k+1)^2 + 4(k+1)^3}{4} = \dfrac{(k+1)^2\left[k^2 + 4(k+1)\right]}{4} = \dfrac{(k+1)^2(k^2+4k+4)}{4}$

$= \dfrac{(k+1)^2(k+2)^2}{4}$

If S_k is true, then S_{k+1} is true. The statement is true for all n.

4. S_1: 2 is a factor of $1^2 + 1 = 2$, since $2 = 2 \cdot 1$.

S_k: 2 is a factor of $k^2 + k$

S_{k+1}: 2 is a factor of $(k+1)^2 + (k+1)$

Simplify:

$(k+1)^2 + (k+1) = k^2 + 2k + 1 + k + 1$

$= k^2 + 3k + 2$

$= k^2 + k + 2k + 2$

$= (k^2 + k) + 2(k+1)$

Because we assume S_k is true, we know 2 is a factor of $k^2 + k$. Since 2 is a factor of $2(k+1)$, we conclude 2 is a factor of the sum $(k^2 + k) + 2(k+1)$. If S_k is true, then S_{k+1} is true. The statement is true for all n.

Exercise Set 10.4

1. $S_n = 1 + 3 + 5 + \cdots + (n-1) = n^2$

$S_1 : 1 = 1^2$

$1 = 1$ true

$S_2 : 1 + 3 = 2^2$

$4 = 4$ true

$S_3 : 1 + 3 + 5 = 3^2$

$9 = 9$ true

3. S_n : 2 is a factor of $n^2 - n$

     S_1 : 2 is a factor of $1^2 - 1 = 0$

       $0 = 0 \cdot 2$ so 2 is a factor of 0 is true.

     S_2 : 2 is a factor of $2^2 - 2 = 2$

       $2 = 1 \cdot 2$ so 2 is a factor of 2 is true.

     S_3 : 2 is a factor of $3^2 - 3 = 6$

       $6 = 3 \cdot 2$ so 2 is a factor of 6 is true.

5. $S_n : 4 + 8 + 12 + \cdots + 4n = 2n(n+1)$

       $S_k : 4 + 8 + 12 + \cdots + 4k = 2k(k+1)$

  $S_{k+1} : 4 + 8 + 12 + \cdots + 4(k+1) = 2(k+1)(k+1+1)$

       $4 + 8 + 12 + \cdots + 4(k+1) = 2(k+1)(k+2)$

7. $S_n : 3 + 7 + 11 + \cdots + (4n-1) = n(2n+1)$

       $S_k : 3 + 7 + 11 + \cdots + (4k-1) = k(2k+1)$

  $S_{k+1} : 3 + 7 + 11 + \cdots + [4(k+1)-1] = (k+1)[2(k+1)+1]$

       $3 + 7 + 11 + \cdots + (4k+3) = (k+1)(2k+3)$

9. S_n : 2 is a factor of $n^2 - n + 2$

     S_k : 2 is a factor of $k^2 - k + 2$

   S_{k+1} : 2 is a factor of $(k+1)^2 - (k+1) + 2$

       $k^2 + 2k + 1 - k - 1 + 2 = k^2 + k + 2$

   S_{k+1} : 2 is a factor of $k^2 + k + 2$.

11. $S_1 : 4 = 2(1)(1+1)$

     $4 = 2(2)$

     $4 = 4$ is true.

       $S_k : 4 + 8 + 12 + \cdots + 4k = 2k(k+1)$

  $S_{k+1} : 4 + 8 + 12 + \cdots 4(k+1) = 2(k+1)(k+1+1)$

Add $4(k + 1)$ to both sides of S_k:

$4 + 8 + 12 + \cdots + 4(k+1) = 2k(k+1) + 4(k+1)$

Simplify the right-hand side:

$= 2k(k+1) + 4(k+1) = (2k+4)(k+1)$

$= 2(k+2)(k+1)$

$= 2(k+1)(k+1+1)$

If S_k is true, then S_{k+1} is true. The statement is true for all n.

13. $S_1 : 1 = 1^2$

$1 = 1$ is true.

$S_k : 1 + 3 + 5 + \cdots + (2k - 1) = k^2$

$S_{k+1} : 1 + 3 + 5 + \cdots + (2k - 1) + [2(k+1) - 1] = (k+1)^2$

$1 + 3 + 5 + \cdots + (2k - 1) + (2k + 1) = (k+1)^2$

Add $(2k + 1)$ to both sides of S_k:

$1 + 3 + 5 + \cdots + (2k - 1) + (2k + 1) = k^2 + (2k + 1)$

Simplify the right-hand side:

$= k^2 + (2k + 1)$

$= (k + 1)^2$

If S_k is true, then S_{k+1} is true. The statement is true for all n.

15. $S_1 : 3 = 1[2(1) + 1)]$

$3 = 3$ is true.

$S_k : 3 + 7 + 11 + \cdots + (4k - 1) = k(2k + 1)$

$S_{k+1} : 3 + 7 + 11 + \cdots + (4k - 1) + [4(k+1) - 1] = (k+1)[2(k+1) + 1]$

$3 + 7 + 11 + \cdots + (4k - 1) + (4k + 3) = (k+1)(2k + 3)$

Add $(4k + 3)$ to both sides of S_k:

$3 + 7 + 11 + \ldots + (4k - 1) + (4k + 3) = k(2k + 1) + 4(k + 3)$

Simplify the right-hand side:

$= k(2k + 1) + (4k + 3) = 2k^2 + k + 4k + 3$

$= 2k^2 + 5k + 3$

$= (k + 1)(2k + 3)$

If S_k is true, then S_{k+1} is true. The statement is true for all n.

17. $S_1 : 1 = 2^1 - 1$

$1 = 1$ is true.

$S_k : 1 + 2 + 2^2 + \cdots + 2^{k-1} = 2^k - 1$

$S_{k+1} : 1 + 2 + 2^2 + \cdots + 2^{k-1} + 2^{k+1-1} = 2^{k+1} - 1$

$1 + 2 + 2^2 + \cdots + 2^{k-1} + 2^k = 2^{k+1} - 1$

Add 2^k to both sides of S_k:

$1 + 2 + 2^2 + \cdots + 2^{k-1} + 2^k = 2^k + 2^k - 1$

Simplify the right-hand side:

$= 2^k + 2^k - 1 = 2\left(2^k\right) - 1$

$= 2^{k+1} - 1$

If S_k is true, then S_{k+1} is true. The statement is true for all n.

19. $S_1 : 2 = 2^{1+1} - 2$

    $2 = 4 - 2$

    $2 = 2$ is true.

      $S_k : 2 + 4 + 8 + \cdots + 2^k = 2^{k+1} - 2$

  $S_{k+1} : 2 + 4 + 8 + \cdots + 2^k + 2^{k+1} = 2^{k+2} - 2$

Add 2^{k+1} to both sides of S_k:

$2 + 4 + 8 + \cdots + 2^k + 2^{k+1} = 2^{k+1} + 2^{k+1} - 2$

Simplify the right-hand side:

$= 2^{k+1} + 2^{k+1} - 1 = 2\left(2^{k+1}\right) - 2$

$= 2^{k+2} - 2$

If S_k is true, then S_{k+1} is true. The statement is true for all n.

21. $S_1 : 1 \cdot 2 = \dfrac{1(1+1)(1+2)}{3}$

    $2 = \dfrac{6}{3}$

    $2 = 2$ is true.

    $S_k : 1 \cdot 2 + 2 \cdot 3 + 3 \cdot 4 + \cdots + k(k+1) = \dfrac{k(k+1)(k+2)}{3}$

$S_{k+1} : 1 \cdot 2 + 2 \cdot 3 + 3 \cdot 4 + \cdots + k(k+1) + (k+1)(k+2) = \dfrac{(k+1)(k+2)(k+3)}{3}$

Add $(k+1)(k+2)$ to both sided of S_k:

$1 \cdot 2 + 2 \cdot 3 + 3 \cdot 4 + \cdots + k(k+1) + (k+1)(k+2) = \dfrac{k(k+1)(k+2)}{3} + (k+1)(k+2)$

Simplify the right-hand side:

$= \dfrac{k(k+1)(k+2)}{3} + (k+1)(k+2) = \dfrac{k(k+1)(k+2) + 3(k+1)(k+2)}{3}$

$= \dfrac{(k+1)(k+2)(k+3)}{3}$

If S_k is true, then S_{k+1} is true. The statement is true for all n.

23. $S_1 : \dfrac{1}{1 \cdot 2} = \dfrac{1}{1+1}$

$\dfrac{1}{2} = \dfrac{1}{2}$ is true.

$S_k : \dfrac{1}{1 \cdot 2} + \dfrac{1}{2 \cdot 3} + \dfrac{1}{3 \cdot 4} + \cdots + \dfrac{1}{k(k+1)} = \dfrac{k}{k+1}$

$S_{k+1} : \dfrac{1}{1 \cdot 2} + \dfrac{1}{2 \cdot 3} + \dfrac{1}{3 \cdot 4} + \cdots + \dfrac{1}{k(k+1)} + \dfrac{1}{(k+1)(k+2)} = \dfrac{k+1}{k+2}$

Add $\dfrac{1}{(k+1)(k+2)}$ to both sides of S_k:

$\dfrac{1}{1 \cdot 2} + \dfrac{1}{2 \cdot 3} + \dfrac{1}{3 \cdot 4} + \cdots + \dfrac{1}{k(k+1)} + \dfrac{1}{(k+1)(k+2)} = \dfrac{k}{k+1} + \dfrac{1}{(k+1)(k+2)}$

Simplify the right-hand side:

$$\dfrac{k}{(k+1)} + \dfrac{1}{(k+1)(k+2)} = \dfrac{k(k+2)+1}{(k+1)(k+2)}$$

$$= \dfrac{k^2 + 2k + 1}{(k+1)(k+2)}$$

$$= \dfrac{(k+1)(k+1)}{(k+1)(k+2)}$$

$$= \dfrac{k+1}{k+2}$$

If S_k is true, then S_{k+1} is true. The statement is true for all n.

25. $S_1 : 2$ is a factor of $1^2 - 1 = 0$, since $0 = 2 \cdot 0$.

$S_k : 2$ is a factor of $k^2 - k$

$S_{k+1} : 2$ is a factor of $(k+1)^2 - (k+1)$

$(k+1)^2 - (k-1) = k^2 + 2k + 1 - k - 1$

$$= k^2 + k$$

$$= k^2 - k + 2k$$

$$= (k^2 - k) + 2k$$

Because we assume S_k is true, we know 2 as a factor of $k^2 - k$. Since 2 is a factor of $2k$, we conclude 2 is factor of the sum $(k^2 + k) + 2k$. If S_k is true, then S_{k+1} is true. The statement is true for all n.

27. S_1: 6 is a factor of $1(1+1)(1+2) = 6$, since $6 = 6 \cdot 1$.

S_k: 6 is a factor of $k(k+1)(k+2)$

S_{k+1}: 6 is a factor of $(k+1)(k+2)(k+3)$

$(k+1)(k+2)(k+3) = k(k+1)(k+2) + 3(k+1)(k+2)$

Because we assume S_k is true, we know 6 as a factor of $k(k+1)(k+2)$. Since either $k+1$ or $k+2$ must be even, the product $(k+1)(k+2)$ is even. Thus 2 is a factor of $(k+1)(k+2)$, and we can conclude that 6 is factor of $3(k+1)(k+2)$. If S_k is true, then S_{k+1} is true.

The statement is true for all n.

29. $\sum\limits_{i=1}^{n} 5 \cdot 6^i = 6\left(6^n - 1\right)$

Show that S_1 is true: $\sum\limits_{i=1}^{1} 5 \cdot 6^i = 6\left(6^1 - 1\right)$

$$5 \cdot 6^1 = 6(6-1)$$

$$5 \cdot 6 = 6 \cdot 5, \quad \text{True}$$

Show that if S_k is true, then S_{k+1} is true:

Assume $S_k : \sum\limits_{i=1}^{k} 5 \cdot 6^i = 6\left(6^k - 1\right)$ is true. Then,

$$\sum\limits_{i=1}^{k} 5 \cdot 6^i + 5 \cdot 6^{k+1} = 6\left(6^k - 1\right) + 5 \cdot 6^{k+1}$$

$$\sum\limits_{i=1}^{k+1} 5 \cdot 6^i = 6^{k+1} - 6 + 5 \cdot 6^{k+1}$$

$$\sum\limits_{i=1}^{k+1} 5 \cdot 6^i = 6 \cdot 6^{k+1} - 6$$

$$\sum\limits_{i=1}^{k+1} 5 \cdot 6^i = 6\left(6^{k+1} - 1\right)$$

The final statement is S_{k+1}. Thus, by mathematical induction, we have proven that $\sum\limits_{i=1}^{n} 5 \cdot 6^i = 6\left(6^n - 1\right)$.

31. $n + 2 > n$

Show that S_1 is true: $1 + 2 > 1$

$$3 > 1, \quad \text{True}$$

Show that if S_k is true, then S_{k+1} is true:

Assume $S_k : k + 2 > k$ is true. Then,

$k + 2 + 1 > k + 1$

$(k+1) + 2 > k + 1$

The final statement is S_{k+1}. Thus, by mathematical induction, we have proven that $n + 2 > n$.

33. $S_1 : (ab)^1 = a^1 b^1$

$ab = ab$ is true.

$S_k : (ab)^k = a^k b^k$

$S_{k+1} : (ab)^{k+1} = a^{k+1} b^{k+1}$

Multiply both sides of S_k by ab:

$(ab)^k (ab) = a^k b^k (ab)$

$(ab)^{k+1} = a^{k+1} b^{k+1}$

If S_k is true, then S_{k+1} is true.

The statement is true for all n.

37. $n^2 > 2n + 1$ for $n \geq 3$

$S_3 : 3^2 > 2 \cdot 3 + 1$

$9 > 7$

$S_k : k^2 > 2k + 1$ for $k \geq 3$

$S_{k+1} : (k+1)^2 > 2k + 3$.

Add $2k + 1$ to both sides of S_k.

$k^2 + (2k+1) > 2k + 1 + (2k+1)$

Write the left side of the inequalities as the square of a binomial and simplify the right side. $(k+1)^2 > 4k + 2$

Since $4k + 2 > 2k + 3$ for $k \geq 3$, we can conclude that $(k+1)^2 > 4k + 2 > 2k + 3$.

By the transitive property,

$(k+1)^2 > 2k + 3$

$(k+1)^2 > 2(k+1) + 1$

If S_k is true, then S_{k+1} is true.

The statement is true for all n.

39. $S_1 = \dfrac{1}{4} = \dfrac{1}{4}$

$S_2 = \dfrac{1}{4} + \dfrac{1}{12} = \dfrac{1}{3}$

$S_3 = \dfrac{1}{4} + \dfrac{1}{12} + \dfrac{1}{24} = \dfrac{3}{8}$

$S_4 = \dfrac{1}{4} + \dfrac{1}{12} + \dfrac{1}{24} + \dfrac{1}{40} = \dfrac{2}{5}$

$S_5 = \dfrac{1}{4} + \dfrac{1}{12} + \dfrac{1}{24} + \dfrac{1}{40} + \dfrac{1}{60} = \dfrac{5}{12}$

$S_n = \dfrac{1}{4} + \dfrac{1}{12} + \dfrac{1}{24} + \cdots + \dfrac{1}{2n(n+1)} = \dfrac{n}{2n+2}$

$S_k = \dfrac{1}{4} + \dfrac{1}{12} + \dfrac{1}{24} + \cdots + \dfrac{1}{2k(k+1)} = \dfrac{k}{2k+2}$

$S_{k+1} = \dfrac{1}{4} + \dfrac{1}{12} + \dfrac{1}{24} + \cdots + \dfrac{1}{2k(k+1)} + \dfrac{1}{2(k+1)(k+2)} = \dfrac{k+1}{2k+4}$

Add $\dfrac{1}{2(k+1)(k+2)}$ to both sides of S_k:

$$\frac{1}{4}+\frac{1}{12}+\frac{1}{24}+\cdots+\frac{1}{2k(k+1)}+\frac{1}{2(k+1)(k+2)}=\frac{k}{2k+2}+\frac{1}{2(k+1)(k+2)}$$

Simplify the right-hand side:

$$\frac{k}{2k+2}+\frac{1}{2(k+1)(k+2)}=\frac{k(k+2)+1}{2(k+1)(k+2)}=\frac{k^2+2k+1}{2(k+1)(k+2)}=\frac{(k+1)^2}{2(k+1)(k+2)}=\frac{k+1}{2k+4}$$

If S_k is true, then S_{k+1} is true. The conjecture is proven.

Section 10.5

Check Point Exercises

1. a. $\dbinom{6}{3}=\dfrac{6!}{3!(6-3)!}=\dfrac{6!}{3!3!}=\dfrac{5\cdot4}{1}=20$

    b. $\dbinom{6}{0}=\dfrac{6!}{0!(6-0)!}=\dfrac{6!}{6!}=1$

    c. $\dbinom{8}{2}=\dfrac{8!}{2!(8-2)!}=\dfrac{8!}{2!6!}=\dfrac{8\cdot7}{2}=28$

    d. $\dbinom{3}{3}=\dfrac{3!}{3!(3-3)!}=\dfrac{3!}{3!0!}=\dfrac{3!}{3!}=1$

2. $(x+1)^4=\dbinom{4}{0}x^4+\dbinom{4}{1}x^3+\dbinom{4}{2}x^2+\dbinom{4}{1}x+\dbinom{4}{0}=x^4+4x^3+6x^2+4x+1$

3. $(x-2y)^5=\dbinom{5}{0}x^5(-2y)^0+\dbinom{5}{1}x^4(-2y)^1+\dbinom{5}{2}x^3(-2y)^2+\dbinom{5}{3}x^2(-2y)^3+\dbinom{5}{4}x(-2y)^4+\dbinom{5}{5}x^0(-2y)^5$

    $=x^5-5x^4(2y)+10x^3(4y^2)-10x^2(8y^3)+5x(16y^4)-32y^5$

    $=x^5-10x^4y+40x^3y^2-80x^2y^3+80xy^4-32y^5$

4. $(2x+y)^9$

    fifth term $=\dbinom{9}{4}(2x)^5y^4=\dfrac{9!}{4!5!}(32x^5)y^4=4032x^5y^4$

Exercise Set 10.5

1. $\dbinom{8}{3}=\dfrac{8!}{3!(8-3)!}=\dfrac{8\cdot7\cdot6}{3\cdot2\cdot1}=56$

3. $\dbinom{12}{1}=\dfrac{12!}{1!11!}=12$

5. $\dbinom{6}{6} = \dfrac{6!}{0!6!} = 1$

7. $\dbinom{100}{2} = \dfrac{100!}{2!98!} = \dfrac{100 \cdot 99}{2} = 4950$

9. $(x+2)^3 = \dbinom{3}{0}x^3 + \dbinom{3}{1}2x^2 + \dbinom{3}{2}4x + \dbinom{3}{3}8 = x^3 + 3x^2 \cdot 2 + 3x \cdot 4 + 8 = x^3 + 6x^2 + 12x + 8$

11. $(3x+y)^3 = \dbinom{3}{0}27x^3 + \dbinom{3}{1}9x^2 y + \dbinom{3}{2}3xy^2 + \dbinom{3}{3}y^3 = 27x^3 + 27x^2 y + 9xy^2 + y^3$

13. $(5x-1)^3 = \dbinom{3}{0}125x^3 - \dbinom{3}{1}25x^2 + \dbinom{3}{2}5x - \dbinom{3}{3} = 125x^3 - 75x^2 + 15x - 1$

15. $(2x+1)^4 = \dbinom{4}{0}16x^4 - \dbinom{4}{1}8x^3 + \dbinom{4}{2}4x^2 + \dbinom{4}{3}2x + \dbinom{4}{4} = 16x^4 + 32x^3 + 24x^2 + 8x + 1$

17. $(x^2 + 2y)^4 = \dbinom{4}{0}(x^2)^4 + \dbinom{4}{1}(x^2)^3(2y) + \dbinom{4}{2}(x^2)^2(2y)^2 + \dbinom{4}{3}(x^2)^1(2y)^3 + \dbinom{4}{4}(2y)^4$

$\qquad = 1(x^8) + 4(x^6)(2y) + 6(x^4)(4y^2) + 4x^2(8y^3) + 1(16y^4)$

$\qquad = x^8 + 8x^6 y + 24x^4 y^2 + 32x^2 y^3 + 16y^4$

19. $(y-3)^4 = \dbinom{4}{0}y^4 + \dbinom{4}{1}y^3(-3) + \dbinom{4}{2}y^2(-3)^2 + \dbinom{4}{3}y(-3)^3 + \dbinom{4}{4}(-3)^4$

$\qquad = y^4 + 4(y^3)(-3) + 6(y^2)(9) + 4(y)(-27) + 81$

$\qquad = y^4 - 12y^3 + 54y^2 - 108y + 81$

21. $(2x^3 - 1)^4 = \dbinom{4}{0}(2x^3)^4 + \dbinom{4}{1}(2x^3)^3(-1) + \dbinom{4}{2}(2x^3)^2(-1)^2 + \dbinom{4}{3}(2x^3)(-1)^3 + \dbinom{4}{4}(-1)^4$

$\qquad = 16x^{12} - 4(8x^9) + 6(4x^6) - 4(2x^3) + 1$

$\qquad = 16x^{12} - 32x^9 + 24x^6 - 8x^3 + 1$

23. $(c+2)^5 = \dbinom{5}{0}c^5 + \dbinom{5}{1}c^4(2) + \dbinom{5}{2}c^3(2^2) + \dbinom{5}{3}c^2(2^3) + \dbinom{5}{4}c(2^4) + \dbinom{5}{5}(2^5)$

$\qquad = c^5 + 5c^4(2) + 10c^3(4) + 10c^2(8) + 5c(16) + 32$

$\qquad = c^5 + 10c^4 + 40c^3 + 80c^2 + 80c + 32$

25. $(x-1)^5 = \dbinom{5}{0}x^5 - \dbinom{5}{1}x^4 + \dbinom{5}{2}x^3 - \dbinom{5}{3}x^2 + \dbinom{5}{4}x - \dbinom{5}{5} = x^5 - 5x^4 + 10x^3 - 10x^2 + 5x - 1$

27. $(3x-y)^5 = \dbinom{5}{0}(3x)^5 - \dbinom{5}{1}(3x)^4 y + \dbinom{5}{2}(3x)^3 y^2 - \dbinom{5}{3}(3x)^2 y^3 + \dbinom{5}{4}3xy^4 - \dbinom{5}{5}y^5$

$\qquad = (1)243x^5 - 5(81x^4)y + 10(27x^3)y^2 - 10(9x^2)y^3 + 5(3x)y^4 - (1)y^5$

$\qquad = 243x^5 - 405x^4 y + 270x^3 y^2 - 90x^2 y^3 + 15xy^4 - y^5$

29. $(2a+b)^6 = \binom{6}{0}(2a)^6 + \binom{6}{1}(2a)^5 b + \binom{6}{2}(2a)^4 b^2 + \binom{6}{3}(2a)^3 b^3 + \binom{6}{4}(2a)^2 b^4 + \binom{6}{5}(2a)b^5 + \binom{6}{6}b^6$

$$= 64a^6 + 6\left(32a^5\right)b + 15\left(16a^4\right)b^2 + 20\left(8a^3\right)b^3 + 15\left(4a^2\right)b^4 + 6(2a)b^5 + b^6$$

$$= 64a^6 + 192a^5 b + 240a^4 b^2 + 160a^3 b^3 + 60a^2 b^4 + 12ab^5 + b^6$$

31.
$$(x+2)^8 = \binom{8}{0}x^8 + \binom{8}{1}x^7 2 + \binom{8}{3}x^6 (2)^2 + \cdots$$

$$= x^8 + 16x^7 + 112x^6 + \cdots$$

33.
$$(x-2y)^{10} = \binom{10}{0}x^{10} - \binom{10}{1}x^9 (2y) + \binom{10}{2}x^8 (2y)^2 - \cdots$$

$$= x^{10} - 20x^9 y + 180x^8 y^2 - \cdots$$

35.
$$(x^2+1)^{16} = \binom{16}{0}(x^2)^{16} + \binom{16}{1}(x^2)^{15} + \binom{16}{2}(x^2)^{14} + \cdots$$

$$= x^{32} + 16x^{30} + 120x^{28} + \cdots$$

37.
$$(y^3-1)^{20} = \binom{20}{0}(y^3)^{20} - \binom{20}{1}(y^3)^{19} + \binom{20}{2}(y^3)^{18} - \cdots$$

$$= y^{60} - 20y^{57} + 190y^{54} - \cdots$$

39. $(2x+y)^6$; third term $= \binom{6}{2}(2x)^4 (y)^2 = 15\left(16x^4 y^2\right) = 240x^4 y^2$

41. $(x-1)^9$; fifth term $= \binom{9}{4}x^5 (-1)^4 = 126x^5$

43. $(x^2+y^3)^8$; sixth term $= \binom{8}{5}(x^2)^3 (y^3)^5 = 56x^6 y^{15}$

45. $(x-\frac{1}{2})^9$; fourth term $= \binom{9}{3}x^6 \left(-\frac{1}{2}\right)^3 = 84x^6 \left(-\frac{1}{8}\right) = -\frac{21}{2}x^6$

47. $\binom{22}{14}(x^2)^8 y^{14} = 319,770x^{16} y^{14}$

49.
$$(x^3+x^{-2})^4 = \binom{4}{0}(x^3)^4 + \binom{4}{1}(x^3)^3 (x^{-2}) + \binom{4}{2}(x^3)^2 (x^{-2})^2 + \binom{4}{3}(x^3)^1 (x^{-2})^3 + \binom{4}{4}(x^{-2})^4$$

$$= \frac{4!}{0!(4-0)!}x^{12} + \frac{4!}{1!(4-1)!}x^9 x^{-2} + \frac{4!}{2!(4-2)!}x^6 x^{-4} + \frac{4!}{3!(4-3)!}x^3 x^{-6} + \frac{4!}{4!(4-4)!}x^{-8}$$

$$= \frac{\cancel{4!}}{0! \cdot \cancel{4!}}x^{12} + \frac{4 \cdot \cancel{3!}}{1! \cdot \cancel{3!}}x^7 + \frac{4 \cdot 3 \cdot \cancel{2!}}{2 \cdot 1 \cdot \cancel{2!}}x^2 + \frac{4 \cdot \cancel{3!}}{\cancel{3!} \cdot 1!}x^{-3} + \frac{\cancel{4!}}{\cancel{4!} \cdot 0!}x^{-8}$$

$$= x^{12} + 4x^7 + 6x^2 + \frac{4}{x^3} + \frac{1}{x^8}$$

51.

$$\left(x^{\frac{1}{3}} - x^{-\frac{1}{3}}\right)^3 = \left(x^{\frac{1}{3}} + \left(-x^{-\frac{1}{3}}\right)\right)^3 = \binom{3}{0}\left(x^{\frac{1}{3}}\right)^3 + \binom{3}{1}\left(x^{\frac{1}{3}}\right)^2\left(-x^{-\frac{1}{3}}\right) +$$

$$+ \binom{3}{2}\left(x^{\frac{1}{3}}\right)^1\left(-x^{-\frac{1}{3}}\right)^2 + \binom{3}{3}\left(-x^{-\frac{1}{3}}\right)^3$$

$$= \frac{3!}{0!(3-0)!}x^1 + \frac{3!}{1!(3-1)!}x^{\frac{2}{3}} \cdot -x^{-\frac{1}{3}} + \frac{3!}{2!(3-2)!}x^{\frac{1}{3}}x^{-\frac{2}{3}} + \frac{3!}{3!(3-3)!} \cdot -x^{-1}$$

$$= \frac{3!}{0! \cdot 3!}x + \frac{3 \cdot 2!}{1! \cdot 2!} \cdot -x^{\frac{1}{3}} + \frac{\cdot 3 \cdot 2!}{2! \cdot 1!}x^{-\frac{1}{3}} + \frac{3!}{3! \cdot 0!} \cdot -x^{-1}$$

$$= x - 3x^{\frac{1}{3}} + \frac{3}{x^{\frac{1}{3}}} - \frac{1}{x}$$

53. $f(x) = x^4 + 7$;

$$\frac{f(x+h) - f(x)}{h}$$

$$= \frac{(x+h)^4 + 7 - \left(x^4 + 7\right)}{h}$$

$$= \frac{\binom{4}{0}x^4 + \binom{4}{1}x^3h + \binom{4}{2}x^2h^2 + \binom{4}{3}xh^3 + \binom{4}{4}h^4 + 7 - x^4 - 7}{h}$$

$$= \frac{\frac{4!}{0!(4-0)!}x^4 + \frac{4!}{1!(4-1)!}x^3h + \frac{4!}{2!(4-2)!}x^2h^2 + \frac{4!}{3!(4-3)!}xh^3 + \frac{4!}{4!(4-4)!}h^4 - x^4}{h}$$

$$= \frac{\frac{4!}{0! \cdot 4!}x^4 + \frac{4 \cdot 3!}{1! \cdot 3!}x^3h + \frac{4 \cdot 3 \cdot 2!}{2! \cdot 2 \cdot 1}x^2h^2 + \frac{4 \cdot 3!}{3! \cdot 1!}xh^3 + \frac{4!}{4! \cdot 0!}h^4 - x^4}{h}$$

$$= \frac{x^4 + 4x^3h + 6x^2h^2 + 4xh^3 + h^4 - x^4}{h}$$

$$= \frac{h(4x^3 + 6x^2h + 4xh^2 + h^3)}{h}$$

$$= 4x^3 + 6x^2h + 4xh^2 + h^3$$

55.   Find the $(5+1) = 6^{th}$ term.

$$\binom{n}{r}a^{n-r}b^r = \binom{10}{5}\left(\frac{3}{x}\right)^{10-5}\left(\frac{x}{3}\right)^5 = \frac{10!}{5!(10-5)!}\left(\frac{3}{x}\right)^5\left(\frac{x}{3}\right)^5$$

$$= \frac{10 \cdot 9 \cdot 8 \cdot 7 \cdot 6 \cdot 5!}{5! \cdot 5 \cdot 4 \cdot 3 \cdot 2 \cdot 1}\left(\frac{3}{x}\right)^5\left(\frac{x}{3}\right)^5 = 252 \cdot \frac{3^5}{x^5} \cdot \frac{x^5}{3^5} = 252$$

57.   a. $f(x) = -x^3 + 11x^2 + x + 31$

$$f(x+3) = -(x+3)^3 + 11(x+3)^2 + (x+3) + 31$$

$$g(x) = -(x^3 + 9x^2 + 27x + 27) + 11(x^2 + 6x + 9) + x + 3 + 31$$

$$= -x^3 - 9x^2 - 27x - 27 + 11x^2 + 66x + 99 + x + 3 + 31$$

$$= -x^3 + 2x^2 + 40x + 106$$

b. $f(3) = -(3)^3 + 11(3)^2 + (3) + 31 = 106$

       $g(0) = -(0)^3 + 2(0)^2 + 40(0) + 106 = 106$

       These functions model the graph's value of 103 reasonably well.

69. $f_1(x) = (x+1)^4$

      $f_2(x) = x^4$

      $f_3(x) = x^4 + 4x^3$

      $f_4(x) = x^4 + 4x^3 + 6x^2$

      $f_5(x) = x^4 + 4x^3 + 6x^2 + 4x$

      $f_6(x) = x^4 + 4x^3 + 6x^2 + 4x + 1$

      f_2, f_3, f_4, and f_5 are approaching $f_1 = f_6$.

71. $f_1(x) = (x-2)^4$

      $= \binom{4}{0}x^4 + \binom{4}{1}x^3(-2) + \binom{4}{2}x^2(-2)^2 + \binom{4}{3}x(-2)^3 + \binom{4}{4}(-2)^4$

      $= x^4 + 4x^3(-2) + 6x^2(4) + 4x(-8) + 16$

      $= x^4 - 8x^3 + 24x^2 - 32x + 16$

73. a.   False; it contains $n + 1$ terms.

    b.   True

    c.   False; let $a = 1$ and $b = 1$. Thus $\displaystyle\sum_{r=0}^{n} \binom{n}{r} a^{n-r} b^r = \sum_{r=0}^{n} \binom{n}{r} = (1+1)^n = 2^n$.

    d.   False; for example, let $a = 0$ and $b = 0$.

    (b) is true.

75. $\left(x^2 + y^2\right)^5$

      Since $\left(x^2\right)^2 = x^4$, the fourth term will contain x^4 : fourth term $= \binom{5}{3}\left(x^2\right)^2\left(y^2\right)^3 = 10x^4 y^6$

77. $\dbinom{n}{r} + \dbinom{n}{r+1} = \dfrac{n!}{r!(n-r)!} + \dfrac{n!}{(r+1)!(n-(r+1))!}$

$$= \dfrac{n!}{r!(n-r)!} + \dfrac{n!}{(r+1)!(n-r-1)!}$$

$$= \dfrac{n!(r+1)}{(r+1)r!(n-r)!(n-r-1)!} + \dfrac{(n-r)n!}{(n-r)(r+1)!(n-r-1)!}$$

$$= \dfrac{n!(r+1) + n!(n-r)}{(r+1)!(n-r)!}$$

$$= \dfrac{n!(r+1+n-r)}{(r+1)!(n-r)!}$$

$$= \dfrac{n!(n+1)}{(r+1)!(n-r)!}$$

$$= \dfrac{(n+1)!}{(r+1)!(n+1-r-1)!}$$

$$= \dfrac{(n+1)!}{(r+1)!(n+1-(r+1))!}$$

$$= \dbinom{n+1}{r+1}$$

Section 10.6

Check Point Exercises

1. We use the Fundamental Counting Principal to find the number of ways a one-topping pizza can be ordered.
Size : Crust : Topping:

$\quad 3 \ \times \ 4 \ \times \ 6 \ = 72$

There are 72 different ways of ordering a one-topping pizza.

2. We use the Fundamental Counting Principal to find the number of ways we can answer the questions.
Question #1: Question #2: Question #3: Question #4: Question #5: Question #6:

$\quad 3 \ \times \ 3 \ \times \ 3 \ \times \ 3 \ \times \ 3 \ \times \ 3 \ = 3^6 = 729$

There are 729 ways of answering the questions.

3. We use the Fundamental Counting Principal to find the number of different license plates that can be manufactured. Multiply the number of different letters, 26, for the first two places and the number of different digits, 10, for the next three places. $26 \cdot 26 \cdot 10 \cdot 10 \cdot 10 = 26^2 \cdot 1000 = 676,000$ plates There are 676,000 different license plates possible.

4. Your group is choosing $r = 4$ officers from a group of $n = 7$ people. The order in which the officers are chosen matters because the four officers to be chosen have different responsibilities. Thus, we are looking for the number of permutations of 7 things taken 4 at a time.

We use the formula $_nP_r = \dfrac{n!}{(n-r)!}$ with $n = 7$ and $r = 4$. $\quad _7P_4 = \dfrac{7!}{(7-4)!} = \dfrac{7!}{3!} = 840.$

Thus, there are 840 different ways of filling the four offices.

5. Because you are using all six of your books in every possible arrangement, you are arranging $r = 6$ books from a group of $n = 6$ books. Thus, we are looking for the number of permutations of 6 things taken 6 at a time. We use the formula

$$_nP_r = \frac{n!}{(n-r)!} \text{ with } n = 6 \text{ and } r = 6.$$

$$_6P_6 = \frac{6!}{(6-6)!} = \frac{6!}{0!} = 6! = 720.$$

There are 720 different possible permutations. Thus, you can arrange the books in 720 ways.

6. a. The order does not matter; this is a combination.

   b. Since what place each runner finishes matters, this is a permutation.

7. The order in which the four people are selected does not matter. This is a problem of selecting $r = 4$ people from a group of $n = 10$ people. We are looking for the number of combinations of 10 things taken 4 at a time. We use the formula

$$_nC_r = \frac{n!}{(n-r)!\ r!} \text{ with } n = 10 \text{ and } r = 4.$$

$$_{10}C_4 = \frac{10!}{(10-4)!4!} = \frac{10!}{6!4!} = \frac{10 \cdot 9 \cdot 8 \cdot 7 \cdot 6!}{6! \cdot 4 \cdot 3 \cdot 2 \cdot 1} = \frac{10 \cdot 9 \cdot 8 \cdot 7}{4 \cdot 3 \cdot 2 \cdot 1} = 210$$

Thus, 210 committees of 4 people each can be found from 10 people at the conference on acupuncture.

8. Because the order in which the 4 cards are dealt does not matter, this is a problem involving combinations. We are looking for the number of combinations of $n = 16$ cards drawn $r = 4$ at a time. We use the formula

$$_nC_r = \frac{n!}{(n-r)!\ r!} \text{ with } n = 16 \text{ and } r = 4.$$

$$_{16}C_4 = \frac{16!}{(16-4)!4!} = \frac{16!}{12!4!} = \frac{16 \cdot 15 \cdot 14 \cdot 13 \cdot 12!}{12! \cdot 4 \cdot 3 \cdot 2 \cdot 1} = 1820$$

Thus, there are 1820 different 4-card hands possible.

Exercise Set 10.6

1. $_9P_4 = \dfrac{9!}{5!} = 3024$

3. $_8P_5 = \dfrac{8!}{3!} = 8 \cdot 7 \cdot 6 \cdot 5 \cdot 4 = 6720$

5. $_6P_6 = \dfrac{6!}{0!} = 720$

7. $_8P_0 = \dfrac{8!}{8!} = 1$

9. $_9C_5 = \dfrac{9!}{4!5!} = \dfrac{9 \cdot 8 \cdot 7 \cdot 6}{4 \cdot 3 \cdot 2 \cdot 1} = \dfrac{3 \cdot 7 \cdot 6}{1} = 126$

11. $_{11}C_4 = \dfrac{11!}{7!4!} = \dfrac{11 \cdot 10 \cdot 9 \cdot 8}{4 \cdot 3 \cdot 2 \cdot 1} = \dfrac{11 \cdot 10 \cdot 3}{1} = 330$

13. $_7C_7 = \dfrac{7!}{0!7!} = 1$

15. $_5C_0 = \dfrac{5!}{5!0!} = 1$

17.   combinations; The order in which the volunteers are chosen does not matter.

19.   permutations; The order of the letters matters because ABCD is not the same as BADC.

21. $\dfrac{_7P_3}{3!} - {_7C_3} = \dfrac{\dfrac{7!}{(7-3)!}}{3!} - \dfrac{7!}{(7-3)!3!} = \dfrac{\dfrac{7!}{4!}}{3!} - \dfrac{7!}{4!3!} = \dfrac{7!}{4!3!} - \dfrac{7!}{4!3!} = 0$

23. $1 - \dfrac{_3P_2}{_4P_3} = 1 - \dfrac{\dfrac{3!}{(3-2)!}}{\dfrac{4!}{(4-3)!}} = 1 - \dfrac{\dfrac{3!}{1!}}{\dfrac{4!}{1!}} = 1 - \dfrac{3!}{4!} = 1 - \dfrac{3!}{4\cdot 3!} = 1 - \dfrac{1}{4} = \dfrac{3}{4}$

25. $\dfrac{_7C_3}{_5C_4} - \dfrac{98!}{96!} = \dfrac{\dfrac{7!}{(7-3)!3!}}{\dfrac{5!}{(5-4)!4!}} - \dfrac{98\cdot 97\cdot 96!}{96!} = \dfrac{\dfrac{7!}{4!3!}}{\dfrac{5!}{1!4!}} - 95067 = \dfrac{\dfrac{7\cdot 6\cdot 5\cdot \cancel{4!}}{\cancel{4!}3\cdot 2\cdot 1}}{\dfrac{5\cdot \cancel{4!}}{1!\cancel{4!}}} - 9506 = \dfrac{35}{5} - 9506 = 7 - 9506 = -9499$

27. $\dfrac{_4C_2\cdot {_6C_1}}{_{18}C_3} = \dfrac{\dfrac{4!}{(4-2)!2!}\cdot\dfrac{6!}{(6-1)!1!}}{\dfrac{18!}{(18-3)!3!}} = \dfrac{\dfrac{4!}{2!2!}\cdot\dfrac{6!}{5!1!}}{\dfrac{18!}{15!3!}} = \dfrac{\dfrac{4\cdot 3\cdot \cancel{2!}}{\cancel{2!}2\cdot 1}\cdot\dfrac{6\cdot \cancel{5!}}{\cancel{5!}1!}}{\dfrac{18\cdot 17\cdot 16\cdot \cancel{15!}}{\cancel{15!}3\cdot 2\cdot 1}} = \dfrac{36}{816} = \dfrac{3}{68}$

29. $9\cdot 3 = 27$ ways

31. $2\cdot 4\cdot 5 = 40$ ways

33. $3^5 = 243$ ways

35. $8\cdot 2\cdot 9 = 144$ area codes

37. $5\cdot 4\cdot 3\cdot 2\cdot 1\cdot 1 = 120$ ways

39. $1\cdot 3\cdot 2\cdot 1\cdot 1 = 6$ paragraphs

41. $_{10}P_3 = \dfrac{10!}{7!3!} = 10\cdot 9\cdot 8 = 720$ ways

43. $_{13}P_7 = \dfrac{13!}{6!} = 13\cdot 12\cdot 11\cdot 10\cdot 9\cdot 8\cdot 7$
              $= 8,648,640$ ways

45. $_6P_3 = \dfrac{6!}{3!} = 6\cdot 5\cdot 4 = 120$ ways

47. $_9P_5 = \dfrac{9!}{4!} = 9\cdot 8\cdot 7\cdot 6\cdot 5 = 15{,}120$ lineups

49. $_6C_3 = \dfrac{6!}{3!3!} = \dfrac{6\cdot 5\cdot 4}{3\cdot 2\cdot 1} = 20$ ways

51. $_{12}C_4 = \dfrac{12!}{8!4!} = \dfrac{12\cdot 11\cdot 10\cdot 9}{4\cdot 3\cdot 2\cdot 1}$
        $= 495$ collections

53. $_{17}C_8 = \dfrac{17!}{9!8!} = \dfrac{17\cdot 16\cdot 15\cdot 14\cdot 13\cdot 12\cdot 11\cdot 10}{8\cdot 7\cdot 6\cdot 5\cdot 4\cdot 3\cdot 2\cdot 1}$
        $= 24{,}310$ groups

55. $_{53}C_6 = \dfrac{53!}{47!6!} = 22{,}957{,}480$ selections

57. $_6P_4 = \dfrac{6!}{2!} = 6\cdot 5\cdot 4\cdot 3 = 360$ ways

59. $_{13}C_6 = \dfrac{13!}{7!6!} = \dfrac{13\cdot12\cdot11\cdot10\cdot9\cdot8}{6\cdot5\cdot4\cdot3\cdot2\cdot1}$
$= 1716$ ways

61. $_{20}C_3 = \dfrac{20!}{17!3!} = \dfrac{20\cdot19\cdot18}{3\cdot2\cdot1} = 1140$ ways

63. $_7P_4 = \dfrac{7!}{3!} = 840$ passwords

65. $_{15}P_3 = \dfrac{15!}{12!} = 15\cdot14\cdot13 = 2730$ cones

77. a. False; the number of ways is $_{10}C_4$.

b. False;
$$_nP_r = \dfrac{n!}{(n-r)!} > \dfrac{n!}{(n-r)!r!} = {}_nC_r \text{ if } r>1$$

c. True; $_7P_3 = \dfrac{7!}{4!} = 3!\dfrac{7!}{4!3!} = 3!\,_7C_3$

d. False;
the number of ways is $20\cdot19 = {}_{20}P_2$.
(c) is true.

79. $2\cdot6\cdot6\cdot2 = 144$ numbers

Section 10.7

Check Point Exercises

1. a. $P(\text{positive test}) = \dfrac{\text{\# women w/positive test}}{\text{total number of women}} = \dfrac{7664}{100{,}000} = \dfrac{479}{6250} \approx 0.077$

b. $P(\text{positive test}) = \dfrac{\text{\# women w/breast cancer and positive test}}{\text{total number of women w/breast cancer}} = \dfrac{720}{800} = \dfrac{9}{10} = 0.9$

c. $P(\text{breast cancer}) = \dfrac{\text{\# women w/breast cancer and positive test}}{\text{total number of women w/positive test}} = \dfrac{720}{7664} = \dfrac{45}{479} = 0.094$

2. The sample space of equally likely outcomes is $S = \{1, 2, 3, 4, 5, 6\}$. There are six outcomes in the sample space, so $n(S) = 6$. The event of getting a number greater than 4 can be represented by $E = \{5, 6\}$. There are two outcomes in this event, so $n(E) = 2$.

The probability of rolling a number greater than 4 is $P(E) = \dfrac{n(E)}{n(S)} = \dfrac{2}{6} = \dfrac{1}{3}$.

3. We have $n(S) = 36$. The phrase "getting a sum of 5" describes the event $E = \{(1,4),(2,3),(3,2),(4,1)\}$. This

event has 4 outcomes, so $n(E) = 4$. Thus, the probability of getting a sum of 5 is $P(E) = \dfrac{n(E)}{n(S)} = \dfrac{4}{36} = \dfrac{1}{9}$.

4. Let E be the event of being dealt a king. Because there are 4 kings in the deck, the event of being dealt a king can occur in 4 ways, i.e., $n(E) = 4$. With 52 cards in the deck, $n(S) = 52$.

The probability of being dealt a king is $P(E) = \dfrac{n(E)}{n(S)} = \dfrac{4}{52} = \dfrac{1}{13}$.

5.   Because the order of the six numbers does not matter, this is a situation involving combinations. With one

lottery ticket, there is only one way of winning so $n(E) = 1$. Using the combinations formula $_nC_r = \dfrac{n!}{(n-r)!r!}$

to find the number of outcomes in the sample space, we are selecting $r = 6$ numbers from a collection of $n = 49$
numbers.

$_{49}C_6 = \dfrac{49!}{43! \cdot 6!} = 13,983,816$ So $n(S) = 13,983,816$. If a person bought one lottery ticket, the probability of

winning was $P(E) = \dfrac{n(E)}{n(S)} = \dfrac{1}{13,983,816}$

The probability of winning the state lottery was 0.0000000715.

6. $P(\text{not in Marines}) = 1 - P(\text{in Marines}) = 1 - \dfrac{170 + 10}{1430} = \dfrac{1250}{1430} = \dfrac{125}{143}$

7.   We find the probability that either of these mutually exclusive events will occur by adding their individual
probabilities.

$P(4 \text{ or } 5) = P(4) + P(5) = \dfrac{1}{6} + \dfrac{1}{6} = \dfrac{2}{6} = \dfrac{1}{3}$

The probability of selecting a 4 or a 5 is $\dfrac{1}{3}$.

8.   It is possible for the pointer to land on a number that is odd and less than 5. Two of the numbers , 1 and 3, are
odd and less than 5. These events are not mutually exclusive. The probability of landing on a number that is odd
and less than 5 is P (odd or less than 5)

$= P \text{ (odd)} + P \text{ (less than 5)} - P \text{ (odd and less than 5)} = \dfrac{4}{8} + \dfrac{4}{8} - \dfrac{2}{8} = \dfrac{6}{8} = \dfrac{3}{4}$

The probability that the pointer will stop on an odd number or a number less than 5 is $\dfrac{3}{4}$.

9. $P(\text{Navy or man}) = P(\text{Navy}) + P(\text{man}) - P(\text{both}) = \dfrac{380}{1430} + \dfrac{1210}{1430} - \dfrac{320}{1430} = \dfrac{1270}{1430} = \dfrac{127}{143}$

10. The wheel has 38 equally likely outcomes and 2 are green. Thus, the probability of a green occurring on a play

is $\dfrac{2}{38}$, or $\dfrac{1}{19}$. The result that occurs on each play is independent of all previous results. Thus,

$P \text{ (green and green)} = P \text{ (green)} \cdot P \text{ (green)} = \dfrac{1}{19} \cdot \dfrac{1}{19} = \dfrac{1}{361} \approx 0.00277$.

The probability of green occurring on two consecutive plays is $\dfrac{1}{361}$.

11. If two or more events are independent, we can find the probability of them all occurring by multiplying the

probabilities. The probability of a baby boy is $\dfrac{1}{2}$, so the probability of having four boys in a row is P (4 boys

in a row) $= \dfrac{1}{2} \cdot \dfrac{1}{2} \cdot \dfrac{1}{2} \cdot \dfrac{1}{2} = \dfrac{1}{16}$.

Exercise Set 10.7

1. $P(\text{female}) = \dfrac{23}{89}$

3. $P(\text{in the Army}) = \dfrac{36}{89}$

5. $P(\text{a woman in the Air Force}) = \dfrac{6}{89}$

7. $P(\text{woman, among Air Force}) = \dfrac{6}{18} = \dfrac{1}{3}$

9. $P(\text{woman in Air Force}) = \dfrac{6}{23}$

11. $P(R) = \dfrac{n(E)}{n(S)} = \dfrac{1}{6}$

13. $P(E) = \dfrac{n(E)}{n(S)} = \dfrac{3}{6} = \dfrac{1}{2}$

15. $P(E) = \dfrac{n(E)}{n(S)} = \dfrac{2}{6} = \dfrac{1}{3}$

17. $P(E) = \dfrac{n(E)}{n(S)} = \dfrac{4}{52} = \dfrac{1}{13}$

19. $P(E) = \dfrac{n(E)}{n(S)} = \dfrac{12}{52} = \dfrac{3}{13}$

21. $P(E) = \dfrac{n(E)}{n(S)} = \dfrac{1}{4}$

23. $P(E) = \dfrac{n(E)}{n(S)} = \dfrac{7}{8}$

25. $P(E) = \dfrac{n(E)}{n(S)} = \dfrac{3}{36} = \dfrac{1}{12}$

27. Buying 1 ticket:

$$P(E) = \dfrac{n(E)}{n(S)} = \dfrac{1}{{}_{51}C_6} = \dfrac{1}{18,009,460}$$

Buying 100 tickets:

$$P(E) = \dfrac{100}{18,009,460} = \dfrac{5}{900,473}$$

29. a. $\quad {}_{52}C_5 = \dfrac{52!}{47!5!}$

$$= \dfrac{52 \cdot 51 \cdot 50 \cdot 49 \cdot 48}{5 \cdot 4 \cdot 3 \cdot 2 \cdot 1} = 2,598,960$$

b. $\quad {}_{13}C_5 = \dfrac{13!}{8!5!} = \dfrac{13 \cdot 12 \cdot 11 \cdot 10 \cdot 9}{5 \cdot 4 \cdot 3 \cdot 2 \cdot 1} = 1287$

c. $\quad P(E) = \dfrac{n(E)}{n(S)} = \dfrac{1287}{2,598,960} \approx 0.0005$

31.

$$P(\text{not completed 4 years of college}) = 1 - P(\text{completed 4 years of college}) = 1 - \dfrac{45}{174} = \dfrac{43}{58}$$

33. $P(\text{completed H.S. or less than 4 yrs college}) = P(\text{completed H.S}) + P(\text{less than 4 yrs college})$

$$= \dfrac{56}{174} + \dfrac{44}{174} = \dfrac{100}{174} = \dfrac{50}{87}$$

35. $P(\text{completed 4 yrs H.S. or man}) = P(\text{completed 4 yrs H.S.}) + P(\text{man}) - P(\text{man who completed 4 yrs H.S})$

$$= \dfrac{56}{174} + \dfrac{82}{174} - \dfrac{25}{174} = \dfrac{113}{174}$$

37. $P(\text{not king}) = 1 - P(\text{king}) = 1 - \dfrac{4}{52} = 1 - \dfrac{1}{13} = \dfrac{12}{13}$

39. $P(2 \text{ or } 3) = P(2) + P(3) = \dfrac{4}{52} + \dfrac{4}{52} = \dfrac{8}{52} = \dfrac{2}{13}$

41. $P(7 \text{ or red card}) = P(7) + P(\text{red card}) - P(7 \text{ and red}) = \dfrac{4}{52} + \dfrac{26}{52} - \dfrac{2}{52} = \dfrac{28}{52} = \dfrac{7}{13}$

43 $P(\text{odd or less than } 6) = P(\text{odd}) + P(\text{less than } 6) - P(\text{odd \# less than } 6) = \dfrac{4}{8} + \dfrac{5}{8} - \dfrac{3}{8} = \dfrac{6}{8} = \dfrac{3}{4}$

45. $P(\text{professor or male}) = P(\text{professor}) + P(\text{male}) - P(\text{male professor}) = \dfrac{19}{40} + \dfrac{22}{40} - \dfrac{8}{40} = \dfrac{33}{40}$

47. $P(2 \text{ and } 3) = P(2) \cdot P(3) = \dfrac{1}{6} \cdot \dfrac{1}{6} = \dfrac{1}{36}$

49. $P(\text{even and greater than } 2) = P(\text{even}) \cdot P(\text{greater than } 2) = \dfrac{3}{6} \cdot \dfrac{4}{6} = \dfrac{1}{3}$

51. $P(\text{all heads}) = \dfrac{1}{2} \cdot \dfrac{1}{2} \cdot \dfrac{1}{2} \cdot \dfrac{1}{2} \cdot \dfrac{1}{2} \cdot \dfrac{1}{2} = \left(\dfrac{1}{2}\right)^{6} = \dfrac{1}{64}$

53. a. $P(\text{hit 2 yrs in a row}) = P(\text{hit in 1}^{\text{st}} \text{ year and 2}^{\text{nd}} \text{ year}) = P(\text{hit 1}^{\text{st}} \text{ year}) \cdot P(\text{hit 2}^{\text{nd}} \text{ year}) = \dfrac{1}{16} \cdot \dfrac{1}{16} = \dfrac{1}{256}$

b. $P(\text{hit 3 yrs in a row}) = \dfrac{1}{16} \cdot \dfrac{1}{16} \cdot \dfrac{1}{16} = \dfrac{1}{4096}$

c.   First find the probability that South Florida will not be hit by a major hurricane in a single year:

$P(\text{not hit}) = 1 - \dfrac{1}{16} = \dfrac{15}{16}$

$P(\text{not hit in next 10 years}) = \left(\dfrac{15}{16}\right)^{10} \approx 0.524$

d. $P(\text{hit at least once}) = 1 - P(\text{hit none}) = 1 - \left(\dfrac{15}{16}\right)^{10} \approx 0.476$

67. a. $P(\text{Democrat who is not a business major})$

$= \dfrac{\text{\# of students who are Democrats but not business majors}}{\text{\# of students}}$

$= \dfrac{29 - 5}{50} = \dfrac{24}{50} = \dfrac{12}{25}$

b. $P(\text{neither Democrat nor business major})$

$= 1 - P(\text{Democrat or business major})$

$= 1 - \big(P(\text{Democrat}) + P(\text{business major}) - P(\text{Democrat and business major})\big)$

$= 1 - \left(\dfrac{29}{50} + \dfrac{11}{50} - \dfrac{5}{50}\right) = 1 - \dfrac{35}{50} = \dfrac{15}{50} = \dfrac{3}{10}$

69. a. The first person can have any birthday in the year. The second person can have all but one birthday.

   b. $\dfrac{365}{365} \cdot \dfrac{364}{365} \cdot \dfrac{363}{365} \approx 0.99$

   c. $100\% - 99\% = 0.01$

   d. $\dfrac{365}{365} \cdot \dfrac{364}{365} \cdot \dfrac{363}{365} \cdots \dfrac{346}{365} \approx 0.59$
       $1 - 0.59 = 0.41$

   e. With 23 people, the probability that at least two people have the same birthday is
$$P(E) = 1 - \frac{365}{365} \cdot \frac{364}{365} \cdot \frac{363}{365} \cdots + \frac{342}{365}$$
$$\approx 1 - 0.4927 \approx 0.5073$$

Chapter 10 Review Exercises

1. $a_n = 7n - 4$
      $a_1 = 7 - 4 = 3$
      $a_2 = 14 - 4 = 10$
      $a_3 = 21 - 4 = 17$
      $a_4 = 28 - 4 = 24$
      First four terms: 3, 10, 17, 24.

2. $a_n = (-1)^n \dfrac{n+2}{n+1}$
      $a_1 = (-1)^1 \dfrac{1+2}{1+1} = -\dfrac{3}{2}$
      $a_2 = (-1)^2 \dfrac{2+2}{2+1} = \dfrac{4}{3}$
      $a_3 = (-1)^3 \dfrac{3+2}{3+1} = -\dfrac{5}{4}$
      $a_4 = (-1)^4 \dfrac{4+2}{4+1} = \dfrac{6}{5}$
      First four terms: $-\dfrac{3}{2}, \dfrac{4}{3}, -\dfrac{5}{4}, \dfrac{6}{5}$.

3. $a_n = \dfrac{1}{(n-1)!}$
      $a_1 = \dfrac{1}{0!} = 1$
      $a_2 = \dfrac{1}{1!} = 1$
      $a_3 = \dfrac{1}{2!} = \dfrac{1}{2}$
      $a_4 = \dfrac{1}{3!} = \dfrac{1}{6}$
      First four terms: $1, 1, \dfrac{1}{2}, \dfrac{1}{6}$.

4. $a_n = \dfrac{(-1)^{n+1}}{2^n}$
      $a_1 = \dfrac{(-1)^2}{2^1} = \dfrac{1}{2}$
      $a_2 = \dfrac{(-1)^3}{2^2} = -\dfrac{1}{4}$
      $a_3 = \dfrac{(-1)^4}{2^3} = \dfrac{1}{8}$
      $a_4 = \dfrac{(-1)^5}{2^4} = -\dfrac{1}{16}$
      First four terms: $\dfrac{1}{2}, -\dfrac{1}{4}, \dfrac{1}{8}, -\dfrac{1}{16}$.

5. $a_1 = 9$ and $a_n = \dfrac{2}{3a_{n-1}}$
      $a_1 = 9$
      $a_2 = \dfrac{2}{3 \cdot 9} = \dfrac{2}{27}$
      $a_3 = \dfrac{2}{3} \cdot \dfrac{27}{2} = \dfrac{54}{6} = 9$
      $a_4 = \dfrac{2}{3 \cdot 9} = \dfrac{2}{27}$
      First four terms: $9, \dfrac{2}{27}, 9, \dfrac{2}{27}$.

6. $a_1 = 4$ and $a_n = 2a_{n-1} + 3$
      $a_1 = 4$
      $a_2 = 2 \cdot 4 + 3 = 8 + 3 = 11$
      $a_3 = 2 \cdot 11 + 3 = 22 + 3 = 25$
      $a_4 = 2 \cdot 25 + 3 = 50 + 3 = 53$
      First four terms: 4, 11, 25, and 53.

7. $\dfrac{40!}{4!\cdot 38!} = \dfrac{40\cdot 39\cdot 38!}{4\cdot 3\cdot 2\cdot 1\cdot 38!} = 65$

8. $\displaystyle\sum_{i=1}^{5}\left(2i^2-3\right)=(2-3)+\left(2\cdot 2^2-3\right)+\left(2\cdot 3^2-3\right)+\left(2\cdot 4^2-3\right)+\left(2\cdot 5^2-3\right)$

$\qquad\qquad\quad = -1+5+15+29+47$

$\qquad\qquad\quad = 95$

9. $\displaystyle\sum_{i=0}^{4}(-1)^{i+1}i! = (-1)^1 0!+(-1)^2 1!+(-1)^3 3!+(-1)^4 4!$

$\qquad\qquad\quad = -1+1-2+6-24$

$\qquad\qquad\quad = -20$

10. $\dfrac{1}{3}+\dfrac{2}{4}+\dfrac{3}{5}+\cdots+\dfrac{15}{17} = \displaystyle\sum_{i=1}^{15}\dfrac{i}{i+2}$

11. $4^3+5^3+6^3+\cdots+13^3 = \displaystyle\sum_{i=1}^{10}(i+3)^3$

12. $a_1 = 7,\ d = 4$

First six terms: 7, 11, 15, 19, 23, 27.

13. $a_1 = -4,\ d = -5$

First six terms: $-4, -9, -14, -19, -24, -29$.

14. $a_1 = \dfrac{3}{2},\ d = -\dfrac{1}{2}$

First six terms: $\dfrac{3}{2}, 1, \dfrac{1}{2}, 0, -\dfrac{1}{2}, -1$.

15. $a_{n+1} = a_n +5,\ a_1 = -2$

First six terms: $-2, 3, 8, 13, 18, 23$.

16. $a_1 = 5,\ d = 3$

$a_n = 5+(n-1)3$

$a_6 = 5+(5)3 = 20$

17. $a_1 = -8,\ d = -2$

$a_n = -8+(n-1)(-2)$

$a_{12} = -8+11(-2) = -30$

18. $a_1 = 14,\ d = -4$

$a_n = 14+(n-1)(-4)$

$a_{14} = 14+(13)(-4) = -38$

19. $-7, -3, 1, 5, \ldots$

$d = -3-(-7) = 4$

$a_n = -7+(n-1)(4)$

$a_n = 4n-11$

$a_{20} = 4(20)-11$

$a_{20} = 69$

20. $a_1 = 200,\ d = -20$

$a_n = 200+(n-1)(-20)$

$a_n = 220-20n$

$a_{20} = 220-20(20)$

$a_{20} = -180$

21. $a_n = a_{n-1}-5,\ a_1 = 3$

$d = -5$

$a_n = 3+(n-1)(-5) = 3-5n+5$

$a_n = 8-5n$

$a_{20} = 8-5(20) = -92$

22. $5, 12, 19, 26, \ldots$

$d = 7$

$a_n = 5+(n-1)(7)$

$a_{22} = 5+21(7) = 152$

$S_{22} = \dfrac{22}{2}(5+152) = 1727$

23. $-6, -3, 0, 3, \ldots$

$d = 3$

$a_n = -6+(n-1)3$

$a_{15} = -6+(14)3 = 36$

$S_{15} = \dfrac{15}{2}(-6+36) = 225$

24. $3 + 6 + 9 + \ldots + 300$

$$S_{100} = \frac{100}{2}(3 + 300) = 15,150$$

25. $\displaystyle\sum_{i=1}^{16}(3i + 2)$

$a_1 = 3 + 2 = 5$

$a_{16} = 3(16) + 2 = 50$

$$S_{16} = \frac{16}{2}(5 + 50) = 440$$

26. $\displaystyle\sum_{i=1}^{25}(-2i + 6)$

$a_1 = -2 + 6 = 4$

$a_{25} = -2(25) + 6 = -44$

$$S_{25} = \frac{25}{2}(4 - 44) = -500$$

27. $\displaystyle\sum_{i=1}^{30}-5i$

$a_1 = -5$

$a_{30} = -5(30) = -150$

$$S_{30} = \frac{30}{2}(-5 - 150) = -2325$$

28. **a.** $a_1 = 31.5$ and $d = -0.54$

$a_n = a_1 + (n-1)d$

$\quad = 31.5 + (n-1)(-0.54)$

$\quad = 31.5 - 0.54n + 0.54$

$\quad = -0.54n + 32.04$

b. Vegetables:

$a_n = -0.54n + 32.04$

$a_{18} = -0.54(18) + 32.04 = 22.32$

29. $a_n = 31,500 + (n-1)2300$

$a_{10} = 31,500 + (9)2300 = 52,200$

$$S_{10} = \frac{10}{2}(31,500 + 52,200) = 418,500$$

The total salary is $418, 500.

30. $a_n = 25 + (n-1)$

$a_{35} = 25 + 34 = 59$

$$S_{35} = \frac{35}{2}(25 + 59) = 1470$$

There are 1470 seats.

31. $a_1 = 3$, $r = 2$

First five terms: 3, 6, 12, 24, 48.

32. $a_1 = \dfrac{1}{2}$, $r = \dfrac{1}{2}$

First five terms: $\dfrac{1}{2}, \dfrac{1}{4}, \dfrac{1}{8}, \dfrac{1}{16}, \dfrac{1}{32}$.

33. $a_1 = 16$, $r = -\dfrac{1}{2}$

First five terms: 16, -8, 4, -2, 1.

34. $a_n = -5a_{n-1}$, $a_1 = -1$

First five terms: -1, 5, -25, 125, -625.

35. $a_1 = 2$, $r = 3$

$a_n = 2 \cdot 3^{n-1}$

$a_7 = 2 \cdot 3^6 = 1458$

36. $a_1 = 16$, $r = \dfrac{1}{2}$

$a_n = 16\left(\dfrac{1}{2}\right)^{n-1}$

$a_6 = 16\left(\dfrac{1}{2}\right)^5 = \dfrac{16}{32} = \dfrac{1}{2}$

37. $a_1 = -3$, $r = 2$

$a_n = -3 \cdot 2^{n-1}$

$a_5 = -3 \cdot 2^4 = -48$

38. $1, 2, 4, 8, \ldots$

$a_1 = 1$, $r = \dfrac{2}{1} = 2$

$a_n = 2^{n-1}$

$a_8 = 2^7 = 128$

39. $100, 10, 1, \dfrac{1}{10}, \ldots$

$a_1 = 100$, $r = \dfrac{10}{100} = \dfrac{1}{10}$

$a_n = 100\left(\dfrac{1}{10}\right)^{n-1}$

$a_8 = 100\left(\dfrac{1}{10}\right)^7 = \dfrac{1}{100,000}$

40. $12, -4, \frac{4}{3}, -\frac{4}{9} \cdots$

$$a_1 = 12, \, r = -\frac{4}{12} = -\frac{1}{3}$$

$$a_n = 12\left(-\frac{1}{3}\right)^{n-1}$$

$$a_8 = 12\left(-\frac{1}{3}\right)^7 = -\frac{4}{729}$$

41. $5, -15, 45, -135, \ldots$

$$r = \frac{-15}{5} = -3$$

$$S_{15} = \frac{5\left[1-(-3)^{15}\right]}{1-(-3)} = 17{,}936{,}135$$

42. $r = \frac{1}{2}, \, a_1 = 8$

$$S_{78} = \frac{8\left[1-\left(\frac{1}{2}\right)^7\right]}{1-\frac{1}{2}} = -16\left(1-\frac{1}{128}\right)$$

$$= -16\left(-\frac{127}{128}\right) = \frac{127}{8}$$

43. $S_6 = \frac{5\left(1-5^6\right)}{1-5} = \frac{5(-15624)}{-4} = 19{,}530$

44. $\displaystyle\sum_{i=1}^{7} 3(-2)^i$

$a_1 = -6, \, r = -2$

$$S_7 = \frac{-6\left[1-(-2)^7\right]}{1-(-2)} = \frac{-6(129)}{3} = -258$$

45. $\displaystyle\sum_{i=1}^{5} 2\left(\tfrac{1}{4}\right)^{i-1}$

$a_1 = 2, \, r = \frac{1}{4}$

$$S_5 = \frac{2\left[1-\left(\frac{1}{4}\right)^5\right]}{1-\frac{1}{4}} = \frac{2\left(\frac{1023}{1024}\right)}{\frac{3}{4}} = \frac{341}{128}$$

46. $a_1 = 9, \, r = \frac{1}{3}$

$$S_\infty = \frac{9}{1-\frac{1}{3}} = \frac{9}{\frac{2}{3}} = 9 \cdot \frac{3}{2} = \frac{27}{2}$$

47. $a_1 = 2, \, r = -\frac{1}{2}$

$$S_\infty = \frac{2}{1-\left(-\frac{1}{2}\right)} = \frac{2}{\frac{3}{2}} = \frac{4}{3}$$

48. $a_1 = -6, \, r = -\frac{2}{3}$

$$S_\infty = \frac{-6}{1-\left(-\frac{2}{3}\right)} = \frac{-6}{\frac{5}{3}} = -\frac{18}{5}$$

49. $r = 0.8$

$$S_\infty = \frac{4}{1-0.8} = 20$$

50. $0.\overline{6} = 0.6 + 0.06 + 0.006 + \cdots$

$$a_1 = \frac{6}{10}, \, r = \frac{1}{10}$$

$$S_\infty = \frac{\frac{6}{10}}{1-\frac{1}{10}} = \frac{\frac{6}{10}}{\frac{9}{10}} = \frac{6}{9} = \frac{2}{3}$$

51. $0.\overline{47} = 0.47 + 0.0047 + 0.000047 + \cdots$

$$a_1 = \frac{47}{100}, \, r = \frac{1}{100}$$

$$S_\infty = \frac{\frac{47}{100}}{1-\frac{1}{100}} = \frac{\frac{47}{100}}{\frac{99}{100}} = \frac{47}{99}$$

52. a. Divide each value by the previous value:

$$\frac{5.9}{4.2} = 1.405$$

$$\frac{8.3}{5.9} = 1.407$$

$$\frac{11.6}{8.3} = 1.398$$

$$\frac{16.2}{11.6} = 1.397$$

$$\frac{22.7}{16.2} = 1.401$$

The population is increasing geometrically with $r = 1.4$.

b. $a_n = 4.2 \cdot 1.4^n$

c. 2080 is 8 decades after 2000 so $n = 8$.

$a_n = 4.2 \cdot 1.4^n$

$a_8 = 4.2 \cdot 1.4^8 \approx 62.0$

In 2080, the model predicts the U.S. population, ages 85 and older, will be 62.0 million

53. $a_1 = 32,000,\ r = 1.06$

$a_6 = 32,000(1.06)^5 \approx \$42,823$

The sixth year salary is $42, 823.

$S_6 = \dfrac{32,000\left(1 - 1.06^6\right)}{1 - 1.06}$

$= \dfrac{32,000\left(1 - 1.06^6\right)}{-0.06}$

$\approx 223,210$

The total salary paid is $223, 210.

54. $A = 200\dfrac{\left(1 + \dfrac{0.1}{12}\right)^{18 \cdot 12} - 1}{\dfrac{0.1}{12}} \approx 120,113$

You will save $120,113.

55. $4(0.7) + 4(0.7)^2 + \cdots;\ r = 0.7$

$S_\infty = \dfrac{4(0.7)}{1 - 0.7} = 9.\overline{3}$

The total spending is $\$9\dfrac{1}{3}$ million.

56. $S_1 : 5 = \dfrac{5(1)(1+1)}{2}$

$5 = \dfrac{5(2)}{2}$

$5 = 5$ is true.

$S_k : 5 + 10 + 15 + \cdots + 5k = \dfrac{5k(k+1)}{2}$

$S_{k+1} : 5 + 10 + 15 + \cdots + 5k + 5(k+1)$

$\qquad = \dfrac{5(k+1)(k+2)}{2}$

Add $5(k+1)$ to both sides of S_k :

$5 + 10 + 15 + \cdots + 5k + 5(k+1)$

$= \dfrac{5k(k+1)}{2} + 5k(k+1)$

Simplify the right-hand side:

$\dfrac{5k(k+1)}{2} + 5(k+1) = \dfrac{5k(k+1) + 10(k+1)}{2}$

$= \dfrac{(5k+10)(k+1)}{2}$

$= \dfrac{5(k+1)(k+2)}{2}$

If S_k is true, then S_{k+1} is true.
The statement is true for all n.

57. $S_1 : 1 = \dfrac{4^1 - 1}{3}$

$1 = \dfrac{3}{3}$

$1 = 1$ is true.

$S_k : 1 + 4 + 4^2 + \cdots + 4^{k-1} = \dfrac{4^k - 1}{3}$

$S_{k+1} : 1 + 4 + 4^2 + \cdots + 4^{k-1} + 4^k = \dfrac{4^{k+1} - 1}{3}$ Add 4^k

to both sides of S_k :

$S_k : 1 + 4 + 4^2 + \cdots + 4^{k-1} = \dfrac{4^k - 1}{3}$

$1 + 4 + 4^2 + \cdots + 4^{k-1} + 4^k = \dfrac{4^k - 1}{3} + 4^k$

Simplify the right-hand side:

$\dfrac{4^k - 1}{3} + 4^k = \dfrac{4^k - 1 + 3 \cdot 4^k}{3}$

$= \dfrac{4 \cdot 4^k - 1}{3}$

$= \dfrac{4^{k+1} - 1}{3}$

If S_k is true, then S_{k+1} is true.
The statement is true for all n.

58. $S_1 : 2 = 2(1)^2$

$2 = 2$ is true.

$S_k : 2 + 6 + 10 + \cdots + (4k - 2) = 2k^2$

$S_{k+1} : 2 + 6 + 10 + \cdots + (4k - 2) + (4k + 2) = 2(k + 1)^2$

Add $(4k + 2)$ to both sides of S_k:

$2 + 6 + 10 + \cdots + (4k - 2) + (4k + 2) = 2k^2 + (4k + 2)$

Simplify the right-hand side:

$2k^2 + 4k + 2 = 2(k^2 + 2k + 1)$

$\qquad\qquad\quad = 2(k + 1)^2$

If S_k is true, then S_{k+1} is true. The statement is true for all n.

59. $S_1 : 1 \cdot 3 = \dfrac{1(1+1)[2(1) + 7]}{6}$

$3 = \dfrac{2 \cdot 9}{6}$

$3 = \dfrac{18}{6}$

$3 = 3$ is true.

$S_k : 1 \cdot 3 + 2 \cdot 4 + 3 \cdot 5 + \cdots + k(k + 2) = \dfrac{k(k+1)(2k+7)}{6}$

$S_{k+1} : 1 \cdot 3 + 2 \cdot 4 + 3 \cdot 5 + \cdots + k(k + 2) + (k+1)(k+3) = \dfrac{(k+1)(k+2)(2k+9)}{6}$

Add $(k + 1)(k + 3)$ to both sides of S_k:

$1 \cdot 3 + 2 \cdot 4 + 3 \cdot 5 + \cdots + k(k + 2) + (k+1)(k+3) = \dfrac{k(k+1)(2k+7)}{6} + (k+1)(k+3)$

Simplify the right-hand side:

$= \dfrac{k(k+1)(2k+7)}{6} + (k+1)(k+3)$

$= \dfrac{k(k+1)(2k+7) + 6(k+1)(k+3)}{6}$

$= \dfrac{(k+1)[k(2k+7) + 6(k+3)]}{6}$

$= \dfrac{(k+1)(2k^2 + 13k + 18)}{6}$

$= \dfrac{(k+1)(k+2)(2k+9)}{6}$

If S_k is true, then S_{k+1} is true. The statement is true for all n.

60. $S_1 : 2$ is a factor of $1^2 + 5(1) = 6$ since $6 = 2 \cdot 3$.

$S_k : 2$ is a factor of $k^2 + 5k$.

$S_{k+1} : 2$ is a factor of $(k + 1)^2 + 5(k + 1)$.

$$(k+1)^2 + 5(k+1) = k^2 + 2k + 1 + 5k + 5$$
$$= k^2 + 7k + 6$$
$$= k^2 + 5k + 2(k+3)$$
$$= (k^2 + 5k) + 2(k+3)$$

Because we assume S_k is true, we know 2 is a factor of $k^2 + 5k$. Since 2 is a factor of $2(k+3)$, we conclude 2 is a factor of the sum $(k^2 + 5k) + 2(k+3)$. If S_k is true, then S_{k+1} is true. The statement is true for all n.

61. $\dbinom{11}{8} = \dfrac{11!}{3!8!} = \dfrac{11 \cdot 10 \cdot 9}{3 \cdot 2 \cdot 1} = 165$

62. $\dbinom{90}{2} = \dfrac{90!}{88!2!} = \dfrac{90 \cdot 89}{2 \cdot 1} = 4005$

63. $(2x+1)^3 = \dbinom{3}{0}(2x)^3 + \dbinom{3}{1}(2x)^2 \cdot 1 + \dbinom{3}{2}(2x)1^2 + \dbinom{3}{3}1^3$
$$= 8x^3 + 3(4x^2) + 3(2x) + 1$$
$$= 8x^3 + 12x^2 + 6x + 1$$

64. $(x^2-1)^4 = \dbinom{4}{0}(x^2)^4 + \dbinom{4}{1}(x^2)^3(-1) + \dbinom{4}{2}(x^2)^2(-1)^2 + \dbinom{4}{3}x^2(-1)^3 + \dbinom{4}{4}(-1)^4$
$$= x^8 - 4x^6 + 6x^4 - 4x^2 + 1$$

65. $(x+2y)^5 = \dbinom{5}{0}x^5 + \dbinom{5}{1}x^4(2y) + \dbinom{5}{2}x^3(2y)^2 + \dbinom{5}{3}x^2(2y)^3 + \dbinom{5}{4}x(2y)^4 + \dbinom{5}{5}(2y)^5$
$$= x^5 + 5(2)x^4y + 10(4)x^3y^2 + 10(8)x^2y^3 + 5(16)xy^4 + 32y^5$$
$$= x^5 + 10x^4y + 40x^3y^2 + 80x^2y^3 + 80xy^4 + 32y^5$$

66. $(x-2)^6 = \dbinom{6}{0}x^6 + \dbinom{6}{1}x^5(-2) + \dbinom{6}{2}x^4(-2)^2 + \dbinom{6}{3}x^3(-2)^3 + \dbinom{6}{4}x^2(-2)^4 + \dbinom{6}{5}x(-2)^5 \dbinom{6}{6}(-2)^6$
$$= x^6 + 6x^5(-2) + 15x^4(4) + 20x^3(-8) + 15x^2(16) + 6x(-32) + 64$$
$$= x^6 - 12x^5 + 60x^4 - 160x^3 + 240x^2 - 192x + 64$$

67. $(x^2+3)^8 = \dbinom{8}{0}(x^2)^8 + \dbinom{8}{1}(x^2)^7 3 + \dbinom{8}{2}(x^2)^6 3^2 + \cdots$
$$= x^{16} + 8x^{14}3 + 28x^{12}9 + \cdots$$
$$= x^{16} + 24x^{14} + 252x^{12} + \cdots$$

68. $(x-3)^9 = \dbinom{9}{0}x^9 + \dbinom{9}{1}x^8(-3) + \dbinom{9}{2}x^7(-3)^2 - \cdots$
$$= x^9 + 9(-3)x^8 + 36(9)x^7 - \cdots$$
$$= x^9 - 27x^8 + 324x^7 - \cdots$$

69. $(x+2)^5$

fourth term $= \binom{5}{3} x^2 (2)^3$

$= 10(8) x^2 = 80x^2$

70. $(2x-3)^6$

fifth term $= \binom{6}{4} (2x)^2 (-3)^4$

$= 15(4x^2)(81) = 4860x^2$

71. $_8 P_3 = \dfrac{8!}{5!} = 8 \cdot 7 \cdot 6 = 336$

72. $_9 P_5 = \dfrac{9!}{4!} = 9 \cdot 8 \cdot 7 \cdot 6 \cdot 5 = 15,120$

73. $_8 C_3 = \dfrac{8!}{5!3!} = \dfrac{8 \cdot 7 \cdot 6}{3 \cdot 2 \cdot 1} = 56$

74. $_{13} C_{11} = \dfrac{13!}{2!11!} = \dfrac{13 \cdot 12}{2 \cdot 1} = 78$

75. $4 \cdot 5 = 20$ choices

76. $3^5 = 243$ possibilities

77. $_{15} P_4 = \dfrac{15!}{11!} = 15 \cdot 14 \cdot 13 \cdot 12 = 32,760$ ways

78. $_{20} C_4 = \dfrac{20!}{16!4!} = \dfrac{20 \cdot 19 \cdot 18 \cdot 17}{4 \cdot 3 \cdot 2 \cdot 1} = 4845$ ways

79. $_{20} C_3 = \dfrac{20!}{17!3!} = \dfrac{20 \cdot 19 \cdot 18}{3 \cdot 2 \cdot 1} = 1140$ sets

80. $_{20} P_4 = \dfrac{20!}{16!}$

$= 20 \cdot 19 \cdot 18 \cdot 17$

$= 116,280$ ways

81. $5! = 120$ ways

82. $P(\text{liberal}) = \dfrac{17}{100}$

83. $P(\text{not conservative}) = 1 - P(\text{conservative})$

$= 1 - \dfrac{33}{100} = \dfrac{67}{100}$

84. $P(\text{moderate or conservative})$

$= P(\text{moderate}) + P(\text{conservative})$

$= \dfrac{50}{100} + \dfrac{33}{100} = \dfrac{83}{100}$

85. $P(\text{conservative or attended college})$

$= P(\text{conservative}) + P(\text{attended college})$

$\quad - P(\text{conservative and attended college})$

$= \dfrac{33}{100} + \dfrac{45}{100} - \dfrac{20}{100} = \dfrac{58}{100} = \dfrac{29}{50}$

86. $P(\text{high school only}) = \dfrac{13}{33}$

87. $P(\text{liberal}) = \dfrac{10}{45} = \dfrac{2}{9}$

88. $P(\text{less than 5}) = P(\text{rolling a 1, 2, 3, 4})$

$= \dfrac{4}{6} = \dfrac{2}{3}$

89. $P(\text{less than 3 or greater than 4})$

$= P(\text{less than 3}) + P(\text{greater than 4})$

$= P(\text{rolling a 1, 2}) + P(\text{rolling a 5, 6})$

$= \dfrac{2}{6} + \dfrac{2}{6} = \dfrac{4}{6} = \dfrac{2}{3}$

90. $P(E) = \dfrac{4}{52} + \dfrac{4}{52} = \dfrac{8}{52} = \dfrac{2}{13}$

91. $P(E) = \dfrac{4}{52} + \dfrac{26}{52} - \dfrac{2}{52} = \dfrac{28}{52} = \dfrac{7}{13}$

92. $P(\text{not yellow}) = 1 - P(\text{yellow}) = 1 - \dfrac{1}{6} = \dfrac{5}{6}$

93. $P(\text{red or greater than 3}) = \dfrac{3}{6} + \dfrac{3}{6} - \dfrac{1}{6} = \dfrac{5}{6}$

94. $P(\text{green, then less than 4}) = \dfrac{2}{6} \cdot \dfrac{3}{6} = \dfrac{6}{36} = \dfrac{1}{6}$

95. a. $P(E) = \dfrac{n(E)}{n(S)} = \dfrac{1}{{}_{20}C_5} = \dfrac{1}{15,504}$

    b. $P(E) = \dfrac{100}{15,504} = \dfrac{25}{3876}$

96. $P(E) = \left(\dfrac{1}{2}\right)^5 = \dfrac{1}{32}$

97. a. $(0.2)^2 = 0.04$

    b. $(0.2)^3 = 0.008$

    c. $(1-0.2)^4 = (0.8)^4 = 0.4096$

Chapter 10 Test

1. $a_n = \dfrac{(-1)^{n+1}}{n^2}$

$a_1 = \dfrac{(-1)^2}{1^2} = 1$

$a_2 = \dfrac{(-1)^3}{2^2} = -\dfrac{1}{4}$

$a_3 = \dfrac{(-1)^4}{3^2} = \dfrac{1}{9}$

$a_4 = \dfrac{(-1)^5}{4^2} = -\dfrac{1}{16}$

$a_5 = \dfrac{(-1)^6}{5^2} = \dfrac{1}{25}$

First five terms: $1, -\dfrac{1}{4}, \dfrac{1}{9}, -\dfrac{1}{16}, \dfrac{1}{25}$.

2. $\displaystyle\sum_{i=1}^{5}(i^2 + 10) = 11 + 14 + 19 + 26 + 35 = 105$

3. $\displaystyle\sum_{i=1}^{20}(3i - 4)$

$a_1 = 3 - 4 = -1$

$d = 3$

$a_n = -1 + (n-1)3$

$a_{20} = -1 + (19)3 = 56$

$S_{20} = \dfrac{20}{2}(-1 + 56) = 550$

4. $\displaystyle\sum_{i=1}^{15}(-2)^i$

$a_1 = -2, \ r = -2$

$S_{15} = \dfrac{-2\left[1 - (-2)^{15}\right]}{1 - (-2)} = -21,846$

5. $\dbinom{9}{2} = \dfrac{9!}{7!2!} = \dfrac{9 \cdot 8}{2 \cdot 1} = 36$

6. ${}_{10}P_3 = \dfrac{10!}{7!} = 10 \cdot 9 \cdot 8 = 720$

7. ${}_{10}C_3 = \dfrac{10!}{7!3!} = \dfrac{10 \cdot 9 \cdot 8}{3 \cdot 2 \cdot 1} = 120$

8. $\dfrac{2}{3} + \dfrac{3}{4} + \dfrac{4}{5} + \cdots + \dfrac{21}{22} = \displaystyle\sum_{i=1}^{20}\dfrac{i+1}{i+2}$

9. $4, 9, 14, 19, \ldots$

$a_1 = 4, \ d = 5$

$a_n = 4 + (n-1) \cdot 5 = 4 + 5n - 1$

$a_n = 5n - 1$

$a_{12} = 5(12) - 1 = 59$

10. $16, 4, 1, \dfrac{1}{4}, \cdots$

$a_1 = 16, \ r = \dfrac{1}{4}$

$a_n = 16\left(\dfrac{1}{4}\right)^{n-1}$

$a_{12} = 16\left(\dfrac{1}{4}\right)^{11} = \dfrac{1}{262,144}$

11. $7, -14, 28, -56, \ldots$

$a_1 = 7, \ r = -2$

$S_{10} = \dfrac{7\left[1 - (-2)^{10}\right]}{1 - (-2)} = \dfrac{7(-1023)}{3} = -2387$

12. $-7, -14, -21, -28, \ldots$

$a_1 = -7, \ d = -7$

$a_n = -7 + (n-1)(-7)$

$a_{10} = -7 + 9(-7) = -70$

$S_{10} = \dfrac{10}{2}(-7 - 70) = -385$

13. $4 + \dfrac{4}{2} + \dfrac{4}{2^2} + \dfrac{4}{2^3} + \cdots$

$\quad r = \dfrac{1}{2}$

$\quad S_\infty = \dfrac{4}{1 - \dfrac{1}{2}} = 8$

14. $0.\overline{73} = 0.73 + 0.0073 + 0.000073 + \cdots$

$\quad a_1 = \dfrac{73}{100}, \ r = \dfrac{1}{100}$

$\quad S_\infty = \dfrac{\dfrac{73}{100}}{1 - \dfrac{1}{100}} = \dfrac{\dfrac{73}{100}}{\dfrac{99}{100}} = \dfrac{73}{99}$

15. $a_1 = 30,000, \ r = 1.04$

$\quad S_8 = \dfrac{30,000\left[1 - (1.04)^8\right]}{1 - 1.04} \approx 276,426.79$

The total salary is $276,427.

16. $S_1 : 1 = \dfrac{1[3(1) - 1]}{2}$

$\quad 1 = \dfrac{2}{2}$

$\quad 1 = 1$ is true.

$\quad S_k : 1 + 4 + 7 + \cdots + (3k - 2) = \dfrac{k(3k - 1)}{2}$

$\quad S_{k+1} : 1 + 4 + 7 + \cdots + (3k - 2) + (3k + 1) = \dfrac{(k + 1)(3k + 2)}{2}$

Add $(3k + 1)$ to both sides of S_k:

$\quad 1 + 4 + 7 + \cdots + (3k - 2) + (3k + 1) = \dfrac{k(3k - 1)}{2} + (3k + 1)$

Simplify the right-hand side:

$\quad \dfrac{k(3k - 1)}{2} + (3k + 1) = \dfrac{k(3k - 1) + 2(3k + 1)}{2}$

$\qquad\qquad\qquad\qquad = \dfrac{3k^2 + 5k + 2}{2}$

$\qquad\qquad\qquad\qquad = \dfrac{(k + 1)(3k + 2)}{2}$

If S_k is true, then S_{k+1} is true. The statement is true for all n.

17. $\left(x^2 - 1\right)^5 = \dbinom{5}{0}\left(x^2\right)^5 + \dbinom{5}{1}\left(x^2\right)^4(-1) + \dbinom{5}{2}\left(x^2\right)^3(-1)^2 + \dbinom{5}{3}\left(x^2\right)^2(-1)^3 + \dbinom{5}{4}x^2(-1)^4 + \dbinom{5}{5}(-1)^5$

$\qquad\qquad = x^{10} - 5x^8 + 10x^6 - 10x^4 + 5x^2 - 1$

18. $\left(x+y^2\right)^8$

First Term $\quad \dbinom{n}{r-1}a^{n-r+1}b^{r-1}=\dbinom{8}{1-1}x^{8-1+1}\left(y^2\right)^{1-1}=\dbinom{8}{0}x^8\left(y^2\right)^0=\dfrac{8!}{0!(8-0)!}x^8\cdot 1=\dfrac{\cancel{8!}}{0!\,\cancel{8!}}x^8$

$\qquad\qquad\qquad = x^8$

Second Term $\quad \dbinom{n}{r-1}a^{n-r+1}b^{r-1}=\dbinom{8}{2-1}x^{8-2+1}\left(y^2\right)^{2-1}=\dbinom{8}{1}x^7\left(y^2\right)^1=\dfrac{8!}{1!(8-1)!}x^7y^2=\dfrac{8\cdot\cancel{7!}}{1\cdot\cancel{7!}}x^7y^2$

$\qquad\qquad\qquad = 8x^7y^2$

Third Term $\quad \dbinom{n}{r-1}a^{n-r+1}b^{r-1}=\dbinom{8}{3-1}x^{8-3+1}\left(y^2\right)^{3-1}=\dbinom{8}{2}x^6\left(y^2\right)^2=\dfrac{8!}{2!(8-2)!}x^6y^4=\dfrac{8\cdot 7\cdot\cancel{6!}}{2\cdot 1\cdot\cancel{6!}}x^6y^4$

$\qquad\qquad\qquad = 28x^6y^4$

$x^8+8x^7y^2+28x^6y^4+\cdots$

19. $\ _{11}P_3=\dfrac{11!}{8!}=11\cdot 10\cdot 9=990\ \text{ways}$

20. $\ _{10}C_4=\dfrac{10!}{6!4!}=\dfrac{10\cdot 9\cdot 8\cdot 7}{4\cdot 3\cdot 2\cdot 1}=210\ \text{sets}$

21. Four digits are open: $10^4=10,000$

22. $P(\text{not brown eyes})=1-P(\text{brown eyes})$

$\qquad\qquad\qquad\quad =1-\dfrac{40}{50}$

$\qquad\qquad\qquad\quad =\dfrac{60}{100}=\dfrac{3}{5}$

23. $P(\text{brown eyes or blue eyes})$

$\quad =P(\text{brown eyes})+P(\text{blue eyes})$

$\quad =\dfrac{40}{100}+\dfrac{38}{100}=\dfrac{78}{100}=\dfrac{39}{50}$

24. $P(\text{female or green eyes})$

$\quad =P(\text{female})+P(\text{green eyes})$

$\qquad -P(\text{female with green eyes})$

$\quad =\dfrac{50}{100}+\dfrac{22}{100}-\dfrac{12}{100}=\dfrac{60}{100}=\dfrac{3}{5}$

25.

$P(\text{male, given blue eyes})=\dfrac{18}{38}=\dfrac{9}{19}$

26. $\ _{15}C_6=\dfrac{15!}{9!6!}=\dfrac{15\cdot 14\cdot 13\cdot 12\cdot 11\cdot 10}{6\cdot 5\cdot 4\cdot 3\cdot 2}=5005$

$P(E)=\dfrac{50}{5005}=\dfrac{10}{1001}$

27. $P(E)=\dfrac{26}{52}+\dfrac{12}{52}-\dfrac{6}{52}=\dfrac{32}{52}=\dfrac{8}{13}$

28. $P(E)=\dfrac{25}{50}+\dfrac{20}{50}-\dfrac{15}{50}=\dfrac{30}{50}=\dfrac{3}{5}$

29. $P(E)=\left(\dfrac{1}{4}\right)^4=\dfrac{1}{256}$

30. $P(E)=\dfrac{2}{8}\cdot\dfrac{2}{8}=\dfrac{1}{16}$

Cumulative Review Exercises (Chapters P–10)

1. Domain: $[-4,1)$; Range: $(-\infty,2]$

2. maximum of 2 at $x=-2$

3. decreasing interval: $(-2,1)$

4. neither

5. $f(-3)=1$ and $f(-1)=1$

6. $(f\circ f)(-4)=f(f(-4))=f(0)=0$

7. $f(x)\to -\infty$ as $x\to 1^-$

8.

$$g(x) = f(x-2) + 1$$

9.

$$h(x) = -f(2x)$$

10. $-2(x-5) + 10 = 3(x+2)$
$-2x + 10 + 10 = 3x + 6$
$14 = 5x$
$x = \dfrac{14}{5}$

The solution set is $\left\{ \dfrac{14}{5} \right\}$.

11. $3x^2 - 6x + 2 = 0$

$x = \dfrac{6 \pm \sqrt{36 - 24}}{6}$

$= \dfrac{6 \pm \sqrt{12}}{6}$

$= \dfrac{6 \pm 2\sqrt{3}}{6}$

$= \dfrac{3 \pm \sqrt{3}}{3}$

The solution set is $\left\{ \dfrac{3+\sqrt{3}}{3}, \dfrac{3-\sqrt{3}}{3} \right\}$.

12. $\log_2 x + \log_2 (2x-3) = 1$
$\log_2 x(2x-3) = 1$
$x(2x-3) = 2$
$2x^2 - 3x - 2 = 0$
$(2x+1)(x-2) = 0$

$2x+1 = 0$ or $x-2 = 0$

$x = -\dfrac{1}{2}$ $\qquad\qquad x = 2$

$x = -\dfrac{1}{2}$ does not check since $\log_2 \left(-\dfrac{1}{2} \right)$ does

not exist.
The solution set is $\{2\}$.

13. $x^{1/2} - 6x^{1/4} + 8 = 0$
Let $t = x^{1/4}$.

$t^2 - 6t + 8 = 0$

$(t-2)(t-4) = 0$

$t-2 = 0$ or $t-4 = 0$

$t = 2$ $\qquad\qquad t = 4$

$x^{1/4} = 2$ $\qquad\quad x^{1/4} = 4$

$x = 16$ $\qquad\qquad x = 256$

The solution set is $\{16, 256\}$.

14. $e^{2x} - 6e^x + 8 = 0$

$(e^x - 4)(e^x - 2) = 0$

$e^x - 4 = 0$ $\qquad\qquad e^x - 2 = 0$

$e^x = 4$ $\quad$ or $\qquad e^x = 2$

$x = \ln 4$ $\qquad\qquad x = \ln 2$

The solution set is $\left\{ \ln 2, \ln 4 \right\}$.

15. $|2x + 1| \le 1$
$-1 \le 2x + 1 \le 1$
$-2 \le 2x \le 0$
$-1 \le x \le 0$ or $[-1, 0]$
The solution set is $\{x | -1 \le x \le 0\}$ or $[-1, 0]$.

16.
$$6x^2 - 6 < 5x$$
$$6x^2 - 5x - 6 < 0$$
$$6x^2 - 5x - 6 = 0$$
$$(3x+2)(2x-3) = 0$$
$$3x + 2 = 0 \text{ or } 2x - 3 = 0$$
$$x = -\frac{2}{3} \qquad x = \frac{3}{2}$$

The test intervals are $\left(-\infty, -\frac{2}{3}\right), \left(-\frac{2}{3}, \frac{3}{2}\right)$, and $\left(\frac{3}{2}, \infty\right)$. Testing a point in each interval shows that the solution is $\left(-\frac{2}{3}, \frac{3}{2}\right)$.

17. $\dfrac{x-1}{x+3} \le 0$

The test intervals are $(-\infty, -3)$, $(-3, 1)$ and $(1, \infty)$.

Testing a point in each interval shows that the solution is $(-3, 1]$.

18.
$$30e^{0.7x} = 240$$
$$e^{0.7x} = 8$$
$$\ln e^{0.7x} = \ln 8$$
$$0.7x = \ln 8$$
$$x = \frac{\ln 8}{0.7} \approx 2.9706$$

The solution set is $\left\{\dfrac{\ln 8}{0.7}\right\}$ or $\{2.9706\}$.

19.
$$2x^3 + 3x^2 - 8x + 3 = 0$$
$p: \pm 1, \ \pm 3$
$q: \pm 1, \ \pm 2$
$$\frac{p}{q}: \pm 1, \pm 3, \pm\frac{1}{2}, \pm\frac{3}{2}$$

$$\begin{array}{r|rrrr}
1 & 2 & 3 & -8 & 3 \\
  &   & 2 & 5 & -3 \\
\hline
  & 2 & 5 & -3 & 0
\end{array}$$

$$(x-1)(2x^2 + 5x - 3) = 0$$
$$(x-1)(2x-1)(x+3) = 0$$
$$x = 1 \text{ or } x = \frac{1}{2} \text{ or } x = -3$$

The solution set is $\left\{-3, \dfrac{1}{2}, 1\right\}$.

20.
$$4x^2 + 3y^2 = 48$$
$$3x^2 + 2y^2 = 35$$
Multiply equation 1 by –2.
Multiply equation 2 by 3.

$$-8x^2 - 6y^2 = -96$$
$$9x^2 + 6y^2 = 105$$
$$\text{Add:} \quad \overline{\quad\quad\quad x^2 = 9\quad}$$
$$x = \pm 3$$

Let $x = -3$:
$$4(-3)^2 + 3y^2 = 48$$
$$36 + 3y^2 = 48$$
$$3y^2 = 12$$
$$y^2 = 4$$
$$y = \pm 2$$

Let $x = 3$:
$$4(3)^2 + 3y^2 = 48$$
$$36 + 3y^2 = 48$$
$$3y^2 = 12$$
$$y^2 = 4$$
$$y = \pm 2$$

The solution set is
$\{(3, 2), (3, -2), (-3, 2), (-3, -2)\}$.

21.
$$x - 2y + z = 16$$
$$2x - y - z = 14$$
$$3x + 5y - 4z = -10$$

$$\left[\begin{array}{rrr|r}
1 & -2 & 1 & 16 \\
0 & -1 & -1 & 14 \\
3 & 5 & -4 & -10
\end{array}\right] \begin{array}{l} \\ -2R_1 + R_2 \\ -3R_1 + R_3 \end{array}$$

$$\left[\begin{array}{rrr|r}
1 & -2 & 1 & 16 \\
0 & 3 & -3 & -18 \\
0 & 11 & -7 & -58
\end{array}\right] \begin{array}{l} \\ \frac{1}{3}R_2 \\ \\ \end{array}$$

$$\left[\begin{array}{rrr|r}
1 & -2 & 1 & 16 \\
0 & 1 & -1 & -6 \\
0 & 11 & -7 & -58
\end{array}\right] \begin{array}{l} \\ 2R_2 + R_1 \\ -11R_2 + R_3 \end{array}$$

$$\left[\begin{array}{rrr|r}
1 & 0 & -1 & 4 \\
0 & 1 & -1 & -6 \\
0 & 0 & 4 & 8
\end{array}\right] \begin{array}{l} \\ \\ \frac{1}{4}R_3 \end{array}$$

$$\left[\begin{array}{rrr|r}
1 & 0 & -1 & 4 \\
0 & 1 & -1 & -6 \\
0 & 0 & 1 & 2
\end{array}\right] \begin{array}{l} R_3 + R_1 \\ R_2 + R_1 \\ \\ \end{array}$$

$$\left[\begin{array}{rrr|r}
1 & 0 & 0 & 6 \\
0 & 1 & 0 & -4 \\
0 & 0 & 1 & 2
\end{array}\right] \begin{array}{l} R_3 + R_1 \\ R_2 + R_1 \\ \\ \end{array}$$

The solution set is $\{(6, -4, 2)\}$.

22.
$$x - y = 1$$
$$x^2 - x - y = 1$$

Multiply $x - y = 1$ by -1, then add

$$-x + y = -1$$
$$\overline{x^2 - x - y = 1}$$
$$x^2 - 2x = 0$$
$$x(x - 2) = 0$$

$x = 0$ or $x = 2$
If $x = 0$, $-y = 1$ so $y = -1$.
If $x = 2$, $2 - y = 1$ so $y = 1$.
The solution set is $\{(0, -1), (2, 1)\}$.

23. $100x^2 + y^2 = 25$

$$4x^2 + \frac{y^2}{25} = 1$$

$$\frac{x^2}{\left(\frac{1}{4}\right)} + \frac{y^2}{25} = 1$$

Ellipse
Foci on the y-axis

$a^2 = 25$ and $b^2 = \frac{1}{4}$, so $\frac{1}{4} = 25 - c^2$.

$$c^2 = \frac{99}{4}$$

$$c = \frac{3\sqrt{11}}{2}$$

Foci: $\left(0, -\frac{3\sqrt{11}}{2}\right), \left(0, \frac{3\sqrt{11}}{2}\right)$

$100x^2 + y^2 = 25$

24.
$$4x^2 - 9y^2 - 16x + 54y - 29 = 0$$
$$4(x^2 - 4x) - 9(y^2 - 6y) = 29$$
$$4(x^2 - 4x + 4) - 9(y^2 - 6y + 9) = 16 - 81 + 29$$
$$4(x - 2)^2 - 9(y - 3)^2 = -36$$
$$\frac{(y - 3)^2}{4} - \frac{(x - 2)^2}{9} = 1$$

Hyperbola with center at $(2, 3)$
Transverse axis vertical
$a^2 = 4$ and $b^2 = 9$, so $9 = c^2 - 4$.
$$c^2 = 13$$

$$c = \sqrt{13}$$
Foci: $\left(2, 3 - \sqrt{13}\right), \left(2, 3 + \sqrt{13}\right)$

$4x^2 - 9y^2 - 16x + 54y - 29 = 0$

25. Symmetry:

$$f(-x) = \frac{x^2 - 1}{-x - 2}$$

No symmetry since $f(-x) \neq f(x)$ and
$f(-x) \neq -f(-x)$.
x-intercepts:
$$x^2 - 1 = 0$$
$$x = \pm 1$$
y-intercept:
$$f(0) = \frac{1}{2}$$
$$y = \frac{1}{2}$$

Vertical asymptote:
$$x - 2 = 0$$
$$x = 2$$
Horizontal asymptote:
$n > m$, so no horizontal asymptote.
Slant asymptote: $n = m + 1$

$$f(x) = x + 2 + \frac{3}{x - 2}$$
$$y = x + 2$$

$$f(x) = \frac{x^2 - 1}{x - 2}$$

26.

$$2x - y \geq 4$$
$$x \leq 2$$

27. $f(x) = x^2 - 4x - 5$

$$x = \frac{-b}{2a} = \frac{4}{2} = 2$$

$$f(2) = 2^2 - 8 - 5 = -9$$

vertex: $(2, -9)$

x-intercepts:

$$x^2 - 4x - 5 = 0$$
$$(x - 5)(x + 1) = 0$$
$$x = 5, -1$$

y-intercept: $f(0) = -5$

$$f(x) = x^2 - 4x - 5$$

28.

29.

30. $f(x) = -x^2 - 2x + 1, \quad g(x) = x - 1$

$$(f \circ g)(x) = f(g(x))$$
$$= -(x-1)^2 - 2(x-1) + 1$$
$$= -x^2 + 2x - 1 - 2x + 2 + 1$$
$$= -x^2 + 2$$
$$(g \circ f)(x) = g(f(x))$$
$$= \left(-x^2 - 2x + 1\right) - 1$$
$$= -x^2 - 2x$$

31. $f(x) = -x^2 - 2x + 1$

$$\frac{f(x+h) - f(x)}{h} = \frac{\left(-(x+h)^2 - 2(x+h) + 1\right) - \left(-x^2 - 2x + 1\right)}{h}$$

$$= \frac{-x^2 - 2xh - h^2 - 2x - 2h + 1 + x^2 + 2x - 1}{h}$$

$$= \frac{-2xh - h^2 - 2h}{h}$$

$$= \frac{h(-2x - h - 2)}{h}$$

$$= -2x - h - 2$$

32. $AB - 4A = \begin{bmatrix} 4 & 2 \\ 1 & -1 \\ 0 & 5 \end{bmatrix} \begin{bmatrix} 2 & 4 \\ 3 & 1 \end{bmatrix} - 4 \begin{bmatrix} 4 & 2 \\ 1 & 1 \\ 0 & 5 \end{bmatrix}$

$= \begin{bmatrix} 14 & 18 \\ -1 & 3 \\ 15 & 5 \end{bmatrix} - \begin{bmatrix} 16 & 8 \\ 4 & -4 \\ 0 & 20 \end{bmatrix} = \begin{bmatrix} -2 & 10 \\ -5 & 7 \\ 15 & -15 \end{bmatrix}$

33. $\dfrac{2x^2 - 10x + 2}{(x-2)(x^2 + 2x + 2)} = \dfrac{A}{x-2} + \dfrac{Bx+C}{x^2 + 2x + 2}$

$2x^2 - 10x + 2 = A(x^2 + 2x + 2) + (Bx + C)(x - 2)$

$\qquad\qquad = Ax^2 + 2Ax + 2A + Bx^2 - 2Bx + Cx - 2C$

$\qquad\qquad = (A + B)x^2 + (2A - 2B + C)x + 2A - 2C$

Thus we have the following system of equations.

$\qquad A + B = 2$

$2A - 2B + C = -10$

$\qquad 2A - 2C = 2$

Add twice the first equation to the second equation.

$\qquad 2A + 2B = 4$

$\dfrac{2A - 2B + C = -10}{4A + C = -6}$

Add twice the resulting equation to the third equation.

$\qquad 8A + 2C = -12$

$\dfrac{2A - 2C = 2}{10A = -10}$

$\qquad\qquad A = -1$

Back-substitute to find B and C.

$2(-1) - 2C = 2$

$\quad -2 - 2C = 2$

$\qquad -2C = 4$

$\qquad\quad C = -2$

$-1 + B = 2$

$\qquad B = 3$

$\dfrac{-1}{x-2} + \dfrac{3x-2}{x^2 + 2x + 2}$

34. $(x^3 + 2y)^5 = \binom{5}{0}(x^3)^5 + \binom{5}{1}(x^3)^4(2y) + \binom{5}{2}(x^3)^3(2y)^2 + \binom{5}{3}(x^3)^2(2y)^3 + \binom{5}{4}(x^3)(2y)^4 + \binom{5}{5}(2y)^5$

$= x^{15} + 5x^{12}(2y) + 10x^9(4y^2) + 10x^6(8y^3) + 5x^3(16y^4) + 32y^5$

$= x^{15} + 10x^{12}y + 40x^9y^2 + 80x^6y^3 + 80x^3y^4 + 32y^5$

35. $\displaystyle\sum_{i=1}^{50}(4i-25)$

$a_1 = 4(1) - 25 = -21$

$a_{50} = 4(50) - 25 = 175$

$S_{50} = \dfrac{50}{2}(-21 + 175) = 3850$

36. Find slope:

$m = \dfrac{y_2 - y_1}{x_2 - x_1} = \dfrac{1-3}{-2-6} = \dfrac{-2}{-8} = \dfrac{1}{4}$

Find equation:

$y - y_1 = m(x - x_1)$

$y - 3 = \dfrac{1}{4}(x - 6)$

$y - 3 = \dfrac{1}{4}x - \dfrac{3}{2}$

$y = \dfrac{1}{4}x + \dfrac{3}{2}$

37. Find the slope:

$x - 5y - 20 = 0$

$-5y = -x + 20$

$\dfrac{-5y}{-5} = \dfrac{-x}{-5} + \dfrac{20}{-5}$

$y = \dfrac{1}{5}x - 4$

$m = -\dfrac{1}{\frac{1}{5}} = -5$

Find the equation:

$y - y_1 = m(x - x_1)$

$y - (-2) = -5(x - 0)$

$y + 2 = -5x$

$y = -5x - 2$

38. $200 + 0.05x = 0.15x$

$200 = 0.1x$

$2000 = x$

At \$2000 in sales, the two earnings will be the same.

39. Let $x =$ the width

Let $900 - 2x =$ the length

$A(x) = x(900 - 2x)$

$A(x) = -2x^2 + 900x$

The maximum occurs at $x = -\dfrac{b}{2a}$.

$x = -\dfrac{b}{2a}$

$x = -\dfrac{900}{2(-2)} = 225$ feet

$900 - 2x = 900 - 2(225) = 450$ feet

The length is 450 feet and the width is 225 feet.
The maximum area is

$450 \text{ ft} \times 225 \text{ ft} = 101,250 \text{ ft}^2$.

40. $10x + 12y = 42$

$5x + 10y = 29$

Multiply second equation by -2 and add:

$\begin{array}{r} 10x + 12y = 42 \\ \underline{-10x - 20y = -58} \\ -8y = -16 \\ y = 2 \end{array}$

Back substitute:

$5x + 10(2) = 29$

$5x = 9$

$x = 1.8$

pen: \$1.80, pad: \$2

41. $s(t) = -16t^2 + 80t + 96$

a. $-16t^2 + 80t + 96 = 0$

$t^2 - 5t - 6 = 0$

$(t + 1)(t - 6) = 0$

$t = -1$ or $t = 6$

The ball will strike the ground after 6 seconds.

b. $t = \dfrac{-b}{2a} = \dfrac{-80}{-32} = \dfrac{5}{2}$ or 2.5

$S(2.5) = -16(2.5)^2 + 80(2.5) + 96 = 196$

The ball reaches a maximum height of 196 feet, 2.5 seconds after it is thrown.

42. $I = \dfrac{k}{R}$

$5 = \dfrac{k}{22}$

$k = 110$

$I = \dfrac{110}{10} = 11$

11 amperes

43. Let x represent the number of years after 1982. The data from 1982 and 2002 are represented as $(0, 179)$ and $(20, 57)$

Find slope: $m = \dfrac{57 - 179}{20 - 0} = -6.1$

Thus, $y = -6.1x + 179$

At this rate there may eventually be no farms growing tobacco in the U.S.

44. $d = 10 \sin \dfrac{3\pi}{4} t$

    a. $|a| = |10| = 10 \; 2a = 20$

        The maximum displacement is 20 inches.

    b. $f = \dfrac{\omega}{2\pi} = \dfrac{\frac{3\pi}{4}}{2\pi} = \dfrac{3}{8}$

        The frequency is $\dfrac{3}{8}$ cycle per second.

    c. period $= \dfrac{2\pi}{\omega} = \dfrac{2\pi}{\frac{3\pi}{4}} = \dfrac{8}{3}$

        The time required for one oscillation is $\dfrac{8}{3}$ seconds.

45. $\tan x + \dfrac{1}{\tan x} = \dfrac{\sin x}{\cos x} + \dfrac{1}{\frac{\sin x}{\cos x}} = \dfrac{\sin x}{\cos x} + \dfrac{\cos x}{\sin x}$

$\qquad\qquad = \dfrac{\sin^2 x + \cos^2 x}{\cos x \cdot \sin x}$

$\qquad\qquad = \dfrac{1}{\cos x \cdot \sin x}$

46. $\dfrac{1 - \tan^2 x}{1 + \tan^2 x} = \dfrac{1 - \frac{\sin^2 x}{\cos^2 x}}{1 + \frac{\sin^2 x}{\cos^2 x}} \cdot \dfrac{\cos^2 x}{\cos^2 x}$

$\qquad\qquad = \dfrac{\cos^2 x - \sin^2 x}{\cos^2 x + \sin^2 x}$

$\qquad\qquad = \dfrac{\cos 2x}{1} = \cos 2x$

47. $y = -2\cos(3x - \pi)$

Amplitude: $|A| = |-2| = 2$

Period: $\dfrac{2\pi}{B} = \dfrac{2\pi}{3}$

Phase shift: $\dfrac{C}{B} = \dfrac{\pi}{3}$

$\left(\dfrac{\pi}{3}, -2\right), \left(\dfrac{\pi}{2}, 0\right), \left(\dfrac{2\pi}{3}, 2\right), \left(\dfrac{5\pi}{6}, 0\right),$

$(\pi, -2)$

$y = -2\cos(3x - \pi)$

48. $4\cos^2 x = 3$

$\cos^2 x = \dfrac{3}{4}$

$\cos x = \pm\sqrt{\dfrac{3}{4}} = \pm\dfrac{\sqrt{3}}{2}$

$x = \dfrac{\pi}{6}, \dfrac{5\pi}{6}, \dfrac{7\pi}{6}, \dfrac{11\pi}{6}$

The solutions in the interval $[0, 2\pi)$ are

$\dfrac{\pi}{6}, \dfrac{5\pi}{6}, \dfrac{7\pi}{6}$, and $\dfrac{11\pi}{6}$.

49. $\qquad 2\sin^2 x + 3\cos x - 3 = 0$

$\qquad 2(1 - \cos^2 x) + 3\cos x - 3 = 0$

$\qquad 2 - 2\cos^2 x + 3\cos x - 3 = 0$

$\qquad 2\cos^2 x - 3\cos x + 1 = 0$

$\qquad (2\cos x - 1)(\cos x - 1) = 0$

$2\cos x - 1 = 0 \quad$ or $\quad \cos x - 1 = 0$

$\quad 2\cos x = 1 \qquad\qquad \cos x = 1$

$\qquad \cos x = \dfrac{1}{2}$

$x = \dfrac{\pi}{3}, \dfrac{5\pi}{3} \quad$ or $\qquad\quad x = 0$

The solutions in the interval $[0, 2\pi)$ are

$0, \dfrac{\pi}{3}$, and $\dfrac{5\pi}{3}$.

50. $\cot\left[\cos^{-1}\left(-\dfrac{5}{6}\right)\right]$

If $\cos\theta = -\dfrac{5}{6}$, θ lies in quadrant II.

$$\cos\theta = -\frac{5}{6} = \frac{x}{r} = \frac{-5}{6}$$

$$x^2 + y^2 = r^2$$

$$(-5)^2 + y^2 = 6^2$$

$$25 + y^2 = 36$$

$$y^2 = 11$$

$$\cot\left[\cos^{-1}\left(-\frac{5}{6}\right)\right] = \frac{x}{y} = \frac{-5}{\sqrt{11}} = -\frac{5\sqrt{11}}{11}$$

51. $r = 1 + 2\cos\theta$

Check for symmetry:

Polar Axis	The Line $\theta = \dfrac{\pi}{2}$	The Pole
$r = 1 + 2\cos(-\theta)$	$-r = 1 + 2\cos(-\theta)$	$-r = 1 + 2\cos\theta$
$r = 1 + 2\cos\theta$	$r = -1 - 2\cos\theta$	$r = -1 - 2\cos\theta$

Graph is symmetric with respect to the polar axis.

θ	0	$\dfrac{\pi}{6}$	$\dfrac{\pi}{3}$	$\dfrac{\pi}{2}$	$\dfrac{2\pi}{3}$	$\dfrac{5\pi}{6}$	π
r	3	2.73	2	1	0	−0.73	−1

Use symmetry to obtain the graph.

$r = 1 + 2\cos\theta$

52. $\dfrac{b}{\sin B} = \dfrac{a}{\sin A}$

$\dfrac{32}{\sin B} = \dfrac{22}{\sin 34°}$

$\sin B = \dfrac{32 \sin 34°}{22} \approx 0.8134$

$B_1 \approx 54°,\ B_2 \approx 180° - 54° = 126°$

$C_1 = 180° - B_1 - A \approx 180° - 54° - 34° = 92°$

$C_2 = 180° - B_2 - A \approx 180° - 126° - 34° = 20$

$\dfrac{c_1}{\sin C_1} = \dfrac{a}{\sin A}$

$\dfrac{c_1}{\sin 92°} = \dfrac{22}{\sin 34°}$

$c_1 = \dfrac{22 \sin 92°}{\sin 34°} \approx 39.3$

$\dfrac{c_2}{\sin C_2} = \dfrac{a}{\sin A}$

$\dfrac{c_2}{\sin 20°} = \dfrac{22}{\sin 34°}$

$c_2 = \dfrac{22 \sin 20°}{\sin 34°} \approx 13.5$

There are two triangles. In the first triangle, the solution is

$B_1 \approx 54°,\ C_1 \approx 92°$, and $c_1 \approx 39.3$.

In the other triangle, $B_2 \approx 126°,\ C_2 \approx 20°$, and

$c_2 \approx 13.5$.

53. $x = \sin t,\ y = 1 + \cos^2 t,\ -\dfrac{\pi}{2} < t < \dfrac{\pi}{2}$

$y = 1 + \cos^2 t = 1 + (1 - \sin^2 t)$

$\quad = 1 + (1 - x^2) = 2 - x^2$

Chapter 11

Check Point Exercises

1. $\lim\limits_{x \to 3} 4x^2$

x	2.99	2.999	$2.9999 \to \;\leftarrow 3.0001$	3.001	3.01
$f(x) = 4x^2$	35.7604	35.9760	$35.9976 \to \;\leftarrow 36.0024$	36.0240	36.2404

The limit of $4x^2$ as x approaches 3 equals the number 36.

2. $\lim\limits_{x \to 0} \dfrac{\cos x - 1}{x}$

x	−0.1	−0.01	$-0.001 \to \;\leftarrow 0.001$	0.01	0.1
$f(x) = \dfrac{\cos x - 1}{x}$	0.0500	0.0050	$0.0005 \to \;\leftarrow -0.0005$	−0.0050	−0.0500

The limit of $\dfrac{\cos x - 1}{x}$ as x approaches 0 equals the number 0.

3. **a.** Figure 12.4 shows that as x approaches -2, $f(x)$ approaches 5. Thus, $\lim\limits_{x \to 2} f(x) = 5$.

   b. In figure 12.4, the graph of $f(x)$ at $x = -2$ is shown by the closed dot with coordinates $(-2, 3)$. Thus, $f(-2) = 3$.

4. Graph the piece defined by the linear function, $f(x) = 3x - 2$, using the y-intercept, -2, and the slope, 3. Because $x = 2$ is not included, show an open dot on the line corresponding to $x = 2$. Complete the graph using $f(x) = 1$ if $x = 2$. This part of the graph is the point $(2, 1)$, shown as a dot.

As x gets closer to 2, the values of $f(x)$ get closer to the y-coordinate of the open dot or 2. We conclude that $\lim\limits_{x \to 2} f(x) = 4$.

5. **a.** As x approaches 0 from the left, the values of $f(x)$ get close to the y-coordinate of 2. Thus
   $$\lim\limits_{x \to 0^-} f(x) = 2.$$

   b. As x approaches 0 from the right, the values of $f(x)$ get close to the y-coordinate of 1. Thus
   $$\lim\limits_{x \to 0^+} f(x) = 1.$$

c.   The $\lim\limits_{x\to 0^-} f(x) = 2$ and $\lim\limits_{x\to 0^+} f(x) = 1$. Because the left and right-hand limits are unequal, $\lim\limits_{x\to 0} f(x)$ does not exist.

d. $f(0) = 1$ because this point is shown as a solid dot.

Exercise Set 11.1

1.   The limit of x^2 as x approaches 2 equals the number 4.

3.   The limit of $\dfrac{\sin 3x}{x}$ as x approaches 0 equals the number 3.

5. $\lim\limits_{x\to 2} 5x^2$

x	1.99	1.999	1.9999 → ← 2.0001	2.001	2.01
$f(x) = 5x^2$	19.801	19.980	19.998 → ← 20.002	20.020	20.201

The limit of $5x^2$ as x approaches 2 equals the number 20.

7. $\lim\limits_{x\to 3} \dfrac{1}{x-2}$

x	2.99	2.999	2.9999 → ← 3.0001	3.001	3.01
$f(x) = \dfrac{1}{x-2}$	1.0101	1.0010	1.0001 → ← 0.9999	0.9990	0.9901

The limit of $\dfrac{1}{x-2}$ as x approaches 3 equals the number 1.

9. $\lim\limits_{x\to 0} \dfrac{x}{x^2+1}$

x	−0.01	−0.001	−0.0001 → ← 0.0001	0.001	0.01
$f(x) = \dfrac{x}{x^2+1}$	−0.0100	−0.0010	−0.0001 → ← 0.0001	0.0010	0.0100

The limit of $\dfrac{x}{x^2+1}$ as x approaches 0 equals the number 0.

11. $\lim\limits_{x\to -2} \dfrac{x^3+8}{x+2}$

x	−2.01	−2.001	−2.0001 → ← −1.9999	−1.999	−1.99
$f(x) = \dfrac{x^3+8}{x+2}$	12.0601	12.0060	12.0006 → ← 11.9994	11.9940	11.9401

The limit of $\dfrac{x^3+8}{x+2}$ as x approaches −2 equals the number 12.

13. $\lim\limits_{x\to 0}\dfrac{2x^2+x}{\sin x}$

x	-0.01	-0.001	$-0.0001 \to \leftarrow 0.0001$	0.001	0.01
$f(x)=\dfrac{2x^2+x}{\sin x}$	0.9800	0.9980	$0.9998 \to \leftarrow 1.0002$	1.0020	1.0200

The limit of $\dfrac{2x^2+x}{\sin x}$ as x approaches 0 equals the number 1.

15. $\lim\limits_{x\to 0}\dfrac{\tan x}{x}$

x	-1	-0.1	$-0.01 \to \leftarrow 0.01$	0.1	1
$f(x)=\dfrac{\tan x}{x}$	1.5574	1.0033	$1.00003 \to \leftarrow 1.00003$	1.0033	1.5574

The limit of $\dfrac{\tan x}{x}$ as x approaches 0 equals the number 1.

17. $\lim\limits_{x\to 0} f(x)$, where $f(x)=\begin{cases} x+1 \text{ if } x<0 \\ 2x+1 \text{ if } x\ge 0 \end{cases}$

x	-0.01	-0.001	$-0.0001 \to \leftarrow 0.0001$	0.001	0.01
$f(x)$	0.99	0.999	$0.9999 \to \leftarrow 1.0002$	1.002	1.02

The limit of $f(x)$ as x approaches 0 equals the number 1.

19. a. The graph shows that as x approaches 3, $f(x)$ approaches -1. Thus, $\lim\limits_{x\to 3} f(x)=-1$.

     b. The graph of $f(x)$ at $x=3$ is the point with coordinates $(3,-1)$. Thus, $f(3)=-1$.

21. a. The graph shows that as x approaches 2, $f(x)$ approaches 2. Thus, $\lim\limits_{x\to 2} f(x)=2$.

     b. The graph of $f(x)$ at $x=2$ is the point with coordinates $(2,1)$. Thus, $f(2)=1$.

23. The graph shows that as x approaches 2, $f(x)$ approaches -3. Thus, $\lim\limits_{x\to 2}(1-x^2)=-3$.

25. The graph shows that as x approaches $-\dfrac{\pi}{2}$, $f(x)$ approaches -1. Thus, $\lim\limits_{x\to -\frac{\pi}{2}}\sin x=-1$.

27. a. As x approaches 2 from the left, the values of $f(x)$ get close to the y-coordinate of 4. Thus
$\lim\limits_{x\to 2^-} f(x)=4$.

     b. As x approaches 2 from the right, the values of $f(x)$ get close to the y-coordinate of 2. Thus
$\lim\limits_{x\to 2^+} f(x)=2$.

c. The $\lim\limits_{x \to 2^-} f(x) = 4$ and $\lim\limits_{x \to 2^+} f(x) = 2$. Because the left and right-hand limits are unequal, $\lim\limits_{x \to 2} f(x)$ does not exist.

d. $f(2) = 4$ because this point is shown as a solid dot.

29. a. As x approaches -3 from the left, the values of $f(x)$ get close to the y-coordinate of 2. Thus $\lim\limits_{x \to -3^-} f(x) = 2$.

b. As x approaches -3 from the right, the values of $f(x)$ get close to the y-coordinate of 2. Thus $\lim\limits_{x \to -3^+} f(x) = 2$.

c. The $\lim\limits_{x \to -3^-} f(x) = 2$ and $\lim\limits_{x \to -3^+} f(x) = 2$, thus $\lim\limits_{x \to -3} f(x) = 2$.

d. $f(-3) = 2$ because this point is shown as a solid dot.

e. As x approaches -1 from the left, the values of $f(x)$ get close to the y-coordinate of 4. Thus $\lim\limits_{x \to -1^-} f(x) = 4$.

f. As x approaches -3 from the right, the values of $f(x)$ get close to the y-coordinate of 3. Thus $\lim\limits_{x \to -1^+} f(x) = 3$.

g. The $\lim\limits_{x \to -1^-} f(x) = 4$ and $\lim\limits_{x \to -1^+} f(x) = 3$. Because the left and right-hand limits are unequal, $\lim\limits_{x \to -1} f(x)$ does not exist.

h. $f(-1)$ does not exist because these points are shown as open dots.

i. As x approaches 3 from the left, the values of $f(x)$ get close to the y-coordinate of 2. Thus $\lim\limits_{x \to 3^-} f(x) = 2$.

j. As x approaches 3 from the right, the values of $f(x)$ get close to the y-coordinate of 2. Thus $\lim\limits_{x \to 3^+} f(x) = 2$.

k. The $\lim\limits_{x \to 3^-} f(x) = 2$ and $\lim\limits_{x \to 3^+} f(x) = 2$, thus $\lim\limits_{x \to 3} f(x) = 2$.

l. $f(3) = 1$ because this point is shown as a solid dot.

31. a. As x approaches 2 from the left, the values of $f(x)$ get close to the y-coordinate of 1. Thus $\lim\limits_{x \to 2^-} f(x) = 1$.

b. As x approaches 2 from the right, the values of $f(x)$ get close to the y-coordinate of 2. Thus $\lim\limits_{x \to 2^+} f(x) = 2$.

c. The $\lim\limits_{x \to 2^-} f(x) = 1$ and $\lim\limits_{x \to 2^+} f(x) = 2$. Because the left and right-hand limits are unequal, $\lim\limits_{x \to 2} f(x)$ does not exist.

d. $f(2) = 2$ because this point is shown as a solid dot.

e.   As x approaches 2.5 from the left, the values of $f(x)$ get close to the y-coordinate of 2. Thus $\lim\limits_{x \to 2.5^-} f(x) = 2$.

f.   As x approaches 2.5 from the right, the values of $f(x)$ get close to the y-coordinate of 2. Thus $\lim\limits_{x \to 2.5^+} f(x) = 2$.

g.   The $\lim\limits_{x \to 2.5^-} f(x) = 2$ and $\lim\limits_{x \to 2.5^+} f(x) = 2$, thus $\lim\limits_{x \to 2.5} f(x) = 2$.

h. $f(2.5) = 2$ because this point is shown as a solid dot.

33. Graph using the y-intercept, 1, and the slope 2.

As x gets closer to 3, the values of $f(x)$ get closer to 7. We conclude that $\lim\limits_{x \to 3}(2x + 1) = 7$.

35. Graph by reflecting the graph of $f(x) = x^2$ across the x-axis, then shifting the graph up 4 units.

As x gets closer to -3, the values of $f(x)$ get closer to -5. We conclude that $\lim\limits_{x \to -3}(4 - x^2) = -5$.

37. Graph by shifting the graph of $f(x) = |x|$ left 1 unit.

As x gets closer to -1, the values of $f(x)$ get closer to 0. We conclude that $\lim\limits_{x \to -1}|x + 1| = 0$.

39. Graph by using the vertical asymptote at $x = 0$, and the horizontal asymptote at $y = 0$.

As x gets closer to -1, the values of $f(x)$ get closer to -1. We conclude that $\lim\limits_{x \to -1}\dfrac{1}{x} = -1$.

41. Graph by first dividing out the factor $x - 1$. Then graph the equivalent function, $f(x) = x + 1$ where $x \neq 1$. Use the y-intercept, 1, and the slope 1. Because $x = 1$ is not included, show an open dot on the line corresponding to $x = 1$.

As x gets closer to 1, the values of $f(x)$ get closer to 2. We conclude that $\lim\limits_{x \to 1} \dfrac{x^2 - 1}{x - 1} = 2$.

43. Graph using the y-intercept, $(0, 1)$, and the properties of the exponential function

$f(x) = a^x$ for $a > 1$.

As x gets closer to 0, the values of $f(x)$ get closer to 1. We conclude that $\lim\limits_{x \to 0} e^x = 1$.

45. Graph using the period $= 2\pi$, amplitude $= 1$, and no phase shift. Use the key points,

$(0, 0),\ \left(\dfrac{\pi}{2}, 1\right),\ (\pi, 0),\ \left(\dfrac{3\pi}{2}, -1\right),$ and

$(2\pi, 0)$.

As x gets closer to π, the values of $f(x)$ get closer to 0. We conclude that $\lim\limits_{x \to \pi} \sin x = 0$.

47. As x approaches 2 from the left and the right, $f(x)$ approaches 3, thus $\lim\limits_{x \to 2} f(x) = 3$.

49. As x approaches 0 from the left, $f(x)$ approaches 3. As x approaches 0 from the right, $f(x)$ approaches 4. The left-hand limit and right-hand limit are not equal, thus the limit does not exist.

51. Graph $f(x) = 2x$ for $x < 1$ by using the y-intercept, 0, and the slope, 2. Because $x < 1$, this line is only graphed on the left side of $x = 1$. Graph $f(x) = x + 1$ for $x \geq 1$ by using the point $(1, 2)$ and the slope, 1. Graph this line on the right side of $x = 1$.

As x gets closer to 1, the values of $f(x)$ get closer to 2. We conclude that $\lim\limits_{x \to 1} f(x) = 2$.

53. As x approaches 0 from the left, $f(x)$ approaches 1. As x approaches 0 from the right, $f(x)$ approaches 0. The left-hand limit and right-hand limit are not equal, thus the limit does not exist.

55. $(f \circ g)(x) = \left(\sqrt{x}\right)^2 - 5 = x - 5$

$\lim\limits_{x \to 2} (f \circ g)(x) = -3$

57. $f^{-1}(x) = \sqrt[3]{x + 2}$

$\lim\limits_{x \to 6} f^{-1}(x) = 2$

59. $\lim\limits_{x \to 3} g(x) = 3$

61. $\lim\limits_{x \to 1^-} g(x) = 0$

63. $\lim\limits_{x \to -3^+} g(x) = 2$

65. $\lim\limits_{x \to 1} g(x) = 0$

67. a. According to the table, $\lim\limits_{x \to 3} f(x) = 8$. As your nose approaches the fan, the speed of the breeze that your nose feels approaches 8 miles per hour.

  b. Answers may vary.

69. $\lim\limits_{x \to 67} f(x) = 45$
The mean score in spatial orientation for someone 67 is 45.

71. a. $\lim\limits_{x \to 100} f(x) = 30$
The cost to rent the car one day and drive it 100 miles is $30.

  b. The rental cost on the first day approaches $40 as the mileage approaches 200.

  c. At the start of the second day, the rental cost is $60.

85.

$$\lim\limits_{x \to 0} \frac{2^x - 1}{x} \approx 0.69315$$

$$\lim\limits_{x \to 0} \frac{2^x - 1}{x} \approx 0.693147$$

87.

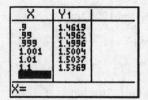

$$\lim\limits_{x \to 1} \frac{x^{3/2} - 1}{x - 1} \approx 1.5000$$

$$\lim\limits_{x \to 1} \frac{x^{3/2} - 1}{x - 1} \approx 1.50000$$

91. Let $x_1 = \dfrac{314}{100}, x_2 = \dfrac{31,415}{10,000},$

$x_3 = \dfrac{3,141,592}{1,000,000},$ and $x_4 = \dfrac{314,159,265}{100,000,000}.$

$3^{x_1} \approx 31.5$

$3^{x_2} \approx 31.541$

$3^{x_3} \approx 31.54426$

$3^{x_4} \approx 31.544281$

3^π is approximately equal to 31.544281.

Section 11.2

Check Point Exercises

1. a. $\lim\limits_{x \to 8} 11 = 11$

  b. $\lim\limits_{x \to 0} (-9) = -9$

2. a. $\lim\limits_{x \to 19} x = 19$

  b. $\lim\limits_{x \to -\sqrt{2}} x = -\sqrt{2}$

3. $\lim\limits_{x \to -3} (x + 16) = \lim\limits_{x \to -3} x + \lim\limits_{x \to -3} 16$
$\qquad\qquad\qquad = -3 + 16$
$\qquad\qquad\qquad = 13$

4. $\lim\limits_{x\to14}(19-x)=\lim\limits_{x\to14}19-\lim\limits_{x\to14}x$
$$=19-14$$
$$=5$$

5. $\lim\limits_{x\to7}(-10x)=\lim\limits_{x\to7}(-10)\cdot\lim\limits_{x\to7}x$
$$=-10\cdot7$$
$$=-70$$

6. a. $\lim\limits_{x\to-5}(3x-7)$
$$=\lim\limits_{x\to-5}3\cdot\lim\limits_{x\to-5}x-\lim\limits_{x\to-5}7$$
$$=3(-5)-7$$
$$=-15-7$$
$$=-22$$

   b. $\lim\limits_{x\to3}8x^2=\lim\limits_{x\to3}8\cdot\lim\limits_{x\to3}x^2$
$$=8\cdot\lim\limits_{x\to3}(x\cdot x)$$
$$=8\cdot\lim\limits_{x\to3}x\cdot\lim\limits_{x\to3}x$$
$$=8\cdot3\cdot3$$
$$=72$$

7. $\lim\limits_{x\to2}(-7x^3)=-7\cdot2^3$
$$=-7\cdot8$$
$$=-56$$

8. $\lim\limits_{x\to2}(7x^3+3x^2-5x+3)$
$$=7\cdot2^3+3\cdot2^2-5\cdot2+3$$
$$=7\cdot8+3\cdot4-5\cdot2+3$$
$$=56+12-10+3$$
$$=61$$

9. $\lim\limits_{x\to4}(3x-5)^3=\left[\lim\limits_{x\to4}(3x-5)\right]^3$
$$=(3\cdot4-5)^3$$
$$=7^3$$
$$=343$$

10. $\lim\limits_{x\to-1}\sqrt{6x^2-4}=\sqrt{\lim\limits_{x\to-1}(6x^2-4)}$
$$=\sqrt{6(-1)^2-4}$$
$$=\sqrt{6-4}$$
$$=\sqrt{2}$$

11. $\lim\limits_{x\to2}\dfrac{x^2-4x+1}{3x-5}=\dfrac{\lim\limits_{x\to2}(x^2-4x+1)}{\lim\limits_{x\to2}(3x-5)}$
$$=\dfrac{2^2-4\cdot2+1}{3\cdot2-5}$$
$$=\dfrac{-3}{1}$$
$$=-3$$

12. a. Because x is less than 1, use the first line of the piecewise function.
$$\lim\limits_{x\to1^-}f(x)=-1$$

   b. Because x is greater than 1, use the second line of the piecewise function.
$$\lim\limits_{x\to1^+}f(x)=\sqrt[3]{2(1)-1}=1$$

   c. Because the left-hand limit and the right-hand limit are unequal, $\lim\limits_{x\to1}f(x)$ does not exist.

13. $\lim\limits_{x\to1}\dfrac{x^2+2x-3}{x-1}=\lim\limits_{x\to1}\dfrac{(x+3)(x-1)}{x-1}$
$$=\lim\limits_{x\to1}(x+3)$$
$$=1+3$$
$$=4$$

14. $\displaystyle\lim_{x\to 0}\frac{\sqrt{9+x}-3}{x} = \lim_{x\to 0}\frac{\sqrt{9+x}-3}{x}\cdot\frac{\sqrt{9+x}+3}{\sqrt{9+x}+3}$

$\qquad = \displaystyle\lim_{x\to 0}\frac{\left(\sqrt{9+x}\right)^2-3^2}{x\left(\sqrt{9+x}+3\right)}$

$\qquad = \displaystyle\lim_{x\to 0}\frac{9+x-9}{x\left(\sqrt{9+x}+3\right)}$

$\qquad = \displaystyle\lim_{x\to 0}\frac{x}{x\left(\sqrt{9+x}+3\right)}$

$\qquad = \displaystyle\lim_{x\to 0}\frac{1}{\sqrt{9+x}+3}$

$\qquad = \dfrac{\displaystyle\lim_{x\to 0}1}{\sqrt{\displaystyle\lim_{x\to 0}(9+x)}+\displaystyle\lim_{x\to 0}3}$

$\qquad = \dfrac{1}{\sqrt{9+0}+3}$

$\qquad = \dfrac{1}{3+3}$

$\qquad = \dfrac{1}{6}$

11. $\displaystyle\lim_{x\to 2}(5x-8)^3 = \left[\lim_{x\to 2}(5x-8)\right]^3$

$\qquad = (5\cdot 2-8)^3$

$\qquad = 2^3$

$\qquad = 8$

13. $\displaystyle\lim_{x\to 1}(2x^2-3x+5)^2 = \left[\lim_{x\to 1}(2x^2-3x+5)\right]^2$

$\qquad = (2\cdot 1^2-3\cdot 1+5)^2$

$\qquad = (2\cdot 1-3\cdot 1+5)^2$

$\qquad = (2-3+5)^2$

$\qquad = 4^2$

$\qquad = 16$

15. $\displaystyle\lim_{x\to -4}\sqrt{x^2+9} = \sqrt{\lim_{x\to -4}(x^2+9)}$

$\qquad = \sqrt{(-4)^2+9}$

$\qquad = \sqrt{16+9}$

$\qquad = \sqrt{25}$

$\qquad = 5$

Exercise Set 11.2

1. $\displaystyle\lim_{x\to 2}8 = 8$

3. $\displaystyle\lim_{x\to 2}x = 2$

5. $\displaystyle\lim_{x\to 6}(3x-4) = \lim_{x\to 6}3\cdot\lim_{x\to 6}x-\lim_{x\to 6}4$

$\qquad = 3\cdot 6-4$

$\qquad = 18-4$

$\qquad = 14$

7. $\displaystyle\lim_{x\to -2}7x^2 = \lim_{x\to -2}7\cdot\lim_{x\to -2}x^2$

$\qquad = 7\cdot\displaystyle\lim_{x\to -2}(x\cdot x)$

$\qquad = 7\cdot\displaystyle\lim_{x\to -2}x\cdot\lim_{x\to -2}x$

$\qquad = 7(-2)(-2)$

$\qquad = 28$

9. $\displaystyle\lim_{x\to 5}(x^2-3x-4) = 5^2-3\cdot 5-4$

$\qquad = 25-15-4$

$\qquad = 6$

17. $\displaystyle\lim_{x\to 5}\frac{x}{x+1} = \frac{\displaystyle\lim_{x\to 5}x}{\displaystyle\lim_{x\to 5}(x+1)}$

$\qquad = \dfrac{5}{5+1}$

$\qquad = \dfrac{5}{6}$

19. $\displaystyle\lim_{x\to 2}\frac{x^2-1}{x-1} = \lim_{x\to 2}\frac{(x+1)(x-1)}{x-1}$

$\qquad = \displaystyle\lim_{x\to 2}(x+1)$

$\qquad = 2+1$

$\qquad = 3$

21. $\displaystyle\lim_{x\to 1}\frac{x^2-1}{x-1} = \lim_{x\to 1}\frac{(x+1)(x-1)}{x-1}$

$\qquad = \displaystyle\lim_{x\to 1}(x+1)$

$\qquad = 1+1$

$\qquad = 2$

23. $\displaystyle\lim_{x\to 2}\frac{2x-4}{x-2} = \lim_{x\to 2}\frac{2(x-2)}{x-2}$

$\qquad = \displaystyle\lim_{x\to 2}2$

$\qquad = 2$

25.
$$\lim_{x\to 1}\frac{x^2+2x-3}{x^2-1}=\lim_{x\to 1}\frac{(x+3)(x-1)}{(x+1)(x-1)}=\lim_{x\to 1}\frac{x+3}{x+1}=\frac{\lim_{x\to 1}(x+3)}{\lim_{x\to 1}(x+1)}=\frac{1+3}{1+1}=\frac{4}{2}=2$$

27.
$$\lim_{x\to 2}\frac{x^3-2x^2+4x-8}{x^4-2x^3+x-2}=\lim_{x\to 2}\frac{x^2(x-2)+4(x-2)}{x^3(x-2)+(x-2)}=\lim_{x\to 2}\frac{(x^2+4)(x-2)}{(x^3+1)(x-2)}=\lim_{x\to 2}\frac{x^2+4}{x^3+1}$$

$$=\frac{\lim_{x\to 2}(x^2+4)}{\lim_{x\to 2}(x^3+1)}=\frac{2^2+4}{2^3+1}=\frac{8}{9}$$

29.
$$\lim_{x\to 0}\frac{\sqrt{1+x}-1}{x}=\lim_{x\to 0}\frac{\sqrt{1+x}-1}{x}\cdot\frac{\sqrt{1+x}+1}{\sqrt{1+x}+1}=\lim_{x\to 0}\frac{\left(\sqrt{1+x}\right)^2-1^2}{x\left(\sqrt{1+x}+1\right)}=\lim_{x\to 0}\frac{1+x-1}{x\left(\sqrt{1+x}+1\right)}=\lim_{x\to 0}\frac{x}{x\left(\sqrt{1+x}+1\right)}$$

$$=\lim_{x\to 0}\frac{1}{\sqrt{1+x}+1}=\frac{\lim_{x\to 0}1}{\sqrt{\lim_{x\to 0}(1+x)}+\lim_{x\to 0}1}=\frac{1}{\sqrt{1+0}+1}=\frac{1}{1+1}=\frac{1}{2}$$

31.
$$\lim_{x\to 2}(x+1)^2(3x-1)^3=\left[\lim_{x\to 2}(x+1)\right]^2\left[\lim_{x\to 2}(3x-1)\right]^3=(2+1)^2\cdot(3\cdot 2-1)^3=3^2\cdot 5^3=1125$$

33.
$$\lim_{x\to 4}\frac{\sqrt{x}-2}{x-4}=\lim_{x\to 4}\frac{\sqrt{x}-2}{x-4}\cdot\frac{\sqrt{x}+2}{\sqrt{x}+2}=\lim_{x\to 4}\frac{\left(\sqrt{x}\right)^2-2^2}{(x-4)\left(\sqrt{x}+2\right)}=\lim_{x\to 4}\frac{x-4}{(x-4)\left(\sqrt{x}+2\right)}$$

$$=\lim_{x\to 4}\frac{1}{\sqrt{x}+2}=\frac{\lim_{x\to 4}1}{\sqrt{\lim_{x\to 4}x}+\lim_{x\to 4}2}=\frac{1}{\sqrt{4}+2}=\frac{1}{2+2}=\frac{1}{4}$$

35.
$$\lim_{x\to 2}\frac{\frac{1}{x}-\frac{1}{2}}{x-2}=\lim_{x\to 2}\frac{\frac{2-x}{2x}}{x-2}=\lim_{x\to 2}\frac{2-x}{2x(x-2)}=\lim_{x\to 2}\frac{-(x-2)}{2x(x-2)}=\lim_{x\to 2}\left(-\frac{1}{2x}\right)=-\frac{1}{2\cdot 2}=-\frac{1}{4}$$

37.
$$\lim_{x\to 4}\frac{\sqrt{x}+5}{x-5}=\frac{\sqrt{\lim_{x\to 4}x}+\lim_{x\to 4}5}{\lim_{x\to 4}x-\lim_{x\to 4}5}=\frac{\sqrt{4}+5}{4-5}=\frac{7}{-1}=-7$$

39.
$$\lim_{x\to 0}\frac{\frac{1}{x+3}-\frac{1}{3}}{x}=\lim_{x\to 0}\frac{\frac{3-(x+3)}{3(x+3)}}{x}=\lim_{x\to 0}\frac{-x}{3x(x+3)}=\lim_{x\to 0}\frac{-1}{3(x+3)}=\frac{\lim_{x\to 0}(-1)}{3\lim_{x\to 0}(x+3)}=\frac{-1}{3(0+3)}=-\frac{1}{9}$$

41.
$$\lim_{x\to 2}\frac{x^2-4}{x^3-8}=\lim_{x\to 2}\frac{(x+2)(x-2)}{(x-2)(x^2+2x+4)}=\lim_{x\to 2}\frac{x+2}{x^2+2x+4}=\frac{\lim_{x\to 2}(x+2)}{\lim_{x\to 2}(x^2+2x+4)}=\frac{2+2}{2^2+2\cdot 2+4}=\frac{4}{12}=\frac{1}{3}$$

43. $f(x) = \begin{cases} x+5 \text{ if } x < 1 \\ x+7 \text{ if } x \geq 1 \end{cases}$

    a. $\lim\limits_{x \to 1^-} f(x) = \lim\limits_{x \to 1^-} (x+5) = 1+5 = 6$

    b. $\lim\limits_{x \to 1^+} f(x) = \lim\limits_{x-1^+} (x+7) = 1+7 = 8$

    c. $\lim\limits_{x \to 1^-} f(x) \neq \lim\limits_{x \to 1^+} f(x)$, therefore, $\lim\limits_{x \to 1} f(x)$ does not exist.

45. $f(x) = \begin{cases} x^2+5 \text{ if } x < 2 \\ x^3+1 \text{ if } x \geq 2 \end{cases}$

    a. $\lim\limits_{x \to 2^-} f(x) = \lim\limits_{x \to 2^-} (x^2+5) = 2^2+5 = 9$

    b. $\lim\limits_{x \to 2^+} f(x) = \lim\limits_{x \to 2^+} (x^3+1) = 2^3+1 = 9$

    c. $\lim\limits_{x \to 2^-} f(x) = \lim\limits_{x \to 2^+} f(x)$, therefore, $\lim\limits_{x \to 2} f(x)$ exists, and is 9

47. $f(x) = \begin{cases} \dfrac{x^2-9}{x-3} \text{ if } x \neq 3 \\ 5 \text{ if } x = 3 \end{cases}$

    a. $\begin{aligned} \lim\limits_{x \to 3^-} f(x) &= \lim\limits_{x \to 3^-} \frac{x^2-9}{x-3} \\ &= \lim\limits_{x \to 3^-} \frac{(x+3)(x-3)}{x-3} \\ &= \lim\limits_{x \to 3^-} (x+3) \\ &= 3+3 \\ &= 6 \end{aligned}$

    b. $\begin{aligned} \lim\limits_{x \to 3^+} f(x) &= \lim\limits_{x \to 3^+} \frac{x^2-9}{x-3} \\ &= \lim\limits_{x \to 3^+} \frac{(x+3)(x-3)}{x-3} \\ &= \lim\limits_{x \to 3^+} (x+3) \\ &= 3+3 \\ &= 6 \end{aligned}$

    c. $\lim\limits_{x \to 3^-} f(x) = \lim\limits_{x \to 3^+} f(x)$, therefore, $\lim\limits_{x \to 3} f(x)$ exists, and is 6

49. $f(x) + \begin{cases} 1 - x & \text{if } x < 1 \\ 2 & \text{if } x = 1 \\ x^2 - 1 & \text{if } x > 1 \end{cases}$

    a. $\lim\limits_{x \to 1^-} f(x) = \lim\limits_{x \to 1^-} (1 - x) = 1 - 1 = 0$

    b. $\lim\limits_{x \to 1^+} f(x) = \lim\limits_{x \to 1^+} (x^2 - 1) = 1^2 - 1 = 0$

    c. $\lim\limits_{x \to 1^-} f(x) = \lim\limits_{x \to 1^+} f(x)$, therefore, $\lim\limits_{x \to 1} f(x)$ exists, and is 0

51. $\lim\limits_{x \to 3}(f \circ g)(x) = \lim\limits_{x \to 3}\left[2^3 - 2^2 + 5(2) - 1 \right] = \lim\limits_{x \to 3} 13 = 13$

    $\lim\limits_{x \to 3}(g \circ f)(x) = \lim\limits_{x \to 3} 2 = 2$

53. $\lim\limits_{x \to 1}(f \circ g)(x) = \lim\limits_{x \to 1} \dfrac{2}{\frac{3}{x-1}} = \lim\limits_{x \to 1} \dfrac{2x - 2}{3} = \dfrac{2(1) - 2}{3} = 0$

    $\lim\limits_{x \to 1}(g \circ f)(x) = \lim\limits_{x \to 1} \dfrac{3}{\frac{2}{x} - 1} = \lim\limits_{x \to 1} \dfrac{3}{\frac{2}{x} - 1} = \dfrac{3}{\frac{2}{1} - 1} = 3$

55. $f^{-1}(x) = \sqrt{x - 4}$

    $\lim\limits_{x \to 8} f^{-1}(x) = \lim\limits_{x \to 8} \sqrt{x - 4} = \sqrt{8 - 4} = 2$

57. $f^{-1}(x) = \dfrac{x + 1}{x - 2}$

    $\lim\limits_{x \to 4} f^{-1}(x) = \lim\limits_{x \to 4} \dfrac{x + 1}{x - 2} = \dfrac{4 + 1}{4 - 2} = \dfrac{5}{2}$

59. **a.** $\lim\limits_{v \to c^-} L = \lim\limits_{v \to c^-} \left[L_0 \sqrt{1 - \dfrac{v^2}{c^2}} \right] = \lim\limits_{v \to c^-} \left[L_0 \sqrt{1 - 1} \right] = \lim\limits_{v \to c^-} 0 = 0$

    b.   The length of the starship appears to approach 0.

    c.   It is not possible to exceed the speed of light.

75. $\lim\limits_{x \to 4} \left(\dfrac{1}{x} - \dfrac{1}{4} \right) \left(\dfrac{1}{x - 4} \right)$

    $= \lim\limits_{x \to 4} \left(\dfrac{4 - x}{4x} \right) \left(\dfrac{1}{x - 4} \right)$

    $= \lim\limits_{x \to 4} \dfrac{-(x - 4)}{4x(x - 4)}$

    $= \lim\limits_{x \to 4} \left(-\dfrac{1}{4x} \right)$

    $= -\dfrac{1}{4 \cdot 4}$

    $= -\dfrac{1}{16}$

77. $\lim\limits_{h \to 0} \dfrac{f(a+h) - f(a)}{h}$

$= \lim\limits_{h \to 0} \dfrac{\sqrt{1+h} - \sqrt{1}}{h}$

$= \lim\limits_{h \to 0} \dfrac{\sqrt{1+h} - 1}{h} \cdot \dfrac{\sqrt{1+h} + 1}{\sqrt{1+h} + 1}$

$= \lim\limits_{h \to 0} \dfrac{\left(\sqrt{1+h}\right)^2 - 1^2}{h\left(\sqrt{1+h} + 1\right)}$

$= \lim\limits_{h \to 0} \dfrac{1 + h - 1}{h\left(\sqrt{1+h} + 1\right)}$

$= \lim\limits_{h \to 0} \dfrac{h}{h\left(\sqrt{1+h} + 1\right)}$

$= \lim\limits_{h \to 0} \dfrac{1}{\sqrt{1+h} + 1}$

$= \dfrac{\lim\limits_{h \to 0} 1}{\sqrt{\lim\limits_{h \to 0}(1+h)} + \lim\limits_{h \to 0} 1}$

$= \dfrac{1}{\sqrt{1+0} + 1}$

$= \dfrac{1}{1+1}$

$= \dfrac{1}{2}$

79. $\lim\limits_{x \to 0} \dfrac{2\sin x + \cos x - 1}{3x}$

$= \lim\limits_{x \to 0} \left(\dfrac{2\sin x}{3x} + \dfrac{\cos x - 1}{3x} \right)$

$= \dfrac{2}{3} \lim\limits_{x \to 0} \dfrac{\sin x}{x} + \dfrac{1}{3} \lim\limits_{x \to 0} \dfrac{\cos x - 1}{x}$

$= \dfrac{2}{3}(1) + \dfrac{1}{3}(0)$

$= \dfrac{2}{3}$

Section 11.3

Check Point Exercises

1. $f(x) = \dfrac{x-2}{x^2-4}$

   a. Is $f(1)$ defined?

$$f(1) = \frac{1-2}{1^2-4} = \frac{1-2}{1-4} = \frac{-1}{-3} = \frac{1}{3}$$

Because $f(1)$ is a real number, $f(1)$ is defined.

Does $\lim\limits_{x\to 1} f(x)$ exist?

$$\lim_{x\to 1} f(x) = \lim_{x\to 1} \frac{x-2}{x^2-4}$$

$$= \frac{\lim\limits_{x\to 1}(x-2)}{\lim\limits_{x\to 1}(x^2-4)}$$

$$= \frac{1-2}{1^2-4}$$

$$= \frac{1-2}{1-4}$$

$$= \frac{-1}{-3}$$

$$= \frac{1}{3}$$

Using the properties of limits, we see that $\lim\limits_{x\to 1} f(x)$ exists.

Does $\lim\limits_{x\to 1} f(x) = f(1)$? Yes.

Because the three conditions for continuity are satisfied, $f(x)$ is continuous at 1.

   b. Is $f(2)$ defined?

$$f(x) = \frac{x-2}{(x+2)(x-2)}$$

Because division by zero is undefined, the domain of f is $\{x \mid x \neq 2, x \neq -2\}$.

Thus, f is not defined at 2. Because one of the three conditions is not satisfied, we conclude that f is discontinuous at 2.

2. $f(x) = \begin{cases} 2x & \text{if } x \le 0 \\ x^2+1 & \text{if } 0 < x \le 2 \\ 7-x & \text{if } x > 2 \end{cases}$

Because $2x$ and $7-x$ are linear functions and x^2+1 is a polynomial function, each is continuous for every number x. However, since the functional form of f changes at $x = 0$ and $x = 2$, we must check for continuity at these two points.

Is $f(0)$ defined?

$f(0) = 2(0) = 0$

Because $f(0)$ is a real number, $f(0)$ is defined.

Does $\lim\limits_{x\to 0} f(x)$ exist?

$$\lim_{x\to 0^-} f(x) = \lim_{x\to 0^-} 2x = 2\cdot 0 = 0$$

$$\lim_{x\to 0^+} f(x) = \lim_{x\to 0^+} (x^2+1) = 0^2+1 = 1$$

Because the left-and right-hand limits are unequal, $\lim\limits_{x\to 0} f(x)$ does not exist.

Because one of the three conditions is not satisfied, we conclude that f is not continuous at 0.

Is $f(2)$ defined?

$f(2) = 2^2 + 1 = 5$

Because $f(2)$ is a real number, $f(2)$ is defined.

Does $\lim\limits_{x\to 2} f(x)$ exist?

$$\lim_{x\to 2^-} f(x) = \lim_{x\to 2^-} (x^2+1) = 2^2+1 = 5$$

$$\lim_{x\to 2^+} f(x) = \lim_{x\to 2^+} (7-x) = 7-2 = 5$$

Because the left- and right-hand limits are equal, $\lim\limits_{x\to 2} f(x) = 5$.

Does $\lim\limits_{x\to 2} f(x) = f(2)$?

$\lim\limits_{x\to 2} f(x) = 5 = f(2)$

Because the three conditions for continuity are satisfied, f is continuous at 2.

In summary, the given function is discontinuous at 0 only.

Exercise Set 11.3

1. $f(1) = 2 \cdot 1 + 5 = 7$

   f is defined at 1.

   $\lim_{x \to 1} f(x) = \lim_{x \to 1}(2x + 5) = 2 \cdot 1 + 5 = 7$

   $\lim_{x \to 1} f(x)$ exists.

   $\lim_{x \to 1} f(x) = 7 = f(1)$, therefore, f is

   continuous at 1.

3. $f(4) = 4^2 - 3 \cdot 4 + 7 = 11$

   f is defined at 4.

   $\lim_{x \to 4} f(x) = \lim_{x \to 4}(x^2 - 3x + 7) = 4^2 - 3 \cdot 4 + 7 = 11$

   $\lim_{x \to 4} f(x)$ exists.

   $\lim_{x \to 1} f(x) = f(4) = 11$, therefore, f is

   continuous at 4.

5. $f(3) = \dfrac{3^2 + 4}{3 - 2} = 13$

   f is defined at 3.

   $\lim_{x \to 3} f(x) = \lim_{x \to 3} \dfrac{x^2 + 4}{x - 2} = \dfrac{3^2 + 4}{3 - 2} = 13$

   $\lim_{x \to 3} f(x)$ exists.

   $\lim_{x \to 3} f(x) = 13 = f(3)$, therefore, f is

   continuous at 3.

7. $f(5)$ results in division by zero, so $f(5)$ is undefined and, therefore, discontinuous at 5.

9. $f(5) = \dfrac{5 - 5}{5 + 5} = 0$

   f is defined at 5.

   $\lim_{x \to 5} f(x) = \lim_{x \to 5} \dfrac{x - 5}{x + 5} = \dfrac{5 - 5}{5 + 5} = 0$

   $\lim_{x \to 5} f(x)$ exists.

   $\lim_{x \to 5} f(x) = 0 = f(5)$, therefore, f is

   continuous at 5.

11. $f(0)$ results in division by zero, so $f(0)$ is undefined and, therefore, discontinuous at 0.

13. $f(x) = \begin{cases} \dfrac{x^2 - 4}{x - 2} & \text{if } x \neq 2 \\ 5 & \text{if } x = 2 \end{cases}$

    $f(2) = 5$, therefore, f is defined at 2.

    $\lim_{x \to 2} f(x) = \lim_{x \to 2} \dfrac{x^2 - 4}{x - 2} = \lim_{x \to 2} \dfrac{(x + 2)(x - 2)}{x - 2}$

    $\qquad = \lim_{x \to 2}(x + 2)$

    $\qquad = 2 + 2$

    $\qquad = 4$

    $\lim_{x \to 2} f(x) \neq f(2)$, therefore, f is

    discontinuous at 2.

15. $f(x) = \begin{cases} x - 5 & \text{if } x \leq 0 \\ x^2 + x - 5 & \text{if } x > 0 \end{cases}$

    $f(0) = 0 - 5 = -5$

    f is defined at 0.

    $\lim_{x \to 0^-} f(x) = \lim_{x \to 0^-}(x - 5) = 0 - 5 = -5$

    $\lim_{x \to 0^+} f(x) = \lim_{x \to 0^+}(x^2 + x - 5) = 0^2 + 0 - 5 = -5$

    $\lim_{x \to 0^-} f(x) = \lim_{x \to 0^+} f(x)$, therefore,

    $\lim_{x \to 0} f(x)$ exists and is -5.

    $\lim_{x \to 0} f(x) = -5 = f(0)$, therefore, f is continuous at 0.

17. $f(x) = \begin{cases} 1 - x & \text{if } x < 1 \\ 0 & \text{if } x = 1 \\ x^2 - 1 & \text{if } x > 1 \end{cases}$

    $f(1) = 0$, therefore, f is defined at 1.

    $\lim_{x \to 1^-} f(x) = \lim_{x \to 1^-}(1 - x) = 1 - 1 = 0$

    $\lim_{x \to 1^+} f(x) = \lim_{x \to 1^+}(x^2 - 1) = 1^2 - 1 = 0$

    $\lim_{x \to 1^-} f(x) = \lim_{x \to 1^+} f(x)$, therefore,

    $\lim_{x \to 1} f(x)$ exists and is 0.

    $\lim_{x \to 1} f(x) = 0 = f(1)$, therefore, f is continuous at 1.

19. $f(x) = x^2 + 4x - 6$ is a polynomial function,

    thus, f is continuous for every number x.

21. $f(x) = \dfrac{x + 1}{(x + 1)(x - 4)}$

    f is not defined at $x = -1$ and $x = 4$, therefore, f is discontinuous at -1 and 4.

23. $f(x) = \dfrac{\sin x}{x}$

f is not defined at $x = 0$, therefore, f is discontinuous at 0.

25. $f(x) = \pi$

f is a constant function, thus, f is continuous for every number x.

27. $f(x) = \begin{cases} x-1 & \text{if } x \le 1 \\ x^2 & \text{if } x > 1 \end{cases}$

$x - 1$ and x^2 are continuous for every number x, but because $f(x)$ changes its functional form at $x = 1$, we must investigate continuity at $x = 1$.

$f(1) = 1 - 1 = 0$

f is defined at 1.

$\lim\limits_{x \to 1^-} f(x) = \lim\limits_{x \to 1^-} (x-1) = 1 - 1 = 0$

$\lim\limits_{x \to 1^+} f(x) = \lim\limits_{x \to 1^+} x^2 = 1^2 = 1$

The left- and right-hand limits are not equal, so $\lim\limits_{x \to 1} f(x)$ does not exist. Therefore, f is discontinuous at 1.

29. $f(x) = \begin{cases} \dfrac{x^2-1}{x-1} & \text{if } x \ne 1 \\ 2 & \text{if } x = 1 \end{cases}$

$\dfrac{x^2-1}{x-1}$ is continuous for every number x except at $x = 1$.

We must investigate continuity at $x = 1$.

$f(1) = 2$

f is defined at 1.

$\lim\limits_{x \to 1} f(x) = \lim\limits_{x \to 1} \dfrac{x^2-1}{x-1}$

$= \lim\limits_{x \to 1} \dfrac{(x+1)(x-1)}{x-1}$

$= \lim\limits_{x \to 1} (x+1)$

$= 1 + 1$

$= 2$

$\lim\limits_{x \to 1} f(x)$ exists.

$\lim\limits_{x \to 1} f(x) = 2 = f(1)$, therefore, f is continuous at 1.

In summary, $f(x)$ is continuous for every number x.

31. $f(x) = \begin{cases} x+6 & \text{if } x \le 0 \\ 6 & \text{if } 0 < x \le 2 \\ x^2+1 & \text{if } x > 2 \end{cases}$

$x + 6$, 6, and $x^2 + 1$ are continuous for every number x. We must investigate continuity at $x = 0$ and $x = 2$.

$f(0) = 0 + 6 = 6$

f is defined at 0.

$\lim\limits_{x \to 0^-} f(x) = \lim\limits_{x \to 0^-} (x+6) = 0 + 6 = 6$

$\lim\limits_{x \to 0^+} f(x) = \lim\limits_{x \to 0^+} 6 = 6$

$\lim\limits_{x \to 0^-} f(x) = \lim\limits_{x \to 0^+} f(x)$, therefore,

$\lim\limits_{x \to 0} f(x)$ exists and is 6.

$\lim\limits_{x \to 0} f(x) = 6 = f(0)$, therefore, f is continuous at 0.

$f(2) = 6$

f is defined at 2.

$\lim\limits_{x \to 2^-} f(x) = \lim\limits_{x \to 2^-} 6 = 6$

$\lim\limits_{x \to 2^+} f(x) = \lim\limits_{x \to 2^+} (x^2+1) = 2^2 + 1 = 5$

The left- and right-hand limits are not equal, therefore, $\lim\limits_{x \to 2} f(x)$ does not exist and $f(x)$ is discontinuous at 2.

In summary, the given function is discontinuous at 2 only.

33. $f(x) = \begin{cases} 5x & \text{if } x < 4 \\ 21 & \text{if } x = 4 \\ x^2+4 & \text{if } x > 4 \end{cases}$

$5x$ and $x^2 + 4$ are continuous for every number x. We must investigate continuity at $x = 4$.

$f(4) = 21$

f is defined at 4.

$\lim\limits_{x \to 4^-} f(x) = \lim\limits_{x \to 4^-} 5x = 5 \cdot 4 = 20$

$\lim\limits_{x \to 4^+} f(x) = \lim\limits_{x \to 4^+} (x^2+4) = 4^2 + 4 = 20$

$\lim\limits_{x \to 4^-} f(x) = \lim\limits_{x \to 4^+} f(x)$, therefore,

$\lim\limits_{x \to 4} f(x)$ exists and is 20.

$\lim\limits_{x \to 4} f(x) \ne f(4)$, therefore, f is discontinuous at 4.

35. $f(x)$ is discontinuous at π.

37. $f(x)$ is discontinuous at each integer.

39.

x	-0.1	-0.01	0.01	0.1
$f(x)$	1.9867	1.9999	1.9999	1.9867

$f(x)$ is continuous for every number x.

41.

x	$\frac{\pi}{2}-0.1$	$\frac{\pi}{2}-0.01$	$\frac{\pi}{2}+0.01$	$\frac{\pi}{2}+0.1$
$f(x)$	-0.9983	-0.9999	-0.9999	-0.9983

$f(x)$ is discontinuous at $\frac{\pi}{2}$.

43. a. $\lim\limits_{t \to t_1} p(t) = 20$ and $p(t_1) = 20$

b. Yes, p is continuous at t_1.
1. p is defined at t_1.
2. the limit exists at t_1.
3. $\lim\limits_{t \to t_1} p(t) = p(t_1)$

c. $\lim\limits_{t \to t_2} p(t) = 40$ and $p(t_2) = 10$

d. No, p is discontinuous at t_2 because $\lim\limits_{t \to t_2} p(t) \neq p(t_2)$.

e. $\lim\limits_{t \to t_3} p(t)$ does not exist because the left-hand and right-hand limits are not the same.
$p(t_3) = 70$

f. No, p is discontinuous at t_3 because the limit does not exist at t_3.

g. $\lim\limits_{t \to t_4^-} p(t) = 100$ and $p(t_4) = 100$

h. As the end of the course approached, the percentage of topics learned by the student approached, and then reached, 100%.

45. a. $\lim\limits_{x \to 4^-} f(x) = \$1.06$

b. $\lim\limits_{x \to 4^+} f(x) = \$1.29$

c. Since the left- and right-hand limits are not equal, $\lim\limits_{x \to 4} f(x)$ does not exist. The graph shows a discontinuity at $x = 4$ ounces.

d. The graph jumps at its discontinuities due to per-ounce charges.

53.

$\lim\limits_{x \to 0^+} (1+x)^{1/x} \approx 2.7183$

$\lim\limits_{x \to 0^+} (1+x)^{1/x} \approx 2.71828$

55. No, it is not possible to define $f(x) = 1/(x-9)$ at $x-9$ such that the function is continuous at 9, since $\lim\limits_{x \to 9} \dfrac{1}{x-9}$ does not exist.

The graph of the function in Exercise 54 is a line with a hole at $x = 9$. In contrast, this function approaches infinity as x approaches 9 from the right-hand side, and negative infinity as x approaches 9 from the left-hand side.

Mid-Chapter 11 Check Point

1. $\lim\limits_{x \to -1^-} f(x) = 2$

2. $\lim\limits_{x \to -1^+} f(x) = 1$

3. $\lim\limits_{x \to -1} f(x)$ does not exist.

4. $\lim\limits_{x \to 1} [f(x) + g(x)] = -2$

5. $\lim\limits_{x \to 0} [f(x) - g(x)] = -1$

6. $(f-g)(0) = f(0) - g(0) = -2 - 1 = -3$

7. $\lim\limits_{x \to 1} \sqrt{10 + f(x)} = \sqrt{10 + (-1)} = \sqrt{9} = 3$

8. $f(x)$ is discontinuous at -1 because the limit does not exist at -1.
$f(x)$ is discontinuous at 0 because $\lim\limits_{x \to 0} f(x)$ does not equal $f(0)$.

9. $\lim\limits_{x \to 0} f(x) = -1$

10. $\lim_{x \to 0} g(x) = 1$

11. $\lim_{x \to 0} \dfrac{4g(x)}{\left[f(x)\right]^2} = \dfrac{4(1)}{(-1)^2} = 4$

12. $\lim_{x \to -2} \left(x^3 - x + 5\right) = (-2)^3 - (-2) + 5 = -1$

13. $\lim_{x \to 3} \sqrt{x^2 - 3x + 4} = \sqrt{3^2 - 3(3) + 4} = \sqrt{4} = 2$

14. $\lim_{x \to 5} \dfrac{2x^2 - x + 4}{x - 1} = \dfrac{2(5)^2 - (5) + 4}{(5) - 1} = \dfrac{49}{4}$

15.
$$\begin{aligned}
\lim_{x \to 5} \frac{2x^2 - 7x - 15}{x - 5} &= \lim_{x \to 5} \frac{(2x + 3)(x - 5)}{x - 5} \\
&= \lim_{x \to 5} (2x + 3) \\
&= 2(5) + 3 \\
&= 13
\end{aligned}$$

16.
$$\begin{aligned}
\lim_{x \to 0} \frac{\sqrt{x^2 + 9} - 3}{x^2} &= \lim_{x \to 0} \left(\frac{\sqrt{x^2 + 9} - 3}{x^2} \cdot \frac{\sqrt{x^2 + 9} + 3}{\sqrt{x^2 + 9} + 3} \right) \\
&= \lim_{x \to 0} \frac{x^2}{x^2 \left(\sqrt{x^2 + 9} + 3\right)} \\
&= \lim_{x \to 0} \frac{1}{\sqrt{x^2 + 9} + 3} \\
&= \frac{1}{\sqrt{0^2 + 9} + 3} \\
&= \frac{1}{6}
\end{aligned}$$

17. The limit does not exist.
$$\begin{aligned}
\lim_{x \to 0} \frac{\dfrac{1}{x + 10} - \dfrac{1}{x}}{x} &= \lim_{x \to 0} \frac{\dfrac{x}{x(x + 10)} - \dfrac{(x + 10)}{x(x + 10)}}{x} \\
&= \lim_{x \to 0} \frac{\dfrac{x - (x + 10)}{x(x + 10)}}{x} \\
&= \lim_{x \to 0} \frac{-10}{x^2(x + 10)} \\
&= \lim_{x \to 0} \frac{-10}{x^3 + 10x^2}
\end{aligned}$$

18. a. $\lim_{x \to 4^-} f(x) = 9 - 2(4) = 1$

b. $\lim_{x \to 4^+} f(x) = \sqrt{4 - 4} = 0$

c. The limit does not exist because the left-hand and right-hand limits are not the same.

19. a.
$$\begin{aligned}
&\lim_{x \to 2^-} f(x) \\
&= \lim_{x \to 2^-} \frac{x^4 - 16}{x - 2} \\
&= \lim_{x \to 2^-} \frac{\left(x^2 + 4\right)(x + 2)(x - 2)}{x - 2} \\
&= \lim_{x \to 2^-} \left[\left(x^2 + 4\right)(x + 2)\right] \\
&= \left(2^2 + 4\right)(2 + 2) \\
&= 32
\end{aligned}$$

b.
$$\begin{aligned}
&\lim_{x \to 2^+} f(x) \\
&= \lim_{x \to 2^+} \frac{x^4 - 16}{x - 2} \\
&= \lim_{x \to 2^+} \frac{\left(x^2 + 4\right)(x + 2)(x - 2)}{x - 2} \\
&= \lim_{x \to 2^+} \left[\left(x^2 + 4\right)(x + 2)\right] \\
&= \left(2^2 + 4\right)(2 + 2) \\
&= 32
\end{aligned}$$

c. $\lim_{x \to 2} f(x) = 32$ because the left-hand and right-hand limits are both 32.

20. $f(x)$ is continuous at 3.

1. $f(x)$ is defined at 3, $f(3) = 0$.
2. $\lim_{x \to 3} f(x) = 0$
3. $\lim_{x \to 3} f(x) = f(3) = 0$

21. $f(x)$ is continuous at 0.

    1. $f(x)$ is defined at 0, $f(0) = 6$.

    2. $\lim\limits_{x \to 0} f(x)$ exists:

$$\lim_{x \to 0} \frac{(x+3)^2 - 9}{x}$$

$$= \lim_{x \to 0} \frac{x^2 + 6x + 9 - 9}{x}$$

$$= \lim_{x \to 0} \frac{x^2 + 6x}{x}$$

$$= \lim_{x \to 0} (x + 6)$$

$$= 0 + 6$$

$$= 6$$

    3. $\lim\limits_{x \to 0} f(x) = f(0) = 6$

22. Each of the three pieces are continuous. The pieces change at -1 and 5 so we must check for continuity at these two values.

Conditions of continuity at -1.

    1. $f(-1) = 2(-1) = -2$ exists.

    2. $\lim\limits_{x \to -1} f(x)$ exists:

$$\lim_{x \to -1^-} \frac{x^2 - 1}{x + 1} \quad \text{and} \quad \lim_{x \to -1^+} 2x$$

$$= \lim_{x \to -1^-} (x - 1) \qquad\qquad = 2(-1)$$

$$= -1 - 1 \qquad\qquad\qquad = -2$$

$$= -2$$

    3. $\lim\limits_{x \to -1} f(x) = f(-1) = -2$

Conditions of continuity at 5.

    1. $f(5) = 2(5) = 10$ exists.

    2. $\lim\limits_{x \to 5} f(x)$ does not exist:

$$\lim_{x \to 5^-} 2x \quad \text{but} \quad \lim_{x \to 5^+} (3x - 4)$$

$$= 2(5) \qquad\qquad = 3(5) - 4$$

$$= 10 \qquad\qquad\quad = 11$$

Thus $f(x)$ is discontinuous at 5.

Section 11.4

Check Point Exercises

1. $f(x) = x^2 - x$

    $(a, f(a)) = (4, 12)$

$$m_{\tan} = \lim_{h \to 0} \frac{f(4+h) - f(4)}{h}$$

$$= \lim_{h \to 0} \frac{(4+h)^2 - (4+h) - (4^2 - 4)}{h}$$

$$= \lim_{h \to 0} \frac{(16 + 8h + h^2 - 4 - h) - 12}{h}$$

$$= \lim_{h \to 0} \frac{h^2 + 7h}{h}$$

$$= \lim_{h \to 0} \frac{h(h + 7)}{h}$$

$$= \lim_{h \to 0} (h + 7)$$

$$= 0 + 7$$

$$= 7$$

2. $f(x) = \sqrt{x}$

    $(a, f(a)) = (1, 1)$

$$m_{\tan} = \lim_{h \to 0} \frac{f(1+h) - f(1)}{h}$$

$$= \lim_{h \to 0} \frac{\sqrt{1+h} - \sqrt{1}}{h}$$

$$= \lim_{h \to 0} \frac{\sqrt{1+h} - 1}{h} \cdot \frac{\sqrt{1+h} + 1}{\sqrt{1+h} + 1}$$

$$= \lim_{h \to 0} \frac{\left(\sqrt{1+h}\right)^2 - 1}{h\left(\sqrt{1+h} + 1\right)}$$

$$= \lim_{h \to 0} \frac{1 + h - 1}{h\left(\sqrt{1+h} + 1\right)}$$

$$= \lim_{h \to 0} \frac{1}{\sqrt{1+h} + 1}$$

$$= \frac{1}{\sqrt{1+0} + 1}$$

$$= \frac{1}{2}$$

$$y - y_1 = m(x - x_1)$$

$$y - 1 = \frac{1}{2}(x - 1)$$

$$y - 1 = \frac{1}{2}x - \frac{1}{2}$$

$$y = \frac{1}{2}x + \frac{1}{2}$$

3.   **a.** $f(x) = x^2 - 5x$

$$f'(x) = \lim_{h \to 0} \frac{f(x+h) - f(x)}{h}$$

$$= \lim_{h \to 0} \frac{(x+h)^2 - 5(x+h) - (x^2 - 5x)}{h}$$

$$= \lim_{h \to 0} \frac{x^2 + 2xh + h^2 - 5x - 5h - x^2 + 5x}{h}$$

$$= \lim_{h \to 0} \frac{h^2 + 2xh - 5h}{h}$$

$$= \lim_{h \to 0} \frac{h(h + 2x - 5)}{h}$$

$$= \lim_{h \to 0} (h + 2x - 5)$$

$$= 0 + 2x - 5$$

$$= 2x - 5$$

   b. $f'(-1) = 2(-1) - 5 = -2 - 5 = -7$

$$f'(3) = 2 \cdot 3 - 5 = 6 - 5 = 1$$

4. $f(x) = x^3$

   a. $\dfrac{f(a+h) - f(a)}{h} = \dfrac{f(4+0.1) - f(4)}{0.1}$

$$= \frac{f(4.1) - f(4)}{0.1}$$

$$= \frac{(4.1)^3 - 4^3}{0.1}$$

$$= 49.21$$

The average rate of change of the volume is 49.21 cubic inches per inch as x changes from 4 to 4.1 inches.

$$\frac{f(a+h) - f(a)}{h} = \frac{f(4+0.01) - f(4)}{0.01}$$

$$= \frac{f(4.01) - f(4)}{0.01}$$

$$= \frac{4.01^3 - 4^3}{0.01}$$

$$= 48.1201$$

The average rate of change of the volume is 48.1201 cubic inches per inch as x changes from 4 to 4.01 inches.

   b. $f'(x) = \lim_{h \to 0} \dfrac{f(x+h) - f(x)}{h}$

$$= \lim_{h \to 0} \frac{(x+h)^3 - x^3}{h}$$

$$= \lim_{h \to 0} \frac{x^3 + 3hx^2 + 3h^2 x + h^3 - x^3}{h}$$

$$= \lim_{h \to 0} \frac{3hx^2 + 3h^2 x + h^3}{h}$$

$$= \lim_{h \to 0} \frac{h(3x^2 + 3hx + h^2)}{h}$$

$$= \lim_{h \to 0} (3x^2 + 3hx + h^2)$$

$$= 3x^2 + 3 \cdot 0 \cdot x + 0^2$$

$$= 3x^2$$

$$f'(4) = 3 \cdot 4^2 = 48$$

The instantaneous rate of change of the volume with respect to x at the moment when $x = 4$ inches is 48 cubic inches per inch.

5. $s(t) = -16t^2 + 96t$

a. $s'(a) = \lim\limits_{h \to 0} \dfrac{s(a+h) - s(a)}{h} = \lim\limits_{h \to 0} \dfrac{-16(a+h)^2 + 96(a+h) - (-16a^2 + 96a)}{h}$

$\qquad = \lim\limits_{h \to 0} \dfrac{-16a^2 - 32ah - 16h^2 + 96a + 96h + 16a^2 - 96a}{h} = \lim\limits_{h \to 0} \dfrac{-16h^2 - 32ah + 96h}{h}$

$\qquad = \lim\limits_{h \to 0} (-16h - 32a + 96) = -32a + 96$

$s'(4) = -32 \cdot 4 + 96 = -32$

After 4 seconds, the ball's instantaneous velocity is –32 feet per second.

b. Set $s(t) = 0$.

$-16t^2 + 96t = 0$

$t^2 - 6t = 0$

$t(t - 6) = 0$

$t = 0 \quad t - 6 = 0$

$\qquad\qquad t = 6$

The ball hits the ground at $t = 6$ seconds.

$s'(6) = -32 \cdot 6 + 96 = -96$

The instantaneous velocity of the ball when it hits the ground is –96 feet per second.

Exercise Set 11.4

1. $f(x) = 2x + 3$ at $(1, 5)$

a.. $m_{\tan} = \lim\limits_{h \to 0} \dfrac{f(1+h) - f(1)}{h} = \lim\limits_{h \to 0} \dfrac{2(1+h) + 3 - [2 \cdot 1 + 3]}{h} = \lim\limits_{h \to 0} \dfrac{2 + 2h + 3 - 5}{h} = \lim\limits_{h \to 0} \dfrac{2h}{h} = \lim\limits_{h \to 0} 2 = 2$

b. $y - y_1 = m(x - x_1)$

$y - 5 = 2(x - 1)$

$y - 5 = 2x - 2$

$y = 2x + 3$

3. $f(x) = x^2 + 4$ at $(-1, 5)$

a. $m_{\tan} = \lim\limits_{h \to 0} \dfrac{f(-1+h) - f(-1)}{h} = \lim\limits_{h \to 0} \dfrac{(-1+h)^2 + 4 - [(-1)^2 + 4]}{h}$

$\qquad = \lim\limits_{h \to 0} \dfrac{1 - 2h + h^2 + 4 - 5}{h} = \lim\limits_{h \to 0} \dfrac{-2h + h^2}{h} = \lim\limits_{h \to 0} (h - 2) = 0 - 2 = -2$

b. $y - y_1 = m(x - x_1)$

$y - 5 = -2(x + 1)$

$y - 5 = -2x - 2$

$y = -2x + 3$

5. $f(x) = 5x^2$ at $(-2, 20)$

    a. $m_{\tan} = \lim_{h \to 0} \dfrac{f(-2+h)-f(-2)}{h} = \lim_{h \to 0} \dfrac{5(-2+h)^2 - 5(-2)^2}{h} = \lim_{h \to 0} \dfrac{5(4-4h+h^2)-5 \cdot 4}{h} = \lim_{h \to 0}(5h-20) = -20$

    b. $y - y_1 = m(x - x_1)$
           $y - 20 = -20(x + 2)$
           $y - 20 = -20x - 40$
               $y = -20x - 20$

7. $f(x) = 2x^2 - x$ at $(2, 6)$

    a. $m_{\tan} = \lim_{h \to 0} \dfrac{f(2+h)-f(2)}{h} = \lim_{h \to 0} \dfrac{2(2+h)^2 - (2+h) - [2 \cdot 2^2 - 2]}{h} = \lim_{h \to 0} \dfrac{2(4+4h+h^2) - 2 - h - 6}{h}$

               $= \lim_{h \to 0} \dfrac{8 + 8h + 2h^2 - 2 - h - 6}{h} = \lim_{h \to 0} \dfrac{7h + 2h^2}{h} = \lim_{h \to 0}(2h + 7) = 2 \cdot 0 + 7 = 7$

    b. $y - y_1 = m(x - x_1)$
            $y - 6 = 7(x - 2)$
           $y - 6 = 7x - 14$
              $y = 7x - 8$

9. $f(x) = 2x^2 + x - 3$ at $(0, -3)$

    a. $m_{\tan} = \lim_{h \to 0} \dfrac{f(0+h)-f(0)}{h} = \lim_{h \to 0} \dfrac{f(h)-f(0)}{h} = \lim_{h \to 0} \dfrac{2h^2 + h - 3 - (0 + 0 - 3)}{h}$

               $= \lim_{h \to 0} \dfrac{2h^2 + h}{h} = \lim_{h \to 0}(2h + 1) = 2 \cdot 0 + 1 = 1$

    b. $y - y_1 = m(x - x_1)$
             $y + 3 = 1(x - 0)$
             $y + 3 = x - 0$
               $y = x - 3$

11. $f(x) = \sqrt{x}$ at $(9, 3)$

    a. $m_{\tan} = \lim_{h \to 0} \dfrac{f(9+h)-f(9)}{h} = \lim_{h \to 0} \dfrac{\sqrt{9+h} - \sqrt{9}}{h} = \lim_{h \to 0} \dfrac{\sqrt{9+h} - \sqrt{9}}{h} \cdot \dfrac{\sqrt{9+h} + \sqrt{9}}{\sqrt{9+h} + \sqrt{9}}$

               $= \lim_{h \to 0} \dfrac{9 + h - 9}{h\left(\sqrt{9+h} + 3\right)} = \lim_{h \to 0} \dfrac{1}{\sqrt{9+h} + 3} = \dfrac{1}{\sqrt{9+0} + 3} = \dfrac{1}{6}$

b.
$$y - y_1 = m(x - x_1)$$
$$y - 3 = \frac{1}{6}(x - 9)$$
$$y - 3 = \frac{1}{6}x - \frac{9}{6}$$
$$y = \frac{1}{6}x + \frac{3}{2}$$

13. $f(x) = \frac{1}{x}$ at $(1, 1)$

a. $m_{\tan} = \lim_{h \to 0} \frac{f(1+h) - f(1)}{h} = \lim_{h \to 0} \frac{\frac{1}{1+h} - \frac{1}{1}}{h} = \lim_{h \to 0} \frac{\frac{1-(1+h)}{1+h}}{h} = \lim_{h \to 0} \frac{1 - 1 - h}{h(1+h)} = \lim_{h \to 0} \frac{-1}{1+h} = \frac{-1}{1+0} = -1$

b.
$$y - y_1 = m(x - x_1)$$
$$y - 1 = -1(x - 1)$$
$$y - 1 = -x + 1$$
$$y = -x + 2$$

15. $f(x) = -3x + 7; x = 1, x = 4$

a. $f'(x) = \lim_{h \to 0} \frac{f(x+h) - f(x)}{h} = \lim_{h \to 0} \frac{-3(x+h) + 7 - (-3x + 7)}{h} = \lim_{h \to 0} \frac{-3x - 3h + 7 + 3x - 7}{h}$

$= \lim_{h \to 0} \frac{-3h}{h} = \lim_{h \to 0} (-3) = -3$

b.
$$f'(1) = -3$$
$$f'(4) = -3$$

17. $f(x) = x^2 - 6; x = -1, x = 3$

a. $f'(x) = \lim_{h \to 0} \frac{f(x+h) - f(x)}{h} = \lim_{h \to 0} \frac{(x+h)^2 - 6 - (x^2 - 6)}{h} = \lim_{h \to 0} \frac{x^2 + 2xh + h^2 - 6 - x^2 + 6}{h}$

$= \lim_{h \to 0} \frac{2xh + h^2}{h} = \lim_{h \to 0} (2x + h) = 2x + 0 = 2x$

b.
$$f'(-1) = 2(-1) = -2$$
$$f'(3) = 2 \cdot 3 = 6$$

19. $f(x) = x^2 - 3x + 5; x = \frac{3}{2}, x = 2$

a. $f'(x) = \lim_{h \to 0} \frac{f(x+h) - f(x)}{h} = \lim_{h \to 0} \frac{(x+h)^2 - 3(x+h) + 5 - (x^2 - 3x + 5)}{h}$

$= \lim_{h \to 0} \frac{x^2 + 2xh + h^2 - 3x - 3h + 5 - x^2 + 3x - 5}{h} = \lim_{h \to 0} \frac{2xh - 3h + h^2}{h}$

$= \lim_{h \to 0} (2x - 3 + h) = 2x - 3 + 0 = 2x - 3$

    b. $f'\left(\dfrac{3}{2}\right) = 2 \cdot \dfrac{3}{2} - 3 = 3 - 3 = 0$

           $f'(2) = 2 \cdot 2 - 3 = 4 - 3 = 1$

21. $f(x) = x^3 + 2$; $x = -1, x = 1$

    a. $f'(x) = \lim\limits_{h \to 0} \dfrac{f(x+h) - f(x)}{h} = \lim\limits_{h \to 0} \dfrac{(x+h)^3 + 2 - (x^3 + 2)}{h} = \lim\limits_{h \to 0} \dfrac{x^3 + 3hx^2 + 3h^2 x + h^3 + 2 - x^3 - 2}{h}$

            $= \lim\limits_{h \to 0} \dfrac{3hx^2 + 3h^2 x + h^3}{h} = \lim\limits_{h \to 0}(3x^2 + 3hx + h^2) = 3x^2 + 3 \cdot 0 \cdot x + 0^2 = 3x^2$

    b. $f'(-1) = 3(-1)^2 = 3 \cdot 1 = 3$

           $f'(1) = 3 \cdot 1^2 = 3 \cdot 1 = 3$

23. $f(x) = \sqrt{x}$; $x = 1, x = 4$

    a. $f'(x) = \lim\limits_{h \to 0} \dfrac{f(x+h) - f(x)}{h} = \lim\limits_{h \to 0} \dfrac{\sqrt{x+h} - \sqrt{x}}{h} = \lim\limits_{h \to 0} \dfrac{\sqrt{x+h} - \sqrt{x}}{h} \cdot \dfrac{\sqrt{x+h} + \sqrt{x}}{\sqrt{x+h} + \sqrt{x}}$

            $= \lim\limits_{h \to 0} \dfrac{x + h - x}{h\left(\sqrt{x+h} + \sqrt{x}\right)} = \lim\limits_{h \to 0} \dfrac{1}{\sqrt{x+h} + \sqrt{x}} = \dfrac{1}{\sqrt{x+0} + \sqrt{x}} = \dfrac{1}{2\sqrt{x}}$

    b. $f'(1) = \dfrac{1}{2\sqrt{1}} = \dfrac{1}{2 \cdot 1} = \dfrac{1}{2}$

           $f'(4) = \dfrac{1}{2\sqrt{4}} = \dfrac{1}{2 \cdot 2} = \dfrac{1}{4}$

25. $f(x) = \dfrac{4}{x}$; $x = -2, x = 1$

    a. $f'(x) = \lim\limits_{h \to 0} \dfrac{f(x+h) - f(x)}{h} = \lim\limits_{h \to 0} \dfrac{\frac{4}{x+h} - \frac{4}{x}}{h} = \lim\limits_{h \to 0} \dfrac{\frac{4x - 4(x+h)}{x(x+h)}}{h} = \lim\limits_{h \to 0} \dfrac{4x - 4x - 4h}{hx(x+h)}$

            $= \lim\limits_{h \to 0} \dfrac{-4}{x(x+h)} = \dfrac{-4}{x(x+0)} = -\dfrac{4}{x^2}$

    b. $f'(-2) = -\dfrac{4}{(-2)^2} = -\dfrac{4}{4} = -1$

           $f'(1) = -\dfrac{4}{1^2} = -\dfrac{4}{1} = -4$

27. $f(x) = 3.2x^2 + 2.1x; \; x = 0, x = 4$

    a. $f'(x) = \lim\limits_{h \to 0} \dfrac{f(x+h) - f(x)}{h} = \lim\limits_{h \to 0} \dfrac{3.2(x+h)^2 + 2.1(x+h) - (3.2x^2 + 2.1x)}{h}$

            $= \lim\limits_{h \to 0} \dfrac{3.2(x^2 + 2xh + h^2) + 2.1x + 2.1h - 3.2x^2 - 2.1x}{h}$

            $= \lim\limits_{h \to 0} \dfrac{3.2x^2 + 6.4xh + 3.2h^2 + 2.1x + 2.1h - 3.2x^2 - 2.1x}{h} = \lim\limits_{h \to 0} \dfrac{6.4xh + 3.2h^2 + 2.1h}{h}$

            $= \lim\limits_{h \to 0} (6.4x + 3.2h + 2.1) = 6.4x + 3.2 \cdot 0 + 2.1 = 6.4x + 2.1$

    b. $f'(0) = 6.4 \cdot 0 + 2.1 = 0 + 2.1 = 2.1$

        $f'(4) = 6.4 \cdot 4 + 2.1 = 25.6 + 2.1 = 27.7$

29. **a. & c.**

    b. $f(3) = 1$, so the tangent line passes through $(3, 1)$.

        $m_{\tan} = \lim\limits_{h \to 0} \dfrac{f(3+h) - f(3)}{h} = \lim\limits_{h \to 0} (h + 2) = 2$

        $y - y_1 = m(x - x_1)$

         $y - 1 = 2(x - 3)$

         $y - 1 = 2x - 6$

           $y = 2x - 5$

31. **a. & c.**

    b. $f(0) = -1$, so the tangent line passes through $(0, -1)$.

        $m_{\tan} = \lim\limits_{h \to 0} \dfrac{f(0+h) - f(0)}{h} = \lim\limits_{h \to 0} \dfrac{\sqrt{h+1} - 1}{h} = \lim\limits_{h \to 0} \dfrac{1}{\sqrt{h+1} + 1} = \dfrac{1}{2}$

        $y - y_1 = m(x - x_1)$

      $y - (-1) = \dfrac{1}{2}\left[x - 0\right]$

         $y + 1 = \dfrac{1}{2}x$

           $y = \dfrac{1}{2}x - 1$

33. a. & c.

b. $f(-1) = 1$, so the tangent line passes through $(-1,1)$.

$$m_{\tan} = \lim_{h \to 0} \frac{f(-1+h) - f(-1)}{h} = \lim_{h \to 0}\left(h^2 - 3h + 3\right) = 3$$

$$y - y_1 = m(x - x_1)$$
$$y - 1 = 3\left[x - (-1)\right]$$
$$y - 1 = 3x + 3$$
$$y = 3x + 4$$

35. a. & c. $x = -3$

b. $f(-2) = -1$, so the tangent line passes through $(-2,-1)$.

$$m_{\tan} = \lim_{h \to 0} \frac{f(-2+h) - f(-2)}{h} = \lim_{h \to 0} \frac{1}{h+1} = 1$$

$$y - y_1 = m(x - x_1)$$
$$y - (-1) = 1(x - (-2))$$
$$y + 1 = x + 2$$
$$y = x + 1$$

37. $f(x) = x^2$

a.
$$\frac{f(a+h) - f(a)}{h} = \frac{f(6+0.1) - f(6)}{0.1}$$
$$= \frac{f(6.1) - f(6)}{0.1}$$
$$= \frac{6.1^2 - 6^2}{0.1}$$
$$= 12.1$$

The average rate of change of the area is 12.1 square inches per inch as x changes from 6 to 6.1 inches.

$$\frac{f(a+h)-f(a)}{h} = \frac{f(6+0.01)-f(6)}{0.01}$$

$$= \frac{f(6.01)-f(6)}{0.01}$$

$$= \frac{6.01^2 - 6^2}{0.01}$$

$$= 12.01$$

The average rate of change of the area is 12.01 square inches per inch as x changes from 6 to 6.01 inches.

b. $$f'(x) = \lim_{h \to 0} \frac{f(x+h)-f(x)}{h}$$

$$= \lim_{h \to 0} \frac{(x+h)^2 - x^2}{h}$$

$$= \lim_{h \to 0} \frac{x^2 + 2xh + h^2 - x^2}{h}$$

$$= \lim_{h \to 0} \frac{2xh + h^2}{h}$$

$$= \lim_{h \to 0} (2x + h)$$

$$= 2x + 0$$

$$= 2x$$

$$f'(6) = 2 \cdot 6 = 12$$

The instantaneous rate of change of the area with respect to x at the moment when $x = 6$ inches is 12 square inches per inch.

39. $f(x) = \pi x^2$

a. $$\frac{f(a+h)-f(a)}{h} = \frac{f(2+0.1)-f(2)}{0.1}$$

$$= \frac{f(2.1)-f(2)}{0.1}$$

$$= \frac{\pi(2.1)^2 - \pi(2)^2}{0.1}$$

$$= 4.1\pi$$

The average rate of change of the area is 4.1π square inches per inch as x changes from 2 to 2.1 inches.

$$\frac{f(a+h)-f(a)}{h} = \frac{f(2+0.01)-f(2)}{0.01}$$

$$= \frac{f(2.01)-f(2)}{0.01}$$

$$= \frac{\pi(2.01)^2 - \pi(2)^2}{0.01}$$

$$= 4.01\pi$$

The average rate of change of the area is 4.01π square inches per inch as x changes from 2 to 2.01 inches.

b. $f'(x) = \lim_{h \to 0} \dfrac{f(x+h) - f(x)}{h}$

$= \lim_{h \to 0} \dfrac{\pi(x+h)^2 - \pi x^2}{h}$

$= \lim_{h \to 0} \dfrac{\pi(x^2 + 2xh + h^2) - \pi x^2}{h}$

$= \lim_{h \to 0} \dfrac{\pi x^2 + 2\pi xh + \pi h^2 + \pi x^2}{h}$

$= \lim_{h \to 0} \dfrac{2\pi xh + \pi h^2}{h}$

$= \lim_{h \to 0} (2\pi x + \pi h)$

$= 2\pi x + \pi \cdot 0$

$= 2\pi x$

$f'(2) = 2\pi \cdot 2 = 4\pi$

The instantaneous rate of change of the area with respect to x at the moment when $x = 2$ inches is 4π square inches per inch.

41. $f(x) = 4\pi x^2$

$f'(x) = \lim_{h \to 0} \dfrac{f(x+h) - f(x)}{h}$

$= \lim_{h \to 0} \dfrac{4\pi(x+h)^2 - 4\pi x^2}{h}$

$= \lim_{h \to 0} \dfrac{4\pi(x^2 + 2xh + h^2) - 4\pi x^2}{h}$

$= \lim_{h \to 0} \dfrac{4\pi(x^2 + 2hx + h^2 - x^2)}{h}$

$= \lim_{h \to 0} \dfrac{4\pi(2hx + h^2)}{h}$

$= \lim_{h \to 0} 4\pi(2x + h)$

$= 4\pi(2x + 0)$

$= 8\pi x$

$f'(6) = 8\pi \cdot 6 = 48\pi$

The instantaneous rate of change of the surface area with respect to x at the moment $x = 6$ inches is 48π square inches per inch.

43. $s(t) = -16t^2 + 64t$

    a.
$$s'(t) = \lim_{h \to 0} \frac{s(t+h) - s(t)}{h}$$

$$= \lim_{h \to 0} \frac{-16(t+h)^2 + 64(t+h) - (-16t^2 + 64t)}{h}$$

$$= \lim_{h \to 0} \frac{-16(t^2 + 2ht + h^2) + 64t + 64b + 16t^2 - 64t}{h}$$

$$= \lim_{h \to 0} \frac{-16t^2 - 32ht - 16h^2 + 64t + 64h + 16t^2 - 64t}{h}$$

$$= \lim_{h \to 0} \frac{-32ht - 16h^2 + 64h}{h}$$

$$= \lim_{h \to 0} (-32t - 16h + 64)$$

$$= -32t - 16 \cdot 0 + 64$$

$$= -32t + 64$$

$$s'(1) = -32(1) + 64 = -32 + 64 = 32$$

The instantaneous velocity of the debris at 1 second is 32 feet per second.

$$s'(3) = -32(3) + 64 = -96 + 64 = -32$$

The instantaneous velocity of the debris at 3 seconds is –32 feet per second.

    b. Set $s(t) = 0$.

$$-16t^2 + 64t = 0$$

$$t^2 - 4t = 0$$

$$t(t-4) = 0$$

$$t = 0 \quad t - 4 = 0$$

$$t = 4$$

$$s'(4) = -32(4) + 64 = -128 + 64 = -64$$

The instantaneous velocity of the debris just before it hits the ground is –64 feet per second.

45. $s(t) = -16t^2 + 96t + 4$

    a.
$$s'(t) = \lim_{h \to 0} \frac{s(t+h) - s(t)}{h}$$

$$= \lim_{h \to 0} \frac{-16(t+h)^2 + 96(t+h) + 4 - (-16t^2 + 96t + 4)}{h}$$

$$= \lim_{h \to 0} \frac{-16(t^2 + 2ht + h^2) + 96t + 96h + 4 + 16t^2 - 96t - 4}{h}$$

$$= \lim_{h \to 0} \frac{-16t^2 - 32ht - 16h^2 + 96t + 96h + 4 + 16t^2 - 96t - 4}{h}$$

$$= \lim_{h \to 0} \frac{-32ht - 16h^2 + 96h}{h}$$

$$= \lim_{h \to 0} (-32t - 16h + 96)$$

$$= -32t - 16 \cdot 0 + 96$$

$$= -32t + 96$$

$s'(2) = -32(2) + 96 = -64 + 96 = 32$

The instantaneous velocity of the ball at 2 seconds is 32 feet per second.

$s'(4) = -32(4) + 96 = -128 + 96 = -32$

The instantaneous velocity of the ball at 4 seconds is -32 feet per second.

b. Set $s'(t) = 0$.

$-32t + 96 = 0$

$32t = 96$

$t = 3$

The ball reaches its maximum height 3 seconds after it was hit.

$s(3) = -16(3)^2 + 96(3) + 4 = -144 + 288 + 4 = 148$

The maximum height obtained by the ball is 148 feet.

47. a. $f(2003 - 1996) = f(7) = 0.1(7) + 0.2 = 0.9$. The piecewise function models the data very well in 2003.

b. $f'(x) = \lim_{h \to 0} \dfrac{f(x+h) - f(x)}{h} = \lim_{h \to 0} \dfrac{\left[0.1(x+h) + 0.2\right] - \left[0.1x + 0.2\right]}{h}$

$= \lim_{h \to 0} \dfrac{0.1x + 0.1h + 0.2 - 0.1x - 0.2}{h} = \lim_{h \to 0} \dfrac{0.1h}{h} = \lim_{h \to 0} 0.1 = 0.1$

c. $f'(2003 - 1996) = f'(7) = 0.1$ million audits per year

65. $f(x) = \dfrac{x}{x - 3}$

dy/dx=-.3333334

$f'(6) \approx -0.33$

67. $f(x) = e^x \sin x$

dy/dx=3.6439141

$f'(2) \approx 3.64$

69. The slope of original graph is a negative constant. The derivative is represented by graph e.

71. The slope of original graph is a constantly increasing. The derivative is represented by graph d.

73. The slope of original graph is increasing then decreasing. The derivative is represented by graph b.

75.

$$A(r) = \pi r^2$$

$$A'(r) = \lim_{h \to 0} \frac{\pi(r+h)^2 - \pi r^2}{h}$$

$$= \lim_{h \to o} \frac{\pi r^2 + 2\pi rh + \pi h^2 - \pi r^2}{h}$$

$$= \lim_{h \to 0} \frac{2\pi rh + \pi h^2}{h}$$

$$= \lim_{h \to 0} 2\pi r + \pi h$$

$$= 2\pi r$$

$2\pi r$ is the diameter of the circle.

Chapter 11 Review Exercises

1. $f(x) = \dfrac{x^3 - 1}{x - 1}$

x	0.99	0.999	0.9999 $\to \leftarrow$ 1.0001	1.001	1.01
$f(x)$	2.9701	2.9970	2.9997 $\to \leftarrow$ 3.0003	3.0030	3.0301

$\lim\limits_{x \to 1} f(x) = 3$

2. $f(x) = \dfrac{\sqrt{x+1} - 1}{x}$

x	−0.01	−0.001	−0.0001 $\to \leftarrow$ 0.0001	0.001	0.01
$f(x)$	0.50126	0.50013	0.50001 $\to \leftarrow$ 0.49999	0.49988	0.49876

$\lim\limits_{x \to 0} f(x) = 0.5$

3. $f(x) = \dfrac{\sin 2x}{x}$

x	−0.1	−0.01	−0.001 $\to \leftarrow$ 0.001	0.01	0.1
$f(x)$	1.9867	1.9999	2.0000 $\to \leftarrow$ 2.0000	1.9999	1.9867

$\lim\limits_{x \to 0} f(x) = 2$

4.   The graph shows that as x approaches −4, $f(x)$ approaches 0. Thus, $\lim\limits_{x \to -4} f(x) = 0$.

5.   The graph shows that as x approaches −1, $f(x)$ approaches 1. Thus, $\lim\limits_{x \to -1} f(x) = 1$.

6.   The graph shows that as x approaches 3, $f(x)$ approaches 3. Thus, $\lim\limits_{x \to 3} f(x) = 3$.

7.   The graph of $f(x)$ at $x = -4$ is the point with coordinates (−4, 2). Thus, $f(-4) = 2$.

8.   The graph of $f(x)$ at $x = 3$ is the point with coordinates (3, 3). Thus, $f(3) = 3$.

9. As x approaches –6 from the right-hand side $f(x)$ approaches 3, therefore, $\lim\limits_{x\to-6^+} f(x) = 3$.

10. As x approaches –4 from the left-hand side $f(x)$ approaches 5, therefore, $\lim\limits_{x\to-4^-} f(x) = 5$.

11. As x approaches –4 from the right-hand side $f(x)$ approaches 3, therefore, $\lim\limits_{x\to-4^+} f(x) = -3$.

12. $\lim\limits_{x\to-4^-} f(x) \neq \lim\limits_{x\to-4^+} f(x)$, therefore,
    $\lim\limits_{x\to-4} f(x)$ does not exist.

13. The graph of $f(x)$ at $x = -4$ is the point with coordinates (–4, 1). Thus, $f(-4) = 1$.

14. As x approaches –1 from the left-hand side $f(x)$ approaches 3, therefore, $\lim\limits_{x\to-1^+} f(x) = 3$.

15. As x approaches –1 from the left-hand side $f(x)$ approaches –3, therefore, $\lim\limits_{x\to-1^-} f(x) = -3$.

16. $\lim\limits_{x\to-1^-} f(x) \neq \lim\limits_{x\to-1^+} f(x)$, therefore,
    $\lim\limits_{x\to-1} f(x)$ does not exist.

17. The graph of $f(x)$ at $x = -1$ is the point with coordinates (–1, 3). Thus, $f(-1) = 3$.

18. The graph has an open dot corresponding to $x = 2$, therefore, $f(2)$ does not exist.

19. As x approaches 2 from the left-hand side $f(x)$ approaches 5, therefore, $\lim\limits_{x\to2^-} f(x) = 5$.

20. As x approaches 2 from the right-hand side $f(x)$ approaches 5, therefore, $\lim\limits_{x\to2^+} f(x) = 5$.

21. $\lim\limits_{x\to2^-} f(x) = \lim\limits_{x\to2^+} f(x)$, therefore, $\lim\limits_{x\to2} f(x)$
    exists, and is 5.

22. As x gets closer to 5 the values of $f(x)$ get closer to 0. We conclude that $\lim\limits_{x\to5} f(x) = 0$.

23. The graph of $f(x)$ at $x = 5$ is the point with coordinates (5, 0). Thus, $f(5) = 0$.

24. $f(x) = \dfrac{x^2 - 9}{x - 3}$

    Graph by first dividing out the factor $x - 3$. Then graph the equivalent function, $f(x) = x + 3$ where $x \neq 3$. Use the y-intercept 3, and the slope, 1. Because $x = 3$ is not included, show an open dot on the line corresponding to $x = 3$.

    As x gets closer to 3, the values of $f(x)$ get closer to 6. We conclude that $\lim\limits_{x\to3} f(x) = 6$.

25. $f(x) = \sin x$
    Graph using the period $= 2\pi$, amplitude $= 1$, and no phase shift. Use the key points, (0, 0), $\left(\dfrac{\pi}{2}, 1\right)$, ($\pi$, 0), $\left(\dfrac{3\pi}{2}, -1\right)$, and ($2\pi$, 0).

    As x gets closer to $\dfrac{3\pi}{2}$, the values of $f(x)$ get closer to –1. We conclude that $\lim\limits_{x\to\frac{3\pi}{2}} f(x) = -1$.

26. $f(x) = \begin{cases} 1 - x \text{ if } x < 0 \\ \cos x \text{ if } x \geq 0 \end{cases}$

Graph $f(x) = 1 - x$ on the left side of $x = 0$ by using the y-intercept, 1, and the slope, -1. Graph $(x) = \cos x$ on the right side of $x = 0$ by using the key points $(0, 1)$, $\left(\dfrac{\pi}{2}, 0\right)$, $(\pi, -1)$, $\left(\dfrac{3\pi}{2}, 0\right)$, and $(2\pi, 1)$.

As x gets closer to 0, the values of $f(x)$ get closer to 1. We conclude that $\lim\limits_{x \to 0} f(x) = 1$.

27. $\lim\limits_{x \to 4}(2x^2 - 5x + 3) = 2(4)^2 - 5(4) + 3 = 15$

28. $\lim\limits_{x \to -1}(-2x^3 - x + 5) = -2(-1)^3 - (-1) + 5 = 8$

29. $\lim\limits_{x \to -3}(x^2 + 1)^3 = \left[\lim\limits_{x \to -3}(x^2 + 1)\right]^3$

$= \left[(-3)^2 + 1\right]^3$

$= 10^3$

$= 1000$

30. $\lim\limits_{x \to 4}\sqrt{x^2 + 9} = \sqrt{\lim\limits_{x \to 4}(x^2 + 9)}$

$= \sqrt{4^2 + 9}$

$= \sqrt{25}$

$= 5$

31.

$\lim\limits_{x \to 5}\dfrac{11x - 3}{x^2 + 1} = \dfrac{\lim\limits_{x \to 5}(11x - 3)}{\lim\limits_{x \to 5}(x^2 + 1)}$

$= \dfrac{11(5) - 3}{5^2 + 1}$

$= \dfrac{52}{26}$

$= 2$

32. $\lim\limits_{x \to -4}\dfrac{x^2 - 16}{x + 4} = \lim\limits_{x \to -4}\dfrac{(x + 4)(x - 4)}{x + 4}$

$= \lim\limits_{x \to -4}(x - 4)$

$= -4 - 4$

$= -8$

33. $\lim\limits_{x \to 7}\dfrac{5x - 35}{x - 7} = \lim\limits_{x \to 7}\dfrac{5(x - 7)}{x - 7}$

$= \lim\limits_{x \to 7} 5$

$= 5$

34. $\lim\limits_{x \to 0}\dfrac{\sqrt{x + 100} - 10}{x}$

$= \lim\limits_{x \to 0}\dfrac{\sqrt{x + 100} - 10}{x} \cdot \dfrac{\sqrt{x + 100} + 10}{\sqrt{x + 100} + 10}$

$= \lim\limits_{x \to 0}\dfrac{x + 100 - 100}{x\left(\sqrt{x + 100} + 10\right)}$

$= \lim\limits_{x \to 0}\dfrac{1}{\sqrt{x + 100} + 10}$

$= \dfrac{1}{\sqrt{0 + 100} + 10}$

$= \dfrac{1}{20}$

35. $\lim\limits_{x \to -1}\dfrac{x^2 - 1}{x^2 + x} = \lim\limits_{x \to -1}\dfrac{(x + 1)(x - 1)}{x(x + 1)}$

$= \lim\limits_{x \to -1}\dfrac{x - 1}{x}$

$= \dfrac{-1 - 1}{-1}$

$= 2$

36. $\lim\limits_{x \to 100}\dfrac{\sqrt{x} - 10}{x - 100} = \lim\limits_{x \to 100}\dfrac{\sqrt{x} - 10}{x - 100} \cdot \dfrac{\sqrt{x} + 10}{\sqrt{x} + 10}$

$= \lim\limits_{x \to 100}\dfrac{x - 100}{(x - 100)\left(\sqrt{x} + 10\right)}$

$= \lim\limits_{x \to 100}\dfrac{1}{\sqrt{x} + 10}$

$= \dfrac{1}{\sqrt{100} + 10}$

$= \dfrac{1}{20}$

37.
$$\lim_{x\to0}\frac{\frac{1}{x+5}-\frac{1}{5}}{x}=\lim_{x\to0}\frac{\frac{5-(x+5)}{5(x+5)}}{x}$$
$$=\lim_{x\to0}\frac{5-x-5}{5x(x+5)}$$
$$=\lim_{x\to0}\frac{-x}{5x(x+5)}$$
$$=\lim_{x\to0}-\frac{1}{5(x+5)}$$
$$=-\frac{1}{5(0+5)}$$
$$=-\frac{1}{25}$$

38. $f(x)=\begin{cases}x^2+1 \text{ if } x<2\\ 3x+1 \text{ if } x\geq2\end{cases}$

   a. $\displaystyle\lim_{x\to2^-}f(x)=\lim_{x\to2^-}(x^2+1)=2^2+1=5$

   b. $\displaystyle\lim_{x\to2^+}f(x)=\lim_{x\to2^+}(3x+1)=3(2)+1=7$

   c. $\displaystyle\lim_{x\to2^-}f(x)\neq\lim_{x\to2^+}f(x)$, therefore,
      $\displaystyle\lim_{x\to2}f(x)$ does not exist.

39. $f(x)=\begin{cases}\sqrt[3]{x^2+7} \text{ if } x<1\\ 4x \qquad\text{ if } x\geq1\end{cases}$

   a. $\displaystyle\lim_{x\to1^-}f(x)=\lim_{x\to1^-}\sqrt[3]{x^2+7}$
                $=\sqrt[3]{1^2+7}$
                $=\sqrt[3]{8}$
                $=2$

   b. $\displaystyle\lim_{x\to1^+}f(x)=\lim_{x\to1^+}4x=4\cdot1=4$

   c. $\displaystyle\lim_{x\to1^-}f(x)\neq\lim_{x\to1^+}f(x)$, therefore,
      $\displaystyle\lim_{x\to1}f(x)$ does not exist.

40. $f(x)=\begin{cases}\frac{x^2-25}{x+5} \text{ if } x\neq-5\\ 13 \qquad\text{ if } x=-5\end{cases}$

   a. $\displaystyle\lim_{x\to-5^-}f(x)=\lim_{x\to-5^-}\frac{x^2-25}{x+5}$
$$=\lim_{x\to-5^-}\frac{(x+5)(x-5)}{x+5}$$
$$=\lim_{x\to-5^-}(x-5)$$
$$=-5-5$$
$$=-10$$

   b.
$$\lim_{x\to-5^+}f(x)=\lim_{x\to-5^+}\frac{x^2-25}{x+5}$$
$$=\lim_{x\to-5^+}\frac{(x+5)(x-5)}{x+5}$$
$$=\lim_{x\to-5^+}(x-5)$$
$$=-5-5$$
$$=-10$$

   c. $\displaystyle\lim_{x\to-5^-}f(x)=\lim_{x\to-5^+}f(x)$, therefore,
      $\displaystyle\lim_{x\to-5}f(x)$ exists, and is -10.

41. $f(x)=3x^2-2x+1$
$$f(4)=3(4)^2-2(4)+1=41$$
$$\lim_{x\to4}(3x^2-2x+1)=3\cdot4^2-2\cdot4+1=41$$
$$\lim_{x\to4}f(x)=f(4), \text{ therefore, } f \text{ is continuous at 4.}$$

42. $f(x)=\dfrac{x^2-9}{x+3}$
$f(x)$ is undefined at $x=-3$, therefore,
f is discontinuous at -3.

43. $f(x) = \begin{cases} \frac{x^2+5x}{x^2-5x} & \text{if } x \neq 0 \\ -2 & \text{if } x = 0 \end{cases}$

$f(0) = -2$

f is defined at 0.

$\displaystyle \lim_{x \to 0} f(x) = \lim_{x \to 0} \frac{x^2+5x}{x^2-5x}$

$\displaystyle = \lim_{x \to 0} \frac{x(x+5)}{x(x-5)}$

$\displaystyle = \lim_{x \to 0} \frac{x+5}{x-5}$

$\displaystyle = \frac{0+5}{0-5}$

$= -1$

$\displaystyle \lim_{x \to 0} f(x) = -1 \neq f(0)$, therefore, f is

discontinuous at 0.

44. $f(x) = \begin{cases} \frac{x^2+x}{x^2-3x-4} & \text{if } x \neq -1 \\ \frac{1}{5} & \text{if } x = -1 \end{cases}$

$f(-1) = \frac{1}{5}$

f is defined at -1.

$\displaystyle \lim_{x \to -1} f(x) = \lim_{x \to -1} \frac{x^2+x}{x^2-3x-4}$

$\displaystyle = \lim_{x \to -1} \frac{x(x+1)}{(x+1)(x-4)}$

$\displaystyle = \lim_{x \to -1} \frac{x}{x-4}$

$\displaystyle = \frac{-1}{-1-4}$

$\displaystyle = \frac{1}{5}$

$\displaystyle \lim_{x \to -1} f(x) = \frac{1}{5} = f(-1)$, therefore, f is

continuous at -1.

45. $f(x) = \begin{cases} 3x & \text{if } x < 2 \\ 5 & \text{if } x = 2 \\ x+4 & \text{if } x > 2 \end{cases}$

$f(2) = 5$

f is defined at 2.

$\displaystyle \lim_{x \to 2^-} f(x) = \lim_{x \to 2^-} 3x = 3 \cdot 2 = 6$

$\displaystyle \lim_{x \to 2^+} f(x) = \lim_{x \to 2^+} (x+4) = 2+4 = 6$

$\displaystyle \lim_{x \to 2^-} f(x) = \lim_{x \to 2^+} f(x)$, therefore, $\displaystyle \lim_{x \to 2} f(x)$

exists and is 6.

$\displaystyle \lim_{x \to 2} f(x) \neq f(2)$, therefore, f is discontinuous at 2.

46. $f(x) = x^3 + 5x^2 - 1$ is a polynomial function and, therefore, continuous for every number x.

47. $f(x) = \dfrac{x-1}{(x-1)(x+3)}$ is undefined at $x = 1$ and

$x = -3$. So, f is discontinuous at 1 and -3.

48. $f(x) = \begin{cases} -1 & \text{if } x < 0 \\ 1 & \text{if } x \geq 0 \end{cases}$

-1 and 1 are continuous for every number x. We must investigate continuity at $x = 0$.

$f(0) = 1$

f is defined at 0.

$\displaystyle \lim_{x \to 0^-} f(x) = \lim_{x \to 0^-} (-1) = -1$

$\displaystyle \lim_{x \to 0^+} f(x) = \lim_{x \to 0^+} 1 = 1$

The left-and right-hand limits are not equal, so $\displaystyle \lim_{x \to 0} f(x)$ does not exist. Therefore, f is

discontinuous at 0.

49. $f(x) = \begin{cases} 4x & \text{if } x < 5 \\ x^2-5 & \text{if } x \geq 5 \end{cases}$

f is continuous for every number x except possibly where f changes its functional form at $x = 5$. We must investigate continuity at $x = 5$.

$f(5) = 5^2 - 5 = 20$

f is defined at 5.

$\displaystyle \lim_{x \to 5^-} f(x) = \lim_{x \to 5^-} 4x = 4 \cdot 5 = 20$

$\displaystyle \lim_{x \to 5^+} f(x) = \lim_{x \to 5^+} (x^2-5) = 5^2 - 5 = 20$

$\displaystyle \lim_{x \to 5^-} f(x) = \lim_{x \to 5^+} f(x)$, therefore, $\displaystyle \lim_{x \to 5} f(x)$

exists and is 20.

$\displaystyle \lim_{x \to 5} f(x) = f(5)$, therefore, f is continuous for

every number x.

50. $f(x) = \begin{cases} \frac{x^2-4}{x+2} & \text{if } x \neq -2 \\ 4 & \text{if } x = -2 \end{cases}$

f is continuous for every number x except possibly at $x = -2$. We must investigate continuity at $x = -2$.

$f(-2) = 4$

f is defined at -2.

$\lim\limits_{x \to -2} f(x) = \lim\limits_{x \to -2} \frac{x^2-4}{x+2} = \lim\limits_{x \to -2} \frac{(x+2)(x-2)}{x+2} = \lim\limits_{x \to -2} (x-2) = -2-2 = -4$

$\lim\limits_{x \to -2} f(x) = -4 \neq f(-2)$, therefore, f is discontinuous at -2.

51. $f(x) = \begin{cases} \frac{x^2-121}{x-11} & \text{if } x \neq 11 \\ 20 & \text{if } x = 11 \end{cases}$

f is continuous for every number x except possibly at $x = 11$. We must investigate continuity at $x = 11$.

$f(11) = 20$

f is defined at 11.

$\lim\limits_{x \to 11} f(x) = \lim\limits_{x \to 11} \frac{x^2-121}{x-11} = \lim\limits_{x \to 11} \frac{(x+11)(x-11)}{x-11} = \lim\limits_{x \to 11} (x+11) = 11+11 = 22$

$\lim\limits_{x \to 11} f(x) = 22 \neq f(11)$, therefore, f is discontinuous at 11.

52. $f(x) = 2x^2 + 5x$ at $(1, 7)$

a. $m_{\tan} = \lim\limits_{h \to 0} \frac{f(a+h) - f(a)}{h} = \lim\limits_{h \to 0} \frac{f(1+h) - f(1)}{h} = \lim\limits_{h \to 0} \frac{2(1+h)^2 + 5(1+h) - [2(1)^2 + 5(1)]}{h}$

$= \lim\limits_{h \to 0} \frac{2 + 4h + 2h^2 + 5 + 5h - 2 - 5}{h} = \lim\limits_{h \to 0} \frac{9h + 2h^2}{h} = \lim\limits_{h \to 0} (9 + 2h) = 9 + 2 \cdot 0 = 9$

b. $y - y_1 = m(x - x_1)$

$y - 7 = 9(x - 1)$

$y - 7 = 9x - 9$

$y = 9x - 2$

53. $f(x) = x^2 - 7x - 4$ at $(-1, 4)$

a. $m_{\tan} = \lim\limits_{h \to 0} \frac{f(a+h) - f(a)}{h} = \lim\limits_{h \to 0} \frac{f(-1+h) - f(-1)}{h} = \lim\limits_{h \to 0} \frac{(-1+h)^2 - 7(-1+h) - 4 - \left[(-1)^2 - 7(-1) - 4\right]}{h}$

$= \lim\limits_{h \to 0} \frac{1 - 2h + h^2 + 7 - 7h - 4 - 1 - 7 + 4}{h} = \lim\limits_{h \to 0} \frac{-9h + h^2}{h} = \lim\limits_{h \to 0} (-9 + h) = -9 + 0 = -9$

b. $y - y_1 = m(x - x_1)$

$y - 4 = -9(x + 1)$

$y - 4 = -9x - 9$

$y = -9x - 5$

54. $f(x) = 3x^2 + 12x - 1;\ x = -2, x = 1$

    a. $f'(x) = \lim_{h \to 0} \dfrac{f(x+h) - f(x)}{h} = \lim_{h \to 0} \dfrac{3(x+h)^2 + 12(x+h) - 1 - (3x^2 + 12x - 1)}{h}$

            $= \lim_{h \to 0} \dfrac{3x^2 + 6hx + 3h^2 + 12x + 12h - 1 - 3x^2 - 12x + 1}{h} = \lim_{h \to 0} \dfrac{6hx + 3h^2 + 12h}{h}$

            $= \lim_{h \to 0}(6x + 3h + 12) = 6x + 3 \cdot 0 + 12 = 6x + 12$

    b. $f'(-2) = 6(-2) + 12 = 0$

        $f'(1) = 6(1) + 12 = 18$

55. $f(x) = 2x^3 - x;\ x = -1, x = 1$

    a. $f'(x) = \lim_{h \to 0} \dfrac{f(x+h) - f(x)}{h} = \lim_{h \to 0} \dfrac{2(x+h)^3 - (x+h) - (2x^3 - x)}{h}$

            $= \lim_{h \to 0} \dfrac{2x^3 + 6hx^2 + 6h^2x + 2h^3 - x - h - 2x^3 + x}{h} = \lim_{h \to 0} \dfrac{6hx^2 + 6h^2x + 2h^3 - h}{h}$

            $= \lim_{h \to 0}(6x^2 + 6hx + 2h^2 - 1) = 6x^2 + 6 \cdot 0 \cdot x + 2 \cdot 0^2 - 1 = 6x^2 - 1$

    b. $f'(-1) = 6(-1)^2 - 1 = 5$

        $f'(1) = 6(1)^2 - 1 = 5$

56. $f(x) = \dfrac{1}{x};\ x = -2, x = 2$

    a. $f'(x) = \lim_{h \to 0} \dfrac{f(x+h) - f(x)}{h} = \lim_{h \to 0} \dfrac{\frac{1}{x+h} - \frac{1}{x}}{h} = \lim_{h \to 0} \dfrac{\frac{x-(x+h)}{x(x+h)}}{h} = \lim_{h \to 0} \dfrac{x - x - h}{xh(x+h)} = \lim_{h \to 0} \dfrac{-1}{x(x+h)}$

        $= \dfrac{-1}{x(x+0)} = -\dfrac{1}{x^2}$

    b. $f'(-2) = -\dfrac{1}{(-2)^2} = -\dfrac{1}{4}$

        $f'(2) = -\dfrac{1}{2^2} = -\dfrac{1}{4}$

57. $f(x) = \sqrt{x};\ x = 36, x = 81$

    a. $f'(x) = \lim_{h \to 0} \dfrac{f(x+h) - f(x)}{h} = \lim_{h \to 0} \dfrac{\sqrt{x+h} - \sqrt{x}}{h} = \lim_{h \to 0} \dfrac{\sqrt{x+h} - \sqrt{x}}{h} \cdot \dfrac{\sqrt{x+h} + \sqrt{x}}{\sqrt{x+h} + \sqrt{x}}$

        $= \lim_{h \to 0} \dfrac{x + h - x}{h(\sqrt{x+h} + \sqrt{x})} = \lim_{h \to 0} \dfrac{1}{\sqrt{x+h} + \sqrt{x}} = \dfrac{1}{\sqrt{x+0} + \sqrt{x}} = \dfrac{1}{2\sqrt{x}}$

    b. $f'(36) = \dfrac{1}{2\sqrt{36}} = \dfrac{1}{12}$

        $f'(81) = \dfrac{1}{2\sqrt{81}} = \dfrac{1}{18}$

58. $f(x) = 5x^2$

a. $\dfrac{f(a+h)-f(a)}{h} = \dfrac{f(2+0.1)-f(2)}{0.1} = \dfrac{f(2.1)-f(2)}{0.1} = \dfrac{5(2.1)^2-5(2)^2}{0.1} = 20.5$

The average rate of change of the volume with respect to x as x changes from 2 to 2.1 inches is 20.5 cubic inches per inch.

$\dfrac{f(a+h)-f(a)}{h} = \dfrac{f(2+0.01)-f(2)}{0.01} = \dfrac{f(2.01)-f(2)}{0.01} = \dfrac{5(2.01)^2-5(2)^2}{0.01} = 20.05$

The average rate of change of the volume with respect to x as x changes from 2 to 2.01 inches is 20.05 cubic inches per inch.

b. $f'(x) = \lim_{h\to 0}\dfrac{f(x+h)-f(x)}{h} = \lim_{h\to 0}\dfrac{5(x+h)^2-5x^2}{h} = \lim_{h\to 0}\dfrac{5x^2+10hx+5h^2-5x^2}{h}$

$= \lim_{h\to 0}\dfrac{10hx+5h^2}{h} = \lim_{h\to 0}(10x+5h) = 10x+5\cdot 0 = 10x$

$f'(2) = 10(2) = 20$

The instantaneous rate of change of the volume with respect to x at $x = 2$ inches is 20 cubic inches per inch.

59. $f(x) = \dfrac{4}{3}\pi x^3$

$f'(x) = \lim_{h\to 0}\dfrac{f(x+h)-f(x)}{h} = \lim_{h\to 0}\dfrac{\frac{4}{3}\pi(x+h)^3-\frac{4}{3}\pi x^3}{h} = \lim_{h\to 0}\dfrac{\frac{4}{3}\pi(x^3+3hx^2+3h^2x+h^3-x^3)}{h}$

$= \lim_{h\to 0}\dfrac{\frac{4}{3}\pi(3hx^2+3h^2x+h^3)}{h} = \lim_{h\to 0}\frac{4}{3}\pi(3x^2+3hx+h^2) = \frac{4}{3}\pi(3x^2+3\cdot 0\cdot x+0^2) = 4\pi x^2$

$f'(5) = 4\pi(5)^2 = 100\pi$

The instantaneous rate of change of the volume with respect to x at $x = 5$ inches is 100π cubic inches per inch.

60. $s(t) = -16t^2 + 80t + 5$

a. $s'(t) = \lim_{h\to 0}\dfrac{s(t+h)-s(t)}{h} = \lim_{h\to 0}\dfrac{-16(t+h)^2+80(t+h)+5-(-16t^2+80t+5)}{h}$

$= \lim_{h\to 0}\dfrac{-16t^2-32ht-16h^2+80t+80h+5+16t^2-80t-5}{h} = \lim_{h\to 0}\dfrac{-32ht-16h^2+80h}{h}$

$= \lim_{h\to 0}(-32t-16h+80) = -32t-16\cdot 0+80 = -32t+80$

$s'(2) = -32(2)+80 = 16$

The instantaneous velocity of the ball 2 seconds after it is thrown is 16 feet per second.

$s'(4) = -32(4)+80 = -48$

The instantaneous velocity of the ball 4 seconds after it is thrown is -48 feet per second.

b. Set $s'(t) = 0$.

$-32t+80 = 0$

$32t = 80$

$t = 2.5$

The ball reaches its maximum height 2.5 seconds after it is thrown.

$s(2.5) = -16(2.5)^2 + 80(2.5) + 5 = 105$

The maximum height of the ball is 105 feet.

Chapter 11 Test

1. $f(x) = \dfrac{9-x}{3-\sqrt{x}}$

x	8.9	8.99	$8.999 \rightarrow \leftarrow 9.001$	9.01	9.1
$f(x)$	5.9833	5.9983	$5.9998 \rightarrow \leftarrow 6.0002$	6.0017	6.0166

     $\lim\limits_{x \to 9} f(x) = 6$

2.   The graph shows that as x approaches -2, $f(x)$ approaches -3. Thus, $\lim\limits_{x \to -2} f(x) = -3$.

3.   The graph of $f(x)$ at $x = -2$ is the point with coordinates $(-2, -5)$. Thus, $f(-2) = -5$.

4.   As x approaches 2 from the left-hand side $f(x)$ approaches 4, therefore, $\lim\limits_{x \to 2^-} f(x) = 4$.

5.   As x approaches 2 from the right-hand side $f(x)$ approaches 6, therefore, $\lim\limits_{x \to 2^+} f(x) = 6$.

6. $\lim\limits_{x \to 2^-} f(x) \neq \lim\limits_{x \to 2^+} f(x)$, therefore, $\lim\limits_{x \to 2} f(x)$ does not exist.

7.   The graph shows that as x approaches 4, $f(x)$ approaches 4. Thus, $\lim\limits_{x \to 4} f(x) = 4$.

8. $\lim\limits_{x \to -2} (x^2 + x + 1)^4 = \left[\lim\limits_{x \to -2} (x^2 + x + 1) \right]^4 = \left[(-2)^2 + (-2) + 1 \right]^4 = 81$

9. $\lim\limits_{x \to -1} \dfrac{x^2 - x - 2}{x + 1} = \lim\limits_{x \to -1} \dfrac{(x+1)(x-2)}{x+1} = \lim\limits_{x \to -1} (x - 2) = -1 - 2 = -3$

10. $\lim\limits_{x \to 9} \dfrac{\sqrt{x} - 3}{x - 9} = \lim\limits_{x \to 9} \dfrac{\sqrt{x} - 3}{x - 9} \cdot \dfrac{\sqrt{x} + 3}{\sqrt{x} + 3} = \lim\limits_{x \to 9} \dfrac{x - 9}{(x-9)\left(\sqrt{x} + 3\right)} = \lim\limits_{x \to 9} \dfrac{1}{\sqrt{x} + 3} = \dfrac{1}{\sqrt{9} + 3} = \dfrac{1}{6}$

11. $f(x) = \begin{cases} \dfrac{x^2 - 1}{x + 1} & \text{if } x \neq -1 \\ 6 & \text{if } x = -1 \end{cases}$

     $f(-1) = 6$
     f is defined at -1.

     $\lim\limits_{x \to -1} f(x) = \lim\limits_{x \to -1} \dfrac{x^2 - 1}{x + 1} = \lim\limits_{x \to -1} \dfrac{(x+1)(x-1)}{x+1} = \lim\limits_{x \to -1} (x - 1) = -1 - 1 = -2$

     $\lim\limits_{x \to -1} f(x) = -2 \neq f(-1)$,

     therefore, f is discontinuous at -1.

12. $f(x) = \begin{cases} 2 - x & \text{if } x \le 2 \\ x^2 - 2x & \text{if } x > 2 \end{cases}$

$f(2) = 2 - 2 = 0$

f is defined at 2.

$\lim\limits_{x \to 2^-} f(x) = \lim\limits_{x \to 2^-} (2 - x) = 2 - 2 = 0$

$\lim\limits_{x \to 2^+} f(x) = \lim\limits_{x \to 2^+} (x^2 - 2x) = 2^2 - 2(2) = 0$

$\lim\limits_{x \to 2^-} f(x) = \lim\limits_{x \to 2^+} f(x)$, therefore, $\lim\limits_{x \to 2} f(x)$ exists and is 0.

$\lim\limits_{x \to 2} f(x) = f(2)$, therefore, f is continuous at 2.

13. $f(x) + x^2 - 5x + 1$

$f'(x) = \lim\limits_{h \to 0} \dfrac{f(x+h) - f(x)}{h} = \lim\limits_{h \to 0} \dfrac{(x+h)^2 - 5(x+h) + 1 - (x^2 - 5x + 1)}{h}$

$= \lim\limits_{h \to 0} \dfrac{x^2 + 2hx + h^2 - 5x - 5h + 1 - x^2 + 5x - 1}{h} = \lim\limits_{h \to 0} \dfrac{2hx + h^2 - 5h}{h}$

$= \lim\limits_{h \to 0} (2x + h - 5) = 2x + 0 - 5 = 2x - 5$

14. $f(x) = \dfrac{10}{x}$

$f'(x) = \lim\limits_{h \to 0} \dfrac{f(x+h) - f(x)}{h} = \lim\limits_{h \to 0} \dfrac{\frac{10}{x+h} - \frac{10}{x}}{h} = \lim\limits_{h \to 0} \dfrac{\frac{10x - 10(x+h)}{x(x+h)}}{h} = \lim\limits_{h \to 0} \dfrac{10x - 10x - 10h}{xh(x+h)} = \lim\limits_{h \to 0} \dfrac{-10}{x(x+h)}$

$= \dfrac{-10}{x(x+0)} = -\dfrac{10}{x^2}$

15. $f(x) = x^2$ at $(-3, 9)$

$m_{\tan} = \lim\limits_{h \to 0} \dfrac{f(x+h) - f(x)}{h} = \lim\limits_{h \to 0} \dfrac{(x+h)^2 - x^2}{h} = \lim\limits_{h \to 0} \dfrac{x^2 + 2hx + h^2 - x^2}{h} = \lim\limits_{h \to 0} \dfrac{2hx + h^2}{h}$

$= \lim\limits_{h \to 0} (2x + h) = 2x + 0 = 2x$

$y - y_1 = m(x - x_1)$

$y - 9 = 2(-3)(x + 3)$

$y - 9 = -6x - 18$

$y = -6x - 9$

16. $s(t) = -16t^2 + 72t$

$s'(t) = \lim\limits_{h \to 0} \dfrac{s(t+h) - s(t)}{h} = \lim\limits_{h \to 0} \dfrac{-16(t+h)^2 + 72(t+h) - (-16t^2 + 72t)}{h}$

$= \lim\limits_{h \to 0} \dfrac{-16t^2 - 32ht - 16h^2 + 72t + 72h + 16t^2 - 72t}{h} = \lim\limits_{h \to 0} \dfrac{-32ht - 16h^2 + 72h}{h}$

$= \lim\limits_{h \to 0} (-32t - 16h + 72) = -32t - 16 \cdot 0 + 72 = -32t + 72$

$s'(3) = -32(3) + 72 = -24$

The instantaneous velocity of the ball 3 seconds after it was thrown is –24 feet per second.

Cumulative Review Exercises (Chapters P–11)

1.
$$\frac{1}{x+2} > \frac{3}{x+1}$$

$$\frac{1}{x+2} - \frac{3}{x+1} > 0$$

$$\frac{x+1-3(x+2)}{(x+2)(x+1)} > 0$$

$$\frac{-2x-5}{(x+2)(x+1)} > 0$$

Find the boundary points.

$-2x-5=0 \qquad x+2=0$

$\qquad x = -\frac{5}{2} \qquad x = -2$

$x+1=0$

$\qquad x = -1$

Interval	Number	Substitute	Conclusion
$\left(-\infty, -\frac{5}{2}\right]$	-3	$\frac{-2(-3)-5}{(-3+2)(-3+1)} > 0$	True
$\left[-\frac{5}{2}, -2\right)$	$-\frac{9}{4}$	$\frac{-2\left(-\frac{9}{4}\right)-5}{\left(-\frac{9}{4}+2\right)\left(-\frac{9}{4}+1\right)} > 0$	False
$(-2, -1)$	$-\frac{3}{2}$	$\frac{-2\left(-\frac{3}{2}\right)-5}{\left(-\frac{3}{2}+2\right)\left(-\frac{3}{2}+1\right)} > 0$	True
$(-1, \infty)$	0	$\frac{-2(0)-5}{(0+2)(0+1)} > 0$	False

The solution set is $\left\{ x \,\middle|\, x \le -\frac{5}{2} \text{ or } -2 < x < -1 \right\}$.

2. $2x^3 + 11x^2 - 7x - 6 = 0$

Use the Rational Zero Theorem.

The constant term is –6, which has factors: $\pm 1, \pm 2, \pm 3,$ and ± 6. The leading coefficient is 2, which has factors: ± 1 and ± 2.

$$\text{Possible rational zeros} = \frac{\text{Factors of the constant term}}{\text{Factors of the leading coefficient}} = \frac{\pm 1, \pm 2, \pm 3, \pm 6}{\pm 1, \pm 2} = \pm 1, \pm 2, \pm 3, \pm 6, \pm \frac{1}{2}, \pm \frac{3}{2}$$

Use trial-and-error and synthetic division to find the first rational zero. Try 1.

```
1 |  2   11   -7   -6
  |       2   13    6
  -------------------
     2   13    6    0
```

1 is a rational zero, so

$$2x^3 + 11x^2 - 7x - 6 = (x-1)(2x^2 + 13x + 6)$$
$$= (x-1)(2x+1)(x+6)$$

$x-1=0 \quad 2x+1=0 \quad x+6=0$

$\quad x=1 \qquad x = -\frac{1}{2} \qquad x = -6$

The solution set is $\left\{ 1, -\frac{1}{2}, -6 \right\}$.

3. $\left|2x+4\right|>3$

$2x+4<-3 \quad$ or $\quad 2x+4>3$

$2x<-7 \quad$ or $\quad 2x>-1$

$x<-\dfrac{7}{2} \quad$ or $\quad x>-\dfrac{1}{2}$

The solution set is $\left\{x \mid x<-\dfrac{7}{2} \text{ or } x>-\dfrac{1}{2}\right\}$.

4. $\cos^2 x + \sin x + 1 = 0, \; 0 \le x < 2\pi$

$0 = (1-\sin^2 x) + \sin x + 1$

$0 = -\sin^2 x + \sin x + 2$

$0 = \sin^2 x - \sin x - 2$

$0 = (\sin x - 2)(\sin x + 1)$

$\sin x - 2 = 0 \quad$ or $\quad \sin x + 1 = 0$

$\sin x = 2 \quad$ or $\quad \sin x = -1$

undefined $\quad$ or $\quad x = \sin^{-1}(-1)$

$x = \dfrac{3\pi}{2}$

The solution set is $\left\{\dfrac{3\pi}{2}\right\}$.

5. $\log_4(x^2-9) - \log_4(x+3) = 3$

$\log_4 \dfrac{x^2-9}{x+3} = 3$

$\dfrac{x^2-9}{x+3} = 4^3$

$x^2 - 9 = 64(x+3)$

$x^2 - 9 = 64x + 192$

$x^2 - 64x - 201 = 0$

$(x-67)(x+3) = 0$

$x - 67 = 0 \quad x+3 = 0$

$x = 67 \quad\quad x = 3$

Because $\log_4((-3)+3) = \log_4 0$ and $\log_4 0$ is undefined, $x=3$ is an extraneous solution. The solution set is $\{67\}$.

6. $f(x) = x^3 + x^2 - 12x$

$= x(x^2 + x - 12)$

$= x(x+4)(x-3)$

7. $f(x) = \dfrac{2x^2 - 5x + 2}{x^2 - 4}$

$= \dfrac{(2x-1)(x-2)}{(x+2)(x-2)}$

$= \dfrac{2x-1}{x+2}, \text{ where } x \ne 2$

8. $f(x) = \begin{cases} -x+1 & \text{if } -1 \le x < 1 \\ 2 & \text{if } x = 1 \\ x^2 & \text{if } x > 1 \end{cases}$

Graph the line $f(x) = -x + 1$ from $x = -1$ to $x = 1$ with a closed dot at $(-1, 2)$ and an open dot at $(1, 0)$. Graph a closed dot at $(1, 2)$, and graph the parabola $f(x) = x^2$ on the right side of $x = 1$.

9. $y = 2\sin\left(2x + \dfrac{\pi}{2}\right)$

period $= \dfrac{2\pi}{B} = \dfrac{2\pi}{2} = \pi$

amplitude $= |A| = |2| = 2$

phase shift $= \dfrac{c}{B} = \dfrac{-\frac{\pi}{2}}{2} = -\dfrac{\pi}{2} \cdot \dfrac{1}{2} = -\dfrac{\pi}{4}$

Graph using the key points

$(0, 2)$, $\left(\dfrac{\pi}{4}, 0\right)$, $\left(\dfrac{\pi}{2}, -2\right)$, $\left(\dfrac{3\pi}{4}, 0\right)$, and $(\pi, 2)$.

10. $y = \dfrac{1}{2}\sec 2\pi x, 0 \le x \le 2$

Use the reciprocal function $y = \dfrac{1}{2}\cos 2\pi x$, with

key points

$\left(0, \dfrac{1}{2}\right), \left(\dfrac{1}{4}, 0\right), \left(\dfrac{1}{2}, -\dfrac{1}{2}\right), \left(\dfrac{3}{4}, 0\right),$ and $\left(1, \dfrac{1}{2}\right).$

Extend the graph one cycle to the right, and
draw vertical asymptotes
at the x-intercepts for guides.

11. $x - 2y \le 4$

$-2y \le -x + 4$

$y \ge \dfrac{1}{2}x - 2, x \ge 2$

12. $\qquad x^2 - 4y^2 - 4x - 24y - 48 = 0$

$x^2 - 4x + 4 - 4(y^2 + 6y + 9) - 48 = 4 - 36$

$(x-2)^2 - 4(y+3)^2 = 16$

$\dfrac{(x-2)^2}{16} - \dfrac{(y+3)^2}{4} = 1$

13. $f(x) = \sqrt{x}, g(x) = \sqrt{x-2} + 1$

$g(x)$ is the graph of $f(x)$ shifted 2 units to the
right and 1 unit up.

14. $x = 3\sin t, y = 4\cos t + 2; 0 \le t \le 2\pi$

15. $2x^2 + 5xy + 2y^2 - \dfrac{9}{2} = 0$

Use the Amount of Rotation formula.

$$\cos 2\theta = \frac{A - C}{B} = \frac{2 - 2}{5} = 0$$

$$\theta = \frac{1}{2}\cos^{-1} 0 = 45°$$

With $\theta = 45°$, the rotation formulas for x and y are $x = \dfrac{\sqrt{2}}{2}(x' - y')$ and $y = \dfrac{\sqrt{2}}{2}(x' + y')$.

Substituting these into the original equation gives the hyperbola $\dfrac{x'^2}{1} - \dfrac{y'^2}{9} = 1$.

16. $f(x) = -2x^2 + 7x - 1$

$$f'(x) = \lim_{h \to 0} \frac{f(x + h) - f(x)}{h} = \lim_{h \to 0} \frac{-2(x + h)^2 + 7(x + h) - 1 - (-2x^2 + 7x - 1)}{h}$$

$$= \lim_{h \to 0} \frac{-2x^2 - 4hx - 2h^2 + 7x + 7h - 1 + 2x^2 - 7x + 1}{h} = \lim_{h \to 0} \frac{-4hx - 2h^2 + 7h}{h}$$

$$= \lim_{h \to 0}(-4x - 2h + 7) = -4x - 2 \cdot 0 + 7 = -4x + 7$$

17. $f(x) = 7x - 1$

$$x = 7y - 1$$

$$x + 1 = 7y$$

$$y = \frac{1}{7}x + \frac{1}{7}$$

$$f^{-1}(x) = \frac{1}{7}x + \frac{1}{7}$$

18. $\displaystyle \lim_{x \to -3} \frac{x^2 + x - 6}{x^2 + 2x - 3} = \lim_{x \to -3} \frac{(x + 3)(x - 2)}{(x + 3)(x - 1)}$

$$= \lim_{x \to -3} \frac{x - 2}{x - 1}$$

$$= \frac{-3 - 2}{-3 - 1}$$

$$= \frac{5}{4}$$

19. $(x^2 - 3y)^4 = \dfrac{4!}{0!(4-0)!}(x^2)^4 + \dfrac{4!}{1!(4-1)!}(x^2)^3(-3y) + \dfrac{4!}{2!(4-2)!}(x^2)^2(-3y)^2 + \dfrac{4!}{3!(4-3)!}x^2(-3y)^3$

$\qquad + \dfrac{4!}{4!(4-4)!}(-3y)^4$

$\qquad = 1 \cdot x^8 + 4x^6(-3y) + 6x^4 \cdot 9y^2 + 4x^2(-27y^3) + 1 \cdot 81y^4$

$\qquad = x^8 - 12x^6 y + 54x^4 y^2 - 108x^2 y^3 + 81y^4$

20. $2x + y - 6 = 0$

$\qquad y = -2x + 6$

The slope is –2.

$y - y_1 = m(x - x_1)$

$\quad y + 3 = -2(x - 2)$

$\quad y + 3 = -2x + 4$

$\qquad y = -2x + 1$

21. $\mathbf{v} = -2\mathbf{i} + \mathbf{j}, \mathbf{w} = 4\mathbf{i} - 3\mathbf{j}$

$\mathbf{v} \cdot \mathbf{w} = (-2\mathbf{i} + \mathbf{j}) \cdot (4\mathbf{i} - 3\mathbf{j})$

$\qquad = -2(4) + 1(-3)$

$\qquad = -8 - 3$

$\qquad = -11$

$\cos\theta = \dfrac{\mathbf{v} \cdot \mathbf{w}}{|\mathbf{v}||\mathbf{w}|}$

$\quad \theta = \cos^{-1}\left(\dfrac{\mathbf{v} \cdot \mathbf{w}}{|\mathbf{v}||\mathbf{w}|}\right)$

$\quad \theta = \cos^{-1}\left(\dfrac{-11}{\sqrt{(-2)^2 + 1^2}\sqrt{4^2 + (-3)^2}}\right)$

$\quad \theta = \cos^{-1}\left(\dfrac{-11}{\sqrt{5}\sqrt{25}}\right)$

$\quad \theta = 170°$

22. $\dfrac{1}{x(x^2 + x + 1)} = \dfrac{A}{x} + \dfrac{Bx + C}{x^2 + x + 1}$

$\qquad 1 = A(x^2 + x + 1) + Bx^2 + Cx$

$\qquad 1 = (A + B)x^2 + (A + C)x + A$

$A = 1 \quad A + B = 0 \qquad A + C = 0$

$\qquad\qquad B = -A \qquad\quad C = -A$

$\qquad\qquad B = -1 \qquad\quad C = -1$

$\dfrac{1}{x(x^2 + x + 1)} = \dfrac{1}{x} - \dfrac{x + 1}{x^2 + x + 1}$

23. $\tan\theta + \cot\theta = \dfrac{\sin\theta}{\cos\theta} + \dfrac{\cos\theta}{\sin\theta}$

$\qquad\qquad\quad = \dfrac{\sin^2\theta + \cos^2\theta}{\cos\theta\sin\theta}$

$\qquad\qquad\quad = \dfrac{1}{\cos\theta\sin\theta}$

$\qquad\qquad\quad = \sec\theta\csc\theta$

24. $\tan(\theta + \pi) = \dfrac{\tan\theta + \tan\pi}{1 - \tan\theta\tan\pi}$

$\qquad\qquad\quad = \dfrac{\tan\theta + 0}{1 - \tan\theta(0)}$

$\qquad\qquad\quad = \tan\theta$

25. $BA = \begin{bmatrix} 1 & 0 \\ 3 & 2 \\ 2 & 1 \end{bmatrix}\begin{bmatrix} 2 & 1 & 3 \\ 1 & -1 & 0 \end{bmatrix}$

$= \begin{bmatrix} 1(2)+0(1) & 1(1)+0(-1) & 1(3)+0(0) \\ 3(2)+2(1) & 3(1)+2(-1) & 3(3)+2(0) \\ 2(2)+1(1) & 2(1)+1(-1) & 2(3)+1(0) \end{bmatrix}$

$= \begin{bmatrix} 2 & 1 & 3 \\ 8 & 1 & 9 \\ 5 & 1 & 6 \end{bmatrix}$

26. $r = 4\sin\theta$

27. $h(x) = (x^2 - 3x + 7)^9$

$h(x) = (f \circ g)(x)$

$f(x) = x^9$

$g(x) = x^2 - 3x + 7$

28. $2x - y - 2z = -1$

$\qquad x - 2y - z = 1$

$\qquad x + y + z = 4$

$\begin{bmatrix} 2 & -1 & -2 & | & -1 \\ 1 & -2 & -1 & | & 1 \\ 1 & 1 & 1 & | & 4 \end{bmatrix} \dfrac{1}{2}R_1$

$= \begin{bmatrix} 1 & -\frac{1}{2} & -1 & | & -\frac{1}{2} \\ 1 & -2 & -1 & | & 1 \\ 1 & 1 & 1 & | & 4 \end{bmatrix} -R_1 + R_2$

$= \begin{bmatrix} 1 & -\frac{1}{2} & -1 & | & -\frac{1}{2} \\ 0 & -\frac{3}{2} & 0 & | & \frac{3}{2} \\ 1 & 1 & 1 & | & 4 \end{bmatrix} -R_1 + R_3$

$= \begin{bmatrix} 1 & -\frac{1}{2} & -1 & | & -\frac{1}{2} \\ 0 & -\frac{3}{2} & 0 & | & \frac{3}{2} \\ 0 & \frac{3}{2} & 2 & | & \frac{9}{2} \end{bmatrix} R_2 + R_3$

$= \begin{bmatrix} 1 & -\frac{1}{2} & -1 & | & -\frac{1}{2} \\ 0 & -\frac{3}{2} & 0 & | & \frac{3}{2} \\ 0 & 0 & 2 & | & 6 \end{bmatrix} -\dfrac{2}{3}R_2$

$= \begin{bmatrix} 1 & -\frac{1}{2} & -1 & | & -\frac{1}{2} \\ 0 & 1 & 0 & | & -1 \\ 0 & 0 & 2 & | & 6 \end{bmatrix} \dfrac{1}{2}R_3$

$= \begin{bmatrix} 1 & -\frac{1}{2} & -1 & | & -\frac{1}{2} \\ 0 & 1 & 0 & | & -1 \\ 0 & 0 & 1 & | & 3 \end{bmatrix} \dfrac{1}{2}R_2 + R_1$

$= \begin{bmatrix} 1 & 0 & -1 & | & -1 \\ 0 & 1 & 0 & | & -1 \\ 0 & 0 & 1 & | & 3 \end{bmatrix} R_3 + R_1$

$= \begin{bmatrix} 1 & 0 & 0 & | & 2 \\ 0 & 1 & 0 & | & -1 \\ 0 & 0 & 1 & | & 3 \end{bmatrix}$

The solution set is $\{(2, -1, 3)\}$.

29. $\displaystyle\sum_{i=1}^{6} 4(-2)^i$

$S_6 = \dfrac{a_1(1 - r^6)}{1 - r} = \dfrac{4(-2)^1\left[1 - (-2)^6\right]}{1 - (-2)} = 168$

30. $\left[\sqrt{2}(\cos 15° + i\sin 15°)\right]^4 = (\sqrt{2})^4\left[\cos 4(15°) + i\sin 4(15°)\right]$

$$= 4(\cos 60° + i\sin 60°)$$

$$= 4\left(\frac{1}{2} + \frac{\sqrt{3}}{2}i\right)$$

$$= 2 + 2i\sqrt{3}$$

31. $0.08(120,000 - x) + 0.18x = 10,000$

$$9600 - 0.08x + 0.18x = 10,000$$

$$0.1x = 400$$

$$x = 4000$$

$116,000 was loaned at 8% and $4000 was loaned at 18%.

32. $V = 9x^2 = 225$

$$x^2 = 25$$

$$x = 5$$

$x + 2(9) = 5 + 18 = 23$

The dimensions of the sheet metal should be $23\,\text{cm} \times 23\,\text{cm}$.

33. $200 = 2x + y, \quad 200 - 2x = y$

$$A(x) = x(200 - 2x)$$

$$= -2x^2 + 200x$$

$$x = \frac{-200}{2(-2)} = 50$$

$$200 - 2x = 200 - 2(50) = 100$$

$$A(100) = 50(200 - 2(50)) = 5000$$

The dimensions are 100 feet by 50 feet and the maximum area is 5000 square feet.

34. $T = C + (T_0 - C)e^{kt}$

a. $75°\text{F} = 72°\text{F} + (375°\text{F} - 72°\text{F})e^{k(60\ \text{min})}$

$$3°\text{F} = (303°\text{F})e^{k(60\ \text{min})}$$

$$\ln\left(\frac{3°\text{F}}{303°\text{F}}\right) = \ln e^{k(60\ \text{min})}$$

$$k = \frac{1}{60\ \text{min}}\ln\left(\frac{1}{101}\right)$$

$$\approx -0.0769\ (\text{min})^{-1}$$

$$T = 72 + 303e^{-0.0769t}$$

b.

$$250\,^\circ\text{F}=72\,^\circ\text{F}+(303\,^\circ\text{F})e^{[-0.0769\,(\text{min})^{-1}]t}$$

$$178\,^\circ\text{F}=(303\,^\circ\text{F})e^{[-0.0769\,(\text{min})^{-1}]t}$$

$$\ln\left(\frac{178\,^\circ\text{F}}{303\,^\circ\text{F}}\right)=\ln e^{[-0.0769\,(\text{min})^{-1}]t}$$

$$t=\frac{\text{min}}{-0.0769}\ln\left(\frac{178}{303}\right)$$

$$\approx 6.9\ \text{min}$$

The temperature of the pie will reach 250° F in approximately 6.9 minutes.

35. $6000 = xy$

$$\frac{6000}{x}=y$$

$$C=25x+5(2y)$$

$$=25x+10\left(\frac{6000}{x}\right)$$

$$=25x+\frac{60,000}{x}$$

36. Set the origin at the harbor with the y-axis pointing north.
Final position of the first ship:

$$x_1 = r\cos\theta = (23)\cos(90^\circ - 42^\circ) = 23\cos 48^\circ \approx 15.4$$

$$y_1 = r\sin\theta$$

$$= 23\sin 48^\circ$$

$$\approx 17.1$$

Final position of the second ship:

$$x_2 = r\cos\theta$$

$$= (72)\cos(90^\circ + 38^\circ)$$

$$= 72\cos 128^\circ$$

$$\approx -44.3$$

$$y_2 = r\sin\theta$$

$$= 72\sin 128^\circ$$

$$\approx 56.7$$

$$d = \sqrt{(x_1 - x_2)^2 + (y_1 - y_2)^2}$$

$$= \sqrt{(15.4 + 44.3)^2 + (17.1 - 56.7)^2}$$

$$\approx 71.6$$

The two ships are approximately 71.6 miles apart.

37. $V = \dfrac{k}{P}$

$40 = \dfrac{k}{22}$

$k = 22(40)$

$k = 880$

$V = \dfrac{880}{30} = 29\dfrac{1}{3}$

The volume of the gas is $29\dfrac{1}{3}$ cubic inches.

38. $s(t) = -16t^2 + 40t$

$s'(t) = \lim\limits_{h \to 0} \dfrac{s(t+h) - s(t)}{h}$

$\qquad = \lim\limits_{h \to 0} \dfrac{-16(t+h)^2 + 40(t+h) - (-16t^2 + 40t)}{h}$

$\qquad = \lim\limits_{h \to 0} \dfrac{-16t^2 - 32ht - 16h^2 + 40t + 40h + 16t^2 - 40t}{h}$

$\qquad = \lim\limits_{h \to 0} \dfrac{-32ht - 16h^2 + 40h}{h}$

$\qquad = \lim\limits_{h \to 0} (-32t - 16h + 40)$

$\qquad = -32t - 16 \cdot 0 + 40$

$\qquad = -32t + 40$

$s'(2) = -32(2) + 40 = -24$

The instantaneous velocity of the ball 2 seconds after it was thrown is –24 feet per second.

39. $V = lwh$

$4 = x \cdot x \cdot y$

$\dfrac{4}{x^2} = y$

$A(x) = x^2 + 4xy$

$A(x) = x^2 + 4x\left(\dfrac{4}{x^2}\right)$

$A(x) = x^2 + \dfrac{16}{x}$

40. $f(x) = -2.32x^2 + 76.58x - 559.87, 12 \le x \le 17$

Set $f(x) = 70$.

$70 = -2.32x^2 + 76.58x - 559.87$

$0 = -2.32x^2 + 76.58x - 629.87$

Use the quadratic formula to solve for x.

$$x = \frac{-B \pm \sqrt{B^2 - 4AC}}{2A}$$

$$= \frac{-76.58 \pm \sqrt{76.58^2 - 4(-2.32)(-629.87)}}{2(-2.32)}$$

≈ 15.6 or 17.5 (17.5 is outside the domain.)

Seventy percent of U.S. students 15.6 years old say that their school is not drug free.